nature

The Living Record of Science

《自然》百年科学经典

英汉对照版　套装共十卷

第八卷
1993-1997

总顾问：李政道（Tsung-Dao Lee）

英方主编：Sir John Maddox
Sir Philip Campbell

中方主编：路甬祥

外语教学与研究出版社 · 麦克米伦教育 · 自然科研

FOREIGN LANGUAGE TEACHING AND RESEARCH PRESS · MACMILLAN EDUCATION · NATURE RESEARCH

北京 BEIJING

图书在版编目（CIP）数据

《自然》百年科学经典：套装共十卷．第八卷：英汉对照／（英）约翰·马多克斯（John Maddox），（英）菲利普·坎贝尔（Philip Campbell），路甬祥主编．－－北京：外语教学与研究出版社，2020.9
　　ISBN 978－7－5213－2021－3

　　Ⅰ．①自… Ⅱ．①约… ②菲… ③路… Ⅲ．①自然科学－文集－英、汉 Ⅳ．①N53

中国版本图书馆 CIP 数据核字 (2020) 第 155155 号

地图审图号：GS (2020) 5244 号

出 版 人　徐建忠
项目统筹　章思英
项目负责　刘晓楠　黄小斌
责任编辑　王丽霞
责任校对　黄小斌
封面设计　高　蕾
版式设计　孙莉明
插图设计　麦克米伦提供原图扫描版
出版发行　外语教学与研究出版社
社　　址　北京市西三环北路 19 号（100089）
网　　址　http://www.fltrp.com
印　　刷　北京华联印刷有限公司
开　　本　787×1092　1/16
印　　张　71
版　　次　2021 年 1 月第 1 版 2021 年 1 月第 1 次印刷
书　　号　ISBN 978-7-5213-2021-3
定　　价　8000.00 元

购书咨询：（010）88819926　电子邮箱：club@fltrp.com
外研书店：https://waiyants.tmall.com
凡印刷、装订质量问题，请联系我社印制部
联系电话：（010）61207896　电子邮箱：zhijian@fltrp.com
凡侵权、盗版书籍线索，请联系我社法律事务部
举报电话：（010）88817519　电子邮箱：banquan@fltrp.com
物料号：320210001

《自然》百年科学经典（英汉对照版）

总顾问：李政道（Tsung-Dao Lee）

英方主编：Sir John Maddox   中方主编：路甬祥
Sir Philip Campbell

编审委员会

英方编委：

Philip Ball

Vikram Savkar

David Swinbanks

中方编委（以姓氏笔画为序）：

许智宏

赵忠贤

滕吉文

本卷审稿专家（以姓氏笔画为序）

王二七	王社江	毛淑德	文 波	方向东	石 磊	田立德
刘冬生	齐利民	许家喜	孙 松	杜 忆	杜爱民	李 彦
李 娟	李军刚	李忠海	李铁刚	杨崇林	吴 晶	吴学兵
吴新智	何香涛	张华伟	张颖奇	陆朝阳	陈 文	欧阳自远
周礼勇	周济林	赵凌霞	胡松年	胡卓伟	段克勤	秦志海
徐永福	郭建栋	黄宝春	常 燎	崔娅铭	梁晓峰	韩汝珊
焦炳华	臧伟呈	翟天瑞	黎 卓			

编译委员会

Contents
目录

Volume VIII

(1993-1997)

The "Flickering Switch" of Late Pleistocene Climate Change

K. C. Taylor *et al.*

Editor's Note

This paper astonished the palaeoclimate community by revealing that significant shifts in climate can occur extremely rapidly, perhaps on timescales of just 5–20 years. Kendrick Taylor and colleagues used measurements of the electrical conductivity of an ice core drilled at Greenland to obtain a record of changes in the dust content of the ice during the last ice age. Alkaline dust alters the conductivity, and changes in airborne dust content reflect climate-induced rearrangements of atmospheric circulation. The researchers found several bursts of sudden changes, which they attribute to abrupt switches between two different climate states. These results suggest that climate change might not be a gradual affair, but could be triggered suddenly when critical thresholds are surpassed.

Polar ice contains a unique record of past climate variations; previous Greenland ice cores have documented relatively warm "interstadial" periods during the last glaciation and short (century-scale) returns to colder conditions during the glacial to interglacial warming (see, for example, ref. 1). These climate features have also been observed to varying degrees in ocean sediment cores[2-4] and terrestrial pollen and insect records[5-7]. Here we report electrical conductivity measurements from a new Greenland ice core, which confirm these previous observations, and also reveal a hitherto unrecognized mode of rapid climate variation. Fluctuations in ice conductivity on the scales of < 5–20 years reflect rapid oscillations in the dust content of the atmosphere. This "flickering" between two preferred states would seem to require extremely rapid reorganizations in atmospheric circulation.

THE Greenland Ice-Sheet Project 2 (GISP2) is coring the summit of the Greenland ice sheet (72.6 ° N, 38.5 ° W) to develop a continuous high-resolution record of climate related parameters going back at least 200,000 years. The electrical conductivity measurement (ECM) measures the ability of an ice core to conduct an electrical current, which is related to the balance of acids and bases in the ice[8-10]. The measurement is made by determining the current flowing between two moving electrodes with a potential difference of a few thousand volts. The current increases with increased concentration of strong acids, especially sulphuric (from volcanic activity[8] and other sources[11]) and nitric (controlled mainly by atmospheric chemistry[12,13]). The current decreases when the acids are neutralized, which is most commonly caused by ammonia (biomass burning and other sources[14,15]) or due to alkaline dust (continental sources[12]).

晚更新世气候变化的"闪电变换"

泰勒等

编者按

本文通过揭示气候可能仅在 5~20 年间就会发生极速变化而使古气候研究学者们感到惊讶。肯德里克·泰勒和同事们测量了在格陵兰钻到的冰芯的电导率，以获取在末次冰期期间冰芯中粉尘含量的变化记录。碱性粉尘改变了电导率，而空气中携带的粉尘含量的变化能够反映大气环流引起的气候变迁。研究人员发现气候发生了数次突然变化，并将其归因为两种不同气候条件之间的突然转换。这些结果表明，气候变化可能不是渐变发生的，而有可能是超过临界值时被突然引发的。

极地冰芯中包含着独特的古气候变化记录；先前对格陵兰冰芯的研究已经证明：末次冰期时存在相对较温暖的"间冰阶"，并且由冰期向间冰期过渡的总变暖趋势下也曾出现过短暂（百年尺度）的回冷气候（参见文献 1）。海洋沉积物岩芯[2-4]及大陆孢粉与昆虫记录[5-7]中也不同程度地观测到了上述气候特征。本文我们将介绍一个格陵兰冰芯电导率的新的测定结果，该测定结果不仅证实了上述观测结果，而且揭示出了一个迄今还未识别出的快速气候变化模式。<5~20 年尺度上的冰芯电导率的波动反映了大气中粉尘含量的快速振荡。两个主要阶段之间出现的这种"闪电式变化"似乎是大气环流极速重组的结果。

格陵兰冰盖计划 2（GISP2）的目的是钻取格陵兰冰盖顶部萨米特冰芯（72.6°N，38.5°W）以获取至少 20 万年以来的连续高分辨率气候记录的相关参数。电导率测量法（ECM）测量的是冰芯传导电流的能力，与冰芯中酸性与碱性的平衡有关[8-10]。该测量方法是通过确定势差数千伏的两个运动电极之间流过的电流来进行的。电流随强酸，特别是硫酸（来自火山活动[8]和其他来源[11]）和硝酸（主要受大气化学作用的控制[12,13]）浓度的增加而增大。当酸性物质被中和时，电流将减小，这种中和作用通常是由氨气（生物体的燃烧以及其他来源[14,15]）或碱性粉尘（来源于大陆[12]）所致。

Changes in the value of the ECM baseline occur when climate or weather patterns change the source strength or transport of the acids and bases. During Wisconsinian times, dust transport to Greenland increased by at least a factor of 40, possibly because of changes in transport paths, wind speeds and surface moisture[16]. The large amounts of alkaline dust present in ice from cold periods during the last glacial period neutralize the acids, reducing the current flow between the electrodes by a factor of ~40 compared with Holocene conditions. This permits clear discrimination between dusty and less dusty conditions. The relationship between the ECM signal and the concentration of alkaline dust at the transition from acidic to alkaline conditions (0 to 10 μA) is not well quantified. At the transition between acidic and alkaline conditions, the effect of small amounts of additional dust on the magnitude (but not the frequency) of the ECM signal may be disproportionately large. In the GISP2 core, however, detailed chemical analysis shows that the order-of-magnitude decreases in ECM that we consider here are associated with order-of-magnitude increases in calcium. The source for the calcium is believed to be airborne calcium carbonate dust. The ECM record has the highest time resolution (> 15 samples per year) of available measurements, and together with the sensitivity to dust, this makes ECM suitable for investigating the rate of rapid atmospheric circulation changes.

The ECM record discussed here covers the time period 10 to 42 thousand years before present (kyr BP), and allows climate variability to be investigated on timescales of seasons to millennia (Fig. 1*a*). The core has been preliminarily dated by counting of annual layers which are identified by visual stratigraphy, ECM and particulate measurements. Every annual layer has been counted for the past 17.4 kyr BP with an estimated accuracy of 3% (ref. 17). Between 17.4 and 40.5 kyr BP, annual layers were counted by visual stratigraphy for one out of every 10 or 20 m. The interim sections were dated by counting interpolated annual layers. At an age of 15 kyr BP, ages of identical events in the GISP2 core and GRIP core[1] (located 30 km to the east) differ by 200 years. This is within expected errors. At an age of 40 kyr BP in the GISP2 core, corresponding events in the GRIP core are dated at 34 kyr BP. Both groups are refining the preliminary dating of the cores and this discrepancy is likely to diminish. A comparison of the two cores will be presented elsewhere.

当气候或天气类型导致酸性或碱性物质的来源或搬运方式发生改变时，ECM 基线值就会出现相应变化。威斯康星冰期时，粉尘向格陵兰岛的输送至少增加了 39 倍，可能是由输送路径、风速以及海表湿度的改变所致[16]。在末次冰期的冷期冰芯中，大量碱性粉尘的出现使酸性物质被中和，使得电极间的电流减少为全新世的 1/40。据此可清楚地辨别出多粉尘和无粉尘环境条件。在酸碱性之间的过渡环境中 (0~10 μA)，ECM 信号与碱性粉尘浓度之间的关系还未得到很好的量化。因为在酸碱性之间的过渡环境中，少量额外粉尘即可能对 ECM 信号的大小（不会影响频率）产生巨大影响。不过，利用 GISP2 冰芯进行详细的化学分析表明，本文我们所关注的 ECM 信号的衰减量级与钙元素的增加量级有关。而降落的碳酸盐粉尘被认为是这些钙的主要来源。由于 ECM 记录具有所有可测量方法中最高的时间分辨率（＞15 个样品每年），并且对粉尘具有较强的敏感性，这使得 ECM 非常适合于大气循环快速变化的研究。

本文所讨论的 ECM 记录跨越了距今 1 万年前到 4.2 万年前的时段，可以据此研究季节性尺度到千年尺度上的气候变化（图 1a）。通过对可视地层学、ECM 和粒子测量分辨出的年层进行计数，学者对冰芯作了初步的定年。从中确定了过去 1.74 万年以来所有的年层年代，年代误差约为 3%（参见文献 17）。从距今 1.74 万年前到 4.05 万年前的年层年代是利用可视地层学方法数出的，这样的地层大约每 10~20 m 一个。中间的部分则是通过内插法确定的。在距今 1.5 万年前，GISP2 冰芯和 GRIP 冰芯[1]（GRIP 位于 GISP2 以东约 30 km 处）中相同事件的年龄相差 200 年。该值位于预期的误差范围以内。在 GISP2 冰芯中测年结果为 4 万年的事件对应于 GRIP 冰芯中的测年结果为 3.4 万年。两组数据都对冰芯的初步测年结果作了改进以尽可能减小这个差异。两冰芯的对比结果将另文给出。

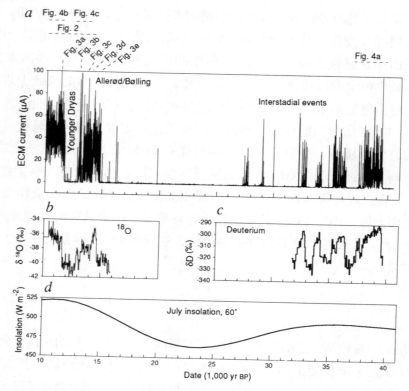

Fig. 1. *a*, GISP2 electrical conductivity measurement (ECM) record for the period of 10–40.5 kyr BP. Low current levels indicate that alkaline dust has neutralized the acidity of the ice. The record is resampled to a rate of one sample per year. The ages of the other expanded-scale figures (Figs 2–4) are indicated. The years indicated are calendar years. We adopt the carbon-14 datum of AD 1950 as present time. *b*, Isotopic ratio $^{18}O/^{16}O$ for the ages 10.5 to 16 kyr BP. *c*, Isotopic ratio D/H for the ages 32 to 40.5 kyr BP. The isotope samples are from contiguous 1-m sections of the core. Because of flow-induced thinning of annual layers, the 1-m sections correspond to one sample every 15 to 37 years in the $^{18}O/^{16}O$ record and one sample every 65 to 80 years in the deuterium/hydrogen record. The correlation between the ECM and the isotope records demonstrates that the ECM record is responding to climatic events. *d*, Mean July insolation for latitude 60° north[23].

The ECM record is characterized by a bimodal high or low pattern that is controlled by the absence or presence of alkaline dust. For comparison we also present stable isotope profiles, which are known to respond to the temperature difference between the moisture source and the ice deposition site, and are used extensively for palaeoclimate reconstructions[18-20]. The synchronous transitions in the ECM and isotope records (Fig. 1*b*, *c*) demonstrate the sensitivity of the ECM to climate conditions. Periods of heavy isotopic composition indicate warmer interglacial or interstadial conditions. The high ECM values during these times indicate that it was also less dusty. The ECM record (Fig. 2) clearly shows well-known millennium-scale Younger Dryas, Allerød, Bølling and Interstadial periods, and century-scale events during the Allerød and Bølling periods. The isolated spikes on the ECM record span at most a few years and are likely to be associated with volcanic activity. Although isotopes and ECM show synchronous transitions in Fig. 1, they do not correlate well on timescales of a few years. This indicates that they respond to different aspects of

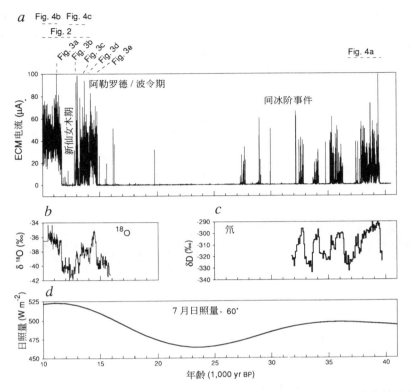

图 1. *a*，距今 1 万年前至 4.05 万年前间，GISP2 电导率测量结果（ECM）记录曲线。电流较低时表示碱性粉尘中和了冰川中的酸性物质。该记录的重复取样率为每年一个样品。图中还给出了局部放大图（图 2~4）的年龄，所标的年龄为历年。其中以 ^{14}C 测年得到的公元 1950 年为当前时间。*b*，距今 1.05 万年前至 1.6 万年前间，氧同位素比值 ^{18}O/^{16}O 的变化曲线。*c*，距今 3.2 万年前至 4.05 万年前间，氢同位素比值 D/H 的变化曲线。同位素样品均来自冰芯中连续长为 1 m 的一段。由于水流引起的年层减薄效应，1 m 间隔相当于 ^{18}O/^{16}O 记录中每 15~37 年一个样品，在 D/H 记录中相当于每 65~80 年一个样品。ECM 与同位素之间的相关性证明，ECM 记录与气候事件是对应的。*d*，北纬 60° 上 7 月份的平均太阳辐射 [23]。

ECM 记录以双峰或双谷为特征，受碱性粉尘存在与否的影响。此外我们还给出了稳定同位素变化曲线，以便于对比。大家都知道该曲线是与水分来源地和冰芯沉积地点之间的温度差异相对应的，并且已在古气候重建中得到广泛应用 [18-20]。ECM 和同位素记录的同步变化（图 1*b* 和 *c*）证明了 ECM 对气候条件变化的敏感性。重同位素组分阶段代表较温暖的间冰期或间冰阶环境。这些时段上出现的高 ECM 值说明当时大气中的粉尘含量较少。ECM 记录（图 2）清楚地显示出了众所周知的千年尺度上的新仙女木期、阿勒罗德期、波令期和间冰阶以及阿勒罗德期和波令期之间百年尺度的气候事件。ECM 记录上的孤立尖峰跨越的时间最大仅为数年，很可能与火山活动有关。虽然从图 1 来看，同位素和 ECM 表现为同步变化，但在数年的时间尺度上两者的相关性并不好。这说明它们反映了气候变化的不同方面（温度和粉尘），

climate (temperature and dust) rather than there being a direct influence of atmospheric particulates on the isotopic composition of snow fall[21,22]. Ice rheology has been observed to covary with ECM in the GISP2 core and other[23] Arctic cores. This phenomenon is most probably due to effects of particulates on grain recrystallization[24], not to an influence of ice rheology on ECM.

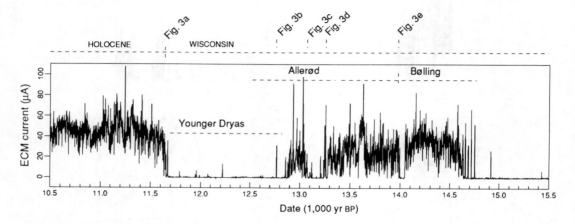

Fig. 2. Yearly averages of ECM in the GISP2 core at Summit, Greenland for the period of 10.5 to 15.5 kyr BP. The ages of expanded figures (Fig. 3a–e) are indicated.

In addition to the well-known millennium-scale stadial and interstadial periods (best viewed in Fig. 1), and the previously recognized century-scale climate events that occur during the Allerød and Bølling periods (best viewed in Fig. 2), we detect a still higher frequency of variability associated with abrupt climate change (Fig. 3a–e). The transitions between century or longer warm and cold periods are characterized by abrupt fluctuations in alkaline dust concentrations that occur over periods of less than 10 years. There are frequent brief (10–20 years) and abruptly terminating (less than 5 years) periods during which the ECM returns to pre-transition values. Although a similar timescale has been reported for temperature change at the end of the Younger Dryas (ref. 25), the fluctuations we have observed are quite different from the smooth transitions previously reported. During the Interstadial periods the fluctuations are continuous (Fig. 4a), in sharp contrast to the more stable Holocene (Fig. 4b). The Allerød and Bølling periods (Fig. 4c) are more stable than the Interstadial periods but not as stable as the Holocene. The transitions at the start and end of the interstadial periods occur within a decade. During the interstadial events and at main climate transitions, the part of the climate system influencing the ECM is behaving like a flickering switch that fluctuates between two states before stabilizing. The instability of the Interstadial events may be related to a prolonged intermediate value of July insolation at 60° north latitude[26] (Fig. 1d), which contrasts with the more stable cold climate that occurs during the low-insolation period. During the Holocene, when climate and the ECM are relatively stable, insolation decreases from 523 W m^{-2} to 475 W m^{-2} (ref. 26), indicating that insolation alone does not control climate stability.

而不是大气中的颗粒对降雪的同位素组成有直接影响[21,22]。据观测，在 GISP2 冰芯及其他[23]北极冰芯中，其海冰流变学特征与 ECM 信号是共变的。该现象并非海冰流变特征对 ECM 影响的反映，而很有可能是由颗粒对重结晶作用的影响所致[24]。

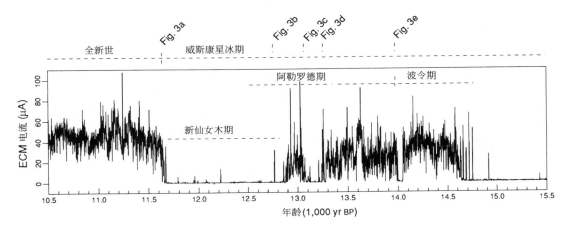

图 2. 格陵兰冰盖顶部 GISP2 冰芯中距今 1.05 万年前至 1.55 万年前间 ECM 记录的年际变化。图中给出了局部放大图（图 3a~e）的年龄。

除了众所周知的千年尺度的冰阶和间冰阶（从图 1 可得到最佳的体现）以及之前已识别出的阿勒罗德期和波令期期间发生的百年尺度的气候事件（图 2 有最佳体现）以外，我们还探测到了一个与气候突变有关的更高频率的变化（图 3a~e）。百年尺度甚至更长时期的冷暖期变化以碱性粉尘浓度在小于 10 年尺度上的突然性波动为标志。在 ECM 回到变化之前的值期间，存在频繁而短暂（10~20 年）的阶段和突然终止（不长于 5 年）阶段。虽然已有新仙女木末期时出现的类似时间尺度的温度变化的相关报道（参见文献 25），但我们所观测到的波动与之前报道的平滑过渡大不相同。间冰阶时，这种波动是连续的（图 4a），与气候更稳定的全新世（图 4b）形成了鲜明对比。阿勒罗德期和波令期（图 4c）则要比间冰阶稳定得多，但仍不如全新世稳定。间冰阶开始和结束的过渡期小于 10 年。间冰阶事件以及主要气候变迁事件期间，影响 ECM 的气候系统像闪烁变化的开关在两种状态间波动，直至稳定。间冰阶事件的不稳定性可能与北纬 60°上 7 月份太阳辐射中值的延长有关[26]（图 1d），这与低太阳辐射时发生的较稳定的寒冷气候不同。全新世时，气候和 ECM 均相对较稳定，太阳辐射由 523 W·m⁻² 降至 475 W·m⁻²（参见文献 26），说明仅仅太阳辐射本身不足以影响气候的稳定性。

The seasonal time resolution of the ECM record portrays an aspect of the climate system that consistently and frequently changes between glacial and near-interglacial conditions in periods of less than a decade, and on occasion as quickly as three years. Instead of being rapid and smooth, the transitions are characterized by flickering between preferred states. It is improbable that the surface area of dust sources such as loess-covered land,

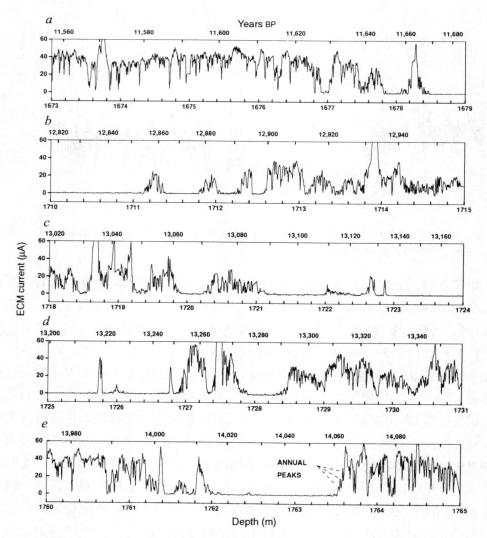

Fig. 3. *a-e*, Expanded ECM records of recent climate transitions plotted against depth (bottom axis) with one sample per millimetre of depth. *a*, Start of Holocene, end of Younger Dryas. *b*, Start of Younger Dryas. *c*, End of inter-Allerød cold period. *d*, Start of inter-Allerød cold period. *e*, Transition. The top axes are age, in years BP. At this scale the annual signal in the ECM can occasionally be resolved as small local peaks that occur once per year. During the transition at 14,060 BP (*e*), three annual peaks can be resolved. The annual layer thickness is ~6 cm per year during warmer, less dusty conditions and 3 cm per year during colder dusty conditions. Occasionally the number of ECM annual peaks and annual layers in a given segment differ slightly because particulate and visual stratigraphy records were also considered when annual layers were identified.

ECM 记录的季节性分辨率反映了气候系统的一个方面，即连续不断地变化于冰期与接近间冰期的环境之间，变化周期小于 10 年，甚至有时仅为 3 年。与快速和平滑的变化相反，此类变迁以在主要环境之间的闪电式转换为特征。以陆地表层的黄土（因冰川和海水的后退而新鲜暴露出来）等为来源的海洋表层粉尘不可能像 ECM

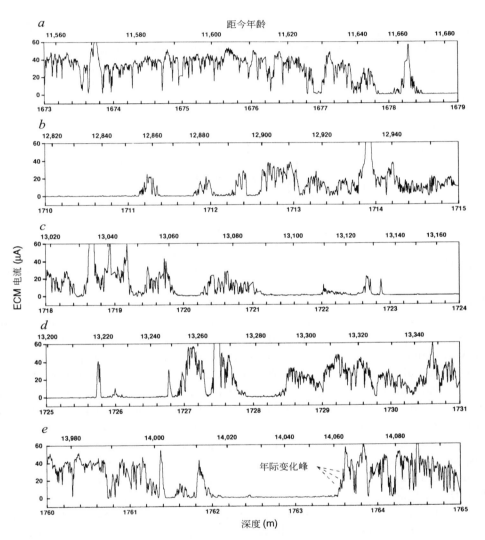

图 3. a~e，近期气候变化的 ECM 放大记录相对于深度（底部横轴）的变化，采样间隔为 1 mm。a，全新世开始时期和新仙女木期末期。b，新仙女木期开始时期。c，阿勒罗德冷期的间期的末期。d，阿勒罗德冷期的间期伊始。e，过渡期。顶部横轴表示距今的年龄，单位为年。在该刻度轴下，ECM 的年际信号有时可分解为较小的局部峰值，一年发生一次。在距今 14,060 年前（e）的过渡时期可以分辨出三个年际峰值。当气候温暖、粉尘较少时，年沉积层的厚度约为 6 cm·yr^{-1}，而在气候相对较冷、粉尘较多的环境下则为 3 cm·yr^{-1}。有时，相同部分上 ECM 的年际峰值与年沉积层会存在些许差异，这是因为在确定年沉积层时我们还考虑了颗粒及可见地层学记录因素。

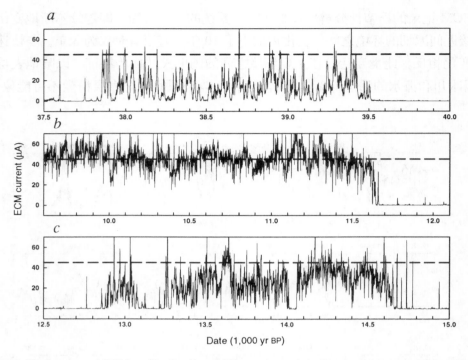

Fig. 4. Yearly averaged ECM profiles for three 2,500-year intervals. *a*, Interstadial event at 37.8 to 39.5 kyr BP; *b*, the start of the Holocene; *c*, the Allerød and Bølling periods.

freshly exposed by retreating ice or water, can change as abruptly as is observed in the ECM record. A re-ordering of atmospheric circulation could rapidly change the surface moisture, wind speeds and air-mass routing and, hence, change the quantity of airborne loess. A re-ordering of atmospheric circulation and increased wind speeds is consistent with observed changes in the temperature gradient between high and mid northern latitudes during glacial conditions[27] and with evidence from ocean sediment cores showing rapid changes in sea surface temperatures[3]. The influence of temperature gradients on atmospheric circulation suggests that the rapid changes observed in the ECM record are a result of changes in the mechanisms influencing high- to mid-latitude Northern Hemisphere temperature gradients. Concepts of mechanisms for rapid changes in ocean and atmospheric circulation, and in sea ice extent, need to be examined to see if they can explain the repeated and rapid changes observed in this record. As additional records from the new Greenland ice cores become available it will be possible to develop and test hypotheses regarding climate mechanisms responsible for the abrupt and frequent climate changes we observe. The increased time resolution provided by these cores may allow analogies to be drawn with the instrumental record, thus opening other ways to understand the mechanism responsible for the flickering switch.

(**361**, 432-436; 1993)

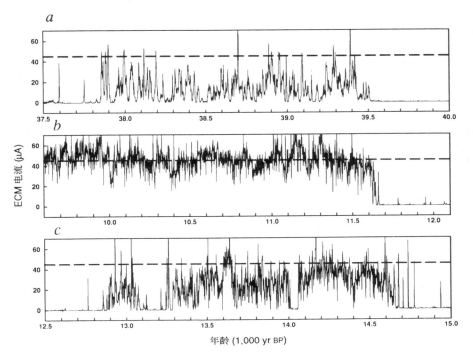

图 4. 三个分别为期 2,500 年的时间段上 ECM 的年平均值剖面。a，距今 3.78 万年至 3.95 万年间的间冰阶事件；b，全新世的开始阶段；c，阿勒罗德期和波令期。

记录中所观测到的突变那样迅速。而大气环流的重新组合则可能快速地改变海表湿度、风速以及气团的路径，进而改变大气输送的黄土的量。此外，大气环流的变化以及风速的提高与已观测到的北半球中高纬度地区冰期环境下温度梯度的变化[27]一致，同时也与海洋沉积物岩芯中显示的海表温度的快速变化[3]一致。温度梯度对大气环流的影响表明，在 ECM 记录中观测到的快速变化是影响北半球由高纬度到中纬度地区温度梯度的机制变化的结果。海洋和大气环流以及海冰范围的快速变化机制有待于进一步研究，以检验是否可以利用它们来解释该记录中所观测到的周期性的快速变化。随着获取的新的格陵兰冰芯越来越多，能够反映我们所观测到的突然且经常性的气候变化的气候机制理论必将得到发展和检验。而随着这些岩芯提供的时间分辨率越来越高，人们将可以从仪器记录中得到类似的结果，由此开辟出其他方法来解释引起快速变换的机制。

（齐红艳 翻译；段克勤 审稿）

K. C. Taylor[*], G. W. Lamorey[†], G. A. Doyle[†], R. B. Alley[‡], P. M. Grootes[§], P. A. Mayewski[||], J. W. C. White[¶] & L. K. Barlow[¶]

[*] Desert Research Institute, University of Nevada System, Reno, Nevada 89506, USA

[†] Hydrology/Hydrogeology Science Program, University of Nevada, Reno, Nevada 89557, USA

[‡] Earth System Science Center and Department of Geosciences, The Pennsylvania State University, University Park, Pennsylvania 16802, USA

[§] Department of Geological Sciences and Quaternary Research Center, University of Washington, Seattle, Washington 98195, USA

[||] Glacier Research Group, Institute for the Study of Earth, Oceans and Space, University of New Hampshire, Durham, New Hampshire 03824, USA

[¶] Institute of Arctic and Alpine Research and Department of Geological Sciences, University of Colorado, Boulder, Colorado 80309, USA

Received 5 October; accepted 22 December 1992.

References:

1. Johnsen, S. *et al. Nature* **359**, 311-313 (1992).

2. Lehman, S. J. & Keigwin, L. D., *Nature* **356**, 757-762 (1992).

3. Ruddiman, W. F. & Macintyre, A. *Palaeogeogr. Palaeoclimatol. Palaeoecol.* **35**, 45-214 (1981).

4. Broeker, W. S. *et al. Palaeoceanography* **5**, 469-477 (1990).

5. Woillard, G. M. & Mode, W. D. *Science* **215**, 159-161 (1982).

6. Kolstrup, E. *Geologie Mijnb.* **69**, 253-262 (1990).

7. Coope, G. R. *Phil. Trans. R. Soc.* B, **280**, 313-2440 (1977).

8. Hammer, C. *et al. J. Glaciol.* **25**, 359-372 (1980).

9. Taylor, K. C. *et al. J. Glaciol.* **38**, 325-332 (1992).

10. Moore, J. C. *et al. J. Geophys. Res.* **97**, 1887-1896 (1992).

11. Bates, T. S. *et al. J. Atmos. Chem.* **14**, 315-337 (1992).

12. Neftel, A. *et al. Am. Geophys. Un. Geophys. Monogr.* **33**, 32-38 (1985).

13. Legrand, M. & Kirchner, S. *J. Geophys. Res.* **95**, 3493-3509 (1990).

14. Legrand, M. *et al. Geophys. Res. Lett.* **19**, 473-477 (1992).

15. Logan, J. *et al. J. Geophys. Res.* **88**, 10785-10807 (1983).

16. Hammer, C. *et al. Am. Geophys. Un. Geophys. Monogr.* **33**, 90-94 (1985).

17. Meese, D. A. *et al. U.S. Army Cold Regions Res. Engng Lab. Rep.* (in the press).

18. Dansgaard, W. *Tellus* **16**, 436-467 (1964).

19. Lorius, C. *et al. Nature* **280**, 644-648 (1979).

20. Dansgaard, W. *et al. Science* **218**, 1273-1277 (1982).

21. Fischer, D. A. *Tellus* B**43**, 401-407 (1991).

22. Fischer, D. A. *The Last Deglaciation: Absolute and Radiocarbon Chronologies*, NATO ASI Series, Vol. 12, 200-212 (1992).

23. Fischer, D. A. *The Physical Basis of Icesheet Modelling*, IAHS Publ. **170**, 45-51 (1987).

24. Paterson, W. S. B. *Cold Regions Sci. Technol.* **20**, 75-98 (1990).

25. Dansgaard, W. *et al. Nature* **339**, 532-523 (1989).

26. Berger, A. & Loutre, M. *Quat. Sci. Rev.* **10**, 297-317 (1991).

27. Frenzel, B. *et al.* (eds) *Atlas of Palaeoclimates and Palaeoenvironments of the Northern Hemisphere*, 39-45 (Geographical Research Institute, Budapest, 1992).

Acknowledgements. We thank the NSF Division of Polar Programs for funding, numerous GISP colleagues, the Science Management Office (University of New Hampshire), the Polar Ice Coring Office (University of Alaska) and TAG 109th (New York Air National Guard) for their assistance.

Recent Change of Arctic Tundra Ecosystems from a Net Carbon Dioxide Sink to a Source

W. C. Oechel *et al.*

Editor's Note

One of the big uncertainties in predictions of future climate change is how the biosphere responds. Living organisms play a central role in the uptake and release of greenhouse gases, particularly carbon dioxide and methane, from and to the atmosphere. If rising temperatures alter this balance, the result could potentially outweigh the human inputs, for better or worse. Here Walter Oechel and co-workers in the US report ominous signs that, for at least one ecosystem (Arctic tundra), the feedback may be positive: changes caused by warming could trigger release of more carbon dioxide. The causes are complex, but most probably linked to the drying of warmer tundra, which alters the rate at which the soil matter decomposes.

Arctic tundra has been a net sink for carbon dioxide during historic and recent geological times[1-4], and large amounts of carbon are stored in the soils of northern ecosystems. Many regions of the Arctic are warmer now than they have been in the past[5-10], and this warming may cause the soil to change from a carbon dioxide sink to a source by lowering the water table[11,12], thereby accelerating the rate of soil decomposition (CO_2 source)[3,13-15] so that this dominates over photosynthesis (CO_2 sink). Here we present data indicating that the tundra on the North Slope of Alaska has indeed become a source of carbon dioxide to the atmosphere. This change coincides with recent warming in the Arctic, whether this is due to increases in greenhouse gas concentrations in the atmosphere or to some other cause. Our results suggest that tundra ecosystems may exert a positive feedback on atmospheric carbon dioxide and greenhouse warming.

THE current, recent and future carbon flux of terrestrial ecosystems is controversial[16,17], and at present, the carbon budget does not balance, implying uncertainty as to the current terrestrial carbon flux. It may be that over the past 30–40 years, the terrestrial biosphere has been a net sink for carbon[11,18] large enough to account for the "missing carbon" injected into the atmosphere and not accounted for in oceanic uptake or atmospheric storage[19,20]. Analyses by Tans *et al.*[17] concluded the likelihood of a net terrestrial sink with high-latitude CO_2 sources to the atmosphere.

Northern ecosystems contain up to 455 Gt (petagrams) of C in the soil active layer and the upper levels of the permafrost, or up to ~60% of the ~750 Gt C currently in the atmosphere as CO_2 (refs 1–4). Arctic tundra ecosystems alone contain more than 50 Gt C

近期北极冻原生态系统
由净二氧化碳汇到源的转变

奥伊赫尔等

编者按

预测未来的气候变化具有很大的不确定性，其中之一便是生物圈会如何响应。在大气循环的过程中，现存生物体在温室气体（特别是二氧化碳和甲烷）的吸收和释放过程中扮演着重要角色。如果升温改变了这种平衡，不论好坏，结果可能会超过人类活动的影响。本文中，美国的沃尔特·奥伊赫尔与其同事报道了至少对于北极冻原来说是糟糕的迹象，这种反馈可能是正向的：由气候变暖所引起的诸多变化可能会引起更多二氧化碳的释放。导致这种结果的原因比较复杂，但是最有可能与冻原变暖而干燥有关，这会改变土壤中物质的分解速率。

无论是地质历史时期还是不久的过去，北极冻原都曾是二氧化碳的一个净汇[1-4]，并且在北部生态系统的土壤中储藏了大量的碳。然而与过去相比，如今北极许多地区都已变暖[5-10]，而这种变暖带来的地下水位的下降可能会导致土壤由二氧化碳的汇变为二氧化碳源[11,12]，从而加快土壤的分解作用（CO_2源）速率[3,13-15]，使之取代光合作用（CO_2汇）成为主导作用。本文我们将给出数据说明位于阿拉斯加北坡上的冻原实际上已经成为大气CO_2的一个源。不论这种变化是由于大气中温室气体浓度的增加还是其他原因所致，它与近期北极地区的变暖是一致的。研究结果表明，冻原生态系统可能在大气CO_2浓度和温室效应中发挥着正反馈作用。

陆地生态系统中过去、现在和将来的碳通量仍饱存争议[16,17]，现今碳的收支并不平衡，意味着当前陆地碳通量存在不确定性。在过去的30~40年里，陆地生物圈一直是一个净的碳汇[11,18]，大到足以达到进入大气中的"遗失碳汇"的量，但还不足以解释海洋吸收和大气储存中的那部分"碳汇"[19,20]的量。根据坦斯等[17]的分析，高纬度地区陆地可能由大气CO_2的净汇变为大气CO_2的源。

北部生态系统的土壤融冻层和上部永冻层中含有高达455 Gt的碳，相当于当前大气中CO_2总量（约750 Gt C）的60%左右（参见文献1~4）。仅北极冻原生态系统就有超过50 Gt碳以死了的有机物的形式埋藏于地下。在历史时期及最近的地质时

below ground as dead organic matter. In the historic and recent geological past, rates of carbon accumulation in tundra worldwide have been ~0.1–0.3 Gt C per year[2-4,12,21,22]. Tussock tundra is estimated to have accumulated carbon at the rate of 23 g C m^{-2} yr^{-1} (0.02 Gt C per year worldwide), wet tundra at the rate of 27 g C m^{-2} yr^{-1} (0.03 Gt C per year worldwide[2,4]) to 40–120 g C m^{-2} yr^{-1} (refs 24, 25).

High-latitude ecosystems are expected to undergo the greatest increases in surface temperature with a doubling of atmospheric CO_2. Surface temperature increases of 4 °C in summer and as much as 17 °C in winter have been predicted for high northern latitudes[5,23], providing the potential for large absolute and relative increases in temperature in arctic regions. The importance of permafrost, ice and snow in controlling arctic ecosystem processes also makes the Arctic particularly sensitive to warming[24].

Regional warming of surface air temperatures[5-8] and permafrost temperatures[9,10] has been experienced over arctic Alaska and Canada and/or central Siberia over the past century. In Alaska, despite complications from heat island effects at Barrow[26], regional summer warming over the past 70 and 20 years at Barrow and Prudhoe Bay, respectively, seems to be reflected in their temperature records (Fig. 1) and agrees with the general trend in global temperature deviations[27-29]. But although the direction of the change observed on the north slope of Alaska is that predicted by general circulation models and climate reconstructions, the temperature rise cannot definitely be ascribed to greenhouse warming[30].

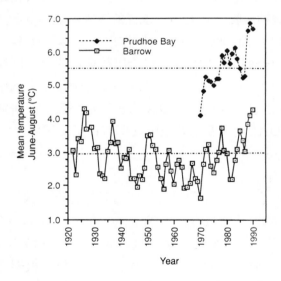

Fig. 1. Mean annual summer (June through August) temperatures from 1921 to 1990 at Barrow Alaska and from 1970 to 1990 at Prudhoe Bay Alaska. Represented are 3-yr sliding mean values from the U.S. Weather Service for Barrow, Alaska and from ARCO for the ARCO airport tower at Prudhoe Bay, Alaska.

Here we report measurements of whole-ecosystem CO_2 flux measured over five seasons (1983–1985, 1987, 1990) at Toolik Lake and along a latitudinal transect in 1990, from the Arctic Ocean at Prudhoe Bay to Toolik Lake, Alaska (Fig. 2). The initial measurements

期中，世界冻原中碳的堆积速率约为 $0.1\sim0.3$ Gt C·yr^{-1}[2-4,12,21,22]。生草丛冻原中碳的堆积速率约为 23 g C·m^{-2}·yr^{-1}（全球约 0.02 Gt C·yr^{-1}），湿地冻原为 27 g C·m^{-2}·yr^{-1}（全球约 0.03 Gt C·yr^{-1}[2,4]）到 $40\sim120$ g C·m^{-2}·yr^{-1}（参见文献 24 和 25）。

我们预期高纬生态系统能够承受大气 CO_2 浓度翻倍导致的地表最大增温。据预测，在北半球高纬地区，夏季地表温度将升高 4 ℃，而冬季的升高值则高达 17 ℃[5,23]，提供了极地地区温度潜在的相对和绝对增加量。永冻层、冰川以及积雪在北极生态系统中的重要性也使得北极地区对温度的升高尤其敏感[24]。

过去一个世纪中，区域性的地表空气升温[5-8]和永冻层升温[9,10]已经在北极阿拉斯加、加拿大和（或）中西伯利亚地区发生。在阿拉斯加，尽管巴罗地区的热岛效应较为复杂[26]，但巴罗和普拉德霍湾地区分别在过去 70 年和 20 年中发生的区域性夏季升温似乎反映于其温度记录中（图 1），并且与全球温度偏差的总趋势一致[27-29]。不过，尽管在阿拉斯加北坡温度观测值的变化方向与大气环流模式及气候重建的预测一致，但还不能将温度的升高明确地归因于温室效应[30]。

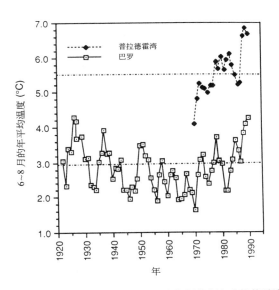

图 1. 1921~1990 年间阿拉斯加的巴罗地区及 1970~1990 年间阿拉斯加普拉德霍湾地区夏季年平均温度（6 月至 8 月）。图中所示为三年的滑动平均值，其中阿拉斯加巴罗地区采用美国气象服务中心的数据，而 ARCO 则代表阿拉斯加普拉德霍湾的 ARCO 机场灯塔。

本文我们将介绍在图利克湖的五个季度（1983~1985、1987、1990）中以及 1990 年沿北冰洋的普拉德霍湾到阿拉斯加的图利克湖的经向断面中的整个生态系统的 CO_2 通量测定结果（图 2）。初始测量结果（1983~1985，1987）是利用一个封闭的、含

(1983–1985, 1987) were made at Toolik Lake using a closed, CO_2 and long-term temperature-controlled, null-balance greenhouse chamber (CO_2LT chamber) system[31]. During the summer of 1990, we made diurnal and seasonal measurements of ecosystem CO_2 flux along a north-south transect from the Arctic Ocean at Prudhoe Bay to Toolik Lake, 200 km to the south, using a portable ecosystem cuvette and gas exchange system[32].

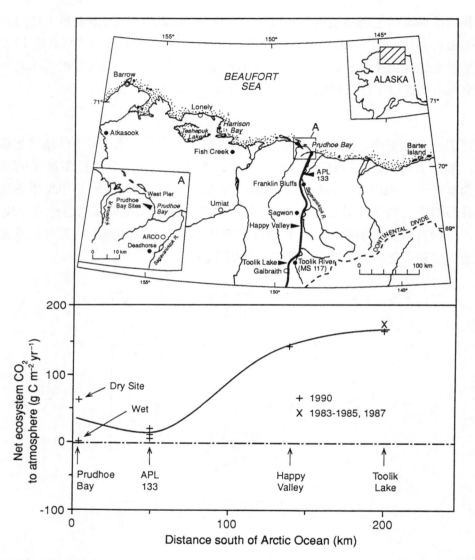

Fig. 2. Site locations on the north slope of Alaska. From north to south: Prudhoe Bay, APL-133, Happy Valley, Toolik Lake (upper panel). Seasonal carbon dioxide flux (as carbon) along a latitudinal gradient from Prudhoe Bay to Toolik Lake, Alaska in 1990 (+), and for four additional years of measurement at Toolik Lake (1983–1985, 1987; ×). The line represents an interpolation of values for 1990. Mean flux for 1983–85 and 1987 is $175 \pm 62\,\mathrm{g\,C\,m^{-2}\,yr^{-1}}$ (mean ± 1 s.e.). Site differences in soil moisture are noted at Prudhoe Bay and APL-133. The three values at APL-133 represent the three areas of differing moisture availability (drained, control and impounded) studied which resulted in higher, medium and lower CO_2 efflux from the tundra to the atmosphere respectively. For the initial measurements (1983–85,

20

CO_2 的且温度长期可控的零平衡温室箱（CO_2LT chamber）系统[31]在图利克湖上得到的。1990 年夏，我们利用一个便携式生态系统模拟仓和气体交换系统[32]测量了沿北冰洋的普拉德霍湾到图利克湖的长 200 km 的南北断面上生态系统中 CO_2 的日通量和季节通量。

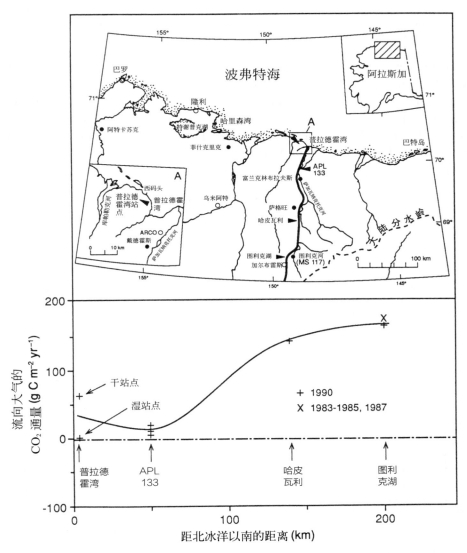

图 2. 阿拉斯加北坡上的测站位置。由北向南依次为：普拉德霍湾、APL-133、哈皮瓦利和图利克湖（上图）。1990 年从阿拉斯加的普拉德霍湾到图利克湖的沿经向梯度的二氧化碳季节通量（+）和在图利克湖测定的其他四个年份的相应值（1983~1985，1987：×）。图中的线表示 1990 年的内插值。1983~1985 和 1987 年的平均通量为 175±62 g C·m⁻²·yr⁻¹（平均值 ±1 个标准差）。在普拉德霍湾和 APL-133 中可以看到各测站中土壤含水量的差异。APL-133 站上的三个值分别代表三种不种的水分情况（排水、对照、蓄水），结果显示，从冻原流向大气的 CO_2 通量分别表现为高、中、低值。对于初始测定结果（1983~1985，1987），在测站周围设置了三个相同的控制室。每 3 分钟测量一次，每 6 分钟求平均值并做记录，贯穿

1987), there were three replicate control chambers running under ambient conditions. Measurements were made every 3 minutes, and averaged and recorded every 6 minutes throughout the day and the season. For 1990, measurements were made from shortly after snow melt to shortly before soil freeze-up in the autumn at each site on each of six replicate plots roughly once every 1.5 h throughout the 24-h measurement period. Seasonal flux was extrapolated to zero at the time of snow melt in the spring and of soil freeze-up in the autumn. The net seasonal flux for each site was determined as the integral under the curve of the seasonal pattern of daily fluxes. There was little variability in daily CO_2 flux rates among the replicates at each site on any day. Because these measurements were made only during the snow-free summer period, they underestimate the seasonal carbon loss to the atmosphere by the presumably small amount of soil and plant respiration that occurs under snow during the unmeasured winter period.

The repeated summer measurements of diurnal CO_2 flux at Toolik Lake made between 1983 and 1987 indicated a loss of CO_2 from the tussock tundra of 0.72–3.9 g C m^{-2} d^{-1} (Table 1). If we assume a nominal active season of 125 days, these annual rates of CO_2 efflux varied from 53 to 286 g C m^{-2} yr^{-1}, reflecting the year-to-year variability in environmental conditions (Table 1). We may have slightly underestimated CO_2 loss by missing some periods of soil and plant respiration in early spring and late autumn (S. A. Zimov, personal communication).

Table 1. Characteristics of research sites and measured CO_2 fluxes

Site	Latitude	Longitude	Distance (km)	Elevation (m)	Tundra type	Moisture	Year	Average summer temperature* (°C)	Summer precipitation* (mm)	Average CO_2 flux (g C m^{-2} d^{-1})
Prudhoe Bay wet	70° 22′	148° 45′	2.5	3	Wet sedge	Wet	1990	6.5¶	49§	+0.034
Prudhoe Bay moist	70° 22′	148° 45′	2.5	3	Wet sedge	Moist	1990	6.5¶	49§	+0.66
APL-133 control	69° 50′	148° 45′	50	80	Wet/ moist sedge	Moist	1990	10.0‡	69‡	+0.216
APL-133 flooded	69° 50′	148° 45′	50	80	Wet/ moist sedge	Wet	1990	10.0‡	69‡	+0.091
APL-133 drained	69° 50′	148° 45′	50	80	Wet/ moist sedge	Moist	1990	10.0‡	69‡	+0.39
Happy Valley	69° 08′	148° 50′	140	366	Tussock	Moist	1990	13.1†	50†	+1.155
Toolik Lake							1990	9.3‡	160‖	+1.34
Toolik Lake							1983	8.9#	N.D.**	+3.8
Toolik Lake	68° 38′	149° 35′	200	732	Tussock	Moist	1984	N.D.**	264‖	+3.9
Toolik Lake							1985	7.5‡:6.5#	213‖	+1.1
Toolik Lake							1987	9.2§	246‖	+0.72

Positive values of flux indicate CO_2 loss to the atmosphere. Daily CO_2 flux measurements are calculated from diurnal measurements, and the integrated seasonal uptake is averaged to provide an average daily flux for the period of biological activity.

* Summer months from June–August.

整个季节的每一天。在 1990 年，每个测站的测定结果都从积雪开始融化不久一直到秋季土壤即将结冰之前，在 24 小时中基本上每 1.5 小时对 6 个相同的样地各进行一次测量。将季节通量在春季积雪融化和秋季土壤冻结时分别外推至零。每个测站的季节通量确定为日通量的季节性变化曲线下的积分值。各测站上每天的重复测定结果之间的 CO_2 日通量差异很小。由于这些测定结果仅是在无雪的夏季测得的，他们假定在未测定的冬季时日里，积雪下发生的土壤和植被呼吸作用是很小的，由此很可能低估了 CO_2 向大气排放量的季节性变化。

1983 年到 1987 年间，对图利克湖夏季的 CO_2 日通量的重复测量结果表明，生草丛冻原的 CO_2 流失量为 0.72~3.9 g C · m^{-2} · d^{-1}（表 1）。倘若我们假定一个活跃季度为 125 天，CO_2 通量的年际速率在 53 g C · m^{-2} · yr^{-1} 到 286 g C · m^{-2} · yr^{-1} 之间变化，反映了环境条件的年际变化（表 1）。由于我们忽略了早春及晚秋时土壤和植被的呼吸作用，二氧化碳的流失量可能略有低估（兹莫夫，个人交流）。

表 1. 研究测站特征及测得的 CO_2 通量值

测站	纬度	经度	距离 (km)	海拔 (m)	冻原类型	水分条件	年代	夏季平均温度 * (℃)	夏季降水量 * (mm)	平均 CO_2 通量 (g C · m^{-2} · d^{-1})
普拉德霍湾湿地	70°22′	148°45′	2.5	3	湿润苔原	湿润	1990	6.5¶	49§	+0.034
普拉德霍湾半湿润地区	70°22′	148°45′	2.5	3	湿润苔原	半湿润	1990	6.5¶	49§	+0.66
APL-133 对照区	69°50′	148°45′	50	80	湿润 / 半湿润苔原	半湿润	1990	10.0‡	69‡	+0.216
APL-133 蓄水区	69°50′	148°45′	50	80	湿润 / 半湿润苔原	湿润	1990	10.0‡	69‡	+0.091
APL-133 排水区	69°50′	148°45′	50	80	湿润 / 半湿润苔原	半湿润	1990	10.0‡	69‡	+0.39
哈皮瓦利	69°08′	148°50′	140	366	生草丛	半湿润	1990	13.1†	50†	+1.155
图利克湖							1990	9.3‡	160‖	+1.34
图利克湖							1983	8.9#	N. D. **	+3.8
图利克湖	68°38′	149°35′	200	732	生草丛	半湿润	1984	N. D. **	264‖	+3.9
图利克湖							1985	7.5‡ : 6.5#	213‖	+1.1
图利克湖							1987	9.2§	246‖	+0.72

通量为正，表示 CO_2 流向大气。每日的 CO_2 通量结果是根据日测定值计算出的，将季度吸收总量平均到每天就可以获得生物活动阶段的平均日通量。

* 6~8 月的夏季月份。

† This study, missing 22 days of data.

‡ Toolik River, MS-117 (D. Kane, personal communication).

§ This study.

‖ Toolik River, MS-117 (R. J. McClure, personal communication).

¶ National Climatic Data Center, Asheville, NC computed from the mean minimum and mean maximum recorded temperatures.

Toolik River, MS-117 (R. H. Haugen, personal communication).

** N.D. Not Determined.

Diurnal and seasonal patterns of carbon flux were dominated by periods of carbon loss to the atmosphere. For example, Happy Valley shows a seasonal increase in the rate of loss of carbon at "night" from early season to peak season. This increase is presumably due to increasing soil temperatures, soil aeration and depth of thaw over this period. Peak net ecosystem carbon uptake also increases from early to mid-season, but on no days measured is the carbon balance positive, and soil decomposition and plant respiration always exceed photosynthetic uptake for the diurnal period. By mid-season, despite increases in midday rates of carbon uptake, carbon loss has increased more than has photosynthetic uptake, and the net loss of carbon has increased compared to early season rates. The measurement period was extended in 1991 to cover almost the entire snow-free period, reducing the extrapolation necessary (W.C.O., unpublished data). The results support those presented here and confirm the carbon loss from spring snow melt to autumn freeze-up along the transect measured.

Net seasonal carbon loss to the atmosphere was found at all sites measured. Carbon loss to the atmosphere during the 1990 season generally increased from north to south (Fig. 2), and on the drier areas within a site (Fig. 2, Table 1). The site closest to the coast, Prudhoe Bay Wet, was the wettest site measured (Table 1). The southern tussock tundra sites, Toolik Lake and Happy Valley, were better drained, and had greater thaw depths and lower water tables. The average rate of annual CO_2 loss for the tussock tundra sites in 1990 was 156 g C m^{-2} yr^{-1}, whereas carbon loss for the wet coastal tundra sites (Prudhoe Bay and APL-133) was ~34 g C m^{-2} yr^{-1} (Table 1). The results for the tussock tundra ecosystems during the 1990 sampling season agree well with the initial measurements made between 1983 and 1987 (Table 1) and with subsequent measurements made in 1991 and 1992 (W.C.O., unpublished data). These data indicate a change in carbon balance of the tundra with respect to the atmosphere, in response to the trend in climate warming for the north slope of Alaska.

We feel that the change from carbon accumulation to carbon loss in these ecosystems is not caused directly by the increase in temperature but indirectly, by enhanced drainage and soil aeration, and a decrease in the water table[11,12]. Decomposition of the soil organic layer in northern peatlands is controlled much more by drainage, and consequently soil aeration, than by temperature[3,13-15]. Warmer periods in the past that resulted in peat accumulation in the Canadian sub-arctic and Alaskan arctic[33], where there is no evidence of current carbon accumulation[3], are thought to reflect the combination of warmer and wetter conditions.

† 本研究缺少 22 天的数据。

‡ 图利克湖，MS-117（凯恩，个人交流）。

§ 本文研究结果。

‖ 图利克湖，MS-117（麦克卢尔，个人交流）。

¶ 位于北卡罗来纳州阿什维尔的国家气候数据中心，根据温度记录的平均最小值和平均最大值计算出的结果。

图利克湖，MS-117（豪根，个人交流）。

** N.D. 表示未测定。

　　碳通量的日变化和季节性变化类型均受控于碳向大气流失的时间。例如，在哈皮瓦利地区，从季度早期到旺季，"夜晚"碳的流失速率呈季节性增加。这种增加可能是由于该时段土壤温度、土壤通气性以及融冻深度的增加所致。从季度伊始至中期，生态系统的最大碳吸收量也在增加，但在日测量结果中未见到正的碳平衡值，而土壤分解和植被的呼吸作用总是会超出一天内光合作用的吸收量。到季度中期时，虽然正午碳的吸收速率增加，但碳的流失量比光合作用的吸收量更大，因此碳的净流失速率高于初期。1991 年时我们延长了测定时段，几乎包含了整个无雪期，减少了外推的必要（奥伊赫尔，未发表的数据）。其结果支持本文所述，并且证实，从春季冰雪融化到秋季结冰时测量断面上的碳是逐渐流失的。

　　所有测站上都发现了碳向大气的净流失。在 1990 年的观测季度中，碳向大气的流失量由北向南增加（图 2），在同一个测站越干的区域其流失量越大（图 2，表 1）。最靠近海岸附近的普拉德霍湾湿地是测站中最湿的一个站（表 1）。南部的生草丛冻原测站，即图利克湖及哈皮瓦利的排水更好一些，并且其融冻深度更大，地下水位更低。1990 年，生草丛冻原的 CO_2 年流失速率为 156 g C·m^{-2}·yr^{-1}，而海岸附近湿润测站（普拉德霍湾和 APL-133）中碳的流失速率则为 34 g C·m^{-2}·yr^{-1} 左右（表 1）。在 1990 年的采样季中，生草丛冻原生态系统的结果与 1983 年和 1987 年间初始测定结果（表 1）以及后续 1991 年和 1992 年得到的结果（奥伊赫尔，未发表的数据）均吻合较好。这些数据指示了冻原碳平衡相对于大气碳平衡的变化，是对阿拉斯加北坡气候变暖趋势的响应。

　　我们认为，这些生态系统中由碳累积到碳流失的变化并不是直接由温度的增加引起的，而是由温度上升引起的排水性增强、土壤通气性提高以及地下水位的降低间接导致的[11,12]。相比于温度来说，北部泥炭区土壤有机层的分解作用更多地受控于排水以及由此带来的土壤通气性的状况[3,13-15]。过去的一系列温暖时期导致加拿大的副极地地区和北极圈内的阿拉斯加地区[33]出现泥炭堆积，这些温暖时期被认为是暖湿组合环境的反映，但并未在这两个地区发现近期的碳堆的证据[3]。

Given the general pattern of warming for the north slope of Alaska and the Canadian arctic[6-10,34], the patterns observed along this transect in Alaska may be widespread and the carbon loss huge. If the average rate of loss in tussock tundra of 156 g C m^{-2} yr^{-1} is typical for circumpolar tussock tundra, the loss of carbon to the atmosphere in 1990 from the 0.90×10^6 km^2 of tussock tundra worldwide[2] would be 0.14 Gt C per year. Similarly, if the 34 g C m^{-2} yr^{-1} of CO_2 evolution from wet tundra is applied to the 1.00×10^6 km^2 of wet coastal tundra, another 0.03 Gt C is lost annually to the atmosphere. Adding 0.02 Gt C for efflux from arctic tundra lakes and rivers[35] results in a total estimated annual loss of 0.19 Gt C from these three circumpolar arctic surface types. This combined efflux can be compared to the 0.2–0.7 Gt C calculated to be lost to the atmosphere from high-latitude ecosystems[17]. Given the large below-ground stores of carbon in arctic, boreal forest and high-latitude bogs, these high-latitude ecosystems could provide a considerable positive feedback on increasing atmospheric CO_2 and global warming.

There are many uncertainties in predicting the long-term effect of global change on arctic ecosystems. The initial response to warming and drying may be a loss of carbon from the system, whereas at longer intervals, invasion by shrub and tree species may result in increased above-ground carbon storage. Other compensatory processes include cooling of the soil surface (following increased insulation from drying of the soil surface and litter or biomass accumulation from elevated CO_2 and/or other climatic effects). Currently there is no evidence that these compensatory processes are acting or will act quickly. Field and laboratory experiments indicate little or no stimulation of photosynthesis in the Arctic by elevated atmospheric CO_2 (ref. 36). It is likely that global warming will lead to significant outgassing of carbon from wet and moist tundra before other processes reincorporate this carbon into arctic areas. Global warming could accelerate the rate of carbon loss in arctic tundra ecosystems by increasing the depth of thaw, increasing soil drainage and aeration, and increasing rates of soil decomposition and plant respiration more than gross primary productivity.

The recent climate patterns may be part of the normal climate variation or an early indication of greenhouse warming. In either case, it is clear that they have affected the current carbon flux from the arctic ecosystem, and that arctic and boreal forest ecosystems could provide a strong positive feedback on atmospheric carbon dioxide concentration.

(**361**, 520-523; 1993)

Walter C. Oechel[*†], Steven J. Hastings[*], George Vourlitis[*], Mitchell Jenkins[*], George Riechers[‡] & Nancy Grulke[§]

[*] Systems Ecology Research Group and Department of Biology, San Diego State University, San Diego, California 92182, USA

[‡] Statewide Air Pollution Research Center, University of California, Riverside, California 92521, USA

[§] USDA Forest Service, 3200 Southwest Jefferson Way, Corvallis, Oregon 97331, USA

[†] To whom correspondence should be addressed.

Received 27 April; accepted 21 December 1992.

考虑到阿拉斯加北坡及加拿大境内的北极圈地区总的变暖趋势[6-10,34]，沿阿拉斯加的断面观测到的类型应该有广泛的分布，而且碳的流失量可能是巨大的。倘若环极附近生草丛冻原的平均流失速率为 156 g C·m^{-2}·yr^{-1}，那么 1990 年世界范围内总面积达 0.90×10^6 km^2 的生草丛冻原中流向大气的碳释放量[2]将达 0.14 Gt C·yr^{-1}。同样地，倘若将湿地冻原中 34 g C·m^{-2}·yr^{-1} 的 CO_2 排放速率应用到 1.00×10^6 km^2 的沿海湿地冻原上，则每年释放到大气的 CO_2 量又将增加 0.03 Gt C。再加上由极地冻原湖泊和河流中流出的 0.02 Gt C[35]，极地附近这三种地表类型每年的碳流失总量应为 0.19 Gt C 左右。该流出量的总和与计算出的由高纬生态系统流向大气的 CO_2 的量 0.2~0.7 Gt C 是相当的[17]。鉴于北极的极北林区和高纬沼泽中巨大的地下碳储量，这些高纬生态系统将对大气中 CO_2 的增加和全球变暖产生明显的正反馈效应。

在预测全球变化对北极生态系统的长期效应方面还存在许多不确定性。碳的流失可能是系统对气候变暖和变干的初始响应，而从长期来看，灌木丛和各种树木的侵入将导致地表之上碳存储量的增加。其他的补偿过程还包括土壤表层的降温（因土壤表层变干导致绝热效应增强，以及 CO_2 升高和（或）其他气候效应引起的垃圾及生物体加积增强所致）等。目前，还没有证据证明这些补偿过程能够或将要很快地发挥作用。野外观测及实验室研究均表明，大气中 CO_2 的增加对北极地区的光合作用的促进作用很弱甚至没有（参见文献 36）。在其他过程将碳重新吸收至北极地区以前，全球变暖可能会导致大量的碳从湿润和半湿润的冻原生态系统中排放出来。全球变暖将使融冻深度增大、土壤的排水性和通气性增强、土壤分解速率和植被呼吸速率增大进而加速北极冻原生态系统中碳的流失，该作用远远高于因初级生产力总量的增加所带来的效应。

近期的气候格局可能是正常气候变化的一部分，也可能是早期温室效应的反映。很显然，无论属于哪种情况，这都已影响到了现今北极生态系统的碳通量，并且北极地区和极北林区生态系统将对大气中的二氧化碳浓度形成强烈的正反馈。

（齐红艳 翻译；徐永福 审稿）

References:

1. Miller, P. C. (ed.) in *Carbon Balance in Northern Ecosystems and the Potential Effect of Carbon Dioxide Induced Climate Change* (CONF-800033118) (NTIS, Springfield, Virginia, 1981).

2. Miller, P. C., Kendall, R. & Oechel, W. C. *Simulation* **40**, 119-131 (1983).

3. Gorham, E. *Ecol. Applic.* **1**, 182-195 (1991).

4. Oechel, W. C. & Billings, W. D. in *Arctic Physiological Processes in a Changing Climate* (eds Chapin, F. S. III, Jeffries, R., Reynolds, J., Shaver, G. & Svoboda, J.) 139-169 (Academic, New York, 1991).

5. Mitchell, J. F. B., Manabe, S., Meleshko, V. & Tokioka, T, in *Climate Change: the IPCC Scientific Assessment 1990* (Cambridge Univ. Press, Cambridge, 1990).

6. Lachenbruch, A. H. & Marshall, B. V. *Science* **234**, 689-696 (1986).

7. Jones, P. D. & Wigley, T. M. L. *Scient. Am.* **263**, 84-91 (1990).

8. Wiley, T. M. L., Jones, P. D. & Kelly, P. M. *Nature* **283**, 17-21 (1980).

9. Hengeveld, H. *A State of the Environment Report, No. 91-2* (Atmospheric Environment Service, Environment Canada, 1991).

10. Beltrami, H. & Mareschal, J. C. *Geophys. Res. Let.* **18**, 605-608 (1991).

11. Wigley, T. M. L. *Global Biogeochem. Cycles* **5**, 373-382 (1991).

12. Post, W. M. *ORNL/ TM-11457* (Oak Ridge National laboratory, Oak Ridge TN, 1990).

13. Billings, W. C., Luken, J. O., Mortensen, D. A. & Peterson, K. M. *Oecologia* **52**, 7-11 (1982).

14. Billings, W. D., Peterson, K. M., Luken, J. O. & Mortenson, D. A. *Oecologia* **65**, 26-29 (1984).

15. Clymo, R. S. *Phil. Trans. R. Soc. Lond.* **303**, 605-654 (1984).

16. Brown, S., Lugo, A. E. & Wisniewski, J. *Science* **257**, 11 (1992).

17. Tans, P., Fung, I. & Takahashi, T. *Science* **247**, 1431-1439 (1990).

18. Sarmiento, J. L., Orr, J. C. & Siegenthaler, U. *Geophys. Res.* **97**, 3621-3645 (1992).

19. Wisniewski, J. & Lugo, A. E. (eds) *Water Air Soil Pollut.* **64** (1, 2) (1992).

20. Lugo, A. E. & Brown, S. *Forest Ecol. Manage.* (in the press).

21. Schell, D. M. *Science* **219**, 1068 (1983).

22. Schell, D. M. & Ziemann, P. J. in *Permafrost. 4th int. Conf.* (National Academy Press, Washington DC, 1983).

23. Schlesinger, M. E. & Mitchell, J. F. B. *Rev. Geophys.* **25**, 760-798 (1987).

24. Chapin, F. S. III, Miller, P. C., Billings, W. D. & Coyne P. I. *An Arctic Ecosystem, the Coastal Tundra at Barrow, Alaska* (eds Brown, J., Miller, P. C., Tieszen, L. L. & Bunnell, F. K.) 458-484 (Dowden, Hutchinson & Ross, Stroudsburg PA, 1980).

25. Coyne, P. I. & Kelley, J. J. *J. Appl. Ecol.* **12**, 587-611 (1975).

26. Dutton, E. G. & Endres, D. J. *Arct. Alp. Res.* **23**, 115-119 (1991).

27. Hansen, J. & Lebedeff, S. *J. Geophys. Res.* **92**, 13345-13372 (1987).

28. Hansen, J. & Lebedeff, S. *Geophys. Lett.* **15**, 323-326 (1988).

29. Folland, C. K., Karl, T. R. & Vinnikov, K. Ya. in *Climate Change: the IPCC Scientific Assessment 1990* (Cambridge Univ. Press, Cambridge 1990).

30. Wigley, T. M. L. & Barnett, T. P. in *Climate Change: the IPCC Scientific Assessment 1990* (Cambridge Univ, Press, Cambridge, 1990).

31. Oechel, W. C. *et al. Funct. Ecol.* **6**, 86-100 (1992).

32. Vourlitis, G. L., Oechel, W. C., Hastings, S. J. & Jenkins, M. A. *Funct. Ecol.* (in the press).

33. Marion, G. M. & Oechel, W. C. *Holocene* (in the press).

34. Lachenbruch, A. H., Cladouhos, T. T. & Saltus, R. W. in *Permafrost Temperature and the Changing Climate, Proc. 5th int. Conf. Permafrost* (ed. Senneset. K.) (Tapir, Trondheim, 1988).

35. King, G. W., Kipphut, G. W. & Miller, M. C. *Science* **251**, 298-301 (1991).

36. Tissue, D. T. & Oechel, W. C. *Ecology* **68**, 401-410 (1987).

Acknowledgements. Supported by the CO_2 Research Program of the Office of Health and Environmental Research of the U.S. Department of Energy. We thank W. Lawrence and T. Prudhomme for assistance in developing the CO_2 LT greenhouse system, S. Cowles for data analysis, and B. Strain, I. Fung, S. Wofsy, F. S. Chapin III, G. Shaver and W. D. Billings for reviewing an earlier draft of this manuscript. Accommodation and support provided by the North Slope Borough, Department of Industrial Development and ARCO, Department of Environmental Compliance at Prudhoe Bay and by the University of Alaska at Toolik Lake are gratefully acknowledged.

Effects of an Endothermic Phase Transition at 670 km Depth in a Spherical Model of Convection in the Earth's Mantle

P. J. Tackley *et al.*

Editor's Note

A long-standing debate over whether mantle convection—the driving force for plate tectonics—happens in one layer or two is given a conciliatory answer in this paper by geophysicist Paul Tackley and colleagues. Taking advantage of the burgeoning advances in computer power, they conduct a simulation of convective flow in a three-dimensional spherical model of the Earth. They find that while convection is mostly double-layered, with a boundary created by a change in mineral structure around 670 km, rising plumes from the core–mantle boundary can sometimes reach through to the upper mantle. Slabs of cold downwelling material in the upper mantle accumulate at the boundary until suddenly flushing through to the lower mantle. So the ultimate answer is "both".

Numerical modelling of mantle convection in a spherical shell with an endothermic phase change at 670 km depth reveals an inherently three-dimensional flow pattern, containing cylindrical plumes and linear sheets which behave differently in their ability to penetrate the phase change. The dynamics are dominated by accumulation of downwelling cold material above 670 km depth, resulting in frequent avalanches of upper-mantle material into the lower mantle. This process generates long-wavelength lateral heterogeneity, helping to resolve the contradiction between seismic tomographic observations and expectations from mantle convection simulations.

THE question of whether an endothermic phase transition associated with the seismic discontinuity at 670 km depth could enforce layered convection in the Earth's mantle has received much attention[1-5], and has profound implications for the Earth's thermal and chemical structure and evolution[6]. Early two-dimensional numerical modelling[1] seemed to show that an unrealistically large Clapeyron slope of -6 MPa K^{-1} would be required for layering to occur. Recent work in two-dimensional cartesian[2,3,48] and spherical axisymmetric[4,5] geometries with realistic phase-change parameters has, however, indicated significant layering, as well as complex new phenomena and modes of time-dependence in the flow.

To understand the Earth it is essential to determine how the effects observed in these two-dimensional studies are modified in three-dimensional geometry. Here we present results

地球内部 670 km 深度处的矿物吸热相变对地幔对流模式的影响

塔克利等

编者按

本文中，地球物理学家保罗·塔克利和他的同事们对一个存在已久的争论——地幔对流（板块构造的驱动力）是发生在一层还是两层——给出了一个和解的答案。得益于计算机性能的突飞猛进，他们开展了地球三维球状模型中地幔对流的模拟。他们发现，尽管对流大多分两层进行，边界由 670 km 深度附近的矿物结构突变产生，但是从核幔边界上升的地幔热柱有时能到达上地幔，而上地幔中冷的下沉物质首先在边界上聚集，直至它们遽然突破边界进入下地幔。因此，最终的答案是二者兼有，即地幔双层对流和单层对流模式共存。

在地球内部 670 km 深度处，地幔矿物会发生吸热相变。基于此，我们建立了三维球壳地幔对流数值模型，揭示了固有的、复杂的地幔流动模式，它包含了圆柱状的地幔柱和线状的地幔薄板，并且具有不同的穿透相变层的能力。地幔对流的动力学特征主要表现为下沉的冷物质在 670 km 的相变面上方堆积，导致上地幔物质频繁涌入下地幔。这种过程产生了长波长的横向不均匀性，它能帮助解决地震层析成像观测与地幔对流模拟预测结果之间存在的矛盾。

地球内部 670 km 深度处存在一个地震不连续面，与其相关的矿物吸热相变是否能促进地幔的分层对流这一科学问题 [1-5]，受到了人们的极大关注。同时，该问题对地球的热和化学结构及演化也具有重大意义 [6]。前期的二维数值模型 [1] 似乎显示出了地幔分层对流的发生需要一个大得不切实际的克拉珀龙斜率 $-6\ \mathrm{MPa \cdot K^{-1}}$。然而，最近带有实际相变参数的二维笛卡儿 [2,3,48] 和球形轴对称 [4,5] 几何结构的数值模拟工作揭示出了明显的地幔分层，在地幔流动中还出现了一些新的、复杂的、并随时间而演化的现象和模式。

为了更好地理解地球内部活动机理，确定这些在二维模型中观察到的效应在三

from a numerical simulation of fully three-dimensional compressible mantle convection in a spherical shell with an endothermic phase change at 670 km depth. The spatial resolution and Rayleigh number are much higher than in previous spherical models with no phase change[7-9]. Although there are some similarities with the two-dimensional results, the simulated flow pattern is inherently three-dimensional, with features that penetrate the phase change being exclusively cylindrical in form. The upper mantle is characterized by interconnected linear downwellings which do not penetrate. At the intersections of these downwelling sheets, cold material accumulates above 670 km depth, building up until huge catastrophic breakthroughs[1,4,5] into the lower mantle are precipitated, flushing the local upper mantle contents through broad cylindrical downwellings to the core–mantle boundary (CMB). These events occur in a globally asynchronous manner, with typically three to four in progress at any particular time. This process generates large-amplitude long-wavelength lateral heterogeneity, which may go some way towards reconciling observations of long-wavelength dominance from seismic tomography[10-15] with the much broader spectrum predicted by high-Rayleigh-number convection simulations[16,17].

The behaviour of downwellings is similar to that observed in a completely basally heated three-dimensional cartesian layer with two phase changes[18]. We find however that the use of spherical geometry and realistic internal heating greatly modifies the heat flow characteristics, geometry of lower-mantle flow, upwelling plume structure and global time-dependence, as well as aiding direct comparison with seismic tomography.

Model Characteristics

Our model incorporates the effect of the endothermic transition from spinel to perovskite plus magnesiowüstite occurring at ~670 km depth, consistent with a peridotitic mantle composition[19]. Some authors have included additional phase changes in their models[2,3,5,18,48]. These slightly alter the propensity towards layering and cause some other second-order effects, but considering the other approximations and uncertainties in current mantle modelling we choose to restrict these calculations to an examination of the first-order effect due to the endothermic phase change at 670 km depth. Our preliminary modelling results with the 400 km phase change added display little qualitative difference in behaviour.

The equations of compressible self-gravitating flow are solved and integrated in time using a spectral-transform method[17], implemented on the Intel Touchstone Delta parallel supercomputer system at the California Institute of Technology. As the mantle is characterized by very high Prandtl number, inertial terms are ignored. The anelastic approximation is used, eliminating acoustic waves which propagate many orders of magnitude faster than convective velocities. Entropy, pressure, gravitational potential and poloidal mass flux potential are expanded laterally in spherical harmonics, up to degree and order 127, and the nonlinear products associated with advection and viscous

维空间中如何变化显得尤为必要。这里我们展示了球壳在 670 km 深度上赋有吸热相变的全三维可压缩地幔对流的数值模拟结果。空间分辨率和瑞利数要比之前无相变的球形模型[7-9]高得多。尽管与二维模拟结果具有一些相似性，但是这里的地幔对流是固有的、三维的，并且穿过相变带的特征（流态）在形态上几乎完全是圆柱状的。相反，上地幔中的线状下沉流相互连接，但几乎都没有穿透相变带。在这些下沉薄板的交汇处，冷物质在 670 km 上方堆积，持续聚集直至最终的突破[1,4,5]而进入下地幔之中，宽大的圆柱状下沉流冲刷局部的上地幔物质直至核幔边界（CMB）。这些事件以全球非同期的方式发生，在任何特定时间一般有三至四个事件进行。这种过程产生了大振幅、长波长的横向不均匀性，这或许可以解释地震层析成像观测到的长波长特征[10-15]与高瑞利数对流模拟预测的十分宽广的范围[16,17]。

下沉流的特征与前人的特定模型中的现象类似，例如一个带有两个相变带的完全底部加热（驱动）的三维笛卡儿模型[18]。然而，我们发现用球形几何结构和更加切合实际的内部加热机制能极大地改变热流特征、下地幔流动的几何形态、涌升柱的结构以及全球的时间依赖性，还有助于直接与地震层析成像进行对比。

模型特征参数

我们的最新模型包含了发生在约 670 km 深度处的从尖晶石到钙钛矿外加镁方铁矿的吸热相变效应，与橄榄岩地幔组分一致[19]。一些学者在他们的模型中加入了一些额外的矿物相变[2,3,5,18,48]。这些相变会略微改变分层的倾向性，产生一些另外的次级影响，但是考虑到在现今地幔模型中存在的其他近似和不确定性，我们选择将计算限定在考察由 670 km 深度上吸热相变产生的主要影响上。我们初步的包含 400 km 深度相变的模拟结果表明几乎没有实质性的差别。

利用谱变换方法[17]对可压缩、自重力的流体动力学方程进行求解和时间积分，程序在加州理工学院的英特尔 Touchstone Delta 并行超算系统上运行。由于地幔具有非常高的普朗特数，方程中的惯性项可以被忽略。采用滞弹性的近似，以消除传播速度比对流速度快许多数量级的声波。熵、压力、重力势能以及极向物质通量势能横向球谐展开至 127 级，与对流和黏性耗散相关的非线性值在 384 个经度格点乘 192 个纬度格点的网格空间进行求解。代表上下地幔的变量均采用离散切比雪夫级

dissipation are evaluated in grid space using 384 longitudinal points by 192 latitudinal points. Variables are expanded vertically in separate Chebyshev series for the upper and lower mantles, with 33 radial levels in the lower and 17 radial levels in the upper mantle. Use of two Chebyshev expansions matched at 670 km depth gives good vertical resolution at the CMB, at 670 km depth and at the surface, where it is most needed. The fields are adequately resolved because the horizontal and vertical variances of variables fall by many orders of magnitude between maximum values and truncation[7-9,17].

As the phase boundary deflection observed in the Earth[20] is at least an order of magnitude smaller than the characteristic size of convective features in our model, it is not necessary (to a good approximation) to resolve the exact details of the phase change. Thus, deflection of the phase change resulting from lateral temperature variations at 670 km depth is represented as a sheet mass anomaly at this depth, resulting in discontinuous normal stress between the two Chebyshev regimes. This approach has the advantage of a phase loop (the pressure or depth interval over which the multivariant phase change occurs) with zero width—important because the phase loop width affects the inhibition of flow across the boundary[5], and recent experiments[19] constrain this width to be a few kilometres at most. For numerical reasons, the latent heat release (absorption) that accompanies upward (downward) motion through the phase change must be spread out 25 km on either side of the interface. This treatment of the phase change has been validated by computing two-dimensional cartesian and spherical axisymmetric results and comparing them to previously published results[1,4].

Parameters. Entropy, pressure and gravitational potential are expanded as perturbations relative to a self-gravitating adiabatic reference state. The Murnaghan equation is assumed, leading to a polytrope[17] (that is $P \propto [\rho^{1+1/n} - \rho_0^{1+1/n}]$, where n is the polytropic index). A constant Grüneisen parameter of 1.0 and polytropic index of 0.5 gives a reasonable fit to the Earth model PREM[21]. Implicit in this treatment is the depth-dependence of material properties such as density bulk modulus and thermal expansivity, with the latter varying from 3.0×10^{-5} at the surface to 2.2×10^{-5} at 670 km depth and 1.2×10^{-5} at the CMB. Heat capacity is assumed constant at 1,250 J kg^{-1} K^{-1}. Thermal conductivity and viscosity are specified as functions of depth only, with dynamic viscosity increasing roughly exponentially from 1.7×10^{22} Pa s at the surface to 1.9×10^{22} Pa s at 670 km depth and 2.1×10^{23} Pa s at the CMB. Thermal conductivity is 2.3 W m^{-1} K^{-1} at the surface, increasing with depth as the fourth power of density, giving a lower-mantle increase consistent with experiments[22] and theory[23]. The boundary conditions at the surface and CMB are stress-free and isothermal, with the temperatures at the CMB and surface fixed at 3,450 K and 1,060 K, respectively. Of the total temperature drop across the mantle, 1,250 K is superadiabatic and 1,140 K is due to adiabatic compression. The unrealistically high surface temperature is a consequence of treating the viscosity as a function of depth only rather than a function of temperature, so rheologically stiff plates are not produced. Absolute temperatures in such a calculation are not meaningful, however, except to the extent that they are adjusted to be realistic at some depth (for example, the upper mantle); only temperature differences are relevant to the convective style and vigour.

Because the ratio of internal to basal heating strongly affects the degree of layering in two-

数垂向地展开，下地幔划分 33 个径向层级，上地幔划分 17 个径向层级。两种切比雪夫展开在 670 km 深度上匹配，这确保了在核幔边界、670 km 深度以及地表上具有良好的垂向分辨率，在这些地方良好分辨率是非常重要的。因为变量的横向和垂向方差在最大值和截断值之间均下降了数个数量级，所以计算空间能得到足够的分辨[7-9,17]。

由于在地球内部观测到的相边界弯曲[20]比我们模型中的对流特征尺度至少小一个数量级，因而不必要去分辨相变的具体细节。因此，在 670 km 深度上由温度横向变化导致的相变弯曲可以表示为该深度上的薄片物质异常，导致两个切比雪夫体系之间法向应力不连续。这种方法具有零宽度相环（发生多元相变的压力或深度间隔）的优点，这是很重要的，因为相环宽度影响流体穿过边界时所受的阻碍力[5]，最近的实验[19]限制这一宽度最多为几千米。出于数值计算考虑，伴随穿过相变界面的向上（向下）运动的潜热释放（吸收）必须在界面两边 25 km 范围扩散。相变的这种处理方式（的合理性）已经通过计算二维笛卡儿和球形轴对称模型及其与前期已发表结果[1,4]的对比得到验证。

参数 熵、压力和重力势能被展开为相对于自身重力绝热参考状态的扰动。假设默纳汉方程，导致了一个多方球[17]（即 $P \propto [\rho^{1+1/n} - \rho_0^{1+1/n}]$，这里 n 为多变指数）。格林艾森常数 1 和多变指数 0.5 能给出对地球模型 PREM[21] 的一个合理拟合。这种处理的隐含意义是物质属性，比如密度体积模量和热膨胀系数，是依赖于深度的，后者从地表上的 3.0×10^{-5} K^{-1} 变化到 670 km 深度上的 2.2×10^{-5} K^{-1} 和核幔边界上的 1.2×10^{-5} K^{-1}。热容假设为常数 1,250 $J \cdot kg^{-1} \cdot K^{-1}$。热导率和黏度都仅设置为深度的函数，动力学黏度大致呈指数增加，从地表的 1.7×10^{22} $Pa \cdot s$ 增加到 670 km 深度上的 1.9×10^{22} $Pa \cdot s$ 和核幔边界上的 2.1×10^{23} $Pa \cdot s$。热导率在地表为 2.3 $W \cdot m^{-1} \cdot K^{-1}$，以密度的四次方随深度增加，进而得到的下地幔增加量与实验[22]和理论[23]结果一致。地表和核幔边界的边界条件均为无剪切应力和等温，核幔边界和地表温度分别固定为 3,450 K 和 1,060 K。穿过地幔总的温度下降，1,250 K 是超绝热的，其中 1,140 K 是绝热压缩所贡献。不切实际的、极高的地表温度是把黏度仅视为深度的函数而非温度的函数的结果，因此并没有生成流变性坚硬的板块。然而，这样计算的绝对温度并没有意义，除非它们在某一深度（例如，上地幔）调整至合理范围。仅温度差异与对流样式和活力相关。

因为内部和底部加热的比率强烈影响二维模型中的分层程度（佩尔蒂埃，个人

dimensional models (W. R. Peltier, personal communication), it is important to match the internal heating rate and core heat flux of the Earth as closely as possible. We therefore use an internal heating rate of 2.75×10^{-12} W kg^{-1}, compatible with chondritic values. The volume averaged Rayleigh numbers resulting from internal heating and super-adiabaticity[9] are 1.8×10^7 and 1.2×10^6 respectively, an order of magnitude higher than in previous studies[7], but almost an order of magnitude less than those characterizing the Earth. Realistic Rayleigh numbers are obtainable in two-dimensional calculations[2,3,5], which are useful for predicting how the effects observed here might scale to the Earth-like regime.

We take the value of the Clapeyron slope to be -4 MPa K^{-1}, the preferred value from recent experimental results[24], although at the high end of the range from previous experiments[19]. We choose a high value so that we can determine and characterize the maximum effect that the phase change could have on the flow. Although this value has been observed to cause very strong layering in one axisymmetric result[4], the inhibiting effect of the phase change in that simulation was greatly enhanced by the use of a much lower thermal expansivity at 670 km depth than is consistent with experimental and theoretical estimates[25], and by the imposed two-dimensionality.

The simulation was started from a case with no phase change and run for about 15,000 timesteps, corresponding to about 3 billion years; the results we present here are characteristic of the last 9,000 timesteps, after the system has overcome the initial transient adjustment to the presence of the phase change.

Observables

We obtain a mean surface heat flow of 2×10^{13} W, of which ~40% comes from the core. The total is similar to that of the Earth, but the basal heatflow is considerably larger than most estimates for the Earth[26-28]. Even so, it drives very little plume activity, as discussed below. It is possible that the mantle heating rate should be substantially augmented by the effect of secular cooling[26,27,29] which is missing from the model because the heating is treated as time-independent, but this is an issue for the future.

Maximum convective velocities are ~40 mm yr^{-1} and average surface velocities typically 6 mm yr^{-1}—an order of magnitude lower than plate velocities, although a direct comparison may be misleading because our simulation lacks rigid plates. The principal difference between our parameters and the Earth probably lies in the use of higher than realistic viscosities, which is necessitated by computing limitations. At the higher Rayleigh number that would result from lower viscosities, the phase change has a stronger inhibitive effect on the flow[1,3]; thus our calculation may underpredict the degree of layering that would occur in the Earth.

Flow pattern. In Fig. 1, which illustrates cold features for the final frame of the calculation,

交流），因此让内部加热率与地核热通量尽可能匹配就显得尤为重要。为此，我们采用的内部加热率为 2.75×10^{-12} W·kg^{-1}，这与球粒陨石相应的值一致。内部加热和超绝热[9] 导致的体积加权瑞利数分别为 1.8×10^7 和 1.2×10^6，比前期研究[7] 要高出一个数量级，但是比代表地球状态的那些数值几乎要小一个数量级。实际的瑞利数在二维模拟计算中[2,3,5] 是可以获得的，这些数值在预测如何将这里观察到的结果归化到地球类似的模型是十分有益的。

我们选取克拉珀龙坡度值为 -4 MPa·K^{-1}，这也是最近实验结果中首选的数值[24]，尽管这个数值位于前期实验[19] 确定的范围的高端。我们选择这样一个高值的目的是确定和描述相变可能对流动产生的最大影响。尽管轴对称模拟[4] 已经发现这一数值会导致非常强烈的分层效应，但是由于在 670 km 深度上采用了一个比实验和理论估计值[25] 要低得多的热膨胀系数以及使用的二维维度，在这种模拟中相变的抑制效应被极大地增强了。

模拟从一个不包含相变的模型开始，运行了大约 15,000 个时间步，相当于 30 亿年。这里展示的结果是最后 9,000 个时间步的特征，此时系统已经克服了初始的、伴随相变作用的瞬变调整。

模型结果及观测量

我们获得了一个 2×10^{13} W 的平均地表热流值，其中约 40% 来自地核。总量与地球的观测值类似，但是底部热流比大多数的地球估计值[26-28] 大得多。即便如此，它几乎没有驱动地幔柱活动，这将在下文中讨论。虽然长期冷却效应可能大大提高了地幔加热率[26,27,29]，可是由于加热被视为与时间无关，所以这一过程并没有被包含在模型中，但这是将来会考虑的问题。

最大对流速度约为 40 mm·yr^{-1}，平均地表速度一般为 6 mm·yr^{-1}，比板块运动速度要低一个数量级，尽管这种直接的对比可能会令人误解，因为我们的模拟缺少坚硬板块。我们的模拟参数与地球真实情况之间最主要的差异很可能在于这里采用了比实际黏度更高的黏度值，这是计算限制需要所致。更低的黏度会导致更高的瑞利数，相变对流动就会产生更强的阻滞效应[1,3]，因此，我们的计算可能低估了地球内部实际出现的分层程度。

流型　图 1 展示的是模拟的最后画面的冷特征，可以看到在上地幔中相互连接

a network of interconnected cold downwelling sheets, which do not penetrate the phase change, is observed in the upper mantle. The distance between sheets that are roughly parallel is typically 3,000–8,000 km, a scale which is consistent with present subduction zones on the Earth. They have some small-scale complexity due to local boundary-layer instabilities, which would probably be suppressed by the high-viscosity lithospheric plates on the Earth. At the intersections of these sheets, large pools of cold material form above the 670 km phase change. This cold material is gravitationally unstable and after building up sufficiently triggers a sudden avalanche into the lower mantle, in the form of a large-diameter (~1,000 km) cylindrical downwelling plume. This downwelling acts as a conduit to the CMB, effectively emptying the cold material from the local upper mantle to a large pool at the base of the mantle, despite the increase in viscosity with depth. The downwelling then shuts off completely and does not recur in exactly the same place during the simulation, although many such events may occur in the same general area, and a total of about 15 events are observed during this part of the simulation. Thus, these events cool all areas of the lower mantle and core. At any one time, several of these flushing events are in progress at different places around the sphere, triggering in a globally asynchronous manner. Owing to the spherical geometry, the surface area of the CMB is ~35% of the surface area of the 670-km interface, and thus the combined effect of flushing events occurring in different places around the sphere is to surround the core with cold material, resulting in a heat flow (40% of surface heat flow) considerably higher than most estimates for the Earth[26-29], but with very little upwelling plume activity.

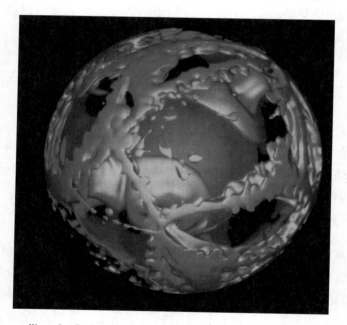

Fig. 1. Cold downwellings for final frame of simulation. Blue surface is an isocontour showing where the temperature is 110 K lower than the horizontally averaged value. Green surface is the core. A network of interconnected linear downwellings is visible in the upper mantle, with three huge cylindrical downwellings in the lower mantle, spreading out into pools of cold material above the core–mantle boundary.

Figure 2 shows the corresponding hot, upwelling regions for the final frame. The most

的冷的沉降薄板交织在一起，它们都没有穿过相变带。相互平行的薄板之间的距离一般为 3,000~8,000 km，这个尺寸与地球现今的俯冲带一致。受局部边界层不稳定性的影响，它们存在某种小尺度的复杂性，地球表层的高黏度岩石圈板块很可能能起到抑制这些复杂性的效果。在这些薄板的交叉部位，大量的冷物质在 670 km 相变带上方形成。这些冷物质是重力不稳定的，在堆积足够量之后它们触发了突然的崩塌，以大直径（~1,000 km）圆柱状沉降柱的形式进入下地幔。这种沉降流起着通向核幔边界的导管作用，有效地将来自上地幔的冷物质输导（或腾空）至地幔底部的大池，尽管黏度随深度增加。然后沉降流完全关闭，在模拟期间在完全相同的位置不再复现，尽管许多类似事件可能出现在同一大区域中，并且在模拟的这部分总共有 15 个事件发生。因此，这些事件冷却了下地幔和地核的全部区域。在任何时间都有数个这类涌流事件在球体的不同位置同时进行，以一个全球非同期的方式触发。由于球形几何结构的缘故，核幔边界的表面积只占 670 km 界面表面积的 35%，因此发生在球体不同位置的涌流事件的综合效应表现为以冷物质围绕地核，导致热流值（40% 的地表热流）显著地高于大部分对地球相应的估计值[26-29]，但是几乎没有涌升柱活动。

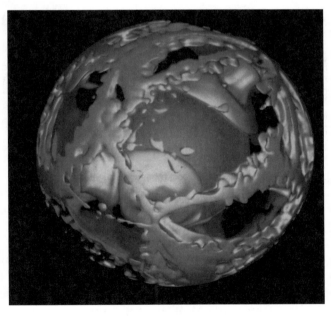

图 1. 模型最终结果中显示的冷的沉降流。蓝色表面显示的是温度低于水平平均值 110 K 的等温面。绿色面代表地核。在上地幔中，可见相互连接的线性沉降流的网状系统；在下地幔中，三个巨大的圆柱状的沉降流发散进入核幔边界上方的冷物质池。

图 2 显示的是最后画面相应的热的、涌升区域。最显著的特征是上地幔中大范

prominent features are the broad hot regions in the upper mantle, which are generally not associated with any deep features in the lower mantle. The lateral heterogeneity is much greater in the upper mantle than in the lower mantle, as shown quantitatively below. At the CMB, ridges of hot material are observed. These are swept around by the enormous injections of cold upper mantle material caused by flushing events, and occasionally a short-lived, transient plume is formed at the intersection of these ridges, rising to the 670-km interface and injecting hot material into the upper mantle. One of these can be observed in Fig. 2. Thus, in both directions, cylindrical forms (plumes) are seen to penetrate the 670-km phase change, whereas linear forms (sheets) do not. The upward flow in the upper mantle and in the top of the lower mantle is generally the weak, distributed return flow characterizing mainly internally heated convection[7-9,30,31].

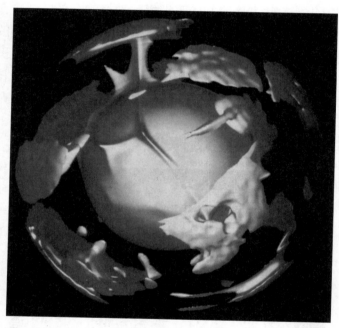

Fig. 2. Hot upwellings for final frame of simulation. Red surface is an isocontour of superadiabatic temperature, showing where the temperature is 110 K higher than the reference-state adiabat. A single plume from the core–mantle boundary feeds a hot region in the upper mantle. Note that most broad hot regions in the upper mantle are not directly linked to lower-mantle structures.

The radial dependence of the flow structure is clearly visible in Fig. 3a and b, which shows the superadiabatic temperature field in two cross-sectional slices for the final frame of the simulation. The upper mantle is extremely heterogeneous on long wavelengths, containing some broad (up to ~10,000 km) regions of anomalously cold or hot material, as well as regions with the classical small aspect-ratio convection cells[32,33]. In the lower mantle, two large cylindrical downwellings are visible (Fig. 3b), and a thick layer of cold material surrounds the core. One broad upwelling plume from the CMB (Fig. 3a) penetrates the 670-km phase change and injects hot material into the upper mantle, but this is the only such feature in the whole lower mantle. The inclusion of realistic temperature-dependent

围的热区域，它们一般没有与下地幔的深部特征相联系。上地幔中的横向不均匀性要比下地幔中的大得多，正如下面要定量展示的一样。在核幔边界上发现有热物质脊。它们被涌流事件造成的上地幔冷物质的大量注入所席卷，偶尔会在这些热脊的交汇处形成一个短暂的瞬态的地幔柱，上升至 670 km 深的相变面，向上地幔注入热物质。图 2 中可以看到其中一个这样的过程。因此，在两个方向上都能看到圆柱状地幔柱穿过 670 km 相变带，然而线性的薄板没有穿过。上地幔和下地幔顶部的上升流一般是弱的分布式的回流，主要表现了内部加热对流的特点 [7-9,30,31]。

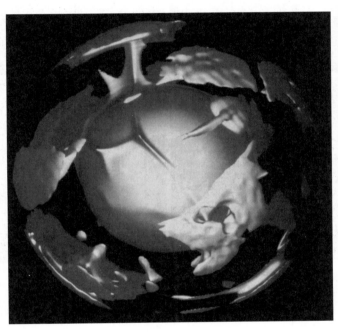

图 2. 模型最终结果中显示的热的涌升流。红色表面代表超绝热温度的等温面，显示的是温度比参考状态绝热温度高 110 K 的区域。来自核幔边界的单个地幔柱供给了上地幔中的一个热区域。注意：上地幔中大部分宽广的热区域并没有与下地幔的结构直接相连。

在图 3a 和 b 中流动结构的径向依赖性清晰可见，它们显示的是模拟最后结果的两个横截面切片中的超绝热温度场。上地幔在长波长尺度上极其不均匀，包含一些广阔的 (达 ~10,000 km) 异常冷或热的物质区域，还有一些区域出现了典型的小纵横比对流圈 [32,33]。在下地幔中可见两个大的圆柱状的沉降流 (图 3b) 和一厚层冷物质围绕地核。一个源自核幔边界的宽广的涌升柱 (图 3a) 穿过了 670 km 相变面，并将热物质注入上地幔，但这是整个下地幔中唯一的这种特征。由于热边界层的影响，把实际依赖于温度的黏度包含进来会立刻导致一个低黏度层出现在核幔边界的

viscosity would result in a low-viscosity layer immediately above the CMB because of the thermal boundary layer, which may result in more upwelling plumes. The lack of strong plume activity in our model is not, however, of concern as plumes on the Earth are merely secondary features, carrying only 10–15% of the total heat flux[28].

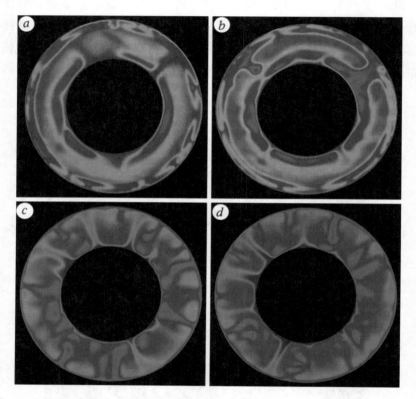

Fig. 3. Superadiabatic temperature field on different cross-sectional slices. *a* and *b*, The final frame of the phase change simulation. Scale ranges from −1,050 K to +350 K. *c* and *d*, A typical case with no phase change. This is representative of mainly internally heated whole-mantle models[7-9,30,31], with Rayleigh numbers for internal and basal heating of 1.4×10^7 and 5.5×10^5 respectively, a factor of 10 viscosity increase with depth, and a basal heat flow of ~16% of the surface heat flow. Scale ranges from −780 K to +220 K.

The ability of the cold downwelling lower mantle plumes to reach the CMB, despite the increasing viscosity and decreasing thermal expansivity with depth, is in marked contrast to a similar case with no phase change illustrated in Fig. 3*c* and *d*, in which the somewhat smaller downwellings slow down and broaden in the lower half of the mantle, allowing the formation of many upwelling plumes, despite the low basal heat flux. It is possible that a larger viscosity increase with depth[28] may slow down the giant drips observed in the phase-change case. They are such large features, however, with so large a reservoir of feeding material, that it seems unlikely that they will be prevented from reaching the CMB.

Radial mass flux. A useful indicator is the radial mass flux diagnostic[5], defined as the spherically averaged absolute radial mass flux, normalized so that the integral over non-

正上方，这可以产生更多的涌升柱。然而，在我们的模型中缺少强烈的地幔柱活动并不是大问题，因为地球上的地幔柱仅仅只是二级特征，它们只携带了总热流量的10%~15%[28]。

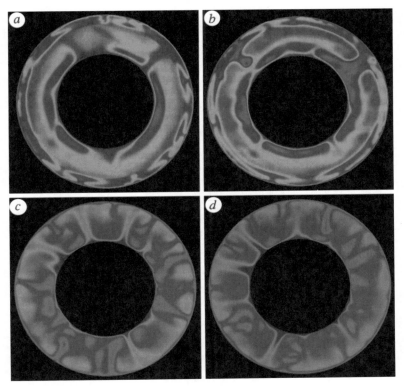

图 3. 不同横截面切片上的超绝热温度场。*a* 和 *b*，包含矿物相变的模型结果，标度从 −1,050 K 到 +350 K。*c* 和 *d* 是一个不含矿物相变的典型模型。这是主要由内部加热的全地幔模型的代表 [7-9,30,31]，内部和底部加热的瑞利数分别为 1.4×10^7 和 5.5×10^5，黏度随深度 10 倍增加，底部热流占地表热流的 ~16%。标度从 −780 K 到 +220 K。

在图 3*c* 和 *d* 展示的无相变的相似模型中，尽管随深度变大黏度增加且热膨胀系数减小，冷的沉降下地幔柱到达核幔边界的能力还是显示出了明显差异，表现为略小的沉降流减缓并在地幔的下半部分变宽，导致了许多涌升柱的形成，尽管底部热流低。黏度随深度更大的增加[28]可能减缓了在含相变带模型中见到的巨大滴落现象。然而，它们是如此巨大，并且拥有如此巨大的供料库，以致阻止它们到达核幔边界看起来都是不可能的。

径向物质通量 径向物质通量因子 [5] 是一个有用的指标，它定义为球面平均绝对径向物质通量，并进行了归一化以使得无量纲深度上的积分是单位一。该因子在模

dimensional depth is unity. This diagnostic for the final frame is shown in Fig. 4, together with the time-series of mass flux through the 670-km discontinuity for the last 9,000 timesteps (~2 Gyr) of the simulation. The phase change is observed to have a marked inhibitive effect on the flow, indicated by the minimum in the radial mass flux at 670 km. Examination of this diagnostic for individual spherical harmonic degrees indicates that long wavelengths of flow are virtually unaffected by the phase change, whereas short wavelengths are increasingly inhibited; for spherical harmonic degrees above ~40, flow is effectively confined to the upper mantle.

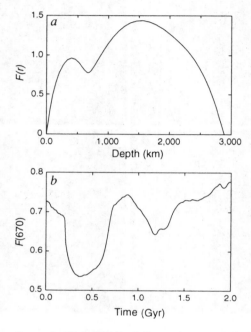

Fig. 4. a, Radial mass flux diagnostic $F(r)$ for the final frame of simulation. b, Time series of $F(670)$ for the last 9,000 timesteps (2 Gyr). $F(r)$, defined in ref. 5, is the spherically averaged modulus of radial mass flux, normalized so that the integral over non-dimensional depth is unity.

From the radial mass flux across the interface at 670 km depth it is possible to calculate a "mixing time", defined as the time required for a mass equal to the mass of the mantle to pass through 670 km. For this case the time is 4.5 Gyr. To scale to the Earth's Rayleigh number (Ra), it is likely that the mass flux (of downwelling cold material) scales roughly as the heat flux, suggesting a $Ra^{1/3}$ scaling[34] which would reduce the mixing time to ~2.1 Gyr for an order of magnitude increase in Ra. This is less than half the age of the Earth, but the increased effect of the phase change at higher $Ra^{1.3}$ may increase this time.

There is some time dependence of the flow through the phase change at 670 km depth, with the mass flux diagnostic at 670 km depth ($F(670)$) varying between 0.5 and 0.8 during this simulation. This time dependence is much weaker than that observed in two-dimensional geometry[4,5,48]. Owing to the large effective aspect ratio in our spherical simulation, several flushing events are typically occurring at any given time, so

型演化最后时段的结果显示于图 4 中，同时显示的还有通过 670 km 不连续界面的物质通量在模型的最后 9,000 个时间步长（~2 Gyr）的演化特征。矿物相变对地幔流动具有显著的抑制作用，表现为径向物质通量在 670 km 深度达到一个极小值。检查该因子在单个球谐度上的变化，结果表明流动的长波长实际不受相变的影响，但是越短的波长受的抑制影响越大。球谐度在 ~40 以上的流态被有效地限定于上地幔之中。

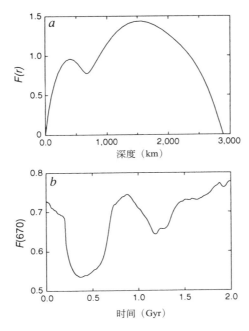

图 4. *a*，模型最终结果中对应的径向物质通量因子 $F(r)$。*b*，$F(670)$ 对于最后 9,000 个时间步长（2 Gyr）的时间演变（或时间序列）。$F(r)$ 是径向物质通量的球面平均模数，其定义可见参考文献 5，由于经过了归一化处理，所以它在无量纲深度上的积分是单位一。

从通过 670 km 深度界面的径向物质通量上可以计算"混合时间"，定义为相当于整个地幔的物质穿过 670 km 不连续面所需要的时间。对于这个模型（或例子），这个时间是 4.5 Gyr。为了对应为地球的瑞利数（Ra），（沉降冷物质的）物质通量可以大致换算为热流，相应的换算系数为 $Ra^{1/3}$[34]，Ra 增加一个数量级，会使混合时间减小至 ~2.1 Gyr。这大约是地球年龄的一半，但是在更高 Ra 情形[1,3]下所增加的相变效应可能会增大这个时间。

通过 670 km 相变带的地幔流动具有某种时间相关性，表现为模型演化期间 670 km 深度上的物质通量因子（$F(670)$）在 0.5 至 0.8 之间变化。这种时间相关性比在二维模型中得到的要弱得多[4,5,48]。由于我们的球形模拟具有大的、有效的纵横比，在任何给定时间一般都有几个全地幔上升流和下降流同时发生，因而在全球尺度上

the convection is never strongly layered on a global scale. As a result globally averaged diagnostics such as $F(670)$, mean temperature, and so on are not greatly affected by an individual flushing event. Given the observed preference for a penetration in cylindrical rather than linear forms, it is also possible that in two-dimensional geometry (where up- or downwellings are restricted to being linear), cold material builds up to a greater extent before it can be flushed into the lower mantle, and thus these events are more violent. It is possible that our flushing events would be more abrupt and violent if we could decrease the viscosity to Earth-like values, as observed in two-dimensional models (ref. 48, and W. R. Peltier, personal communication). We believe, however, that with an Earth-like viscosity, flushing events would still overlap in time, and the global time dependence would be intrinsically weaker in full three-dimensional spherical geometry than in spherical axisymmetric or two-dimensional cartesian geometries.

Spherically averaged temperature. The horizontally averaged ($l = 0$) temperature field is shown in Fig. 5. A temperature drop of several hundred degrees occurs around 670 km depth. In addition a small kink is observed at 670 km, due to the release or absorption of latent heat by material advected across the phase change. The net thermal gradient at 670 km depth is low, and thus the conductive heat flow across the 670-km interface is only ~10% of the surface heat flow, with most of the heat flux across 670 km depth being advected. On local scales, much steeper temperature gradients are observed in regions far from cylindrical downwellings and most of the radial heat flux may be conductive.

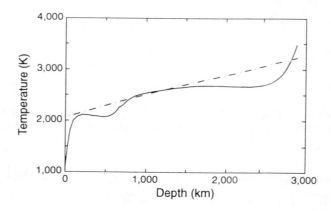

Fig. 5. Solid line, radial profile of spherically averaged temperature for final frame. Dashed line, reference state adiabat.

Lateral Heterogeneity and Seismic Tomography

The effects of the phase change on both the horizontal spectrum of density anomalies and the depth-dependence of total power[5] is pronounced, resulting in a dominance of long-wavelength power in the upper mantle and base of the lower mantle, and a concentration of total power in the same areas (Fig. 6a and b), compatible with seismic tomography[13,15].

对流没有出现强烈的分层现象。全球平均诊断参数，例如 $F(670)$、平均温度等，也因此没有受到单个地幔柱事件的明显的影响。考虑到穿透倾向于以圆柱形式进行而非线性形式，在二维几何结构中（其中涌升流或沉降流被限定为线性形式），冷物质也可能需要更大程度地堆积在相变面之上才能涌进下地幔，因此这些事件会发生得更激烈。如果我们将黏度降低至与地球类似的值，正如在二维模型中见到的一样（参考文献 48，以及和佩尔蒂埃的个人交流），全地幔流动事件可能会变得更突然和更激烈。然而，我们认为就算赋予和地球类似的黏度值，这些事件在时间上仍然会重叠，并且对于全三维球形几何结构中的全球时间相关性，其本质上就比球形轴对称或二维笛卡儿几何结构中的弱。

球面平均温度 图 5 中显示的是水平平均（$l=0$）温度场。在 670 km 深度附近温度下降了几百度。此外，由于被平流输送穿过相变带的物质的潜热释放或吸收，一个小的弯曲出现在 670 km 深度附近。在 670 km 深度上净温度梯度低，因此穿过 670 km 界面的传导热流只占地表热流的 ~10%，大部分穿过 670 km 深度的热流都被平流输送掉了。从局部尺度上来看，远离圆柱状沉降流的区域温度梯度要陡得多，大部分径向热流可能是通过传导传递的。

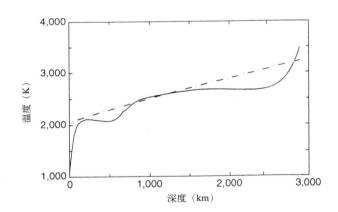

图 5. 实线代表模型最终结果中的球面平均温度的径向剖面；虚线代表参考状态绝热线。

横向不均匀性与地震层析成像

矿物相变对密度异常的水平范围和总能量的深度依赖性的影响[5]都很显著，导致长波长能量集中在上地幔和下地幔底部，总能量也聚集在相同的区域（图 6a 和 b），与地震层析成像结果一致[13,15]。在上地幔中，占优频率为球谐度 $l=2$~7，峰值在 $l=6$ 上；然而在下地幔最深的 400 km 上，$l=2$ 和 $l=3$ 占优，二级峰值出现在

In the upper mantle the dominant frequencies are spherical harmonic degrees $l = 2$–7, with a peak at $l = 6$, whereas in the deepest ~400 km of the lower mantle, $l = 2$ and 3 dominate, with a secondary peak at $l = 5$–6. This is very different from the illustrated result with no phase change (Fig. 6c and d), in which a broad peak is observed in the range $l = 8$–20; and also with basally heated model at Ra = 10^6 (ref. 17; Fig. 1) which peaks at $l = 10$. Indeed, the lateral spectrum is fairly consistent with the observations of long-wavelength dominance from seismic tomography[10-13,15,35], particularly that of Inoue $et\ al.$[35] (plotted in refs 13 and 15). The flow lacks the dominant $l = 2$ component found in some seismic models[10-12]; this is probably due to the absence of tectonic plates and continents, as discussed later. The asymptotic fall-off in power with spherical harmonic degree varies with depth, but is roughly proportional to l^{-2}.

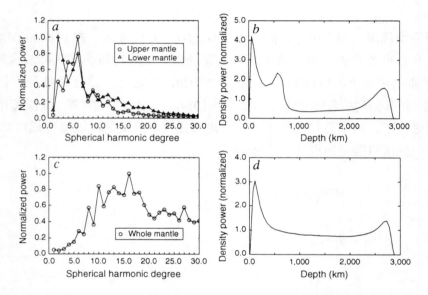

Fig. 6. a, Power in each spherical harmonic degree, vertically averaged through upper and lower mantles, for the final frame. This lateral power spectrum has similarities with that observed by Inoue $et\ al.$ using seismic tomography (plotted in ref. 13, Fig. 5). b, Radial profile of total lateral heterogeneity (in density). A peak is observed at 670 km depth, as with two-dimensional results[5]. c, Power in each spherical harmonic degree, vertically averaged through the whole mantle, for the case with no phase change (illustrated in Fig. 3c and d). d, As b for the case with no phase change.

Even when filtered to seismic tomographic resolution (for example $l = 10$, Chebyshev degree $n = 13$), the effect of the phase change is still clearly discernible, both in the entropy field and in radial correlations between layers[49]. However, all plume-like upwellings on the lower mantle disappear completely. The strongest of the broad cylindrical downwellings are visible as smeared out cold anomalies, and thus may be discernible in tomographic models. The peak in the radial heterogeneity profile (Fig. 6b) is still visible at $n = 13$, but disappears at $n = 6$. Although the lateral heterogeneity spectrum is dominated by long wavelengths, we need to expand to at least $l \approx 31$ to see all the main features.

$l = 5~6$。这与无相变的结果（图 6c 和 d）迥然不同，在无相变的模型中，一个宽广的峰出现在 $l = 8~20$ 的范围内；与 Ra = 10^6 的底部加热模型（参考文献 17 中的图 1）也十分不同，在底部加热模型中峰出现在 $l = 10$ 处。确实，这里的横向范围与地震层析成像观测到的长波长主导的特征相当地一致[10-13,15,35]，尤其是与井上等[35]的结果（见参考文献 13 和 15 的图表）。地幔流动缺少在一些地震模型中发现的占优势的 $l = 2$ 的成分[10-12]，这可能是由于模型缺失构造板块和大陆的缘故，随后会讨论。功率随球谐度渐进下降的趋势随深度而变化，但大体上正比于 l^{-2}。

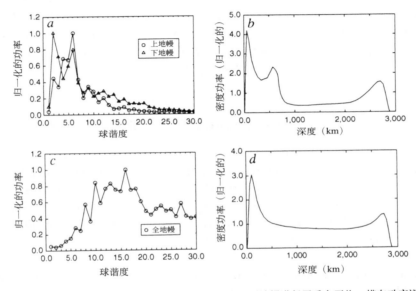

图 6. a，模型最终结果中的每一个球谐度上的功率，对上、下地幔进行了垂向平均。横向功率谱与井上等利用地震层析成像获得的观测结果（见文献 13 的图 5）相似；b，总的横向不均匀性的径向剖面（密度）。一个峰值出现在 670 km 深度上，正如在二维模拟结果一样[5]；c，无相变模型（如图 3c 和 d 所示）对应的每个球谐度的功率，对全地幔进行了垂向平均；d，和 b 一样，对应无相变模型。

即便当滤波至地震层析成像的分辨率（例如，$l = 10$，切比雪夫度 $n = 13$），矿物相变的影响在熵场和层间径向相关上[49]都依然清晰可辨。然而，下地幔中所有类地幔柱的涌升流都完全消失了。最强的宽广圆柱状沉降流逐渐显示为发散的冷异常，因此它们可能在层析成像模型中是可分辨的。径向不均匀剖面的峰值（图 6b）在 $n = 13$ 时仍然可见，但是在 $n = 6$ 时就消失了。尽管横向不均匀性的范围在长波长上占主导，我们仍然需要展开到至少 $l \approx 31$ 阶来观察所有主要的特征。

Slab Penetration

The issue of whether subducting lithospheric slabs penetrate the lower mantle or are deflected by the 670-km discontinuity is central to the question of mantle layering[36-42]. The closest analogues to slabs in our model are the linear downwellings in the upper mantle, and our model results suggest that slabs do not immediately penetrate, but instead build up in the transition zone until enough cold mass has accumulated to precipitate an avalanche into the lower mantle[43]. This picture would be consistent with (1) strong correlations between past locations of subduction and seismically fast ("cold") regions at the base of the upper mantle and top of the lower mantle[44], (2) recent tomography of slabs[39-41] showing that at least in some areas slabs flatten out along the 670-km discontinuity and appear to stagnate in the transition zone, (3) recent global tomography[14] showing broad seismically fast areas at 600 km depth in places where subducted slabs would be expected to accumulate, and (4) global mapping of topography on the 670-km discontinuity[20] favouring models in which subducting slabs are deflected horizontally at the discontinuity.

Differences from the Earth?

Although our model does not include the effects of variable viscosity, tectonic plates or continents, many of the chief characteristics of the Earth are reproduced, such as the predominance of linear downwellings in the upper mantle (analogous to slabs), wavelength of upper-mantle features (compatible with typical plate sizes), the secondary nature of upwelling plumes, and the similarity of lateral heterogeneity spectra at different depths with seismic tomographic models[13,15].

One difference is that junctions of linear downwellings, at which the large pools of cold material build up in our model, are not observed in the Earth except at the intersection of the Pacific, Philippine and Eurasia plates. This may make catastrophic breakthrough more difficult and more violent, as in two-dimensional models[1,4,43,48]. In addition, the cold slab material is highly viscous and if deflected by the phase change, may have a greater tendency to stagnate in the transition zone.

The addition of rigid plates would probably reinforce the long-wavelength nature of the flow[45,46]. The plate-tectonic cycle, including subduction-zone locations, may be controlled by the assembly and breakup of supercontinents[47], which would pump power into the very lowest spherical harmonic degrees[44].

(**361**, 699-704; 1993)

Paul J. Tackley[*] , David J. Stevenson[†], Gary A. Glatzmaier[‡] & Gerald Schubert[§]

[*] Seismological Laboratory, California Institute of Technology, Pasadena, California 91125, USA

[†] Division of Geological and Planetary Sciences, California Institute of Technology, Pasadena, California 91125, USA

板片穿透性

俯冲的岩石圈板片是穿过了下地幔还是被 670 km 不连续面所转向是地幔分层的焦点问题[36-42]。在我们的模型中与板片最为接近的相似物是上地幔中的线性沉降流，我们的模拟结果显示板片不能立即穿透相变带，而是在过渡带上方堆积，直至聚集了足够多的冷物质，骤然雪崩式地陷入下地幔[43]。这种图景与下面的观测现象一致：(1) 过去俯冲带的位置与上地幔底部和下地幔顶部的高地震波速（冷）区域紧密相关[44]，(2) 最近板片层析成像结果[39-41]显示至少在某些区域俯冲板片沿着 670 km 不连续面变平并且似乎在过渡带滞留，(3) 最近全球层析结果[14]显示 600 km 深度上宽广的地震快速区域与预期的俯冲板片的聚集位置一致，(4) 对 670 km 不连续面地形的全球成像结果[20]支持了俯冲板片在不连续面水平转向的模型。

与地球的差异？

尽管我们的模型没有包含可变的黏度、板块构造或大陆所产生的影响，但是地球的许多主要特征都被再现，例如上地幔中线性沉降流（类似于板片）占优势，上地幔的波长特征（与典型的板块尺寸一致），涌升柱的二级特征，以及在不同深度上横向不均匀体的谱与地震层析成像模型的相似性等[13,15]。

一个不同之处在于：我们模型中的冷物质大致汇聚在线性沉降流的结合处，除了在太平洋、菲律宾和欧亚板块的交汇处之外，这并未在地球的其他地方发现。这可能使灾难性地突破地幔转换带变得更加困难和剧烈，正如在二维模型中展示的那样[1,4,43,48]。此外，冷的板片物质具有高黏性，如果被相变带转向，则它们更有可能滞留在地幔过渡带中。

坚硬板块的加入很可能会加强流动的长波长特性[45,46]。板块构造旋回，包括俯冲带的位置，可能受超级大陆的聚合和裂解控制[47]，这也可能促使了非常低的球谐度的形成[44]。

（陈林 翻译；李忠海 审稿）

‡ Earth and Environmental Sciences Division and Institute of Geophysics and Planetary Physics, Los Alamos National Laboratory, Los Alamos, New Mexico 87545, USA

§ Department of Earth and Space Sciences and Institute of Geophysics and Planetary Physics, University of California, Los Angeles, California 90024, USA

Received 30 November 1992; accepted 29 January 1993.

References:

1. Christensen, U. R. & Yuen, D. A. *J. Geophys. Res.* **90**, 10291-10300 (1985).

2. Liu, M., Yuen, D. A., Zhao, W. & Honda, S. *Science* **252**, 1836-1839 (1991).

3. Zhao, W., Yuen, D. A. & Honda, S. *Phys. Earth Planet. Inter.* **72**, 185-210 (1992).

4. Machetel, P. & Weber, P. *Nature* **350**, 55-57 (1991).

5. Peltier, W. R. & Solheim, L. P. *Geophys. Res. Lett.* **19**, 432-324 (1992).

6. Wyllie, P. J. *Rev. Geophys.* **26**, 370-404 (1988).

7. Glatzmaier, G. A., Schubert, G. & Bercovici, D. *Nature* **347**, 274-277 (1990).

8. Bercovici, D., Schubert, G. & Glatzmaier, G. A. *Science* **244**, 950-955 (1989).

9. Schubert, G., Bercovici, D. & Glatzmaier, G. A. *J. Geophys. Res.* **95**, 14105-14129 (1990).

10. Nakanishi, I. & Anderson, D. L. *J. Geophys. Res.* **88**, 10267-10283 (1983).

11. Tanimoto, T. *J. Phys. Earth* **38**, 493-509 (1990).

12. Tanimoto, T. *Geophys. J. Int.* **100**, 327-336 (1990).

13. Su, W. & Dziewonski, A. M. *Nature* **352**, 121-126 (1991).

14. Su, W., Woodward, R. L. & Dziewonski, A. M. *Nature* **360**, 149-152 (1992).

15. Su, W.-J. & Dziewonski, A. M. *Phys. Earth Planet. Inter.* **74**, 29-54 (1992).

16. Jarvis, G. T. & Peltier, W. R. in *Mantle Convection: Plate Tectonics and Global Dynamics* (ed. Peltier, W. R.) 479-594 (Gordon and Breach, New York, 1989).

17. Glatzmaier, G. A. *Geophys. Astrophys. Fluid Dyn.* **43**, 223-264 (1988).

18. Honda, S., Yuen, D. A., Balachandar, S. & Reuteler, D. *Science* (in the press).

19. Ito, E. & Takahashi, E. *J. Geophys. Res.* **94**, 10637-10646 (1989).

20. Shearer, P. M. & Masters, T. G. *Nature* **355**, 791-796 (1992).

21. Dziewonski, A. M. & Anderson, D. L. *Phys. Earth Planet. Inter.* **25**, 297-356 (1981).

22. Osako, M. & Ito, E. *Geophys. Res. Lett.* **18**, 239-242 (1991).

23. Anderson, D. L. *Phys. Earth Planet. Inter.* **45**, 307-323 (1987).

24. Ito, E., Akaogi., M. Topor, L. & Navrotsky, A. *Science* **249**, 1275-1278 (1990).

25. Anderson, O. L., Oda, H. & Isaak, D. *Geophys. Res. Lett.* **19**, 1987-1990 (1992).

26. Schubert, G. *Ann. Rev. Earth Planet. Sci.* **7**, 289-342 (1979).

27. Schubert, G., Stevenson, D. J. & Cassen, P. *J. Geophys. Res.* **85**, 2531-2538 (1980).

28. Davies, G. F. & Richards, M. A. *J. Geol.* **100**, 151-206 (1992).

29. Sharpe, H. N. & Peltier, W. R. *Geophys. Res. Lett.* **5**, 737-740 (1978).

30. Houseman, G. *Nature* **332**, 346-349 (1988).

31. Travis, B. Weinstein, S. & Olson, P. *Geophys. Res. Lett.* **17**, 243-246 (1990).

32. Christensen, U. & Yuen, D. *Geophys. Res. Lett.* **15**, 597-600 (1988).

33. Busse, F. H. in *Mantle Convection: Plate Tectonics and Global Dynamics* (ed. Peltier, W. R.) 23-95 (Gordon and Breach, New York, 1989).

34. Turcotte, D. L. & Schubert, G. *Geodynamics: Applications of Continuum Physics to Geological Problems* 279-285 (Wiley, New York, 1982).

35. Inoue, H., Fukao, Y., Tanabe, K. & Ogata, Y. *Phys. Earth Planet. Inter.* **59**, 294-328 (1990).

36. Creager, K. C. & Jordan, T. H. *J. Geophys. Res.* **91**, 3573-3589 (1986).

37. Vidale, J. E. & Garcia-Gonzales, D. *Geophys. Res. Lett.* **15**, 369-372 (1988).

38. Zhou, H. W. & Anderson, D. L. *Proc. Natl. Acad. Sci. U.S.A.* **86**, 8602-8606 (1989).

39. Zhou, H. W. & Clayton, R. W. *J. Geophys. Res.* **95**, 6829-6851 (1990).

40. van der Hilst, R., Engdahl, R., Spakman, W. & Nolet, G. *Nature* **353**, 37-43 (1991).

41. Fukao, T., Obayashi, M., Inoue, H. & Nenbau, M. *J. Geophys. Res.* **97**, 4809-4822 (1992).

42. Christensen, U. R. & Yuen, D. A. *J. Geophys. Res.* **89**, 4389-4402 (1984).

43. Solheim, L. P. & Peltier, W. R. *J. Geophys. Res.* (in the press).

44. Scrivner, C. & Anderson, D. L. *Geophys. Res. Lett.* **19**, 1053-1056 (1992).

45. Davies, G. F. *J. Geophys. Res.* **93**, 10451-10466 (1988).

46. Gurnis, M. & Zhong, S. *Geophys. Res. Lett.* **18**, 581-584 (1991).

47. Gurnis, M. *Nature* **332**, 695-699 (1988).

48. Weinstein, S. A. *Geophys. Res. Lett.* **20**, 101-104 (1993).

49. Jordan, T. H., Puster, P., Glatzmaier, G. A. & Tackley, P. J. *Nature* (submitted).

Acknowledgements. We thank W. R. Peltier, D. L. Anderson, D. A. Yuen, M. Gurnis, V. Solomatov and the participants of the Los Alamos Mantle Convection Workshop for discussions, U. Christensen for his review and H. X. Qian for photographic assistance. The Intel Touchstone Delta System was operated by the California Institute of Technology on behalf of the Concurrent Supercomputing Consortium. Access to this facility was provided by the institute. P.T. thanks the NSF for financial support.

SNAP Receptors Implicated in Vesicle Targeting and Fusion

T. Söllner *et al.*

Editor's Note

Vesicle merging—the fusion of tiny sac-like structures to a membrane—has been implicated in numerous processes, including nerve cell communication and various secretory pathways. Here cell biologist (and future Nobel laureate) James E. Rothman and colleagues propose a mechanism to explain how different vesicles reach and merge with their specific target in the brain. They show that vesicles and target membranes contain different types of synaptic receptors called SNARE proteins, and suggest that specificity occurs when compartment-specific SNAREs in the vesicle and target membrane pair up. The classification of SNAREs into vesicle-associated (v-SNAREs) and target membrane-associated (t-SNAREs) remains today, although the proteins can also be characterised according to their structure.

The N-ethylmaleimide-sensitive fusion protein (NSF) and the soluble NSF attachment proteins (SNAPs) appear to be essential components of the intracellular membrane fusion apparatus. An affinity purification procedure based on the natural binding of these proteins to their targets was used to isolate SNAP receptors (SNAREs) from bovine brain. Remarkably, the four principal proteins isolated were all proteins associated with the synapse, with one type located in the synaptic vesicle and another in the plasma membrane, suggesting a simple mechanism for vesicle docking. The existence of numerous SNARE-related proteins, each apparently specific for a single kind of vesicle or target membrane, indicates that NSF and SNAPs may be universal components of a vesicle fusion apparatus common to both constitutive and regulated fusion (including neurotransmitter release), in which the SNAREs may help to ensure vesicle-to-target specificity.

TRANSACTIONS among the membrane-bound compartments in the cytoplasm of eukaryotic cells are generally executed by transport vesicles which bud from one membrane and fuse selectively with another[1]. The mechanism by which each vesicle chooses its target is currently unknown, but must embody the essence of compartmental specificity. Choice of target is implicit in all vesicular fusion events, from the ubiquitous steps in the constitutive secretory and endocytotic pathways (such as the fusion of a vesicle from the endoplasmic reticulum with the Golgi) to specialized and tightly regulated forms of exocytosis (such as the triggered fusion of a synaptic vesicle containing neurotransmitter with the axonal membrane). Here we describe a fundamental relationship between these processes, suggesting that a general apparatus is used to bring about fusion, and that specificity is established by the pairing of compartment-specific proteins in the transport vesicle and target membrane, respectively.

囊泡靶向及融合过程中 SNAP 受体的功能

泽尔纳等

编者按

囊泡融合（微小的囊状结构与膜的融合）涉及神经细胞交流和各种分泌途径等众多过程。在这篇文章中，细胞生物学家、之后的诺贝尔奖获得者詹姆斯·罗思曼及其同事提出了一种机制，来说明大脑中不同的囊泡如何到达它们的特异性靶位点并与之融合。他们指出囊泡和靶细胞膜包含不同类型的突触受体（称为 SNARE 蛋白），并提出当囊泡和靶细胞膜上的区室特异性 SNARE 蛋白配对时会发生特异性融合。虽然现在可以根据 SNAREs 的结构特点分类，但是按照定位将 SNARE 分为囊泡相关蛋白（v-SNAREs）和靶细胞膜相关蛋白（t-SNAREs）两类的分类方法到现在仍在沿用。

N– 乙基马来酰亚胺敏感融合蛋白（NSF）和可溶性 NSF 附着蛋白（SNAPs）似乎是细胞内膜融合装置的必需组分。根据这些蛋白与它们靶分子的天然结合特性建立了一种亲和纯化方法，利用该方法从牛的脑组织中分离 SNAP 受体（SNAREs）。值得注意的是，分离出来的四种主要蛋白质都是与神经突触有关的蛋白。其中一种分布于突触小泡上，另一种则定位在细胞膜上，这提示它们可能参与囊泡停靠过程中的某种简单机制。目前已经发现了大量的 SNARE 相关蛋白，并且每种蛋白都特异地对应某种囊泡或者靶细胞膜，这表明 NSF 和 SNAP 可能是组成型和调控型囊泡融合（包括神经递质的释放）装置的通用组分，而 SNARE 则可能负责保证囊泡与靶位点结合的特异性。

真核细胞的细胞质中，由膜包裹的区室间的运输通常都是通过运输小泡来实现的。这些囊泡从一个区室的膜表面出芽形成，之后选择性地与另一个膜发生融合 [1]。目前对于囊泡选择靶位点的机制尚不了解，但其肯定与细胞内的区室特异性有关。从组成型分泌和内吞途径中普遍存在的步骤（例如来源于内质网的囊泡与高尔基体融合）到特异性的、高度调控的胞吐过程（例如含有神经递质的突触囊泡与神经轴突细胞膜的融合），所有的囊泡融合事件都涉及靶位点的选择。在这篇文章中，我们描述了这些过程之间的基本关系，并提出细胞内融合过程具有一个通用装置，而融合的特异性则是分别通过运输小泡和靶细胞膜上的区室特异性蛋白之间的配对实现的。

The *N*-ethylmaleimide-sensitive fusion protein is a soluble tetramer of 76K subunits which was purified[2,3] on the basis of its ability to restore intercisternal Golgi transport in a cell-free system[4,5]. It is required for transport vesicle fusion, as vesicles accumulate at the acceptor membrane in its absence[6,7]. In yeast, NSF is encoded by the *SEC18* gene[8], originally shown to be necessary for transport from the endoplasmic reticulum (ER) to the Golgi[9]. The SEC18 protein can replace NSF in a mammalian system for cell-free Golgi transport[8] and is required at every discernible step of the secretory pathway *in vivo*[10]. NSF thus appears to participate in a variety of intracellular fusion processes.

NSF requires additional cytoplasmic factors to attach to Golgi membranes[11]. Three species of monomeric soluble NSF attachment proteins, termed α-, β- and γ-SNAP (M_rs of 35, 36 and 39K, respectively), have been purified from brain[12,13] and SNAP activity is necessary for vesicle fusion *in vitro*[13]. α-SNAP (but not β- or γ-SNAP) can restore animal cell Golgi transport activity to cytosol prepared from *sec17* mutant yeast, implying[13] that the *SEC17* gene encodes α-SNAP in yeast. SEC17 is now known to be functionally equivalent to α-SNAP[14], and the two proteins are clearly related[15]. In the absence of functional SEC17 (or SEC18), ER to Golgi transport stops in yeast, and transport vesicles accumulate[16]. SNAPs, like NSF, thus appear to be components of a general intracellular membrane fusion apparatus common to all eukaryotic cells.

SNAPs bind to distinct sites in membranes which up until now have only been operationally defined, and NSF will only interact with SNAPs that are already attached to these sites[17]. α-SNAP and β-SNAP compete for binding to the same receptor site with low nM affinity. γ-SNAP binds to a noncompetitive site in the same complex[17], and, although not essential for NSF binding, increases the complexes' affinity for NSF[18]. Crosslinking studies suggest that the SNAP receptor contains an α-SNAP-binding subunit of 30–40K (ref. 17). When membrane-bound NSF–SNAP–SNAP receptor complexes are solubilized with detergent, they sediment as a distinct multisubunit particle at 20S (ref. 18), which may form the core of a generalized apparatus catalysing bilayer fusion at its point of assembly[6,13]. The 20S particles are also formed when detergent extracts of Golgi membranes containing SNAP receptors are mixed with SNAPs and NSF. When NSF and SNAPs are added in excess, all SNAP receptor activity in the membrane extract is incorporated into 20S particles[18].

NSF is an ATPase containing two ATP-binding sites in separate domains[19], and the binding and hydrolysis of ATP are critical in determining the stability of NSF[3] and its attachment to membranes[2,18]. Stable 20S particles can be formed in the presence of either Mg–ATP-γS (a non-hydrolysable analogue of ATP) or ATP without magnesium. In the presence of Mg–ATP, however, particles rapidly dissociate even at 0 °C, liberating NSF in a process that requires ATP hydrolysis[18]. This disassembly may be an intrinsic step in the fusion mechanism[18].

NSF 是一个可溶的四聚体，亚基分子量为 76K，是基于其可以在一个无细胞系统中恢复高尔基体各片层间转运的性质 [4,5] 而分离纯化 [2,3] 出来的。NSF 是运输小泡融合所必需的，如果没有 NSF 就会导致囊泡在受体膜附近积累 [6,7]。NSF 在酵母中由 *SEC18* 基因编码 [8]，最初发现它在内质网（ER）到高尔基体的转运中起着必不可少的作用 [9]。在无细胞高尔基体转运实验中 [8]，SEC18 蛋白可以替代哺乳动物系统中 NSF 的功能，并且对于体内分泌途径的每个可辨别的步骤来说都是必需的 [10]。因此，NSF 似乎参与多种细胞内融合过程。

NSF 需要额外的细胞质因子才能结合到高尔基体膜上 [11]。研究人员从脑组织中纯化出了三种可以与 NSF 结合的单体可溶性蛋白，分别命名为 α-，β- 和 γ-SNAP（分子量分别为 35K，36K 和 39K）[12,13]。SNAP 的活性是体外囊泡融合所必需的 [13]。α-SNAP（而非 β- 和 γ-SNAP）可以恢复利用 *sec17* 酵母突变体制备的胞质溶胶辅助的动物细胞高尔基体转运的活性，说明 [13] 在酵母中 *SEC17* 基因编码 α-SNAP。现在已知 SEC17 具有与 α-SNAP 相同的功能 [14]，并且这两种蛋白是明确相关的 [15]。当缺失功能性 SEC17（或 SEC18）时，酵母中 ER 到高尔基体的转运过程便停止了，运输小泡则会出现积累 [16]。因此，与 NSF 一样，SNAP 也是所有真核细胞中膜融合装置的一个通用组分。

SNAP 可以与膜上的特异性位点结合。到现在为止，对特异性位点的定义仍停留在操作性定义的层面上。NSF 只能与已经结合到膜上的 SNAP 相互作用 [17]。α-SNAP 和 β-SNAP 以纳摩尔级别的亲和力竞争结合同一个受体位点，而 γ-SNAP 则以非竞争的形式与相同的复合物结合 [17]。尽管 γ-SNAP 并不是 NSF 的结合所必需的，但是其可以提高 NSF 与复合物相互作用的亲和力 [18]。交联实验表明，SNAP 受体包含一个可以与 α-SNAP 结合的 30K~40K 的亚基（参考文献 17）。当使用去垢剂溶解结合在膜上的 NSF–SNAP–SNAP 受体复合物时，这个复合物会以一个多亚基颗粒的形式沉淀下来，沉降系数为 20S（参考文献 18）。这一复合物在组装时可以形成某种通用装置的核心，用以催化脂双层膜的融合 [6,13]。用去垢剂抽提高尔基体膜得到的膜抽提物中含有 SNAP 受体，当将其与 SNAP 和 NSF 混合时，也会形成 20S 的颗粒。当加入过量的 NSF 和 SNAP，膜抽提物中所有 SNAP 受体的活性都会融合到 20S 颗粒中去 [18]。

NSF 是一种 ATP 酶，它的两个分开的结构域中分别含有一个 ATP 结合位点 [19]。ATP 的结合以及水解对于 NSF 的稳定性 [3] 以及其与膜的结合过程 [2,18] 具有重要的影响。当存在 Mg–ATP-γS（一种不能被水解的 ATP 类似物）或者存在 ATP 但无 Mg 时，都可以形成稳定的 20S 颗粒。然而当 Mg–ATP 存在时，这些颗粒即使在 0 ℃ 也会迅速地解离，并随着 ATP 的水解而释放出 NSF[18]。这一解离的过程或许是膜融合过程中固有的一个步骤 [18]。

Purification of SNAP Receptors

To purify SNAP receptors, we used the specificity inherent in the assembly and disassembly of 20S particles as the basis of an affinity purification technique (schematized in Fig. 1): 20S particles were formed and attached to a solid matrix, allowing purified SNAP receptor to be released by particle disassembly when ATP was subsequently hydrolysed.

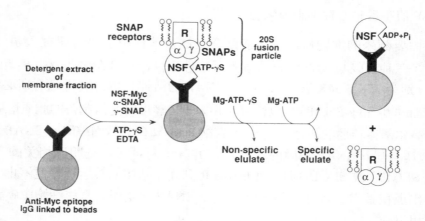

Fig. 1. Procedure used to purify SNAP receptors (SNAREs). Recombinant NSF, α-SNAP, and γ-SNAP are assembled into 20S particles by SNAREs present in a crude detergent extract of membranes. The SNAREs are incorporated stoichiometrically into the particles, which are then bound to beads by means of NSF. For this purpose, the NSF is epitope-tagged with Myc, and an anti-Myc monoclonal IgG is linked to the beads. The beads are washed and then eluted first with Mg–ATP-γS (nonspecific eluate) and then with Mg–ATP (specific eluate). The bound 20S particles disassemble in the presence of Mg–ATP (but not Mg–ATP-γS), releasing stoichiometric amounts of SNAPs and SNAREs. NSF remains bound to the beads. Experimental details are given in Fig. 2 legend.

A recombinant form of NSF, epitope-tagged with a Myc peptide[20] (EQKLISEEDL) at its carboxy terminus, was expressed in *E. coli* and shown to be functional[21]. The 20S particles were formed in solution by mixing a Triton X-100 extract of membranes with pure, recombinant α- and γ-SNAPs expressed in *E. coli* and NSF–Myc at 0 °C (ref. 15) in the presence of ATP-γS and EDTA (to chelate any magnesium). A monoclonal anti-Myc IgG (9E10; ref. 22) attached to protein G beads was then added to bind the 20S particles through their NSF–Myc subunits. The anti-Myc IgG does not inhibit NSF–Myc function in cell-free transport assays (our unpublished results).

The beads were formed into a column and washed extensively before a first (nonspecific) elution with Mg–ATP-γS to elute any proteins attached in a Mg^{2+}-sensitive fashion, or by Mg–ATP-γS *per se*. A second (specific) elution was then done with Mg–ATP (replacing Mg–ATP-γS). Only proteins released as the immediate consequence of ATP hydrolysis on the column will be recovered in this specific eluate. This scheme is based on that described

SNAP 受体的纯化

为了纯化 SNAP 受体，我们使用了一种亲和纯化技术。这一技术基于 20S 颗粒在组装和解离方面所固有的特性（如图 1 所示）：20S 颗粒形成后附着到固体基质上，然后再通过 ATP 水解，使颗粒解离，从而得到纯化的 SNAP 受体。

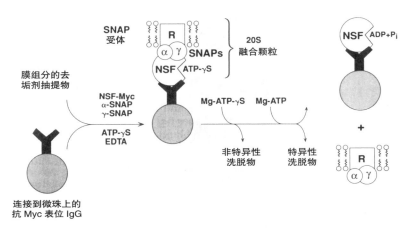

图 1. SNAP 受体（SNARE）的纯化步骤。重组 NSF、α-SNAP 和 γ-SNAP 被加入到使用去垢剂抽提得到的细胞膜粗提物中，并与其中的 SNARE 结合，形成 20S 颗粒。SNARE 会按化学计量比包含在 20S 颗粒中，并进一步通过其中的 NSF 与微珠结合。为了实现这个目的，NSF 的 C 端加上了一个 Myc 表位标签，同时微珠的表面偶联了抗 Myc 单克隆 IgG。微珠用缓冲液冲洗后，首先用 Mg-ATP-γS 溶液洗脱一次（非特异性洗脱），然后再用 Mg-ATP 进行洗脱（特异性洗脱）。在 Mg-ATP（而不是 Mg-ATP-γS）存在的情况下，20S 颗粒会发生解离，从而将一定化学计量数的 SNARE 和 SNAP 释放出来，而 NSF 则仍然结合在微珠上。实验细节请见图 2 注。

我们在大肠杆菌中表达了在 C 端加一个 Myc 表位标签[20]（EQKLISEEDL）的重组 NSF 蛋白，并且实验证明该蛋白是有活性的[21]。利用 Triton X-100 抽提膜组分，然后与纯化的、在大肠杆菌中表达的重组 α-SNAP、γ-SNAP 和纯化的 NSF–Myc 在 0 ℃混合（参考文献 15），并向体系中加入 ATP-γS 和 EDTA（以螯合溶液中的镁离子），促进 20S 颗粒的形成。另一方面，将抗 Myc 单克隆 IgG（9E10；参考文献 22）连接到表面包被了蛋白 G 的微珠上，将它们加入含有 20S 颗粒的溶液中，从而可以通过抗 Myc IgG 与 NSF–Myc 的特异结合将 20S 颗粒分离出来。在无细胞转运系统中，抗 Myc IgG 并不会抑制 NSF–Myc 的功能（未发表数据）。

将分离出来的微珠填充到一个柱子中，用大量缓冲液冲洗，然后首先（非特异性）使用含有 Mg-ATP-γS 的溶液洗脱附着在上面的所有对镁离子或 Mg-ATP-γS 敏感的蛋白，再用 Mg-ATP 溶液（替代 Mg-ATP-γS）进行第二次（特异性）洗脱。在特异性洗脱过程中只有那些在 ATP 水解后立即被释放出来的蛋白质才会被收集到特异性洗

previously[18] but includes a number of key modifications detailed in the figure legends. As NSF remains on the beads, the specific eluate should consist of a fraction of the added SNAPs, together with additional polypeptides representing SNAP receptors, ideally in stoichiometric amounts.

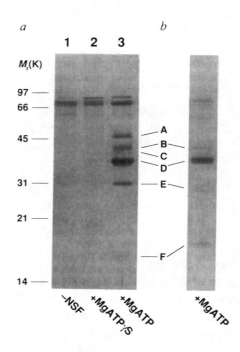

Fig. 2. Identification of proteins released from NSF after ATP hydrolysis. *a*, Polyacrylamide gel stained with Coomassie blue. Lane 1, control, Mg–ATP eluate of control binding reaction in the absence of NSF; lane 2, "nonspecific" eluate from complete binding reaction with NSF–Myc and Mg–ATP-γS; lane 3, "specific" eluate of the same column as for lane 2 following the exchange of ATP for ATP-γS (in the presence of EDTA) and addition of Mg^{2+} to allow ATP hydrolysis (Fig. 1). *b*, Silver-stained Laemmli gel of the specific (Mg–ATP) eluate.

Methods. All manipulations were performed at 0–4 °C. Bovine brain tissue was initially stripped of meninges, and all but the grey matter removed and discarded. The resulting tissue (30 g) was homogenized with 30 strokes of a Dounce homogenizer in buffer A (20 mM Tris–HCl, pH 8.0, 1 M KCl, 250 mM sucrose, 2 mM $MgCl_2$, 1 mM DTT, 1 mM phenylmethylsulphonyl fluoride (PMSF). A total particulate fraction was isolated by centrifugation in a Ti-45 rotor (Beckman) for 60 min at 33,000 r.p.m. The pellet was then resuspended in buffer A by Dounce homogenization and the membranes collected by centrifugation. The resulting pellet was washed once in buffer B (10 mM HEPES/KOH, pH 7.8, 100 mM KCl, 2 mM $MgCl_2$, 1 mM DTT) and then resuspended in 100 ml buffer B. Triton X-100 was added slowly with mixing to a final concentration of 4% (v/v), and the suspension incubated on ice with frequent mixing. After 45 min, the suspension was clarified by centrifugation (Ti-45 rotor) for 60 min at 33,000 r.p.m. and the supernatant dialysed overnight against 100 vol 25 mM Tris–HCl, pH 7.8, 50 mM KCl, 1 mM DTT, 1% (v/v) Triton X-100. After dialysis, the material was clarified by centrifugation (Ti-45 rotor for 60 min at 33,000 r.p.m.), aliquoted, and stored at −80 °C. Protein concentration was measured using the BCA reaction (Pierce) with ovalbumin as standard. This bovine brain extract (2 mg protein) was preincubated in the presence of His₆-α-SNAP (12 μg protein), His₆-γ-SNAP (4 μg protein) and NSF–Myc (12 μg protein) in buffer C (25 mM HEPES/KOH, pH 7.0, 0.75% (w/v) Triton X-100, 75 mM KCl, 1 mM DTT, 2 mM

脱物中。这一实验流程是基于以前的一篇报道[18]形成的，但对一些关键的步骤进行了修改（如图注中所示）。由于 NSF 会继续与免疫微珠结合，因此特异性的洗脱液中会含有一部分 SNAP 和额外的代表 SNAP 受体的多肽，并且这两种蛋白的分子数理论上应该是符合一定化学计量比例的。

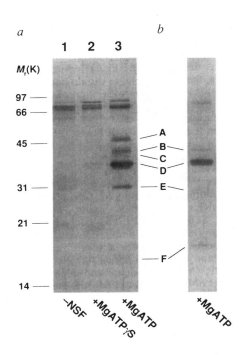

图 2. ATP 水解后，从 NSF 上解离下来的蛋白质的鉴定。a，使用考马斯蓝染色的聚丙烯酰胺凝胶。1 道为没有加 NSF 的对照，也使用 Mg–ATP 洗脱；2 道为使用 Mg–ATP-γS 洗脱的、与 NSF–Myc 非特异性结合的样品；3 道为使用 Mg–ATP（含 EDTA）洗脱的、与 NSF–Myc 特异性结合的样品（图 1）。b，Mg–ATP 特异性洗脱下来的样品，使用银染显色的莱氏凝胶电泳。

方法。所有的操作都在 0~4 ℃ 进行。剥去牛脑组织的脑膜，然后将除灰质以外的部分都丢弃。将约 30 g 的灰质在杜恩斯匀浆器中使用缓冲液 A（20 mM Tris–HCl，pH 8.0，1 M KCl，250 mM 蔗糖，2 mM MgCl$_2$，1 mM DTT，1 mM 苯甲基磺酰氟（PMSF））匀浆 30 次。使用 Ti-45 转子（贝克曼公司）33,000 rpm，离心 60 分钟。用溶液 A 重悬沉淀并用杜恩斯匀浆器再次匀浆，离心后收集膜组分。离心后的沉淀使用缓冲液 B（10 mM HEPES/KOH，pH 7.8，100 mM KCl，2 mM MgCl$_2$，1 mM DTT）冲洗一次，然后在 100 ml 缓冲液 B 中重悬。缓慢加入 Triton X-100 至终浓度为 4%（体积比）。将悬浮液在冰上孵育并不时混匀。45 分钟后，使用 Ti-45 转子 33,000 rpm，离心 60 分钟，将上清液使用 100 倍体积的 25 mM Tris–HCl，pH 7.8，50 mM KCl，1 mM DTT，1%（体积比）Triton X-100 混合溶液透析过夜。第二天，使用 Ti-45 转子 33,000 rpm，离心 60 分钟，将上清液分装并储存于 −80 ℃ 冰箱中。使用 BCA 法（皮尔斯公司）测定溶液中的蛋白浓度，以卵清蛋白为标准。在 4 ℃ 条件下，将牛脑组织抽提物（2 mg 蛋白质）与 His$_6$-α-SNAP（12 μg 蛋白质）、His$_6$-γ-SNAP（4 μg 蛋白质）和 NSF–Myc（12 μg 蛋白质）在缓冲液 C（25 mM HEPES/KOH，pH 7.0，0.75%（质量体积比）Triton X-100，75 mM KCl，1 mM DTT，2 mM EDTA，0.5 mM ATP（1 道）或 0.5 mM ATP-γS（2 道和 3 道），1%（质量体积比）聚乙二醇（PEG）4000，0.4 mM PMSF）中

EDTA, 0.5 mM ATP (for lane 1) or 0.5 mM ATP-γS (for lanes 2 and 3), 1% (w/v) polyethylene-glycol (PEG) 4000, 0.4 mM PMSF) for 30 min at 4 °C in a final volume of 2 ml. Mouse anti-Myc monoclonal antibody (200 µg protein, termed 9E10; ref. 22) covalently coupled to protein G–Sepharose 4 fast-flow (Pharmacia) was added and the incubation continued for 2 h with constant agitation. (The anti-Myc IgG was covalently coupled to the protein G–Sepharose using 20 mM dimethyl suberimidate as described[47].) The beads were packed into a column, washed with 10 vol buffer D (20 mM HEPES/KOH, pH 7.0, 0.5% (w/v) Triton X-100, 100 mM KCl, 1 mM DTT, 2 mM EDTA, 0.5 mM ATP (lane 1) or 0.5 mM ATP-γS (lanes 2 and 3), 0.4 mM PMSF) and the proteins eluted with 6 column-volumes of buffer D containing 8 mM MgCl$_2$ (resulting in a concentration of free Mg^{2+} of 4 mM). The column containing ATP-γS (lanes 2 and 3) was washed with an additional 2 column-volumes of buffer D containing 4 mM EDTA to complex the free Mg^{2+}, 3 column-volumes of buffer D containing ATP to exchange for bound ATP-γS, and then eluted with 6 column-volumes of buffer D containing 8 mM MgCl$_2$ to allow ATP hydrolysis. The appropriate fractions containing the eluate were pooled, precipitated with trichloroacetic acid, boiled in sample buffer[48] and analysed by electrophoresis on Tris–urea/SDS–polyacrylamide (18% acrylamide, 6 M urea, 750 mM Tris–HCl, pH 8.85, 50 mM NaCl, 0.1% SDS[49]) and stained with Coomassie blue R-250. For sequencing, the reaction was scaled up 25-fold.

A detergent extract of a crude, salt-washed total particulate fraction from the grey matter of bovine brain was used as the source of potential SNAP receptors. Membranes were washed with 1 M KCl before use to remove most of their endogenous SNAP supply[12]. As recombinant SNAPs were added in great excess for the binding reaction (Fig. 1), these should compete out the remaining endogenous SNAPs, preventing them from forming particles on the beads. Figure 2a shows a Coomassie blue-stained SDS–urea–high Tris–polyacrylamide gel of the specific eluate (lane 3), the nonspecific eluate fraction (lane 2), and the specific eluate from a control experiment omitting NSF–Myc (lane 1). Several bands (labelled A–F) appear only in the specific (Mg–ATP) eluate and depend on the presence of NSF. A set of bands at about M_r 70K are present in all three lanes, but apart from these, bands A–F are substantially pure in the specific eluate fraction. Band F runs as a sharper band in a standard Laemmli gel (Fig. 2b; specific eluate, stained with silver) than in the high Tris–urea gel (Fig. 2a). Bands A and C virtually co-electrophorese with the abundant band D in a Laemmli gel (Fig. 2b; see below).

Identification of SNAP Receptors

To identify specific bands, they were excised from blots and digested with trypsin, giving peptides that were then separated by high-pressure liquid chromatography and microsequenced (see Fig. 3 for details). Bands B and D co-electrophoresed with recombinant γ-SNAP and α-SNAP, respectively, both of which were His$_6$-tagged[15] and thus slightly larger than their endogenous counterparts (not shown). These identifications were confirmed by microsequencing peptides from bands B and D (not shown).

预孵育 30 分钟，最后总体积为 2 ml。加入共价偶联到蛋白 G-Sepharose 4 fast-flow（法玛西亚公司）上的小鼠抗 Myc 单克隆抗体（200 μg，称为 9E10；参考文献 22），继续孵育 2 小时，并持续振荡。（使用 20 mM 的辛二亚氨酸二甲酯作为交联剂可以将抗 Myc 抗体共价偶联到蛋白 G-Sepharose 上[47]）然后将微珠装入层析柱中，使用 10 倍体积的缓冲液 D（20 mM HEPES/KOH，pH 7.0，0.5%（质量体积比）Triton X-100，100 mM KCl，1 mM DTT，2 mM EDTA，0.5 mM ATP（1 道）或 0.5 mM ATP-γS（2 道和 3 道），0.4 mM PMSF）冲洗，使用 6 倍柱体积的含有 8 mM MgCl$_2$（游离的 Mg^{2+} 浓度为 4 mM）的缓冲液 D 洗脱结合在柱子上的蛋白。使用额外的 2 倍柱体积的缓冲液 D（含有 4 mM EDTA）冲洗含有 ATP-γS 的柱子（2 和 3 道）以螯合游离的 Mg^{2+}，再使用 3 倍柱体积的缓冲液 D（含有 ATP）置换 ATP-γS，然后再用 6 倍柱体积的缓冲液 D（含有 8 mM MgCl$_2$）洗脱，使得 ATP 水解。收集洗脱下来的蛋白组分用三氯乙酸沉淀后，用样品缓冲液[48]煮沸，然后使用 Tris-尿素/SDS-聚丙烯酰胺（18% 丙烯酰胺，6 M 尿素，750 mM Tris-HCl，pH 8.85，50 mM NaCl，0.1% SDS[49]）凝胶电泳分离，考马斯蓝 R-250 染色。如果所得样品用于测序，则将反应体系扩大 25 倍。

使用去垢剂抽提并经盐冲洗后的牛脑灰质粗提物作为潜在的 SNAP 受体来源。首先使用 1 M KCl 溶液冲洗膜组分以去除大部分内源性的 SNAP[12]。当过量的重组 SNAP 被加入到样品中之后（图 1），它们应该可以竞争过残余的内源性 SNAP，阻止其在微珠上形成微粒。图 2a 显示了经 SDS-尿素-高 Tris-聚丙烯酰胺凝胶分离的特异洗脱样品（3 道）、非特异洗脱的样品（2 道）和对照组（未加入重组 NSF-Myc 蛋白）的特异洗脱样品（1 道）用考马斯蓝染色后的结果。只有在实验组的特异洗脱（使用 Mg-ATP）且存在 NSF 的样品中才可以看到多个条带（分别标记为 A~F），而 1 道和 2 道都没有。三个道中都有一条分子量约为 70K 的条带。除此以外，在特异洗脱部分中，条带 A~F 基本上是纯的。使用标准的莱氏凝胶（图 2b；特异性洗脱，银染）可以得到比高浓度 Tris-尿素凝胶（图 2a）边缘更清晰的条带 F，在莱氏凝胶中条带 A 和 C 会与大量的条带 D 共电泳（图 2b；见下文）。

SNAP 受体的鉴定

为了鉴定这些特异的条带，我们将这些条带从印迹中切下来并用胰蛋白酶消化得到多肽，然后使用高压液相层析法（HPLC）将其分离并进行微量测序（详细信息见图 3）。条带 B 和 D 分别与重组的 γ-SNAP 和 α-SNAP 共电泳。由于这两个重组的 SNAP 都带有一个 His$_6$ 标签[15]，因此比细胞内的 SNAP 要稍大一些（数据未展示）。对从条带 B 和 D 中得到的多肽进行微量测序进一步证实了这一结果（数据未展示）。

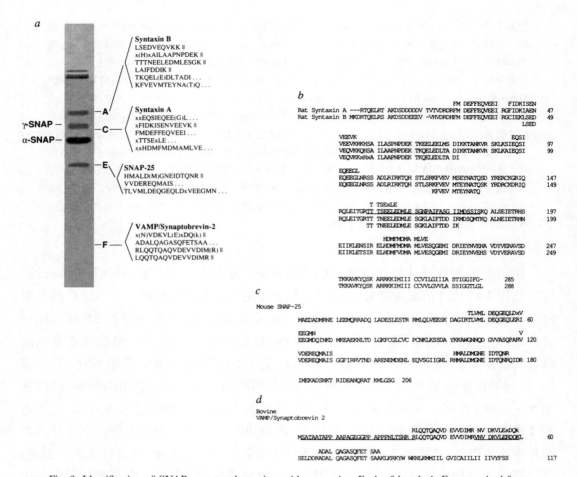

Fig. 3. Identification of SNAP receptors by amino-acid sequencing. Each of bands A–F was excised from an electroblot onto a nitrocellulose membrane after staining with Ponceau S, digested with trypsin, and the fragments separated by reverse-phase HPLC. *a*, Peptide sequences from each of the indicated bands are shown on the right (one-letter code). An "X" means that no residue could be identified at this position. A capital letter in parentheses means that the residue was identified with a lower degree of confidence; a lower-case letter in parentheses means that the residue was present but in very small amounts. The symbol ‖ indicates that the C terminus of the peptide was known. A dotted line means no more interpretable signals were obtained, but that this was unlikely to be the C terminus. The identify of bands B and D (Fig. 2) as γ-SNAP and α-SNAP, respectively, was confirmed by peptide sequencing. In the case of the syntaxin A peptide XTTSExLE... (from band C), only this limited sequence was obtained because of instrument failure. However, mass analysis of this peptide (on 1/25th of the sample) gave a value of $m/z = 3,274.8$; this is in good agreement with the value ($MH^+ = 3,276.67$) calculated for the predicted tryptic peptide (residues 156–186 of syntaxin A) which contains the limited sequence, so confirming the identify of the entire peptide. Mass analysis was also critical in the identification of band F as VAMP/synaptobrevin-2, confirming the presence of an *N*-acetylated peptide corresponding to residues 2–31 in the digest of band F (see text for details). *b*, Amino-acid sequences of syntaxins A (top) and B (below) from rat brain[23]. Shown above syntaxin A are the peptide sequences obtained from band C, and below syntaxin B are the peptide sequences obtained from band A. *c*, Complete amino-acid sequence of synaptosome-associated protein 25 (SNAP-25) from mouse brain[24]. Above are the peptide sequences obtained from band E. Underlined sequences in *d* and *b* are peptides identified by mass analysis.

Methods. Tryptic digestions and peptide separation. Ponceau S staining bands were excised, digested

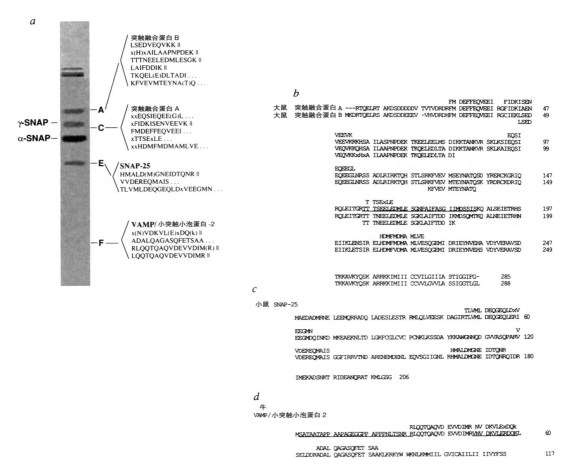

图 3. 通过氨基酸测序鉴定 SNAP 受体。蛋白转印到硝酸纤维素膜上后，用丽春红 S 染色，然后将 A~F 的各个条带切下来并使用胰蛋白酶消化，最后使用反相 HPLC 对消化得到的肽段进行分离。a，各个条带分析得到的多肽序列标记在各个带的右侧（使用氨基酸单字母代码）。其中"X"表示该位点的多肽残基未测出来；括号中的大写字母表示该位点鉴定的残基可信度较低；括号中的小写字母表示存在该残基，但量非常少；"‖"表示该多肽的 C 端已知；虚线表示虽然没有可以识别的信号，但这不太可能是 C 端。在图 2 中，已经鉴定出条带 B 和 D 分别是 γ-SNAP 和 α-SNAP，多肽测序的结果证实了这一点。由于仪器错误，在突触融合蛋白 A 的一个肽段中只测出了有限的序列 XTTSExLE…（从条带 C 中）。然而，这一多肽的质谱分析（1/25 的样品量）结果显示，其质荷比为 3,274.8，与理论预计的包含有限序列的胰蛋白酶消化肽段（突触融合蛋白 A 的残基 156~186）的质荷比（3,276.67）非常吻合，因此可以确定这一多肽就是突触融合蛋白 A 的片段。在鉴定条带 F 就是 VAMP / 小突触小泡蛋白-2 的过程中，质谱分析也提供了有力的证据。其证明在 2~31 位的多肽中存在 N-乙酰化修饰（详情请见正文）。b，大鼠脑组织中突触融合蛋白 A（上面）和 B（下面）的氨基酸序列[23]。图中所示的突触融合蛋白 A 的序列来自条带 C，而突触融合蛋白 B 的序列来自条带 A。c，小鼠脑组织中突触小体相关蛋白 25（SNAP-25）的氨基酸全序列[24]。其多肽序列来自条带 E。在 b 和 d 中带下划线的序列是质谱中鉴定出的片段。

方法。胰蛋白酶酶解与多肽的分离。经丽春红 S 染色的条带剪切后使用胰蛋白酶原位消化（1 μg 测序级的胰蛋白酶，伯林格 - 曼海姆公司），所产生的多肽使用 RP-HPLC（参考文献 50）进行分离。HPLC 系统如文献所述[50]，采用的是 Separations Group 公司（希斯皮里亚市，美国加利福尼亚州）的

in situ with trypsin (1 μg sequencing grade trypsin; Boehringer–Mannheim), and the resulting fragments separated by RP-HPLC (ref. 50). Generally, HPLC systems were as described[50] and equipped with a 2.1 × 250 mm Vydac C4 (214TP54) column from the Separations Group (Hesperia, CA). Peptides resulting from digests of band F were fractionated on a 1 × 100 mm Inertsil 100GL-I-ODS-110/5 C18 column from SGE (Ringwood, Australia). The 1-mm column was operated in a system consisting of a model 140B syringe pump (ABI, Foster City, CA) and an ABI model 783 detector, fitted with a LC-Packings Kratos-compatible capillary flow cell which was directly connected to the column outlet (system assembly by C. Elicone); gradient slope was 1% B per min at a flow of 30 μl min⁻¹. Fractions were stored at −70 °C before sequence or mass analysis. Peptide sequencing: Peptides were sequenced with the aid of an ABI model 477A automated sequencer, optimized for femtomol phenylthiohydantoin analysis as described[51,52]. Fractions were always acidified (20% TFA final concentration) before application on the sequencer disc. Mass analysis: Aliquots (typically 1/50–1/25) of selected peak fractions were analysed by matrix-assisted laser desorption time-of-flight mass spectrometry using a Vestec (Houston, TX) LaserTec instrument with a 337 nm output nitrogen laser operated according to ref. 53. The matrix was α-cyano-4-hydroxy cinnamic acid and a 25 kV ion acceleration and 3 kV multiplier voltage were used. Laser power was adjusted manually as judged from optimal deflections of specific maxima, using a Tektronix TDA 520 digitizing oscilloscope.

Sequences from six major peptides containing a total of 70 residues were obtained from band A, each precisely matching the sequence of syntaxin B (p35B) from rat brain[23] (Fig. 3*b*). The sequences of these and peptides from the other specific bands are shown in association with the band from which they were obtained (Fig. 3*a*). No sequences or fragments attributable to any other protein were found, indicating that the bulk of material in band A is syntaxin B.

Five major peptides containing a total of 53 residues were sequenced from band C (Fig. 3*a*), and proved to differ at only one position from the published sequence of syntaxin A from rat brain[23]; the difference presumably reflects the species involved. Expected sequence differences between the 84% identical syntaxins A and B were found in the peptides from bands C and A (Fig. 3*b*). The syntaxins run more slowly than expected from their relative molecular masses (about 35K) in the high percentage Tris–SDS–urea–polyacrylamide gels were used, although they virtually co-electrophorese with α-SNAP (35K) in standard Laemmli gels (Fig. 2*b*, and data not shown).

Three major peptides (Fig. 3*a*) from band E gave sequences (Fig. 3*c*) matching a protein predicted from a mouse brain complementary DNA clone which by coincidence has been termed SNAP-25 (for synaptosome-associated protein of 25K; ref. 24). Of 45 residues obtained, 42 were identical to the published sequence of mouse SNAP-25. The discrepancies, two of which are conservative, are probably due to species differences. SNAP-25 migrates at M_r 31K in the SDS–urea gel.

All five peptides (containing 43 identified residues) sequenced from band F (Fig. 3*a*) exactly matched the sequence of VAMP/synaptobrevin-2 from bovine brain[25] (Fig. 3*d*). VAMP-2, the major isoform of VAMP/synaptobrevin in brain, differs slightly from VAMP-1 (refs 26, 27); all the sequences obtained from band F correspond to VAMP-2. All HPLC peptide peaks from band F, other than those attributable to trypsin autodigestion, were shown to be derived from VAMP/synaptobrevin. As a control, the region corresponding to band F

2.1 mm×250 mm 的 Vydac C4 (214TP54) 柱子。条带 F 中消化得到的多肽则使用 SGE 公司 (灵伍德, 澳大利亚) 的 1 mm×100 mm 的 Inertsil 100GL-I-ODS-110/5 C18 柱进行分离。1 mm 的柱子是在含有 140B 型注射泵 (ABI 公司, 福斯特城, 美国加利福尼亚州) 和 ABI 783 型检测器的系统下进行操作, 并通过一个 LC-Packings Kratos-compatible 毛细管流动吸收池与柱子流出管直接相连 (该系统由 C. Elicone 组装)。梯度为每分钟 1% B, 流速为 30 μl·min⁻¹。各组分在进行测序或质谱分析前在 −70 ℃ 中保存。多肽测序: 使用 ABI 477A 型自动序列分析仪进行多肽序列分析。针对飞摩尔级乙内酰苯硫脲分析进行了优化, 实验方法如文献所述 [51,52]。在上样前, 各组分通常都会先进行酸化处理 (使用终浓度为 20% 的三氟乙酸)。质谱分析: 将等份的 (一般是 1/50~1/25) 收集的峰组分使用 "基质辅助激光解吸时间飞行质谱" 进行分析, 激光器是 Vestec 公司 (休斯敦, 美国得克萨斯州) 的 LaserTec 仪器, 氮气激光, 波长为 337 nm, 操作方法如文献 53 所述。使用的基质是 α-氰基-4-羟基桂皮酸, 离子加速电压 25 kV, 倍增器电压 3 kV。使用 Tektronix TDA 520 数字示波器, 激光的功率根据特定峰值的最佳偏转来手动调节。

对从条带 A 中得到的 6 个主要多肽 (总共含有 70 个氨基酸残基) 进行测序, 发现每个肽段都可以精确地与大鼠脑组织中的突触融合蛋白 B(p35B) 的序列吻合 [23] (图 3b)。条带 A 和其他特异条带的多肽序列分别显示在其对应的条带旁 (图 3a)。从条带 A 中消化得到的序列或片段没有一个与其他蛋白吻合, 说明条带 A 中的主要物质就是突触融合蛋白 B。

从条带 C 中得到的 5 个主要的多肽 (总共含有 53 个氨基酸残基) 同样经测序后发现 (图 3a): 除了一个位点不同外, 其与已公布的来源于大鼠脑组织的突触融合蛋白 A[23] 均相同。这一差别可能反映了物种的差异。突触融合蛋白 A 和 B 的序列相似性为 84%, 这一序列差异也在条带 C 和 A 的测序结果中得到体现 (图 3b)。尽管在标准的莱氏凝胶中突触融合蛋白几乎与分子量为 35K 的 α-SNAP 共电泳, 但是在高比例 Tris-SDS-尿素-聚丙烯酰胺凝胶中它们的迁移速度远低于其相对分子质量 (约 35K) 对应的预期速度 (图 2b, 数据未显示)。

从条带 E 中得到的 3 个主要多肽 (图 3a) 的序列 (图 3c) 可以与小鼠脑组织中 cDNA 克隆编码的一个名为 SNAP-25 (名字源于 25K 的突触小体相关蛋白; 参考文献 24) 的蛋白相匹配。45 个已获得的残基中, 有 42 个与已公布的小鼠 SNAP-25 的序列吻合。另外 3 个序列中有 2 个是保守的, 这种差异可能是由于物种不同引起的。在 SDS-尿素凝胶中, SNAP-25 迁移速度与分子量为 31K 的蛋白相同。

从条带 F 中得到的 5 个多肽 (含有 43 个已鉴定的残基) 的序列 (图 3a) 与牛脑组织中的 VAMP(突触小泡相关膜蛋白) / 小突触小泡蛋白 -2 [25] 完全吻合 (图 3d)。VAMP-2 是 VAMP / 小突触小泡蛋白在大脑中的主要亚型, 其与 VAMP-1 有细微的差别 (参考文献 26, 参考文献 27); 从条带 F 中得到的所有序列都与 VAMP-2 匹配。在 HPLC 分析中, 除了胰蛋白酶自身消化的片段外, 所有的肽段峰都来自 VAMP /

from the blot of the gel of the nonspecific (Mg–ATP-γS) eluate was subject to tryptic digestion and HPLC analysis in parallel with band F from the Mg–ATP eluate in two separate experiments. None of the VAMP/synaptobrevin-2 peptide peaks from band F were present in the HPLC profile of the control; only the autolytic tryptic peptides were detected.

Two peptides from the digest of band F failed to give any sequence, suggesting that they had blocked N termini. Mass spectroscopy indicated that these components had m/z values of 2,680.90 and 2,838.36 respectively, differing by 157.46, or approximately the molecular mass of Arg (156.19 average isotopic mass). The tryptic cleavage site closest to the N terminus in bovine VAMP/synaptobrevin-2 consists of an Arg-Arg sequence (at positions 30–31), so the expected partial cleavage would yield two N-terminal-derived peptides. If it is assumed that the initiator Met is removed, and that the newly generated N-terminal Ser is acetylated, adding 42.04 to the M_r, the two masses correspond almost perfectly with the predicted M_rs [MH$^+$] of the bovine VAMP/synaptobrevin-2 peptides spanning residues 2–30 and 2–31 (2,681.90 and 2,838.09, respectively). The N terminus of VAMP/synaptobrevin-2 thus appears to be processed and acetylated.

The material in the 70K region of all three eluates (specific, nonspecific and control) (Fig. 2) was microsequenced (from the specific eluate) in an attempt to determine if any synaptotagmin/p65 was present, as this protein can be immunoprecipitated together with syntaxins[23]. No evidence for its presence was found, although it cannot be excluded. Of three peptides sequenced, two were from Hsp70, an ATP-binding protein[28], and one was from a protein not found in the Genbank database.

Scanning and integrating the Coomassie blue stain in the gel shown in Fig. 2a gives the following ratios when staining is corrected for molecular weight, expressed as a fraction of α-SNAP; syntaxin B, 0.18; SNAP-25, 0.15; VAMP/synaptobrevin-2, 0.23. The syntaxin A band (band C) is weak compared with syntaxin B and could not readily be quantitated. The sum of all of the SNAP receptor species is 0.56 mol per mol α-SNAP, and so is approximately stoichiometric, given that proteins vary in staining by Coomassie blue, and the stoichiometry of SNAP and receptor in complexes does not need to be 1:1. The relative amounts of the different SNAP receptors in such a co-purified mixture may not reflect their relative abundance in the starting material, as their affinities for SNAPs may differ. The ratio of γ-SNAP to α-SNAP was ~0.2.

The role of syntaxins, SNAP-25, and synaptobrevin as SNAP receptors is supported by (1) their absence when NSF was omitted from the purification; (2) the need for ATP hydrolysis, rather than the mere presence of ATP, to elute them from the beads; (3) the approximately stoichiometric amounts purified relative to SNAP itself; and (4) the substantial purity of the proteins obtained. The fact that all of these proteins originate from the synapse further strengthens this conclusion.

As further confirmation, we attempted to follow the incorporation of α-SNAP receptor into

小突触小泡蛋白。作为对照，我们将非特异性洗脱（Mg–ATP-γS）样品的凝胶中与条带 F 位置相同的区域切下来后，和 Mg–ATP 洗脱中的条带 F 分别在两个独立实验中平行进行胰蛋白酶消化和 HPLC 分析。结果发现除了胰蛋白酶自溶肽段外，对照组的 HPLC 色谱图中不含任何条带 F 中的 VAMP / 小突触小泡蛋白 –2 的多肽峰。

条带 F 的消化产物中有两个多肽的序列不能够被测定，说明他们具有封闭的 N 端。质谱分析显示它们的质荷比分别为 2,680.90 和 2,838.36，相差 157.46，大约为一个精氨酸（平均同位素量 156.19）的分子量。胰蛋白酶在牛 VAMP / 小突触小泡蛋白 –2 上最靠近 N 端的切割位点是一个 Arg-Arg 序列（位于多肽残基的第 30~31 位）。因此，预期的不完全切割可能会产生两种 N 端来源的肽段。假使起始的甲硫氨酸被去除，而新的 N 端——丝氨酸发生乙酰化，那么该 N 端肽段的分子量将增加约 42.04。这样计算的话，牛 VAMP / 小突触小泡蛋白 –2 第 2~30 位和第 2~31 位肽段的分子量分别为 2,681.90 和 2,838.09，与上面质谱的结果相吻合。因此，VAMP / 小突触小泡蛋白 –2 的 N 端似乎发生了乙酰化。

对三种洗脱情况（特异、非特异及对照组）（图 2）中，分子量为 70K 的物质也进行了微量测序，以确定是否有突触结合蛋白 / p65 存在。这是由于该蛋白被证明可以与突触融合蛋白免疫共沉淀[23]。虽然无法完全排除其存在的可能性，但没有证据表明 70K 条带含有该蛋白。对所有三个多肽的测序发现，其中两个来自于 Hsp70（一种 ATP 结合蛋白[28]），另一个在 Genbank 数据库中找不到与之匹配的蛋白。

当染色经分子量校正后，扫描并分析考马斯蓝染色的胶（图 2a）发现，各蛋白以占 α-SNAP 的比例表示如下：突触融合蛋白 B，0.18；SNAP-25，0.15；VAMP / 小突触小泡蛋白 –2，0.23。与突触融合蛋白 B 相比，突触融合蛋白 A（条带 C）的含量太低以至于无法定量。所有的 SNAP 受体与 α-SNAP 的摩尔比为 0.56∶1。由于不同蛋白经考马斯蓝染色深度不一样，且 SNAP 和受体结合时并不一定要 1∶1 结合，因此这是一个近似的化学计量比例。在共纯化的混合物中，不同 SNAP 受体之间的相对含量并不一定能够反映出它们在起始物质中的相对丰度，这是因为不同受体与 SNAP 的亲和力可能不一样。γ-SNAP 和 α-SNAP 的比率大约为 0.2。

以下证据支持突触融合蛋白、SNAP-25 和小突触小泡蛋白是 SNAP 受体：（1）不加入 NSF 纯化时，不存在这些蛋白；（2）只有当 ATP 存在且发生水解的情况下，它们才能够从微珠上洗脱下来；（3）纯化下来的这些蛋白与 SNAP 具有近似的化学计量数；（4）获得的这些蛋白纯度都很高。此外，这些蛋白都来自于突触的事实也进一步巩固了这一结论。

为了进一步验证上述结论，我们制备了一个抗 SNAP-25 的一个 C 端多肽的抗

20S particles formed from crude extracts of bovine brain membranes using an antibody raised against a C-terminal peptide from SNAP-25. Detergent extract from salt-washed membranes was incubated with excess recombinant α- and γ-SNAPs with (Fig. 4c) or without (Fig. 4b) excess recombinant NSF, and the products were separated by velocity centrifugation in a linear glycerol gradient. In the absence of NSF, SNAP-25 sedimented at about 5S, but in its presence, almost all SNAP-25 cosedimented with NSF, α-SNAP, and γ-SNAP in the 20S particle (Fig. 4d). Assembly of NSF and SNAPs into the 20S particle required bovine brain membrane extract (Fig. 4a), as expected from earlier studies with Golgi membranes[18].

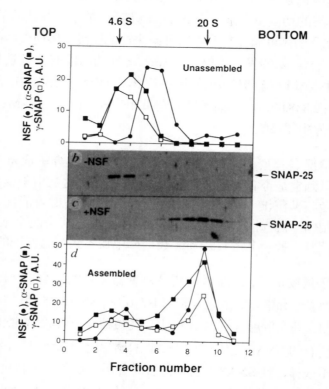

Fig. 4. Incorporation of SNAP-25 and other components into 20S fusion particles. a, b, Conditions in which 20S particles do not form (for example, controls); c, d, conditions in which 20S particles assemble. Components of the 20S fusion particle were incubated and then fractionated by glycerol gradient centrifugation, and the fractions analysed by SDS–PAGE to determine the location of α-SNAP and γ-SNAP, and to determine the locations of NSF and SNAP-25. Bovine serum albumin (4.6S) and α_2-macroglobulin (20S) were used as standards.

Methods. Reaction conditions were arranged so that the protein of interest would be maximally incorporated into 20S particles; thus, results in a and d are composites of several experiments. In the case in which the SNAPs were examined, in vitro-translated ^{35}S-labelled α-SNAP (■) and γ-SNAP (□) (ref. 17) (~2.1×10^6 c.p.m. for α- and 1.4×10^5 c.p.m. for γ-SNAP) were incubated on ice with bovine brain extract (1.2 mg protein), in the absence (a) or presence (d) of His$_6$-NSF (100 µg protein) in 20 mM HEPES–KOH, pH 7.4, 100 mM KCl, 2 mM DTT, 2 mM EDTA, 0.5 mM ATP, 0.5% (v/v) Triton X-100 in a final volume of 0.5 ml. After 15 min, reactions were loaded onto a 10–35% (w/v) glycerol gradient[18] and centrifuged in an SW41 rotor (Beckman) for 18 h at 40,000 r.p.m. Gradients were fractionated from the bottom at 1 ml per min, and an aliquot of each fraction analysed by SDS–PAGE and autofluorography. Recovery of both radiolabelled SNAPs

体，以此来追踪 α-SNAP 受体整合到 20S 颗粒（来自于牛脑组织细胞膜粗提物）的过程。我们将盐冲洗过的细胞膜抽提物在加（图 4c）或不加（图 4b）过量的重组 NSF 蛋白的情况下与过量的重组 α-SNAP 和 γ-SNAP 蛋白孵育，然后使用线性甘油梯度离心法分离产物。当不加 NSF 时，SNAP-25 的沉降系数为 5S；而加入 NSF 后，几乎所有的 SNAP-25 都与 NSF、α-SNAP 和 γ-SNAP 一起沉淀于 20S 的颗粒中（图 4d）。此外，与早期使用高尔基体膜的实验得到的预期[18] 一致的是，由 NSF 和 SNAP 组成的 20S 颗粒的形成需要牛脑组织细胞膜抽提物（图 4a）。

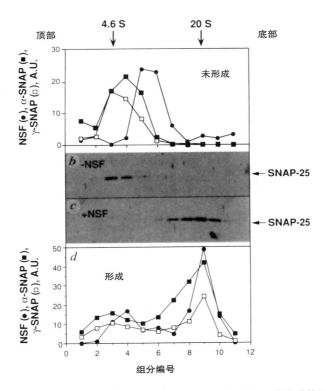

图 4. SNAP-25 与其他组分组装成 20S 融合颗粒的过程。a, b, 没有形成 20S 颗粒的情况（例如，对照组）；c, d，形成 20S 颗粒的情况。20S 颗粒的组分在孵育后使用甘油梯度离心的方法进行分离，然后不同的组分再使用 SDS–PAGE 进行分析，来鉴别出哪些是 α-SNAP 和 γ-SNAP，哪些是 NSF 和 SNAP-25。以牛血清白蛋白（4.6S）和 α_2- 巨球蛋白（20S）为标准。

方法。我们对反应条件进行了优化，使得我们感兴趣的蛋白能够最大限度地组装成 20S 颗粒。因此，a 和 d 所示的结果是由多次实验产生的。在检验 SNAP 的实验中，我们使用了体外翻译的 ^{35}S 标记的 α-SNAP（■）和 γ-SNAP（□）（参考文献 17）（浓度分别约为 2.1×10^6 cpm 和 1.4×10^5 cpm），分别在 His$_6$-NSF（100 μg 蛋白）存在（d）和不存在（a）的情况下，在冰上与牛脑组织抽提物（1.2 mg 蛋白）共同孵育，溶液中含有 20 mM HEPES–KOH，pH 7.4，100 mM KCl，2 mM DTT，2 mM EDTA，0.5 mM ATP，0.5%（体积比）Triton X-100，总体积为 0.5 ml。15 分钟后，将反应产物加到 10%~35%（质量体积比）甘油梯度[18] 中，使用 SW41 转子（贝克曼公司）40,000 rpm，离心 18 小时。离心结束后，将各梯度的组分从离心管底部以 1 ml·min^{-1} 的速度放出，分别收集，然后用 SDS–PAGE 和放射自显影法分析各组分。结果表明，放

exceeded 90%. Autofluorographs were scanned with a ScanJet Plus (Hewlett Packard) and the images integrated using Scan Analysis software (BioSoft, Cambridge). To examine NSF (●), His$_6$-NSF (ref. 15) (10 μg protein) was incubated with each of the His$_6$-SNAPs (20 μg each protein), either in the absence (*a*) or presence (*d*) of bovine brain extract (1.5 mg protein). Samples were incubated and fractionated as described. Aliquots were analysed by western blotting using an anti-His$_6$ antibody and blots were scanned as described[17]. To determine the extent to which SNAP-25 is incorporated into the 20S particle, bovine brain extract was added in limiting amounts (300 μg protein) and incubated either in the absence (*b*) or presence (*c*) of both His$_6$-SNAPs and His$_6$-NSF (30 μg each protein). Samples were processed and aliquots of each fraction analysed by western blotting using an antibody generated against the C-terminal peptide of SNAP-25. For this purpose, a peptide of the sequence used in ref. 24 was synthesized but with an additional cysteine at the N terminus, and affinity-purified antibodies generated. Blots were visualized using the ECL System (Amersham). AU, arbitrary unit.

Discussion

In this study, we have purified SNAP receptors from a crude brain membrane fraction on the basis of their ability to assemble 20S particles from SNAPs and NSF, and their release from NSF upon ATP hydrolysis (studies using Golgi membranes as source material will be described elsewhere). The simplest explanation for the fact that multiple polypeptides are obtained is that each is a distinct SNAP receptor. In particular, there is no evidence that any of these polypeptides associate, for example, as heterodimers[54]. All of them must thus have either the capacity to assemble a 20S particle, or a very high affinity for one that has been assembled. As our method is biased to isolating receptors of the highest abundance and affinity, we have probably isolated only some of the receptor types that are present.

By exploiting the same enzyme cycle used in the vesicle fusion process to offer two layers of biological specificity, we have purified SNAP receptors on the basis of their function, giving a largely pure preparation of four proteins from the crudest possible extract of brain, all of which originate from synapses. This striking selection for synaptic components probably reflects the degree to which the brain is specialized for synaptic vesicle fusion. The fact that each SNAP receptor purified corresponds to a previously cloned and sequenced gene no doubt reflects the exhaustive structural characterization of synaptic components by molecular biologists who have focused on the synapse because of its central importance in neuronal development and function[29,30,54]. Despite this effort, however, the roles of these proteins are unknown because of the lack of functional assays.

Of the SNAP receptors we have isolated, SNAP-25 is found in the presynaptic terminals of neurons[24] but has not been more precisely localized. Although its sequence suggests it is hydrophilic, it behaves as an integral membrane protein[24] and is palmitylated at one or more of the four cysteine residues between positions 85 and 92 (ref. 55). Fatty acyl-CoA is required for NSF-dependent fusion[56], and SNAP-25 or related proteins may serve as the relevant acyl acceptors. Multiple acylations of such proteins could create a hydrophobic surface as a trigger for fusion.

VAMP/synaptobrevin is inserted into synaptic vesicles by a single hydrophobic C-terminal

射性标记的 SNAP 的回收率超过 90%。放射自显影的图像使用 ScanJet Plus 扫描仪（惠普公司）扫描，并使用扫描分析软件（BioSoft 公司，剑桥）对图像进行整合。为了检测 NSF（●），我们分别在牛脑组织抽提物（1.5 mg 蛋白）存在（d）和不存在（a）的情况下，将 His$_6$-NSF（10 μg 蛋白）（参考文献 15）与 His$_6$-SNAP（每种蛋白 20 μg）一起孵育。样品采用相同的方法进行孵育和分离，然后使用抗 His$_6$ 的抗体进行蛋白质印迹检测，并采用与上述相同的方法对那些杂交出来的点进行扫描和分析[17]。为了确定 SNAP-25 整合在 20S 颗粒中的比例，我们向一定量（300 μg 蛋白）的牛脑组织抽提物中分别加入（c）或不加（b）His$_6$-SNAP 蛋白和 His$_6$-NSF 蛋白（每种蛋白均 30 μg）并进行孵育。然后再采用与上述相同的方法分离样品，并使用抗 SNAP-25 C 端多肽位点的抗体进行蛋白质印迹检测。为了达到这个目的，我们合成了文献 24 中所述的多肽序列并在 N 端加上一个额外的半胱氨酸，以此作为抗原，制备亲和纯化的抗体。蛋白质印迹杂交的结果使用电化学发光（ECL）系统（安马西亚公司）进行显色。AU，任意单位。

讨　论

本研究中，我们利用 SNAP 受体可以与 SNAP 和 NSF 结合形成 20S 颗粒并可以随着 ATP 的水解而从 NSF 上解离下来的性质（利用高尔基体膜作为材料源进行的研究发表在别的杂志上），从脑组织细胞膜组分粗提物中纯化出了 SNAP 受体。对于这些纯化出来的多肽，最简单的解释就是他们每一个都是 SNAP 受体。尤其值得注意的是，没有任何证据表明这些多肽之间会相互结合，例如形成异源二聚体等[54]。因此，所有这些多肽要么具有组装成 20S 颗粒的能力，要么具有与那些已经形成的颗粒高亲和力结合的能力。由于我们的实验方法偏好于分离出具有最高丰度和亲和力的受体，因此我们可能只分离出了存在的受体中的一部分。

通过探索在囊泡融合过程中提供两层生物特异性的同一种酶循环，我们利用 SNAP 受体的功能将其纯化出来，最终从脑组织的粗提物中分离出了四种很纯的蛋白质。这些蛋白质都来自于突触，这一惊人发现很可能反映出大脑为突触囊泡融合而特化的程度。此次纯化出的各个 SNAP 受体分别与之前克隆或基因序列分析的结果一致的事实也毫无疑问地体现了分子生物学家对突触结构鉴定的巨大努力。这些分子生物学家之所以会关注突触，是因为突触在神经元发育和功能中具有核心作用[29,30,54]。虽然如此，由于缺乏相应的功能性实验，目前对于这些蛋白的功能仍缺乏了解。

在分离得到的 SNAP 受体中，我们发现 SNAP-25 分布于神经元的突触前末端[24]，但更精确的定位尚不清楚。尽管其序列表明它是一个亲水性的蛋白，但是其种种表现却更像是一个整合膜蛋白[24]。另外，在 SNAP-25 的 85 到 92 位的四个半胱氨酸残基中，有一个或多个发生了棕榈酰基化修饰（参考文献 55）。由于依赖 NSF 的融合过程需要脂酰辅酶 A 的参与[56]，SNAP-25 或其他相关蛋白可能扮演着相关酰基受体的角色。这一类蛋白质的多重酰化可以形成一个疏水的界面从而引发膜融合过程。

VAMP／小突触小泡蛋白通过其 C 端一个疏水性的片段插入到突触囊泡上，而

segment, and the remainder of the protein is cytoplasmic. Both tetanus and botulinum B toxins, potent inhibitors of neurotransmitter release, are proteases specific for VAMP/synaptobrevin-2 (ref. 31), suggesting that this SNAP receptor is essential for synaptic vesicle fusion *in vivo*. Syntaxin[23] has the same topography as VAMP/synaptobrevin, but is concentrated in "active zones" of the presynaptic membrane[23] at which a subpopulation of synaptic vesicles is docked[32] to allow fusion within 200 μs of the calcium influx induced by an action potential[33]. Components of the fusion machinery may have to be largely preassembled at these sites to allow such a rapid response.

In this light, the fact that 20S particles can contain VAMP/synaptobrevin (from the synaptic vesicle) and syntaxin (from the plasma membrane) is of interest, because these complexes might form part of the fusion apparatus docking the vesicle to its target in the active zone. It is not yet possible to say whether syntaxin and VAMP/synaptobrevin exist together in a single 20S particle (Fig. 5a), or whether separately assembled particles join together to form an attachment site (Fig. 5b), perhaps with the aid of additional proteins.

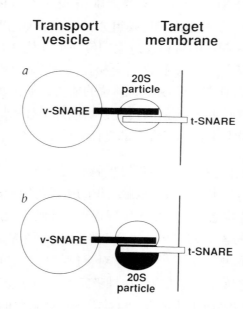

Fig. 5. Models to explain vesicle targeting based on the finding that SNAREs isolated in 20S fusion particles can originate from either the transport vesicle (v-SNAREs) or from the target membrane (t-SNAREs). A 20S particle (containing NSF and SNAPs) that simultaneously binds a v-SNARE and a t-SNARE (a) would attach a vesicle to its target. Alternatively (b), 20S particles, each capable of binding only one SNARE at a time, could interact to attach vesicle to target, a process that perhaps requires other proteins to assemble together.

The fact that molecules previously implicated in regulated exocytosis at the synapse are SNAP receptors implies that the same NSF- and SNAP-dependent machinery necessary for many constitutive fusion events also underlies triggered release of neutotransmitters at synapses. By extension, we would expect that NSF and SNAP are similarly employed in other forms of regulated exocytosis[34].

其余的部分则仍位于细胞质中。破伤风毒素和肉毒杆菌 B 毒素（有效的神经递质释放抑制剂）都是 VAMP / 小突触小泡蛋白–2 的特异性蛋白酶（参考文献 31）。这表明在体内 SNAP 受体对于突触囊泡的融合来说至关重要。突触融合蛋白 [23] 具有与 VAMP / 小突触小泡蛋白相同的拓扑结构，但是却集中分布于突触前膜的"活性区"[23]——在这些区域有一个亚群的突触囊泡停靠 [32]，当有动作电位引发钙离子内流时，在 200 μs 内便可以发生囊泡的融合 [33]。融合装置的各个组分需要预先在这些位点大量组装好，从而可以在很短的时间内迅速作出反应。

这样看来，20S 颗粒中含有 VAMP / 小突触小泡蛋白（来自突触囊泡）和突触融合蛋白（来自细胞膜）就显得很有意思了，这意味着这些复合物也许可以形成将囊泡停靠在特定活性区域所需的融合装置的一部分。不过目前仍无法肯定在单个 20S 颗粒中是否同时含有突触融合蛋白和 VAMP / 小突触小泡蛋白（图 5a），也不确定是否由各个独立的颗粒来联合组装成一个附着位点（图 5b）。也许另外还有别的蛋白对这一过程有辅助作用。

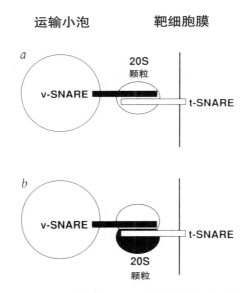

图 5. 囊泡靶向机理模式图。20S 融合颗粒中的 SNARE 有的来自运输小泡（v-SNAREs），有的来自靶细胞膜（t-SNAREs）。当一个 20S 颗粒（含有 NSF 和 SNAP）同时与 v-SNARE 和 t-SNARE(a)结合时，便会将囊泡与其靶位点结合在一起。或者如(b)所示，如果每个 20S 颗粒一次只能结合一个 SNARE，则可以通过颗粒间的相互作用将囊泡与靶位点结合在一起，这一过程可能需要借助其他蛋白来完成组装。

突触的调控型胞吐过程有 SNAP 受体的参与，说明参与组成型融合的 NSF 及 SNAP 机器也同样参与了诸如突触神经递质释放这样的调控型融合过程。引申开来，我们认为 NSF 和 SNAP 在其他形式的调控型胞吐过程中也具有类似的功能 [34]。

How can constitutive fusion machinery also be used in triggered exocytosis? An inhibitory component(s) must apparently prevent the 20S fusion particle from engaging, or from completely assembling in the first place. Such a fusion clamp could either cover an active site in NSF, SNAP or the SNAP receptors, or could prevent any of the additional cytoplasmic subunits of the fusion machinery[35] from binding. In the case of the synapse, a calcium trigger would remove the clamp. A strong candidate for such a clamp is the synaptic vesicle membrane protein synaptotagmin[36,37]. Synaptotagmin co-immunoprecipitates with syntaxin[23], and the recombinant proteins can bind each other[23]. It also undergoes a calcium-dependent conformational change[38]. Although synaptotagmin is not one of the major components of the 20S particles characterized here, this is not surprising, as the interaction between syntaxin and synaptotagmin is disrupted by 0.5 M salt[23], and we used a 1 M salt wash.

Rab3A, a Ras-related GTP-binding protein, is another candidate for a clamp, as this protein dissociates from synaptic vesicles upon stimulation of fusion[39]. Fusion clamps may respond to a variety of second messengers such as cyclic AMP, activated G proteins, protein phosphorylation, and so on, in addition to calcium, depending on cell type and physiological context.

SNAREs may Encode Specificity

Both syntaxin and VAMP/synaptobrevin have homologues in yeast[40,42]. The yeast protein SED5 is related to syntaxin[40], and its absence blocks ER-to-Golgi transport, leading to the accumulation of transport vesicles; it appears to reside in the Golgi[40]. Another homologue, PEP12, is found primarily on the vacuole membrane, and is required for Golgi-to-vacuole transport[41]. The yeast SEC22, BET1 and BOS1 gene products are related to VAMP/synaptobrevin, and are required for fusion with the Golgi in vivo. BOS1 at least is a component of ER-derived transport vesicles[16,42-45]. Other recent examples are discussed in ref. 46. SNAP-25 is distantly related to SED5, PEP12, and the syntaxins.

The synaptic SNAP receptors we have identified are thus members of a family of proteins which appear to be distributed in a compartmentally specific fashion, with one set attached to the transport vesicles (v-SNAREs) and another set attached to target membranes (t-SNAREs). This suggests a model in which each transport vesicle contains one or more members of the v-SNARE superfamily obtained on budding from a corresponding donor compartment, and every target compartment in a cell contains one or more members of the t-SNARE superfamily. Specificity in membrane transactions would be assured by the unique and non-overlapping distribution of v-SNAREs and t-SNAREs among the different vesicles and target compartments. In the simplest view, that is, if there were no other source of specificity, only when complementary v-SNARE and t-SNARE pairs engage would a productive fusion event be initiated. Thus, a v-SNARE from the ER (possibly SEC22)

组成型融合装置在引发胞吐的过程中如何发挥作用呢？应该有某种（或多种）抑制性组分可以显著抑制 20S 融合颗粒的啮合或全部组装。这种融合"钳子"要么会掩盖 NSF、SNAP 或 SNAP 受体的活性位点，要么会阻止融合装置中其他胞质亚基[35]的结合。对于突触而言，钙触发剂可以移除这种"钳子"。突触囊泡膜蛋白——突触结合蛋白[36,37]是这种"钳子"强有力的候选蛋白。突触结合蛋白可以与突触融合蛋白免疫共沉淀[23]，并且这两种重组蛋白可以相互结合[23]。此外，突触结合蛋白还会受钙离子的调控发生构象变化[38]。虽然在 20S 颗粒中，突触结合蛋白并没有作为一个主要成分被鉴定出来，但我们对此并不感到奇怪，因为突触融合蛋白和突触结合蛋白的相互作用会被 0.5 M 的盐破坏[23]，而我们在实验中却使用了 1 M 的盐进行冲洗。

Rab3A 是一个 Ras 相关的 GTP 结合蛋白，它是"钳子"的另一个候选蛋白。当融合过程被激活时，这个蛋白会从突触囊泡上解离下来[39]。除了钙离子之外，融合"钳子"还可能会随着细胞种类和生理环境的不同而对多种第二信使发生应答，比如环腺苷酸（cAMP）、激活的 G 蛋白、蛋白质磷酸化等等。

SNARE 也许是特异编码的

突触融合蛋白和 VAMP / 小突触小泡蛋白在酵母中都有同源蛋白[40,42]。酵母中的 SED5 蛋白与突触融合蛋白同源[40]，其缺失会抑制从 ER 到高尔基体的转运，导致运输小泡的积累。SED5 似乎分布于高尔基体中[40]。另一个同源分子——PEP12 则主要分布于液泡膜上，是从高尔基体到空泡转运所必需的[41]。酵母 *SEC22*，*BET1* 和 *BOS1* 基因的产物是 VAMP / 小突触小泡蛋白的同源分子，对于体内高尔基体的融合来说是必需的。BOS1 至少是来自 ER 运输小泡的一种成分[16,42-45]。其他最近的例子在参考文献 46 中进行了讨论。SNAP-25 与 SED5、PEP12 和突触融合蛋白的关系比较远。

因此，我们已经鉴定出来的突触 SNAP 受体属于一个蛋白家族，他们的分布具有区室特异性，其中一部分与运输小泡（v-SNARE）结合，另一部分与靶细胞膜（t-SNARE）结合。这提示了一种囊泡靶向机制——每个运输小泡中含有一种或多种 v-SNARE 超家族的成员，这些 v-SNARE 来自于囊泡出芽的相应供体区；细胞中每个靶向区域则含有一个或多个 t-SNARE 超家族的成员。通过 v-SNARE 和 t-SNARE 在不同囊泡和靶位点上独特的、无重叠的分布，可以实现特异的膜融合。简而言之，如果没有其他决定特异性的因素的话，那么只有当 v-SNARE 和 t-SNARE 相匹配的时候，囊泡的融合过程才能够被启动。因此，来自 ER 的 v-SNARE（可能是 SEC22）可以与来自高尔基体的 t-SNARE（可能是 SED5）结合，而不与来自溶酶体（可能是

could engage a t-SNARE from the Golgi (possibly SED5), but not one from the lysosome (possibly PEP12). For the proposed mechanism to work (again, assuming no other source of specificity), non-complementary SNAREs would have to be excluded from the same 20S particle (Fig. 5a) or multi-particle assemblies (Fig. 5b), although any one SNARE might be able to form a 20S particle by itself while waiting for a partner to arrive. If this is correct, the 20S fusion particle assembly reaction might be used as a cell-free "read-out" system to test whether candidate proteins are SNAREs (as shown here for SNAP-25), and to establish which SNAREs, if any, form specific cognate pairs. Localization of the SNARE proteins *in situ* would then establish which are v-SNAREs and which are t-SNAREs and which compartments are involved in each pairing.

A related mechanistic question is whether the SNAPs (and NSF) are associated primarily with a v-SNARE or with a t-SNARE, or whether an essentially symmetrical structure is formed at the junction of vesicle and target. NSF and SNAPs can associate with Golgi membranes to form 20S particles in the absence of transport vesicles[18], implying that 20S particles can be formed with only one SNARE partner. As native NSF is a tetramer of subunits with two ATPase domains each, it is easy to imagine several ways in which a 20S particle containing one NSF could form a symmetrical vesicle–target junction by simultaneously binding a v-SNARE and a t-SNARE (Fig. 5a).

Although many important details need to be established, our findings imply a general role for NSF and SNAP in regulated and constitutive intracellular membrane fusion processes, and in synaptic transmission in particular. The SNAREs we have identified appear to be members of compartment-specific membrane protein multigene families which may form attachment sites between specific vesicles and their correct target membranes together with NSF and SNAPs.

(**362**, 318-324; 1993)

**Thomas Söllner, Sidney W. Whiteheart, Michael Brunner, Hediye Erdjument-Bromage, Scott Geromanos, Paul Tempst &
James E. Rothman**
Rockefeller Research Laboratory, Memorial Sloan-Kettering Cancer Center, 1275 York Avenue, New York, New York 10021,
USA

Received 25 February; accepted 9 March 1993.

References:

1. Palade, G. E. *Science* **189**, 347-358 (1975).

2. Glick, B. S. & Rothman, J. E. *Nature* **326**, 309-312 (1987).

3. Block, M. R., Click, B. S., Wilcox, C. A., Wieland, F. T. & Rothman, J. E. *Proc. Natl. Acad Sci. U.S.A.* **85**, 7852-7856 (1988).

4. Fries, E. & Rothman, J. E. *Proc. Natl. Acad. Sci. U.S.A.* **77**, 3870-3874 (1980).

5. Balch, W. E., Dunphy, D. W., Braell, W. A. & Rothman, J. E. *Cell* **39**, 405-416 (1984).

6. Malhotra, V., Orci, L., Glick, B. S., Block, M. R. & Rothman, J. E. *Cell* **54**, 221-227 (1988).

7. Orci, L., Malhotra, V., Amherdt, M., Serafini, T. & Rothman, J. E. *Cell* **56**, 357-368 (1989).

8. Wilson, D. W. *et al. Nature* **399**, 355-359 (1989).

PEP12）的某种蛋白结合。为使所假设的机制成立（再一次假设没有其他决定特异性的因素存在），尽管任何一个 SNARE 也许都能够形成 20S 颗粒，但非互补性的 SNARE 将不会存在于同一个 20S 颗粒（图 5a）或多颗粒的复合体（图 5b）中。如果这个推论正确的话，那么 20S 融合颗粒的组合实验也许可以被作为一个无细胞体系，用于检验候选蛋白是否为 SNARE（例如这里说的 SNAP-25），还可以用于研究哪些 SNARE 可以形成特异的配对。SNARE 蛋白的原位定位实验则可以用于鉴别哪些是 v-SNARE，哪些是 t-SNARE，以及哪些细胞内的区室参与配对。

对于这个机制来说，仍存在一个问题，即是否 SNAP（以及 NSF）主要与某种 v-SNARE 或 t-SNARE 结合，或者在囊泡和靶位点结合的时候是否会形成一种基本对称的结构。在没有运输小泡存在的情况下，NSF 和 SNAP 也可以与高尔基体膜结合形成 20S 颗粒[18]，这表明即使只有一个 SNARE 配体也可以形成 20S 颗粒。由于天然 NSF 由 4 个亚基组成，每个亚基有两个 ATP 酶结构域，因此很容易想象含有一个 NSF 的 20S 颗粒通过同时结合 v-SNARE 和 t-SNARE 形成一个对称的囊泡 – 靶位点汇合处的多种方法（图 5a）。

尽管许多重要的细节仍有待研究，但我们的发现揭示了 NSF 和 SNAP 在调控型和组成型细胞内膜融合过程中，尤其是在突触信号的传递中的普遍性作用。我们所鉴定的多种 SNARE 蛋白似乎是某种区室特异性膜蛋白家族的成员，它们可以与 NSF 和 SNAP 一起介导囊泡与其靶位点形成特异的结合。

（张锦彬 翻译；石磊 审稿）

9. Novick, P., Ferro, S. & Schekman, R. *Cell* **25**, 461-469 (1981).

10. Graham, T. R. & Emr, S. D. *J. Cell Biol.* **114**, 207-218 (1991).

11. Weidman, P. J., Melancon, P., Block, M. R. & Rothman, J. E. *J. Cell Biol.* **108**, 1589-1596 (1989).

12. Clary, D. O. & Rothman, J. E. *J. Biol. Chem.* **265**, 10109-10117 (1990).

13. Clary, D. O., Griff, I. C. & Rothman, J. E. *Cell* **61**, 709-721 (1990).

14. Griff, I. C., Schekman, R., Rothman, J. E. & Kaiser, C. A. *J. Biol. Chem.* **267**, 12106-12115 (1992).

15. Whiteheart, S. W. *et al. Nature* **362**, 353-355 (1993).

16. Kaiser, C. A. & Schekman, R. *Cell* **61**, 723-733 (1990).

17. Whiteheart, S. W., Brunner. M., Wilson, D. W., Wiedmann, M. & Rothman, J. E. *J. Biol. Chem.* **267**, 12239-12243 (1992).

18. Wilson, O. W., Whiteheart, S. W., Wiedman, M., Brunner, M. & Rothman, J. E. *J. Cell Biol.* **117**, 531-538 (1992).

19. Tagaya, M., Wilson, D. W., Brunner, M., Arango, N. & Rothman, J. E. *J. Biol. Chem.* **269**, 2662-2666 (1993).

20. Munro, S. & Pelham, H. R. B. *Cell* **48**, 899-907 (1987).

21. Wilson, D. W. & Rothman, J. E. *Meth. Enzym.* **219**, 309-318 (1992).

22. Evan, G. I., Lewis, G. K., Ramsey, G. & Bishop, M. J. *Molec. Cell. Biol.* **5**, 3610-3616 (1985).

23. Bennett, M. K., Calakos, N. & Schelller, R. H. *Science* **257**, 255-259 (1992).

24. Oyler, G. A. *et al. J. Cell Biol.* **109**, 3030-3052 (1989).

25. Sudhof, T. C. *et al. Neuron* **2**, 1475-1481 (1989).

26. Elferink, L. A., Trimble, W. S. & Scheller, R. H. *J. Biol. Chem.* **264**, 11061-11064 (1989).

27. Archer, B. T., Ozcelik, T., Jahn, R., Franke, U. & Sudhof, T. C. *J. Biol. Chem.* **265**, 17267-17273 (1990).

28. Chappell, T. G. *Cell* **45**, 3-13 (1986).

29. Greengard, P., Valturta, F., Czernik, A. J. & Benfenati, F. *Science* **259**, 780-785 (1993).

30. Trimble, W. S., Linial, M. & Sheller, R. H. *A. Rev. Neurosci.* **14**, 93-122 (1991).

31. Schiavo, G. *et al. Nature* **359**, 832-835 (1992).

32. Landis, D. M. D., Hall, A. K., Weinstein, L. A. & Reese, T. S. *Neuron* **1**, 201-209 (1988).

33. Llinas, R., Steinberg, I. Z. & Walton, K. *Biophys. J.* **33**, 323-352 (1981).

34. Kelley, R. B., *Science* **230**, 25-32 (1985).

35. Waters, R. G., Clary, D. O. & Rothman, J. E. *J. Cell Biol.* **118**, 1015-1026 (1992).

36. Perin, M. S., Fried, V. A., Mignery, G. A., Jahn. R. & Sudhof, T. C. *Nature* **34**, 260-263 (1990).

37. Wendland, B., Miller. K. G., Schilling, J. & Scheller, R. H. *Neuron* **6**, 993-1007 (1991).

38. Brose, N., Petrenko, A. G., Sudhof, T. C. & Jahn, R. *Science* **256**, 1021-1025 (1992).

39. Fischer von Mollard, G., Sudhof, T. C. & Jahn, R. *Nature* **349**, 79-81 (1991).

40. Hardwick, K. G. & Pelham, H. R. B. *J. Cell Biol.* **119**, 513-521 (1992).

41. Preston, R. A. *et al. Molec. Cell. Biol.* **11**, 5801-5812 (1991).

42. Dascher, C., Ossig, R., Gallwitz, D. & Schmitt, H. D. *Molec. Cell. Biol.* **11**, 872-885 (1991).

43. Newman, A. P., Groesch, M. E. & Ferro-Novick, S. *EMBO J.* **11**, 3609-3617 (1992).

44. Newman, A. P. *et al. Molec. Cell. Biol.* **12**, 3663-3664 (1992).

45. Shim, J., Newman, A. P. & Ferro-Novick, S. *J. Cell Biol.* **113**, 55-64 (1991).

46. Bennett, M. K. & Scheller, R. H. *Proc. Natl. Acad. Sci. U.S.A.* (in the press).

47. Harlow, E. & Lane, O. *Antibodies: A Laboratory Manual* (Cold Spring Harbor Laboratory Press, New York, 1988).

48. Laemmli, U. K, *Nature* **227**, 680-685 (1970).

49. Schlenstedt, G., Gudmundsson, G. H., Boman, H. G. & Zimmermann, R. *J. Biol. Chem.* **265**, 13960-13968 (1990).

50. Tempst, P., Link, A. J., Riviere, L. R., Fleming, M. & Elicone, C. *Electrophoresis* **11**, 537-553 (1990).

51. Tempst, P. & Riviere, L. *Analyt. Biochem.* **183**, 290-300 (1989).

52. Erdjument-Bromage, H., Geromanos, S., Chodera, A. & Tempst, P. *Techniques in Protein Chemistry IV* (Academic, San Diego, in the press).

53. Beavis, R. C. & Chait, B. T. *Rapid Commun. Mass Spect.* **3**, 432-435 (1989).

54. Sudhof, T. C. & Jahn, R. *Neuron* **6**, 665-677 (1991).

55. Hess, D. T., Slater, T. M., Wilson, M. C. & Skene, J. H. P. *J. Neurosci.* **12**, 4634-4641 (1992).

56. Pfanner, N., Glick, B. S., Arden, S. R. & Rothman, J. E. *J. Cell Biol.* **110**, 955-961 (1990).

Acknowledgements. We thank M. Hum, L. Lacomis and M. Lui for help with protein digestions, HPLC separations and peptide sequencing; C. Elicone for custom assembly of the microbore HPLC system; M. Wiedmann for discussion; and W. Patton for gel scans and analysis. This work was supported by the Mathers Charitable Foundation, and by an NIH grant (to J.E.R.), a Fellowship of the Deutsche Forschungsgemeinschaft (to T.S.), a Fellowship from the Jane Coffin Childs Memorial Fund for Medical Research (to S.W.W.), and by an EMBO postdoctoral fellowship (to M.B.). The Sloan-Kettering microchemistry core facility is supported, in part, by an NCI core grant.

Discovery of the Candidate Kuiper Belt Object 1992 QB₁

D. Jewitt and J. Luu

Editor's Note

In 1951 it was hypothesized that the outer solar system (beyond Neptune's orbit) contains a population of icy bodies, in the so-called Kuiper Belt. Many searches were made, which revealed a couple of bodies beyond Saturn's orbit. By the early 1990s, telescopes were being equipped with semiconductor-based cameras that were hundreds or thousands of times more sensitive than earlier technology, such as photographic film. Here David Jewitt and Jane Luu use such a camera to find the first Kuiper Belt object. More objects were rapidly found, and by 2000 it was clear that the "planet" Pluto was really just another Kuiper Belt object. Pluto was demoted from planetary status in 2006.

The apparent emptiness of the outer Solar System has been a long-standing puzzle for astronomers, as it contrasts markedly with the abundance of asteroids and short-period comets found closer to the Sun. One explanation for this might be that the orbits of distant objects are intrinsically short-lived, perhaps owing to the gravitational influence of the giant planets. Another possibility is that such objects are very faint, and thus they might easily go undetected. An early survey[1] designed to detect distant objects culminated with the discovery of Pluto. More recently, similar surveys yielded the comet-like objects 2060 Chiron[2] and 5145 Pholus[3] beyond the orbit of Saturn. Here we report the discovery of a new object, 1992 QB₁ moving beyond the orbit of Neptune. We suggest that this may represent the first detection of a member of the Kuiper belt[4,5], the hypothesized population of objects beyond Neptune and a possible source of the short-period comets[6-8].

OUR observations are part of a deep-imaging survey[9] of the ecliptic, made with the University of Hawaii 2.2-m telescope on Mauna Kea. The survey uses Tektronix $1{,}024 \times 1{,}024$ pixel and $2{,}048 \times 2{,}048$ pixel charge-coupled devices (CCDs) at the $f/10$ Cassegrain focus. Both CCDs have anti-reflection coatings which yield quantum efficiencies of $\sim90\%$ at wavelength $\lambda \approx 7{,}000$ Å (K. Jim, personal communication). Survey observations are obtained in sets of four images per field with a total timebase of 2 or more hours. Each image is exposed for 900 s while autoguiding at sidereal rate. Because objects in the outer Solar System have small proper motions, our survey was optimized to detect slowly moving objects (SMOs). The angular motions of SMOs are sufficiently small that little trailing-loss results from sidereal tracking. This strategy is found to provide optimum

柯伊伯带天体候选体 1992 QB$_1$ 的发现

朱维特，刘丽杏

编者按

1951 年，人们猜测外太阳系（太阳系内海王星轨道之外的空间）在后来被称为"柯伊伯带"的区域内有很多冰冷的天体。人们进行了很多搜寻，但仅在土星轨道之外找到了一些天体。到了 20 世纪 90 年代早期，人们开始在望远镜上安装基于半导体的相机，其灵敏度比照相胶片等早期技术提高了成百上千倍。大卫·朱维特和刘丽杏使用这样的相机找到了第一个柯伊伯带天体。很快更多天体被发现了。到 2000 年，人们清楚地意识到"行星"冥王星其实只是另一个柯伊伯带天体而已。冥王星于 2006 年被排除行星范围。

外太阳系表观上的空旷一直都是困扰天文学家的疑团，这与在更靠近太阳的地方发现的大量小行星及短周期彗星形成了鲜明的对比。对此，一种解释是，或许远处天体的轨道寿命本身就较短，寿命短可能是因为巨型行星的引力作用。另一种可能的解释是，这类天体非常暗淡，因此可能很难被探测到。以探测太阳系远距离天体为目的的一次早期巡天[1]发现了冥王星的存在。后来，类似的巡天在土星轨道之外发现了类彗天体 2060 喀戎[2]和 5145 福鲁斯[3]。在此我们报告运行于海王星轨道之外的新天体 1992 QB$_1$ 的发现。我们认为这可能是第一次探测到的柯伊伯带成员[4,5]，柯伊伯带即人们猜测中的海王星之外的一族天体，也是短周期彗星的一个可能来源[6-8]。

我们的观测是利用位于冒纳凯阿火山的夏威夷大学 2.2 米望远镜进行的黄道深空成像巡天[9]项目的一部分。该观测使用 $f/10$ 的卡塞格林焦点处的美国泰克 1,024 × 1,024 像素和 2,048 × 2,048 像素电荷耦合元件（CCD）。以上两种 CCD 都有减反射镀膜，这使得波长 7,000 Å 处的量子效率达到 90% 左右（吉姆，个人交流）。在实际观测中对每个视场都拍了四幅图片，总的时间是 2 小时或者更长。在以恒星周天转速自动跟踪时，每幅图像的曝光时间是 900 s。由于外太阳系天体具有微小的自行，所以我们的巡天优先探测那些缓慢运动天体（SMOs）。这些 SMO 由于自身的角运动足够小，几乎没有跟踪造成的拖尾损失。人们发现这种观测方法对于预期的 SMO 的线性的、相

sensitivity to the linear, correlated motion expected of slowly moving objects. By restricting observations to stellar images of full width at half maximum (FWHM) $\leqslant 1.0$ arcsec, and to moon-less skies, we obtain limiting magnitudes $m_R \sim 25$. To date, a sky area of 0.7 square degrees has been imaged to this depth. We are extending our coverage to 1 square degree.

We confine our observations to the opposition direction, where the angular motion of distant objects is retrograde and primarily due to the Earth's motion. At opposition, the parallactic angular motion $\dot{\theta}$ (arcsec per hour) is given by $\dot{\theta} = 148[(1-R^{-1/2})/(R-1)]$, where R (in astronomical units, AU) is the heliocentric distance[9]. Thus, a measurement of $\dot{\theta}$ yields R directly. Our observations are restricted to the spring and autumnal equinoxes to benefit further from the large galactic latitude of the opposition point, and from the resultant low density of background stars. In fact, field galaxies pose a worse contamination problem than do field stars in our observations.

The object 1992 QB$_1$ was detected in real time on UT 1992 August 30 (ref. 10). The discovery images are shown in Fig. 1, where the faster motion of a nearby, unnumbered main-belt asteroid emphasizes the remarkably small angular motion (and hence large distance) of QB$_1$. The slow motion of the SMO (2.6 arcsec h^{-1} west and 1.1 arcsec h^{-1} south) was confirmed on UT August 31 and September 01. Absence of detectable diurnal parallax confirmed that the object was not a near-Earth asteroid whose proper motion fortuitously resembled that of a SMO. Positions of 1992 QB$_1$ were obtained with reference to stars in the Hubble Guide Star Catalogue. Measurements relative to these stars suggested an absolute astrometric accuracy of ± 1 arcsec, and the relative positions were precise to about ± 0.3 arcsec. Astrometric positions were communicated to B. Marsden at the Center for Astrophysics. Follow-up astrometry from the 2.2-m telescope was obtained on UT 1992 September 25, and other observers have reported astrometric measurements in the following three months[11-13]. Observations from 1992 August 30 to December 25 yielded a current heliocentric distance $R \approx 41$ AU, and were used to calculate the orbital parameters listed in Table 1 (ref. 13).

Table 1. Preliminary orbital parameters

Semi-major axis	a	44.4 AU
Eccentricity	e	0.11
Inclination	i	2.2°
Orbital period	P	296 years
Perihelion date	T	AD 2023
Perihelion distance	q	39.6
Aphelion distance	Q	49.1

Based on astrometry in the interval 1992 August 30 to December 25. Orbit solution is by Marsden[13].

关的运动最为灵敏。通过限制观测星像的半峰全宽（FWHM），在不大于 1.0 arcsec、无月夜的条件下，我们得到的极限星等为 $m_R \sim 25$。迄今，我们对 0.7 平方度的天区进行了这种深度的成像。我们正在将覆盖范围扩大到 1 平方度。

我们将观测限制在冲日方向，在那里，遥远天体的角运动主要是由于地球运动导致的逆行。在冲日点，视差角运动 $\dot{\theta}$(arcsec·h⁻¹) 为 $\dot{\theta} = 148[(1-R^{-1/2})/(R-1)]$，其中 R（单位为天文单位，AU）是与太阳的距离[9]。因此，由 $\dot{\theta}$ 的测量就可以直接算出 R。我们的观测限制在了春分点和秋分点附近，进一步得益于冲日点的高银纬以及此处背景星的低密度。事实上，在我们的观测中，场星系造成的污染比场星造成的污染严重。

1992 QB₁ 是在世界时 1992 年 8 月 30 日实时发现的（参考文献 10）。图 1 显示了发现 1992 QB₁ 时的图像，图中其附近较快速运动的未编号的主带小行星凸现了 QB₁ 天体非常小的角运动（是由于距离遥远）。该 SMO 的缓慢运动（以 2.6 arcsec·h⁻¹ 向西、1.1 arcsec·h⁻¹ 向南运动）在世界时 8 月 31 日和 9 月 1 日得到了证实。基于没有发现周日视差可以确定，该天体不是一颗运动恰好类似于 SMO 的近地小行星。1992 QB₁ 的位置是参考哈勃导星星表的恒星得到的。相对于这些星的测量，给出的天体测量的绝对精度为 ±1 arcsec，相对位置的精度约为 ±0.3 arcsec。天体测量位置是和天体物理中心的马斯登交流过结果的。世界时 1992 年 9 月 25 日我们用 2.2 米望远镜进行了后续天体测量，其他观测者在接下来的三个月内报告了天体测量结果[11-13]。从 1992 年 8 月 30 日到 12 月 25 日的观测结果得出了现在的日心距 $R \approx 41$ AU，并且被用来计算轨道参数，相应的轨道参数列于表 1 中（参考文献 13）。

表 1. 轨道参数初步结果

半长轴	a	44.4 AU
偏心率	e	0.11
轨道倾角	i	2.2°
轨道周期	P	296 年
过近日点日期	T	AD 2023
近日点距离	q	39.6
远日点距离	Q	49.1

基于 1992 年 8 月 30 日到 12 月 25 日的天体测量。轨道解算由马斯登完成[13]。

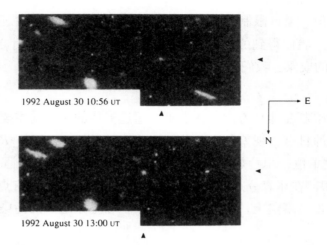

Fig. 1. Discovery images of 1992 QB₁ (marked by arrows), obtained UT 1992 August 30 at the University of Hawaii 2.2-m telescope, using a Mould R filter (central wavelength $\lambda_c = 6{,}500$ Å, FWHM $\Delta\lambda = 1{,}250$Å). The images show regions of a $2{,}048 \times 2{,}048$ pixel Tektronix CCD (each pixel subtends 0.22 arcsec). Stellar images are about 0.8 arcsec FWHM. The elongated object to the lower right in the top image is a main-belt asteroid: it appears in the top left of the bottom image and demonstrates the extraordinarily slow motion of 1992 QB₁. The field shown is ~90 arcsec in width.

At distance $R = 41$ AU, geocentric distance $\Delta = 40$ AU and phase angle $\alpha = 0.5°$, the apparent red magnitude $m_R = 22.8 \pm 0.2$ on August 30 corresponds to absolute magnitude $\overline{H_R} = 6.6 \pm 0.2$. For comparison, the absolute magnitude of the distant comet 2060 Chiron in its faint state is $\overline{H_R} \approx 6.3 \pm 0.1$ (ref. 14). Lacking a measurement of the albedo, we cannot determine the size of 1992 QB₁. However, an albedo $p_R = 0.04$, similar to that of a comet nucleus, suggests a diameter $d \approx 250$ km, roughly one-eighth the size of Pluto. The Kron-Cousins colours of 1992 QB₁ were measured on UT 1992 August 30 and September 01. Our best estimates are $m_V - m_R = 0.6 \pm 0.1$ and $m_R - m_I = 1.0 \pm 0.2$, to be compared with solar colours $m_V - m_R = 0.32$ and $m_R - m_I = 0.4$, respectively. Here m_V, m_R and m_I are the stellar magnitudes measured with V (5,500 Å), R (6,500 Å) and I (8,000 Å) filters. The $m_R - m_I$ colour is based on a single I filter image. Nevertheless, it seems that 1992 QB₁ is substantially redder than sunlight, inconsistent with a surface of pure ice but consistent with dirty ice, or one contaminated with organic compounds. For comparison, the corresponding colours of the distant object 5145 Pholus are $m_V - m_R \approx 0.7$ and $m_R - m_I \approx 0.7$ (ref. 15), and all other known cometary nuclei are substantially less red[16]. Both Pholus and 1992 QB₁ may retain primitive organic mantles produced by prolonged cosmic-ray irradiation. Such mantles would be disrupted or buried by rubble mantles on active, near-Sun comets[15,16].

Figure 2 shows the surface brightness profile measured from images taken UT 1992 September 01. The profile of a nearby field star is shown for comparison. Figure 2 supplies no evidence for a resolved coma down to surface brightness 29 mag per square arcsec, at a distance of 1.5 arcsec from the centre of the image. The absence of resolved coma allows us to place a model-dependent limit on the mass loss rate from 1992 QB₁, using a profile-

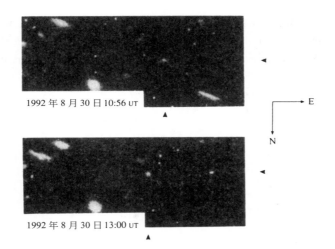

1992 年 8 月 30 日 10:56 UT

1992 年 8 月 30 日 13:00 UT

图 1. 1992 QB₁(用箭头标出)的发现图。于世界时 1992 年 8 月 30 日用夏威夷大学 2.2 米望远镜得到，所用的是 R 滤光片(中心波长为 $\lambda_c = 6{,}500$ Å，半峰全宽为 $\Delta\lambda = 1{,}250$ Å)。这幅图像显示 2,048 × 2,048 像素美国泰克 CCD(每个像素对应于 0.22 arcsec)的观测区域。恒星图像半峰全宽大约为 0.8 arcsec。上图中右下角被拉长的天体是主带小行星：它在下面一幅图中出现在了左上角，这说明了 1992 QB₁ 极其缓慢的运动。该区域宽度约为 90 arcsec。

　　在日心距 $R = 41$ AU，地心距离 $\Delta = 40$ AU 和相位角为 $\alpha = 0.5°$ 的情况下，8 月 30 日的红视星等 $m_R = 22.8 \pm 0.2$，对应绝对星等 $\overline{H_R} = 6.6 \pm 0.2$。作为比较，遥远彗星 2060 喀戎在暗弱态的绝对星等为 $\overline{H_R} \approx 6.3 \pm 0.1$(参考文献 14)。由于缺乏对星体反照率的测量，我们无法确定 1992 QB₁ 的大小。不过假设其具有类似于彗核的反照率 $p_R = 0.04$，则可以估算其直径 $d \approx 250$ km，大约为冥王星大小的八分之一。1992 QB₁ 的克朗-卡曾斯色指数是在世界时 1992 年 8 月 30 日到 9 月 1 日之间测量的。我们的最佳估计是 $m_V - m_R = 0.6 \pm 0.1$ 和 $m_R - m_I = 1.0 \pm 0.2$，相较而言太阳的值是 $m_V - m_R = 0.32$ 和 $m_R - m_I = 0.4$。这里 m_V、m_R 和 m_I 分别是用 V(5,500 Å)、R(6,500 Å)和 I(8,000 Å)波段的滤光片测量的恒星星等。$m_R - m_I$ 的色指数基于单幅 I 波段图像。似乎 1992 QB₁ 比太阳光红很多，和纯净冰的表面的性质不一致，而和脏冰或者受了有机化合物污染的冰的表面性质一致。相较而言，遥远天体 5145 福鲁斯相对应的色指数值为 $m_V - m_R \approx 0.7$ 和 $m_R - m_I \approx 0.7$(参考文献 15)，而所有其他已知彗核都没这么红 [16]。福鲁斯和 1992 QB₁ 可能保留了长期宇宙线的辐射产生的原始有机幔。在活动的近日彗星上，这样的幔很可能会被破坏或被碎石幔掩盖 [15,16]。

　　图 2 显示了世界时 1992 年 9 月 1 日拍摄的图像中测得的天体面亮度轮廓。另一颗临近场星的亮度分布被用于比较。在距图像中心 1.5 arcsec 处，暗至面亮度 29 mag·arcsec⁻²，图 2 中没有可分辨的彗发的迹象。没有可分辨的彗发让我们可以利用一种轮廓拟合方法 [17]，给出依赖模型的 1992 QB₁ 的质量损失率的上限。这个上限是 $dm/dt < 0.7$ kg·s⁻¹，故 1992 QB₁ 的活动程度至多是靠近太阳的哈雷型彗星活动

fitting method[17]. This limit is $dm/dt < 0.7$ kg s^{-1}, so 1992 QB$_1$ is at least 10^4 times less active than a Halley-class, near-Sun comet and probably less active than 2060 Chiron $(dm/dt \approx 1$ kg s$^{-1})$[18]. Weaker activity cannot be constrained by existing observations, however.

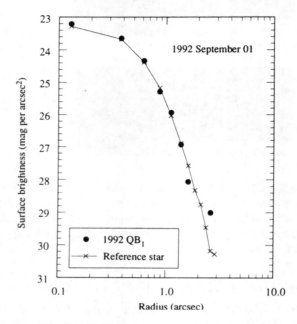

Fig. 2. Surface brightness profile of 1992 QB$_1$, measured UT 1992 September 01 with 0.8 arcsec FWHM images. The profile was computed from four separate R-filter images of total integration time 3,600 s. A scaled profile of a nearby field star is shown for reference. The image of 1992 QB$_1$ is consistent with a point source down to surface brightness ~29 magnitudes per square arcsec.

As our survey is still in progress, we will not discuss in detail the statistics implied by the detection of 1992 QB$_1$. It is, however, interesting to make a crude estimate of the Kuiper belt population. We note that 1992 QB$_1$ was detected in a survey that has so far covered 0.7 square degree. The implied surface density of similar objects is of order 1 per square degree. The inclination of 1992 QB$_1$ is 2 degrees (Table 1), so the angular width of the belt is at least 4 degrees, and is presumably much larger. A lower limit to the projected area of the Kuiper belt is $360 \times 4 = 1{,}440$ square degree, and the number of similar objects is thus $N \geqslant 1{,}440$. A minimal belt mass, based on an assumed diameter of 250 km and density of 10^3 kg m^{-3} for each object, is $M \geqslant 1 \times 10^{22}$ kg $\approx 2 \times 10^{-3}$ M_{Earth} (about 1 Pluto mass). This is compatible with the upper limit to the belt mass inferred from dynamical observations of P/Halley, $M \approx 1$ M_{Earth} (refs 19–21), and with the minimal mass needed to supply the observed flux of short period comets, $M \approx 0.02$ M_{Earth} (ref. 6). The estimated mass must be augmented to account for Kuiper belt comets too small or too distant to be detected in the present survey, but this depends on the (poorly known) mass and spatial distribution of cometary nuclei. M is a lower limit to the true mass.

The faintness of 1992 QB$_1$ makes it unlikely that earlier observations will be identified, so limiting the accuracy of the derived orbital parameters. The astrometric timebase

程度的 1 / 10,000，可能比 2060 喀戎（$\mathrm{d}m / \mathrm{d}t \approx 1\ \mathrm{kg \cdot s^{-1}}$）[18] 的活动程度低。然而，更弱的活动性以现在的观测水平就无法限制了。

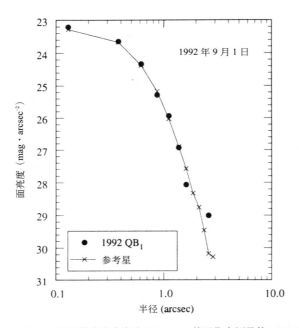

图 2. 在世界时 1992 年 9 月 1 日得到的半峰全宽为 0.8 arcsec 的图像中测量的 1992 QB₁ 面亮度轮廓。该图是由四块独立的 R 滤光片总积分时间为 3,600 s 的图像计算而来的。一颗标度过面亮度轮廓的临近场星也显示出来作为参考。1992 QB₁ 的图像和面亮度暗至 29 mag · arcsec⁻² 的点源一致。

　　由于我们的巡天还在进行中，所以我们不详细讨论 1992 QB₁ 探测的统计结果。然而对柯伊伯带天体数量进行粗略的估计还是很有意义的。我们注意到 1992 QB₁ 是在覆盖了 0.7 平方度的巡天中被发现的。这暗示了类似天体的表面密度为每平方度 1 个的量级。1992 QB₁ 的轨道倾角是 2°（表 1），所以柯伊伯带的角宽度至少有 4°，或者更宽。对于柯伊伯带的投影面积的下限估计是 $360 \times 4 = 1,440$ 平方度，因此类似天体的数量是 $N \geqslant 1,440$。基于直径为 250 km 和密度为 $10^3\ \mathrm{kg \cdot m^{-3}}$ 的假定，可得柯伊伯带的最小质量为 $M \geqslant 1 \times 10^{22}\ \mathrm{kg} \approx 2 \times 10^{-3}\ M_{\mathrm{Earth}}$（大约一个冥王星的质量）。这与对哈雷彗星（P/Halley）动态观测推得的柯伊伯带质量上限数据一致，即 $M \approx 1\ M_{\mathrm{Earth}}$（参考文献 19~21）；并且与对应观测到的短周期彗星流量所需最小质量也是吻合的，即 $M \approx 0.02\ M_{\mathrm{Earth}}$（参考文献 6）。对总质量的估计应该对目前无法被观测到的太小或太远的柯伊伯带彗星而作出补偿，但这种补偿又依赖于目前尚知之甚少的彗核的质量和空间分布。M 是真实质量的下限。

　　由于 1992 QB₁ 暗弱，所以在之前的观测中不大可能被证认出来，故而限制了推导的轨道参数的精度。得到表 1 中参数的天体测量时基只是轨道周期的千分之

used to obtain the parameters in Table 1 is only 10^{-3} of the orbit period. Although these parameters are not finalized, it is likely that the perihelion lies beyond the orbits of the gas giant planets (the expected perihelion $q \approx 40$ AU, compared with the Neptune aphelion $Q_N = 30.3$ AU)[13]. It thus seems that 1992 QB$_1$ escapes strong planetary perturbations and is, in this sense, more primitive than its presumed cousins at smaller distances, 2060 Chiron and 5145 Pholus. Theory suggests that, although many orbits between the giant planets are unstable on timescales short compared with the age of the Solar System, orbits beyond Neptune may be stable for longer times[22-27]. In particular, low-eccentricity orbits with semi-major axes of ~44 AU (Table 1) have lifetimes in excess of 10^9 yr (ref. 27), supporting the idea that 1992 QB$_1$ is a Kuiper belt comet.

Note added in proof: On UT 1993 March 28 we detected a second slow moving object (*IAU Circ.* 5370, 29 March 1993). This object, 1993 FW, has the same magnitude and angular motion as 1992 QB$_1$, and is presumably also resident in the Kuiper belt. Our detection of 1993 FW supports the Kuiper belt population estimate given above.

(**362**, 730-732; 1993)

David Jewitt* & Jane Luu[†]
* Institute for Astronomy, University of Hawaii, 2680 Woodlawn Drive, Honolulu, Hawaii 96822, USA
[†] Department of Astronomy, 601 Campbell Hall, University of California at Berkeley, Berkeley, California 94720, USA

Received 13 January; accepted 30 March 1993.

References:

1. Tombaugh, C. W. in *Planets and Satellites* (eds Kuiper G. P. & Middlehurst, B. M.) 12-30 (Univ. Chicago Press, Chicago, 1961).
2. Kowal, C., Liller, W. & Marsden, B. in *Dynamics of the Solar System. Proc. IAU Symp.* No. 81 (ed. Duncombe R.) 245-249 (Reidel, Dordrecht, 1979).
3. Scottie, J. V. *IAU Circ.* No. 5434 (1992).
4. Edgeworth, K. E. *Mon. Not. R. astr. Soc.* **109**, 600-609 (1949).
5. Kuiper, G. P. in *Astrophysics* (ed. Hynek, J. A.) 357-424 (New York, McGraw-Hill. 1951).
6. Duncan, M., Quinn, T. & Tremaine, S. *Astrophys. J.* **328**, L69-L73 (1988).
7. Whipple, F. *Proc. Natl. Acad. Sci.* **51**, 711-717 (1964).
8. Fernandez, J. A. *Mon. Not. R. astr. Soc.* **192**, 481-491 (1980).
9. Luu, J. X. & Jewitt, D. C. *Astr. J.* **95**, 1256-1262 (1988).
10. Jewitt, D. C. & Luu, J. X. *IAU Circ.* No. 5611 (1992).
11. McNaught, R. & Steel, D. *Minor Planet Circ.* 20878 (1992).
12. Hainault, O. & Elst, E. *Minor Planet Circ.* 20902 (1992).
13. Marsden, B. G. *IAU Circ.* No. 5684 (1992).
14. Luu, J. X. & Jewitt, D. C. *Astr. J.* **100**, 913-932 (1990).
15. Mueller, B., Tholen, D., Hartmann, W. & Cruikshank, D. *Icarus* **97**, 150-154 (1992).
16. Jewitt, D. C. *Cometary Photometry* in *Comets in the Post-Halley Era* (ed. Newburn, R.) 19-65 (Kluwer, Dordrecht, 1990).
17. Luu, J. X. & Jewitt, D. C. *Icarus* **97**, 276-287 (1992).
18. Luu, J. X. & Jewitt, D. C. *Astr. J.* **100**, 913-932 (1990).
19. Hamid, S. E., Marsden, B. & Whipple, F. *Astr. J.* **73**, 727-729 (1968).
20. Yeomans, D. K. *Proc. 20th ESLAB Symp.* 419-425 (ESA SP-250, Heidelberg, 1986).
21. Hogg, D. W., Quinlan, G. D. & Tremaine, S. *Astr. J.* **101**, 2274-2286 (1991).
22. Torbett, M. V. *Astr. J.* **98**, 1477-1481 (1989).
23. Torbett, M. V. & Smoluchowski, R. *Nature* **345**, 49-51 (1990).

一。尽管这些参数还没有最终确定，但该彗星的近日点可能位于气态巨行星轨道之外（预期的近日点距 $q \approx 40\,\text{AU}$，相比较海王星远日点距 $Q_N = 30.3\,\text{AU}$）[13]。所以看起来 1992 QB₁ 逃过强烈行星摄动，从这种意义上来说，相对距离更近的 2060 喀戎和 5145 福鲁斯，它更为原始。理论认为，尽管在与太阳系年龄相比较短的时标上许多在巨型行星之间的轨道不稳定，但在更长的时标 [22-27] 上海王星之外的轨道可能是稳定的。特别是，半长轴 ~44 AU（表 1）的低偏心率轨道的寿命超过 10^9 年（参考文献 27），这支持 1992 QB₁ 是一颗柯伊伯带彗星的观点。

附加说明： 在世界时 1993 年 3 月 28 日我们探测到了第二个缓慢运动的天体（国际天文学联合会快报 *IAU Circ.* 5370，1993 年 3 月 29 日）。1993 FW 这个天体和 1992 QB₁ 有着相同的星等和角运动，它也很有可能是柯伊伯带中的天体。我们探测到 1993 FW 支持了上文中对柯伊伯带天体数量的估计。

（冯翀 翻译；周礼勇 审稿）

24. Quinn, T., Tremaine, S. & Duncan, M. *Astrophys. J.* **355**, 667-679 (1990).

25. Duncan, M. & Quinn, T. in *Protostars and Planets III* (Tucson, in the press).

26. Holman, M. J. & Wisdom, J. *Astr. J.* (in the press).

27. Levison, H. & Duncan, M. *Astrophys. J.* (in the press).

Acknowledgements. We thank B. Marsden for discussions about 1992 QB$_1$. G. Luppino for CCD cameras, the Institute for Astronomy TAC for consistent allocation of time to this project, and A. Pickles for obtaining supporting astrometric images. The Planetary Astronomy program of NASA provides financial support at the UH 2.2-m telescope. J.X.L. is in receipt of a Hubble Fellowship.

Superconductivity above 130 K in the Hg–Ba–Ca–Cu–O System

A. Schilling *et al.*

Editor's Note

In 1986, physicists in Switzerland discovered a ceramic material that became superconducting at temperatures below about 30 K when doped with impurities. Hitherto, many physicists suspected that superconductivity would be impossible above about 20 K, and the discovery of so-called high-temperature superconductivity kicked off a race both to explain the effect and to design new materials with even higher transition temperatures (T_c). By 1993, the record had reached 125 K; here Andreas Schilling and colleagues improve on that with a material having a T_c of 133 K. Since then the record for copper-oxide materials has been raised to 138 K. But a definitive theory to explain the phenomenon remains an outstanding problem in physics.

The recent discovery[1] of superconductivity below a transition temperature (T_c) of 94 K in $HgBa_2CuO_{4+\delta}$ has extended the repertoire of high-T_c superconductors containing copper oxide planes embedded in suitably structured (layered) materials. Previous experience with similar compounds containing bismuth and thallium instead of mercury suggested that even higher transition temperatures might be achieved in mercury-based compounds with more than one CuO_2 layer per unit cell. Here we provide support for this conjecture, with the discovery of superconductivity above 130 K in a material containing $HgBa_2Ca_2Cu_3O_{1+x}$ (with three CuO_2 layers per unit cell), $HgBa_2CaCu_2O_{6+x}$ (with two CuO_2 layers) and an ordered superstructure comprising a defined sequence of the unit cells of these phases. Both magnetic and resistivity measurements confirm a maximum transition temperature of ~133 K, distinctly higher than the previous established record value of 125–127 K observed in $Tl_2Ba_2Ca_2Cu_3O_{10}$ (refs 2, 3).

THE structural similarity of $HgBa_2CuO_{4+\delta}$ (Hg-1201, ref. 1) to a member of the thallium-containing family of copper oxides, $TlBa_2CuO_5$ (Tl-1201), suggests the existence of compounds with the general composition $HgBa_2Ca_{n-1}Cu_nO_{2n+2+\delta}$. The transition temperatures of the thallium-containing analogues, $TlBa_2Ca_{n-1}Cu_nO_{2n+3}$, range from < 10 K ($n = 1$, ref. 4) to ~110 K ($n = 3$, ref. 5). In this sense, transition temperatures exceeding 100 K may be expected also in the Hg–Ba–Ca–Cu–O (HBCCO) system. Although the successful synthesis of $HgBa_2RCu_2O_{6+x}$ (Hg-1212) with R being (Eu, Ca) has been reported, no superconductivity was found in that system[6].

We prepared the samples following the procedure described in ref. 1 for Hg-1201.

Hg–Ba–Ca–Cu–O 体系
在 130 K 以上时的超导性

席林等

编者按

1986 年，两位瑞士物理学家发现了一种氧化物陶瓷材料，在温度低于约 30 K 时具有超导性。此前，许多物理学家们推测超导温度不可能高于 20 K，而高温超导的发现开启了理论解释和实验探索具有更高转变温度（T_c）的新超导材料的竞赛。在 1993 年以前，T_c 记录值已达到 125 K。本文中的安德烈亚斯·席林及其同事们发现一种 T_c 为 133 K 的新型超导材料。从此，铜氧化物材料的 T_c 温度记录提升至 138 K。但是目前在物理上并没有一种明确的理论解释。

最近对于 $HgBa_2CuO_{4+\delta}$ 在低于 94 K 转变温度（T_c）的超导性的发现[1]，进而扩大到对适当（层状）结构中含有铜氧面的高 T_c 超导体的研究。以前用含铋和铊而不是汞的类似复合物所进行的实验表明，每个单胞中 CuO_2 层多于一个的汞基复合物有可能达到更高的转变温度。本文对这一猜测提供了支持：因为发现高于 130 K 的超导性存在于含有 $HgBa_2Ca_2Cu_3O_{1+x}$（每个单胞中有三个 CuO_2 层）、$HgBa_2CaCu_2O_{6+x}$（含两个 CuO_2 层）的材料中，而且这两相的单胞以确定的序列形成有序的超结构。磁性和电阻测量都确认最大转变温度约为 133 K，明显高于过去在 $Tl_2Ba_2Ca_2Cu_3O_{10}$（参考文献 2，3）中观测到的记录值 125~127 K。

$HgBa_2CuO_{4+\delta}$（Hg–1201，参考文献 1）与铊系铜氧化物，如 $TlBa_2CuO_5$（Tl–1201），在结构上的相似性暗示着具有组成通式为 $HgBa_2Ca_{n-1}Cu_nO_{2n+2+\delta}$ 的化合物的存在。含铊化合物 $TlBa_2Ca_{n-1}Cu_nO_{2n+3}$ 的转变温度范围在小于 10 K（$n=1$，参考文献 4）至约 110 K（$n=3$，参考文献 5）之间。从这种意义上来看，我们可以预期 Hg–Ba–Ca–Cu–O（HBCCO）体系也会有超过 100 K 的转变温度。尽管已有 $HgBa_2RCu_2O_{6+x}$（Hg–1212）（R 为 Eu，Ca）的成功合成的报道，但却没有在该体系中发现超导性[6]。

我们根据参考文献 1 中所描述的制备 Hg–1201 的过程制备了样品。将每种金

A precursor material with the nominal composition $Ba_2CaCu_2O_5$ was obtained from a well ground mixture of the respective metal nitrates, sintered at 900 °C in O_2. After regrinding and mixing with powdered HgO, the pressed pellets were sealed in evacuated quartz tubes. These tubes were placed horizontally in tight steel containers and held at 800 °C for 5 hours. On opening the containers, we found that the quartz tubes were broken. It was not possible to reconstruct at which stage of the heating, cooling or opening procedure this happened. Some of the pellets were finally annealed for 5 hours at 300 °C in flowing oxygen. During the preparation and the characterization of the samples, all possible measures were taken to avoid any contamination with toxic mercury or mercury-containing compounds.

After annealing, the resulting black material was characterized by X-ray diffraction using the Guinier technique, by energy-dispersive X-ray spectrometry (EDS), and by selected-area electron-diffraction techniques (SAED) and high-resolution transmission electron microscopy (HRTEM). The EDX analysis showed that the samples are composites of isolated grains of $BaCuO_2$ (~30%), CuO (~30%), an unidentified oxide containing Hg, Ca and Cu (~15%), an oxide with Ca and Cu (~5%), and ~5% impurities with unspecified composition. About 15% of the total sample volume consisted of plate-like grains containing Hg, Ba, Ca and Cu. Some of these were investigated in detail by SAED and HRTEM techniques on a Phillips CM 30-ST transmission electron microscope. Both techniques showed clearly that these identified grains consist mostly of pure $HgBa_2Ca_2Cu_3O_{8+x}$ (Hg-1223), disordered mixtures of Hg-1223 and Hg-1212, and a periodic stacking sequence of the latter unit cells. We found no grains or intergrowths associated with the Hg-1201 structure. As the volume fraction of the phases of interest is fairly small, we could not measure the lattice parameters precisely with the X-ray Guinier technique. Nevertheless, from the SAED patterns, we deduce the lattice constants $c = 12.7(2)$ Å and $c = 16.1(3)$ Å for the tetragonal Hg-1212 and Hg-1223 units, respectively, and $a = 3.93(7)$ Å, valid for both types of compounds. The results for Hg-1212 are in good agreement with the values obtained in ref. 6. Figure 1 is a representative HRTEM image showing, as an example, a stacking containing both Hg-1212 and Hg-1223 layers. The stacking sequence 1223/1223/1212/1212/1223/1212 with a supercell c-axis $c \approx 86.4$ Å extends beyond 2,000 Å, thus qualifying this superstructure as a proper phase. HRTEM images as well as SAED patterns gave no evidence for the presence of HgO-double layers.

属的硝酸盐的混合物充分研磨，在 900 ℃于氧气中烧结，得到一种具有标称成分为 $Ba_2CaCu_2O_5$ 的前驱物。烧结物与 HgO 粉末混合并重新研磨后，压制成片并密封于抽成真空的石英管中。再将石英管水平地放置于钢质密闭容器中，于温度为 800 ℃下保持 5 小时。打开容器时，我们发现石英管已经破裂。我们无法推想破裂发生在加热、冷却或开启过程中的哪个阶段。最后将部分的样片在流动的氧气中于 300 ℃退火 5 小时。在样品的制备和表征过程中，采用了各种可能的措施以避免有毒的汞或含汞化合物的污染。

在退火之后，将所得黑色物质采用吉尼耶技术的 X 射线衍射、能量色散 X 射线光谱（EDS）、选区电子衍射技术（SAED）和高分辨透射电子显微镜（HRTEM）进行表征。EDX 分析表明，样品是由下列物质的分离的颗粒所组成：包括 $BaCuO_2$（约 30%）、CuO（约 30%）、一种含 Hg、Ca 和 Cu 组成不明的氧化物（约 15%）、一种含 Ca 和 Cu 的氧化物（约 5%）和约 5% 含未确定成分的杂质。样品总体积中约 15% 的部分是由含 Hg、Ba、Ca 和 Cu 的片状颗粒组成。我们对其中某些区域用菲利普斯 CM 30-ST 透射电子显微镜进行了 SAED 和 HRTEM 技术的详细研究。两种技术都清楚地表明，上述所检验的颗粒主要包含纯的 $HgBa_2Ca_2Cu_3O_{8+x}$（Hg-1223）、无序的 Hg-1223 与 Hg-1212 的混合物，以及这两种单胞的周期性堆垛序列。我们没有发现与 Hg-1201 结构有关的颗粒或共生物。由于有意义的相只占相当小的体积分数，我们未能用 X 射线吉尼耶技术精确地测量其晶格参数。尽管如此，根据 SAED 图像，我们推测四方晶系 Hg-1212 和 Hg-1223 的晶格常数分别为 $c = 12.7$ (2) Å 和 $c = 16.1$ (3) Å，以及对两种化合物都有效的 $a = 3.93$ (7) Å。对 Hg-1212 的观测结果与参考文献 6 所得到的数值非常吻合。图 1 是典型的 HRTEM 图像，例如，它显示的堆垛同时含有 Hg-1212 和 Hg-1223 层。具有超晶格 c 轴 $c \approx 86.4$ Å 按照 1223/1223/1212/1212/1223/1212 堆垛序列延展到超过 2,000 Å，因而可将这种超结构视为本征相。HRTEM 和 SAED 图像都未能证明有 HgO 双层的存在。

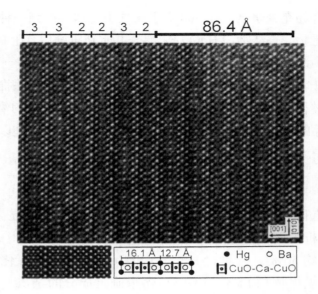

Fig. 1. HRTEM image of a grain in [100] orientation, containing layers of Hg-1212 and Hg-1223. Here, they are stacked in a periodic sequence forming a supercell with $c \approx 86.4$ Å (see text). A contrast simulation ($c_s = 1.1$ mm, $E = 300$ keV, defocus -870 Å, specimen thickness 23 Å) is inserted. The stacking sequence in terms of the number of Cu–O planes and an enlarged schematic drawing of the involved unit cells are included.

We measured the magnetic susceptibility of the specimens using a SQUID-magnetometer (Quantum Design). Figure 2 shows the result obtained for an oxygen-annealed sample. In an external field $H = 27$ Oe, the zero-field cooling susceptibility (ZFC) amounts to ~100% of $1/4\pi$ at temperature $T = 6$ K, indicating complete magnetic screening. For this estimate, we assumed an average density $\rho \approx 6$ g cm^{-3}. The field-cooling (FC) susceptibility reaches ~10% of the maximum possible value. This value represents a lower-bound value for the true superconducting volume fraction in the sample, indicating the bulk nature of superconductivity. The onset temperature of diamagnetism is $T_c \approx 133.5$ K, seen both in FC and ZFC experiments (see Fig. 2, inset). The FC susceptibility reaches ~60% of its full low-temperature value at 125 K, strongly indicating that the phase with $T_c \approx 133.5$ K dominates all other superconducting phases. In the ZFC curves, additional features are seen at 126 K and 112 K, which we ascribe to different superconducting phases with lower transition temperatures.

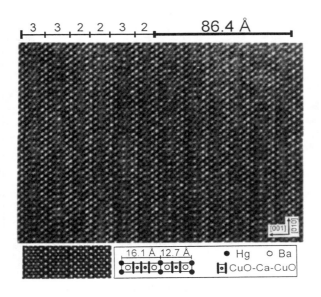

图 1. 晶粒在 [100] 取向上的 HRTEM 图像，包含 Hg-1212 和 Hg-1223 层。按照周期顺序，它们堆垛形成 $c \approx 86.4$ Å（见正文）的超晶格。插图是一个衬度模拟（$c_s = 1.1$ mm，$E = 300$ keV，散焦 −870 Å，样品厚度 23 Å）。右下方表示的是以 Cu–O 平面层的数目表示的堆垛序列和有关晶胞的放大示意图。

我们使用一台超导量子干涉磁强计（量子设计）测量了样品的磁化率。图 2 显示的是有氧退火样品所测得的结果。在 $H = 27$ Oe 的外场下，零场冷却磁化率（ZFC）相当于温度 $T = 6$ K 时达到 $1/4\pi$ 的 100% 左右，显示出完全的磁屏蔽。基于这一点估计，我们假定其平均密度 ρ 约为 6 g·cm⁻³。场冷却（FC）磁化率达到最大可能值的 10% 左右。这个数值相当于样品中真正超导部分的体积分数的下限值，表明了体超导特性。抗磁性的起始温度 T_c 约为 133.5 K，在 FC 和 ZFC 实验中均是如此（见图 2 中插图）。FC 磁化率在温度为 125 K 时达到其完全低温数值的 60% 左右，强烈地表明 $T_c \approx 133.5$ K 的相比其他所有超导相都有优势。在 ZFC 曲线中，在温度为 126 K 和 112 K 处可以看到其他的特征，我们将其归结为另外的具有较低转变温度的不同超导相所引起的。

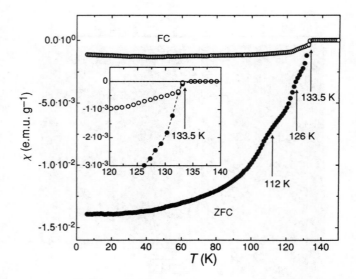

Fig. 2. Zero-field cooling (ZFC) and field cooling (FC) susceptibilities $\chi(T)$ of one of the investigated oxygen-annealed HBCCO samples, measured in $H = 27$ Oe. The ZFC curve indicates the presence of several different superconducting phases.

The resistivity R as a function of temperature T of an annealed sample is shown in Fig. 3. At $T \approx 132.5$ K, $R(T)$ drops sharply with a maximum in the differential dR/dT, and reaches zero at $T = 95$ K within the resolution of the four-probe a.c.-resistance bridge used. This temperature is still considerably higher than the zero-resistance temperature $T \approx 35$ K, reported for Hg-1201 (ref. 1) The final oxygen treatment was very effective in increasing the critical temperature; the as-sintered samples showed a maximum T_c of only ~ 117 K.

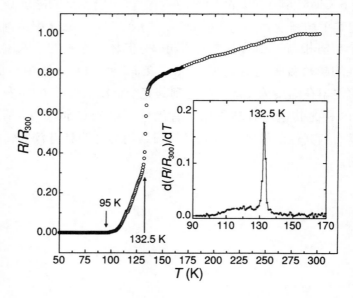

Fig. 3. Resistivity $R(T)$ of an annealed HBCCO specimen, normalized with respect to the resistance value $R(300) \approx 0.10\ \Omega$. The inset displays the temperature derivative dR/dT to show the maximum resistivity drop at $T \approx 132.5$ K. Zero resistance is attained at $T = 95$ K.

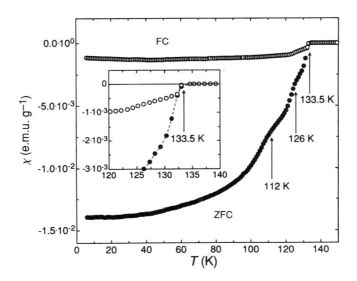

图 2. 一份有氧退火的 HBCCO 研究样品的零场冷却 (ZFC) 和场冷却 (FC) 磁化率 $\chi(T)$，在 $H = 27$ Oe 中测得。ZFC 曲线指出若干个不同超导相的存在。

　　图 3 中显示了经退火处理样品的电阻 R 作为温度 T 的函数的变化。在温度 T 约为 132.5 K 处，$R(T)$ 急剧下降，其微分值 dR/dT 达到最大值，并且在四电极交流电阻桥的分辨率下观测到在温度 T 为 95 K 处达到零电阻。这个温度比起对于 Hg–1201 所报道的 (参考文献 1) 零电阻温度 T 约 35 K 还是高出很多。最后的氧处理对于提高临界温度非常有效；那些原始烧结的样品具有的最高温度 T_c 只有约 117 K。

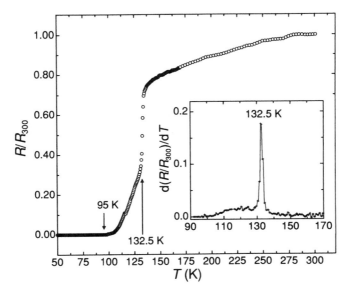

图 3. 一份经退火处理的 HBCCO 样品的电阻 $R(T)$，以阻值 $R(300) \approx 0.10\ \Omega$ 为标准。插图显示了温度的导数 dR/dT 以表明 $T \approx 132.5$ K 处的最大电阻降。在 $T = 95$ K 时得到零电阻。

At present we cannot relate the different superconducting phases to crystallographic phases. There is no unambiguous proof that the occurrence of superconductivity in our samples stems from the $HgBa_2Ca_{n-1}Cu_nO_{2n+2+\delta}$ phases. In analogy with the thallium- and bismuth-based copper oxides[5], however, we suggest that in the HBCCO system T_c also increases with the number of Cu–O planes per unit cell, and conclude that Hg-1223 is responsible for superconductivity at ~133 K. This would be consistent with the large relative superconducting volume fraction at 125 K, in view of the dominance of Hg-1223 observed in the grains investigated microscopically.

(**363**, 56-58; 1993)

A. Schilling, M. Cantoni, J. D. Guo & H. R. Ott
Laboratorium für Festkörperphysik, ETH Hönggerberg, 8093 Zürich, Switzerland

Received 14 April; accepted 15 April 1993.

References:

1. Putilin, S. N., Antipov, E. V., Chmaissem, O. & Marezio, M. *Nature* **362**, 226-228 (1993).

2. Kaneko, T., Yamauchi, H. & Tanaka, S. *Physica* C**178**, 377-382 (1991).

3. Parkin, S. S. P. *et al. Phys. Rev. Lett.* **60**, 2539-2542 (1988).

4. Gopalakrishnan, I. K., Yakhmi, J. V. & Iyer, R. M. *Physica* C**175**, 183-186 (1991).

5. Parkin, S. S. P. *et al. Phys. Rev. Lett.* **61**, 750-753 (1988).

6. Putilin, S. N., Bryntse, I. & Antipov, E. V. *Mat. Res. Bull.* **26**, 1299-1307 (1991).

Acknowledgements. We thank S. Ritsch for his help in the structural characterization. This work was supported in part by the Schweizerische Nationalfonds zur Förderung der wissenschaftlichen Forschung.

目前我们还无法将不同的超导相与各个晶相一一对应起来。还没有明确的证据表明我们的样品的超导性是源于 $HgBa_2Ca_{n-1}Cu_nO_{2n+2+\delta}$ 相。不过，与铊基和铋基铜的氧化物[5] 类比，我们认为，HBCCO 体系的 T_c 也会随着每个单胞中 Cu–O 平面数目的增加而升高，并断言 Hg–1223 是温度约为 133 K 时超导性产生的原因。考虑到用显微镜研究颗粒时所观测到的 Hg–1223 占优势，这与 125 K 时大的相对超导体积分数是一致的。

（王耀杨 翻译；韩汝珊 郭建栋 审稿）

Single-shell Carbon Nanotubes of 1-nm Diameter

S. Iijima and T. Ichihashi

Editor's Note

The observation of multi-walled carbon nanotubes by Japanese microscopist Sumio Iijima in 1991 stimulated intense interest in these nanostructures, for example as ultra-strong fibres, capsules and electrically conductive wires. But understanding their properties from theory was complicated, because they tended to consist of several nested tubes, which were difficult to model. Here Iijima and his coworker Toshinari Ichihashi describe how to make carbon nanotubes with single-layer walls of carbon sheets. They grew them from a carbon-rich vapour in which vapourized iron atoms act as a catalyst. This finding was critical to the current widespread use of carbon nanotubes in nanotechnology, especially as nanoelectronic devices.

Carbon nanotubes[1] are expected to have a wide variety of interesting properties. Capillarity in open tubes has already been demonstrated[2-5], while predictions regarding their electronic structure[6-8] and mechanical strength[9] remain to be tested. To examine the properties of these structures, one needs tubes with well-defined morphologies, length, thickness and a number of concentric shells; but the normal carbon-arc synthesis[10,11] yields a range of tube types. In particular, most calculations have been concerned with single-shell tubes, whereas the carbon-arc synthesis produces almost entirely multi-shell tubes. Here we report the synthesis of abundant single-shell tubes with diameters of about one nanometre. Whereas the multi-shell nanotubes are formed on the carbon cathode, these single-shell tubes grow in the gas phase. Electron diffraction from a single tube allows us to confirm the helical arrangement of carbon hexagons deduced previously for multi-shell tubes[1].

WE found the single-shell tubules in soot-like deposits formed in a carbon-arc chamber similar to that used for fullerene production. Two vertical electrodes are installed in the centre of the chamber. The anode, which is the upper electrode, is a graphitic carbon rod 10 mm in diameter, and the cathode, a 20-mm-diameter carbon rod, has a shallow dimple used to hold a small piece of iron during evaporation. The evaporation chamber is filled with a gas mixture typically consisting of 10 torr methane and 40 torr argon. The carbon discharge arc was generated by running a d.c. current of 200 A at 20 V between the electrodes. The iron fillings melted to form a droplet, and so generated iron vapour which cooled and condensed into small particles of iron carbide above the cathode. The vaporization of iron takes place simultaneously with the production of soot, both from methane and by evaporation from the carbon cathode. We noticed that no tubules were formed when the carbon arc reactor was operated with any one of the three components argon, iron and methane absent.

直径 1 nm 的单层碳纳米管

饭岛澄男，市桥俊成

编者按

1991 年，日本电镜专家饭岛澄男报道了对于多壁碳纳米管的观测结果，从此激发了人们对于诸如超强纤维、胶囊剂以及电学导线等纳米结构的强烈兴趣。但是要从理论上理解它们的性质是复杂的，因为它们倾向于形成多层嵌套微管，因而难于进行建模。这里，饭岛与他的合作者市桥俊成，描述了如何制备单层碳壁的纳米管的方法。他们利用富碳蒸气来生长碳纳米管，并用气化的铁原子来充当催化剂。这一发现对于当时碳纳米管在纳米技术，尤其是纳米电子器件领域的广泛应用是至关重要的。

预期碳纳米管[1]具有各种各样的有趣性质。开口管中的毛细现象已被发现[2-5]，但关于其电子结构[6-8]和机械强度[9]的预测仍有待检验。要检测这些结构的性质，需要具有确定的形态、长度、厚度及多个同心壳层的纳米管；但是正常的碳弧合成[10,11]生成的是一系列类型的纳米管。特别是，大多数计算考虑的都是单层管，而碳弧合成产生的却几乎完全是多层管。本文我们要报道大量直径约为 1 nm 的单层管的合成。多层纳米管是在碳阴极上形成的，而这些单层管则生长于气相中。单层管的电子衍射使我们得以确认此前针对多层管推导出来的碳六边形的螺旋形排布[1]。

我们在类似制备富勒烯所用的碳弧反应室中形成的烟灰状沉积物中发现了单层微管。反应室中心安装着两个垂直的电极。阳极，也就是上电极，是一根直径 10 mm 的石墨碳棒，而阴极，是一根直径 20 mm 的碳棒，上面有一道浅槽，用来在气化过程中固定一小块铁片。气化室中充入混合气体，典型组成为 10 torr 的甲烷和 40 torr 的氩气。通过在电极之间施加 20 V 下 200 A 的直流电产生碳放电电弧。铁填充物熔融形成小滴，继而产生铁蒸气，在阴极上方冷却并凝结成碳化铁小颗粒。铁的气化过程与烟灰的产生同时发生，后者既有来自于甲烷的部分也有来自碳阴极气化的部分。我们注意到，在缺少氩气、铁和甲烷这三种成分中任何一种时，碳弧反应器中都不会形成微管。

The catalytic role of iron is well known in carbon fibre production, in which iron particles are found on the fibre tips and act as heterogeneous deposition centres for carbon atoms from the vapour phase[12]. In the present experiment, we did not find iron particles at the tubule tips. We suspect, however, that atomic iron particles, presumably as a homogeneous catalyst in the vapour phase, somehow assist the formation of single-shell tubules. Specimens for electron microscopy were prepared from acetone suspensions of soot collected over the electrodes in the evaporation chamber. Nanotubes were placed on a microscope specimen grid by drying a drop of the suspension taken up on the grid. We used either an ultra-high-vacuum (JEM 200FXV) or conventional transmission electron microscope (Topcon 002B) at 120 kV or 200 kV accelerating voltage.

A typical electron micrograph showing a general view of the specimen is reproduced in Fig. 1a. Threads are curved and tangled together to form bundles in some regions. All the threads are found to be single-shell carbon nanotubes. Round, dark objects attached to the tubules are cementite (Fe$_3$C), as indicated by powder diffraction measurements and measurement of the d spacings of lattice fringes (lattice images with spacings of around 0.2 nm were recorded on individual particles); these particles range in size from a few nanometres to several tens of nanometres, which were mostly coated with a few graphite layers. Some of the particles were soluble in nitric acid.

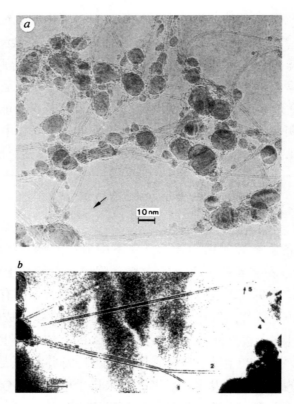

Fig. 1. a, Electron micrograph showing bundles of single-shell carbon nanotubes which are curved and entangled. Dark blobs are cementite particles which assist in tubule growth. A terminated tubule is indicated by an arrow. b, Electron micrograph showing individual single-shell nanotubes. The tubule labelled 1 is 0.75 nm in diameter and tubule 2 is 1.37 nm in diameter. A straight tubule (3) and two terminated ones (4 and 5) can also be seen.

铁在碳纤维制备中的催化作用是人所共知的，铁颗粒出现在纤维末端，充当来自蒸气相的碳原子的异相沉积中心[12]。在当前实验中，我们没有在微管末端发现铁颗粒。但是我们猜想，蒸气相中铁原子颗粒作为均相催化剂在某种程度上促进了单层微管的形成。我们利用从气化室中电极上收集到的烟灰的丙酮悬浊液制备供电子显微镜观测的样品。将样品悬浊液滴在网上风干，从而将碳纳米管置于电镜样品网上。我们使用超高真空（JEM 200FXV）或者传统的透射电子显微镜（拓普康公司 002B），加速电压为 120 kV 或 200 kV。

图 1a 中再现了一幅典型的电子显微图像，显示出样品的概貌。某些区域，丝状物弯曲并纠缠在一起，形成了束。我们发现所有的丝状物都是单层碳纳米管。粉末衍射测定和晶格条纹间隔 d 的测定（对单个颗粒记录了具有约 0.2 nm 间隔的晶格像）表明附着在微管上的圆形深色物体是渗碳体（Fe$_3$C）；这些颗粒的尺寸范围从几个纳米到几十个纳米，大部分为几个石墨层所覆盖。某些颗粒可以溶于硝酸中。

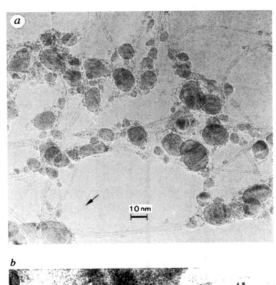

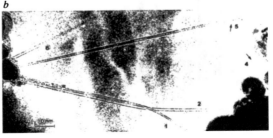

图 1. a, 电子显微图像, 显示出弯曲和纠缠着的单层碳纳米管束。深色斑点是参与微管生长的渗碳体颗粒。箭头所指的是一根微管的尾端。b, 分立的单层纳米管的电子显微图像。标记为 1 的微管, 直径是 0.75 nm, 微管 2 的直径是 1.37 nm。还可以看到一根直微管（3）和两根（4 和 5）微管的末端。

The nanotubes often form as bundles, but isolated and single tubules are also present. Three tubules which bridge two cementite particle agglomerates are seen in Fig. 1*b*. On the upper right-hand side, a graphitic layer showing an image of the basal plane with lattice spacing 0.34 nm can be recognized. From this, we calibrated the magnifications of the tubules. All micrographs were recorded at optimum focus[13], so that two dark lines in the tubule image correspond to side portions of the cylinders. The thinnest tube in this micrograph (labelled 1) is 0.75 nm in diameter, and is attached to a thicker (13 nm) tube (labelled 2). Tubules 1 and 2 are slightly curved, but tubule 3 (diameter 0.92 nm) spans straight across a 140-nm opening between two cementite particle agglomerates. The longest single-shell tubule was 700 nm long with a diameter of 0.9 nm.

Short and terminated tubules are commonly observed (4 and 5 in Fig. 1*b*). The terminated tubule labelled 6 moved gradually during the observation so that one end appears to be fading out. No cementite particles were found on the free tips of the tubules, but they are entangled with cementite particle agglomerates. The tubules are capped in shapes that have been reported previously[14,15] (arrow 4 in Fig. 1*b*).

We carefully measured the diameters on the electron micrographs of individual tubules. Figure 2 shows a histogram of the diameters of about 60 tubules, which range from about 0.7 nm to 1.6 nm. Two peaks are seen at tubule diameters of around 0.8 nm and 1.05 nm; we believe that these peaks are significant. The origin of the preferred tubule diameters is interesting to consider in terms of the tubule helicity and growth.

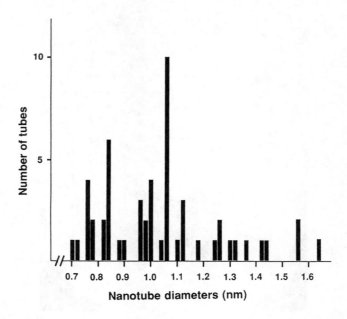

Fig. 2. Histogram showing frequency of single-shell nanotubes of different tubule diameters. Two peaks, at 0.8 nm and 1.05 nm, are dominant.

纳米管经常形成束，但是分离的和单个的微管也会出现。图 1b 中可以看到桥联着两个渗碳体颗粒团块的三根微管。图上方右手侧，可以识别出一个石墨层，图像中基面的晶格间距为 0.34 nm。我们据此来校准微管的放大倍率。所有显微图像都是在最佳聚焦时记录的[13]，因此微管图像中的两条暗线对应于圆柱的边缘部分。这张显微图像中最细的管（标记为 1）直径为 0.75 nm，它附着在一根较粗（13 nm）的管（标记为 2）上。微管 1 和 2 略为弯曲，但微管 3（直径 0.92 nm）笔直地横向跨过两个渗碳体颗粒团块之间 140 nm 的间隔。最长的单层管有 700 nm 长，直径为 0.9 nm。

通常观测到的都是短的终止微管（图 1b 中的 4 和 5）。标记为 6 的终止微管在观测过程中逐渐移动，因此其一端看来像是淡退了。在微管的自由端没有发现渗碳体颗粒，但是它们与渗碳体颗粒团块纠缠在一起。微管的帽具有以前曾报道过的形状[14,15]（图 1b 中的箭头 4）。

我们在电子显微镜上仔细地测定了单个微管的直径。图 2 显示出大约 60 根微管的直径分布柱状图，直径分布从 0.7 nm 到 1.6 nm。在管径约 0.8 nm 和 1.05 nm 处可以看到两个峰；我们认为这两个峰的出现是有重要意义的。从微管螺旋性和生长的角度来考虑，优势管径的起因是值得注意的。

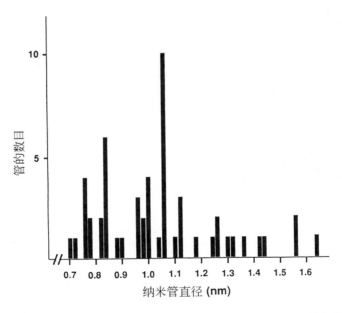

图 2. 具有不同管径的单层纳米管直径分布的柱状图。0.8 nm 和 1.05 nm 的管径最为常见。

Figure 3a shows an electron diffraction pattern taken from a 1.37-nm single-shell tubule together with its corresponding electron micrograph (Fig. 3b). The tubule is attached to the bundle of tubules seen at the left-hand side. An electron beam (20 nm diameter) was focused on to the tubule, so that the area diffracting the electrons comprised about 2,000 carbon atoms. This small scattering volume and the cylindrical structure are responsible for the extremely weak and diffused diffraction intensities. There are two hexagonal ($hk0$) diffraction patterns rotated $\pm\alpha/2$ from perfect alignment along the tube axis, and these patterns show mirror symmetry both along and perpendicular to the tube axis. The mirror symmetry confirms helicity in the single-shell tubule structure, as was found previously for multi-shell tubules[1]. All electron diffraction patterns observed in the present sample showed the $2mm$ symmetry. The ($00l$) spots coming from the graphite basal lattice plane, which were observed for the multi-shell tubes, are completely absent (see Fig. 3 of ref. 1).

The spots are streaked vertically because of the fibrous structure. Each streaked spot in Fig. 3a has intensity maxima appearing with a period (indicated by triple arrows) of 0.73 nm^{-1}. The value corresponds to the diameter measured on the tubule (1.37 nm). The modulation can be explained by Fraunhofer diffraction from two vertical portions of the tubule parallel to the incident electron waves.

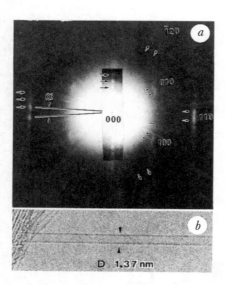

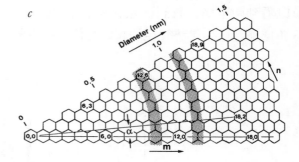

Fig. 3. a, Electron diffraction pattern taken from a single-shell nanotubule of diameter 1.37 nm. b, Electron micrograph of same tubule. The pattern comprises two sets of the hexagonal patterns which give rise to splitting of the ($hk0$) spots. Each spot has periodic intensity maxima in the vertical direction, caused by Fraunhofer diffraction from the two portions of the tube imaged as two dark lines in b. c, Schematic representation of helical tubules according to Hamada's notation[6]. A tubule is represented by an index (m, n) or (m, α), where m is mth hexagon from the origin (0, 0), and n and α are defined as shown. α is a pitch angle. If the tubule diameter D and angle α are known, the tubule structure is uniquely determined. Hatched hexagons represent the tubules corresponding to the two peaks in Fig. 2.

图 3*a* 显示出 1.37 nm 单层微管的一幅电子衍射图案及其相应的电子显微图像（图 3*b*）。这根管附着在左手侧的管束上。直径 20 nm 的电子束聚焦在微管上，所以衍射电子的区域中包含大约 2,000 个碳原子。小的散射体积和圆柱形结构导致了极其微弱且弥散的衍射强度。沿完美平行于管轴的方向旋转 ±α/2 有两种六方 (*hk*0) 衍射图案，并且这些图案显示出同时沿管轴和垂直于管轴方向的镜面对称性。如同之前在多层微管中所发现的[1]那样，镜面对称性确认了单层微管结构中的螺旋性。当前样品中观测到的所有电子衍射图案都显示出 2*mm* 对称性。在多层管中能观测到的来自石墨晶格基平面的 (00*l*) 衍射点，完全没有出现（见参考文献 1 中的图 3）。

衍射点上由于纤维状结构而出现垂直条纹。图 3*a* 中每个出现条纹的点都有以 0.73 nm^{-1} 周期（用三个箭头指出）出现的强度极大值。这个值对应于从微管测得的直径（1.37 nm）。利用微管平行于入射电子波的两个垂直部分的夫琅禾费衍射，可以解释调制问题。

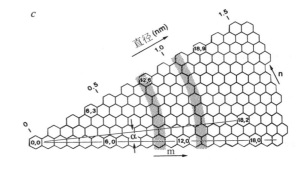

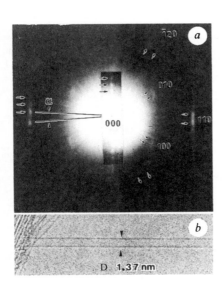

图 3. *a*，直径为 1.37 nm 的单层纳米管的电子衍射图案。*b*，同一微管的电子显微图像。图像由两组六边形图案组成，它们导致 (*hk*0) 点的分裂。每个点在垂直方向上有周期性的强度极大值，这是由管的两部分——其图像为 *b* 中的两条暗线——之间的夫琅禾费衍射造成的。*c*，用哈马达符号[6] 表示的螺旋形微管的示意图。一根微管是用指标 (*m*, *n*) 或 (*m*, α) 来表示的，其中 *m* 是从原点 (0, 0) 起的第 *m* 个六边形，*n* 和 α 则如图中所示般定义。α 是螺旋角。如果已知微管直径 *D* 和角度 α，就可以唯一确定微管的结构。涂上阴影的六边形表示对应于图 2 中两个峰的微管。

By knowing the tubule diameter D and its pitch angle α with respect to the fibre axis (Fig. 3a), the helicity and thus the tubule structure can be determined uniquely. To describe the tubule helicity, we follow Hamada's notation[6] as illustrated in Fig. 3c, where a tubule can be represented by an index (m, n). This tubule can be realized by rolling up a sheet of hexagons so as to superimpose the origin $(0, 0)$ on the hexagon (m, n). A tubule $(m, -n)$ is chiral with the opposite handedness to (m, n), and thus they should be optically active, but they cannot be distinguished by the diffraction experiment. The tubules which were observed frequently on the histogram (Fig. 2) have values of (m, n) in the hatched areas. On the electron diffraction pattern in Fig. 3a, α and D are measured as 7° and 1.37 nm, respectively. This tube can be indexed as $(18, 2)$ or its enantiomer $(18, -2)$, and should behave as a semiconductor according to electronic band structure calculations[6,16]. We should mention here that α, or helicity, varies for a given tubule diameter.

We speculate that the single-shell tubules might be the embryo for the multi-shell tubules. In our proposed model for the nanotube growth[17,18], the tubule ends are open so that carbon atoms are easily captured at dangling bonds, and the multi-shell tubules grow in the direction of the tube axis and also perpendicular to it. The latter growth is associated with layer-by-layer growth on the tubule surface. In the single-shell tubes, we assume that axial growth dominates over layer growth. We speculate that the iron in the present experiments acts as a homogeneous catalyst in the vapour phase.

(**363**, 603-605; 1993)

Sumio Iijima & Toshinari Ichihashi
Fundamental Research Laboratories, NEC Corporation, 34 Miyukigaoka, Tsukuba, Ibaraki 305, Japan

Received 23 April; accepted 1 June 1993.

References:

1. Iijima, S. *Nature* **354**, 56-58 (1991).
2. Ajayan, P. M. & Iijima, S. *Nature* **361**, 333-334 (1993).
3. Ajayan, P. M. *et al. Nature* **362**, 522-523 (1993).
4. Tsang, S. C., Harris, P. J. F. & Green, M. L. *Nature* **362**, 520-522 (1993).
5. Pederson, M. R. & Broughton, J. O. *Phys. Rev. Lett.* **69**, 2687-2692 (1992).
6. Hamada, N., Sawada, S. & Oshiyama, S. *Phys. Rev. Lett.* **68**, 1579-1581 (1992).
7. Mintmire, J. W., Dunlap, B. I. & White, C. T. *Phys. Rev. Lett.* **68**, 631-634 (1992).
8. Saito, R., Fujita, F., Dresselhaus, G. & Dresselhaus, M. S. *Phys. Rev.* B**46**, 1804-1811 (1992).
9. Robertson, D. H., Brenner, D. W. & Mintmire, J. W. *Phys. Rev.* B**45**, 12592-12595 (1992).
10. Ebbesen, T. W. & Ajayan, P. M. *Nature* **368**, 220-222 (1992).
11. Ando, Y. & Iijima, S. *Jpn. J. Appl. Phys.* **32**, L107-L109 (1993).
12. Oberlin, A. & Endo, M. *J. Cryst. Growth* **32**, 335-349 (1976).
13. Iijima, S. *Chem. Scripta* **14**, 117-123 (1978-79).
14. Iijima, S., Ichihashi, T. & Ando, Y. *Nature* **356**, 776-778 (1992).
15. Ajayan, P. M. Ichihashi, T. & Iijima, S. *Chem. Phys. Lett.* **202**, 384-388 (1992).
16. White, C. T., Robertson, D. H. & Mintmire, J. W. *Phys. Rev.* B**47**, 5485-5488 (1993).
17. Iijima, S., Ajayan, P. M. & Ichihashi, T. *Phys. Rev. Lett.* **69**, 3100-3103 (1992).
18. Iijima, S. *Mat. Sci. Enging* B. (in the press).

通过了解微管直径 D 和相对于纤维轴的夹角 α（图 3a），可以唯一确定螺旋性进而确定微管结构。为描述微管螺旋性，我们使用如图 3c 中所显示的哈马达符号 [6]，其中微管可以用一组指数 (m, n) 来表示。以把原点 $(0, 0)$ 叠加到六边形 (m, n) 上的方式将一个六边形平面层卷起就可形成微管。微管 $(m, -n)$ 与 (m, n) 具有相反的手性，因此它们应该是有光学活性的，但是通过衍射实验无法区分它们。在柱状图（图 2）中频繁出现的微管具有涂阴影区域中的 (m, n) 值。在图 3a 的电子衍射图案中，测得的 α 和 D 的数值分别是 7° 和 1.37 nm。这根管可以记为 $(18, 2)$，其对应异构体则是 $(18, -2)$，而且根据电子能带结构计算 [6,16]，它应该具有半导体的性质。这里我们应该指出，对于给定的微管直径来说，α 或螺旋性可以是不同的。

我们推测单层微管可能是多层微管的雏形。在我们为纳米管生长提出的模型中 [17,18]，微管末端是开放的，因此碳原子可以很容易地被悬挂键捕获，从而使多层微管沿垂直和平行于管轴的方向生长。多层管的生长与微管表面上的逐层生长有关。在单层管中，我们设想轴向生长主导于层的生长。我们推测当前实验中铁在蒸气相中起到了均相催化剂的作用。

（王耀杨 翻译；李彦 审稿）

Cobalt-catalysed Growth of Carbon Nanotubes with Single-atomic-layer Walls

D. S. Bethune *et al.*

Editor's Note

Following the discovery of carbon nanotubes—nested tubes of graphite-like carbon just a few nanometres across—it became evident that their properties could be better compared with theoretical predictions if they could be made from just a single layer of carbon. Here a team at IBM's Almaden Research Center in California show how to do that. They make single-walled tubes by vaporizing carbon along with cobalt metal, which they suspect forms small clusters that catalyse the tube growth: new carbon atoms are attached to the growing tube circumference where it adjoins the metal particles. A related metal-catalysed method for making single-walled nanotubes was reported at the same time by Sumio Iijima in Japan, the discoverer of carbon nanotubes.

Carbon exhibits a unique ability to form a wide range of structures. In an inert atmosphere it condenses to form hollow, spheroidal fullerenes[1-4]. Carbon deposited on the hot tip of the cathode of the arc-discharge apparatus used for bulk fullerene synthesis will form nested graphitic tubes and polyhedral particles[5-8]. Electron irradiation of these nanotubes and polyhedra transforms them into nearly spherical carbon "onions"[9]. We now report that covaporizing carbon and cobalt in an arc generator leads to the formation of carbon nanotubes which all have very small diameters (about 1.2 nm) and walls only a single atomic layer thick. The tubes form a web-like deposit woven through the fullerene-containing soot, giving it a rubbery texture. The uniformity and single-layer structure of these nanotubes should make it possible to test their properties against theoretical predictions[10-13].

THE initial aim of our experiments was to produce metallofullerenes and graphite-encapsulated nanocrystals of magnetic atoms. Electrodes were prepared by boring 4-mm-diameter holes in 6-mm-diameter graphite rods and filling them with mixtures of pure powdered metals (Fe, Ni or Co) and graphite. These filled anodes (~2 at % metal) were vaporized with a current of 95–105 A in 100–500 torr of He in our arc fullerene generator. The results obtained with cobalt were unique.

When a Co-containing rod was used, what looked like spider webs formed in the chamber, draping between surfaces. The soot on the chamber walls was rubbery and could be peeled off in long strips. Normal fullerene soots (and those made with Fe- or Ni-containing rods) are crumbly. The soot and the web material were ferromagnetic. A transmission electron microscope (TEM) image of the web material (Fig. 1) shows that the web consists of rounded

具有单原子层管壁的碳纳米管的钴催化生长

编者按

随着碳纳米管的发现——只有几个纳米大小的石墨型碳的嵌套微管——人们逐渐了解到，如果能够只用单一碳层来制备碳纳米管，那么它们的性质就可以更好地与理论预期相对照。这里，来自加利福尼亚的 IBM 阿尔马登研究中心的一个团队说明了如何实现这一目标的方法。他们制备单层壁纳米管的方法是将碳与金属钴一起气化，他们猜测钴可以形成微小团簇，从而催化纳米管的生长：新的碳原子可以附着在与金属颗粒连接的生长中的管表面。与此同时，碳纳米管的发现者，日本的饭岛澄男也报道了一种与之相关联的通过金属催化来制备单层壁纳米管的方法。

碳具有一种形成很多种结构的独特能力。在一种惰性气氛中，它聚集成空心球形富勒烯 [1-4]。沉积在用于合成块状富勒烯的电弧放电装置热尖端的碳，会形成嵌套式的石墨管和多面体颗粒 [5-8]。对这些碳纳米管和多面体的电子照射使其转化为近乎球形的碳"洋葱" [9]。现在我们报道的是，在电弧发生器中同时气化碳和钴导致碳纳米管的形成，它们都有很小的直径 (约 1.2 nm) 和只有一个原子层厚度的外壁。这些管在含富勒烯的烟灰中形成网状的沉积布，具有橡胶样的质地。这些纳米管的均一性和单层结构将使得对其性质的测试与理论预测进行对照成为可能 [10-13]。

我们实验的最初目的是制备金属富勒烯化合物和石墨包裹的磁性原子纳米晶体。通过在 6 mm 直径的石墨棒上钻一个 4 mm 直径的洞并注入纯金属粉末 (Fe、Ni 或 Co) 和石墨来制备电极。在我们的电弧富勒烯发生器中，于 100~500 torr 的 He 中用 95~105 A 电流将这些填充阳极 (金属百分比约为 2%) 气化。用钴得到了与其他材料不同的结果。

在使用含钴的石墨棒时，反应室中形成了看起来像蛛网一样的东西，交织在表面上。反应室壁上的烟灰为橡胶状，能够一长条一长条地剥离下来。正常的富勒烯灰 (以及那些用含铁或镍的棒制得的) 是疏松的。烟灰和网络状物质是铁磁性的。透射电子显微镜 (TEM) 图像 (图 1) 表明，网状物质是由几十个纳米大小的圆形烟灰颗

soot particles a few tens of nanometres across, linked together by fine fibres. Individual threads can be traced for several micrometres. In some cases several fibres converge on a soot particle. Embedded within the soot particles are round cobalt clusters with diameters ranging from a few nanometres to roughly 20 nm. Both electron and X-ray diffraction patterns showed that these clusters are face-centred-cubic Co. This indicates that the clusters were rapidly quenched, as Co is normally hexagonal-close-packed below 400 °C.

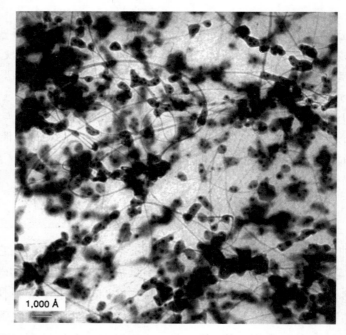

Fig. 1. Transmission electron microscope of web-like material showing strands of thread-like fibres and cobalt clusters (dark spots) embedded in carbon soot particles. This image and those in Figs 2 and 3 were obtained using a Topcon 002B microscope operating at 200 kV and a Gatan Model 679 slow-scan camera to acquire digital images, which can then have the contrast enhanced to reveal the nanotubes.

Scanning electron microscope (SEM) images show that the rubber soot deposits from the chamber walls contain thin fibres and soot particles similar to those in the web material, but with the particles in greater relative abundance. The carbon around the cobalt clusters consists partly of fullerenes, which can be extracted from the soot in typical amounts using toluene. Laser-desorption/laser-ionization mass-spectrometry of the raw soot showed a CoC_{60} peak, but this species was not found in a toluene extract of the soot.

A higher-magnification TEM image (Fig. 2) reveals the structures underlying the fibre and web formation. Carbon nanotubes with single-atomic-layer walls and diameters of 1.2 ± 0.1 nm are ubiquitous. The tubules apparently crossed, aggregated and tangled before being encased. Although the tubules are mostly coated with non-graphitic carbon, bare sections are also evident. Figure 3 (at still higher magnification) shows a bare nanotube with several round objects, comparable in size to fullerenes with 60–100 carbons, adhering to it. The circumference of the nanotubes would

116

粒通过细纤维连接在一起而成的。单根细丝可以长达几个微米。在某些情况下，几根细丝汇集在一个烟灰粒子上。嵌入烟灰颗粒中的是圆形的钴团簇，其直径从几个纳米到约 20 nm 不等。电子和 X 射线衍射图案表明，这些团簇是面心立方的 Co。这意味着团簇是快速凝结形成的，因为正常情况下 Co 在 400 ℃ 以下时是六方密堆积的。

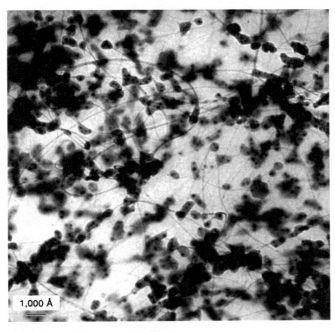

图 1. 网状物质的透射电子显微镜图像展示出丝状纤维束和包裹在烟灰粒子中的钴团簇（黑点）。此图和图 2 和图 3 中的图像是用拓普康公司 002B 显微镜在 200 kV 条件下获得的，并且用美国加登公司 679 型慢扫描相机来获取数字图像，从而能够增强至可分辨出碳纳米管的对比度。

扫描电子显微镜（SEM）图像显示，沉积在反应室壁上的橡胶状烟灰中包含细纤维和类似于网状材料中的烟灰颗粒，但颗粒占有更大的比例。钴团簇周围的碳部分地由富勒烯组成，用甲苯能够从烟灰中提取出一定量的富勒烯。粗烟灰的激光解吸 / 激光电离质谱呈现出一个 CoC_{60} 峰，但是在烟灰的甲苯提取物中没有发现该物质。

更高放大倍率的 TEM 图像（图 2）揭示出纤维和网状物的更精细结构。随处可见具有单原子层管壁和 1.2±0.1 nm 直径的碳纳米管。微管在被包住之前就已明显地交叉、聚集、缠结。尽管微管大多为非石墨碳所覆盖，裸露的纳米管仍然可以见到。图 3（在更高的放大倍率下）显示出一个周围附着几个圆形物体的裸露的纳米管，圆形物体的尺寸与含 60~100 个碳原子的富勒烯相当。纳米管的周长相当于一根由 15

correspond to a belt of 15 or 16 edge-sharing hexagons with 0.142-nm sides.

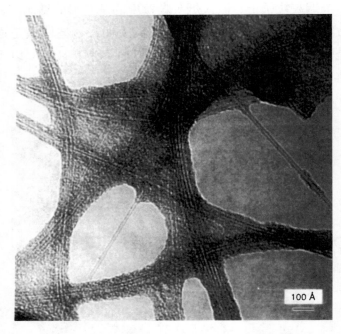

Fig. 2. TEM image at higher magnification showing details of the web-like material. Running through the deposited non-graphitic carbon are single-walled nanotubes about 1.2 nm in diameter. Bare portions of these nanotubes are also evident. The dark spot in the upper-right corner is a cobalt cluster.

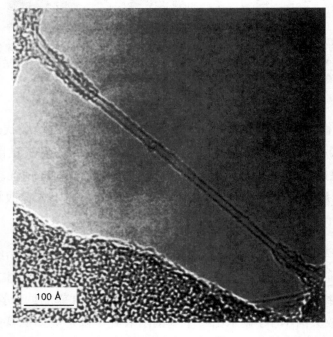

Fig. 3. TEM image of a bare section of a single-walled nanotube. The round objects adhering to the tube have diameters corresponding to fullerenes with 60–100 carbons.

或 16 个边长为 0.142 nm 的共边六边形组成的带子。

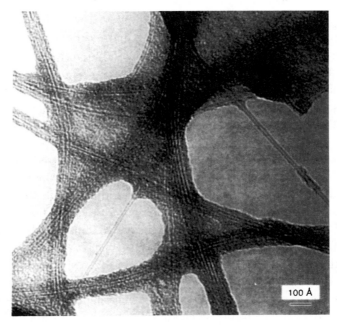

图 2. 较高放大倍率的 TEM 图像，显示出网络状物质的细节。穿过沉积非石墨碳的是直径约为 1.2 nm 的单壁纳米管。这些纳米管的裸露部分仍是明显的。右上角的黑点是一个钴团簇。

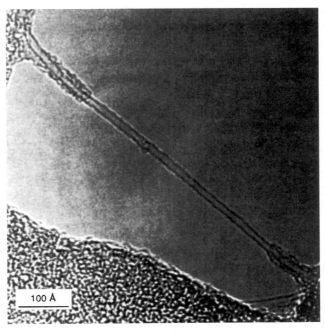

图 3. 单壁纳米管裸露部分的 TEM 图像。挨着管的圆形物体具有相当于含 60~100 个碳原子的富勒烯的直径。

Carbon fibres grow under diverse conditions[14-16]. Graphitic whiskers 1–5 μm in diameter and centimetres in length can be grown on the extremely hot cathode of a carbon arc run in high-pressure argon[17]. Under similar conditions (but at lower pressures), tubular graphitic structures with 2–30 nm diameters and micrometre lengths form in the cathode deposits in an arc-fullerene generator[5-7]. These nanotubes typically have walls 2–50 atomic layers thick. On the other hand, in the presence of transition-metal catalyst particles, vapour-grown carbon fibre can be produced by pyrolysing a hydrocarbon/carrier-gas mixture at temperatures between 500 °C and 1,200 °C (refs 14–16). Yacaman et al.[18] recently reported that some fibres produced by this method resemble the hollow graphitic tubes seen in fullerene-generator cathode deposits.

In contrast to these multilayered fibres and tubes, our cobalt-catalysed nanotubes have single-atomic-layer walls and a common diameter ($\sim$1.2 nm). They grow from carbon vapour (with no dissociation of hydrocarbon needed) at helium pressures in the range 100–500 torr. Fullerenes form abundantly at the same time. Under the conditions we used, no fibre growth was observed using Fe, Ni or a 50:50 Ni:Cu mixture, all of which catalyse fibre growth in the presence of hot gaseous hydrocarbons[19,20]. We believe, therefore, that cobalt plays a special role in catalysing the formation of these single-walled tubules, and suggest that a specific nucleation process may be responsible for their highly uniform diameter. For the moment the relationship between the nanotubes and the cobalt clusters is obscured by the encasing layer of carbon. The nanotubes are found in relatively cold regions of the chamber, co-condensed with (and mostly coated by) fullerene soot. It may be possible to control the amount of carbon that forms on the nanotubes by modifying the growth conditions, and the crystallinity of this carbon by post-annealing the coated nanotubes at high temperature. Such measures have been used to modify vapour-grown carbon fibres[14], and could be important in attempting to exploit the uniformity of these vapour-grown nanotubes to develop new types of carbon fibres.

It may also be possible to isolate bulk quantities of bare, single-walled nanotubes. Such structures constitute a new type of all-carbon polymer. Theoretical calculations predict that they can be metallic or semiconducting, depending on their helical pitch[10,11]. They might draw species into their interiors by capillary action, and they may be useful as catalytic containers, nanowires and solenoids[21]. The recent success of Ajayan et al.[22] in filling nanotubes with lead supports some of these ideas. The availability of the single-walled carbon nanotubes reported here should permit characterization and further experiments.

(**363**, 605-607; 1993)

D. S. Bethune, C. H. Klang*, **M. S. de Vries, G. Gorman, R. Savoy, J. Vazquez & R. Beyers**
IBM Research Division, Almaden Research Center, 650 Harry Road, San Jose, California 95120-6099, USA
* Affiliated with the Materials and Molecular Simulation Center, Beckman Institute, California Institute of Technology, Pasadena, California 91125, USA.

Received 24 May; accepted 3 June 1993.

碳纤维在各种条件下生长出来[14-16]。在高压氩气中实验时，碳电弧的极热的阴极上可以生长出直径为 1~5 μm、长度为厘米量级的石墨晶须[17]。在类似的条件下（但是压力较低），在电弧–富勒烯发生器中的阴极沉积物里，形成了直径为 2~30 nm、长度为微米量级的管状石墨结构[5-7]。典型情况下，这些纳米管有 2~50 个原子层的厚度。另一方面，在有过渡金属催化剂颗粒存在时，气相生长的碳纤维可以通过在 500 ℃ 到 1,200 ℃ 之间的温度时热解碳氢化合物 / 载气混合物得到（参考文献 14~16）。亚卡曼等人最近报道，利用这种方法生产出的一些纤维很像在富勒烯发生器的阴极沉积物中所看到的空心石墨管[18]。

对比这些多层纤维和管，我们的钴催化纳米管具有单原子层厚度的管壁和均一的直径（约 1.2 nm）。它们在压强为 100~500 torr 的氦气氛中由碳蒸气生成（不需要烃类物质的解离）。与此同时形成大量的富勒烯。在我们所用的条件下，使用 Fe、Ni 或者 50:50 的 Ni:Cu 混合物时，都没有观测到纤维的生长，而在有热的气态烃类物质存在时，它们都能催化纤维的生长[19,20]。因此我们相信，在这些单壁微管的形成中钴的催化起到了特殊的作用，并且暗示着一种特殊的成核过程是导致它们的直径具有高度的一致性的原因。目前纳米管与钴团簇之间的关系由于管外面碳的覆盖还不清楚。在反应室中的相对冷的区域中发现了纳米管，它们与富勒烯烟灰凝聚在一起（并且大部分被富勒烯覆盖）。也许有可能通过调节生长条件来控制纳米管上形成的碳的量，并通过高温下被覆盖的纳米管的后退火来控制这些碳的结晶度。这些方法已经被用来调控蒸气生长的碳纤维[14]，而且它们对于探索通过实现蒸气生长的纳米管的均一性来制造新型碳纤维来说，可能是重要的。

分离出大量裸露的单壁纳米管是可能的。这些结构构成了一种新型的全碳聚合物。理论计算预测它们可以是金属性的或者半导体性的，这取决于其螺距[10,11]。它们能够通过毛细管作用将物质拉入其内部，而且可以用作催化容器，纳米线和螺线管[21]。最近阿加延等人用铅填充纳米管的成功[22] 部分地支持了上述一些设想。这里所报道的单壁碳纳米管的获得应该有助于表征和进一步的实验。

（王耀杨 翻译；李彦 审稿）

121

References:

1. Kroto, H. W., Heath, J. R., O'Brien, S. C., Curl, R. F. & Smalley, R. E. *Nature* **318**, 162-163 (1985).

2. Krätschmer, W., Fostiropoulos, K. & Huffman, D. R. *Chem. Phys. Lett.* **170**, 167-170 (1990).

3. Krätschmer, W., Lamb, L. D., Fostiropoulos, K. & Huffman, D. R. *Nature* **347**, 354-358 (1990).

4. Meijer, G. & Bethune, D. S. *J. Chem. Phys.* **93**, 7800-7802 (1990).

5. Iijima, S. *Nature* **354**, 56-58 (1991).

6. Iijima, S., Ichihashi, T. & Ando, Y. *Nature* **356**, 776-778 (1992).

7. Ebbesen, T. W. & Ajayan, P. M. *Nature* **358**, 220-222 (1992).

8. Saito, Y., Yoshikawa, T., Inagaki, M., Tomita, M. & Hayashi, T. *Chem. Phys. Lett.* **204**, 277-282 (1993).

9. Ugarte, D. *Nature* **359**, 707-708 (1992).

10. Hamada, N., Sawada, S. & Oshiyama, A. *Phys. Rev. Lett.* **68**, 1579-1581 (1992).

11. Mintmire, J. W., Dunlap, B. I. & White, C. T. *Phys. Rev. Lett.* **68**, 631-634 (1992).

12. Saito, R., Fujita, M., Dresselhaus, G. & Dresselhaus, M. S. *Phys. Rev.* B46, 1804-1811 (1992).

13. Robertson, D. H., Brenner, D. W. & Mintmire, J. W. *Phys. Rev.* B45, 12592-12595 (1992).

14. Endo, M. *Chemtech* **18**, 568-576 (1998).

15. Baker, R. T. *Carbon* **27**, 315-323 (1989).

16. Tibbetts, G. G. *J. Cryst. Growth* **73**, 431-438 (1985).

17. Bacon, R. *J. Appl. Phys.* **31**, 283-290 (1960).

18. Jose-Yacaman, M., Miki-Yoshida, M., Rendon, L. & Santiesteban, J. G. *Appl. Phys. Lett.* **62**, 657-659 (1993).

19. Baker, R. T. & Harris, P. S. in *Chemistry and Physics of Carbon*, Vol. 14, 83-165 (Marcel Dekker, New York, 1978).

20. Kim, M. S., Rodriguez, N. M. & Baker, R. T. *J. Catal.* **131**, 60-73 (1991).

21. Pederson, M. R. & Broughton, J. Q. *Phys. Rev. Lett.* **69**, 2689-2692 (1992).

22. Ajayan, P. M. & Iijima, S. *Nature* **361**, 333-334 (1993).

Acknowledgements. We thank W. A. Goddard III, R. D. Johnson, C. S. Yannoni, C. T. Rettner and J. R. Salem for discussions. C. H. K. acknowledges partial support by the NSF and the Materials and Molecular Simulation Center (supported by DOE-AICD, Allied-Signal, BP America, Asahi Chemical, Asahi Glass, Chevron, B. F. Goodrich and Xerox).

122

The Displacement Field of the Landers Earthquake Mapped by Radar Interferometry

D. Massonnet *et al.*

Editor's Note

Understanding, and perhaps ultimately predicting, earthquakes depends on having a detailed knowledge of how the Earth's crust accumulates stresses before an event and how these are dissipated when a fault slips. This paper by Didier Massonnet and co-workers in France supplied a landmark in that quest. It reports a map of the movements associated with the 1992 earthquake at Landers in California, obtained by using satellite-based "synthetic aperture radar interferometry"—a technique in which the topography of the surface is deduced from the reflection of radar waves. The superposition of images taken before and after the earthquake produces interference bands owing to the offsets of surface features caused by displacement, from which the slip motions can be calculated.

Geodetic data, obtained by ground- or space-based techniques, can be used to infer the distribution of slip on a fault that has ruptured in an earthquake. Although most geodetic techniques require a surveyed network to be in place before the earthquake[1-3], satellite images, when collected at regular intervals, can capture co-seismic displacements without advance knowledge of the earthquake's location. Synthetic aperture radar (SAR) interferometry, first introduced[4] in 1974 for topographic mapping[5-8] can also be used to detect changes in the ground surface, by removing the signal from the topography[9,10]. Here we use SAR interferometry to capture the movements produced by the 1992 earthquake in Landers, California[11]. We construct an interferogram by combining topographic information with SAR images obtained by the ERS-1 satellite before and after the earthquake. The observed changes in range from the ground surface to the satellite agree well with the slip measured in the field, with the displacements measured by surveying, and with the results of an elastic dislocation model. As a geodetic tool, the SAR interferogram provides a denser spatial sampling (100 m per pixel) than surveying methods[1-3] and a better precision ($\sim$3 cm) than previous space imaging techniques[12,13].

THE magnitude 7.3 (M_w) Landers earthquake of 28 June 1992 ruptured over 85 km along a fault system that included the Johnson Valley, Homestead Valley, Emerson, and Camp Rock faults (Fig. 1). Field[11] and seismological[14] investigations show right-lateral slip reaching maxima of 4 m and 6 m, respectively 10 km and 40 km north of the main shock, for which the hypocentral depth[11] was between 3 and 8 km. This event was followed 3 hours later by the Big Bear earthquake (M_w 6.2), for which no surface rupture was reported. Co-seismic horizontal displacements as large as 3 m were measured geodetically and are

雷达干涉测量技术得到的兰德斯地震位移场

马索内等

编者按

对地震的认识以及最终可能的预测，需要对地球的地壳在事件发生前如何积累应力，以及这些应力在断层滑动时如何被释放等方面有详尽的了解和认识。法国的迪迪埃·马索内及其合作者的这篇文章是相关研究的一座里程碑。它报道了与 1992 年的加利福尼亚兰德斯地震有关的地形变化，研究使用了星载的"合成孔径雷达干涉测量法"——一种可以从雷达波的反射中推导地表上的拓扑结构的技术。通过叠加地震发生时间前后的雷达图像得到了由于地表位移补偿产生的干涉带，从中滑动运动即可计算得出。

地基或空基技术获得的大地测量数据，能够用于推断发震断裂的滑移量分布。虽然大部分的大地测量所需的勘测网络需要在地震发生前就安置就位 [1-3]，但以规律时间间隔采集的卫星图像能够获取同震位移，而不需要预先知道地震地点。合成孔径雷达（SAR）干涉测量技术，于 1974 年被首次提出 [4] 并随后被用于地形测量 [5-8]，该技术也能够通过去除地形信号，而被用于探测地表的变化 [9,10]。本文我们使用 SAR 干涉测量来获取 1992 年的加利福尼亚兰德斯地震产生的（地形）运动 [11]。我们通过合成地形测量信息和 ERS-1 卫星在地震前后获得的 SAR 图像得到了影像干涉图。由卫星观察到雷达视线方向（雷达至地表方向）的形变与实地测量得到的滑动、勘测得到的位移、弹性位错模型的结果均吻合得很好。作为一种大地测量工具，SAR 干涉图具备比传统勘测方法更加密集的空间采样（每像素 100 米）[1-3] 以及比先前的空间成像测量技术更好的精度（约 3 厘米）[12,13]。

震级 7.3（矩震级 M_w）的兰德斯地震发生于 1992 年 6 月 28 日，沿着包括约翰逊峡谷、霍姆斯特德峡谷、埃默森断层以及坎普岩石断层在内的断层系，形成了长达 85 千米的断裂带（图 1）。野外测量 [11] 和地震学研究 [14] 显示右旋走滑达到了最大 4 米和 6 米，分别位于主震北部 10 千米和 40 千米处，震源深度 [11] 在 3 千米和 8 千米之间。大贝尔地震（矩震级 6.2 级）于兰德斯地震后的 3 小时发生，关于大贝尔地震并没有地面破裂的报道。大地测量得到的同震水平位移达到了 3 米，与简单弹性位

in good agreement with simple elastic dislocation models[1-3,15]. Near the fault, co-seismic displacements of the order of a metre were detected by pixel correlation of SPOT satellite images[13] and up to 6 cm of post-seismic displacement was observed by surveys in the month following the earthquake[16]. The sequence of earthquakes altered the state of stress on the San Andreas fault system[17,18] and triggered seismicity elsewhere in North America[19].

The ERS-1 satellite passes over the rupture area (Fig. 1) at an altitude of 785 km, transmitting along ray paths pointed west at an average angle of 23° from the vertical. Each SAR image is a map of the ground reflectivity sorted by range, the distance from the radar antenna to the ground. The phase of each 4 by 20 m pixel measures both the range and the phase shift due to reflection of the wave from the ground surface. The latter quantity can be eliminated between two images of the same area if the dielectric characteristics of the ground remain constant and the orbits satisfy the conditions necessary for coherence[6,20]. The remaining path difference, known only to within an integer number of wavelengths, contains information from three sources: (1) relative orbital positions, (2) topography as seen in stereo by the satellite from slightly different orbital passes and (3) any change in position of the ground reflector between the acquisition times of the two images[8,10].

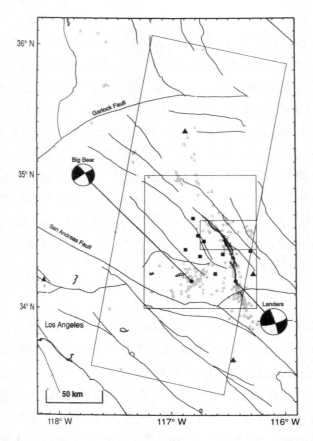

Fig. 1. Active faults in the region of the Landers and Big Bear earthquakes. Heavy solid lines indicate

错模型[1-3,15]吻合得很好。在断层附近，通过 SPOT 卫星图像基于像素相关的方法[13]测量到了量级为米的同震位移，而且在地震发生的一个月后勘测观察到了高达 6 厘米的震后位移[16]。地震序列改变了圣安德烈亚斯断层系统的应力状态[17,18]并触发了北美洲其他地区的地震活动[19]。

ERS-1 卫星在 785 千米的海拔高度上经过地震破裂地区（图 1），沿着指向垂直方向西面的平均角度 23 度的射线路径发射信号。每张 SAR 图像是根据雷达天线到地表地物的距离（这个距离的方向称为距离向）而排列的地面反射率的强度地图。每个像素点（约 4 米乘 20 米覆盖面积）的相位测量了雷达天线至地面的距离和由于地表反射导致的相位偏移。后者的量能够通过同一地区的两张雷达相位图之间的差分相抵消，如果地面的介电特性保持常数，而且卫星轨道满足相干所需的条件[6,20]。剩余的路径差，一般在波长的整数倍之内，包含了以下三方面的信息：（1）相对轨道位置，（2）卫星在细微差别的轨道路径上观察到的立体地形，（3）在两幅图的采集时间间隔中发生的任何地面反射体的位置改变[8,10]。

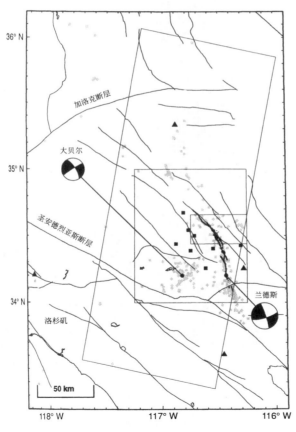

图 1. 兰德斯和大贝尔地震地区的活动断层。粗实线指出了兰德斯事件导致的地表破裂[11]。大贝尔事件

surface rupture associated with the Landers event[11]. No surface break was reported for the Big Bear event. Solid circles are epicentres[11] of Landers and Big Bear main shocks with focal mechanisms (G. Ekström and M. Salganik, personal communication). Gray spots are earthquakes with magnitude greater than 3 between 25 June and 8 August 1992. Rectangles denote the areas covered by Fig. 2a (large), Fig. 2b and c (small) and Fig. 3a and b (medium). Squares and triangles denote geodetic stations where the co-seismic displacement has been estimated by the U.S. Geological Survey[3] and the Permanent GPS Geodetic Array[1,2], respectively.

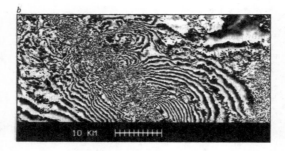

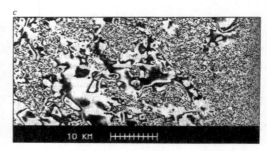

Fig. 2. a, Post-processing interferometric fringes obtained with the pair of ERS-1 SAR images taken before (24 April) and after (7 August) the earthquake. The image covers the 125 by 275 km area outlined by the large rectangle in Fig. 1. One cycle of gray shading represents a range difference of 28 mm between the two images. It is a measure of the component of the displacement vector which points toward the satellite. The number of fringes increases from zero at the northern edge of the image, where no co-seismic displacement is assumed, to at least 20 (representing 560 mm in range difference) in the cores of the lobes adjacent to the fault.

中并没有地表破裂的报道。实心圈是由震源机制解给出的兰德斯和大贝尔主要冲击区的震中 [11](埃克斯特伦和萨尔加尼克,个人交流)。灰色点是在 1992 年 6 月 25 日和 8 月 8 日之间的震级超过 3 的地震区。矩形框代表图 2a(大),图 2b 和 c(小),以及图 3a 和 b(中)所覆盖的区域。方块和三角代表大地测量站,其中同震位移分别由美国地质调查局 [3] 和永久 GPS 大地测量阵列 [1,2] 估计得到。

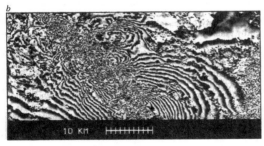 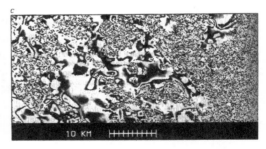

图 2. a,通过 ERS-1 SAR 在地震前(4 月 24 日)和地震后(8 月 7 日)的一对图像获得的后处理干涉测量条纹。这幅图像覆盖了图 1 中的大矩形框注明的 125 千米乘 275 千米的区域。每一个由白至黑的颜色周期(色周)代表了两幅图之间的 28 毫米的距离向的位移差异。它测量了地表指向卫星的方向上的位移分量。条纹的数量在图片的北方边缘从零开始增加,那里假设没有同震位移,直至断层附近的波瓣中心位置的至少 20 条(代表着 560 毫米的距离向形变)。断层两侧的(色周条纹的)不对称性是由断层的曲率

129

The asymmetry between the two sides of the fault is due to the curvature of the fault and the geometry of the radar. Displacements with different azimuths on opposite sides of the fault produce different fringe patterns because the radar resolves only the range component of the displacement vector. b, Detail of the fringe map in a, covering an area 64 km by 33 km as outlined by the small rectangle in Fig. 1. The orbital separation, or baseline, between the images taken 24 April and 7 August measures approximately 60 m and 126 m, in the vertical and horizontal components, respectively. These values imply that an error in the elevation model of 72 m would produce a shift of one full cycle. c, Fringes obtained using the same processing and area for b, but with SAR images acquired on 3 July and 7 August (after the 28 June earthquakes). The maximum post-seismic displacement observed[16] in the area and time covered by this image pair is 4 cm, which would produce a change in range of less than 0.2 cycles. The fringes are apparently due to errors in the elevation model because the interferogram exhibits characteristic topographic fringes and local incoherence in areas of high relief[20]. The orbital separation of this pair of images measures 22 m and 496 m in the vertical and horizontal components, respectively. These values imply that an error of 16 m in the elevation model would create one fringe. This interferogram is thus 4.5 times more sensitive to such errors than the co-seismic image pair (a and b). Since this post-seismic image pair (c) exhibits a noise level of about 1.5 cycles, we infer about 24 m of noise in the elevation model, in agreement with the published uncertainty[22] of 30 m. This noise level would in turn contribute about one third of a cycle, or 9 mm to the range changes in the co-seismic interferogram (a and b).

SAR images of the rupture zone were acquired by ERS-1 on four separate dates in 1992: 24 April, 3 July, 7 August, and 11 September. Among the three pairs spanning the earthquake date, the April 24–August 7 pair provides the optimum conditions for image correlation because the orbital separation best meets the coherence condition and the reflective surface was well preserved despite the intervening 105 days.

From these images, we reconstruct the phase of each pixel using a phase-preserving correlator[21]. We adjust the satellite orbital parameters (1) to minimize the number of fringes at the four corners of the image, assuming that the far field displacement is negligible. The stereoscopic path difference (2) is eliminated using a digital elevation model[22]. The interferometric fringes (3) are calculated in the geometry of the radar image and then mapped into the cartographic geometry. There they are resampled on the 90 by 110 m pixels of the elevation model to improve the signal-to-noise ratio.

The resulting interferogram (Fig. 2a and b) is a contour map of the change in range, that is the component of the displacement which points toward the satellite. It includes all the co-seismic and some of the post-seismic deformation. Each fringe corresponds to one cycle, equivalent to 28 mm (half the 56-mm wavelength of the ERS-1 SAR). For the nine geodetic stations located in the coherent part of the interferogram, the range changes are comparable to those calculated from surveying observations of horizontal displacement[1-3] with an r.m.s difference of 1.2 cycles, or 34 mm. This value represents the uncertainty, in an absolute sense, of the range change for a given point in the interferogram, and probably reflects mostly orbital errors.

Figures 2b and c show two different interferograms of the same area near the fault. Figure 2c was processed in the same way as Fig. 2b, but using a pair of images taken after the earthquake on 3 July and 7 August. Comparison of these two images clearly shows that the fringes in Fig. 2a and b are due to the earthquake. The comparison also indicates that errors in the elevation model propagate into the ranges in Fig. 2a and b at the level of

和雷达的几何位置造成的，因为雷达只分辨距离向的位移矢量，在断层对侧的不同方位向上的位移产生了不同的色周条纹特征。b，图 a 中干涉条纹图的细节（放大图），覆盖了图 1 中的小矩形框对应的 64 千米乘 33 千米的区域。4 月 24 日和 8 月 7 日测量的图像间，卫星（两次获取影像的）轨道差异，或称基线，其垂直和水平分量分别大约为 60 米和 126 米。这些值暗示高程模型（若）有 72 米的误差会导致（相位图）一个色周条纹的偏移。c，使用同样方法获得的 b 图区域的条纹，但是 SAR 图像在 7 月 3 日和 8 月 7 日获得（在 6 月 28 日地震之后）。这组图像对覆盖的面积和时间内观察到 [16] 的最大震后位移是 4 厘米，会产生距离向小于 0.2 个色周的变化。这些条纹显然是由于高程模型的误差产生的，因为干涉测量图在高峻地形区域内显示了典型的地形条纹以及局部非相干 [20]。这组图像对所对应的轨道分离的垂直和水平分量分别测得为 22 米和 496 米。这些值意味着高程模型的 16 米误差会产生一个条纹。因此这幅干涉图对地形误差的敏感度相较于同震图像对（a 和 b）对地形误差的敏感度要高出 3.5 倍。由于震后图像对（c）显示了大约 1.5 个色周的噪声水平，我们推断高程模型中有大约 24 米的噪声，这与已发表的 30 米误差水平 [22] 是吻合的。这个（高程模型）噪声水平会转而贡献大约三分之一个色周，或者同震干涉测量图（a 和 b）中的 9 毫米距离向的变化。

地震破裂地区的 SAR 图像是由（欧洲宇航局）ERS-1（雷达成像卫星）在 1992 年的四个日期采集的：4 月 24 日，7 月 3 日，8 月 7 日和 9 月 11 日。在跨越地震日期的三组图像对中，4 月 24 日和 8 月 7 日这一组图像对具备最佳的图像校准像素相关的条件：因为轨道差异满足相干条件，而且反射面（地表）保持得很好，尽管（影像对时间）间隔达到了 105 天。

基于这些图像，我们使用一种相位保持的相关算法 [21] 重构了每个像素的相位。我们调整了卫星的轨道参数（1）以最小化图像四角的相位条纹，假定远场位移是可忽略的。立体影像的路径差（2）通过一种数字高程模型消除了 [22]。干涉测量的条纹（3）在雷达影像坐标系下计算得到，然后投影到地图坐标系。因此它们被重新采样为高程模型中的 90 米乘 110 米（的空间分辨率），以提高信噪比。

结果得到的干涉图（图 2a 和 b）是距离改变量（即指向卫星方向的位移成分）的等高线图。其中包含了全部同震和部分震后引起的变形。每个条纹对应一个颜色周期，等于 28 毫米（ERS-1 SAR 的 56 毫米波长的一半）。对于位于干涉测量图的相干区域的 9 个大地测量站来说，距离向位移改变与那些由勘测站对水平位移 [1-3] 的观测计算出的数据是相当的，均方差偏离为 1.2 个色周或 34 毫米。这个值代表了在绝对意义上的干涉测量图上特定点的距离向位移的不确定性，可能大多反映的是轨道误差。

图 2b 和 c 显示了断层附近的同一地区的两幅有差异的干涉测量图。图 2c 与图 2b 的处理方法相同，但是使用的是一对在震后 7 月 3 日和 8 月 7 日采集的图像。这两幅图的比较清晰地显示了图 2a 和 b 中的条纹是由地震形成的。比较还指出，由于高程模型的误差所导致的在图 2a 和 b 的距离向位移误差达到了约 9 毫米，如图注所

9 mm, as quantified in the caption. This value represents the uncertainty of the relative change in range between two nearby points in the interferogram.

The co-seismic interferogram (Figs. 2a, 2b and 3a), shows no organized fringes in a band within 5–10 km of the fault trace. In this area, the displacement gradient is sufficiently large that the change in range across a radar pixel exceeds a critical value, and coherence is lost[6,20]. Rotations of small crustal blocks may also reduce the coherence[23]. Indeed, the band of incoherence is not observed in the post-earthquake interferogram (Fig. 2c).

25 km

Fig. 3. a, Detail of the earthquake area showing the same interferogram as in Fig. 2 and b a synthetic interferogram calculated with an elastic half-space dislocation model as described in the text. One cycle of gray shading represents 28 mm of change in the range, as in Fig. 2a and b. White segments depict the

量化的。这个值代表了干涉测量图中的临近两点的距离向相对位置的改变的不确定度。

　　同震干涉测量图（图 2a，2b 和 3a）显示了在断层迹线附近约 5~10 千米的带状区域中没有规则的条纹。在这一区域中，形变位移的梯度足够大，以致于在一个雷达像素的距离向位置改变超过了临界值，失去了相干性[6,20]。小型地壳块的转动可能也会减弱相干作用[23]。实际上，在震后干涉测量图中没有观察到非相干带（图 2c）。

25 km

图 3. a，地震区域的细节图，与图 2 中一样的干涉图；b，使用文中描述的弹性半空间位错模型计算得到合成干涉图。白色到黑色的一个颜色周期变化代表 28 毫米的距离向位移，如图 2a 和 b 所示。白色线段

fault geometry as mapped in the field[11] (*a*), and as used in the model (*b*). Both images cover the 90 by 110 km area outlined by the medium rectangle in Fig. 1. The observed (*a*) and modelled (*b*) fringe patterns differ mostly in the short-wavelength features near the rupture zone. These local concentrations of strain occur at the ends of fault segments. They are highly sensitive to the detailed geometry of the fault (*a*) and poorly explained by the simple geometry adopted in the model (*b*). The band of incoherence in the rupture zone (*a*) is delimited in many places by two parallel fault splays. These areas are also affected by intense secondary faulting, especially along the northern and southern parts of the Homestead Valley fault[11]. The loss of correlation might be explained by a large displacement gradient imposed by slip on these secondary faults and possibly rotation of blocks between them.

For comparison, we calculate the theoretical change in range (Fig. 3*b*) using a dislocation model which describes the rupture zone as an elastic half space[15]. The earthquake fault is treated as eight vertical planar segments which represent the surface rupture and the aftershock distribution[11]. Each segment is subdivided into rectangular patches 2 km in length. For the Landers event, the slip on each patch matches the offset mapped in the field (K. Hudnut, personal communication, published in ref. 14). The modelled rupture extends from 0 to 15 km below the surface, to match the moment[11] of 10^{20} N m. For the Big Bear event, where no surface rupture was observed, the model includes the geometry from previous studies[1,2], a simple triangular slip distribution extending from 3 to 15 km below the surface, and a moment[2] of 4×10^{18} N m.

The outstanding resemblance between the modelled and observed fringe patterns, which were obtained independently, validates both calculations. They agree to within two fringes (56 mm) in both the near and far field. Larger, but local, differences within 10 km of the fault are due to the simple discretization of the elastic model. The large lobes are adjacent to the central section of the fault, where the maximum slip was observed[11]. On both sides of the fault, the fringes converge toward points where the fault slip vanishes. This occurs at both ends of the fault and 20 km north of the epicentre, between the two main ruptures[11,14].

The modelled and observed changes in range agree to within 30 mm in a profile perpendicular to the central section of the fault (Fig. 4*a*). The agreement in the decay of displacement with distance out to 40 km from the fault suggests that the rupture depth of 15 km in the model is correct in this section of the fault. The right-lateral slip on the fault can be estimated from the interferogram by assuming that the observed change in range is due only to horizontal right-lateral strike slip on a plane trending N20°W. The estimated slip (see Fig. 4*b* and associated caption) agrees in magnitude and general distribution with the field observations[11].

描绘了通过野外测绘得到的断层几何走势[11](a)，以及在模型中使用的断层几何走势(b)。两张图片均覆盖了图 1 中的中等矩形框标明的 90 千米乘 110 千米的区域。干涉测量得到的(a)和模型模拟得到的(b)的条纹图主要在靠近破裂区域的短波特征上出现区别。这些局部张力的集中发生在断层片段的末端。它们对断层(a)的几何形状的细节高度敏感，而难以用模型(b)中采用的简单几何形状进行解释。破裂区域(a)中的非相干带(的范围)在许多地方由两条平行断层外扩部分的范围所划定。这些区域还受到密集的次级断层的影响，尤其沿着霍姆斯特德峡谷断层的北部和南部[11]。失相干可能是由于这些次级断层上的滑动而造成的大位移梯度及其间地层块可能的转动。

作为比较，我们应用把破裂地区描述为弹性半空间的位错模型[15]计算了距离向位移的理论变化(图 3b)。地震断层被当作八个垂直平面部分，代表着地表破裂和余震的分布[11]。每个部分被进一步划分为长度为 2 千米的矩形块。对兰德斯地震来说，每个片上的滑动与实地观测的偏移相匹配(赫德纳特，个人交流，发表于参考文献 14)。用于建模的破裂延伸到地表以下 0 至 15 千米的范围，以匹配 10^{20} N · m 的力矩[11]。对大贝尔事件来说，没有观察到地表破裂，模型用到了以前研究[1,2]中建议的几何形状———一种延伸到地表以下 3 千米至 15 千米范围的简单三角滑动分布，力矩[2] 为 4×10^{18} N · m。

模型模拟和观察分别独立获得的干涉条纹图具有显著的相似度，由此证实了各自计算的正确性。它们在近场和远场的吻合度达到两条条纹(56 毫米)之内。更大的、但是局部的、断层 10 千米以内的差异是由于弹性模型的简单离散化造成的。大的弧型突出处(干涉条纹)处于断层中央部分的附近，在此处发现了最大的滑动[11]。在断层的两侧，条纹向着断层滑动消失点汇聚。这种情况发生于两个主要破裂之间的断层的两端以及震中以北 20 千米处[11,14]。

在垂直于断层中央部分的剖面中，理论上的和观测到的距离向变化的吻合度在 30 毫米范围内(图 4a)。理论和观测得到了一致的结论：位移随着距断层的距离(距断层最远 40 千米)发生衰减，因此意味着模型得到的该部分断层破裂深度为 15 千米的结论是正确的。假设观测到的距离向形变仅来源于朝向北偏西 20 度平面上水平方向上的右旋走滑，断层的右旋走滑能够在干涉图中被(观测)估计出来。估计得到的滑移量(如图 4b 及其图注)与野外测量得到的观测值在量级和总体分布上是一致的[11]。

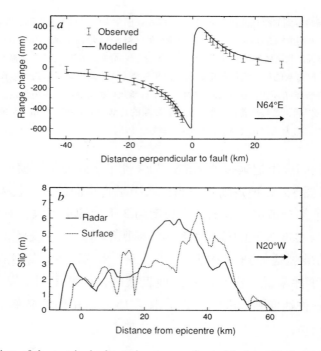

Fig. 4. *a*, Comparison of the co-seismic change in range as observed (points with error bars) and modelled (solid line) along a profile striking N64°E perpendicular to the fault trace at 34.44° N, where the maximum slip was observed[11]. The observed values are estimated by integrating the phase difference in Fig. 2*a* along the profile. The level of the observed values west and east of the fault is determined by counting fringes along a closed path passing north of the incoherent band in the rupture zone. The origin, with zero change in range, is taken to be where the path crosses the black-to-white fringe contour emanating from the northernmost part of Fig. 2*a*, where we assume no co-seismic displacement. *b*, Comparison of slip distribution along the fault estimated by integration of interferometric fringes (solid line) and from field measurements[11] of surface rupture (dashed line). Both quantities are projected onto a line striking N20°W and distance is reckoned positive to the north of the main shock epicentre (34.20° N, 116.44° W). Fringes are counted along two profiles following the western and eastern edges of the incoherent band, at a distance of 5–10 km from the fault. The fringes are extrapolated across the band of incoherence by projecting them in a direction perpendicular to the N20°W strike of the fault. Horizontal slip is derived from the measured slant-range displacement by assuming purely horizontal, right-lateral strike-slip displacement on the N20°W trend. In this approximation, the ratio between slant-range and horizontal slip is the product $\sin\alpha\sin\phi$, where α is the angle between the fault and the satellite nadir ground track and ϕ is the radar incidence angle. The apparent offset of 10 km between the maxima of the two curves results from the right-angle projection of fringes which appear to intersect the fault at an oblique angle. The interferometric estimate of slip does not show all the short wavelength features of the field estimate because the slip on the fault is inferred by extrapolating slip observed at points away from the fault.

The Landers earthquake, because of its large and clear surface rupture, provides a positive validation of the use of radar interferometry for measuring co-seismic displacements. Changes in range have been estimated under realistic conditions including actual topography and unexceptional orbits. The resulting map of the displacement field is unprecedented in its combination of precision (34 mm) and dense spatial sampling (100 m per pixel). These attributes could be refined with an improved elevation model and a more precise orbital calculation. Displacements of 1 cm have been detected for artificial

136

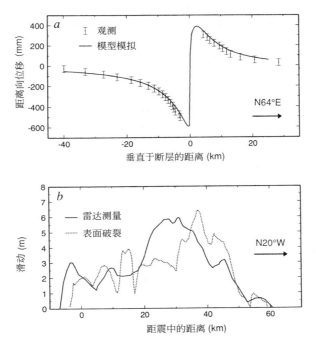

图 4. *a*，观测到的（带有误差棒的点）和模型模拟的（实线）获得的同震距离向位移的比较，两种情况都是沿着垂直于北纬 34.44 度断层线的朝向北偏东 64 度的剖面得到的，在北纬 34.44 度断层线处观察到了最大滑动 [11]。观测值是通过积分图 2*a* 中剖面上的相位差估计得到的。断层以西和以东的观测值水平是通过对破裂区域非相干带北部的闭合路径上的条纹进行计数得到的。起点（距离向位移为零）被认为是位于路径与从图 2*a* 最北侧开始发出的黑色至白色条纹等值线相交的位置上，我们假定此处没有同震位移。*b*，沿着断层滑动分布的比较，分别由测量图条纹积分估计而来（实线），以及从表面破裂的野外测量 [11] 而来（虚线）。两种值均被投影至穿越朝北偏西 20 度平面的线上，且认为震中（北纬 34.2 度，西经 116.44 度）北面相对于震中的距离为正。沿着非相干带的边缘（约位于距断层 5 千米至 10 千米的距离），我们分别在西侧和东侧边缘的两个剖面上对干涉条纹进行了计数。通过被投影至垂直于朝北偏西 20 度走向平面的方向上，条纹外插穿过非相干带。假定水平滑动为朝北偏西 20 度走向上的纯水平方向的右旋走滑位移，（该滑动量）可以通过测量（雷达干涉测量的）斜距形变推导而来。在这个近似条件下，斜距形变和水平滑动的比值是 $\sin\alpha\sin\phi$ 的乘积，α 是断层和卫星星下轨道的夹角，ϕ 是雷达的入射角。两条曲线最大值处有显著的 10 千米的偏差，这来自于干涉条纹的右视投影与断层倾斜相交。干涉测量估计的滑动并未展现出野外测量估计的所有短波特征，因为断层上的滑动受到了在断层外的点上观察到的外推滑动的影响。

　　兰德斯地震，由于其大型和清晰的表面破裂，正面验证了使用雷达干涉测量技术测量同震位移的准确性。距离向位移已经在真实的数据条件下进行了计算，包括真实的地形和正常的轨道（参数）。最终获得的位移场在精度（34 毫米）和密集空间采样（每像素 100 米）方面是前所未有的。这些因素能够通过更高精度的高程模型和更加精确的轨道计算得到进一步的提高。1 厘米的位移已经在人工目标 [24,25] 上被探

targets[24,25] and the ultimate precision of the technique is at the millimetre level[26]. For this shallow earthquake, the range changes measured by radar agree extremely well with both the field observations at the fault and the dislocation model in the intermediate and far fields. The detailed features of the radar fringes near the fault require more sophisticated modelling. For deeper earthquakes associated with little or no surface rupture, radar interferometry will become a powerful tool for measuring surface displacement in the intermediate and far fields. Unlike surveying techniques, there is no need to install ground stations before the earthquake. To ensure a pre-earthquake observation, one needs only to archive radar images of the potentially seismogenic area each time the satellite passes over it, as ERS-1 currently does once every 35 days.

(**364**, 138-142; 1993)

Didier Massonnet, Marc Rossi, César Carmona, Frédéric Adragna, Gilles Peltzer[*]**, Kurt Feigl**[*] **& Thierry Rabaute**[†]

Centre National d'Etudes Spatiales, 18 Ave. E. Belin, 31055 Toulouse, France

[*] Observatoire Midi-Pyrénées, 14 Ave. E. Belin, 31400 Toulouse, France

[†] Scot Conseil, 1 rue Hermès, 31520 Ramonville, France

Received 21 April 1993; accepted 2 June 1993.

References:

1. Blewitt, G. *et al. Nature* **361**, 340-342 (1993).

2. Bock, Y. *et al. Nature* **361**, 337-340 (1993).

3. Murray, M. H., Savage, J. C., Lisowski, M. & Gross, W. K. *Geophys. Res. Lett.* **20**, 623-626(1993).

4. Graham, L. C. *Proc. Inst. Elect. Electron. Engrs.* **62**, 763-768 (1974).

5. Zebker, H. & Goldstein, R. *J. Geophys. Res.* **91**, 4993-5001 (1986).

6. Gabriel, A. K. & Goldstein, R. M. *Int. J. Remote Sensing* **9**, 857-872 (1988).

7. Li, F. K. & Goldstein, R. M. *IEEE Trans. Geosci. Remote Sensing* **28**, 88-97 (1990).

8. Massonnet, D. *Proc. Int. Geophys. Remote Sensing Symp.* **1**, 1431-1434 (1990).

9. Massonnet, D. *Etude de Principe d'une Détection de Mouvements Tectoniques par Radar* Internal memo No. 326 (Centre Nationale d'Etudes Spatiales, Toulouse, 1985).

10. Gabriel, A. K., Goldstein, R. M. & Zebker, H. A. *J. Geophys. Res.* **94**, 9183-9191(1989).

11. Sieh, K. *et al. Science* **260**, 171-176(1993).

12. Crippen, R. E. *Episodes* **15**, 56-61 (1992).

13. Crippen, R. E. & Blom, R. G. *Eos* (Supplement, 27 Oct.) **73**, 364 (1992).

14. Kanamori, H., Thio, H.-K., Dreger, D. & Hauksson, E. *Geophys. Res. Lett.* **19**, 2267-2270 (1992).

15. Okada, Y. *Bull. Seism. Soc. Am.* **75**, 1135-1154 (1985).

16. Shen, Z., Jackson, D., Feng, Y., Kim, M. & Cline, M. *Bull. Seism. Soc. Am.* (submitted).

17. Jaumé, S. C. & Sykes, L. R. *Science* **258**, 1325-1328(1992).

18. Stein, R. S., King, G. L. P. & Lin, J. *Science* **258**, 1328-1332 (1992).

19. Hill, D. P. *et al. Science* **260**, 1617-1623 (1993).

20. Massonnet, D. & Rabaute, T. *IEEE Trans. Geosci. Remote Sensing* **31**, 455-464 (1993).

21. Massonnet, D., Rossi, M. & Adragna, F. Paper presented at PRISME, *CEOS workshop on SAR calibration*, Oberpfaffenhofen, Germany, October 9-11 (1991).

22. Elassal, A. A. & Caruso, V. M. *USGS Digital Cartographic Data Standards: Digital Elevation Models* (National Cartographic Information Center, Reston, 1984).

23. Zebker, H. A. & Villasenor, J. *IEEE Trans. Geosci. Remote Sensing* **30**, 950-959 (1992).

24. Cafforio, C., Prati, C. & Rocca, F. *IEEE Trans. Aero. Elect. Syst.* **27**, 194-207 (1991).

25. FRINGE SAR Interferometry Working Group, *Proceedings of First Workshop*, 12 Oct, 1992, Frascati, Italy (1992).

26. Gray, A. L. & Farris-Manning, P. J. *IEEE Trans. Geosci. Remote Sensing* **31**, 180-191(1993).

Acknowledgements. We thank T. Farr for providing the USGS elevation model quickly and K. Sieh, K. Hudnut and A. Lilje for sharing their rupture map in advance of publication.

测到，而这种技术的终极精度在毫米量级[26]。对这个浅源地震，雷达测量到的距离向位移与断层的野外勘测以及中远场位错模型符合得非常好。断层附近的雷达条纹细节特征需要更加复杂精细的模型。对发生轻微地表破裂或未发生地表破裂的深震，雷达干涉测量会成为测量中远场地表位移的有力工具。不同于勘测技术，该技术无需在地震发生前安装地面站。为了确保震前观测，只需要存档潜在的地震发生地区每次卫星飞越时的雷达图像，正如 ERS-1 现在每 35 天即飞越并采集一次一样。

（元旭津 翻译；吴晶 审稿）

Climate Instability during the Last Interglacial Period Recorded in the GRIP Ice Core

Greenland Ice-core Project (GRIP) Members

Editor's Note

This paper from the international team working on the Greenland Ice-core Project (GRIP) confirmed earlier hints that past climate change has happened with shocking speed. Several indicators of climate in ice cores that supply a record for the past 200,000 years, such as oxygen and hydrogen isotope ratios and electrical conductivity measurements of dust content, reveal that the last warm (interglacial) period was punctuated by many abrupt switches to a colder climate. Some of these began and ended very suddenly, lasting for only a few decades. This record suggested that our present warm climate has been curiously stable in comparison, and that natural feedbacks seem able to precipitate a very sudden change to a new climate state.

Isotope and chemical analyses of the GRIP ice core from Summit, central Greenland, reveal that climate in Greenland during the last interglacial period was characterized by a series of severe cold periods, which began extremely rapidly and lasted from decades to centuries. As the last interglacial seems to have been slightly warmer than the present one, its unstable climate raises questions about the effects of future global warming.

THE Eemian interglacial period is a prime target for palaeoclimate reconstruction[1]. A variety of evidence indicates that during isotope stage 5e of the marine oxygen isotope record ($\sim$125 to 115 kyr BP), usually correlated with the Eemian interglacial period in Europe and Sangamon in North America, conditions were at least as warm as today[2,3] and probably fairly stable[4]. Some evidence suggests that there may have been strong regional differences, with cyclical climate changes in areas bordering the north Atlantic[3]. Thus there is some hope of examining the behaviour of the physical and chemical climate of the Earth under conditions rather warmer than present, a possible analogue for future climate evolution.

Polar ice cores drilled in optimum locations allow the reconstruction of highly resolved climate records. The Vostok core[5] from central Antarctica was the first to yield an environmental record spanning the entire last glacial–interglacial cycle. At this site, ice deposited during the Eemian period is still $\sim$300 m thick, and as it lies about halfway through the total ice depth the record can be considered robust against distortion due to flow irregularities close to bedrock. Generally, higher annual snowfall and thinner ice cover in Greenland ensure that the Eemian ice will be found relatively deeper in this

GRIP 冰芯记录的末次间冰期气候的不稳定性

格陵兰冰芯计划组（GRIP）成员

编者按

本文来自格陵兰冰芯计划（GRIP）的国际团队，其研究工作证明此前的气候变化速度之快令人震惊。冰芯中反映气候的众多指标（如氢氧同位素比率、粉尘的电导率）提供了过去 20 万年来的气候记录，显示最后一次暖期（间冰期）被许多突然的冷冰阶所打断。有些阶段的开始和结束都非常迅速，仅仅持续几十年。这些记录表明，目前的温暖气候相对来说出奇地稳定，自然界的反馈将可能促成向新的气候阶段的突变。

对格陵兰中部最高点得到的 GRIP 冰芯（萨米特冰芯）的同位素和化学分析显示，末次间冰期时，格陵兰岛的气候以一系列极寒的冷期为特征，这些冷期开始得非常迅速并且持续数十年到数百年。由于末次间冰期的气候似乎比现今的略暖，其气候的不稳定性引出了关于未来全球变暖影响的问题。

埃姆间冰期是古气候重建的一个主要目标[1]。各种证据均显示，海洋氧同位素记录的 5e 阶段（距今约 12.5 万至 11.5 万年前），通常与欧洲的埃姆间冰期和北美的桑加蒙间冰期相对应，当时的环境条件至少与现今同样温暖[2,3]，并且可能相当稳定[4]。有证据表明，可能存在强烈的区域性差异，伴随着北大西洋周边地区气候的周期性变化[3]。因此，有望通过研究在比现今气温还高的环境下地球的物理、化学气候特征，来预测未来气候的变化。

利用在最佳位置上钻取的极地冰芯可获取高分辨率气候记录的重建结果。从南极洲中部获得的沃斯托克冰芯（也称东方站冰芯）[5]是第一个跨越了整个末次冰期–间冰期旋回的环境记录冰芯。在该站点上，埃姆间冰期的冰芯沉积仍厚达 300 m 左右，并且由于其大致位于整根冰芯的中间深度位置，可认为该记录是完整的，不存在基岩附近由于不规则流动而引起的扰动。一般来说，格陵兰年降雪量较大而冰盖厚度较薄，因而埃姆冰层应该位于该冰盖中相对较底部的位置。在格陵兰岛西北

ice sheet. The deep Camp Century core from northwest Greenland[6] may have reached the Eemian period, but probably did not penetrate it; in this period, at least the detailed record seems to have been strongly modified by rapid shear in the basal ice.

Here we present data obtained from an ice core drilled close to bedrock at Summit, central Greenland, which penetrates the Eemian period. The data cast doubt on some of our present conceptions of this period. Although the timing and amplitude of low-frequency variations (> 5 kyr period) in primary indices of climate and atmospheric circulation throughout the last glacial cycle closely mirror those recorded in the Vostok core, there are striking differences at higher frequencies[7]. These are most marked in the Eemian period, for which the record is highly structured. Most constituents examined so far show evidence for a series of shifts from levels typical of warm interglacial conditions to levels more typical of the mid-glacial period. The changes can be transient (lasting only a few decades to centuries), seemingly analogous to the series of climate "mode-switches" previously identified in the late glacial period[8], or they can remain latched for up to 5 kyr.

Record of the Eemian at Summit

The GRIP ice core, drilled into silty ice close to bedrock at Summit on the main ice divide ($72° 34'$N, $37° 37'$W) in summer 1992 (refs 7, 9) and the parallel core being drilled about 30 km to the west by the United States Greenland Ice-Sheet Project (GISP2)[10] were positioned to obtain records of the best quality possible through at least the last complete glacial cycle. The stable isotope profile for the complete core is presented in ref. 7. Although detailed analysis of the core is still under way, several constituents were measured continuously at the drill site, or shortly afterwards. These have allowed a partial characterization of the Eemian sequence, which is ~80 m thick and extends from about 163 to 238 m above bedrock. The observed thickness is broadly consistent with model predictions based on the assumption that Greenland was covered by an ice sheet of similar maximum thickness to the present throughout the Eemian interglacial period[11].

A preliminary chronology for the GRIP core going back to 14.5 kyr BP has been proposed[9] based on the stratigraphy. The chronology has been extended through the Eemian section of the core by ice-flow modelling[7], and confirmed by demonstrating a close correlation between low-frequency features (> 5 kyr period) in the GRIP stable isotope profile with corresponding features in the Vostok profile[5], in the SPECMAP marine sediment standard isotope curve[12] and in the Devils Hole terrestrial isotope record[13]. The stable isotope composition is a well established climate indicator, depending to first order on air temperature[5,14], but also contains information on conditions in the source regions for atmospheric moisture, and hence is linked also to atmospheric circulation changes[15]. However, the closely paralleled behaviour of stable isotopes in Greenland and Antarctica applies to other constituents such as calcium, as can be seen in Fig. 1. Calcium is mainly derived from terrestrial dusts, correlating closely with aluminium[16], and temporal variations are connected with large-scale changes in the transport and loading of terrestrial dusts[17].

部钻取的更深的世纪营地冰芯[6]应该达到了埃姆间冰期，但很可能并未完全贯穿。在该时期，至少基底冰层的快速剪切应力似乎强烈地改变了冰芯记录的细节。

本文我们将给出在格陵兰中部最高点钻取的萨米特冰芯的有关数据，该冰芯贯穿了整个埃姆间冰期。这些数据使我们对关于该时期的一些观点产生质疑。虽然在末次冰期旋回中，气候和大气洋流的主要指标中低频变化（周期 > 5,000 年）的时间和振幅与沃斯托克冰芯记录极为相似，但对于高频变化两者差异却很大[7]。高频变化的差异在埃姆间冰期最为显著，该时期冰芯记录的变化特征很明显。目前已研究过的大部分组成成分已证明，其间存在一系列的由典型的间冰期温暖环境到相当于冰期中期典型环境的转换。这种变化可能比较短暂（仅持续数十年到数百年），与之前在冰期晚期中发现的气候"模式转换"序列[8]相似，但它也可能可以持续长达 5,000 年。

萨米特冰芯中埃姆间冰期的记录

GRIP 冰芯是 1992 年夏在格陵兰顶部的主分冰岭（72°34′ N, 37°37′ W）上钻取的，钻到了基岩附近的粉砂质冰层（参考文献 7 和 9）。其对照冰芯（美国格陵兰冰盖计划（GISP2）[10]）是在该冰芯以西约 30 km 处取得的，选择该位置是为了能得到至少整个末次冰期旋回的最佳记录。整根冰芯的稳定同位素记录曲线见参考文献 7。尽管对于冰芯的详细分析还在进行中，但在钻探现场及之后不久，我们就已得到了一些组成成分的连续测量记录。这些数据能够部分地反映出埃姆序列的一些特征。埃姆序列厚约 80 m，位于基岩上部 163~238 m 处。该观测厚度与模型预测结果基本一致。而模拟结果是假定埃姆间冰期的格陵兰岛被与今天相似的最大厚度的冰盖所覆盖[11]。

根据年层结果，GRIP 冰芯的年代可以初步追溯至距今 1.45 万年前[9]。利用冰川流动模型[7]已将该年表延伸至冰芯的埃姆间冰期，而 GRIP 冰芯中稳定同位素曲线的低频特征（周期 > 5,000 年）与沃斯托克冰芯曲线[5]、SPECMAP 海洋沉积物标准同位素曲线[12]以及魔鬼洞的陆相同位素记录[13]中相应特征之间的密切相关性也证实了这一点。稳定同位素组成是一个良好的气候指示因子，它主要取决于空气温度[5,14]，但也包含一些源区大气水汽的相关信息，因此也与大气环流变化有关[15]。然而，在格陵兰冰芯与南极冰芯之间，稳定同位素变化的一致性也可在其他组分上看到，比如钙，如图 1 所示。钙主要来自陆源粉尘，与铝元素密切相关[16]，其随时间的变化则与陆源粉尘的输送和沉降的大尺度变化有关[17]。在海洋氧同位素第 5 阶

Throughout marine isotope stage 5 (MIS-5) with the exception of a brief period between MIS-5a and -5c, calcium concentrations are uniformly low and roughly equal those in the Holocene. There are, however, striking differences between the appearance of MIS-5e at Summit and that at Vostok, Fig. 1. At Summit, there is a highly structured pattern of variation on both long (> 1 kyr) and short (sub-century) timescales. By contrast, Vostok[5] shows smooth trends across the whole stage, which can only partially be explained by the coarser resolution of this record.

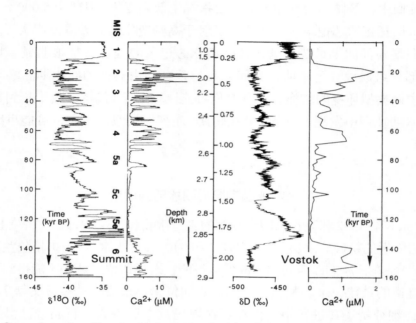

Fig. 1. Comparison of profiles of stable isotopes and calcium ion concentrations through the last glacial cycle in central Greenland and Antarctica. a, 200 yr mean $\delta^{18}O$, from Summit[7]; b, 200 yr mean Ca, from Summit (based on 3-mm continuous measurements below 1,300 m depth, using continuous-flow analysis[38]); c, δD (1 m core-length average) from Vostok[5] with new timescale[39]; d, Ca (~2 kyr average) from Vostok[16].

At Summit, only in the first part of MIS-5e are conditions mainly interglacial in character. Even here there is considerable fine structure with a series of transient returns to apparently cool interstadial conditions. This stage seems to correspond with the warmest stage of the Vostok profile where the temperature changes are believed to have preceded sea-level changes[18] by about 4 kyr. This sub-stage may represent less than 10 kyr of MIS-5e, more in accord with the ~11-kyr duration of MIS-5e derived from the SPECMAP curve[12].

The climate over central Greenland seems to be highly sensitive to changes in circulation in the north Atlantic region. The GRIP[7,9] and GISP2[10,19] records, and previous Greenland deep-core records extending into the last glaciation[8], all show evidence for series of "mode switches" in the isotopic record in the late glacial period which are considered to reflect rapid shifts in the position of the Arctic frontal system, in turn believed to be connected with changes in ocean circulation[20]. Evidence for the most recent event[21], the Younger Dryas (YD), has been traced in many independent media throughout areas under the

144

（MIS-5）中，除了 MIS-5a 和 MIS-5c 之间有一小段时间以外，其他部分中钙的含量均异常低，大致相当于全新世时期的含量。但萨米特冰芯和沃斯托克冰芯的 MIS-5e 阶的特征却存在明显的差异，见图 1。在萨米特冰芯中，不论长期（＞1,000 年）还是短期（不到百年）变化都非常明显。相反，在沃斯托克冰芯[5]中该阶段上的变化趋势整体较平缓，部分原因是因为该记录分辨率较低。

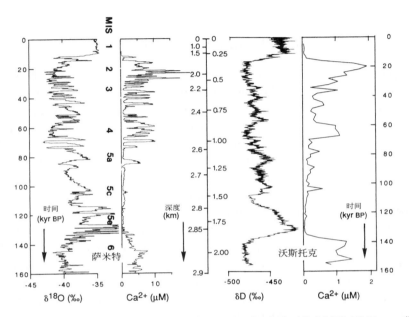

图 1. 格陵兰中部和南极冰芯记录的末次冰期旋回的稳定同位素和钙离子浓度剖面对比图。a，萨米特冰芯每 200 年的 $\delta^{18}O$ 平均值[7]。b，萨米特冰芯每 200 年的钙离子浓度平均值（基于在 1,300 m 深度以下每 3 mm 的连续测量，采用连续流动测量[38]）。c，采用新时间尺度[39]的沃斯托克冰芯平均每 1 m 的 δD 值[5]。d，沃斯托克冰芯每 2,000 年的钙离子浓度平均值[16]。

在萨米特冰芯中，仅 MIS-5e 的第一部分属于间冰期的环境特征。即使在这一段上也存在许多细微的变化，通过一系列的过渡又回到明显较冷的间冰阶时段。该段应该对应着沃斯托克曲线中最温暖的时期，而这一段的温度变化被认为[18]超前于海平面变化约 4,000 年左右。该亚阶可能代表了 MIS-5e 中不到 1 万年的一段时间，而与 SPECMAP 曲线[12]上为期 1.1 万年的 MIS-5e 更为一致。

格陵兰中部的气候似乎对北大西洋地区的环流变化特别敏感。GRIP[7,9]和 GISP2[10,19]记录，以及之前延伸至末次冰期的格陵兰深孔冰芯记录[8]，均给出了冰期晚期同位素记录中"模式转换"序列的证据。这些模式转换被认为是北极冷锋系统位置的快速变化的反映，从而被认为与大洋环流的变化有关[20]。在北大西洋气候影响

influence of the north Atlantic, but it is a rather weak feature in Antarctic records[22,23]. There is also evidence for an abrupt transition at the end of the Eemian in pollen records from northeast France[24,25] and in coastal marine sediment sequences from western Norway[26] and off northwest Africa[27]. An isotopic record from an exposure of ancient ice at the margin of the Greenland ice sheet also appears to show structure in ice suggested to be of Eemian age[28]. It seems that the sharp termination of the Eemian and some of the structural features observed at the start of the Eemian may have parallels in other systems and in other regions.

Climatic Characteristics of the Eemian

Figure 2 shows the isotopic and dust (Ca) content, and electrical properties of the solid ice during the Eemian period. The low-frequency conductivity of the ice, measured by dielectric profiling (DEP[29]), is controlled by both the neutral salt (probably chloride) and the free acid concentration[30]. This parameter was closely paralleled by the d.c. electrical conductivity (ECM[31]) profile, reflecting only the total acidity along this section of the record. Chloride is mainly derived from sea spray, and concentrations observed in the ice are strongly regulated by atmospheric circulation. The acidic content of the ice is controlled by various sources (marine biogenic, sporadic volcanoes and NO_x), and by transport and neutralization in the atmosphere. On the other hand, calcium levels strongly depend on a source that is known to have varied substantially throughout the course of the last glacial cycle—the extent of loess deposits[32] and of evaporites deposited on the continental shelves. Although we cannot at this stage separate out the various controls on these species, they undoubtedly have very different sensitivity to climate and circulation changes. We suggest that a similar pattern of composition should indicate broadly similar conditions of climate and atmospheric circulation.

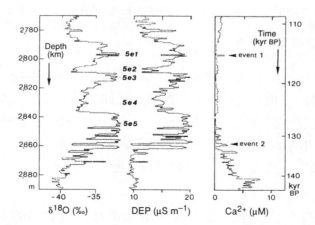

Fig. 2. Detailed profiles of selected isotopic and chemical constituents (averaged along 55 cm segments) through the Eemian (MIS-5e) section of the GRIP Summit core. MIS-5e is divided into three principal warm substages separated by up to 5 kyr of sustained cool periods, which we have named MIS-5e1 to 5e5. The profile for DEP[40] corresponds to the limiting high-frequency conductivity.

下的不同地区的独立介质中都找到了最近气候事件[21]——新仙女木期（YD）的相关证据，但在南极冰芯记录中其信号却极微弱[22,23]。在法国东北部的孢粉记录[24,25]、挪威西部[26]和非洲西北部近岸[27]的沿海沉积物序列中，也可以找到埃姆间冰期末气候快速转换的证据。在格陵兰冰盖边缘暴露的古冰的同位素记录也显示出了埃姆间冰期的某些特征[28]。埃姆间冰期的突然结束以及在埃姆间冰期伊始见到的一些变化特征似乎也可以在其他系统和其他地区发现。

埃姆间冰期的气候特征

图 2 为埃姆间冰期冰芯中同位素和粉尘（Ca）以及固体冰电导率的变化曲线。冰芯电导率的低频变化是利用电介质剖面测量法（DEP[29]）得到的，期间通过中性盐（很可能是氯化物）和游离酸的浓度来控制[30]。该参数与直流电电导率曲线（ECM[31]）非常相似，而后者仅反映该记录剖面上的总酸度。氯化物主要来自海洋飞沫，在冰芯中观测到的浓度进一步受到大气环流的强烈影响。冰川中的酸性组分则受不同来源（海洋生物成因、偶尔的火山作用以及氮氧化物）以及在大气中的搬运与中和作用的控制。另一方面，钙的浓度主要取决于以下来源，即黄土的沉积范围[32]以及在大陆架沉积的蒸发岩的范围，这些来源在末次冰期旋回中已发生了巨大的变化。虽然我们无法从该时期中区分出不同因素的影响程度，但毫无疑问，它们对气候和环流变化的敏感程度是不同的。我们认为，类似的组成特征所指示的气候条件和大气环流应该是大致相同的。

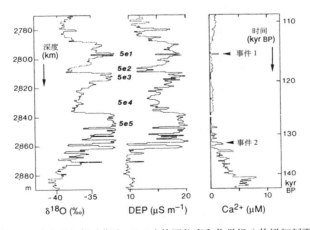

图 2. 节选的萨米特 GRIP 冰芯埃姆间冰期（MIS-5e）的同位素和化学组分的详细剖面（每隔 55 cm 求平均值）。MIS-5e 被分成 3 个次一级的暖期，这 3 个暖期被最长持续近 5,000 年的持续冷期分开，这些阶段我们命名为 5e1 至 5e5。DEP[40] 剖面对应的是高频极限电导率。

In Fig. 2 we have identified three clear, warm substages of (MIS)-5e, which we have named 5e1, 5e3 and 5e5, apparent in all constituents measured. In each of these, isotopically derived temperatures at least as high as in the Holocene levels were attained. Table 1 gives the comparative ice composition for different stages of the last glacial cycle. The isotopic and chemical signature of the warm stages of the Eemian is consistent with a similar atmospheric circulation to the Holocene. (Similar mean concentrations were obtained for Na, Mg, Cl, SO_4^{2-} and NO_3^-.) The difference in mean oxygen isotope ratios (1.4‰) suggests that temperatures were ~2 °C warmer than now during the warm stages of the Eemian (this is based on an isotope–temperature gradient for Greenland of 1.5 °C per 1‰ change[9]). Deuterium excess ($d = \delta D - 8 \times \delta^{18}O$) is sensitive to conditions in the moisture source region[15] and, in turn, to shifts in atmospheric circulation which could affect the stable isotope–temperature gradient. The similar values for mean deuterium excess in the Holocene and in the warm stages of the Eemian (Table 1) strengthen the idea that circulation changes are unlikely to have perturbed the gradients in the Eemian warm stages. Our dating of the record indicates that the unbroken warm stages characterize only 2 kyr of substage 5e5, < 1 kyr of 5e3 and ~3 kyr of 5e1 (except for one major transient event). The isotopic and chemical evidence suggests that conditions overall during the cool stage 5e4 were similar to the mid-glacial warm stages (interstadials), ~5 °C cooler than the Holocene. A marked antiphase variation between Ca concentration and $\delta^{18}O$ during the last glacial cycle has been reported previously in both Greenland and Antarctica[17,33]. This is reflected strongly in Table 1, where the relationship clearly extends through the sub-stages of the Eemian.

Table 1. Mean ice-core parameters for stages of the last climatic cycle

	$\delta^{18}O$ (‰)	D excess (‰)	Ca (µM)	DEP (µS m^{-1})	ECM (relative units)
Holocene	−34.8	8	0.203	23.9	1.43
Last Glacial Maximum	−42	6	10.11		
Stade	−41	8	4.72	11.01	0.01
Interstade	−38	4	1.4	12.6	0.25
Warm Eemian	−33.4	8.5	0.28	17.7	1.07
Event 1	−39	7	4.37	11.36	0.0054
Event 2	−38.4	6	2.12	9.66	0.0036
5E4	−36.8	7	0.451	14.75	0.616

Mean isotopic and chemical composition of ice deposited during the Eemian warm and cool stages in comparison with ice drawn from the principle climate stages of the last glacial cycle.

Although the isotope and chemical signature of ice laid down during the Eemian warm stages suggests that climate and circulation patterns were similar to those prevailing in the Holocene, at least in the north Atlantic region, the overall pattern of behaviour during MIS-5e is strikingly different. Figure 3 compares the frequency distribution of $\delta^{18}O$ values for MIS-5 in comparison with those obtained for the Holocene and for the glacial sequence MIS-2 to 4. The marked bimodal behaviour of the mid-glacial sequence reflects the now

在图 2 中，我们已从 MIS-5e 中确定出了三个比较清晰的温暖亚阶，分别将其称为 5e1、5e3 和 5e5，这三个阶段在所有测定的组成成分中都非常明显。在每个亚阶中，根据同位素记录得出的温度显示，当时的温度都至少达到了全新世的水平。表 1 给出了末次冰期旋回中不同阶段冰芯组成成分的对比。埃姆间冰期暖期的同位素及化学特征与全新世相似大气环流下的结果是一致的(Na、Mg、Cl、SO_4^{2-} 以及 NO_3^- 的平均浓度在两个时期是相近的)。平均氧同位素比率的对比差值(1.4‰)表明，埃姆间冰期暖期时的温度比现今高 2 ℃ 左右(这是根据格陵兰的同位素每变化 1‰，温度变化 1.5 ℃ 得出的[9])。过量氘值($d = \delta D - 8 \times \delta^{18}O$)对源区的湿度条件非常敏感[15]，从而对大气环流的变化敏感，而后者又会影响稳定的同位素 – 温度梯度。全新世中与埃姆间冰期暖期在平均过量氘值上的相似性(表 1)更有力地证明了环流变化并未改变埃姆间冰期暖期同位素 – 温度梯度这一观点。我们对该记录进行的测年结果表明，连续的温暖阶段在 5e5 中仅持续了约 2,000 年，5e3 中不到 1,000 年，5e1 中约为 3,000 年(其间存在一次较大的气候变化事件)。同位素及化学证据显示，在整个 5e4 冷阶中，其环境条件与冰期中期的暖期(间冰阶)差不多，温度比全新世低 5 ℃ 左右。之前在格陵兰冰芯和南极冰芯中都曾报道过末次冰期旋回中 Ca 元素浓度和 $\delta^{18}O$ 的明显反相变化[17,33]。这一点在表 1 中反映非常明显，这种关系清楚地贯穿于埃姆间冰期的亚阶。

表 1. 末次气候旋回各阶段冰芯的参数均值

	$\delta^{18}O$ (‰)	过量氘 (‰)	Ca (μM)	DEP ($\mu S \cdot m^{-1}$)	ECM (相对单位)
全新世	−34.8	8	0.203	23.9	1.43
末次冰盛期	−42	6	10.11		
冰阶	−41	8	4.72	11.01	0.01
间冰阶	−38	4	1.4	12.6	0.25
埃姆间冰期暖期	−33.4	8.5	0.28	17.7	1.07
事件 1	−39	7	4.37	11.36	0.0054
事件 2	−38.4	6	2.12	9.66	0.0036
5e4	−36.8	7	0.451	14.75	0.616

埃姆间冰期暖期、冷期的冰芯与末次冰期旋回主要气候阶段的冰芯在同位素和化学组分均值方面的对比。

虽然埃姆间冰期暖期冰芯中同位素和化学特征显示，至少在北大西洋地区其气候和环流模式与全新世是相近的，但 MIS-5e 期间总的特征类型却存在显著差异。图 3 对比了 MIS-5 中 $\delta^{18}O$ 值的频率分布与全新世以及 MIS-2~MIS-4 冰芯序列之间的差别。末次冰期中期序列中显著的双峰特征反映的是如今在所有格陵兰冰芯都已观测

well documented climate switching observed in all Greenland ice cores[8]. It seems that this behaviour was even more pronounced during MIS-5e, with a strongly defined intermediate mode. This contrasts with the single-mode isotope trend for the past 8 kyr of the Holocene, which seems to have a similar distribution to each of the component modes in the other stages, underlining the unusual stability of the present climate[7].

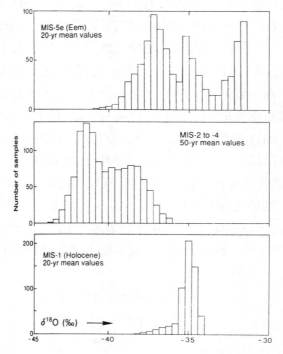

Fig. 3. Frequency distribution of the isotope data measured throughout MIS-5e in comparison with that observed during the last glaciation (MIS-2–4) and during the past 8 kyr of the Holocene. The distinctive single-mode characteristic of the Holocene contrasts with the bi- and trimodal behaviour observed through the last glaciation and during MIS-5e.

The cool events between the principal substages of the Eemian indicate a marked change in climate in Greenland and adjacent regions, and given the sharp changes in chemical signature, these seem to be connected either with a sudden change in the larger-scale atmospheric circulation or with a sustained shift, for example in the position of the polar front, leading effectively to a systematic change in the average source regions of constituents in the atmosphere over central Greenland. Their persistence suggests that there may have been large-scale changes in oceanic circulation in the north Atlantic region. Measurements on the gas content of the ice should establish the global significance of these findings. Our first measurements of methane trapped in bubbles in the ice show concentrations of 620 p.p.b.v. and 650 p.p.b.v. at points within MIS-5e3 and 5e5 respectively, similar to the values reported for the last interglacial in the Vostok core[34]. A single point so far measured in the MIS-5e4 cool substage gives the significantly lower value of 530 p.p.b.v., at the lower limit of the noise envelope cited for the Vostok core for this period, and a value typical for an interstadial.

到并已得到充分证明的气候转变过程[8]。在 MIS-5e 中该特征似乎表现得更显著，明显属于中间型模式。这与最近 8,000 年来的全新世中单峰模式的同位素趋势形成对比，全新世的单峰模式与其他阶段的每个组成模式都呈相似分布，说明现今的气候异常稳定[7]。

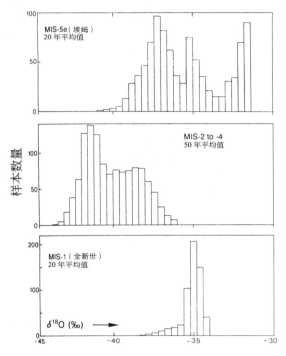

图 3. MIS-5e、末次冰期 (MIS-2~MIS-4) 及全新世最近 8,000 年来的同位素数据的频率分布对比图。全新世具有与众不同的单峰特征，末次冰期为双峰，MIS-5e 为三峰。

埃姆间冰期主要亚阶之间的变冷事件暗示格陵兰及其周边地区的气候发生了显著变化，此时再考虑到化学特征出现的急剧变化，这些变化可能是由于大尺度大气环流发生了突然的变化或者发生了一个持久的变化 (如北极冷锋位置的变化)，从而导致格陵兰中部地区大气组分的平均源区发生系统性改变。这些变化的持续性说明，北大西洋地区的大洋环流可能发生过多次大规模变化。对冰芯中气体组分的测定将可以确定上述发现在全球气候中的意义。我们第一次在 MIS-5e3 和 5e5 的冰川气泡中测得甲烷浓度分别为 620 ppbv 和 650 ppbv，与从沃斯托克冰芯中得到的末次间冰期的相应值[34]相似。目前为止，在 MIS-5e4 亚冷冰阶中单点上测得的明显偏低的值，530 ppbv，相当于沃斯托克冰芯同一时期中甲烷浓度波动廓线的最下限，或间冰阶的典型值。

Rapid Climate Change during the Eemian

The most striking feature of MIS-5e is a series of high-amplitude, high-frequency oscillations seen in all constituents measured continuously along the core (Fig. 2). We have examined two contrasting events in greater detail. Event 1 (Fig. 4) is a catastrophic event within MIS-5el at the culmination of the Eemian, where the oxygen isotope values plunge to mid-glacial levels (−41‰). The event is estimated to have lasted ~70 years to judge from an annual layer thickness of 2.5 mm (estimated from the relationship between accumulation-rate[7] and δ, and from flow modelling). Event 2 (Fig. 5) is one of the lengthy series of massive and sustained oscillations that marked the first ~8 kyr of the Eemian and the end of the previous deglaciation sequence. Stable isotope values approach YD levels (~−40‰) and were sustained for about 750 yr, comparable with the length of the YD itself. Maximum temperature decreases associated with these events are estimated at 14 °C and 10 °C respectively, on the basis of the suggested isotope–temperature relationship[9]. The deuterium excess is significantly reduced during both events, pointing to a lowering of associated moisture source temperatures. This suggests that any correction to the isotope–temperature gradient would only serve to increase the estimated temperature shifts.

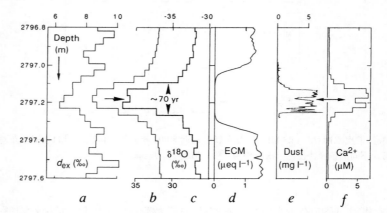

Fig. 4. Profiles of five parameters through "event 1", a rapid climatic oscillation (~70 yr duration) at the culmination of the Eemian interglacial, ~115 kyr BP. a, Deuterium excess[15]; b, oxygen isotope ratio[7]; c, same as b, but deconvoluted to account for diffusion (estimated diffusion length 3 cm); d, acidity measured by ECM in microequivalents per litre[31]; e, dust concentration measured from scattered laser light and calibrated by Coulter Counter by integrating size distribution[33]; f, calcium ion concentration[38].

埃姆间冰期的快速气候变化

MIS-5e 中最显著的特征是，沿该段冰芯连续测量出的所有组分中都存在一系列高振幅、高频率的振荡（图 2）。我们对其中两个相对照的事件进行了详细研究。事件 1（图 4）是埃姆最顶部 MIS-5e1 中的一次灾难事件，其氧同位素值暴跌至冰期中期时的水平（−41‰）。据估计，该事件持续了约 70 年，这是按年层厚度为 2.5 mm确定出的（根据积累率[7]与 δ 值的关系以及冰川流动模拟结果得来）。事件 2（图 5）是埃姆期前 8,000 年和之前的冰退阶段中出现的典型的持续时间长且连续大幅度波动的气候事件之一。其稳定同位素值接近新仙女木期的水平（约 −40‰），并持续了约 750 年，相当于整个新仙女木期的时间长度。根据同位素与温度之间的关系[9]估计，在这两次事件中，温度的最大降幅分别为 14 ℃和 10 ℃。两次事件中过量氘值都显著降低，意味着水汽来源地的温度也在降低。这样的话，如果校正同位素－温度梯度值，只会使估算出的温度变化值更大。

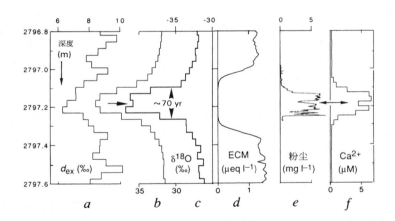

图 4. 事件 1 中 5 个参数的剖面曲线。事件 1 是在埃姆间冰期的顶端的一次快速的气候振荡（持续近 70年），约为 11.5 万年前。a，过量氘[15]。b，氧同位素比值[7]。c，同 b，但退卷积以计算扩散值（估计扩散长度为 3 cm）。d，通过电导率测得的酸度（单位为微升当量／升）[31]。e，粉尘浓度，由激光散射测量并由库尔特微粒计数器粒径分布积分进行了校正[33]。f，钙离子浓度[38]。

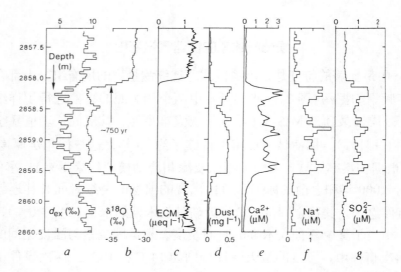

Fig. 5. Profiles of oxygen isotope ratio[7], calcium ion concentration[38], acidity by ECM[31], dust[33], deuterium excess[15], sodium and sulphate[41] through "event 2", a climate oscillation sustained for ~750 yr in the initial stages of the Eemian interglacial ~131 kyr BP.

The chemical signature of major species is broadly similar in both events. Strong negative correlation between $\delta^{18}O$ and Ca evidently persisted in the more transient events within the Eemian, although peak Ca concentrations, similar to YD levels, are much lower than late glacial concentrations. Calcium concentrations in the warm stages either side of events 1 and 2 are roughly equal to Holocene levels.

Although many features of the Eemian cool events seem to parallel the changes in the YD, there is a striking difference in the signal for deuterium excess which is strongly in phase with $\delta^{18}O$ throughout the Eemian, including events 1 and 2. During the late glacial and including the YD event, these parameters are strongly in antiphase[21]. It seems clear that although a similar mode switching in ocean–atmosphere circulations may be implicated in both the Eemian and late glacial events (including YD), there has been a fundamental difference in the oceanic source regions involved. The vast production of melt water from decaying ice sheets could have been involved in the YD, but was not available at least for event 1, which occurred in the final part of the Eemian.

There is some indication in event 1 of a catastrophic start to the event with a more tapered recovery. This can be seen in the dust profile, a parameter that suffers least from smoothing by diffusion and has been measured at millimetre resolution. Surging of (for example) the west Antarctic ice sheet could have provided the necessary trigger to the system[35], but the rapidity of the start of the event as seen in Greenland would be surprising, especially as it seems to have passed unrecognized in the Vostok core. Alternatively, a sudden weakening of the north Atlantic current could have allowed the Greenland current to carry icebergs much further south. A general cooling of the north Atlantic associated with such events could, in part, account for the observed lower deuterium excess. Whatever the "trigger" for these events, their duration of up to several hundred years is most probably connected with a re-ordering of

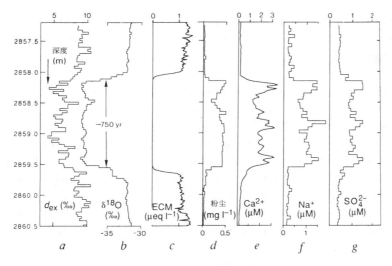

图 5. 埃姆间冰期最初阶段（约为 13.1 万年前）持续约 750 年的气候振荡（即"事件 2"）中各物理量的曲线图：a，过量氚[15]；b，氧同位素比率剖面[7]；c，ECM 测得的酸度[31]；d，粉尘浓度[33]；e，钙离子浓度[38]；f 和 g，钠离子浓度和硫酸盐浓度[41]。

两事件中主要组分的化学特征大体相近。在埃姆间冰期，$\delta^{18}O$ 值与 Ca 离子浓度含量之间呈显著负相关，尤其是在气候过渡期，不过 Ca 的最大浓度仅与新仙女木期的水平相当，远低于冰期晚期的浓度。不论事件 1 还是事件 2 中，其暖期中钙的浓度都与全新世的大体相当。

虽然埃姆间冰期中变冷事件的许多特征似乎都与新仙女木期的变化类似，但在过量氚信号中却存在显著差异，而在整个埃姆间冰期（包括事件 1 和事件 2），过量氚的变化都与 $\delta^{18}O$ 的情况同相。冰期晚期（包括新仙女木事件）中，这些参数则表现为强烈的反相关系[21]。很显然，尽管在埃姆间冰期和晚冰期事件（包括新仙女木期）中可能存在相似的海洋－大气环流的模式转换，但其中包含的海洋源区有着根本差异。新仙女木事件与冰盖融化导致的大量冰川融水有关，但至少在埃姆间冰期最后阶段的事件 1 中并非如此。

从事件 1 中可以看出，事件的发生是灾难性的迅速，而结束却相对较为平缓。这也可以从微粒含量的粉尘记录中看出，粉尘记录是受扩散平滑影响最小的指标，而且该指标的测定分辨率可达毫米量级。例如西南极冰盖等的跃动可能是诱发该系统变化的原因所在[35]，但是如在格陵兰看到的，该事件的发生迅速得令人震惊，尤其是它似乎在南极沃斯托克冰芯中都未能记录到。另一方面，北大西洋暖流的突然减弱使得格陵兰洋流携带冰山能到达更南部的地区。伴随上述事件的北大西洋的总体变冷，在某种程度上也是导致较低的过量氚值出现的原因。不管是什么因素"触发"了这些气候事件，其持续时间之所以能达到数百年很可能与大洋环流的重组有关。

the oceanic circulation. Such features have not, however, been observed through the Holocene, despite important climate changes during this period—these include the Climatic Optimum and the Little Ice Age.

We have considered the possibility that the events may have been generated or sharpened by processes occurring within the ice sheets, but several factors argue strongly against this. First, the events are located ~200 m above bedrock. Visible examination of the core revealed no evidence for significant disturbance of the layering down to 2,847 m, or ~50 m below the depth of event 1, although examination of cloudy bands showed that the layering was becoming inclined by up to 21° by the depth of event 2. Although this might indicate some migration of the position of the ice divide since the Eemian[7], no indication of any discontinuity in the record was observed after the start of the Eemian. Observations on the core have revealed a strong anti-correlation between crystal size and dust or Ca content, with sharp changes at the boundaries of both events 1 and 2. Studies on the ice adjacent to and within event 1 show a significant strengthening of the fabric (pattern of preferred orientation) within the smaller crystals inside the event. It is not clear how far this could influence the rate at which the ice thins. Paterson[36] has argued that the effect should not be important near an ice divide where little shearing is expected.

Second, transition times at the start and at the end of the events are similar to those observed for the mid- and late-glacial events, even allowing for peak broadening due to diffusion. Some diffusion is indicated by the symmetry and broader appearance of the ECM (H^+), DEP and $\delta^{18}O$ profiles with respect to the dust profiles. If dust is considered to be immobile, and it is also assumed the shifts were originally simultaneous, then we can estimate a mean diffusion length of ~8 cm for both H^+ and $\delta^{18}O$. This can be compared with a diffusion length for ice molecules of 3–4 cm calculated on the basis of a mean ice temperature of −15 °C, a vertical strain rate of 3×10^{-5} yr^{-1} estimated for the Eemian ice, and a self-diffusion coefficient for ice of 2.5×10^{-8} m^2 yr^{-1}. If we therefore assume that the dust signal represents the broad shift in atmospheric circulation pattern at the boundaries of these events, this suggests that the shift was largely completed within ~10 years for event 1 and ~30 years for event 2. These rates of change are comparable with the rates indicated previously for both YD termination[21] and for the late glacial events[7,8].

At this stage, estimates of the rate of change of climate parameters must be tentative, but such processes cannot affect the amplitude of the events themselves. The overall picture of an atmospheric circulation system oscillating between two well-defined modes is unaffected.

What the Ice Cores Tell Us

Although we knew that abrupt and large climatic oscillations could occur during the cold stages of the glacial–interglacial cycle, the oscillations seen during a warm stage are new. They are prevalent in the early to mid-stages of the warmest part of the Eemian interglacial

不过，在全新世虽然也出现了许多重要的气候变化——包括气候最宜期及小冰期等，却还未发现类似上述特征。

我们也考虑了发生于冰盖内部的过程导致或加剧了这些事件的可能性，但多个因素都不支持这一想法。首先，两个事件在冰芯中的位置都处于基岩上约 200 m 处。虽然对冰芯不透光带层理的检查发现在事件 2 的深度位置上，冰层的倾斜度达到了 21°，但根据对冰芯的肉眼观察结果，直到 2,847 m 深处，即事件 1 下部约 50 m 的地方都未见到明显的冰层扰动。也许这意味着自埃姆间冰期以来分冰岭的位置发生过迁移[7]，不过在埃姆间冰期开始后，并未在该记录中见到任何冰层不连续的迹象。对冰芯的观察结果揭示，晶体大小与粉尘或 Ca 含量之间呈显著的反相关关系，同时在事件 1 和事件 2 的边界附近都存在急剧的变化。对事件 1 及其附近的冰的研究表明，事件内部较小的冰晶结构中纤维状定向（晶体择优取向的模式）明显加强。这一点对冰层减薄速率的影响程度尚不清楚。帕特森[36]提出，在分冰岭附近由于剪切作用较弱该影响不重要。

其次，事件开始和结束的过渡阶段均与在其他冰期中期和晚期事件中观察到的结果类似，即使在由于扩散作用导致峰值变宽的情况下也是如此。ECM(H^+)、DEP 和 $\delta^{18}O$ 剖面相对于粉尘剖面较宽且对称分布也指示了扩散作用的存在。如果认为粉尘在冰内是不移动的，同时假设粉尘变化记录了当时形成时瞬间的状况，那么由此可得到 H^+ 和 $\delta^{18}O$ 的平均扩散距离约为 8 cm。这和当平均冰温为 $-15\,℃$，且埃姆冰层的垂直应变率为 $3 \times 10^{-5}\,yr^{-1}$ 以及冰的自扩散系数为 $2.5 \times 10^{-8}\,m^2 \cdot yr^{-1}$ 时计算出的冰分子的扩散距离（3~4 cm）具有可比性。因而，当我们假定粉尘信号能够表示在这些事件的时间边界上大气环流形式发生的较大的转变，那么对于事件 1 来说这种气候突变在 10 年内就完成了，而事件 2 的相应时间约为 30 年。这样的变化速率与之前指示新仙女木期结束[21]和晚冰期事件[7,8]的速率具有可比性。

目前对气候参数变化速率的估计只是试探性的，不过这并不会对气候事件本身的变化幅度产生影响。大气环流系统在两种已定义好的模式之间振荡的总体形式也不受影响。

冰芯带给我们的启示

尽管我们知道在冰期–间冰期旋回的冷期中会发生突发性的大规模气候振荡，但暖期中见到如此规模的振荡还是首次。这种振荡在埃姆间冰期最温暖阶段的早中

but occur throughout MIS-5e. The mode switches may be completed in as little as 1–2 decades and can become latched for anything between 70 yr and 5 kyr. The signature of these events revealed in the chemical profiles in the GRIP core is consistent with large changes in atmospheric circulation patterns in the north Atlantic, and important climate changes at least over Greenland and adjacent regions are indicated. The length of these events indicates that shifts in ocean circulation were involved, as is believed to have been the case with the YD event, so the effects are likely to have been much more widespread.

Given the history of the last 150 kyr, the past 8 kyr has been strangely stable; only during the final ~2 kyr of the warmest stage of the Eemian interglacial do our data demonstrate a similar period of stability. The unexpected finding that the remainder of the Eemian period was interrupted by a series of oscillations, apparently reflecting reversals to a "mid-glacial" climate is extremely difficult to explain. Perhaps the most pressing question is why similar oscillations do not persist today, as the Eemian period is often considered as an analogue for a world slightly warmer than today's. It has been suggested that the north Atlantic Oscillation or related processes may have a bearing on decadal-frequency features[10,37], as they are linked to strong inter-annual variability at coastal Greenland stations, but clearly this has not left significant evidence in the Holocene ice-core records. If such an oscillation caused the earlier features, it must have been far stronger. Moreover we need to explain how a mode switch can be sustained for 70 yr–5 kyr after being induced by, perhaps, a higher frequency switching in the atmospheric system, or by some catastrophic event such as ice-sheet surging.

As the GISP2 drilling nears bedrock, we can rapidly expect both confirmation of these findings and new clues as the sister cores are subjected to closer scrutiny. The analysis of new parameters should allow us to narrow down the range of possible changes in ocean and atmosphere that favoured instability in the climate. Coordinated analysis of the two cores should allow much firmer dating than has hitherto been possible in any single ice-core, and remove beyond reasonable doubt any question relating to local interferences on the records. Jointly, they may provide the vital clue to answer the question of what it might take to induce Eemian-type instability into the Holocene pattern of climate. Man is already perturbing one of the factors that may be involved, the greenhouse gases, and our first tentative measurements indicate that they may be linked to climatic changes within the Eemian.

(**364**, 203-207; 1993)

Greenland Ice-core Project (GRIP) Members[*]

[*] M. Anklin, J. M. Barnola, J. Beer, T. Blunier, J. Chappellaz, H. B. Clausen, D. Dahl-Jensen, W. Dansgaard, M. De Angelis, R. J. Delmas, P. Duval, M. Fratta, A. Fuchs, K. Fuhrer, N. Gundestrup, C. Hammer, P. Iversen, S. Johnsen, J. Jouzel, J. Kipfstuhl, M. Legrand, C. Lorius, V. Maggi, H. Miller, J. C. Moore, H. Oeschger, G. Orombelli, D. A. Peel, G. Raisbeck, D. Raynaud, C. Schøtt-Hvidberg, J. Schwander, H. Shoji, R. Souchez, B. Stauffer, J. P. Steffensen, M. Stievenard, A. Sveinbjörnsdottir, T. Thorsteinsson, E. W. Wolff.

Received 5 April; accepted 3 June 1993.

期比较常见，但其实在整个 MIS-5e 阶段都有发生。气候模式转换所需的时间大概仅为 10~20 年，但持续时间可在 70~5,000 年间变化。GRIP 冰芯的化学剖面揭示出的此类事件的特征与北大西洋地区大气环流模式的大规模变化一致，至少揭示了包括格陵兰及其邻近地区的重大气候变化。此类事件的持续时间说明这与大洋环流转换有关，并且人们普遍认为这些气候事件可以与新仙女木事件相提并论，因此这一结论的影响将是深远的。

在过去的 15 万年中，最近的 8,000 年异乎寻常地稳定。我们获得的数据表明，仅在埃姆间冰期最温暖的最后 2,000 年出现过类似的稳定阶段。让人意想不到的是，埃姆间冰期的其余阶段均被一系列的振荡所打断，气候反转回末次冰期中期的水平，令人难以解释。也许最紧迫的问题是：为什么类似的振荡没有持续到今天呢？要知道通常认为埃姆间冰期与现今气候是类似的，只是温度略高。有学者提出，北大西洋涛动或相关过程可能影响着年代际频率尺度上的波动[10,37]，而这与格陵兰沿岸站点的强烈年际变化相关，但显然在全新世的冰芯记录中并未留下明显的相关证据。如果是由这样一类振荡引起之前的特征的话，则其强度应该要大得多。此外，我们还需要解释为什么由大气系统中的更高频率的气候转换所触发的，或由一些灾难性事件（如冰盖的跃动）所触发的气候模式可以维持 70~5,000 年。

GISP2 冰芯已钻到了基岩附近，随着对该姊妹冰芯的深入研究，我们有理由期待上述发现很快就可以得到证实，并从中找到新的线索。通过对新参数的分析，我们可以缩小导致气候变化不稳定性的海洋与大气可能的变化范围。通过对两根冰芯的交叉分析得到的测年结果将比目前在单根冰芯中得到的任一结果都更加准确，并能消除对这些记录中局部干扰方面的质疑。连带地，还有可能为回答是什么诱导埃姆型不稳定性进入全新世气候格局这个问题提供重要线索。温室气体作为一种可能因素，已然引起人们的不安，而我们的首次尝试性的测定结果也表明该因素确实可能与埃姆间冰期的气候变化有关。

（齐红艳 翻译；田立德 审稿）

References:

1. IGBP *Global Change, 12, IGBP: A Study of Global Change. The Initial Core Projects* (International Geosphere-Biosphere Programme, 1990).

2. Dansgaard, W. in *The Climate of Europe: Past, Present and Future* (eds Flohn, H. & Fantechi, R.) 208-225 (Reidel, Dordrecht, 1984).

3. Anderson, P. *et al. Quat. Int.* **10-12**, 9-28 (1991).

4. Müller, H., in *Man's Impact on Climate* (eds Bach, W., Pankreth, J. & Kellog, W.) 29-41 (Elsevier, Amsterdam, 1979).

5. Jouzel, J. *et al. Nature* **329**, 403-408 (1987).

6. Dansgaard, W. *et al. Science* **218**, 1273-1277 (1982).

7. Dansgaard, W. *et al. Nature* **364**, 218-220 (1993).

8. Oeschger, H. & Arquit, A. in *Global Changes of the Past* (ed. Bradley, R. S.) 175-200. (UCAR/ Office for Interdisciplinary Earth Studies, Boulder, Colorado, 1991).

9. Johnsen, S. J. *et al. Nature* **359**, 311-313 (1992).

10. Taylor, K. C. *et al. Nature* **361**, 432-436 (1993).

11. Letréguilly, A., Reeh, N. & Huybrechts, P. *Glob. Planet. Change* **90**, 385-394 (1991).

12. Martinson, D. G. *et al. Quat. Res.* **27**, 1-29 (1987).

13. Winograd, I. J. *et al. Science* **258**, 255-260 (1992).

14. Dansgaard, W. *Tellus* **16**, 436-468 (1964).

15. Johnsen, S. J., Dansgaard, W. & White, J. W. C. *Tellus* B**41**, 452-468 (1989).

16. Legrand, M. R., Lorius, C., Barkov, N. I. & Petrov, V. N. *Atmos. Envir.* **22**, 317-331 (1988).

17. Delmas, R. J. & Legrand, M., in *Dahlem Konferenzen, The Environmental Record in Glaciers and Ice Sheets* (eds Oeschger, H. & Langway, C. C. Jr) 319-341 (Wiley, Chichester, 1989).

18. Sowers, T., Bender, M., Raynaud, D., Korotkevich, Y. S. & Orchardo, J. *Paleoceanography* **6**, 679-696 (1991).

19. Alley, R. B. *et al. Nature* **362**, 527-529 (1993).

20. Broecker, W. S., Bond, G., Klas, M., Bonani, G. & Wolfli, W. *et al Paleoceanography* **5**, 469-477 (1990).

21. Dansgaard, W., White, J. W. C. & Johnsen, S. J. *Nature* **339**, 532-534 (1989).

22. Jouzel, J., Lorius, C., Merlivat, L. & Petit, J.-R. in *NATO ASI Series C, 216, Abrupt Climatic Change* (eds Berger, W. H. & Labeyrie, L. D.) 235-245 (Reidel, Dordrecht, 1987).

23. Jouzel, J. *et al.*, in *NATO ASI Series 12, The Last Deglaciation: Absolute and Radiocarbon Chronologies* (eds Bard, E. & Broecker, W. S.) 229-226 (1992).

24. Woillard, G. *Nature* **281**, 558-562 (1979).

25. Guiot, J., Pons, A., de Beaulieu, J. L. & Reille, M. *Nature* **338**, 309-313 (1989).

26. Mangerud, J., Sønstegaard, E. & Sejtup, H.-P. *Nature* **227**, 189-192 (1979).

27. Eglinton, G. *et al. Nature* **356**, 423-126 (1992).

28. Reeh, N., Oerter, H., Letreguilly, A., Miller, H. & Hubberten, H-W. *Palaeogeogr. Palaeoclimatol. Palaeoecol.* **90**, 373-383 (1991).

29. Moore, J. C., Mulvaney, R. & Paren, J. G. *Geophys. Res. Lett.* **16**, 1177-1180 (1989).

30. Moore, J. C., Paren, J. G. & Oerter, H. *J. Geophys. Res.* **97**, 19803-19812 (1992).

31. Hammer, C. U. *J. Phys. Chem.* **87**, 4099-4103 (1983).

32. Pye, K. *Aeolian Dust and Dust Deposits* (Academic, London, 1987).

33. Hammer, C. U. *et al.* in *Greenland Ice Core: Geophysics, Geochemistry and the Environment* (eds Langway, C. C. Jr, Oeschger, H. & Dansgaard, W.) 90-94 (Am. Geophys. Un. Geophys. Monogr. 33, Washington DC, 1985).

34. Chappellaz, J., Barnola, J. M., Raynaud, D., Korotkevich, Y. S. & Lorius, C. *Nature* **345**, 127-131 (1990).

35. Hollin, J. T. *Boreas* **6**, 33-52 (1977).

36. Paterson, W. S. B. *Cold Reg. Sci. Technol.* **20**, 75-98 (1991).

37. Lehman, S. *Nature* **361**, 404-405 (1993).

38. Fuhrer, K., Neftel, A., Anklin, M. & Maggi, V. *Atmos. Envir.* (in the press).

39. Jouzel, J. *et al. Nature* (in the press).

40. Moore, J. C., Wolff, E. W., Clausen, H. B. & Hammer, C. U. *J. Geophys. Res.* **97**, 1887-1896 (1992).

41. Steffensen, J. P. *Ann. Glaciol.* **10**, 171-177 (1988).

Acknowledgements. This work is a contribution to the Greenland Ice-core Project (GRIP), co-ordinated and supported by the European Science Foundation. We thank the national funding agencies and organizations in Belgium, Denmark, France, Germany, Iceland, Italy, Switzerland and the United Kingdom together with the XII Directorate of CEC for financial support. We thank the many individuals who have supported this project.

Evidence for General Instability of Past Climate from a 250-kyr Ice-core Record

W. Dansgaard *et al.*

Editor's Note

This paper by Willi Dansgaard of the University of Copenhagen and coworkers added to growing evidence that natural climate change can happen very suddenly—in a matter of decades. This offered a sobering perspective for concerns over the consequences of current global warming. The researchers report an ice-core climate record from Greenland stretching back over the past 250,000 years, which embraces not only the last ice age and the previous warm period (interglacial) but part of the ice age before that. Abrupt climate instabilities are seen during all of these periods, in contrast to the apparently stable climate of the Holocene (the past 12,000 years or so). The reasons for these sudden shifts are still being debated.

Recent results[1,2] from two ice cores drilled in central Greenland have revealed large, abrupt climate changes of at least regional extent during the late stages of the last glaciation, suggesting that climate in the North Atlantic region is able to reorganize itself rapidly, perhaps even within a few decades. Here we present a detailed stable-isotope record for the full length of the Greenland Ice-core Project Summit ice core, extending over the past 250 kyr according to a calculated timescale. We find that climate instability was not confined to the last glaciation, but appears also to have been marked during the last interglacial (as explored more fully in a companion paper[3]) and during the previous Saale–Holstein glacial cycle. This is in contrast with the extreme stability of the Holocene, suggesting that recent climate stability may be the exception rather than the rule. The last interglacial seems to have lasted longer than is implied by the deep-sea SPECMAP record[4], in agreement with other land-based observations[5,6]. We suggest that climate instability in the early part of the last interglacial may have delayed the melting of the Saalean ice sheets in America and Eurasia, perhaps accounting for this discrepancy.

IN 1990–92, the joint European Greenland Ice-core Project (GRIP) drilled an ice core to near the bedrock at the very top of the Greenland ice sheet (72.58° N, 37.64° W; 3,238 m above sea level[7]; annual mean air temperature −32 °C). The 3,028.8-m-long core was recovered by an electromechanical drill, ISTUK[8]. Less than 1 m of core in total was lost in the drilling process. The deepest 6 m is composed of silty ice with pebbles. The core quality is excellent, except for a "brittle zone" in the depth interval between 800 and 1,300 m.

Here we discuss a timescale for the entire core and present a continuous profile of $\delta^{18}O$ (hereafter denoted by δ, the relative deviation of the $^{18}O/^{16}O$ ratio in a sample from that

冰芯记录的过去 25 万年来总体
气候不稳定性的证据

丹斯果等

编者按

本文中，来自哥本哈根大学的维利·丹斯果及其同事们的研究成果是越来越多的证明自然气候可以在短短几十年内迅速改变的证据之一。由此，当今气候变暖的结果令人担忧。这项研究报道了一根格陵兰冰芯可延伸至过去 25 万年的气候记录，其时间跨度不仅包括末次冰期及前一次大暖期（末次间冰期），还包括倒数第二次冰期的部分时段。在这些时期内都可观察到气候的多次突变，与全新世（距今约 1.2 万年以前）的稳定气候形成鲜明对比。这些突变的原因仍存在争议。

在格陵兰岛中部钻取的两根冰芯获得的最新研究结果[1,2]显示，末次冰期晚期存在至少是区域性尺度的大规模、突发性气候变化，这表明北大西洋地区的气候本身就可以快速重组，可能仅需几十年的时间。本文我们将给出格陵兰冰芯计划中萨米特冰芯（在格陵兰顶部萨米特站钻取的冰芯）完整而详细的稳定同位素记录，根据计算得到的时间结果，该冰芯跨越的时间尺度约为 25 万年。我们发现，气候的不稳定性并不限于末次冰期，在末次间冰期（在另一篇文章[3]中有详细阐释）以及之前的萨勒-荷尔斯泰因冰期旋回中也曾出现过。这与全新世异常稳定的特性形成鲜明对比，说明近期气候的稳定性可能是一个例外，而非通例。末次间冰期持续的时间可能比由深海 SPECMAP 记录[4]得出的时间要长，这一点与其他陆地观测结果亦相吻合[5,6]。我们认为，末次间冰期早期气候的不稳定性可能推迟了美洲及欧亚地区萨勒冰川的融化时间，这有可能是上述差异产生的原因所在。

1990~1992 年间，欧洲格陵兰冰芯计划（GRIP）在格陵兰冰盖的最顶层（72.58°N，37.64°W，海平面以上 3,238 m[7]，年平均气温为 -32 ℃）钻取了到达基岩附近的冰芯。该冰芯长 3,028.8 m，是利用 ISTUK 电动钻机获取的[8]。在钻取过程中损失的冰芯总长度不足 1 m。冰芯最下部的 6 m 由含卵石的粉砂质冰层组成。冰芯的品质是非常好的，仅在 800~1,300 m 深度之间有一段"脆冰带"。

本文我们将讨论整根冰芯的时间尺度，并给出其连续的 $\delta^{18}O$（后文将以 δ 表示，

in standard mean ocean water). In polar glacier ice, δ is mainly determined by its temperature of formation[9]. Profiles of several climate-related parameters spanning the last interglacial period (known as the Eemian period, or Eem) are being investigated by GRIP participants[3].

The timescale back to 14.5 kyr BP (thousands of years before present) is derived by counting annual layers downward from the surface[1]. Beyond 14.5 kyr BP a timescale is calculated as

$$t = \int_0^z \mathrm{d}z / \lambda_z$$

t being the age of the ice and λ_z the annual layer thickness at depth z. A steady-state ice flow model[10] is modified by introducing a sliding layer at bedrock[11], and using a δ-dependent accumulation rate (λ_H) derived from all available λ_z data, $\lambda_H = \lambda_{H0} \exp[0.144 (\delta + 34.8)]$ m of ice equivalent per year, λ_{H0} being the present value, 0.23 m yr^{-1} (ref. 1).

The other flow model parameters are as follows: The total thickness of the ice sheet $H = 3{,}003.8$ m of ice equivalent; the thickness of the intermediate shear layer $h = 1{,}200$ m; the ratio between the strain rates at the top of the silty ice and at the surface, $f_b = 0.15$; and the thickness of the silty ice layer, $\mathrm{d}h = 6$ m. The latter value may be too low, but higher values would significantly influence only the calculated ages of the deepest 50 m (ice older than 250 kyr) which will not be discussed here.

The h and f_b values are chosen so as to assign well-established ages to two characteristic features in the δ record: 11.5 kyr for the end of the Younger Dryas event[1,12] and 110 kyr for the marine isotope stage (MIS) 5d[4], which appear at depths of 1,624 m and 2,788 m, respectively, in the δ record. These are points a and b in Fig. 1B. Back to 35 kyr BP the calculated timescale agrees essentially with that presented in ref. 1.

One of the assumptions behind the timescale calculation is that the stratigraphy has remained undisturbed, so that all annual layers are represented in a continuous sequence and thinned according to the depth-dependent vertical strain described by the flow model. This may fail at great depths if there is folding close to a hilly bedrock, and/or random thinning of layers of different rigidity (boudinage effect[13]).

Large-scale folding caused by bedrock obstacles hardly exists in the Summit area, however, because the bedrock is gently sloping ($\leqslant 40$ m per km) in a large area around the drill site[14]. Furthermore, according to radio-echo sounding records (L. Hempel, personal communication) the shape of internal reflection layers suggests that the long-term position of the ice divide was only 5 km west of the present Summit. Consequently, the ice movement at Summit has been essentially vertical in the past, confirming that the ice cannot have travelled long distances over hilly bedrock. Nonetheless, at great depths the boudinage effect may have caused small-scale disturbances. Some layers may have thickened at the expense of others now missing in the core. If so, the layer sequence may not be strictly continuous, but even then the broad outline of the timescale may still be valid.

是指样品中 $^{18}O/^{16}O$ 的比值相对于标准海洋水中 $^{18}O/^{16}O$ 平均值的偏差）记录。在极地冰川冰中，δ 值主要是由其形成时的温度决定的[9]。GRIP 成员已对跨越末次间冰期（称为依米安期或埃姆期）的多个气候参数剖面作了研究[3]。

1.45 万年前至今的年代是通过自表层向下数年层的方法来获得的[1]。比 1.45 万年前更早的冰芯定年的计算如下：

$$t = \int_0^z \mathrm{d}z / \lambda_z$$

其中 t 为冰层年龄，λ_z 表示 z 深度处的年层厚度。通过在基岩上引入一个滑动层[11]，并引用一个依赖于 δ 值的积累率（λ_H），对稳态冰流模型[10]作了修改，λ_H 是从所有可以得到的 λ_z 值中推算出来的：$\lambda_H = \lambda_{H0} \exp[0.144\,(\delta + 34.8)]$ m，单位是每年冰川积累量的冰当量。λ_{H0} 表示当前的值，为每年 0.23 m（参考文献 1）。

其他的冰流模型参数如下：冰盖的总厚度 $H = 3{,}003.8$ m 冰当量，中部剪切层的厚度 $h = 1{,}200$ m，粉砂质冰层顶部和表层冰芯的应变率比值 $f_b = 0.15$，粉砂质冰层的厚度 $dh = 6$ m。最后一个值可能有些过低，不过即使该值再高也只会对最下部 50 m（老于 25 万年的冰层）的定年结果产生显著影响，而本文将不讨论该部分内容。

h 与 f_b 值的确定要满足 δ 记录中年龄已明确确定了的两次特征事件：新仙女木事件的结束时间为 1.15 万年前[1,12]，海洋氧同位素（MIS）5d 阶为 11 万年前[4]。在 δ 记录中它们分别出现于 1,624 m 和 2,788 m 深度，即图 1B 中的 a 点和 b 点。自距今 3.5 万年前以来，所计算出的年龄与参考文献 1 中的结果基本一致。

该时间计算基于一个前提，即假设冰芯年层未受扰动，从而年层自上而下都是按顺序，并且按照冰川流动模型描述的那样，随深度变化的垂向应力减薄。当深度很深时，如果陡峭的基岩附近存在褶皱和（或）不同硬度层出现随机减薄（香肠构造的影响[13]），这种方法将可能失效。

不过，在萨米特站区域很难存在因基岩阻碍而形成的大规模褶皱，因为在冰芯钻取点附近的广大区域上基岩的坡度均比较小（≤40 m·km⁻¹）[14]。而且，根据无线电回波记录（亨普尔，个人交流）的内部反射层的形状显示，分冰岭长期处于现今的萨米特站以西仅 5 km 处的位置。因此，过去萨米特站区域冰川的运动基本是垂向的，由此证明，冰川并未在起伏的基岩上做远距离运动。尽管如此，当深度较大时，香肠构造的影响仍可能形成小规模的扰动。有些年层可能因此而变厚，其代价就是冰芯中有些层位出现缺失。倘使如此，那么这些层序就并非严格连续，不过即便如此，总体时间序列仍然是可信的。

Visible cloudy bands, probably indicative of former surfaces[15], lie almost perpendicular to the core axis down to ~2,900 m depth, corresponding to 160 kyr BP. Then follows a 54-m increment of apparently disturbed stratigraphy (S. Kipfstuhl, personal communication), possibly caused by the boudinage effect. Finally, the regular layer sequence is re-established from 2,954 m (210 kyr BP), but special caution should be applied beyond 160 kyr BP. The American GISP2 deep ice core being drilled 30 km west of Summit[2], may provide verification of the timescale.

A continuous δ record along the upper 3,000 m of the GRIP core is plotted on a linear depth scale in two sections of Fig. 1. The upper half of the record (Fig. 1A, δ scale on top) spans nearly the past 10 kyr, and each δ value represents the snow deposition through a few years near surface, increasing to 20 years at 10 kyr BP. Apart from the δ minimum at 8,210 ± 30 yr BP[1], the record indicates a remarkably stable climate during the past 10 kyr.

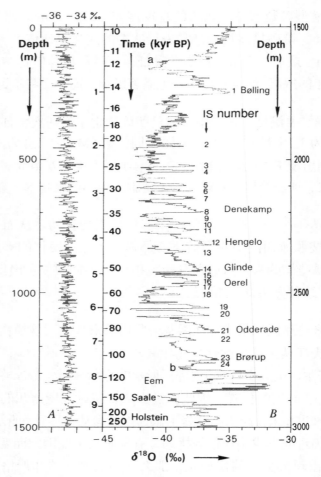

Fig. 1. The continuous GRIP Summit $\delta^{18}O$ record plotted in two sections on a linear depth scale: *A*, from surface to 1,500 m; *B*, from 1,500 to 3,000 m depth. Each point represents 2.2 m of core increment. Glacial

可见的不透光带很有可能是以前的冰层表面[15]，近乎垂直于冰芯轴分布，直至 2,900 m 深处，这里对应的年代为距今 16 万年前。再往下是一段 54 m 长的明显扰动层（基普夫斯图赫尔，个人交流），很可能是由香肠构造效应所致。最终，从 2,954 m 深处开始重新恢复到有规律的层序（距今 21 万年前），不过对于比距今 16 万年前更早的冰芯定年应格外谨慎。美国 GISP2 深层冰芯是在萨米特站以西约 30 km 处钻取的[2]，有可能对定年结果进行检验。

GRIP 冰芯上部 3,000 m 的 δ 值随深度线性变化的连续记录见图 1，分两段列出。记录的上半部分（图 1A，δ 的刻度位于顶部）基本上跨越了最近 1 万年的时间，在表层，每个 δ 值仅代表几年的积雪量，而到距今 1 万年前，所代表的年份增加至 20 年。从该记录上看，除在距今 8,210±30 年前 δ 有一个最小值[1]外，最近 1 万年来的气候非常稳定。

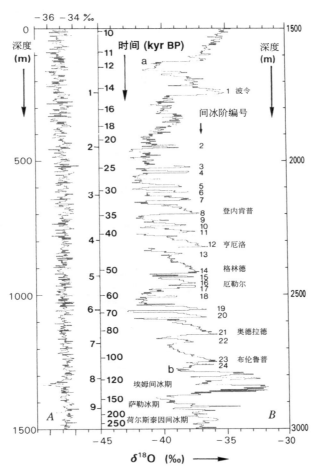

图 1. GRIP 萨米特冰芯中 δ^{18}O 连续记录的值随深度的两段线性变化曲线：A 为表层到 1,500 m 深度段；B 为 1,500~3,000 m 深度段。每个点代表冰芯深度增加 2.2 m。对冰期的间冰阶作了编号，标于图中曲线

interstadials are numbered to the right of the *B* curve. The timescale in the middle is obtained by counting annual layers back to 14.5 kyr BP, and beyond that by ice flow modelling. The glacial interstadials of longest duration are reconciled with European pollen horizons[16].

In the contrast, the rest of the record shown in Fig. 1*B* is dominated by large and abrupt δ shifts. Because of plastic thinning of the layers as they approach the bedrock, these 1,500 m of ice represent a much longer period of time than the 1,500 m above. On the right side of the record is an extension of the numbering of glacial interstadials (IS) introduced previously[1]. Furthermore, a series of European pollen horizons[16] (^{14}C dated back to 60 kyr BP) is reconciled with the longest lasting δ-based interstadials. The ^{14}C datings are all in essential agreement with our timescale once recent corrections to the ^{14}C scale[12] have been considered.

Figure 2 is a composite of five different chronological records. Figure 2*D* shows the upper 2,982 m of the Summit δ record plotted on the linear timescale in 200 yr increments. The vertical line is drawn for comparison with the Holocene mean δ value, −35‰. On the right-hand side of this line is a division of the last glacial cycles in European terminology. The adopted timescale is further supported, first by the numerous common features (particularly during the last glaciation) between the smoothed version and the other four records in Fig. 2 (exemplified by dashed arrows); second, because a maximum entropy spectrum[17] comprising the total Summit record contains significant signals on the two Milankovitch cycles 41 kyr (obliquity) and, considerably weaker, 24/18 kyr (precession).

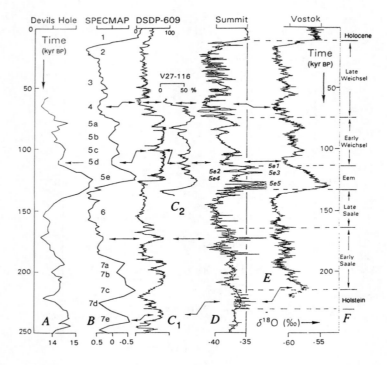

Fig. 2. Four climate records spanning the last glacial cycles and plotted on a common linear timescale. *A*, $\delta^{18}O$ variations in vein calcite from Devils Hole, Nevada[6]. Dating by U/Th. *B*, The SPECMAP standard

B 的右侧。中间的时间尺度可以通过自上而下数年层定年至 1.45 万年前，比 1.45 万年前更早的年代则是通过冰流模型确定的。持续时间最长的冰期间冰阶通过欧洲的孢粉层位进行了校正[16]。

相反，图 1*B* 中所示的其余记录则以较大的突变性的 δ 值变化为主要特征。随着冰层向基岩的接近，由于塑性减薄作用，这 1,500 m 的冰层所代表的时段要远大于上部的 1,500 m。在记录的右侧是之前曾介绍过[1]的冰期间冰阶(IS)的序号。此外，一系列的欧洲孢粉层位[16]([14]C 测年至距今 6 万年前)也与根据 δ 值得出的持续时间最长的间冰阶一致。考虑到新近对 [14]C 定年结果作出的校正[12]后，其结果与我们的时间序列亦基本一致。

图 2 是 5 种不同时间序列记录的对比图。图 2*D* 所示为萨米特冰芯上部 2,982 m 的 δ 值记录，纵坐标为以 200 年为间隔的线性时间尺度。图中画出的垂向线条是为了与全新世 δ 的平均值 −35‰ 相比较。该线的右侧标注了末次冰期旋回各部分的欧洲术语。所采用的时间序列从以下的对比结果中得到了进一步的支持：首先，在图 2 中(以虚箭头指示)平滑线与其他四个记录存在许多共同特征(尤其是在末次冰期中)；其次，组成整个萨米特冰芯记录的最大熵谱[17]分析结果包含了两个米兰科维奇旋回周期，4.1 万年(地轴倾角)周期和相对较弱的 2.4 万 / 1.8 万年(岁差)周期。

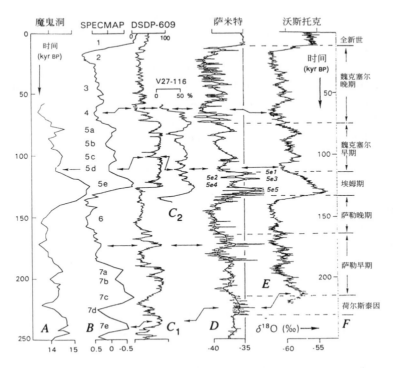

图 2. 跨越末次冰期旋回的四种不同气候记录，图中的时间统一到一致的线性时间尺度。*A*，内华达魔鬼洞[6]方解石脉的 δ^{18}O 变化情况，采用的是 U/Th 测年法。*B*，SPECMAP 标准同位素曲线[4]及传统的

isotope curve[4] with conventional marine isotope stages and sub-stages. Dating by orbital tuning. C, part 1. Grey-scale measurements along 14.3 m of ocean sediment cores DSDP site 609. Part 2. Percent $CaCO_3$ in V27-116 (through stage 5) from locations west-southwest and west of Ireland. Scale in arbitrary units on top[24]. Dating by orbital tuning. D, $\delta^{18}O$ record along the upper 2,982 m of the GRIP Summit ice core. Each point represents a 200-yr mean value. The heavy curve is smoothed by a 5-kyr gaussian low-pass filter. Dating by counting annual layers back to 14.5 kyr BP, and beyond that by ice flow modelling. Along the vertical line, which indicates the Holocene mean δ value, is added an interpretation in European terminology. E, δD record from Vostok, East Antarctica[5], converted into a $\delta^{18}O$ record by the equation $\delta D = 8\delta^{18}O + 10‰$. Dating by ice flow modelling.

The violent δ shifts observed in Greenland cores are less pronounced in the δ record along the Vostok, East Antarctica, ice core[5] (Fig. 2E), probably because the shifts in Greenland are connected to rapid ocean/atmosphere circulation changes in the North Atlantic region[18,19]. Both records, as well as the δ record from Devils Hole[6] (Fig. 2A), and the records in Fig. 2C introduced below, imply MIS 5e (Eem) as an interglacial of considerably longer duration than estimated from sea sediment δ records, such as the SPECMAP record[4] in Fig. 2B. The disagreement may be explained, in part, by the climate instability recorded (Fig. 2D) in the early stages of Eem, which must have slowed the melting of the Saalean ice sheets in America and Eurasia. Further evidence of delayed sea level rise is found in records of the isotopic composition of atmospheric oxygen in the Vostok core[5]. If MIS 5e is defined as the period between the first and last years of higher than Holocene δ, it lasted nearly 20 kyr, from 133 to 114 kyr BP, according to the Summit record.

In Fig. 2D (and in other Summit records[3]), 5e stands out as an interglacial abruptly interrupted several times by periods as cool as 5a and 5c. A similar episode in 5e was previously demonstrated in the Camp Century and Devon Island ice cores[20,21], and given the new timescale, it could well be identical with one of the 5e cool spells indicated in Fig. 2D. The duration of 5e2 and 5e4 was apparently 2 and 6 kyr, and they define a tripartition of 5e. Carbon dioxide analyses along the Vostok ice core also suggest a partition of 5e[22], but Fig. 2D differs remarkably from most pollen and deep sea records, which show the Eem as a generally warm and stable period (see for example, ref. 16 and Fig. 2B).

The apparent disagreement may not be serious. Substantial global climate changes are generally more pronounced at higher latitudes. The cooling in western Europe corresponding to the long-lasting δ minimum 5e4 in Fig. 2D may therefore not have been deep enough to cause any marked change in the vegetation, and thereby in the pollen records. Sea sediment δ records are primarily indicative of the continental ice volume, which does not necessarily vary with temperature during times of no ice in North America and Eurasia. Furthermore, the resolution is limited by bioturbation and coarse sampling. Significant fluctuations of 5e have been recorded, however, in North Atlantic areas of high sedimentation rate ($\geqslant 5$ cm kyr^{-1}), for example in core V28-56 from the Norwegian sea[23], and as colour and $CaCO_3$ concentration changes in central North Atlantic sediment cores[24].

The colour record from Deep Sea Drilling Project site 609 is plotted in Fig. 2C, part 1, on a timescale tuned[25] to orbital variations. This record has a resolution comparable to that

海洋同位素阶与亚阶,轨道参数调谐定年。C_1 为 DSDP 609 孔上 14.3 m 的海洋沉积物岩芯的灰度测定结果。C_2 为在爱尔兰西和西－西南方向上 V27-116 孔(穿过第 5 阶)的 $CaCO_3$ 的百分比。顶部用任意单位标度[24],轨道参数调谐定年。D,GRIP 萨米特冰芯上部 2,982 m 的 $\delta^{18}O$ 记录。每个点代表一个 200 年的均值。粗线经 5,000 年高斯低通滤波平滑。数年层的方法可以定年到 1.45 万年前,而比 1.45 万年前更早的定年则是根据冰流模型计算而来。沿表示全新世平均 δ 值的垂向线条,增加了有关的欧洲术语。E,沃斯托克冰芯的 δD 记录。该冰芯取自东南极洲的沃斯托克站(也称东方站)[5],根据方程 $\delta D = 8\delta^{18}O + 10‰$ 将其转化为 $\delta^{18}O$ 记录。测年结果来自冰川流动模型的模拟。

 格陵兰冰芯中见到的 δ 值的突变在东南极洲的沃斯托克冰芯 δ 记录中表现并不显著[5](图 2E),这很可能是因为格陵兰冰芯中记录的变化只与北大西洋地区海洋／大气环流的快速变化有关[18,19]。上述两记录、魔鬼洞[6]的 δ 记录(图 2A)以及下面将要介绍的图 2C 中的记录均显示,MIS 5e(埃姆期)作为一个间冰期,持续时间远长于根据海洋沉积物 δ 记录所推测的时间,比如图 2B 中的 SPECMAP 记录[4]。其中部分原因可能是埃姆早期的气候不稳定记录(图 2D)导致分布在美洲和欧亚大陆的萨勒冰盖融化的速度减缓。在沃斯托克冰芯的大气氧同位素组成记录中发现了海平面上升被推迟的进一步的证据[5]。倘若将 MIS 5e 间冰阶定义为 δ 值高于全新世的起始和结束年份之间的时段,则根据萨米特冰芯记录,其持续时间接近 2 万年,即从距今 13.3 万年前到 11.4 万年前。

 在图 2D(以及其他萨米特冰芯记录[3])中,5e 间冰阶多次被寒冷如 5a 和 5c 的时段突然打断。在之前的世纪营地和德文岛冰芯中也发现了类似 5e 的事件[20,21],并且按照上述新的时间尺度来看,它与图 2D 所示 5e 的寒冷时段之一相吻合。5e2 和 5e4 的持续时间分别为 2,000 年和 6,000 年,它们将 5e 分为三部分。对沃斯托克冰芯的二氧化碳分析结果同样显示出 5e 的各部分划分[22],但图 2D 与大多数孢粉和深海记录有着明显区别,后者显示的埃姆期总体上是一段温暖而稳定的时期(参见文献 16 和图 2B)。

 它们之间明显的分歧并不严重。全球大幅度的气候变化一般在高纬地区更加显著。图 2D 中的 5e4 段存在持续的 δ 最小值,对应 5e4 段的西欧地区降温还不足以导致植被发生显著变化,因而孢粉记录中也没有显著的变化。海洋沉积物 δ 记录主要指示大陆的冰川体积,并不一定会随着北美洲和欧亚大陆无冰时的温度变化而变化。此外,生物扰动作用以及取样间隔较大等也会影响其分辨率。不过,在北大西洋中沉积速率较高($\geq 5\ cm \cdot kyr^{-1}$)的地区,如取自挪威海的 V28-56 孔岩芯[23]也记录到了 5e 的明显波动,同样在北大西洋中部的沉积物岩芯中,其颜色和 $CaCO_3$ 浓度的变化也有相应记录[24]。

 深海钻探计划(DSDP)609 孔的色度记录见图 $2C_1$,其时间尺度已根据轨道参数作了调整[25]。该记录的分辨率与图 2D 相当。倘若不考虑受碳酸盐颗粒的影响而导

of Fig. 2*D*. Disregarding MIS 2 and 3, where detrital grains of carbonate corrupt the grey scale, nearly all of the δ shifts can be recognized in the colour record, including some of the δ shifts in 5e. The colour scale reaches "saturation" (note that 5a, and 5c and the warm phases of 5e appear equally dark), which may be why only one of the cool stages in 5e looks significantly different in colour. Several fluctuations in 5e are registered in cores recovered farther north[24]; for example see the inset of per cent $CaCO_3$ (indicative of biological activity) through MIS 5 from V27-116 in Fig. 2*C*, part 2.

The glacial cycles spanned by the Summit ice core appear different in Fig. 2*D*. For example, MIS 6 (late Saale) was apparently less cold and variable than late Weichsel, and a few spells of extreme warmth occurred in early Saale. Furthermore, the Holstein interglacial[26] (possibly MIS 7e) seems more stable than Eem, but less stable than Holocene.

In conclusion high resolution records suggest that, apart from the Holocene, instability has dominated the North Atlantic climate over the last 230,000 years. This applies to the Weichsel glaciation (MIS 2 to 5d), to the Eem interglacial (MIS 5e) whose progress was very different from the Holocene, the Saale glaciation (MIS 6 to 7d), and Holstein, the preceding interglacial (MIS 7e), according to the interpretation given in Fig. 2*D*. This emphasizes the question of whether the Holocene will remain stable in spite of the growing atmospheric pollution.

(**364**, 218-220; 1993)

W. Dansgaard[*], S. J. Johnsen[*†], H. B. Clausen[*], D. Dahl-Jensen[*] N. S. Gundestrup[*], C. U. Hammer[*], C. S. Hvidberg[*], J. P. Steffensen[*], A. E. Sveinbjörnsdottir[†], J. Jouzel[‡] & G. Bond[§]

[*] The Niels Bohr Institute, Department of Geophysics, University of Copenhagen, Haraldsgade 6, DK-2200 Copenhagen N, Denmark

[†] Science Institute, Department of Geophysics, University of Iceland, Dunhaga 3, IS-107, Reykjavik, Iceland

[‡] Laboratoire de Modélisation du Climat et de l'Environment, CEA/DSM, CE Saclay 91191, and Laboratoire de Glaciologie et Géophysique de l'Environment, BP 96, 38402 St Martin d'Héres Cedex, France

[§] Lamont-Doherty Geological Observatory, Columbia University, Palisades, New York 10964, USA

Received 4 April; accepted 3 June 1993.

References:

1. Johnsen, S. J. *et al. Nature* **359**, 311-313 (1992).

2. Taylor, K. C. *et al. Nature* **361**, 432-436 (1993).

3. GRIP Members *Nature* **364**, 203-207 (1993).

4. Martinson, D. G. *et al. Quat. Res.* **27**, 1-29 (1987).

5. Jouzel, J. *et al. Nature* (in the press).

6. Winograd, I. J. *et al. Science* **258**, 255-260 (1992).

7. Ekholm, S. & Keller, K. *Nat. Survey and Cadastre, Geodetic Div., Tech. Rep.* No. 6 (Copenhagen, Denmark, 1993).

8. Gundestrup, N. S. & Johnsen, S. J. in *Greenland Ice Cores: Geophysics, Geochemistry and Environment* (eds Langway, C. C. Jr, Oeschger, H. & Dansgaard, W.) 19-22 (Am. Geophys. Un. Geophys. Monogr. **33**, (Washington DC, 1985).

9. Johnsen, S. J., Dansgaard, W. & White, J. W. C. *Tellus* **B41**, 452-468, (1992).

10. Dansgaard, W. & Johnsen, S. J. *J. Glaciol.* **8**, 215-223 (1969).

11. Johnsen. S. J. & Dansgaard, W. in *The Last Deglaciation: Absolute and Radiocarbon Chronologies* (eds Bard, E. & Broecker, W. S.) (NATO ASI Series 2, 1992).

致灰度记录遭破坏的 MIS 2 和 MIS 3，基本上所有的冰芯 δ 值波动都可以在该色度记录中找到，其中包括 5e 中 δ 值的一些变化。该色度记录达到了"饱和"状态（注意 5a 和 5c 以及 5e 中较温暖的阶段上其颜色深度相当），这可能正是 5e 中仅有一个冷阶的颜色明显不同的原因所在。在更北部的岩芯中记录到了 5e 内的多次波动[24]，见图 $2C_2$ 中 V27-116 中 MIS 5 的 $CaCO_3$ 百分比（表征生物活动）插图。

在图 2D 中，萨米特冰芯覆盖的冰期旋回存在差异。例如，MIS 6（萨勒晚期）明显不如魏克塞尔晚期冷，且波动较小，同时，在萨勒早期还曾出现几个极端温暖的时段。此外，荷尔斯泰因间冰期[26]（可能为 MIS 7e）比埃姆间冰期更稳定，但不如全新世稳定。

总之，高分辨率记录显示，除全新世以外，在近 23 万年中，北大西洋气候一直处于不稳定状态。这些阶段包括图 2D 所示的魏克塞尔冰期（MIS 2 至 MIS 5d）、与现代全新世气候变迁完全不同的埃姆间冰期（MIS 5e）、萨勒冰期（MIS 6 至 MIS 7d）以及在萨勒之前的荷尔斯泰因间冰期（MIS 7e）。这使得"随着大气污染的不断加重，全新世气候能否继续保持稳定"的问题显得更加突出。

（齐红艳 翻译；田立德 审稿）

12. Bard, E. *et al. Radiocarbon* (in the press).

13. Staffelbach, T., Stauffer, B, & Oeschger, H. *Ann. Glaciol.* 10. 167-170 (1988).

14. Hodge, S. M. *et al. J. Glaciol.* 36, 17-27 (1990).

15. Hammer, C. U. *et al. J. Glaciol.* 20, 3-26 (1978).

16. Behre, K.-E. & van der Plicht, J. *Veg. Hist. Archaeobot.* 1, 111-117 (1992).

17. Ulrych, T. J. & Bishop, T. N. *Rev. Geophys. Space Phys.* 13, 183-200 (1975).

18. Oeschger, H. *et al.* in *Climate Processes and Climate Sensitivity* (ed. Hansen, F.) 299-306 (Am. Geophys. Un. Geophys. Monogr. 29, Washington DC, 1984).

19. Broeker, W. S., Bond G., Klas, M., Bonani, G. & Wolfli, W. *Palaeoceanography* 5, 469-477 (1990).

20. Dansgaard, W., Clausen, H. B., Johnsen, S. J. & Langway, C. C. *Quat. Res.* 2, 396-398 (1972).

21. Paterson, W. S. B. *et al. Nature* 266, 508-511(1977).

22. Raynaud, D. *et al. Science* 259, 926-934 (1993).

23. Kellogg, T. B. *Marine Micropaleontol.* 2, 235-249 (1977).

24. Bond, G., Broecker, W., Lotti, R. S. & McManus, J. in *Start of a Glacial* (eds Kukla, G. J. & Went, E.) 185-205 (NATO ASI Series I 3, Springer, Heidelberg, 1992).

25. Ruddiman, W. F., Raymo, M. E., Martinson, D. G., Clement, B. M. & Backman, J. *Palaeoceanogr.* 4, 353-412 (1989).

26. Linke, G., Katzenberg, O. & Grün, R. *Quat. Sci. Rev.* 4, 319-331 (1985).

Acknowledgements: We thank C. C. Langway and H. Tauber for reading the manuscript and making corrections and additions. This work is a contribution of the international Greenland Ice-core Project (GRIP) organized by the European Science Foundation. We thank the GRIP participants and supporters for their cooperative effort. We also thank the funding agencies in Belgium, Denmark, France, Germany, Iceland, Italy, Switzerland and the United Kingdom, as well as the XII Directorate of CEC, the University of Iceland Research fund, the Carlsberg Foundation, and the Commission for Scientific Research in Greenland, for financial support.

Extending the Vostok Ice-core Record of Palaeoclimate to the Penultimate Glacial Period

J. Jouzel *et al.*

Editor's Note

In this paper, scientists working on ice-core climate records from Antarctica extend them significantly further, analysing an ice core drilled 2.5 km into the 3.7-km-thick ice sheet at the Russian Vostok station. This allows a record of temperature and atmospheric greenhouse-gas (methane and carbon dioxide) concentrations to be obtained back into the penultimate ice age, which ended around 150,000 years ago. As a result, understanding the links between these factors was no longer dependent on data from a single ice age. Cause and effect between temperature and greenhouse-gas levels still cannot be unambiguously assigned, but the lag in CO_2 concentrations relative to temperature seen in the last ice age does not show up in the previous one.

The ice-core record of local temperature, dust accumulation and air composition at Vostok station, Antarctica, now extends back to the penultimate glacial period (~140–200 kyr ago) and the end of the preceding interglacial. This yields a new glaciological timescale for the whole record, which is consistent with ocean records. Temperatures at Vostok appear to have been more uniformly cold in the penultimate glacial period than in the most recent one. Concentrations of CO_2 and CH_4 correlate well with temperature throughout the record.

IN 1985 Lorius *et al.*[1] presented the first ice-core climate record spanning a full glacial–interglacial cycle. The record, which went back to the end of the penultimate glacial period about 150,000 years ago (150 kyr before present, BP) was based on ice drilled at Vostok, the Russian station in central East Antarctica (78° 28′ S and 106° 48′ E, mean annual temperature −55 °C, elevation 3,490 m). The Vostok records show that East Antarctica was colder and drier during glacial periods than during the Holocene[1-4], demonstrate that the large-scale atmospheric circulation was more vigorous during glacial times[5,6], support evidence from deep-sea sediment studies for orbital forcing of Pleistocene climate[2,7] and reveal direct correlations of carbon dioxide and methane concentrations with temperature. The last point suggests that variations in greenhouse gas concentrations have contributed to glacial–interglacial changes in climate[8-11]. Most of this work was based on the study of ice from the surface to 2,083 m depth in the 3Γ core.

Here we extend the record of Vostok geochemistry to the bottom of a new core, 4Γ, drilled

把沃斯托克冰芯的古气候记录延伸
至倒数第二次冰期

编者按

本文中，科学家对南极的冰芯气候记录作了大幅度的延伸，分析了从俄罗斯沃斯托克站（也称东方站）3.7 km 厚的冰盖中钻取的 2.5 km 的冰芯，获取了一个约在 15 万年前结束的倒数第二次冰期中温度和大气中温室气体浓度（甲烷和二氧化碳浓度）的记录，因此揭示出它们之间的联系不再依赖于唯一的一个冰期记录。温度和温室气体浓度之间的因果关系尚不明确，但在末次冰期中 CO_2 的浓度变化相对滞后于所观测到的温度变化这一现象在倒数第二次冰期中并未出现。

南极沃斯托克站冰芯中温度、粉尘浓度以及空气成分的记录如今已可延伸到倒数第二次冰期（约 14 万至 20 万年前）和之前的间冰期末期。由此提供了一个新的与海洋记录一致的冰川时间序列。倒数第二次冰期时，沃斯托克地区的温度似乎普遍低于末次冰期时的温度。整个记录中 CO_2 和 CH_4 的浓度均与温度呈现出很好的相关性。

1985 年，洛里于斯等[1]介绍了首个覆盖完整的冰期–间冰期旋回的冰芯气候记录。该记录是根据在东南极中部的俄罗斯沃斯托克站（78°28′ S，106°48′ E，年平均温度 −55 ℃，海拔 3,490 m，也称东方站）钻取的冰芯得到的，可一直追溯至约 15 万年前的倒数第二次冰期的末期。该沃斯托克冰芯记录显示，冰期时的东南极地区要比全新世时的更加寒冷和干燥[1-4]，这证明冰期时大尺度的大气环流更为强烈[5,6]，进一步支持了深海沉积物记录中地球轨道参数驱动更新世气候变化的证据[2,7]，揭示出二氧化碳和甲烷浓度与温度之间的直接关系。最后一项说明，温室气体浓度的变化对气候的冰期–间冰期变化有一定的贡献[8-11]。该项工作中很大一部分是根据 3Γ 冰芯从表面到深 2,083 m 冰层的研究得到的。

本文我们试图将沃斯托克冰芯的地球化学记录延伸至 4Γ 这一新冰芯的底部，

down to 2,546 m. We include details of deuterium and dust concentrations measured in the ice and three parameters measured in the air bubbles entrapped in the ice: CO_2, CH_4 and the oxygen isotope ratio (given as $\delta^{18}O$) of O_2. Each parameter contains climate-related information. The new results (Table 1) are plotted against depth in Fig. 1, along with data from the bottom part of core 3Γ. The shallowest depth plotted, 1,500 m, corresponds to the end of the last interglacial period (LIG) and is dated at about 110 kyr BP. In addition, we will use information on changes in accumulation rate at Vostok contained in a new [10]Be profile also measured down to 2,546 m. Details on experimental procedures may be found elsewhere[2,6,8,9,12,13]. The depth profiles of CO_2, CH_4 and $\delta^{18}O$ in O_2 will undoubtedly evolve as additional samples are analysed.

Table 1. Carbon dioxide, methane and oxygen

CO_2 (p.p.m.v.)			CH_4 (p.p.b.v.)			$\delta^{18}O$ (‰)		
Depth (m)	Age (kyr)	Mean	Depth (m)	Age (kyr)	Mean	Depth (m)	Age (kyr)	Mean
2078	150.1	197.7	2089	151.5	356	2089	151.6	0.60
2116	155.4	192.6	2102	153.6	400	2101	153.4	0.74
2157	160.3	189.7	2127	156.7	395	2109	154.5	0.82
2164	161.4	186.2	2153	159.8	382	2129	157.0	0.98
2203	166.9	205.1	2177	163.5	403	2139	158.1	0.89
2225	169.6	192.3	2196	166.1	376	2158	160.5	0.88
2247	172.9	184.5	2225	169.6	405	2167	161.9	0.80
2280	177.8	198.6	2273	176.9	478	2188	165.0	0.87
2302	180.9	198.5	2302	180.9	456	2198	166.3	0.79
2325	184.1	191.0	2325	184.1	468	2220	169.0	0.66
2333	185.3	190.8	2348	187.5	503	2233	170.7	0.38
2348	187.5	208.5	2373	191.1	464	2251	173.6	0.09
2363	189.6	214.0	2425	199.8	440	2278	177.6	0.11
2372	190.9	218.5	2475	207.5	460	2290	179.2	−0.13
2386	193.1	200.5	2501	211.5	558	2298	180.4	−0.10
2399	195.2	204.2	2525	214.9	612	2309	181.9	0.04
2414	197.9	211.5	2543	217.5	482	2329	184.7	−0.01
2425	199.8	232.2				2338	186.1	0.24
2437	201.6	232.3				2350	187.9	0.47
2451	203.7	218.8				2369	190.5	0.88
2475	207.5	220.9				2388	193.4	0.87
2499	211.2	243.5				2402	195.7	0.72
2525	214.9	251.9				2413	197.6	0.53
2533	216.0	240.0				2423	199.4	0.47
2543	217.5	248.6				2433	201.0	0.38

该冰芯的钻取深度为 2,546 m。我们的研究内容包括在冰芯中测定的氘和粉尘浓度的详细情况以及冰芯包裹的气泡中测到的三个参数：CO_2、CH_4 和 O_2 的氧同位素比值（表示为 $\delta^{18}O$）。每个参数都包含着与气候相关的信息。上述新测定结果（表 1）随深度的变化情况见图 1，同时我们还给出了 3Γ 冰芯底部的相关数据。图中所画的最浅深度 1,500 m 对应着末次间冰期（LIG）的末期，定年结果为距今 11 万年左右。此外，我们还将用到 ^{10}Be 剖面中获得的沃斯托克冰芯积累速率的变化信息，其中 ^{10}Be 剖面的深度同样向下测至 2,546 m 处。实验过程的详细情况见其他文章[2,6,8,9,12,13]。毫无疑问，随着更多样品的分析，CO_2、CH_4 和 O_2 中 $\delta^{18}O$ 的深度剖面关系还将进一步完善。

表 1. 二氧化碳、甲烷和氧气

CO₂ (ppmv)			CH₄ (ppbv)			δ¹⁸O (‰)		
深度（m）	年龄（kyr）	平均	深度（m）	年龄（kyr）	平均	深度（m）	年龄（kyr）	平均
2078	150.1	197.7	2089	151.5	356	2089	151.6	0.60
2116	155.4	192.6	2102	153.6	400	2101	153.4	0.74
2157	160.3	189.7	2127	156.7	395	2109	154.5	0.82
2164	161.4	186.2	2153	159.8	382	2129	157.0	0.98
2203	166.9	205.1	2177	163.5	403	2139	158.1	0.89
2225	169.6	192.3	2196	166.1	376	2158	160.5	0.88
2247	172.9	184.5	2225	169.6	405	2167	161.9	0.80
2280	177.8	198.6	2273	176.9	478	2188	165.0	0.87
2302	180.9	198.5	2302	180.9	456	2198	166.3	0.79
2325	184.1	191.0	2325	184.1	468	2220	169.0	0.66
2333	185.3	190.8	2348	187.5	503	2233	170.7	0.38
2348	187.5	208.5	2373	191.1	464	2251	173.6	0.09
2363	189.6	214.0	2425	199.7	440	2278	177.6	0.11
2372	190.9	218.5	2475	207.5	460	2290	179.2	−0.13
2386	193.1	200.5	2501	211.5	558	2298	180.4	−0.10
2399	195.2	204.2	2525	214.9	612	2309	181.9	0.04
2414	197.9	211.5	2543	217.5	482	2329	184.7	−0.01
2425	199.8	232.2				2338	186.1	0.24
2437	201.6	232.3				2350	187.9	0.47
2451	203.7	218.8				2369	190.5	0.88
2475	207.5	220.9				2388	193.4	0.87
2499	211.2	243.5				2402	195.7	0.72
2525	214.9	251.9				2413	197.6	0.53
2533	216.0	240.0				2423	199.4	0.47
2543	217.5	248.6				2433	201.0	0.38

Continued

CO₂ (p.p.m.v.)			CH₄ (p.p.b.v.)			δ¹⁸O (‰)		
Depth (m)	Age (kyr)	Mean	Depth (m)	Age (kyr)	Mean	Depth (m)	Age (kyr)	Mean
						2441	202.2	0.12
						2452	203.9	−0.11
						2462	205.5	−0.03
						2469	206.6	−0.11
						2489	209.7	−0.14
						2500	211.3	−0.06
						2510	212.7	0.04
						2518	213.8	0.20
						2528	215.3	0.39
						2544	217.6	0.66

The deuterium and dust data are available from the authors on request.

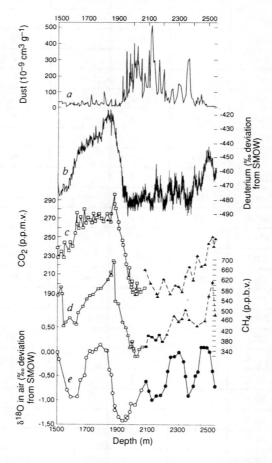

Fig. 1. Depth profiles *a*, Dust concentration. Data are from core 3Γ down to 2,200 m (6) and from core 4Γ

续表

CO₂ (ppmv)			CH₄ (ppbv)			δ¹⁸O (‰)		
深度 (m)	年龄 (kyr)	平均	深度 (m)	年龄 (kyr)	平均	深度 (m)	年龄 (kyr)	平均
						2441	202.2	0.12
						2452	203.9	−0.11
						2462	205.5	−0.03
						2469	206.6	−0.11
						2489	209.7	−0.14
						2500	211.3	−0.06
						2510	212.7	0.04
						2518	213.8	0.20
						2528	215.3	0.39
						2544	217.6	0.66

氘和粉尘的数据可向作者索取。

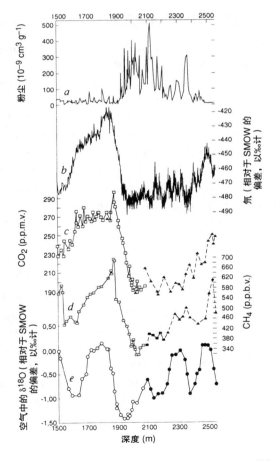

图 1. 深度剖面图。*a*，粉尘浓度。2,200 m 以上的数据来自 3Γ 冰芯，以下的部分来自 4Γ（每隔 8 m 进

below (discontinuous measurements every ~8 m). *b*, Deuterium content (δD in ‰ deviation from SMOW). In core 4Γ, δD was measured continuously below 1,920 m on 1-m ice increments down to 2,200 m (~150 yr), at higher resolution (0.5 m, ~70 yr) down to 2,414 m, and on 1-m increments from this depth down to 2,546 m. Data from 3Γ are reported for the 1,800–2,083-m depth interval. The agreement between 3Γ and 4Γ profiles is excellent over their common part. The comparison shows that there is no sizeable age difference between similar depth horizons in the cores despite small differences in the inclination of the two holes. *c*, *d*, *e*, Concentrations of CO_2, CH_4 and $\delta^{18}O$ of O_2 within air bubbles. Individual measurements are indicated by symbols: open symbols correspond to published data, and filled symbols to new data; for CH_4, squares and triangles correspond to different sets of measurements. Filled symbols are joined by a dotted line because the bottom part of the profile will undoubtedly evolve as additional samples are analysed.

We first describe a new timescale for the entire Vostok core. After discussing the reconstructed Vostok temperature record, we test our chronology by comparing various Vostok climate records with climate records from deep-sea sediments and, where relevant, curve of insolation. We then discuss the climate information contained in our new data set which covers the entire penultimate glacial period and extends through a part of the next to last interglacial down to $\simeq 220$ kyr BP.

Extending the Glaciological Dating Approach

To interpret the Vostok data, we need a chronology for the ice, expressed as a curve of age against depth. We derive this chronology from the following four assumptions. First, the accumulation rate at Vostok has varied in the past as the derivative of the water vapour saturation pressure with respect to temperature at the level where the precipitation forms; that is, above the inversion layer[1,14]. Second, the accumulation (*A*) upstream of Vostok, where ice found at depth originates, increases with distance upstream according to $A(x)/A(x=0) = 1.00+0.65(x/X)$, where *x* is distance upstream of Vostok and *X* is distance of site Dome B upstream of Vostok (320 km). This equation invokes the observation that the Holocene as reflected by the δD or $\delta^{18}O$ records starts at a depth of ~300 m at Vostok and ~500 m at Dome B[15]. Third, ice at a depth of 1,534 m has an age of 110 kyr BP[16,17]. Finally, the strain-induced thinning of annual layers with depth is accurately described by the two-dimensional glaciological model of Ritz[18].

With these assumptions, we calculate the accumulation rate at Vostok today to be 1.98 g cm^{-2} yr^{-1}, 13% lower than the value of 2.3 g cm^{-2} yr^{-1} (ref. 1) based on estimates over the past 10 years, but in good agreement with the value of 2.00 ± 0.4 g cm^{-2} yr^{-1} estimated over the past 170 years using the Tambora eruption as a marker[19]. Back to 110 kyr BP, the biggest discrepancy with the chronology of Lorius *et al.*[1] is 3.5 kyr (Fig. 2). The age of the bottom of the core is 220 kyr BP. We refer to our age-depth curve as the "extended glaciological timescale" (EGT). The uncertainty in the age of the bottom of the 4Γ core (2,546 m), largely dominated by the uncertainty in the current accumulation rate[18], is estimated to be ± 20 kyr.

行不连续测定）。b，氘含量（δD 以相对于 SMOW（标准平均海水）的千分偏差计）。在 4Γ 冰芯中 1,920~2,200 m 之间（约 150 年）δD 的值是以 1 m 间隔连续测定的。从 2,200~2,414 m 取样的分辨率更高（间隔 0.5 m，约 70 年），从 2,414 m 往下至 2,546 m 采样间隔为 1 m。图中还给出了 3Γ 芯 1,800~2,083 m 之间的数据。在重叠部分中 3Γ 和 4Γ 剖面的一致性非常好。比较结果显示，尽管两冰芯的倾斜度有微小差异，在相同深度上它们之间几乎不存在明显的年代差异。c、d、e 分别为空气气泡中 CO_2、CH_4 的浓度以及 O_2 的 δ18O 值。不同的测量结果以不同的符号表示：空心符号对应已发表数据，实心符号表示新数据；在 CH_4 浓度曲线上，正方形和三角形代表不同的测量结果。实心符号以虚线相连是因为随着对额外样品的分析，毫无疑问将勾勒出剖面的底部的情况。

首先我们对整个沃斯托克冰芯的新的时间序列进行描述。讨论了沃斯托克冰芯温度记录的重建后，我们通过将不同的沃斯托克气候记录与深海沉积物气候记录及太阳辐射曲线相比较来检验我们的定年结果。随后再对我们得到的新数据库中所包含的气候信息加以讨论，该新的冰芯数据库包含整个倒数第二次冰期并向前延伸到 22 万年前的倒数第二次间冰期的部分记录。

冰川测年方法的延伸

为了解释沃斯托克冰芯数据，我们需要对冰芯建立一条时间序列，以年龄随深度的变化曲线来表示。我们的定年结果基于以下四个假定。首先，过去沃斯托克站积累速率的变化是降水形成高度处（即逆温层之上）饱和蒸汽压对温度的导数[1,14]。其次，沃斯托克站上游（即指向冰起源方向）的积累速率（A）随上游距离的变化遵循 $A(x)/A(x=0) = 1.00 + 0.65 (x/X)$，其中 x 为上游到沃斯托克站的距离，X 为上游 Dome B 站到沃斯托克的距离（320 km）。该方程隐含着一个已知的观测结果，即 δD 和 δ18O 记录反映出的全新世起始的深度在沃斯托克站为 300 m 左右，而在 Dome B 站则为 500 m[15]。第三，深度 1,534 m 处的冰层年龄为距今 11 万年[16,17]。第四，里茨的二维冰川模型[18]准确地描述了因压力导致的年层随深度的减薄作用。

利用上述假设，我们计算出现今沃斯托克站的积累速率为 1.98 g·cm^{-2}·yr^{-1}，该值比近 10 年来的估算值 2.3 g·cm^{-2}·yr^{-1}（参考文献 1）低了 13%，但与利用坦博拉火山喷发作为标志层得出的过去 170 年的平均积累速率为 2.00 ± 0.4 g·cm^{-2}·yr^{-1}[19]的结论是一致的。一直回溯到距今 11 万年前时，最大的差异是与洛里于斯等[1]给出的定年结果相差 3,500 年（图 2）。冰芯底部的年龄为距今 22 万年。我们将我们的年龄–深度曲线称为"延伸冰川时间序列"（EGT）。在 4Γ 冰芯底部（2,546 m），其年龄的不确定性主要是当前积累速率[18]的不确定性导致的，其变化范围为 ±2 万年。

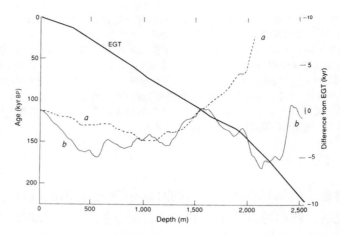

Fig. 2. The depth-age relationship for the EGT, together with differences between this and (*a*) the original timescale of Lorius *et al.*,[1] and (*b*) the "[10]Be" timescale derived assuming a constant [10]Be flux and assigning the 110-kyr BP level at 1,534 m. Differences (right scale) are negative when the EGT gives older ages.

Raisbeck *et al.*,[13] obtained [10]Be concentrations in Vostok and have subsequently analysed the 3Γ and 4Γ cores in higher resolution (Raisbeck *et al.*, manuscript in preparation). We have used these data to calculate a curve of accumulation rate against depth for Vostok, assuming that the [10]Be deposition rate is constant and the same as the average value observed over the top 1,534 m (as above, we assume an age of 110 kyr BP for this depth). Complications that might introduce errors in such an estimate of accumulation are discussed in refs 20 and 21. Combining this accumulation rate with the flow model used above, we can calculate a [10]Be chronology which differs by no more than ~5 kyr from the EGT (Fig. 2). Although we believe this concordance tends to support the overall correctness of the EGT, it does not preclude significant differences in detail, particularly over periods when there were important climatic changes. For example, this [10]Be chronology gives a duration for the Holocene ~30% shorter than that given by the EGT.

The Isotope Temperature Record

Precipitation is isotopically enriched with respect to atmospheric water vapour, and the vapour remaining in a given air mass is depleted at each condensation step both in δD and $\delta^{18}O$. Simple models[22,23] predict that δ should vary linearly with temperature, T, in mid- and high latitudes. This predicted dependence is well documented from observations of present-day Antarctic precipitation[24,25]. We use the modern δ-T relationship to translate the δ change observed going back in time, at one given location, into a curve of temperature against age. This approach is supported by results from the general climate model studies[26,27] and independent glaciological estimates of glacial–interglacial temperature changes[28].

Temperature reconstructed from the isotopic profile is plotted against EGT age in Fig. 3 (curve 3*b*). We calculate the change from the present temperature using the equation $\Delta T_a = (1\ °C$

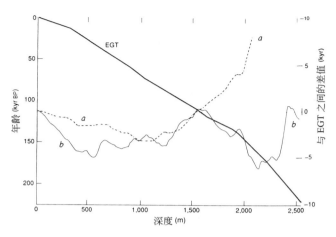

图 2. EGT 定年深度与年龄的关系，以及它分别与 (a) 和 (b) 的差异随深度的变化。(a) 洛里于斯等[1]原来标定的定年结果，(b) 假定 [10]Be 通量为常数并指定 1,534 m 深度上的年龄为距今 11 万年前时得到的 "[10]Be" 定年结果。当 EGT 给出的年龄偏老时，它们之间的差（右侧标度）表示为负。

　　雷兹贝克等[13]测得了沃斯托克冰芯的 [10]Be 浓度，并对 3Γ 和 4Γ 冰芯进行了高分辨率分析（雷兹贝克等，稿件准备中）。我们利用这些数据计算出了沃斯托克冰芯中积累速率随深度的变化曲线，前提是假定 [10]Be 的沉积速率为常数，并等于冰芯上部 1,534 m 的平均值（如前所述，我们假设该深度上的年龄为距今 11 万年）。参考文献 20 和 21 已对该积累速率研究方法中可能引起误差的地方作了讨论。将该积累速率与之前采用的流动模型相结合，我们就可计算出 [10]Be 的定年结果，该结果与 EGT 法得到的结果相差不到 5,000 年（图 2）。虽然我们相信这种一致性可能有利于证明整个 EGT 结果的正确性，但并不排除细节上会存在明显差异，特别是当有重要气候变化发生时。例如，该 [10]Be 法定年结果得到的全新世的持续时间就要比 EGT 法的定年结果短 30%。

同位素温度记录

　　相对于大气中的水汽来说，大气降水中的同位素更加富集，因而在每个凝结步骤中，给定气团中剩余水汽的 δD 和 $\delta^{18}O$ 都会越来越贫化。简单的模型[22,23]预测认为，在中高纬度地区，δ 值应当随温度 T 呈线性变化。今天对南极降水的观测结果[24,25]也很好地证明了上述预测关系。我们利用现今的 $\delta-T$ 关系将之前观测到的某一地点的 δ 变化转换为温度相对于年龄的变化曲线。该方法得到了一般气候模式研究结果[26,27]及独立的冰期–间冰期温度变化研究[28]的支持。

　　根据同位素曲线重建的温度结果相对于 EGT 年龄的变化见图 3（曲线 3b）。我们利用方程 $\Delta T_a = (1\,℃ / 9‰) \times (\delta D_{ice} - 8\delta^{18}O_{sw})$ 计算出了相对于现今温度的变化。式

per 9‰) × ($\delta D_{ice} - 8\delta^{18}O_{sw}$). T_a is the temperature immediately above the inversion layer where Antarctic precipitation forms[14]. The first term on the right is the inverse of the dependence of δD on temperature observed for this sector of East Antarctica[24], and the $8\delta^{18}O_{sw}$ term corrects for the variation of δD with ice volume[29]. The variation of $\delta^{18}O_{sw}$ as a function of Vostok age is taken from Sowers *et al.*[16].

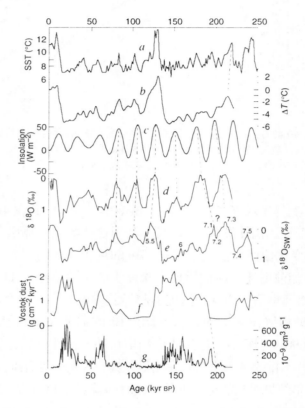

Fig. 3. Variations with time. *a*, Summer sea surface temperature (SST) at Indian Ocean site RC11-120 (16° 37′ N, 59° 52′ E). *b*, Atmospheric temperature change at Vostok (above the inversion) as derived from the deuterium profile. We used published deuterium data down to 1,920 m (ref. 2) and extended this record down to 2,083 m by averaging 3Γ and 4Γ data and to 2,546 m using 4Γ data alone; we then smoothed the entire record. *c*, Summer insolation at 20° N (ref. 49). *d*, $\delta^{18}O$ of O_2 measured in the air bubbles on the EGT. *e*, Change in the isotopic composition of sea water derived from the V19-30 $\delta^{18}O$ foraminifera record and extended back to 250 kyr BP[16]; the record is normalized so that the average Holocene value is 0‰. *f*, Mass accumulation rate (MAR) in the Indian Ocean site RC27-61 (adapted from ref. 32). *g*, The dust concentration in the Vostok ice. The Vostok records are reported using the EGT and the deep-sea records using the SPECMAP[31] timescale. Horizons in the Vostok and deep-sea cores which are believed to be correlative are joined by dotted lines (see text).

The new record shows a long cold period from ~140 to 200 kyr BP. During this cold period, the amplitude of temperature variation is smaller than during the last ice age. In central Antarctica this entire period was nearly as cold as the Last Glacial Maximum (LGM) (~6 °C colder than the Holocene). Temperature is warmer before ~200 kyr BP, with a well marked peak around 215 kyr BP.

中 T_a 为形成南极降水的逆温层上部的温度[14]。等号右边的第一项为东南极研究区域 δD 对温度依赖性的倒数[24]，而表达式 $8\delta^{18}O_{sw}$ 则是以冰体积对 δD 的变化进行校正[29]。索尔斯等[16]研究发现 $\delta^{18}O_{sw}$ 的变化是沃斯托克冰芯年龄的函数。

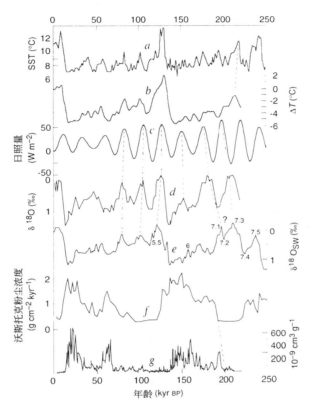

图 3. 各参量指标随时间的变化。a，印度洋 RC11-120 孔（16°37′ N，59°52′ E）的夏季表层海水温度（SST）。b，根据沃斯托克冰芯氘剖面数据得到的大气温度（在逆温层之上）的变化。在 1,920 m 以上我们采用的是已发表的氘数据（参考文献 2），并利用 3Γ 和 4Γ 数据的平均值将该记录延伸到了 2,083 m，再仅采用了 4Γ 芯的数据向下延伸至 2,546 m，最后我们对整个记录作了平滑处理。c，20° N 处的夏季太阳辐射（参考文献 49）。d，EGT 定年下测得的空气气泡中 O_2 的 $\delta^{18}O$ 值。e，根据 V19-30 孔浮游有孔虫的 $\delta^{18}O$ 值记录得到的海水同位素组成的变化情况，并将该记录延伸到了距今 25 万年前[16]，我们对该记录作了归一化处理以使全新世中的平均值为 0‰。f，印度洋 RC27-61 孔的物质积累速率（MAR）（改自参考文献 32）。g，沃斯托克冰芯中的粉尘浓度。所介绍的沃斯托克冰芯记录采用 EGT 定年，而深海记录采用的则是 SPECMAP[31] 时间序列。沃斯托克冰芯和深海记录中相关的层位以虚线相连（见正文）。

新记录显示，从距今 14 万前到 20 万年前是一段很长的冷期。在该冷期中，温度的变化幅度要小于末次冰期。在南极中部地区该时期的温度相当于末次冰盛期（LGM）时的温度（约比全新世低 6 ℃）。从距今 20 万年前再向前，温度变温暖一些，并在距今 21.5 万年左右时达到峰值。

Correlating Vostok and Oceanic Records

We now extend to the bottom of the core the previous efforts to correlate the Vostok and the SPECMAP timescales by curve-matching records of temperature[17,30], dust[6], and $\delta^{18}O$ of O_2 and sea water[12,16]. We plot changes in the isotopic composition of sea water, and hence inferred continental ice volume, against age (curve 3e).

The Vostok temperature record compares well with sea surface temperature (SST) in various Indian ocean cores[17,30]. For example, in the summer SST record of RC11-120 (ref. 31), stages 7.1 and 7.3 are colder than the Holocene and much colder than the Last Interglacial (curve 3a), in agreement with the Vostok temperature record. Correlating the Vostok temperature peak at 215 kyr BP with the RC11-120 peak at 218 kyr BP suggests that the bottom of the Vostok core corresponds to marine stage 7.4. The comparison with RC11-120 thus supports our glaciological timescale.

The dust concentration is plotted against EGT age in curve 3g High values are observed throughout the penultimate glacial period (140–200 kyr BP). There is a small maximum at about 160 kyr BP and a broad minimum between 170 and 190 kyr BP. Low values are recorded before 200 kyr BP, consistent with our interpretation that this depth interval lies in the stage 7 interglacial period. We compare dust concentration at Vostok and the mass accumulation rate (MAR) in core RC27-61 from the Indian Ocean which gives a good record of aeolian input[32]. Both (curve 3f) are highest during glacial stages (2, 4 and 6), and low during the interglacial stages (1, 5 and 7). The two records are almost always in phase to within ±10 kyr; the exception is between 170–190 kyr, where the low values in Vostok have no parallel in the RC27-61 record. At around 200 kyr BP, dust rises at Vostok 10 kyr before MAR rises at RC27-61, and at 145 kyr BP decreases at Vostok again about 10 kyr before the MAR decreases at RC 27-61. It is not clear whether these differences reflect errors in the chronologies or true differences in phasing.

The $\delta^{18}O$ of past atmospheric O_2 is plotted against EGT age in curve 3d, after correction for differences between gas age and ice age[33], and for gravitational fractionation[34]. Variations of $\delta^{18}O$ of O_2 are governed mainly by processes associated with oxygen isotope exchange of O_2 and sea water due to photosynthesis and respiration[35]. These variations are thought to be closely related to variations in the $\delta^{18}O$ of sea water: when the composition of sea water changes, the composition of O_2 produced by photosynthesis changes, transmitting the sea water variations to the atmospheric O_2 reservoir[36]. For the sake of simplicity, we do not consider the small additional variations in the $\delta^{18}O$ of O_2 associated with glacial–interglacial variations in oxygen isotope fractionation by biogeochemical and hydrologic processes[16] (that is, changes in the Dole effect).

The record of variations in $\delta^{18}O$ of O_2 looks similar to the record of variations in $\delta^{18}O$

沃斯托克冰芯与海洋记录的关联

现在我们利用温度[17,30]、粉尘[6]以及 O_2 和海水的 $\delta^{18}O$ 值记录[12,16]曲线之间的对应关系，将沃斯托克冰芯与 SPECMAP 时间序列的相互关系延伸至冰芯底部。我们画出了海水同位素变化曲线，而该曲线可以反映过去大陆上的冰的体积随时间的变化（曲线 3e）。

沃斯托克冰芯的温度记录与印度洋中各岩芯显示的表层海水温度 (SST)[17,30]具有很好的一致性。比如，在 RC11-120 孔的夏季表层海水温度记录（参考文献 31）中，7.1 阶和 7.3 阶的温度要低于全新世，同时也远远低于末次间冰期（曲线 3a）的温度，这与沃斯托克冰芯的温度记录是一致的。将沃斯托克冰芯在距今 21.5 万年时的温度峰值与 RC11-120 在距今 21.8 万年时的峰值关联起来发现，沃斯托克冰芯底部对应着海洋氧同位素 7.4 阶。因此，与 RC11-120 的对比结果证实了我们标定的冰川时间序列。

粉尘浓度相对于 EGT 年龄的变化如曲线 3g 所示。整个倒数第二次冰期（距今 14 万至 20 万年）该观测值都很高。距今约 16 万年时曾有一个小的高值，而在距今 17 万至 19 万年间总体为一个低值段。距今 20 万年以前记录到的值较低，与我们提出的该深度段处于间冰期第 7 阶的解释一致。我们还比较了沃斯托克冰芯的粉尘浓度和印度洋 RC27-61 孔上的物质积累速率 (MAR)，RC27-61 孔很好地记录了风尘的输入[32]。两者（曲线 3f）均在冰阶（2、4 和 6）时达最高值，而在间冰阶（1、5 和 7）时则较低。除在距今 17 万至 19 万年间，沃斯托克冰芯中的低值记录未在 RC27-61 中找到对应记录以外，两条记录几乎都是同步变化的，相差不到 ±1 万年。在距今 20 万年左右时，沃斯托克冰芯中粉尘浓度的升高比 RC27-61 中 MAR 的升高早出现了 1 万年；而在距今 14.5 万年时，沃斯托克冰芯中粉尘浓度的降低再次比 RC27-61 中 MAR 提早了 1 万年。上述差异反映的到底是定年上的误差还是位相上的真实差异尚不清楚。

对气体年龄和冰川年龄之间的差异[33]以及重力分馏作用[34]进行校正后，得到的过去大气中 O_2 的 $\delta^{18}O$ 值相对于 EGT 年龄的变化见曲线 3d。O_2 中 $\delta^{18}O$ 值的变化主要受光合作用和呼吸作用引起的 O_2 和海水之间氧同位素交换等相关过程的影响[35]。人们普遍认为这种变化与海水中 $\delta^{18}O$ 值的变化密切相关：当海水组成发生变化时，光合作用产生的 O_2 的组成也随之变化，将海水的变化转化为大气中 O_2 库的变化[36]。生物地球化学过程和水文过程变化[16]（即道尔效应的变化）使得冰期–间冰期期间发生了氧同位素分馏，为了简便起见，我们并未考虑与此相关的 O_2 中 $\delta^{18}O$ 值的微弱变化。

O_2 中 $\delta^{18}O$ 值的变化记录与海水中 $\delta^{18}O$ 值的变化（曲线 3e）记录类似。同时还

of sea water (curve 3*e*). It also resembles the curve of June insolation at 20° N (curve 3*c*), because variations in $\delta^{18}O$ of sea water and variations in the Dole effect are both linked to insolation. We therefore test the EGT chronology by comparing $\delta^{18}O$ of O_2 with $\delta^{18}O$ of sea water and with insolation. Uncertainties restrict the comparison to about ± 10 kyr; within this uncertainty, variations in $\delta^{18}O$ of O_2 as dated by the EGT chronology are consistent with sea water $\delta^{18}O$ and insolation curve. Thus the $\delta^{18}O$ measurements, as well as dust and temperature comparisons, support the EGT chronology.

The duration of the Last Interglacial, now highly controversial, is crucial for new insights on the causes of glacial–interglacial cycles[37-39]. Relevant information is summarized in Fig. 4. Here we plot the Vostok temperature record using the adopted EGT and other timescales which would be derived from different starting assumptions. In the figure, we also show the $\delta^{18}O$ of sea water, the curve of sea surface temperature derived from core MD 84-551 (ref. 17) and the recently published[37] isotopic record of vein calcite from Devils Hole (Nevada). The LIG lasts twice as long at Vostok in the chronology of Lorius *et al.* than in the deep-sea record of the sea-level change[1,2].

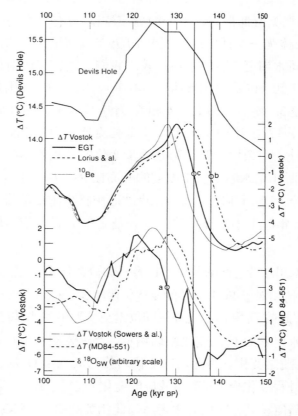

Fig. 4. The Vostok temperature record on various timescales for the 100–150 kyr BP period encompassing the LIG. Upper curve: the Devils Hole record; middle curves: Vostok temperature using three different

与 20°N 处六月份的太阳辐射曲线类似（曲线 $3c$），这是因为海水中 $\delta^{18}O$ 值的变化以及道尔效应的变化均与太阳辐射有关。因此，我们通过比较 O_2 中 $\delta^{18}O$ 值与海水中 $\delta^{18}O$ 值的变化，及 O_2 中 $\delta^{18}O$ 值与太阳辐射的变化来检验 EGT 定年结果。比较的结果把误差的范围限定在 ±1 万年左右，在该不确定范围内，利用 EGT 定年结果得到的 O_2 中 $\delta^{18}O$ 值的变化与海水中 $\delta^{18}O$ 值的变化以及与太阳辐射的变化均一致。因此，$\delta^{18}O$ 值的测定结果以及粉尘和温度的比较均支持 EGT 定年结果。

对于末次间冰期的持续时间，目前仍存在很大争议，这一持续时间对于找到导致冰期 – 间冰期旋回的起因至关重要[37-39]。相关信息总结于图 4。这里我们利用 EGT 法和根据不同假设得到的其他时间尺度画出了沃斯托克冰芯温度记录。在该图中我们还给出了从 MD84-551 孔岩芯得到的海水 $\delta^{18}O$ 值变化、海洋表面温度的变化（参考文献 17）以及新近发表[37]的魔鬼洞站（内华达）上脉状方解石的同位素记录。根据洛里于斯等对沃斯托克冰芯的定年结果得出的末次间冰期的持续时间是根据海平面变化的深海记录定年结果的两倍[1,2]。

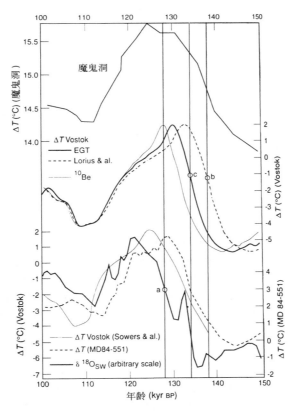

图 4. 距今 10 万至 15 万年之间（其中包含末次间冰期），不同时间尺度下的沃斯托克冰芯温度记录。最上部的曲线为魔鬼洞站的记录；中间曲线为采用三种不同时间尺度（"^{10}Be"，EGT 和洛里于斯等）得到

timescales ("[10]Be", EGT and Lorius *et al.*); lower curves: Vostok temperature (using the timescale obtained by Sowers *et al.*[16] in correlating sea water $\delta^{18}O$ with ^{18}O of O_2); the sea surface temperature estimated from core MD84-551[17]; and the sea water $\delta^{18}O$ (similar to 3*e* with an arbitrary scale chosen in such a way this curve is comparable to the temperature records). The three vertical lines correspond to: a, mid-transition in sea water $\delta^{18}O$, a proxy of sea-level and ice volume change (128 kyr BP); b, mid-transition in Vostok temperature using the Lorius *et al.* timescale (138 kyr BP); and c, mid-transition according to the EGT reference timescale (134 kyr BP).

Both the use of air $\delta^{18}O$ (ref. 16) and the correlation with Southern Ocean SST[17] have recently confirmed that the temperature at Vostok rose before (~5 kyr at mid-transition) sea level rose for this termination (termination 2). As the EGT is, at mid-transition, ~4 kyr younger than that of Lorius *et al.*, the EGT and SPECMAP timescales now appear in agreement for this termination 2 (but differences of up to 6 kyr still exist at the LIG peak). The EGT timescale supports the observation, now well documented, that the duration of this interglacial is longer in the Vostok temperature and Southern Ocean SST records than in the record of sea-level change. This conclusion is fairly insensitive to our assumption about Vostok age at 1,534 m depth (a 5% change in age at 110 kyr BP will modify the duration by only 1 kyr or so). The duration which would be derived from the ^{10}Be chronology is similar, within 2 kyr, to that obtained with the EGT (but note the uncertainties of the ^{10}Be method mentioned above). Finally, the Vostok and Devils Hole records[37] agree less convincingly with the EGT than with the timescale of Lorius *et al.*[1].

Climate Interpretation

We now examine how the extension of the records, and the new information they contain, complement or modify our current climatic interpretation of Vostok data. In turn, we discuss the dust record, the link between orbital forcing and climate, and the record of greenhouse-gas concentrations.

The dust throughout the Vostok record begins to increase rapidly when Vostok atmospheric temperature drops by more than ~4 °C below its modern value. We interpret this result as indicating that the penultimate glacial period, like the last glacial period, was characterized by more extensive deserts, more intense surface winds in the desert source regions and/or more efficient meridional transport. The isotopic composition from the LGM dust in the Dome C core[40] suggests that the Patagonia desert might be the main contributor to dust fallout in East Antarctica. During the end of the previous interglacial, as during the LIG and today, dust fallout was very low.

An intriguing feature of the records is that dust at Vostok covaries so closely with Vostok isotopic temperature whereas MAR at RC27-61 covaries so closely with sea water $\delta^{18}O$. The dust record is similar to the record of mass accumulation rate for the Northern Hemisphere Indian Ocean core RC27-61. Over the entire Vostok record, there are similarities between dust and indicators of dust source strength in Central Asia analysed in Chinese loesses[41,42]. These

的沃斯托克冰芯的温度记录；最下方曲线分别为：沃斯托克冰芯温度（采用了索尔斯等[16]得出的时间尺度，该方法将海水 δ^{18}O 值和 O₂ 中的 [18]O 含量进行关联），从 MD84-551 孔[17]岩芯中得到的海洋表层温度，以及海水的 δ^{18}O 值（与 3e 相似，人工选定的尺度以使其与温度记录可以相比较）。三条垂线分别对应：a，海水 δ^{18}O 曲线的过渡期中值，它是海平面和冰体积变化的一个替代指标（距今 12.8 万年）；b，采用洛里于斯等的时间尺度得到的沃斯托克冰芯曲线的过渡期中值（距今 13.8 万年）；c，根据 EGT 相关时间尺度得到的过渡期中值（距今 13.4 万年）。

利用空气 δ^{18}O 值（参考文献 16）以及它与南大洋表层海水温度的相关关系[17]都已证明，在该结束期（倒数第二次冰期结束期），沃斯托克冰芯揭示的温度上升的时间早于海平面上升的时间（在中间过渡期时约早 5,000 年）。由于 EGT 时间序列在中间过渡期要比洛里于斯等的定年结果年轻 4,000 年左右，所以对于倒数第二次冰期结束期来说，EGT 和 SPECMAP 的时间标度似乎是一致的（但末次间冰期最盛期两者存在最高达 6,000 年的差异）。沃斯托克温度和南大洋 SST 记录到的间冰期的持续时间要长于海平面变化记录的时间，这一结果已被充分证实，并得到 EGT 时间尺度的支持。该结论对于沃斯托克冰芯 1,534 m 处的定年假定极不敏感（倘若距今 11 万年时的年龄改变 5%，则定年结果只改变 1,000 年左右）。如果用 [10]Be 来定年的话，其持续时间与 EGT 的接近，两者相差不到 2,000 年（但是需要注意上述提到的 [10]Be 测年法的不确定性）。最后，沃斯托克冰芯记录和魔鬼洞记录[37]与 EGT 的一致性不如它们与洛里于斯等[1]建立的时间尺度的一致性更具说服力。

气候解释

现在我们来研究延伸的记录以及其中所包含的新信息如何补充和改变当前我们对沃斯托克冰芯数据的气候解释。反过来，我们还将讨论粉尘记录、地球轨道参数驱动与气候之间的关系以及温室气体浓度记录。

当沃斯托克站地区大气温度较于现今温度降幅大于 4 ℃时，沃斯托克冰芯的粉尘含量快速升高。我们将该结果解释为：与末次冰期一样，倒数第二次冰期以沙漠范围更广、沙漠源区地表风力更强和（或）经向搬运效率更高为特征。Dome C 冰芯中末次冰盛期的粉尘同位素组成[40]表明，巴塔哥尼亚沙漠可能是东南极地区降落的粉尘的主要来源。就像末次间冰期和现代一样，在上一个间冰期末时，落尘率是很低的。

该记录中一个有趣的特征是沃斯托克冰芯的粉尘与其同位素温度的变化高度同步，而 RC27-61 中的 MAR（物质积累速率）与海水 δ^{18}O 记录的变化亦非常相近。粉尘记录与北半球印度洋中的 RC27-61 孔岩芯的物质积累率记录相似。在整个沃斯托克冰芯记录中，粉尘和在中国黄土中[41,42]已分析过的中亚地区粉尘来源强度指标之间

similarities indicate that large-scale changes in dust fallout reflect global changes in climate.

We examine the link between Vostok temperature and orbital forcing through spectral analysis using a multi-taper method[7,43]. The analysis was done (1) for the entire 2,546-m record, and (2) for the same series limited to 2,083 m using either the EGT or the Lorius *et al.* timescale. Using the EGT instead of the chronology of Lorius *et al.* causes a slight shift in the period of the obliquity peak (from 41.7 to 40.3 kyr), retains the strong significance of this peak and makes the significance of the precessional peak stronger, probably because of the shortening of the LIG. Using the full time series (EGT chronology) leads to a decrease in the amplitude of the obliquity peak (41.01 kyr) which is even more significant; but the precessional peak (24.6 kyr) is now weaker and less significant. This decrease in amplitude of orbital frequencies is the quantitative expression of uniformly cold temperatures throughout the period between 140–200 kyr BP. During most of the record there is a strong relationship between local annual insolation, which primarily reflects obliquity, and temperature[2]. This relationship is absent, however, between 140 and 200 kyr BP: the insolation maximum at ~170 kyr BP has no clear temperature counterpart.

Polar ice cores provide the most direct evidence of past changes in greenhouse gas concentrations. These changes are well documented for CO_2 and CH_4 and to a lesser degree for N_2O (ref. 44 for a review). Previously published results obtained on Vostok and other ice cores highlight the correlation between CO_2 concentration, CH_4 concentration and temperature throughout the last climate cycle. Results from Vostok also reveal phase differences between CO_2 and temperature. At the end of the penultimate interglacial, for example, the CO_2 decrease lags behind the Antarctic cooling leading to glacial conditions.

The CO_2 and CH_4 concentrations for the entire Vostok core profiles are plotted against age in Fig. 5 using the EGT after correction for the difference between gas age and ice age[33,45]. CO_2 concentrations are low during the penultimate glacial period, from 140 to 190 kyr BP. These values are similar to the concentrations observed during the last glacial period between ~60 and 18 kyr BP. Before 190 kyr BP, the CO_2 values are higher. At the very bottom of the core, the CO_2 concentration is about 250 p.p.m.v., intermediate between full glacial concentrations and preindustrial values. The lowest CH_4 concentrations are similar to, or slightly lower than, those in the LGM, and are observed only during the final stage of the penultimate glaciation. The measurements are too scarce to discuss in detail this new part of the CH_4 record. Nevertheless, the increasing trend towards the bottom should be noted, especially the marked peak at the bottom with a maximum concentration of 610 p.p.b.v. Again, the concentrations measured near the very bottom are intermediate between full glacial and preindustrial values. This is consistent with the dating, indicating that the bottom ice is from the end of the previous interglacial period.

存在相似性。这种相似性说明，大空间尺度的降尘量的变化反映了全球气候的变化。

我们利用多窗谱分析法[7,43]通过光谱分析研究了沃斯托克温度和地球轨道参数驱动之间的关系。我们对(1)全部 2,546m 长的冰芯记录时间序列和(2)利用 EGT 法或洛里于斯等得出的上部 2,083m 的时间序列作了此类分析。利用 EGT 法代替洛里于斯等的定年方法后所得到的地轴倾角频率的峰值有微小的偏移(由 4.17 万年移到 4.03 万年)，不但保留了这一峰值的显著性，也使岁差峰信号的显著性更强，这很可能是因为末次间冰期的持续时间被缩短了的缘故。采用完整时间序列(EGT 定年)时，更为重要的变化是所得到的地轴倾角峰(4.101 万年)幅度减小，而岁差峰值(2.46 万年)变弱且相对不那么重要。轨道频率幅度的降低是距今 14 万至 20 万年间温度始终较低的定量表现。大部分该记录中反映地轴倾角变化的当地年均太阳辐射和温度之间都存在很强的相关性[2]。然而，这种关系在距今 14 万至 20 万年之间则不存在：距今约 17 万年时出现的太阳辐射最大值并没有与之对应的温度峰值存在。

极地冰芯为过去温室气体的变化情况提供了最直接的证据。CO_2、CH_4 的变化已经充分证实了这些变化情况，而 N_2O 的变化也可以在一定程度上作为证据(参见文献 44)。之前发表的关于沃斯托克冰芯及其他冰芯的相关结果已强调了末次气候旋回中 CO_2 浓度、CH_4 浓度和温度之间的关系。对沃斯托克冰芯的研究结果还揭示出了 CO_2 和温度之间的位相差。例如，在倒数第二次间冰期末期，CO_2 浓度的降低要滞后于导致冰期形成的南极温度的降低。

整个沃斯托克冰芯中 CO_2 和 CH_4 浓度随时间的变化剖面见图 5，该定年基于 EGT 方法并对气体年龄和冰川年龄之差进行了校正[33,45]。在距今 14 万至 19 万年之间的倒数第二次冰期时 CO_2 浓度一直较低。其 CO_2 浓度值与末次冰期时在距今约 6 万至 1.8 万年间观测到的浓度相近。而在距今 19 万年以前，CO_2 的浓度值则高得多。在该冰芯的最底部，CO_2 浓度约为 250 ppmv，处于整个冰期浓度与工业化之前浓度的中间值。CH_4 浓度的最低值与末次冰盛期时相当或略低，并且仅见于倒数第二次冰期的最末端。由于测定结果太少因而无法对 CH_4 记录中的新的部分作详细讨论。但向底部靠近时呈现出的这种增加趋势值得注意，特别是在最底部存在一个最大浓度达 610 ppbv 的峰值。再一次，接近冰芯最底部附近测得的浓度处于整个冰期浓度和工业化以前浓度的值之间。这与测年结果是一致的，说明底部的冰层来自前一个间冰期末。

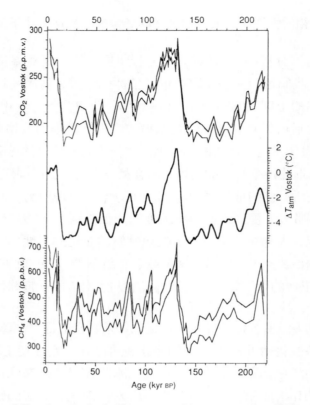

Fig. 5. CO_2, CH_4 and Vostok atmospheric temperature with respect to time (EGT) with the air-ice age difference calculated following Barnola *et al.*[33], taking into account the temperature dependence of the ice density[50]. For CO_2 and CH_4, the envelope corresponds to the measurement accuracy.

The strong covariation between CO_2 and temperature and CH_4 and temperature observed for the last 160 kyr is also present in the new part of the Vostok record. The CO_2–temperature correlation coefficient (r^2) over the past 220 kyr is 0.81 (0.76 for CH_4) instead of 0.78, in each case, over the last 160 kyr. In contrast to the lag of CO_2 behind temperature observed around 110 and 70 kyr BP, the CO_2 decrease between 220 and 190 kyr BP is in phase with the temperature change. A notable feature of the CH_4 results is the absence of clear oscillations during the penultimate glacial period. These would be expected from the link between the methane record and a monsoonal precipitation index largely dominated by the precession cycle[46] which was suggested for the past 160 kyr (ref. 9). This feature is directly reflected in the CH_4 spectrum: the amplitude and significance of the precession peak are smaller for the full record than for the last 160 kyr. The CO_2 spectrum also differs between the longer and shorter records, although in a different way. The 220-kyr CO_2 record now shows significant peaks at obliquity and both precession periodicities, whereas only the precession peak was present for the last climate cycle[7]. This also reflects, in the spectral domain, what is clearly seen in the CO_2 record: the long penultimate glacial period and the last ice age have different characteristics. Obviously, all these features would need to be confirmed by further measurements.

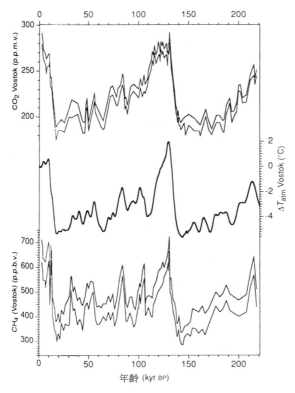

图 5. CO_2、CH_4 和沃斯托克冰芯的大气温度三者随时间（EGT）的变化情况，其中空气和冰川冰的年龄差异是根据巴诺拉等[33]的方法计算而来的，同时考虑了冰密度对温度的依赖性[50]。对 CO_2 和 CH_4 来说，包络线代表测量结果的精度。

　　沃斯托克记录的新增部分中，也显示了近 16 万年来观测到的 CO_2 随温度以及 CH_4 随温度的强烈共变。过去 22 万年中 CO_2– 温度的相关系数（r^2）为 0.81（CH_4 为 0.76）而非近 16 万年来的 0.78。与在距今 11 万至 7 万年间观测到的 CO_2 变化滞后于温度的变化不同，在距今 22 万至 19 万年之间，CO_2 的降低与温度是同步变化的。CH_4 结果的一个显著特征是倒数第二次冰期时缺乏显著的波动。这一点可以由甲烷记录和由岁差周期控制的季风降水指数的联系[46]预见，在过去的 16 万年中就是如此（参考文献 9）。该特征直接反映于 CH_4 的波谱分析中：整个记录中岁差周期的幅度和显著性要小于最近 16 万年的结果。CO_2 的谱分析结果中，长期和短期的记录也存在差异，但是表现形式不同。近 22 万年来的长期 CO_2 记录谱分析结果出现了地轴倾角和岁差两个周期的显著峰值，而在末次气候旋回中则仅有岁差峰[7]。这一点还反映了 CO_2 浓度记录中清晰可见的谱分析结果：漫长的倒数第二次冰期和末次冰期存在不同的特征。显然，所有这些特征还有待于进一步测量结果的证实。

Conclusions

Our new chronology appears to correlate well with oceanic records. In particular, the EGT chronology resolves half of the 10-kyr discrepancy in the duration of the LIG that arose when the previous Vostok chronology was compared to the deep-sea record. With the EGT chronology, the duration of the LIG at Vostok is still 5 kyr longer than its duration in deep-sea sediments. We believe that this important difference reflects the fact that, during termination 2, Antarctic temperatures rose ~5 kyr before the Northern Hemisphere ice sheets began to melt[12,17]. In general, matching Vostok climate records with deep-sea sediments records and insolation curves supports our entire chronology to ± 10 kyr.

The isotopic temperature record shows that there is a long cold period in East Antarctica which we date from about 140 to 200 kyr BP. The coldest isotopic temperatures measured during this period are similar to those measured during the last glacial maximum, but the duration of the cold period is much longer. Isotopic temperatures rise in the bottom of the Vostok 4Γ core corresponding to interstadial–interglacial periods of marine stage 7. The overall covariation of climate variables in the newly examined section of the Vostok ice core is similar to that observed for the last glacial–interglacial cycle[8,9]. Thus concentrations of CO_2 and CH_4 are lowest during the penultimate glacial period, where their values are comparable to those of the LGM. CO_2 and CH_4 are positively correlated with isotopic temperatures with correlations similar to those found during the last climate cycle. Throughout the record, dust concentrations at Vostok rise during cold periods, and are very low when temperatures are less than ~4 °C colder than modem values.

There is still much more climate information to extract from Vostok drilling. There is more than 1 km of ice below the 2,546 m reached by core 4Γ (the ice thickness is ~3,700 m), which may represent more than 500 kyr of time. At the same time, the new data discussed here, together with the results of the GRIP[47] and GISP2[48] cores, will allow comparison of climate change in Antarctica and Greenland beyond 200 kyr BP.

(**364**, 407-412; 1993)

J. Jouzel[*†], N. I. Barkov[‡], J. M. Barnola[§], M. Bender[∥†], J. Chappellaz[§], C. Genthon[§], V. M. Kotlyakov[¶], V. Lipenkov[‡], C. Lorius[§], J. R. Petit[§*], D. Raynaud[§], G. Raisbeck[#], C. Ritz[§], T. Sowers[∥], M. Stievenard[*], F. Yiou[#] & P. Yiou[*]

[*] Laboratoire de Modélisation du Climat et de l'Environnement, CEA/DSM CE Saclay, 91191, Gif sur Yvette Cedex, France
[‡] Arctic and Antarctic Research Institute, Beringa Street 38, 199226, St Petersburg, Russia
[§] Laboratoire de Glaciologie et Géophysique de l'Environnement, CNRS, BP96, 38402, Saint Martin d'Hères Cedex, France
[∥] Graduate School of Oceanography, University of Rhode Island, Narragansett, Rhode Island 02882-1197, USA
[¶] Institute of Geography, Staromonetny, per 29, 109017, Moscow, Russia
[#] Centre de Spectrométrie Nucléaire et de Spectrométrie de Masse, 91405, Orsay, France
[†] J. J. is also at the Laboratoire de Glaciologie et Géophysique de l'Environnement. M.B. is on sabbatical leave at the Centre des Faibles Radioactivités, CNRS-CEA 91198, Gif-sur-Yvette Cedex, France.

Received 22 March; accepted 10 June 1993.

结　论

我们的新定年结果与海洋记录之间具有很好的一致性。特别是，EGT 定年结果使得之前的沃斯托克冰芯与深海记录定年结果中存在的末次间冰期持续时间的 1 万年的差异缩短了一半。根据 EGT 定年结果，沃斯托克冰芯中末次间冰期的持续时间仍比深海沉积物长 5,000 年。我们认为，这一巨大差异反映了一个事实，即在倒数第二次冰期结束期时南极温度的上升比北半球冰川开始融化的时间早 5,000 年[12,17]。总之，将沃斯托克冰芯气候记录与深海沉积物记录以及太阳辐射曲线相匹配证实了，我们的整个冰芯定年结果的误差在 ±1 万年以内。

同位素温度记录显示，东南极地区在距今 14 万至 20 万年之间曾有一段漫长的冷期。在这一段时期内测得的最低同位素温度与末次冰盛期最低温度相当，不过该段冷期的持续时间要长得多。沃斯托克 4Г 冰芯底部同位素温度的上升对应于海洋氧同位素第 7 阶的间冰阶 – 间冰期阶段。沃斯托克冰芯最新这一部分所揭示的气候参量总体共变性与以前观测到的末次冰期 – 间冰期旋回中的情况类似[8,9]。因此，倒数第二次冰期时 CO_2 和 CH_4 的浓度最低，与末次冰盛期时相当。CO_2 和 CH_4 的浓度与同位素温度呈正相关，该相关关系与末次气候旋回中的类似。在整个冰芯记录中，冷期时沃斯托克地区的粉尘浓度上升，而当温度低于现今温度 4 ℃ 以内时粉尘浓度变得极低。

在沃斯托克冰芯中还存在许多气候信息有待于提取。在 4Г 冰芯已经达到的 2,546 m 以下，仍有厚达 1 km 以上的冰层存在（冰层的厚度约 3,700 m），所代表的时间尺度可能达 50 万年以上。同时，结合本文所讨论的新数据，和 GRIP[47] 与 GISP2[48] 冰芯的相关数据，可以对距今 20 万年以前南极地区和格陵兰的气候变化加以比较。

（齐红艳 翻译；田立德 审稿）

References:

1. Lorius, C. *et al. Nature* **316**, 591-596 (1985).

2. Jouzel, J. *et al. Nature* **329**, 403-408 (1987).

3. Yiou, F., Raisbeck, G. M., Lorius, C. & Barkov, N. I. *Nature* **316**, 616-617 (1985).

4. Jouzel, J. *et al. Quat. Res.* **31**, 135-150 (1989).

5. De Angelis, M., Barkov, N. I. & Petrov, V. N. *Nature* **325**, 318-321 (1985).

6. Petit, J. R. *et al. Nature* **343**, 56-58 (1990).

7. Yiou, P. *et al. J. Geophys. Res.* **96**, 20365-20378 (1991).

8. Barnola, J. M., Raynaud, D., Korotkevich, Y. S. & Lorius, C. *Nature* **329**, 408-414 (1987).

9. Chappeiiaz, J., Barnola, J. M., Raynaud, D., Korotkevich, Y. S. & Lorius, C. *Nature* **345**, 127- 131 (1990).

10. Genthon, C. *et al. Nature* **329**, 414-418 (1987).

11. Lorius, C., Jouzel, J., Raynaud, D., Hansen, J. E. & Le Treut, H. *Nature* **347**, 139-145 (1990).

12. Sowers, T., Bender, M., Raynaud, D., Korotkevich, Y. S. & Orchado, J. *Paleoceanography* **6**, 679-696 (1991).

13. Raisbeck, G. M. *et al. Nature* **326**, 273-277 (1987).

14. Robin, G. de Q. *Phil. Trans. R. Soc.* B**280**, 143-148 (1977).

15. Vaikmae, R., Jouzel, J. & Petit, J. R., presentation at mtg on *Application of Isotope Techniques in Studying Past and Current Environmental Changes in the Hydrosphere and the Atmosphere*, Vienna, April 1993.

16. Sowers, T. *et al. Paleoceanography* (submitted).

17. Pichon, J. J. *et al. Paleoceanography* **7**, 289-318 (1992).

18. Ritz, C. *J. Glaciol.* (in the press).

19. Legrand, M. & Delmas, R. *Nature* **327**, 671-676 (1987).

20. Raisbeck, G. M. *et al. The Last Deglaciation: Absolute and Radiocarbon Chronologies* (eds Bard, E. & Broecker W.S.) 127-139 (NATO ASI Series 12, Springer, Berlin, 1992).

21. Raisbeck, G. M. & Yiou, F. *Nuclear Instrum. Meth.* B**5**, 91-99 (1984).

22. Dansgaard, W. *Tellus* **16**, 436-468 (1964).

23. Jouzel, J. & Merlivat, L. *J. Geophys. Res.* **89**, 11749-11758 (1984).

24. Lorius, C. & Merlivat, L. *IAHS Publ.* **118**, 127-137 (1979).

25. Dahe, Q., Petit, J. R., Jouzel, J. & Stievenard, M. *J. Glaciol.* (in the press).

26. Joussaume, S. & Jouzel, J. *J. Geophys. Res.* **98**, 2807-2830 (1993).

27. Jouzel, J., Koster, R. D., Suozzo, R. & Russell, G. *EOS* (Spring Meeting supplement, 7 April) (1992).

28. Johnsen, S. J. *et al. Nature* **359**, 311-313 (1992).

29. Craig, H. *Science* **133**, 1702-1703 (1961).

30. Shackleton, N. J., Mix, A. & Hall, M. A. *Quat. Sci. Rev.* **11**, 387-400 (1992).

31. Martinson, D. G. *et al. Quat. Res.* **27**, 1-29 (1987).

32. Clemens, S. & Prell, W. *Paleoceanography* **5**, 109-145 (1992).

33. Barnola, J. M., Pimentia, P., Raynaud, D. & Korotkevich, Y. S. *Tellus* B**43**, 83-90 (1991).

34. Craig, H., Horibe, Y. & Sowers, T. A. *Science* **242**, 1675-1678 (1988).

35. Dole, M., Lane, G. A., Rudd, D. P. & Zaukelies, D. A. *Geochim. Cosmochim. Acta* **6**, 65-78 (1954).

36. Bender, M., Labeyrie, L. D., Raynaud, D. & Lorius, C. *Nature* **318**, 349-352 (1985).

37. Winograd, I. J. *et al. Science* **258**, 255-260 (1992).

38. Lambeck, K. & Nakada, M. *Nature* **357**, 125-128 (1992).

39. Imbrie, J., Mix, A. C. & Martinson, D. G. *Nature* **363**, 531-533 (1993).

40. Grousset, F. *et al. Earth Planet Sci. Lett.* **111**, 175-182 (1992).

41. Kukla, G., An, Z. S., Melice, J. L., Gavin, J. & Xiao, J. L. *Trans. R. Soc. Edin.* **81**, 263-288 (1990).

42. Beer, J. *et al. Geophys. Res. Lett.* **20**, 57-60 (1993).

43. Thomson, D. J. *Proc. IEEE* **70**, 1055-1096 (1982).

44. Raynaud, D. *et al. Science* **259**, 926-934 (1993).

45. Sowers, T. A., Bender, M. L., Raynaud, D. & Korotkevich, Y. L. *J. Geophys. Res.* **97**, 15683-15697 (1992).

46. Prell, W. & Kutzbach, J. E. *J. Geophys. Res.* **92**, 8411-8425 (1987).

47. Dansgaard, W. *et al. Nature* **364**, 218-220 (1993).

48. Taylor, K. T. *et al. Nature* **361**, 432-436 (1993).

49. Berger, A. L. *J. Atmos. Sci.* **35**, 2362-2367 (1978).

50. Martinerie, P., Raynaud, D., Etheridge, D., Barnola, J. M. & Mazaudier, D. *Earth Planet Sci. Lett.* **112**, 1-13 (1992).

Acknowledgements. Vostok is a joint project between Russia, France and the United States. We thank participants in drilling, field work and ice sampling. We acknowledge the Russian Antarctic Expeditions, the Institut Français de Recherches et Technologies Polaires and the NSF Division of Polar Programs for logistic support. The project is supported in Russia by the Russian Ministry of Sciences, in France by the Programme National d'Études de la Dynamique du Climat, Fondation de France and the Commission of European Communities Environment Programme, and in the U.S., by the NSF. We thank J. Meyssonnier for discussions, J. C. Pugno for the figures and C. Alba, P. Doira and M. Delmotte for isotope analyses.

B-cell Apoptosis Induced by Antigen Receptor Crosslinking is Blocked by a T-cell Signal Through CD40

T. Tsubata *et al.*

Editor's Note

The controlled elimination of self-reactive lymphocytes by programmed cell death (apoptosis) is an essential feature of the immune system that helps prevent autoimmunity. Here Takeshi Tsubata and colleagues use a mouse B cell line, which can readily be induced to apoptose, to study anti-apoptotic mechanisms. The team show that co-culture with T helper cells prevents B-cell apoptosis, and that the effect may be due to the interaction of the B cell CD40 protein binding to its ligand on the T helper cell. They conclude that the presence or absence of T-cell help through CD40 may be crucial in determining whether B cells are activated or killed upon interaction with antigens, with implications for understanding and treating autoimmune disease.

In mice transgenic for an autoantibody, self-reactive B cells have been shown to be eliminated upon interaction with membrane-bound self-antigens in the periphery[1,2] as well as in the bone marrow[3-5], suggesting that both immature and mature B cells are eliminated by multimerization of surface immunoglobulins (sIg). Activation of mature B cells by antigens may thus require a second signal that inhibits sIg-mediated apoptosis. Such a second signal is likely to be provided by T helper cells, because B-cell tolerance is more easily induced in the absence of T helper cells[6-9]. To assess the molecular nature of the signal that inhibits sIg-mediated apoptosis, we used anti-IgM-induced apoptotic death of WEHI-231 B lymphoma cells[10,11] as a model system. Here we report that the signal for abrogating sIg-mediated apoptosis is generated by association of the CD40L molecule on T cells with the CD40 molecule on WEHI-231 cells. T-cell help through CD40 may thus determine whether B cells are eliminated or activated upon interaction with antigens.

WEHI-231 cells undergo apoptotic cell death when the sIg is crosslinked by anti-IgM antibody[10,11]. To test whether T helper cells are able to block sIg-mediated apoptosis of B cells, we treated WEHI-231 cells with anti-IgM in the presence or absence of A3.4C6 helper T hybridoma cells[12]. After 2 days, cells were collected and stained with phycoerythrin-labelled anti-IgM and fluorescein-labelled anti-B220. A known number of sIgM$^-$/sIgG$^+$ B lymphoma K46 cells were added to the collected cells before staining so that we could calculate the number of WEHI-231 cells in the culture. Flow cytometry analysis separated and quantified WEHI-231 cells (sIgM$^+$, B220$^+$), K46 cells (sIgM$^-$, B220$^+$) and T cells (sIgM$^-$, B220$^-$) in the mixture (Fig. l*a*). Treatment with anti-IgM

T 细胞通过 CD40 抑制抗原受体交联引起的 B 细胞凋亡

锷田武志等

编者按

免疫系统的一个基本特征是能够通过程序性细胞死亡（凋亡）有计划地清除自身反应性淋巴细胞，从而防止自身免疫病发生。在这篇文章中锷田武志及其同事利用容易发生诱导性凋亡的小鼠细胞系研究了 B 细胞的抗凋亡机制。结果显示，B 细胞凋亡在有辅助 T 细胞存在时被显著抑制，而 B 细胞的 CD40 蛋白与其在辅助 T 细胞上配体的结合可能介导了这种抑制作用。该研究证明，B 细胞能否通过 CD40 获得 T 细胞的帮助可能决定了抗原结合后 B 细胞的命运（活化或死亡），为理解和治疗自身免疫病提供了启示。

在自身抗体转基因小鼠的外周血 [1,2] 和骨髓 [3-5] 中，自身反应性 B 细胞与膜表面结合的自身抗原结合后被清除，这说明非成熟或者成熟 B 细胞在表面免疫球蛋白 (sIg) 的多聚化后均会死亡。因此，成熟 B 细胞在被抗原活化时也许需要通过第二信使来抑制 sIg 介导的细胞凋亡。在缺失辅助 T 细胞时 [6-9]，B 细胞更容易产生抗原耐受。因而，辅助 T 细胞极有可能提供了抑制 B 细胞凋亡的第二信使。我们利用抗 IgM 抗体诱导 B 淋巴瘤细胞系 WEHI-231 凋亡模型 [10,11] 来研究了第二信使抑制 sIg 介导凋亡的分子机理。研究发现，表达于 T 细胞的 CD40 配体与 WEHI-231 细胞上 CD40 结合后能够产生抑制信号，影响 sIg 介导的 B 细胞凋亡。因此，通过 CD40 获得 T 细胞的帮助决定了 B 细胞在抗原结合后是被活化还是被清除。

抗 IgM 抗体可以引起 sIg 的交联，并进一步诱发 WEHI-231 细胞的凋亡性死亡 [10,11]。为了验证辅助 T 细胞是否可以阻断 sIg 介导的 B 细胞凋亡，我们分别在 A3.4C6 辅助 T 杂交瘤细胞 [12] 存在或不存在时检验了抗 IgM 抗体对 WEHI-231 细胞的作用。反应 2 天后，将这些细胞收集起来并使用藻红蛋白标记的抗 IgM 抗体和荧光素标记的抗 B220 抗体染色。并且在染色前，我们向收集的细胞中加入了一定数量的 sIgM⁻/sIgG⁺ K46 B 淋巴瘤细胞，以便计算 WEHI-231 细胞的数量。我们使用流式细胞术分析将细胞混合液中的 WEHI-231 细胞（sIgM⁺，B220⁺）、K46 细胞（sIgM⁻，

alone markedly reduced the number of WEHI-231 cells, whereas the growth of anti-IgM-treated WEHI-231 cells was restored in the presence of A3.4C6 cells. A similar result was obtained when a T helper clone DB14 (ref. 13) was used (data not shown). On the other hand, other T-helper hybridoma lines 2B4 (ref. 14) and N3-6-71 (ref. 15), as well as a cytotoxic T-cell clone CTLL-2, failed to rescue anti-Ig-treated WEHI-231 cells from apoptotic death (Fig. 1b). These results indicate that some T-helper lines are able to block sIg-mediated apoptotic death of B cells.

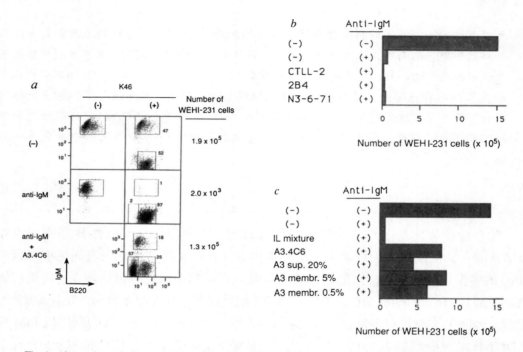

Fig. 1. Abrogation of sIg-mediated cell death of WEHI-231 cells by T helper cells. WEHI-231 cells were cultured with 10 μg ml⁻¹ of goat anti-mouse IgM antibody (Cappel) in the presence or absence of various cells or reagents in 1 ml RPMI-1640 medium supplemented with 10% fetal calf serum, 50 μM 2-mercapto-ethanol and antibiotics for 2 days. Cells were subsequently collected and, after adding 2×10^5 K46 cells into each sample, stained by fluorescein-conjugated anti-B220 (RA3-6B2) and phycoerythrin-conjugated goat anti-mouse IgM antibody (Southern Biotechnology). Cells were analysed on a FACScan (Becton–Dickinson), and the fraction of WEHI-231 cells and K46 cells in the culture determined. The number of WEHI-231 cells was calculated as (the fraction of WEHI-231/fraction of K46) × (2×10^5). a, Two-colour flow cytometry analysis for the growth of WEHI-231 cells. WEHI-231 cells (2×10^4) were cultured with anti-IgM in the presence or absence of 1×10^5 A3.4C6 cells for 2 d. Percentages of WEHI-231 (IgM⁺B220⁺), K46 (IgM⁻B220⁺) and A3.4C6 (IgM⁻B220⁻), and calculated numbers of WEHI-231 cells recovered from each culture are indicated. As controls for staining, untreated or anti-Ig-treated WEHI-231 cells were stained in parallel without adding K46 cells. Note that the condition of flow cytometry for untreated WEHI-231 cells is slightly different from that for the others and that sIgM expression of anti-Ig treated WEHI-231 cells is significantly higher than that of K46 cells, although anti-Ig treatment reduced sIgM expression of WEHI-231 cells 20-fold. b, Growth of anti-IgM-stimulated WEHI-231 cells cultured with T-cell lines. WEHI-231 (1×10^5) were cultured with 10 μg ml⁻¹ of anti-IgM in the presence of 1×10^5 cells of the T-cell lines CTLL-2, 2B4 or N3-6-71 for 2 days. c, Growth of anti-IgM-stimulated WEHI-231 cells cultured with reagents to replace helper T cells. A3.4C6 cells (1×10^5), the culture supernatant

B220[+])和 T 细胞(sIgM[-],B220[-])进行了分离并计算了数量(图 1a)。单独使用抗 IgM 抗体处理会导致 WEHI-231 细胞数量显著减少,而在 A3.4C6 细胞存在时,抗 IgM 抗体处理过的 WEHI-231 细胞恢复生长。使用 DB14 辅助 T 细胞(参考文献 13)也可以获得类似的结果(结果未展示)。然而另一些辅助 T 杂交瘤细胞系——2B4(参考文献 14)、N3-6-71(参考文献 15)和杀伤性 T 细胞 CTLL-2 则不能阻断抗 IgM 抗体所引起的 WEHI-231 细胞凋亡(图 1b)。这些结果表明,某些辅助 T 细胞系可以阻断 sIg 介导的 B 细胞凋亡。

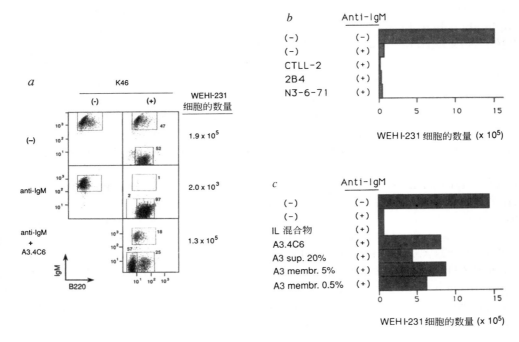

图 1. 辅助 T 细胞阻断 sIg 介导的 WEHI-231 细胞死亡。在有或没有各种细胞或因子条件下,WEHI-231 细胞在含 10% 胎牛血清、50 µM 2−巯基乙醇和抗生素的 1 ml RPMI-1640 培养基中与 10 µg·ml[-1] 的羊抗鼠 IgM 抗体(Cappel 公司)共同培养 2 天。随后收集细胞,在每个样品中加入 2×10^5 个 K46 细胞后,用荧光素标记的抗 B220 抗体(RA3-6B2)和藻红蛋白标记的羊抗鼠 IgM 抗体(Southern Biotechnology 公司)染色并使用流式细胞仪(美国贝克顿−迪金森公司)进行分析,确定 WEHI-231 与 K46 的比例。WEHI-231 细胞的数量等于 WEHI-231 与 K46 荧光强度之比乘以 2×10^5。a,WEHI-231 细胞的双染流式细胞术分析。在 1×10^5 个 A3.4C6 存在和不存在的情况下,将 2×10^4 个 WEHI-231 细胞与抗 IgM 抗体共培养 2 天。每个培养基中 WEHI-231 细胞(IgM[+]B220[+])、K46 细胞(IgM[-]B220[+])和 A3.4C6 细胞(IgM[-]B220[-])的百分比以及 WEHI-231 细胞的数量都标注在图中。在没加 K46 细胞的情况下,未处理或抗 IgM 抗体共培育处理的 WEHI-231 细胞平行染色作为对照。需要注意的是未处理的 WEHI-231 细胞进行流式分析的条件与其他的细胞有轻微的不同,并且尽管使用抗 IgM 抗体处理的 WEHI-231 细胞的 sIgM 的表达量降低为 1/20,但仍然显著高于 K46 细胞。b,抗 IgM 抗体刺激的 WEHI-231 细胞与 T 细胞系共培养。1×10^5 个 WEHI-231 细胞和 10 µg·ml[-1] 的抗 IgM 抗体一起分别与 1×10^5 个 T 细胞系 CTLL-2、2B4、N3-6-71 共培养 2 天。c,抗 IgM 抗体刺激的 WEHI-231 细胞与各种物质共培养。1×10^5 个 WEHI-231

of A3.4C6 (A3 sup.), the crude membrane fraction of A3.4C6 (A3 membr.), or a mixture of interleukins (IL) were cultured with 1×10^5 WEHI-231 cells in the presence of 10 μg ml^{-1} anti-IgM for 2 days. Culture supernatants of A3.4C6 were added at concentrations of 5 or 20%. The crude membrane fraction was prepared from 5×10^7 A3.4C6 cells as described[31] and suspended in 500 μl phosphate-buffered saline. The membrane fraction was subsequently added to the culture at concentrations of 0.5 or 5%. Culture with the interleukin mixture contained 25 U recombinant IL-1, 1 nM recombinant IL-2, 100 U recombinant IL-5, 1,300 U recombinant IL-6, and 5% culture supernatant of X63Ag8.653 cells transfected with an expression vector carrying mouse IL-4 cDNA[32].

To identify a molecule responsible for the inhibition of sIg-mediated B-cell death, we tested whether the membrane fraction and the culture supernatant of A3.4C6 cells could replace intact T cells for the rescuing activity. The membrane fraction of A3.4C6 completely substituted for the intact A3.4C6 cells, and the culture supernatant from A3.4C6 cells partially rescued WEHI-231 cells from sIg-mediated death (Fig. 1c). But none of interleukins 1, 2, 4, 5 and 6, either alone or in combination, were able to rescue WEHI-231 cells. These results suggest that sIg-mediated death of WEHI-231 cells may be prevented by interaction with membrane-bound molecules on A3.4C6, a fraction of which are also released into the supernatant, presumably by proteolysis.

T cells express the membrane-bound ligands for CD40 (ref. 16) and CD72 (ref. 17), which are expressed on the B-cell surface and are capable of transducing a signal for activation of B cells[18,23]. Furthermore, signalling through CD40 blocks spontaneous apoptosis of human germinal centre B cells cultured *in vitro*[24] and may thus play a part in the selection of B cells undergoing somatic hypermutation in germinal centres. To test whether either of the ligands for CD72 or CD40, that is, Ly1 or CD40L, respectively, is responsible for rescuing WEHI-231 cells, we tested A3.4C6 cells for expression of these molecules. As controls we examined 2B4 and N3-6-71 cells, which are inactive in rescuing anti-Ig-treated WEHI-231. Ly1 is expressed on all the T cell hybridomas tested (data not shown). In contrast, CD40L messenger RNA is expressed in A3.4C6 cells but not in 2B4 nor N3-6-71 cells (Fig. 2)

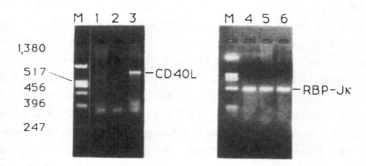

Fig. 2. Assay of CD40L by reverse transcriptase–polymerase chain reaction (RT-PCR). Total RNA was prepared from 2B4 (lanes 1 and 4), N3-6-71 (lanes 2, 5) and A3.4C6 (lanes 3, 6), followed by cDNA synthesis as described[33]. One μg of each cDNA was amplified using the pair of primers for CD40L (lanes 1–3): 5'-CG GAATTCAGTCAGCATGATAGAAAC-3' (sense) and 5'-AAGTCGACAGCGCACTGTTCAGAGT-3' (antisense). After 30 cycles, PCR products were resolved by agarose gel electrophoresis, followed by staining with ethidium bromide. As controls, the same cDNA samples were analysed for expression of RBP-Jκ[34]

细胞和 10 µg·ml⁻¹ 的抗 IgM 抗体一起分别与 $1×10^5$ 个 A3.4C6 细胞、A3.4C6 细胞培养上清（A3 sup.）、A3.4C6 细胞膜粗提物（A3 membr.）或白介素（IL）的混合物共培育 2 天。加入的 A3.4C6 细胞培养上清浓度为 5% 或 20%。细胞膜粗提物组分是参照文献描述从 $5×10^7$ 个 A3.4C6 细胞中制备的 [31]，并最终悬于 500 µl 磷酸盐缓冲液。加入的该粗提物浓度为 0.5% 或 5%。白介素混合物包括 25 U 重组 IL-1、1 nM 重组 IL-2、100 U 重组 IL-5、1,300 U 重组 IL-6 和 5% 转染了小鼠 IL-4 cDNA 的 X63Ag8.653 细胞的培养上清 [32]。

为了进一步鉴定抑制 sIg 介导的 B 细胞凋亡的分子，我们分别测试了 A3.4C6 细胞的细胞膜成分和培养上清是否能够代替完整的 T 细胞发挥阻断作用。结果发现 A3.4C6 的细胞膜成分可以完全替代完整细胞的功能，而细胞培养上清则可以部分抑制 sIg 介导的 WEHI-231 细胞的凋亡（图 1c）。我们也测试了 IL-1、IL-2、IL-4、IL-5、IL-6，发现它们单独或联合使用都不具有上述功能。这些结果表明 WEHI-231 细胞通过与 A3.4C6 膜表面结合分子相互作用从而抑制 sIg 介导的凋亡作用，而小部分结合分子据推测经由蛋白质水解作用释放到细胞培养上清中。

此前的研究表明 T 细胞可以表达 CD40（参考文献 16）和 CD72（参考文献 17）的膜结合型配体，而 CD40 和 CD72 在 B 细胞表面有表达，并介导信号传递促进 B 细胞的激活 [18,23]。此外，CD40 介导的信号还可以阻断体外培养的人生发中心 B 细胞的自然凋亡 [24]，并且其也许能将在生发中心进行体细胞高频突变的 B 细胞筛选出来。鉴于此，为了验证 CD72 或 CD40 的配体（即 Ly1 或 CD40L）是否与抑制 WEHI-231 细胞的凋亡有关，我们首先检测了 A3.4C6 细胞中这两个分子的表达情况，并使用 2B4 和 N3-6-71 这两个不具有抑制 B 细胞凋亡功能的细胞作为对照。结果表明，Ly1 在所有检测的 T 杂交瘤细胞中都有表达（结果没显示），而 CD40L mRNA 只表达于 A3.4C6 细胞中，而在 2B4 和 N3-6-71 细胞中没有表达（图 2）。

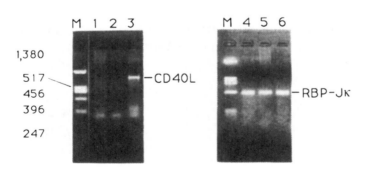

图 2. 使用逆转录聚合酶链式反应（RT-PCR）检测 CD40L 的表达。我们首先提取了 2B4（1 道，4 道）、N3-6-71（2 道，5 道）和 A3.4C6（3 道，6 道）细胞的所有 RNA，然后合成了 cDNA[33]。取 1 µg cDNA，使用下列引物扩增 CD40L（1~3 道）：5′-CGGAATTCAGTCAGCATGATAGAAAC-3′（正义链），5′-AAGTCGACAGCGCACTGTTCAGAGT-3′（反义链）。经过 30 个循环后，用琼脂糖凝胶电泳分离 PCR 产物，并用溴化乙锭（EB）染色。另外，使用下列引物扩增 RBP-Jκ[34] 作为对照（4~6 道）：

by RT-PCR using the pair of primers (lanes 4–6): 5'-TGGACGACGACGAGTCGGAA-3' (sense) and 5'-CTTGAGAAAGGCAGAAGTAC-3' (antisense). M, molecular size marker (*Hin*fI-digested BS-KS plasmid (Stratagene)); sizes are shown on the left in base pairs.

To test whether CD40L on the T-cell surface is responsible for rescuing B cells from apoptosis, we stimulated WEHI-231 cells with anti-CD40, together with anti-IgM. As antibodies against mouse CD40 are not available, we introduced the expression plasmid pMIK-hCD40 encoding human CD40 into WEHI-231 cells and treated the transfectant WEHI-hCD40 with anti-IgM and anti-human CD40 antibodies. Growth of WEHI-hCD40 cells was measured by the number of cells recovered after treatment (Fig. 3*a*) and by tritiated thymidine (^{3}H-TdR) uptake (Fig. 3*b*). Anti-Ig treatment markedly inhibited cell growth. This growth inhibition was mostly abrogated in the presence of anti-CD40 antibody, indicating that sIg-mediated apoptosis is inhibited by signalling through CD40. This conclusion is supported by a quantitative assay for apoptosis using propidium iodide[25] (Fig. 3*c*). WEHI-hCD40 cells were treated with anti-IgM and/or anti-CD40, and nuclei were prepared by treating cells with hypotonic solution. DNA contents of nuclei were measured by staining with propidium iodide, followed by flow cytometry. Almost all nuclei of the WEHI-hCD40 cells treated with anti-IgM contained reduced amounts of DNA, indicating extensive fragmentation of nuclei, presumably as a result of apoptosis. In contrast, the DNA contents of almost all nuclei were intact in cells treated with both anti-Ig and anti-CD40 antibodies. Moreover, growth inhibition of anti-IgM-treated WEHI-231 cells is blocked by co-culture with X63Ag8.653 myeloma cells transfected with an expression vector for CD40L (X63CD40L), but not with parent X63Ag8.653 cells (Fig. 3*d*). Taken together, signal transduction through CD40 that is induced by either anti-CD40 antibody or the ligand for CD40 inhibits sIg-mediated apoptotic cell death of WEHI-231 cells. It is, however, unlikely that signalling through CD40 blocks all the pathways of signal transduction generated by sIg multimerization. Indeed, treatment of WEHI-hCD40 cells with anti-Ig and anti-CD40 antibodies gives enhanced Ia expression, one of the markers for B-cell activation[26], whereas the increase in Ia expression by stimulation with anti-CD40 alone is marginal (Fig. 4). Moreover, Ia expression of the few WEHI-hCD40 cells that survived anti-IgM treatment was enhanced, but was less than that of WEHI-hCD40 cells treated with both anti-IgM and anti-CD40 antibodies. This result indicates that B cells are activated by a combination of signals through CD40 and sIg.

5′-TGGACGACGACGAGTCGGAA-3′(正义链)，5′-CTTGAGAAAGGCAGAAGTAC-3′(反义链)。M 道为分子大小标尺(使用 HinfI 消化的 BS-KS 质粒，Stratagene 公司)。标尺的大小以碱基对为单位标注在左侧。

接下来，为了验证 T 细胞表面的 CD40L 是否与抑制 B 细胞凋亡有关，我们同时使用了抗 CD40 抗体和抗 IgM 抗体刺激 WEHI-231 细胞。由于目前还没有抗鼠 CD40 的抗体，于是我们向 WEHI-231 细胞中转染了可以表达人 CD40 的 pMIK-hCD40 质粒(所得转染细胞记为 WEHI-hCD40)，然后再用抗 IgM 抗体和抗人 CD40 抗体来处理这个细胞。我们分别使用了细胞计数(图 3a)和 ^{3}H 胸腺嘧啶(^{3}H-TdR)示踪(图 3b)的方法来测量 WEHI-hCD40 细胞的生长。结果显示，抗 Ig 抗体处理后可以显著地抑制细胞的生长；如果同时使用抗人 CD40 抗体来处理细胞，则可以消除细胞的生长抑制。这表明 CD40 介导的信号可以抑制 sIg 介导的细胞凋亡。使用碘化丙啶[25] 定量检测凋亡的实验结果进一步支持了上述结论(图 3c)。我们首先使用抗 IgM 抗体和(或)抗 CD40 抗体刺激 WEHI-hCD40 细胞，然后使用低渗溶液处理细胞从而分离出细胞核；接下来再用碘化丙啶给细胞核中的 DNA 染色并用流式细胞仪检测。结果发现几乎所有经抗 IgM 抗体处理过的细胞的细胞核中的 DNA 含量都减少了，表明细胞核的碎片化较严重，而这可能是细胞凋亡引起的结果。相反，同时使用抗 IgM 抗体和抗 CD40 抗体处理的细胞其细胞核中的 DNA 含量几乎不变，相应地 DNA 的含量也较高。此外，使用转染了 CD40L 基因的 X63Ag8.653 骨髓瘤细胞(X63CD40L)与抗 IgM 抗体处理的 WEHI-231 细胞共培养，也可以阻断抗 IgM 抗体引起的 WEHI-231 细胞的生长抑制，而亲代 X63Ag8.653 骨髓瘤细胞则不具有这种作用(图 3d)。综合考虑上述结果，我们可以得出结论——使用抗 CD40 抗体或者 CD40 配体都可以引发 CD40 产生信号转导从而抑制 sIg 介导的 WEHI-231 细胞的凋亡。不过，上述 CD40 介导的信号似乎不能阻断所有的 sIg 多聚化引发的信号转导通路。事实上，同时使用抗 IgM 抗体和抗 CD40 抗体处理 WEHI-hCD40 细胞可以引起该细胞中 Ia(B 细胞激活的标志分子之一 [26]) 表达水平的升高，而单独使用抗 CD40 抗体则不会产生显著的效果(图 4)。此外，在那些经抗 IgM 抗体处理后仍存活下来的细胞中，Ia 的表达水平也是升高的，只不过比同时使用抗 IgM 抗体和抗 CD40 抗体处理的细胞要低一些。这表明 B 细胞的激活是 CD40 介导的信号和 sIg 共同作用的结果。

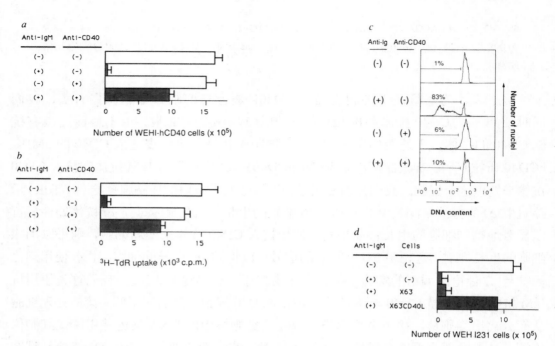

Fig. 3. Signalling through CD40 abrogates sIg-mediated cell death of WEHI-231 cells. Human CD40 transfectants of WEHI-231 (WEHI-hCD40) were cultured with 10 μg ml⁻¹ anti-IgM, 10 μg ml⁻¹ anti-human CD40 (5C3; a gift from H. Kikutani), or both, for 2 days. Alternatively, WEHI-231 cells were cultured either with X63Ag8.653 (X63) cells or X63 cells transfected with a CD40L vector (X63CD40L) for 2 days. *a*, Growth of WEHI-hCD40 cells. WEHI-hCD40 cells (1×10^5) were cultured in 1 ml culture medium with antibodies as indicated. All cells in the culture were collected and viable cells excluding trypan blue counted. Data represent mean cell number ± s.d. *b*, Proliferation of WEHI-hCD40 cells. WEHI-231 cells (4×10^4) were cultured in triplicate in 200 μl culture medium with the antibodies indicated for 2 days. Cultures were pulsed with 0.2 μCi ³H-TdR (Amersham) for the last 16 h of culture. Cells were collected and ³H-TdR uptake measured by liquid scintillation counting (Packard). Data represent the mean ³H-TdR uptake (c.p.m.) ± s.d. *c*, Apoptosis of WEHI-hCD40 cells. WEHI-hCD40 cells (1×10^5) were cultured in 1 ml culture medium with the antibodies indicated. Cells were lysed in a hypotonic solution (0.1% sodium citrate, 0.1% Triton-X100) containing 10 μg ml⁻¹ of propidium iodide, and the DNA content of the nuclei analysed on a FACScan as described[25]. The percentage of fragmented nuclei is indicated. *d*, Growth of WEHI-231 cells. WEHI-231 cells (1×10^5) were cultured with either 1×10^5 X63 cells or the same number of X63CD40L cells. All cells were collected and viable cells excluding trypan blue were counted. The number of WEHI-231 cells was determined by using flow cytometry analysis as in Fig. 1. Data represent mean cell number ± s.d.

Methods. The expression plasmid pMIK-hCD40 coding for human CD40 was constructed by cloning the *Xho*I fragment of CDM8/CDw40[35] containing human CD40 cDNA into *Xho*I-digested pMIKNeo (−) plasmid (gift from K. Maruyama). The pMIK-hCD40 plasmid was introduced into WEHI-231 cells by electroporation and the transfectant WEHI-hCD40 obtained by G418 selection. For generating X63CD40L cells, murine CD40L cDNA was amplified from A3.4C6 cells by RT-PCR (Fig. 2 legend) using the following primers: 5′-CGGAATTCAGTCAGCATGATAGAAAC-3′ (sense) and 5′-AAGTCGACAGCGCACTGTTCAGAGT-3′ (antisense). The amplified cDNA was digested with *Eco*RI and *Sal*I, and cloned into the pMIKneo plasmid digested with both *Eco*RI and *Xho*I, resulting in the pMIK-CD40L vector. X63Ag8.653 cells were transfected with the pMIK-CD40L vector and transfectants obtained by G418 selection.

210

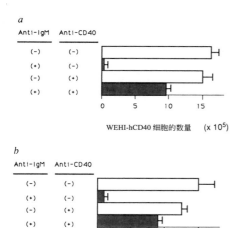

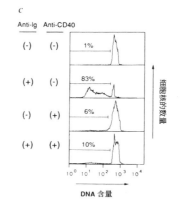

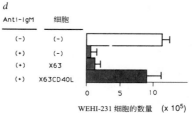

图 3. CD40 介导的信号能抑制 sIg 介导的 WEHI-231 细胞的凋亡。人 CD40 基因转染的 WEHI-231 细胞（WEHI-hCD40）与 10 μg·ml⁻¹ 的抗 IgM 抗体和（或）10 μg·ml⁻¹ 的抗人 CD40 抗体（5C3；菊谷惠赠）培养 2 天。或者，WEHI-231 细胞与 X63Ag8.653（X63）骨髓瘤细胞或转染了 CD40L 基因的 X63 细胞（X63CD40L）共培养 2 天。a, WEHI-hCD40 细胞的生长情况。1×10^5 个 WEHI-hCD40 细胞在 1 ml 培养基中与抗体共培养后，收集细胞，用台盼蓝染色后计算活细胞数量。数据以细胞平均数 ± 标准差的形式表示。b, WEHI-hCD40 细胞的增殖。4×10^4 个 WEHI-hCD40 细胞在 200 μl 培养基中与抗体共培养 2 天。每个都做了 3 个平行实验。在培养的最后 16 小时使用 0.2 μCi ³H-TdR（安马西亚公司）冲击，收集细胞，使用液体闪烁计数器计算 ³H-TdR 被细胞摄入的量。数据以 ³H-TdR 摄入平均值 ± 标准差（cpm）的形式表示。c, WEHI-hCD40 细胞的凋亡。1×10^5 个 WEHI-hCD40 细胞在 1 ml 培养基中与抗体共培养。然后使用含 10 μg·ml⁻¹ 碘化丙啶的低渗溶液（0.1% 柠檬酸钠，0.1% Triton-X100）裂解细胞，使用流式细胞仪分析细胞核中 DNA 含量[25]。图中显示了细胞核碎片化的百分比。d, WEHI-231 细胞的生长情况。1×10^5 个 WEHI-231 细胞与 1×10^5 个 X63 细胞或同样数量的 X63CD40L 细胞共培养。收集细胞后使用台盼蓝染色计算活细胞数量。WEHI-231 细胞的数量采用与图 1 相同的流式细胞术分析。数据以细胞平均数 ± 标准差的形式表示。

方法。通过克隆含人 CD40 cDNA 的 CDM8/CDw40[35] XhoI 片段，并将其插入有 XhoI 酶切位点的 pMIKNeo(−) 质粒（丸山惠赠），构建出编码人 CD40 的 pMIK-hCD40 质粒。通过电穿孔将 pMIK-hCD40 质粒转入 WEHI-231 细胞，使用 G418 筛选出 WEHI-hCD40 细胞。为了获得 X63CD40L 细胞，使用如下引物从 A3.4C6 细胞中通过 RT-PCR 扩增鼠 CD40L cDNA（图 2 图注）：5′-CGGAATTCAGTCAGCATGATAGAAAC-3′（正义链），5′-AAGTCGACAGCGCACTGTTCAGAGT-3′（反义链）。使用 EcoRI 和 SalI 酶切扩增出的 cDNA，插入到 EcoRI 和 XhoI 酶切后的 pMIKneo 质粒中，构建得到 pMIK-CD40L 载体。用 pMIK-CD40L 载体转染 X63Ag8.653 细胞并使用 G418 筛选得到 X63CD40L 细胞。

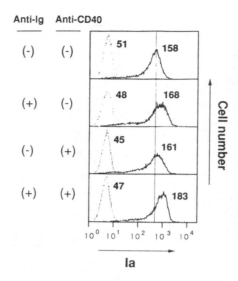

Fig. 4. Expression of the Ia antigen on the surface of WEHI-hCD40 cells. WEHI-hCD40 cells were cultured with anti-CD40 alone, anti-IgM alone, or both anti-IgM and anti-CD40, as described for Fig. 3a. After 2 days, cells were collected and stained for Ia expression (thick traces) by incubating with rat anti-mouse Ia (M5/114.15.2), followed by reaction with fluorescein-conjugated MARK1 (mouse anti-rat κ). Cells were subsequently analysed on a FACScan. As a control, cells were stained with fluorescein-conjugated MARK1 alone (thin traces). Mean fluorescence intensities are indicated. The vertical line in the flow cytometry histograms shows the peak channel for Ia expression of unstimulated WEHI-231 cells.

We have shown here that CD40L-producing T hybridoma cells A3.4C6, anti-CD40 antibody, or myeloma transfectants producing CD40L, can all rescue WEHI-231 cells from apoptosis induced by sIg multimerization. These results indicate that signalling through CD40 alone is sufficient for abrogating sIg-mediated apoptosis of WEHI-231 cells. Signalling through CD40 not only inhibits sIg-mediated apoptosis but also, together with signalling through sIg, activates WEHI-231 cells. T-helper cell lines not only express CD40L on the surface[16,23] but also secrete CD40L (ref. 27). The rescuing ability for WEHI-231 cells detected in the culture supernatant of A3.4C6 cells may thus be attributed to secreted CD40L.

Mature B cells undergo apoptosis by signalling through sIg *in vivo* (ref. 1; and T.T., unpublished observation). Activation of mature resting B cells *in vivo* probably requires an additional signal that abrogates sIg-mediated apoptosis. Our results indicate that such a signal is likely to be generated through the CD40 molecule, which is expressed on almost all B cells. The presence or absence of T-cell help through CD40 may, therefore, be crucial in determining whether antigen-stimulated B cells are activated or killed. As we have detected significant enhancement of bcl-2 protein production in WEHI-hCD40 cells after anti-CD40 treatment (data not shown), bcl-2 may be involved in CD40-mediated abrogation of B-cell apoptosis. But constitutive expression of bcl-2 does not prevent the death of WEHI-231 cells treated with anti-Ig (ref. 28; and A. Strasser and S. Cory, personal communication), nor does it abrogate clonal deletion of self-reactive B cells in autoantibody transgenic mice[29], suggesting that bcl-2 alone is not sufficient to block apoptosis of B cells. As CD40L

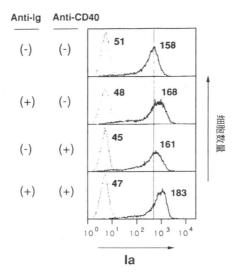

图 4. WEHI-hCD40 细胞表面 Ia 抗原的表达。如图 3a 所述，分别使用抗 CD40 抗体、抗 IgM 抗体或二者一起与 WEHI-hCD40 细胞共同培养。2 天后收集细胞，将该细胞与大鼠抗小鼠 Ia 抗体（M5/114.15.2）共培养，然后与荧光素标记的 MARK1（小鼠抗大鼠 κ 链）反应，检测 Ia 抗原的表达情况（图中的粗线）。利用流式细胞仪分析细胞数量。仅使用荧光素标记的 MARK1 直接染色的细胞作为对照（图中的细线）。图中标出了平均荧光强度。图中的垂直线为未刺激的 WEHI-hCD40 细胞中 Ia 抗原表达的峰值。

在这篇文章中，我们证明了表达 CD40L 的 T 杂交瘤细胞 A3.4C6、抗 CD40 抗体或转了 CD40L 的骨髓瘤细胞都可以抑制 sIg 多聚化所引起的 WEHI-231 细胞的凋亡。这些结果表明 CD40 介导的信号途径完全可以抑制 sIg 介导的 WEHI-231 细胞的凋亡。不仅如此，CD40 介导的信号还可以与 sIg 信号一起激活 WEHI-231 细胞。有研究表明辅助 T 细胞系不仅在细胞表面表达 CD40L[16,23]，而且可以分泌 CD40L 到细胞外（参考文献 27）。这也解释了 A3.4C6 细胞培养上清为什么也可以部分抑制 WEHI-231 细胞的凋亡——可能归功于分泌的 CD40L。

在体内实验中，sIg 信号会引起成熟 B 细胞的凋亡（参考文献 1 以及锷田武志尚未发表的观察结果）。在体内，处于静息期的成熟 B 细胞的激活可能需要额外的信号来阻断 sIg 介导的凋亡。我们的实验结果证明这个信号很可能是通过 CD40 分子来产生的。这一分子几乎在所有的 B 细胞中都有表达。因此，是否有辅助 T 细胞激活 B 细胞上的 CD40 信号成为那些被抗原激活的 B 细胞是活化还是死亡的决定性因素。我们在实验中观察到经抗 CD40 抗体处理过的 WEHI-hCD40 细胞中 bcl-2 蛋白的表达水平也有显著的提高（结果未展示），这表明 bcl-2 也可能参与了 CD40 介导的阻断 B 细胞凋亡过程。不过组成型表达的 bcl-2 并不能抑制抗 IgM 抗体处理的 WEHI-231 的凋亡（参考文献 28；以及与斯特拉瑟和科里的个人交流），也不能消除自身抗体转

is expressed on activated T helper cells but not on resting T cells[16,23,30], inhibition of sIg-mediated apoptosis and activation of B cells probably take place in an antigen-specific manner only in the presence of antigen-presenting cells, antigens, and helper T cells specific for the antigens. Self-reactive B cells may thus be deleted, presumably as a result of the absence of self-reactive T cells. But if T-cell tolerance breaks down, autoreactive T cells may initiate the pathogenesis of antibody-mediated autoimmunity by antagonizing clonal deletion of self-reactive mature B cells.

(**364**, 645-648; 1993)

Takeshi Tsubata, Jing Wu & Tasuku Honjo
Department of Medical Chemistry, Kyoto University Faculty of Medicine, Kyoto 606, Japan

Received 31 December 1992; accepted 4 June 1993.

References:

1. Murakami, M. *et al. Nature* 357, 77-80 (1992).

2. Russell, D. M. *et al. Nature* 354, 308-311 (1991).

3. Nemazee, D. A. & Bürki, K. *Nature* 337, 562-566 (1989).

4 Hartley, S. B. *et al. Nature* 353, 765-769 (1991).

5. Okamoto, M. *et al. J. Exp. Med.* 175, 71-79 (1992).

6. Nossal, G. J. V. *A. Rev. Immun.* 1, 33-62 (1983).

7. Goodnow, C. C. *A. Rev. Immun.* 10, 489-518 (1992).

8. Metcalf, E. S. & Klinman, N. R. *J. Exp. Med.* 143, 1327-1340 (1976).

9. Metcalf, E. S. & Klinman, N. R. *J. Immun.* 118, 2111-2116 (1977).

10. Benhamou, L. E., Cazenave, P. A. & Sarthou, P. *Eur. J. Immun.* 20, 1405-1407 (1990).

11. Hasbold, J. & Klaus, G. G. B. *Eur. J. Immun.* 20, 1685-1690 (1990).

12. Ozaki, S., Durum, S. K., Muegge, K., York-Jolley, J. & Berzofsky, J. A. *J. Immun.* 141, 71- 78 (1988).

13. Ogasawara, K., Maloy, W. L., Beverly, B. & Schwartz, R. H. *J. Immun.* 142, 1448-1456 (1989).

14. Ashwell, J. D., Cunningham, R. E., Noguchi, P. D. & Hernandez, D. *J. Exp. Med.* 165, 173- 194 (1987).

15. Odaka, C., Kizaki, H. & Tadakuma, T. *J. Immun.* 144, 2096-2101 (1990).

16. Armitage, R. J. *et al. Nature* 357, 80-82 (1992).

17. Van de Velde, H., von Hoegen, I., Luo, W., Parnes, J. R. & Thielemans, K. *Nature* 351, 662-664 (1991).

18. Clark, E. A. & Ledbetter, J. A. *Proc. Natl. Acad. Sci. U.S.A.* 83, 4494-4498 (1986).

19. Paulie, S. *et al. J. Immun.* 142, 590-595 (1989).

20. Rousset, F., Garcia, E. & Banchereau, J. *J. Exp. Med.* 173, 705-710 (1991).

21. Subbarao, B. & Mosier, D. E. *J. Immun.* 130, 2033-2037 (1983).

22. Subbarao, B. & Mosier, D. E. *J. Exp. Med.* 159, 1796-1801 (1984).

23. Noelle, R. J. *et al. Proc. Natl. Acad. Sci. U.S.A.* 89, 6550-6554 (1992).

24. Liu, Y.-J. *et al. Nature* 342, 929-931 (1989).

25. Nicoletti, I., Migliorati, M. C., Grignani, F. & Riccardi, C. *J. Immun. Meth.* 139, 271-279 (1991).

26. Mond, J. J., Seghal, E., Kung, J. & Finkelman, F. D. *J. Immun.* 127, 881-888 (1981).

27. Armitage, R. J. *et al. Eur. J. Immun.* 22, 2071-2176 (1992).

28. Cuende, E. *et al. EMBO J.* 12, 1555-1560 (1993).

29. Hartley, S. B. *et al. Cell* 72, 325-335 (1993).

30. Noell, R. J., Ledbetter, J. A. & Aruffo, A. *Immun. Today* 13, 431-433 (1992).

31. Robb, R. J. *Proc. Natl. Acad. Sci. U.S.A.* 83, 3992-3996 (1986).

32. Karasuyama, H. & Melchers, F. *Eur. J. Immun.* 18, 97-104 (1988).

基因小鼠中自身反应性 B 细胞的克隆排除[29]。这表明只有 bcl-2 是不足以阻断 B 细胞的凋亡。由于 CD40L 只在激活的辅助 T 细胞上表达而不在静息的 T 细胞中表达[16,23,30]，因此抑制 sIg 介导的凋亡和促进 B 细胞的激活可能是抗原特异性的。也就是说，只有当抗原呈递细胞、抗原以及针对该抗原特异性的辅助 T 细胞一起存在时才能激发 B 细胞的第二信使。如果自身反应性 B 细胞发生凋亡，那么极有可能是没有自身反应性 T 细胞导致的。但是如果 T 细胞耐受被打破，自身反应性 T 细胞就会通过对抗自身反应性成熟 B 细胞的克隆排除，从而引发自身抗体介导的自身免疫疾病。

（张锦彬 翻译；秦志海 审稿）

33. Shimizu, A., Nussenzweig, M. C., Mizuta, T.-R., Leder, P. & Honjo, T. *Proc. Natl. Acad. Sci. U.S.A.* **86**, 8020-8023 (1989).

34. Matsunami, N. *et al. Nature* **342**, 934-937 (1989).

35. Stamenkovic, I., Clark, E. A. & Seed, B. *EMBO J.* **8**, 1403-1410 (1989).

Acknowledgements. We thank S. Ozaki, J. A. Berzofsky, K. Ogasawara, E. A. Clark, H. Kikutani, K. Maruyama, A. Tominaga and J. Reed for reagents, M. Paumen for critically reading the manuscript, R. Sakai for technical help, and K. Hirano for help in preparing the manuscript. This work was supported in part by a grant from the Ministry of Education, Science and Culture of Japan.

Correlations between Climate Records from North Atlantic Sediments and Greenland Ice

G. Bond *et al.*

Editor's Note

Scientists studying climate change on the ancient Earth rely on records preserved in geological media. For the past several hundred million years, the two most revealing records are those in polar ice (which affords, among other things, temperature and greenhouse-gas concentrations) and in marine sediments. But do the two sources match up? Here Gerard Bond and other palaeoclimatologists assess this crucial question for climate records in the North Atlantic and in Greenland ice cores over the past 90,000 years. Not only do they find good agreement between the two, but also they find evidence that relatively rapid climate fluctuations are linked to ice-sheet collapse and the discharge of icebergs—a process thought to influence ocean circulation and the associated heat transport.

Oxygen isotope measurements in Greenland ice demonstrate that a series of rapid warm–cold oscillations—called Dansgaard–Oeschger events—punctuated the last glaciation[1]. Here we present records of sea surface temperature from North Atlantic sediments spanning the past 90 kyr which contain a series of rapid temperature oscillations closely matching those in the ice-core record, confirming predictions that the ocean must bear the imprint of the Dansgaard–Oeschger events[2,3]. Moreover, we show that between 20 and 80 kyr ago, the shifts in ocean–atmosphere temperature are bundled into cooling cycles, lasting on average 10 to 15 kyr, with asymmetrical saw-tooth shapes. Each cycle culminated in an enormous discharge of icebergs into the North Atlantic (a "Heinrich event"[4,5]), followed by an abrupt shift to a warmer climate. These cycles document a previously unrecognized link between ice sheet behaviour and ocean–atmosphere temperature changes. An important question that remains to be resolved is whether the cycles are driven by external factors, such as orbital forcing, or by internal ice-sheet dynamics.

MEASUREMENTS of $\delta^{18}O$ in the new GRIP ice core from Summit, Greenland provide the first record of air temperatures over the ice cap spanning the last 250 kyr[1]. We have correlated the last 90 kyr of that record with a proxy of sea surface temperature in two North Atlantic cores, DSDP site 609 and V23-81 (Fig. 1). The proxy of sea surface temperature is the abundance of *Neogloboquadrina pachyderma* (s.), a planktic foraminifera which lives in waters $< 10\,°C$ and comprises about 95% of the fauna at summer temperatures $< 5\,°C$[6,7]. Correlation among the foraminiferal records is constrained by depths of Heinrich events and AMS ^{14}C measurements (Figs 2, 3; and Table 1). Bioturbation of

北大西洋沉积物与格陵兰冰芯气候记录之间的相关性

邦德等

编者按

科学家们根据地质媒介中保存的记录研究早期地球的气候变化。在过去几亿年中，两个最能说明问题的记录是极地冰川记录（能提供包括温度和温室气体浓度在内的相关信息）和海洋沉积物记录。但是这两种记录可以对应吗？杰勒德·邦德和其他的古气候学家将在本文中通过北大西洋沉积物和格陵兰冰芯过去9万年的气候记录探讨这个至关重要的问题。他们发现二者之间不仅有良好的匹配性，而且有证据显示相对较快的温度波动与冰盖崩塌、冰山流出有关，这一过程影响了海洋环流和相应的热传输。

格陵兰冰芯的氧同位素测定结果证明，末次冰期曾被一系列的快速冷暖变化——丹斯果–厄施格尔事件——所打断[1]。我们将在本文中介绍北大西洋沉积物中记录的近9万年来的表层海水温度，其中包含一系列快速的温度振荡，与冰芯记录具有良好的匹配性，由此证实关于海洋曾受到丹斯果–厄施格尔事件的影响的预测[2,3]。此外，我们还将证明距今2万至8万年之间海洋–大气温度的变迁与降温循环有关，其持续时间平均约1万至1.5万年，表现为不对称的锯齿状。每个循环都以大量冰山流入北大西洋而告终（一次"海因里希事件"[4,5]），随后就突然转为较温暖的气候。这些循环为之前未曾认识到的冰盖行为与海洋–大气循环温度变化之间的关系提供了证据。还有待于解决的另一个重要问题是：这些循环的驱动因子到底是外部因素，如轨道驱动，还是内部的冰川动力。

格陵兰顶部萨米特站最新GRIP冰芯中的$\delta^{18}O$测定结果提供了近25万年来该冰盖上的首个空气温度记录[1]。我们将该记录中距今9万年的部分与两个北大西洋沉积岩芯（DSDP609孔和V23-81孔（图1））的表层海水温度替代指标进行了关联。表层海水温度的替代指标是厚壁新方球虫的丰度，厚壁新方球虫是一种生活在温度低于10℃水体中的浮游有孔虫，并且当夏季温度低于5℃时，其在整个种群中的丰度可达到95%左右[6,7]。有孔虫记录之间的相关性由海因里希事件的深度和加速器质谱^{14}C测年结果来约束（图2和3以及表1）。在两个岩芯中沉积物的生物扰动作用很

sediment is so low in both cores that we were able to sample at a resolution of 300–500 yr. In addition, by avoiding burrows and other sediment disturbances in V23-81, our new AMS ^{14}C ages have no reversals, a problem that hampered previous radiocarbon dating of that core[8]. We note that ^{14}C measurements in V23-81 and V30-101k revise previous age estimates for Heinrich events 3 and 4 (refs 4, 5) from 28 to 27 kyr BP (before present) and from 41 to 35.5 kyr, respectively (Table 1).

Table 1. Radiocarbon ages for cores DSDP 609, V23-81, and V30-101k

Core	Depth (cm)	Corrected age* (yr)	Error (± yr)	Core	Depth (cm)	Corrected age* (yr)	Error (± yr)
DSDP 609	73–75	12,350#	220	V23-81	154–155	10,900‡	140
DSDP 609 (G.b.)	79–81	13,250#	90	V23-81	198–199	12,320‡	220
DSDP 609	84–85	14,590#	230	V23-81	210	13,440§	120
DSDP 609	87–88	15,960#	240	V23-81	213	13,600§	120
DSDP 609	90–91	16,360#	150	V23-81	217	13,610§	100
DSDP 609	98–99	16,960#	120	V23-81	219	13,630§	100
DSDP 609	105–107	18,940#	220	V23-81	221	14,150§	110
DSDP 609	110–111	19,970#	330	V23-81	223	14,330§	100
DSDP 609	111–112	20,550#	260	V23-81	227	14,770§	110
DSDP 609	112–113	21,110#	220	V23-81	229	15,040§	110
DSDP 609	115–116	21,370#	220	V23-81	321	20,420§	180
DSDP 609	118–120	22,380#	340	V23-81	323	20,470§	160
DSDP 609 (G.i.)	139–141	25,260#	440	V23-81	327	20,570§	180
DSDP 609	147–149	26,170#	310	V23-81	329	20,990§	170
DSDP 609	153–155	29,170#	660	V23-81	331	21,210§	170
DSDP 609	166–167	30,080#	680	V23-81	333	21,700§	180
DSDP 609 (G.i.)	174–176	30,720#	730	V23-81	337	21,960§	190
V30-101k	56–57	23,570§	210	V23-81	371	24,680§	200
V30-101k · H4†(80cm)–	70	33,250§	510	V23-81	381	26,270§	260
V30-101k	85	36,570§	650	V23-81	391	28,980§	320
				V23-81	393	29,050§	310

Ages of interstadial 1e and the "W" (levels a, b and c) in Fig. 3			
Level	[14]C age (yr) in marine cores	Calendar age (yr) in marine cores‖	Ice core age¶
1e	12,300	14,300	14,500
a	13,550	16,000	16,400
b	15,400	18,440	18,800
c	18,400	21,970	21,070

* Corrected for assumed 400-yr difference between surface-water carbon and atmospheric carbon; G.b. = analyses on *G. bulloides*; G.i. = analyses on *G. inflata;* all other analyses done on *N. pachyderma* (s).

弱，使得我们的取样分辨率可达 300~500 年。此外，在 V23-81 孔上，由于避开了潜穴和其他沉积物扰动，我们得到的新加速质谱 [14]C 测年结果中并未出现倒置现象，而这正是之前阻碍对该岩芯进行放射性测年[8]的问题所在。我们注意到 V23-81 孔和 V30-101k 孔上 [14]C 的测年结果修正了之前对海因里希事件 3 和事件 4 的估算年龄（参考文献 4，5），分别由距今 2.8 万年和 4.1 万年变为 2.7 万年和 3.55 万年（表 1）。

表 1. DSDP 609 孔、V23-81 孔和 V30-101k 孔的放射性碳测年结果

岩芯名称		深度 (cm)	校正年龄 * (yr)	误差 (±yr)	岩芯名称	深度 (cm)	校正年龄 * (yr)	误差 (±yr)
DSDP 609		73~75	12,350#	220	V23-81	154~155	10,900‡	140
DSDP 609 (G.b.)		79~81	13,250#	90	V23-81	198~199	12,320‡	220
DSDP 609		84~85	14,590#	230	V23-81	210	13,440§	120
DSDP 609		87~88	15,960#	240	V23-81	213	13,600§	120
DSDP 609		90~91	16,360#	150	V23-81	217	13,610§	100
DSDP 609		98~99	16,960#	120	V23-81	219	13,630§	100
DSDP 609		105~107	18,940#	220	V23-81	221	14,150§	110
DSDP 609		110~111	19,970#	330	V23-81	223	14,330§	100
DSDP 609		111~112	20,550#	260	V23-81	227	14,770§	110
DSDP 609		112~113	21,110#	220	V23-81	229	15,040§	110
DSDP 609		115~116	21,370#	220	V23-81	321	20,420§	180
DSDP 609		118~120	22,380#	340	V23-81	323	20,470§	160
DSDP 609 (G.i.)		139~141	25,260#	440	V23-81	327	20,570§	180
DSDP 609		147~149	26,170#	310	V23-81	329	20,990§	170
DSDP 609		153~155	29,170#	660	V23-81	331	21,210§	170
DSDP 609		166~167	30,080#	680	V23-81	333	21,700§	180
DSDP 609 (G.i.)		174~176	30,720#	730	V23-81	337	21,960§	190
V30-101k		56~57	23,570§	210	V23-81	371	24,680§	200
V30-101k	H4†(80cm)~	70	33,250§	510	V23-81	381	26,270§	260
V30-101k		85	36,570§	650	V23-81	391	28,980§	320
					V23-81	393	29,050§	310
图 3 中的间冰阶 1e 和 "W" (a,b,c 层位) 的年龄								
层位		海洋岩芯中的 [14]C 年龄		海洋岩芯中的历年 ‖			冰芯年龄 ¶	
1e		12,300		14,300			14,500	
a		13,550		16,000			16,400	
b		15,400		18,440			18,800	
c		18,400		21,970			21,070	

* 假定表层海水中的碳和大气中的碳之间的差别为 400 年进行校正；G.b. 代表对泡抱球虫的分析结果；G.i. 代表对膨形抱球虫的分析结果；其他结果都是根据厚壁新方球虫的分析得到的。

† H4 in V30-101k is Heinrich layer 4 (this layer was initially identified as H3 in ref. 4; subsequent analyses of that core now demonstrate that it is H4).

‡ ref. 8.

§ AMS ^{14}C ages from analyses done at ETH-Zurich for this work.

‖ ref. 14.

¶ ref. 12.

ref. 4.

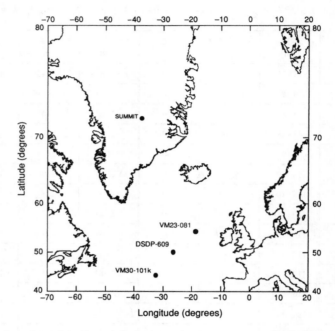

Fig. 1. Locations of the Summit ice core and the deep-sea cores described in this work.

A conspicuous feature common to both the ice and ocean records enabled us to correlate them in spite of their uncertain chronologies. That feature is a bundling of the millennial-scale Dansgaard–Oeschger cycles into longer cooling cycles, each terminated by an abrupt shift from cold to warm temperatures (Fig. 3). We matched the records at the points of abrupt temperature shifts and then "stretched" the ice-core record linearly until the points were aligned. That alignment is justified by the fact that at the latitudes of our cores (50–54 ° N), shifts in sea surface temperatures must be in phase with air temperature changes above Greenland, especially at the sharp terminations of Dansgaard–Oeschger cycles.

† V30-101k 孔中的 H4 为海因里希 4 层（该层最早在文献 4 中标识为 H3；对该岩芯后续的分析证明应该为 H4）。

‡ 文献 8。

§ 加速器质谱仪（AMS）测量 ¹⁴C 年龄，该分析工作是在苏黎世的 ETH 进行的。

‖ 文献 14。

¶ 文献 12。

文献 4。

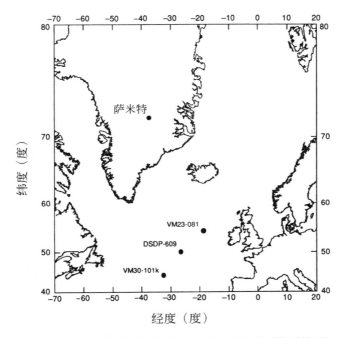

图 1. 本文所研究的格陵兰萨米特冰芯和深海沉积物岩芯的取样位置。

　　冰芯与海洋沉积物记录之间存在共同的显著特征使我们能把两种记录联系起来，尽管它们的年代序列存在不确定性。该特征就是长周期降温循环中一系列千年尺度的丹斯果-厄施格尔循环，每个循环都以由低温到高温的突然转变为结束（图 3）。我们根据温度突变点来匹配两条记录，然后对冰芯记录作线性"拉伸"以使这些温度突变点都能对应上。该校准方法得到以下事实的支持，即我们取样位置所在的纬度（北纬 50°~54°）上表层海水温度的变化与格陵兰上空大气温度的变化一定是同步的，特别是在丹斯果-厄施格尔循环突然结束时。

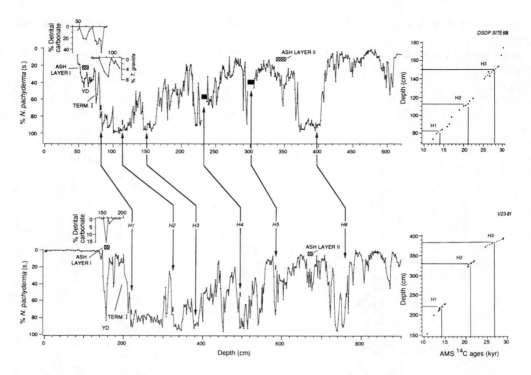

Fig. 2. Abundances of *N. pachyderma* (s.) in two North Atlantic cores, DSDP site 609 (top) and V23-81 (bottom). Samples from DSDP site 609 are from every centimetre; in V23-81, samples are from every 2 cm. Also shown for both sites are new measurements of % detrital carbonate (inset, top and bottom) across the levels of the Younger Dryas (YD) event, demonstrating large discharges of icebergs at that time, presumably from the Laurentide ice sheet. The % of *T. gravida*, a polar diatom (inset, top), indicates a warm-cold oscillation within isotope stage 2 at DSDP site 609. Depths of Ash Layer I and II are based on peak concentrations of the rhyolitic glass that defines those horizons. Heinrich events, shown as H1 to H6, are brief intervals of increased discharge of icebergs and reduced foraminiferal fluxes that serve as excellent markers for correlation among the marine cores[4]. The AMS ^{14}C ages to the right of the records are listed in Table 1. In both cores, detrital carbonate-bearing layers within Heinrich deposits are indicated by the black bars (Fig. 2). At DSDP site 609 the detrital carbonate-rich layers at H2, H4 and H5 accumulated nearly instantaneously[4] and are so thick that they must be removed before constructing the time series. In core V23-81, none of the layers containing detrital carbonate are thick enough to require removal.

What makes the correlation convincing is that down core, the changes in shapes and internal structures of the longer cycles is nearly the same in all the records (Fig. 3). The stepped pattern of cooling between the Younger Dryas (YD) and ice-core interstadial le is closely matched in V23-81, a pattern recognized previously in this core[8,9] and in the Norwegian Sea[10]. Between ice-core interstadials le and 2, a "W"-like pattern with superimposed, short oscillations appears in the ice and sediment, especially in V23-81. Two short interstadials just below the "W" also appear in V23-81. Between ice-core interstadials 2 and 20 are five asymmetrical cycles, each containing progressively cooler interstadials and culminating in a prominent cold stadial. Much of the structure within these cycles also appears in the foraminiferal records. Finally, the two oscillations on the stage 4/5 boundary and the cooling within marine stage 5b are present in all three records[11].

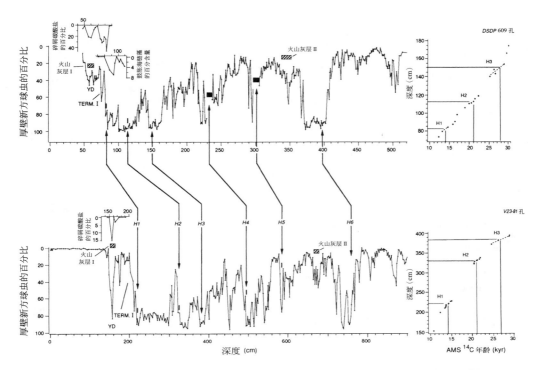

图 2. 北大西洋 DSDP609 孔（上图）和 V23-81 孔（下图）厚壁新方球虫的丰度。DSDP609 孔的采样间隔
为 1 cm，V23-81 孔为 2 cm。图中还给出了两个孔位上新仙女木事件层位上碎屑碳酸盐百分比的最新测
定结果（上、下插图），证明当时有大量冰山流出，并且很可能来自劳伦太德冰盖。鼓胀海链藻（一种极
地硅藻）的百分含量（上插图）显示，DSDP609 孔的氧同位素 2 阶中存在一个冷暖振荡过程。火山灰
层 I 和 II 的深度是根据流纹岩玻璃的最大浓度确定的。图中 H1 到 H6 代表的海因里希事件是冰山流出
增加和有孔虫通量降低之间的一个短暂时期，作为绝佳的标志层，可以很好地将不同的海洋沉积物岩
芯相互联系起来[4]。图右侧的 AMS [14]C 年龄记录列于表 1。两岩芯的海因里希沉积中的碎屑碳酸盐层
位均以黑色条带标出（图 2）。在 DSDP609 孔的 H2、H4 和 H5 阶段中的富碎屑碳酸盐层几乎是瞬时
沉积[4]并且沉积厚度很大，以致进行时间序列重建前需首先将其剔除。在 V23-81 孔中则不存在厚度
达到需要剔除程度的碎屑碳酸盐层。

　　使这种相关性更有说服力的是：随着深度的增加，所有记录中长期循环的形状
和内部特征的变化几乎完全相同（图 3）。在 V23-81 孔中，新仙女木期与冰芯 1e 间
冰阶之间阶梯式的降温模式也极为匹配，这种模式是之前研究该岩芯[8,9]和挪威海岩
芯[10]时发现的。在冰芯中的 1e 间冰阶和 2 间冰阶之间，冰芯和沉积物记录中都出
现了呈"W"形重叠的短期振荡，特别是在 V23-81 孔中。在 V23-81 孔记录中，"W"
之下还存在两个短暂的间冰阶。冰芯间冰阶 2 和 20 之间是五个不对称的循环，每个
循环都包含多个愈来愈冷的间冰阶并在一个主冰阶达到顶点。这些循环的大部分特
征也见于有孔虫记录中。最后，三条记录中都可以看到海洋氧同位素第 4 阶段和第
5 阶段分界处的两次振荡以及海洋氧同位素 5b 阶的变冷事件[11]。

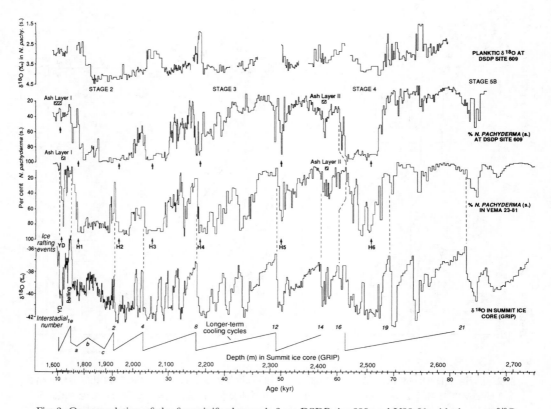

Fig. 3. Our correlation of the foraminiferal records from DSDP site 609 and V23-81 with the new $\delta^{18}O$ record from GRIP, Summit, Greenland. (Note that the timescale is not an age model for the ice core.) The interstadial numbers in the ice-core record are from the numbering system in ref. 1. Also shown are the longer-term cooling cycles, defined by bundling of millennium scale cycles (Dansgaard–Oeschger cycles) and abrupt shifts to markedly warm interstadials. The dashed lines were used as tie points for matching the ice-core and marine records. The bend in the tie point corresponding to interstadial 16 probably reflects a small decrease in the sedimentation rate at this depth in V23-81 relative to DSDP 609. See text for construction of the timescale. At the top of the figure is the planktic $\delta^{18}O$ measured in *N. pachyderma* (s.)[4]. The heavy arrows mark the locations of the IRD peaks within the Heinrich events (H1 to H6) and the peak concentrations of detrital carbonate IRD in the Younger Dryas event. The boxes filled with slanted lines are the levels of Ash Layers I and II in the marine cores; the correlatives of these layers in the ice core should occur at depths of ~1,630 m (Ash Layer I) and ~2,426 m (Ash Layer II). It should be noted that the short cooling cycle at about 13,000 ^{14}C yr BP in DSDP site 609, a contemporaneous decrease in the rate of warming in V23-81 and the cold peak containing H1 in V23-81 between 14,000 and 15,000 ^{14}C yr were not recognized previously[4,5]. These revisions are a consequence of our new foraminiferal measurements in both cores and the improved ^{14}C dating in V23-81.

The only direct confirmation of our correlation so far comes from the upper parts of the records where ice-core dating and radiocarbon to calendar age conversions are reasonably well established[12-14]. There, except for the oldest layer, calendar ages of correlated ice and sediment differ by no more than a few hundred years (Table 1, Fig. 3). Two other tests yet to be performed are the depths predicted for marine Ash layers I and II in the ice core (Figs 2, 3).

Our timescale is constrained by ^{14}C dating for the past ~35,500 years. Below the level of

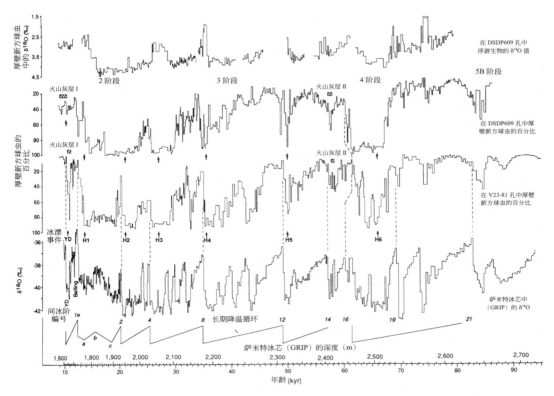

图 3. 我们得到的 DSDP609 孔和 V23-81 孔的有孔虫记录与格陵兰 GRIP 萨米特冰芯中新 δ^{18}O 记录之间的相关性。（注意该时间序列并不是作为冰芯定年的一个模型。）冰芯记录中的间冰阶的编号是根据参考文献 1 中的计数系统得出的。图中还给出了长期降温循环，这些循环由多个千年尺度的循环（丹斯果－厄施格尔循环）组成，并且通常会突然转变为显著温暖的间冰阶。虚线表示冰芯与海洋记录匹配点的连接线。与 16 间冰阶对应的连接线出现的弯曲很可能说明，相对于 DSDP609 孔来说，在该深度上 V23-81 孔的沉积速率略有下降。关于时间尺度的建立见正文。在图的最顶部为根据厚壁新方球虫测得的浮游生物的 δ^{18}O 值[4]。粗体箭头表示海因里希事件（H1~H6）中 IRD 峰的位置以及新仙女木事件中碎屑碳酸盐的 IRD 最大浓度。带斜线的方框表示海洋岩芯中火山灰层 I 和 II 的位置，它们在冰芯中的对应物应分别出现在 1,630 m（火山灰层 I）和 2,426 m（火山灰层 II）深度上。应当注意的是，距今 13,000 [14]C 年时 DSDP609 孔中曾出现的短暂降温循环、同一时代在 V23-81 孔上出现的升温速率降低现象以及 14,000~15,000 [14]C 年之间 V23-81 孔的 H1 中包含的冷峰，都是之前未曾识别出的[4,5]，上述修改都是我们在两岩芯中采用了新的有孔虫测定方法并对 V23-81 孔 [14]C 测年改进的结果。

　　到目前为止，我们取得的直接可靠的相关关系只存在于冰芯记录的上部，这是因为只有这一部分冰芯定年与碳放射性年龄转换结果的时间序列已被合理地建立起来[12-14]。除了最老的层位之外，对应的冰芯与沉积物的年龄相差不过几百年（表 1 和图 3）。海洋火山灰层 I 和 II 这两次事件还有待于从冰芯中对应的深度去证实（图 2 和 3）。

　　近 3.55 万年以来的时间尺度经过了 [14]C 测年结果的限定。V23-81 孔 [14]C 年层以下，

[14]C dating in V23-81 we assigned ages from DSDP site 609 to H5 (50 kyr), to H6 (66 kyr) and to the sharp peak in stage 5b (84.4 kyr) and then interpolated linearly between them. To date the level below 5b in V23-81, we extrapolated the sedimentation rate between H6 and the sharp peak in 5b. Whereas our timescale is broadly consistent with previous dating of the ice core[1] and with the SPECMAP chronology[15], we emphasize that it is not intended to be an age model for the ice core. Conversion of ^{14}C ages to calendar ages is uncertain, especially beyond ~20 kyr, and sedimentation rates in the marine cores are probably not linear. In fact, the spacing of the ice-core depth intervals should increase steadily down core, and the deviation from that spacing below about 2,200 m (Fig. 3) may be an artefact of changes in sedimentation rates in DSDP site 609.

Our new findings are the strongest evidence so far that Dansgaard–Oeschger cycles are imprinted in the marine sediments of the North Atlantic. The temperature shifts, especially in V23-81, occur on millennium timescales and have asymmetric shapes, sharp boundaries and strong amplitudes (up to a change in temperature of ~5 °C), features which characterize the Dansgaard–Oeschger cycles. A number of the Dansgaard–Oeschger cycles even appear to have direct correlatives in the marine records (Fig. 3). Clearly, for at least 80 kyr the atmosphere and ocean surface were a coupled system, repeatedly undergoing massive reorganizations on timescales of centuries or less. At the abrupt cold-to-warm shifts that terminate Dansgaard–Oeschger cycles (Fig. 2), rates of change in ocean temperatures must have been nearly the same as in the ice core: that is, several degrees within decades[9,13,16,17]. The large amplitudes and high rates of these temperature shifts are independent of ice volumes, occurring during deglaciation, during the glacial maximum, during the warmer isotope stage 3 and even during the inception of large ice sheets at the stage 4/5 boundary.

Perhaps the most important finding of our study is evidence of an unexpectedly close relation between the ice-core temperature cycles and one of the most prominent features of North Atlantic records, the Heinrich events. Heinrich events occur during times of sea surface cooling, reduced fluxes of foraminifera and brief, exceptionally large discharges of icebergs from the Laurentide ice sheet that left conspicuous layers of detrital carbonate in deep sea sediment[4,5,18]. Accompanying these events were large decreases in planktic $\delta^{18}O$ (Fig. 3), evidence of lowered surface salinities probably caused largely by melting of the drifting ice[4]. Our correlation demonstrates that the iceberg discharges and salinity drops must have occurred during times of particularly cold stadials (Fig. 3). Supporting this is evidence that H1 has the same calendar age, within error, as the younger cold cycle in the "W" (cycle a, Fig. 3, Table 1). In addition, the Younger Dryas, which unquestionably correlates with a prominent stadial in the ice core (Fig. 3), has features in common with Heinrich events. During the Younger Dryas, North Atlantic sea surface temperatures dropped[19], salinities decreased[20], and Laurentide ice advanced through Hudson Strait, depositing detrital carbonate-bearing sediment in the Labrador Sea[21]. We have now found elevated percentages of detrital carbonate in sediments of Younger Dryas age (Fig. 2), indicating that, just as during the Heinrich events, icebergs drifted from the Labrador Sea far into the North Atlantic[4]. We note that the match of Heinrich events to cold stadials confirms our earlier suggestion that Heinrich events formed during periods of extreme atmospheric cooling[4].

我们用 DSDP609 孔确定到 H5 阶段（5 万年）、H6 阶段（6.6 万年）和 5b 阶段的尖峰（8.44 万年）的年龄，然后再通过线性内插定年。为了确定 V23-81 孔 5b 阶以下的年龄，我们对 H6 和 5b 阶段尖峰之间的沉积作用速率进行了外推。虽然我们获得的时间序列和之前的冰芯定年[1]以及 SPECMAP 定年结果[15]基本一致，但我们强调它不应成为一个确定冰芯年龄的模型。由 [14]C 年龄到历年的转换还存在不确定性，特别是对于距今 2 万年以前，并且海洋岩芯的沉积速率也有可能并不是线性的情况。实际上，冰芯的取样深度的时间间隔应该是向下逐渐增大的，而 2,200 m 以下间隔的偏差（图 3），可能是 DSDP609 孔沉积速率变化的产物。

目前为止，我们的新发现有力地证明了，北大西洋深海沉积物记录中保存了丹斯果-厄施格尔循环。温度的变化，特别是在 V23-81 孔中，通常发生在千年时间尺度，呈不对称形态，边界处很陡且振幅很大（温度的变化可达 5 ℃左右），而这正是丹斯果-厄施格尔循环的典型特征。数个丹斯果-厄施格尔循环甚至与海洋记录存在直接的相关性（图 3）。显然，在过去至少 8 万年中大气和海洋表层是一个耦合系统，重复地经历着百年时间尺度以内的大规模重组。在丹斯果-厄施格尔循环末期由冷到暖的突然转变时（图 2），海洋温度的变化速率必定与冰芯接近，即数十年内变化几度左右[9,13,16,17]。这些大幅度、高速率的温度转换与冰体积无关，它们既发生于冰消期和冰期最盛期，也发生于海洋氧同位素第 3 阶段暖期，甚至还发生于海洋氧同位素第 4 阶段和第 5 阶段交界处大冰川开始形成的时期。

也许本研究得到的最重要的收获就是发现了冰芯温度循环与北大西洋记录最重要的特征之一——海因里希事件——之间超乎想象的密切关系。海因里希事件发生于海洋表层温度下降时期，有孔虫通量下降，异常大量的冰山在这段时间内从劳伦太德冰盖上脱离下来并在深海沉积物中留下了明显的碎屑碳酸盐层[4,5,18]。与之相伴的是浮游生物 $\delta^{18}O$ 值的大幅下降（图 3），证明表层海水盐度下降主要是由冰山的融化所致[4]。我们得出的相关性证明，冰山的融化和盐度的降低尤其发生在冷冰阶中（图 3）。支持该观点的证据就是：在误差范围以内 H1 和 "W" 中的年龄较新的冷循环（a 循环）具有相同的历年（图 3 和表 1）。此外，新仙女木期，毫无疑问与冰芯记录的显著冰阶相关（图 3），也与海因里希事件之间存在共同特征。新仙女木期时，北大西洋海洋表层温度降低[19]、盐度下降[20]，且劳伦太德冰盖沿哈得孙海峡前移，在拉布拉多海中形成了含碳酸盐碎屑的沉积物[21]。现在我们已发现，新仙女木期时，沉积物中碎屑碳酸盐的比例明显升高（图 2），这说明正如海因里希事件发生时一样，冰山穿过拉布拉多海进入到北大西洋内部深处[4]。我们注意到海因里希事件与冷冰阶的一致性证实了我们先前提出的海因里希事件形成于大气极端降温时期的观点[4]。

It is also significant that except for H1, the Heinrich events, and the Younger Dryas ice rafting event as well, consistently occur near the ends of the bundled Dansgaard–Oeschger cycles that constrain much of our correlation (Fig. 3). The bundles form a series of saw-tooth shaped cycles, each defined by a succession of progressively cooler interstadials (Fig. 3), probably reflecting a progressive strengthening of the polar cell. Each cycle culminates in a prolonged cold period (stadial) during which a Heinrich event occurs. Following the stadial is a rapid termination-like shift to a prominent warm interstadial marking the beginning of the next cycle (Fig. 3). This complex pattern, known previously only from deglacial records[8-10], persists through almost all of the last glaciation, the only exceptions being the intervals through the "W" and stage 5b.

The series of saw-tooth shaped cooling cycles is clearly a fundamental structure of the atmosphere and sea-surface records, and must bear a close relation to the Heinrich events and the repeated, massive collapses of the Laurentide ice sheets. With the evidence in hand we cannot be certain whether the cooling cycles were caused entirely by internal oscillations of the ice sheet[22], or whether they reflect a mode of climate forcing that caused ice sheets to grow, culminating each time in a prolonged, cold stadial, ice-sheet instability and massive calving. If internal oscillations of the ice sheet are sole mechanisms, they must have operated during times such as the Younger Dryas when ice volumes had decreased. We note however, that because H1 comes at the end of a different type of cycle, the "W", its relation to climatic and ice-sheet mechanisms may well have been different from that of the others.

The abrupt warmings that followed the Heinrich events and that caused the asymmetry of the cooling cycles, on the other hand, could have been a direct consequence of the ice. Collapse of the ice sheet and landward retreat of ice streams after each event must have reduced the flux of icebergs to the open ocean. The resulting increase in surface salinity could have been large enough to strengthen thermohaline circulation, rapidly bringing heat into the North Atlantic. If so, that further supports our suggestion[4] that iceberg meltwater strongly influenced the North Atlantic's thermohaline circulation during glaciation.

Whatever their origin, the series of asymmetric cooling cycles and the prominent warmings that terminate them are so conspicuous in the atmospheric and ocean surface records of the North Atlantic that they must be imprinted in other records from the last glaciation. In fact, a series of prominent cycles on timescales of several thousands of years appears within marine stage 3 in summer sea surface temperature estimates from other North Atlantic deep-sea cores[23,24], in the Grande Pile pollen record[25], and in high-resolution benthic $\delta^{18}O$ records from core V19-30 in the eastern equatorial Pacific[26]. Perhaps the sea-level highstands demarked in the flights of the marine terraces of the last glaciation[27] are the consequence of massive ice sheet collapses during Heinrich events and the warmings at the ends of the cycles. To test these ideas, however, will require the analysis of records with more precise chronologies and at much higher resolution than has been attempted to date.

Our new findings still leave unexplained the Dansgaard–Oeschger oscillations in air

还有很重要的一点，除 H1 以外，海因里希事件以及新仙女木冰漂事件，均发生在丹斯果 – 厄施格尔循环的末期（图 3），这让我们看到它们之间的必然相关性。同位素曲线这种一个接一个的大幅流动形成了一系列的锯齿状循环，每个循环又由一系列逐渐变冷的间冰阶来确定（图 3），这很可能反映了极地流环的逐渐增强。每个循环都结束于一个持续时间较长的冰阶，而海因里希事件就发生在冰阶期间。紧随冰阶之后是向温暖间冰阶的一次快速转换，标志着这次循环的结束以及下一个循环的开始（图 3）。之前人们对这种复杂模式的认识仅限于冰退记录研究[8-10]，实际上它近乎贯穿着差不多整个末次冰期，唯一的例外出现在"W"到 5b 阶之间。

一系列锯齿状降温循环显然是大气和海洋表层记录的基本结构，并且与海因里希事件和劳伦太德冰盖的反复、大规模崩塌有密切关系。依据手头的证据我们还不能确定降温循环是完全由冰盖的自身振荡所致[22]，还是它们只是反映了一种气候驱动模式导致冰盖增大，并且每次都以一个很长的冷冰阶、冰盖不稳定和大规模的冰解作为结束。倘若冰盖的自身振荡是唯一机制，那么它们一定是在冰盖体积减小时（如新仙女木期）发挥作用。然而，我们注意到，由于 H1 出现于一种不同类型循环（"W"）的末期，它与气候和冰盖机制之间的关系应该与其他事件有差别。

另一方面，海因里希事件之后的突然变暖以及导致不对称降温循环事件的原因，应该是冰川作用的直接结果。每次事件后冰盖的崩塌以及冰流向陆地退却都减少了向开阔大洋中输送的冰山。由此导致的表层盐度的升高已足以引起热盐环流增强，从而快速将热量带入北大西洋。倘若如此，将能进一步支持我们以前的观点[4]，即冰期时冰山融水强烈影响北大西洋的热盐环流。

不论其起因是什么，在北大西洋的大气和海洋表层记录中，这一系列不对称的降温循环以及终结它们的快速升温是如此显著，因而有理由相信在其他末次冰期记录中必定也留有它们的痕迹。事实上，在北大西洋深海岩芯的夏季海洋表层温度记录[23,24]的、大皮勒（法国东北部的地名）孢粉记录[25]的以及东赤道太平洋 V19-30 孔的高分辨率海洋 $\delta^{18}O$ 记录[26]的海洋氧同位素 3 阶段中也存在一系列数千年尺度上的显著循环。或许末次冰期海岸台地的各阶地中可区分显示的海平面高水位期[27]就是海因里希事件中大规模冰盖崩塌及其后各循环末期变暖事件的结果。然而，要想验证上述观点，就需要利用更精确的定年方法在更高的分辨率下对记录加以分析。

我们的新发现仍未能解释格陵兰气温的丹斯果 – 厄施格尔振荡，这些气温振荡

temperature over Greenland that punctuate the intervals between the Heinrich events. Perhaps, as we suggested earlier[3], these reflect the salt-induced ocean circulation oscillations caused by an interaction between the ocean heat-pump and the Scandinavian ice sheets. Although many questions remain unanswered, our correlation of the Heinrich events so prominent in the ice cores with the more frequent Dansgaard–Oeschger events in the ice cores brings us significantly closer to understanding the complex link between ice-sheet dynamics and ocean operation.

(365, 143-147; 1993)

Gerard Bond*, Wallace Broecker*, Sigfus Johnsen[†‡], Jerry McManus*, Laurent Labeyrie[§], Jean Jouzel[‖¶] & Georges Bonani[#]

* Lamont-Doherty Earth Observatory of Columbia University, Palisades, New York 10964, USA

† The Niehls Bohr Institute, Department of Geophysics, University of Copenhagen, Haraldsgade 6, DK-2200, Copenhagen N, Denmark

‡ Science Institute, Department of Geophysics, University of Iceland, Dunghaga 3, IS-107 Reykjavik, Iceland

§ CFR Laboratoire mixte CNRS-CEA, Domaine du CNRS, 91198, Gif-sur-Yvette, Cedex, France

‖ Laboratorie de Modélisation du Climat et de l'Environnement, CEA/DSM, CE Saclay 91191, France

¶ Laboratorie de Glaciologie et Géophysique de l'Environnement, CNRS, BP96, 38402 St. Martin d'Hères Cedex, France

Institute fur Mittelenergiephysik, ETH Honggerberg, CH-8093 Zurich, Switzerland

Received 21 April; accepted 16 July 1993.

References:

1. Dansgaard, W. *et al. Nature* **364**, 218-220 (1993).

2. Broecker, W. S. *et al. Quat. Res.* **30**, 1-6 (1988).

3. Broecker, W. S., Bond, G. & Klas, M. *Paleoceanogr.* **5**(4), 469-477 (1990).

4. Bond, G. *et al. Nature* **360**, 245-249 (1992).

5. Broecker, W. S., Bond, G., Klas, M., Clark, E. & McManus, J. *Clim. Dynamics* **6**, 265-273 (1992).

6. Bé, A. W. H. & Tolderlund, D. S. *Micropaleontology of Oceans* (eds Funnell, B. M. & Riedel, W. R.) 105-149 (Cambridge Univ. Press, 1971).

7. Kellogg, T. B. *Boreas* **9**, 115-137 (1980).

8. Broecker, W. S. *Paleoceanogr.* **3**(1), 1-19 (1988).

9. Lehman, S. J. & Keigwin, L. D. *Nature* **356**, 757-762 (1992).

10. Karpuz, N. C. & Jansen, E. *Paleoceanogr.* **7**(4), 499-520 (1992).

11. Bond, G., Broecker, W., Lotti, R. & McManus, J. in *Start of a Glacial* (eds Kukla, G. J. & Went, E.) 185-205 (Springer, Berlin, 1992).

12. Johnsen, S. J. *et al. Nature* **359**, 311-313 (1992).

13. Alley, R. B. *et al. Nature* **362**, 527-529 (1993).

14. Bard, E., Arnold, M., Fairbanks, R. G. & Hamelin, B. *Radiocarbon* **3**(1), 191-199 (1993).

15. Martinson, D. G. *et al. Quat. Res.* **27**, 1-29 (1987).

16. Dansgaard, W., White, J. W. C. & Johnsen, S. J. *Nature* **339**, 532-533 (1989).

17. Taylor, K. C. *et al. Nature* **361**, 432-136 (1993).

18. Heinrich, H. *Quat. Res.* **29**, 142-152 (1988).

19. Ruddiman, W. F. & McIntyre, A. *Paleogeogr. Palaeoclimatol. Palaeoecol.* **35**, 145-214 (1981).

20. Duplessy, J-C., Labeyrie, L., Juillet-LeClerc, A. & Duprat, J. in *The Last Deglaciation: Absolute and Radiocarbon Chronologies* (eds Bard, E. & Broecker, W. S.) 201-208 (Springer, Berlin, 1992).

21. Andrews, J. T., Tedesco, K., Briggs, W. M. & Evans, L. W. *Can. J. Earth Sci.* (in the press).

22. MacAyeal, D. R. *Nature* **359**, 29-32 (1992).

23. Ruddiman, W. F. in *Northern America and Adjacent Oceans during the Last Deglaciation: The Geology of North America* (eds Ruddiman, W. F. & Wright, H. E. Jr) 137-154 (Geol. Soc. of Am., Boulder, 1987).

24. Sancetta, C., Imbrie, J, & Kipp, N. G. *Quat. Res.* **3**, 110-116 (1973).

25. Woillard, G. & Mook, W. G. *Science* **215**, 159-161 (1982).

事件穿插于海因里希事件之间。也许，正如我们之前提出的那样[3]，这些反映出海洋热泵与斯堪的纳维亚冰盖之间的交互作用引起了海盐诱导的大洋环流振荡。尽管尚存在许多问题有待解决，但我们把冰芯记录中特别突出的海因里希事件与冰芯记录中发生频率更高的丹斯果－厄施格尔事件关联起来，这使我们向更好地理解冰盖动力与海洋机制之间的复杂关联性方面又前进了一大步。

（齐红艳 翻译；田立德 审稿）

26. Shakleton, N, J., Imbrie, J. & Hall, M. A. *Earth Planet. Sci. Lett.* **65**, 233-244 (1983).

27. Bloom, A. L., Broecker, W. S., Chappell, J. M. A., Matthews, R. K. & Mesolella, K. J. *Quat. Res.* **4**, 185-205 (1974).

Acknowledgements. This research was supported in part by grants from the US National Science Foundation (NSF) and NOAA. The ice-core data are from the Greenland Ice Core Project (GRIP) organized by the European Science Foundation. The measurement of planktic $\delta^{18}O$ was supported by the French CNRS, CEA and CEE(EPOCH). We thank the Ocean Drilling Program for permission to sample cores from DSDP site 609. Support for the core collection of Lamont-Doherty Geological Observatory is provided by the NSF and the Office of Naval Research. We thank C. Sancetta for providing her unpublished diatom data from DSDP site 609. We also thank G. Denton, E. Jansen, S. Leyman, D. MacAyeal and P. Mayewski for comments on the manuscript.

Music and Spatial Task Performance

F. H. Rauscher *et al.*

Editor's Note

In appearing to verify the long-standing suspicion that music enhances intelligence, this report presented by Frances Rauscher and colleagues in California attracted immense interest. They reported that college students show slightly better results in spatial reasoning tests (boosting IQ by 8–9 points) after listening to ten minutes of Mozart's music than after either listening to a "relaxation tape" or sitting in silence. Follow-up studies drew diverse conclusions: some apparently supported the claim, others found no effect, or results not specific to Mozart. It now seems that such effects are minor and transient, and are caused by mood and arousal rather than anything specific to music. All the same, "brain music" for children has become a small marketing industry.

THERE are correlational[1], historical[2] and anecdotal[3] relationships between music cognition and other "higher brain functions", but no causal relationship has been demonstrated between music cognition and cognitions pertaining to abstract operations such as mathematical or spatial reasoning. We performed an experiment in which students were each given three sets of standard IQ spatial reasoning tasks; each task was preceded by 10 minutes of (1) listening to Mozart's sonata for two pianos in D major, K488; (2) listening to a relaxation tape; or (3) silence. Performance was improved for those tasks immediately following the first condition compared to the second two.

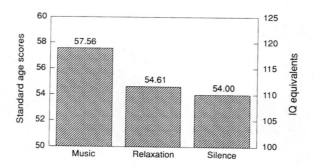

Standard age scores for each of the three listening conditions.

Testing procedure. In the music condition, the subject listened to 10 min of the Mozart piece. The relaxation condition required the subject to listen to 10 min of relaxation instructions designed to lower blood pressure. The silence condition required the subject to sit in silence for 10 min. One of three abstract reasoning tests taken from the Stanford–Binet intelligence scale[4] was given after each of the listening conditions. The abstract/spatial reasoning tasks consisted of a pattern analysis test, a multiple-choice matrices test and a multiple-choice paper-folding and cutting test. For our sample, these three tasks correlated at the 0.01 level of significance. We were thus able to treat them as equal measures of abstract reasoning ability.

Scoring. Raw scores were calculated by subtracting the number of items failed from the highest item number administered. These were then converted to SAS using the Stanford–Binet's SAS conversion table of normalized standard scores with a mean set at 50 and a standard deviation of 8. IQ equivalents

音乐和空间任务表现

劳舍尔等

编者按

这篇由加利福尼亚大学的弗朗西丝·劳舍尔和她的同事所写的报告似乎证实了人们长期以来的怀疑，即音乐可以提高智力。这引起了人们极大的兴趣。在他们的报告中，大学生在听了十分钟莫扎特的音乐之后在空间推理测试中的成绩比听放松磁带或静坐的情况下稍微好些（IQ 提高了 8~9 分）。然而，后续研究却得到了不同的结论：一些显然支持这种说法，一些没有发现相同的效果或是效果不特定于莫扎特的音乐。现在看来，这种效果较小且短暂，更可能是由情绪和唤醒状态而不是由音乐特定引起的。尽管如此，儿童的"大脑音乐"已经成为一个小的营销行业。

音乐认知和其他"高级脑功能"在相关性上[1]、历史上[2]和民间传闻中[3]都有关联。但音乐认知和与抽象操作（数学或者空间推理等）有关的认知之间的因果关系至今还没有被证实。我们进行了一项实验，在实验中每个学生都被要求完成三套标准 IQ 空间推理测试，学生在每份测试之前先进行 10 分钟的活动：(1) 听莫扎特的 D 大调双钢琴奏鸣曲 K488，(2) 听一盘放松的磁带，或者 (3) 静坐。相比第二和第三项活动，学生在紧跟着第一项活动后的测试中表现有所提高。

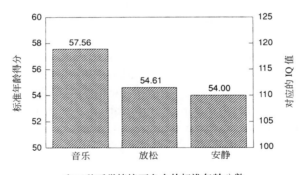

在三种听觉情境下各自的标准年龄分数

测试步骤。在音乐情境下，测试者听 10 分钟莫扎特的作品。在放松情境下，测试者听 10 分钟可降低血压的放松磁带。在安静情境下，测试者静坐 10 分钟。在每一种听力情境结束后，测试者完成斯坦福-比奈智力量表[4]中三份抽象推理测验中的一份。抽象（空间）推理任务包括一个图形分析测试、一个多项选择矩阵测试和一个多项选择的折纸剪纸测试。对于我们的样本，这三项测试在 0.01 水平下显著相关，因此我们把它们作为对抽象推理能力的等效测试。

得分。原始分数由测试所给最高次数减去失误总次数得到。该分数再通过斯坦福-比奈标准年龄得分 (SAS) 转化表转化成平均值为 50，标准差为 8 的 SAS 值。对应 IQ 值的计算方法为先将每个 SAS 值乘

were calculated by first multiplying each SAS by 3 (the number of subtests required by the Stanford–Binet for calculating IQs). We then used their area score conversion table, designed to have a mean of 100 and a standard deviation of 16, to obtain SAS IQ equivalents.

Thirty-six college students participated in all three listening conditions. Immediately following each listening condition, the student's spatial reasoning skills were tested using the Stanford–Binet intelligence scale[4]. The mean standard age scores (SAS) for the three listening conditions are shown in the figure. The music condition yielded a mean SAS of 57.56; the mean SAS for the relaxation condition was 54.61 and the mean score for the silent condition was 54.00. To assess the impact of these scores, we "translated" them to spatial IQ scores of 119, 111 and 110, respectively. Thus, the IQs of subjects participating in the music condition were 8–9 points above their IQ scores in the other two conditions. A one-factor (listening condition) repeated measures analysis of variance (ANOVA) performed on SAS revealed that subjects performed better on the abstract/spatial reasoning tests after listening to Mozart than after listening to either the relaxation tape or to nothing ($F_{2,35} = 7.08$; $P = 0.002$). The music condition differed significantly from both the relaxation and the silence conditions (Scheffe's $t = 3.41$, $P = 0.002$; $t = 3.67$, $P = 0.0008$, two-tailed, respectively). The relaxation and silence conditions did not differ ($t = 0.795$; $P = 0.432$, two-tailed). Pulse rates were taken before and after each listening condition. A two-factor (listening condition and time of pulse measure) repeated measures ANOVA revealed no interaction or main effects for pulse, thereby excluding arousal as an obvious cause. We found no order effects for either condition presentation or task, nor any experimenter effect.

The enhancing effect of the music condition is temporal, and does not extend beyond the 10–15-minute period during which subjects were engaged in each spatial task. Inclusion of a delay period (as a variable) between the music listening condition and the testing period would allow us quantitatively to determine the presence of a decay constant. It would also be interesting to vary the listening time to optimize the enhancing effect, and to examine whether other measures of general intelligence (verbal reasoning, quantitative reasoning and short-term memory) would be similarly facilitated. Because we used only one musical sample of one composer, various other compositions and musical styles should also be examined. We predict that music lacking complexity or which is repetitive may interfere with, rather than enhance, abstract reasoning. Also, as musicians may process music in a different way from non-musicians, it would be interesting to compare these two groups.

(**365**, 611; 1993)

Frances H. Rauscher , Gordon L. Shaw*, Katherine N. Ky
Center for the Neurobiology of Learning and Memory, University of California, Irvine, California 92717, USA
* Also at Department of Physics.

References:
1. Hassler, M., Birbaumer, N. & Feil, A. *Psychol. Music* **13**, 99-113(1985).
2. Allman, G. J. *Greek Geometry from Thales to Euclid* p. 23 (Arno, New York, 1976).
3. Cranberg, L. D. & Albert, M. L. in *The Exceptional Brain* (eds Obler, L. K. & Fein, D.) 156 (Guilford, New York, 1988).
4. Thorndike, R. L., Hagen, E. P. & Sattler, J. M. *The Stanford–Binet Scale of Intelligence* (Riverside, Chicago, 1986).

以 3（斯坦福－比奈量表测试 IQ 值需要的子测验数目）。然后我们使用各项对应的分数换算表得到平均值为 100，标准差为 16 的 SAS 对应 IQ 值。

36 名大学生参与了所有三种情景下的测试。每种听觉情景结束后，我们立刻通过斯坦福－比奈智力量表 [4] 测试他们的空间推理能力。三种情景下测试所得的平均标准年龄得分（SAS）如图所示。听音乐情景下平均 SAS 为 57.56；听放松磁带情景下平均 SAS 为 54.61；安静情景下平均 SAS 为 54.00。为了评估这些分数的影响，我们将它们"翻译"为空间 IQ 分数，该分数分别为 119，111 和 110。因此，测试对象在音乐情境下的 IQ 分数要比另外两种情境下的 IQ 分数高 8~9 分。标准年龄得分的单因素（听觉情境）重复测量方差分析（ANOVA）显示，测试对象听完莫扎特音乐后在抽象（空间）推理能力测试中的表现好于听放松磁带或者什么都不听（$F_{2,35} = 7.08$；$P = 0.002$）。听音乐后的表现与听放松磁带后或者安静情况下的表现有显著区别（Scheffe 差别检验法，$t = 3.41$，$P = 0.002$；$t = 3.67$，$P = 0.0008$，双尾检验）。而听放松磁带后的表现和安静情况下的表现无差异（$t = 0.795$；$P = 0.432$，双尾检验）。我们在三种听觉活动前后分别测量了测试者的脉搏次数。对脉搏次数的双因素（听觉情境和脉搏测量时间）重复测量的 ANOVA 表明听觉情境和测量时间对脉搏次数没有交互作用或主效应，因此排除了唤醒状态这一明显的导致因素。我们没有发现听觉情境或任务的顺序效应，也未发现实验者效应。

音乐情境的增强效应是暂时的，没有超过测试对象完成空间测试任务所需的 10~15 分钟。在听音乐和测试阶段之间加入时间延迟（作为一个变量）可以让我们定量地测定音乐效应的衰减常数。改变听音乐的时间长短来优化音乐的增强效应，并且检测听音乐对其他一般智力（语言推理、计量推理、短时记忆）是否有相似的提升作用，将会很有趣。因为我们只用了一位作曲家的一首乐曲，其他的曲目和音乐风格也应该被研究。我们预测缺少复杂性的或者重复的音乐将会妨碍而不是提高抽象推理能力。另外，因为音乐家加工音乐的方式可能与非音乐家不同，比较这两个组的表现也将会很有趣。

（苏怡汀 翻译；杜忆 审稿）

Possible Gravitational Microlensing of a Star in the Large Magellanic Cloud

C. Alcock *et al.*

Editor's Note

The existence of dark matter—invisible matter that exceeds the amount of visible matter in the universe by a factor of 5–6—is supported by several observations, not least that it is required to bind galaxies together. But almost nothing is known about what it consists of. A possibility explored in the early 1990s was that it is in the form of small bodies collectively known as "massive compact halo objects", or MACHOs, because much of the dark matter in galaxies seems to be in their outer spherical "halos". Such bodies should produce a "microlensing" effect: the relativistic bending of light (gravitational lensing) by bodies smaller than galaxies. This paper is one of two to report the first microlensing signals ever seen. But it now appears that MACHOs are too rare to account for dark matter.

There is now abundant evidence for the presence of large quantities of unseen matter surrounding normal galaxies, including our own[1,2]. The nature of this "dark matter" is unknown, except that it cannot be made of normal stars, dust or gas, as they would be easily detected. Exotic particles such as axions, massive neutrinos or other weakly interacting massive particles (collectively known as WIMPs) have been proposed[3,4], but have yet to be detected. A less exotic alternative is normal matter in the form of bodies with masses ranging from that of a large planet to a few solar masses. Such objects, known collectively as massive compact halo objects[5] (MACHOs), might be brown dwarfs or "jupiters" (bodies too small to produce their own energy by fusion), neutron stars, old white dwarfs or black holes. Paczynski[6] suggested that MACHOs might act as gravitational microlenses, temporarily amplifying the apparent brightness of background stars in nearby galaxies. We are conducting a microlensing experiment to determine whether the dark matter halo of our Galaxy is made up of MACHOs. Here we report a candidate for such a microlensing event, detected by monitoring the light curves of 1.8 million stars in the Large Magellanic Cloud for one year. The light curve shows no variation for most of the year of data taking, and an upward excursion lasting over 1 month, with a maximum increase of ~2 mag. The most probable lens mass, inferred from the duration of the candidate lensing event, is ~0.1 solar mass.

THE MACHO Project[7,8] uses the gravitational microlens signature to search for evidence of MACHOs in the Galactic halo, which is thought to be at least three times as massive as the visible disk[2]. (Two other groups are attempting a similar search[9,10].)

大麦哲伦云的一颗恒星可能存在微引力透镜效应

阿尔科克等

编者按

种种证据表明，宇宙中存在暗物质，尤其是暗物质是束缚星系所必需的。这种不可见物质的含量是宇宙中可见物质含量的 5~6 倍。然而我们对其物质组成却几乎一无所知。20 世纪 90 年代初，由于发现星系中大部分暗物质似乎存在于星系晕的外层，人们提出了一种可能性，即认为暗物质是以一种被统称为"晕族大质量致密天体 (MACHOs)"的小天体的形式存在的。这样的小天体可以产生微引力透镜效应：比星系小的天体产生的对光的相对论性偏折（引力透镜效应）。这篇文章是发现首例微引力透镜信号的两篇文章之一（另一篇文章请见本书第 253 页）。然而现在看来 MACHO 的数目似乎太少了，不足以解释暗物质。

现在有充分的证据表明，在正常星系周围存在着大量看不见的物质，包括我们的银河系 [1,2]。我们不了解这种"暗物质"的性质，但它不可能由普通的恒星、尘埃或气体组成，否则它们就会被轻易地探测到。人们已经提出若干种奇异粒子模型，如轴子、有质量中微子或者其他弱相互作用大质量粒子（简称为 WIMPs）[3,4]，但目前还没有探测到其中任何一种。另一种不太奇异的可能性是各种天体中的正常物质，质量范围从一个大行星到几个太阳。这类天体统称为晕族大质量致密天体 [5]（MACHOs），可能是褐矮星、类木星天体（这类天体质量太小，不能通过自身核聚变产生能量）、中子星、老年的白矮星或者黑洞。帕金斯基提出 [6]，MACHO 可能会产生微引力透镜现象，暂时放大近邻星系中背景星的视亮度。我们正在进行一项微引力透镜实验，检验我们银河系的暗物质晕是否由 MACHO 构成。我们在本文中报告了通过监测大麦哲伦云的 180 万颗恒星的光变曲线一年而探测到的一个微引力透镜候选事件。该事件中恒星的光变曲线存在持续超过一个月的向上偏移，且最大增量大约为 2 mag（星等），但是在这一年中其他绝大部分数据采集期间里没有变化。从候选透镜事件持续的时间可以推断，最可能的透镜天体质量大约相当于 0.1 倍太阳质量。

MACHO 项目 [7,8] 利用微引力透镜信号来搜寻银晕中存在 MACHO 的证据，一般认为银晕的质量至少是可见银盘的 3 倍 [2]（另外两个研究组也在进行类似的搜寻 [9,10]）。如果我们银河系的大部分暗物质都集中在 MACHO 中，则大麦哲伦云

If most of our Galaxy's dark matter resides in MACHOs, the "optical depth" for microlensing towards the Large Magellanic Cloud (LMC) is about 5×10^{-7} (independent of the mass function of MACHOs), so that at any given time about one star in two million will be microlensed with an amplification factor $A > 1.34$ (ref. 5). Our survey takes advantage of the transverse motion of MACHOs relative to the line-of-sight from the observer to a background star. This motion causes a transient, time-symmetric and achromatic brightening that is quite unlike any known variable star phenomena, with a characteristic timescale $t = 2r_E / v_\perp$ where r_E is the Einstein ring radius and $v_\perp$ is the MACHO velocity transverse to the line-of-sight. For typical halo models the time $t \sim 100 \sqrt{M_{\mathrm{macho}}/M_\odot}$ days[5] (where $M_\odot$ is the mass of the Sun). The amplification can be large, but these events are extremely rare; for this reason our survey was designed to follow > ten million stars over several years.

The survey employs a dedicated 1.27-m telescope at Mount Stromlo. A field-of-view of 0.5 square degrees is achieved by operating at the prime focus. The optics include a dichroic beam-splitter which allows simultaneous imaging in a "red" beam (6,300–7,600 Å) and a "blue" beam (4,500–6,300 Å). Two large charge-coupled device (CCD) cameras[11] are employed at the two foci; each contain a 2×2 mosaic of $2,048 \times 2,048$ pixel Loral CCD imagers. The 15-µm pixel size corresponds to 0.63 arcsec on the sky. The images are read out through a 16-channel system, and written into dual ported memory in the data acquisition computer. Our primary target stars are in the LMC. We also monitor stars in the Galactic bulge and the Small Magellanic Cloud. As of 15 September 1993, over 12,000 images have been taken with the system.

The data are reduced with a crowded-field photometry routine known as Sodophot, derived from Dophot[12]. First, one image of each field that was obtained in good seeing is reduced in a manner similar to Dophot to produce a "template" catalogue of star positions and magnitudes. Normally, bright stars are matched with the template and used to determine an analytic point spread function (PSF) and a coordinate transformation. Photometric fitting is then performed on each template star in descending order of brightness, with the PSF for all other stars subtracted from the frame. When a star is found to vary significantly, it and its neighbours undergo a second iteration of fitting. The output consists of magnitudes and errors for the two colours, and six additional useful parameters (such as the χ^2 of the PSF fit and crowding information). These are used to flag questionable measurements, that arise from cosmic ray events in the CCDs, bad pixels and so on.

These photometric data are subjected to an automatic time-series analysis which uses a set of optimal filters to search for microlensing candidates and variable stars (which we have detected in abundance[13]). For each microlensing candidate a light curve is fitted, and the final selection is done automatically using criteria (for example, signal-to-noise, quality of fit, wave-length independence of the light curve and colour of the star) that were established empirically using Monte Carlo addition of fake events into real light curves.

This analysis has been done on four fields near the centre of the LMC, containing 1.8

(LMC) 方向的微引力透镜的"光深"大约为 5×10^{-7}（与 MACHO 的质量函数无关）。这样在任意给定时刻下，200 万颗恒星中就大约有一颗可以被微引力透镜放大，放大因子为 $A > 1.34$（参考文献 5）。我们的巡天观测借助于 MACHO 相对于观察者到背景星视线的横向运动。这种运动可以引起一种暂现的、时间对称且无色差的增亮现象，这种现象不同于任何已知的变星现象，其特征时标为 $t = 2r_E/v_\perp$，其中 r_E 为爱因斯坦环半径，$v_\perp$ 为 MACHO 相对视线的横向运动速度。对于典型的晕模型，时间 t 大约为 $100\sqrt{M_{macho}/M_\odot}$ 天 [5]，其中 $M_\odot$ 为太阳质量。这种放大效应可以很强，但是这类事件却极为罕见。因此，我们就需要在数年内对超过 1,000 万颗恒星进行巡天观测。

这次巡天观测使用了位于澳洲斯特朗洛山的 1.27 m 专用望远镜，该望远镜在主焦点工作状态下的视场为 0.5 平方度。其光学系统包括一个双色分束器，可以同时用红波段光束 (6,300~7,600 Å) 和蓝波段光束 (4,500~6,300 Å) 分别成像。在两条光束的焦点上分别放置电荷耦合器件 (CCD) 照相机 [11]，每台相机含有一个 2×2 的 Loral 成像器 (2,048×2,048 像素)。像素大小为 15 μm，对应于天空中的 0.63 arcsec。图像数据通过一个 16 通道系统读取，然后写入数据采集计算机中的双端存储器中。我们主要的目标恒星位于大麦哲伦云中，我们也监测银河系核球与小麦哲伦云中的恒星。截止到 1993 年 9 月 15 日，该系统已经获得超过 12,000 张图像。

这些数据通过密集星场测光程序 Sodophot 进行处理，该程序源自 Dophot [12]。首先，对每个星场中视宁度较好的图像通过和 Dophot 相似的方式进行处理，从而生成关于恒星位置及星等的"模板"星表。一般情况下，将较亮的恒星与模板相匹配，这样可以用来确定其解析的点扩散函数（简称为 PSF）和坐标转换。在对其他所有恒星用 PSF 修正之后，按照模版恒星亮度递减的顺序，我们对每颗模板恒星进行光度拟合。当发现一颗恒星的亮度变化显著时，则对该星及其邻星进行第二次迭代拟合。输出结果包括两种颜色的相应星等和误差，以及其他六种有用的参数（如 PSF 拟合的 χ^2 和星场密集分布信息），这些参数被用来标记有问题的测量数据，诸如 CCD 中的宇宙线事件、坏像元，等等。

随后，我们对这些测光数据进行一种自动时间序列分析，该分析通过使用一组最优滤波器来寻找微透镜候选体和变星（我们已经探测到很多 [13]）。对于每一个微引力透镜候选体，我们进行光变曲线拟合，然后自动地根据判断标准（例如，信噪比、拟合品质、与光变曲线无关的波长以及恒星的颜色）作出最后筛选。这些判断标准是经验性地用蒙特卡罗方法在真实的光变曲线中加入伪事件得出的。

这种分析被应用于靠近大麦哲伦云中心附近的四个区域。这些区域包含了

million stars, with approximately 250 observations for each star. The candidate event reported here occurs in the light curve of a star at coordinates $\alpha = 05$ h 14 min 44.5 s, $\delta = -68° \, 48' \, 00''$ (J2000). (A finding chart is available on request from C.A.). The star has median magnitudes $V \sim 19.6$, $R \sim 19.0$, consistent with a clump giant (metal-rich helium core burning star) in the LMC. These magnitudes are estimated using colour transformations from our filters to V and R that have been derived from observations of standard stars.

Our photometry for this star, from July 1992 to July 1993, is shown in Fig. 1, and the candidate event is shown on an expanded scale in Fig. 2, along with the colour light curve. The colour changes by < 0.1 mag as it brightens and fades (the candidate "event"). A mosaic, showing portions of some of the CCD images used, is shown in Fig. 3, with the relevant star at the centre. The integrated number of PSF photoelectrons detected above the sky background in the template image is $\sim 10^4$, for a 300 s exposure. The increase in counts during the peak is highly significant, as is clear from the figures. Also shown in Fig. 2 is a fit to the theoretical microlensing light curve (see ref. 6). The four parameters fit are (1) the baseline flux, (2) the maximum amplification $A_{max} = 6.86 \pm 0.11$, (3) the duration $t = 33.9 \pm 0.26$ d, (4) the centroid in time 433.55 ± 0.04 d. The quoted errors are formal fit errors. Using the PSF fit uncertainties as determined by the photometry program, the best-fit microlensing curve gives a χ^2 per degree of freedom of 1.6 (for 443 d.f.).

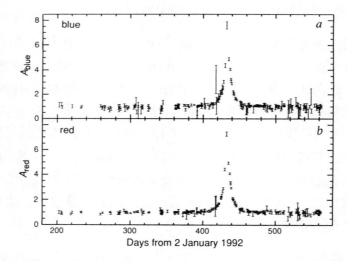

Fig. 1. The observed light curve with estimated $\pm 1\sigma$ errors. *a*, Shows A_{blue}, the flux (in linear units) divided by the median observed flux, in the blue passband. *b*, Is the same, for the red passband.

180 万颗恒星，每颗恒星大约进行了 250 次观测。这里报告候选事件产生于坐标为 $\alpha = 05$ h 14 min 44.5 s，$\delta = -68°\ 48'\ 00''$（J2000）的恒星的光变曲线中（如果需要可以从阿尔科克处得到认证图）。该恒星的中位星等 $V \sim 19.6$、$R \sim 19.0$，与大麦哲伦云中的团簇巨星（富含金属且正经历氦核燃烧的恒星）相符。这些星等是通过我们的观测波段与 V、R 波段的颜色转换关系估计出来的，所采用的颜色转换关系是通过对标准星的观测导出的。

我们从 1992 年 7 月至 1993 年 7 月对该星的测光结果，如图 1 所示；候选事件的放大的光变曲线以及颜色光变曲线如图 2 所示。随着它的明暗变化（候选"事件"），其颜色变化小于 0.1 mag。图 3 给出了部分分析使用的 CCD 照片图，其中心位置为我们研究的恒星。对于 300 s 的曝光时间，我们在模板照片中探测到高于天空背景的 PSF 光电子的积分数为 $\sim 10^4$。从图中我们可以清楚地看到峰值期间的计数增长非常明显。我们在图 2 中也相应给出了理论微透镜光变曲线的拟合结果[6]。四个拟合参数分别为：(1) 基线流量，(2) 最大放大率 $A_{max} = 6.86 \pm 0.11$，(3) 持续时间 $t = 33.9 \pm 0.26$ d，(4) 放大峰值时刻，第 433.55 ± 0.04 d。引用的误差是标准的拟合误差。使用由测光程序给出的 PSF 拟合不确定度，最佳拟合微引力透镜曲线给出每个自由度的 χ^2 为 1.6（对于 443 个自由度）。

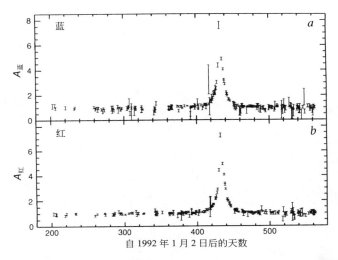

图 1. 观测到的光变曲线，估计误差为 $\pm 1\sigma$。a，给出了蓝光波段的放大率 $A_蓝$，即流量（线性坐标）除以观测中值流量（蓝光波段）。b，与 a 一样，但针对红光波段。

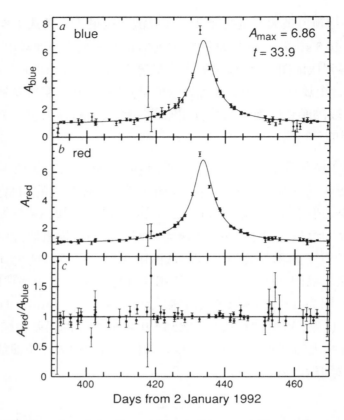

Fig. 2. As in Fig.1, with an expanded scale around the candidate event. The smooth curve shows the best-fit theoretical microlensing model, fitted simultaneously to both c is the colour light curve, showing the ratio of red to blue flux, normalized so that the median is unity.

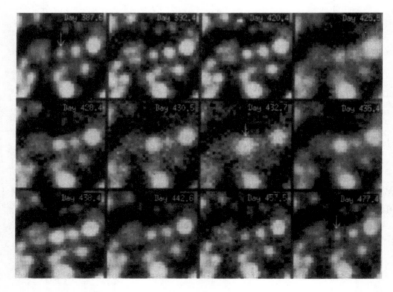

Fig. 3. Selected red CCD frames centred on the microlens candidate, showing observations before, during and after the event. The numbers on each frame indicate the days after 2 January 1992.

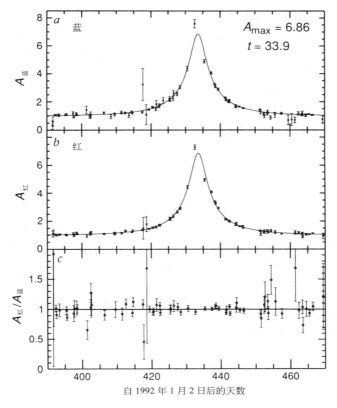

图 2. 如图 1，该图只是将候选事件附近的光变曲线进行了放大。图中的平滑曲线代表最佳拟合的理论微引力透镜模型，拟合过程同时拟合红光和蓝光两个波段的数据。c 图为颜色光变曲线图，给出的是红光和蓝光波段流量的比值。这里流量均已归一化，从而使得各自波段的中位值为 1。

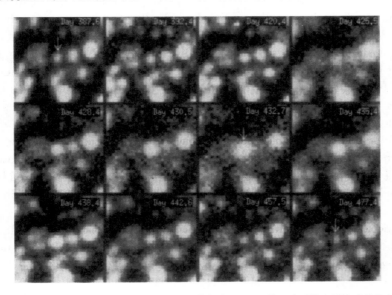

图 3. 筛选以微引力透镜候选天体为中心的红光波段的部分 CCD 图片，分别给出了该事件发生前、发生中和发生后的观测图像。每张图片上的数字表示 1992 年 1 月 2 日后的天数。

A number of features of the candidate event are consistent with gravitational microlensing: the light curve is achromatic within measurement error, and it has the expected symmetrical shape. If this is a genuine microlensing event, the mass of the deflector can be estimated. Because the duration depends upon the lens mass, the relative velocity transverse to the line-of-sight and the distance to the lens (none of which are known), the lens mass cannot be uniquely determined from the duration. But by using a model of the mass and velocity distributions of halo dark matter, one can find the relative probability that a MACHO of mass M_{macho} gave rise to the event. Thus, if this is genuine microlensing, Fig. 9 of ref. 5 implies the most likely mass is ~ 0.12 $M_\odot$, with masses of 0.03 $M_\odot$ and 0.5 $M_\odot$ being roughly half as likely. However, this method does not properly take into account our detection efficiencies, and should be considered only a rough estimate.

The mass range given above includes brown dwarfs and main sequence stars. Any microlensing star is very unlikely to be a red dwarf of the Galactic stellar halo, because one can show that the optical depth τ_s for microlensing by main sequence stars of the stellar halo is very low. Even if the mass function of the stellar halo rises as steeply as $dN/dM \propto M^{-4}$, as suggested recently[14] (here N is the number of stars per unit stellar mass interval), τ_s is still a few hundred times smaller than the 5×10^{-7} optical depth estimated for MACHO microlensing. The chance of finding such a stellar microlensing event among our 1.8 million stars is therefore very small.

The prospects for direct observation of a lensing object are not favourable. Even a star of 0.5 $M_\odot$, for example, would have $V \sim 24$, and for many years would be within a small fraction of an arcsecond of the much brighter LMC star.

We emphasize that the observed stellar brightening could be due to some previously unknown source of intrinsic stellar variability. The fit discrepancy near the peak is not yet understood; a more refined analysis of the data is under way. We do not yet have a spectrum of the star. A crucial test of the hypothesis that we are seeing gravitational microlensing by MACHOs in the galactic halo will be the detection of other candidates. So far, we have analysed only $\sim 15\%$ of our first year's frames and we plan to continue observations until 1996; this should allow us to determine if microlensing is really the cause. Additional events should show the theoretical distribution of maxima, and should be representative of both the colour–magnitude diagram and the spatial structure of the LMC. No repeats should be seen in any given star. (While this paper was in preparation, we were informed by J. Rich (personal communication) of the candidate events reported by the EROS collaboration. Note that the two groups use different definitions of characteristic time.)

If such candidates do result from microlensing we should be able to determine the contribution of MACHOs to the dark matter in the Galactic halo. The results presented here encourage us to believe this will happen.

(365, 621-623; 1993)

该候选事件的许多特征与微引力透镜现象相符：在测量误差范围内，光变曲线是无色差的，而且具有预期的对称形状。如果这是一个真实的微引力透镜事件，则可以估算出偏折天体的质量。因为持续时间依赖于透镜质量、横穿视线的相对速度以及与透镜天体的距离（这些量都是未知的），因此透镜质量不能由持续时间唯一确定。但是通过使用晕暗物质的质量和速度分布模型，我们可以计算出一颗质量为 M_{macho} 的 MACHO 导致该事件的相对概率。因此，如果这是真实的微引力透镜事件，从参考文献 5 中的图 9 可推出其最可能的质量约为 0.12 $M_\odot$，而质量分别为 0.03 $M_\odot$ 和 0.5 $M_\odot$ 的概率大致降低一半。然而，以上方法并没有很好地将我们的探测效率考虑进去，因此只能认为是一种粗略的估计。

上面给出的质量范围涵盖了褐矮星和主序星。任何形成微引力透镜事件的恒星都不太可能是银河系恒星晕中的红矮星，因为可以发现恒星晕中的主序星形成的微引力透镜事件的光深 τ_s 都是非常小的。即使根据最近提出的按照 $dN/dM \propto M^{-4}$ 变化[14] 的恒星晕的质量函数（这里的 N 代表每单位恒星质量间隔的恒星数量），τ_s 仍然比 MACHO 微引力透镜事件的光深估计值（5×10^{-7}）小数百倍。因此，在我们观测的 180 万颗恒星中发现这样一个恒星微引力透镜事件的概率是很小的。

而直接观测到透镜天体的前景也并不乐观。比如即使对于一颗质量为 0.5 $M_\odot$ 的恒星，其星等 $V \sim 24$，在许多年间它可能还是处在大麦哲伦云中比它亮得多的一颗恒星附近若干分之一角秒范围之内。

在这里我们需要强调一下，观测到的恒星变亮还可能是由一些以前未知的恒星内禀变化导致的。峰值附近的拟合偏差还不能很好地给出解释，我们正在对这些数据进行更加细致的分析。我们还没有这颗恒星的光谱。关于观测到银晕中 MACHO 形成微引力透镜事件的假设，关键的检验是能否进一步探测到其他候选天体。迄今，我们仅分析了第一年图像的大约 15%，我们打算将观测持续到 1996 年，这将帮助我们确定造成这一现象的真正原因是不是微引力透镜事件。其他事件将揭示出最大放大倍数的理论分布，并可以反映大麦哲伦云的颜色 - 星等图和空间结构，在任何给定的恒星中都不应该看到重复事件。（就在本文准备过程中，里奇通知我们，EROS 合作研究小组也报道了一些候选事件（个人交流）。但是请注意，两个研究小组采用的特征时间定义不同。）

如果这类候选事件的确源于微引力透镜现象，那么我们应该可以确定 MACHO 对于银晕暗物质的贡献。本文结果使我们相信上述推论可以被确认。

（金世超 翻译；何香涛 审稿）

C. Alcock[*†], C. W. Akerlof[†¶], R. A. Allsman[*], T. S. Axelrod[*], D. P. Bennett[*†], S. Chan[‡], K. H. Cook[*†], K. C. Freeman[‡], K. Griest[†‖], S. L. Marshall[†§], H-S. Park[*], S. Perlmutter[†], B. A. Peterson[‡], M. R. Pratt[†§], P. J. Quinn[‡], A. W. Rodgers[‡], C. W. Stubbs[†§] & W. Sutherland[†]

[*] Lawrence Livermore National Laboratory, Livermore, California 94550, USA

[†] Center for Particle Astrophysics, University of California, Berkeley, California 94720, USA

[‡] Mt Stromlo and Siding Spring Observatories, Australian National University, Weston, ACT 2611, Australia

[§] Department of Physics, University of California, Santa Barbara, California 93106, USA

[‖] Department of Physics, University of California, San Diego, California 92039, USA

[¶] Department of Physics, University of Michigan, Ann Arbor, Michigan 48109, USA

Received 22 September; accepted 30 September 1993.

References:

1. Trimble, V. *A. Rev. Astr. Astrophys.* **25**, 425-472 (1987).

2. Fich, M. & Tremaine, S. *A. Rev. Astr. Astrophys.* **29**, 409-445 (1991).

3. Primack, J. R., Seckel, D. & Sadoulet, B. *A. Rev. Nucl. Part. Sci.* B**38**, 751-807 (1988).

4. Kolb, E. W. & Turner, M. S. *The Early Universe* (Addison Wesley, New York, 1990).

5. Griest, K. *Astrophys. J.* **366**, 412-421 (1991).

6. Paczynski, B. *Astrophys. J.* **304**, 1-5 (1986).

7. Bennett, D. *et al. Ann. N.Y. Acad. Sci.* **688**, 612-618 (1993).

8. Alcock, C. *et al. Astr. Soc. Pacif. Conf. Ser.* **34**, 193-202 (1992).

9. Magneville, C. *Ann. N.Y. Acad. Sci.* **688**, 619-625 (1993).

10. Udalski, A. *et al. Ann. N.Y. Acad. Sci.* **688**, 626-631 (1993).

11. Stubbs, C. W. *et al.* in *Charge-coupled Devices and Solid State Optical Sensors III* (ed. Blouke, M.) *Proc. of the SPIE* **1900**, 192-204 (1993).

12. Schechter, P. L., Mateo, M. L. & Saha, A. *Publ. Astron. Soc. Pac.* **105**, 1342-1353 (1993).

13. Cook, K. H. *et al. Bull. Am. Astr. Soc.* **24**, 1179 (1993).

14. Richer, H. B. & Fahlman, G. G. *Nature* **358**, 383-386 (1992).

Acknowledgements. We are grateful for the support given our project by the technical staff at the Mt Stromlo Observatory. Work performed at LLNL is supported by the DOE. Work performed by the Center for Particle Astrophysics on the UC campuses is supported in part by the Office of Science and Technology Centers of the NSF. Work performed at MSSSO is supported by the Bilateral Science and Technology Program of the Australian Department of Industry, Technology and Commerce. K.G. acknowledges a DOE OJI grant, and C.W.S. thanks the Sloan Foundation for their support.

Evidence for Gravitational Microlensing by Dark Objects in the Galactic Halo

E. Aubourg *et al.*

Editor's Note

The unseen "dark matter" that is needed to account for the gravitational cohesion of rotating spiral galaxies is one of the most profound current mysteries of science. This matter apparently exceeds its visible counterpart by a factor of 5–6, yet there is still no real understanding of what it consists of. In this paper a team of French astronomers explore the possibility that it could be constituted of dark, massive compact bodies in the spherical "halos" of galaxies like our own, which are called MACHOs. Such objects would occasionally be expected to bend and amplify the light from stars beyond, an effect called microlensing. The paper is one of two that report the first detection of microlensing by MACHOs, and it concludes that the objects are probably 0.01–1 times the mass of our sun.

The flat rotation curves of spiral galaxies, including our own, indicate that they are surrounded by unseen haloes of "dark matter"[1,2]. In the absence of a massive halo, stars and gas in the outer portions of a galaxy would orbit the centre more slowly, just as the outer planets in the Solar System circle the Sun more slowly than the inner ones. So far, however, there has been no direct observational evidence for the dark matter, or its characteristics. Paczyński[3] suggested that dark bodies in the halo of our Galaxy can be detected when they act as gravitational "microlenses", amplifying the light from stars in nearby galaxies. The duration of such an event depends on the mass, distance and velocity of the dark object. We have been monitoring the brightness of three million stars in the Large Magellanic Cloud for over three years, and here report the detection of two possible microlensing events. The brightening of the stars was symmetrical in time, achromatic and not repeated during the monitoring period. The timescales of the two events are about thirty days and imply that the masses of the lensing objects lie between a few hundredths and one solar mass. The number of events observed is consistent with the number expected if the halo is dominated by objects with masses in this range.

THE "EROS" (Expérience de Recherche d'Objets Sombres) collaboration is searching for microlensing events using the European Southern Observatory at La Silla, Chile[4,5]. We have two complementary programmes. The first uses $5° \times 5°$ Schmidt plates of the Large Magellanic Cloud (LMC) that allow us to monitor about eight million stars with a sampling rate of no more than two measurements per night. This makes the programme primarily sensitive to lens masses in the range $10^{-4} M_\odot < M < 1 M_\odot$ (where $M_\odot$ is the

利用微引力透镜效应发现银晕中
存在暗天体的证据

奥堡等

编者按

为了解释转动的旋涡星系的引力束缚问题（旋转曲线），我们需要引入看不见的"暗物质"，这是当今科学最重大的未解之谜之一。这种暗物质的含量是可见物质含量的 5~6 倍，但对其具体的物质组成我们尚无真正的了解。在这篇文章中，一组法国天文学家探索了暗物质由与我们银河系类似星系的球状晕中的大质量致密暗天体（这些天体被称为 MACHO）组成的可能性。预期这些天体偶尔会使背后恒星发出的光偏折、变亮，这种效应称为微引力透镜效应。这篇文章是报告发现首例 MACHO 微引力透镜信号的两个工作之一，其结果表明这些小天体的质量可能只是我们太阳质量的 0.01~1 倍。

包括我们自己银河系在内的旋涡星系有着平坦的自转曲线，这暗示着它们都被不可见的"暗物质"[1,2]晕包围着。如果没有这样大质量晕的存在，星系靠外部分的恒星以及气体将绕中心转得更慢，正如太阳系带外行星绕太阳转动的速度要比带内行星慢一样。然而，迄今为止还没有关于暗物质及其性质的直接观测证据。帕金斯基[3]提出，可以通过我们星系晕中暗天体作为引力"微透镜"使临近星系中恒星发出的放大来探测它们。这种微引力透镜事件所持续的时间和暗天体的质量、距离及速度有关。我们已经对大麦哲伦云中 300 万颗恒星的亮度进行了长达三年的监测，在此报告两个可能的微引力透镜事件。这些恒星的亮度变化在时间上对称，在不同波段一致并且在观测期间没有重复。这两次微引力透镜事件的时标约为 30 天，表明透镜天体的质量介于百分之几到一倍太阳质量之间。观测到的微引力透镜事件数量与假设晕由这种质量范围的天体主导所预期的数量相符。

经验性探测暗天体（EROS）合作项目利用位于智利拉西亚的欧南台来寻找微引力透镜事件[4,5]。我们有两个互补的计划。第一个计划是使用大麦哲伦云（LMC）的 $5° \times 5°$ 施密特底片，这可以使我们以每晚不超过两次观测的采样率对约 800 万颗恒星进行监测。这使得该项目易于探测质量在 $10^{-4} M_\odot < M < 1 M_\odot$（其中 $M_\odot$ 是太阳质量）范围之内的透镜天体，对应的透镜事件的平均持续时间在 $1\,d < \tau < 100\,d$ 之间。

solar mass), corresponding to mean lensing durations in the range 1 d $< \tau < 100$ d. The probability that a given star in the LMC is amplified by more than 0.3 magnitudes at a given time is calculated to be $\sim 0.5 \times 10^{-6}$ (refs 3, 6). For a deflector of mass M the typical timescale for the amplification is $\tau = 70 \sqrt{M/M_\odot}$ d. The light curve of such an event should be symmetric in time, achromatic, and the event should not be repeated. Over the period 1990–93, a total of 304 Schmidt plates of the LMC were taken for us at La Silla with red or blue filters. Exposure times were typically one hour, permitting us to monitor stars down to the twentieth magnitude with a mean photometric precision of about 15% (r.m.s.). The transparency of the plates is digitized in 10 μm (0.67 arcsec) steps by the "MAMA" (Machine Automatique a Mesurer pour l'Astronomie) at the Observatoire de Paris[7]. The relation between transparency and star luminosity has been established using charge-coupled device (CCD) images scattered through the Schmidt-plate field.

The second programme uses a CCD camera consisting of a mosaic of sixteen 579×400 pixel Thomson THX 31157 CCDs covering about $1° \times 0.4°$. It is mounted on a 40-cm reflector (f/10) refurbished with the help of the Observatoire de Haute Provence. We have used this to observe one field in the bar of the LMC from December 1991 to March 1992 and from August 1992 to March 1993. As of March 1993, a total of 8,100 exposures had been taken with red and blue filters. About 100,000 stars are seen on each image, with a mean photometric precision of about 6%. Compared to the Schmidt-plate programme, the number of stars is a factor 80 smaller but the rapid sampling time (an image pair every 22 minutes) makes the CCD programme sensitive to deflector masses in the range $10^{-7} M_\odot < M < 10^{-3} M_\odot$, corresponding to event durations in the range 1 h $< \tau < 3$ d.

After preliminary processing (digitizing the Schmidt plates and flat-fielding the CCD images), the data reduction for both programmes follows basically the same procedure. First, one reference image for each colour was constructed by combining ten plates or 50 CCD images taken with good atmospheric conditions. We used a star finding algorithm to establish a star catalogue for each reference image. Next, each image is aligned with the reference using bright, isolated stars. The positions of the stars on the reference image then serve as input to a photometric fitting programme to determine the luminosity of each catalogue star on the new image. The image is then aligned "photometrically" with the reference by requiring that the mean luminosity of stars in a given luminosity band equal the mean luminosity in the catalogue. (The small number of intrinsically variable stars in the catalogue does not affect this procedure.) Successive images then add one point to the blue or red light curve of each star in the catalogue.

After data reduction, each light curve is tested for the presence of time variations using a variety of algorithms. For microlensing-like events, we use a simple algorithm that scans curves for sequences of measurements that are significantly above the mean value. The light curve is selected as a microlensing candidate if it exhibits one and only one such sequence simultaneously in both colours. The precise value of the threshold for acceptance is chosen using estimates of measurement errors so that random fluctuations

根据计算，大麦哲伦云中某一恒星在指定时间变亮超过 0.3 星等的概率约为 0.5×10^{-6}（参考文献 3，参考文献 6）。对于一个质量为 M 的天体所产生的光偏折，其光度变亮的典型时标为 $\tau = 70\sqrt{M/M_\odot}$ 天。这种微引力透镜事件的光变曲线应该在时间上具有对称性、在不同波段一致并且不可重复。1990~1993 年间，我们在拉西亚天文台用红或蓝滤光片共得到 304 块大麦哲伦云的施密特底片。典型曝光时间为一小时，这使我们可以在平均测光精度为 15%（rms，均方根）的条件下监测到暗至 20 星等的恒星。这些施密特底片的透明度在巴黎天文台 [7] 被天文自动测量仪器（MAMA）以 10 μm（0.67 arcsec）为步长进行了数字化。利用整个施密特底片视场的电荷耦合器件（CCD）图像，我们得到了透明度和恒星光度的关系。

第二个项目是采用由 16 个 579×400 像素的 Thomson THX 31157 型 CCD 拼接组成的 CCD 照相机，覆盖大约 $1° \times 0.4°$ 范围的天区。该照相机被安装在了由上普罗旺斯天文台参与修复的 40 cm 口径的反射望远镜（f/10）上。用此 CCD 照相机，我们从 1991 年 12 月到 1992 年 3 月及 1992 年 8 月到 1993 年 3 月之间观测了大麦哲伦云棒的一个天区。至 1993 年 3 月，我们使用红和蓝滤光片总共得到 8,100 次曝光。在平均测光精度约为 6% 的条件下，每张图像上约可看见 100,000 颗恒星。这和前面提到的施密特底片项目相比，虽然恒星的数量是施密特底片项目中恒星数量的 1/80，但是较短的采样时间（每幅图像平均只要 22 分钟）使得这个 CCD 项目易于探测质量在 $10^{-7} M_\odot < M < 10^{-3} M_\odot$ 范围之内的偏折天体，对应透镜事件的平均持续时间在 $1 \text{ h} < \tau < 3 \text{ d}$ 之间。

在初期处理（施密特底片信号的数字化和 CCD 图像的平场处理）后，两个项目的数据处理都遵循基本相同的步骤。首先，通过结合良好大气条件下拍摄的 10 幅施密特底片或者 50 幅 CCD 图像，我们得到了每种颜色下的参考图像。利用一种寻找恒星的算法，我们为每幅参考图像建立一个星表。随后，通过亮的孤立星将每一幅图像和参考图像对齐。这些参考图像上恒星的位置随即作为一个测光拟合程序的输入值，以确定新图像星表中每颗恒星的光度。然后，这些图像在“测光”上和参考图像对齐，要求在指定的某一光度范围内恒星的平均光度和星表中的平均光度相同。（星表中少数内禀变星不会对此步骤产生影响。）于是接连观测的图像就在星表中每颗恒星的蓝或红的光变曲线上增加了一个点。

在数据处理之后，我们可以对每条光变曲线采用多种算法测试其时变性。对于类微引力透镜事件，我们采用一种简单的算法，即扫描光变曲线中明显超过平均值的测量序列。如果有且只有一个这种序列可以在蓝和红波段同时出现，则此光变曲线被选为微引力透镜候选事件。我们通过估计误差范围来选择接受阈值的准确数值，从而排除非变星的随机涨落。每幅图像的测光误差可以近似看作是星等的函数，但

of intrinsically stable stars are not accepted. The photometric errors are estimated as a function of magnitude for each image but may still vary from one star to another by 20% according to the star's environment. We estimate the efficiency of the cuts to accept real microlensing events using Monte Carlo-generated lensing events, produced with the observed photometric resolution and observing sequence. We superimposed the Monte Carlo signature of microlensing events onto both observed (flat) light curves and simulated light curves. These curves were then subjected to the same algorithms as the real data. For simulated events with peak amplifications > 1.34 inserted into the data during the period of the observing seasons, the efficiency ranges from $\sim 25\%$ for events with timescales of 6 days to 50% for events with timescales of 30 days. These numbers differ from 100% because of the sampling period and the photometric resolution for faint stars.

Measured curves passing the above selection criteria were then inspected visually and subjected to further analysis to determine their compatibility with the microlensing hypothesis. At this stage, we found it necessary to eliminate only those light curves that exhibit variations on a timescale comparable to that of the total observing period. Such events cannot be tested for the presence of subsequent variations. Remaining events are fitted for the theoretical microlensing light curve. The parameters of the fit are the off-lensing luminosity, the maximum amplification, the time of maximum amplification, and the timescale of the microlensing. The light curves of the two colours are fitted separately (to test for wavelength independence) and then simultaneously.

We found no candidates in an analysis performed on the 1991–92 CCD data (20% of the total data). For this data, we expected about three candidates if the halo is entirely comprised of dark objects in the range 10^{-7} to $10^{-5}\,M_\odot$.

A preliminary analysis of 40% of the Schmidt-plate data has revealed two events that are consistent with the microlensing hypothesis. The light curves are shown in Figs 1 and 2, with the event characteristics listed in Table 1. They are the only curves so far analysed that show one significant amplification event with no further variations. (No curves have been found that show two or more examples of microlensing-like behaviour.) The curves are consistent with the theoretical curve; χ^2s are good within the estimated 20% uncertainty in the photometric errors. The events are wavelength independent at the 10% level, that is within errors. The amplification is near the median amplitude expected ($\delta m = 1.0$) for detectable events with these time-scales. Neighbouring stars show no variations over the whole observing period. The off-lensing magnitudes of the two stars are near the average for stars in our catalogue. Candidate 2 is on the main sequence while candidate 1 is between the main sequence and giant branch of the colour–magnitude diagram. Only the observation of further events will tell us if there is an accumulation of events in a given region of the diagram indicating variable-star phenomena.

是仍可能因为恒星的环境不同而在不同恒星间变化 20%。我们用蒙特卡罗方法模拟得到的透镜事件（用观测的测光分辨率和观测序列产生）估计阈值对于接受真实微引力透镜事件的效率。我们在观测到的（平坦的）光变曲线和模拟的光变曲线上叠加微引力透镜事件的蒙特卡罗特征信号。这些曲线将在之后同真实数据一样用同样的算法进行分析。对于在观测时间段的数据中插入峰值放大率大于 1.34 的模拟透镜信号的模拟事件，探测效率的范围从时标为 6 天事件的 25% 到时标为 30 天事件的 50%。而对于暗星而言，由于不同的采样周期以及测光分辨率，探测效率可以相差 100%。

对满足上述选择判据的观测到的光变曲线，我们随即再通过人眼检验以及进一步的分析，以确定它们是否符合微引力透镜假设。在此阶段，我们发现只需剔除那些光度变化时标和整个观测周期差不多的光变曲线。这样的事件不能被用于检验之后的变化。剩下的事件将利用微引力透镜的理论光变曲线进行拟合。拟合参数包括未发生透镜现象时的光度、放大率的最大值、放大率达到最大的时刻以及微引力透镜事件的时标。两种颜色的光变曲线被分别（以此来检验波长的独立性）拟合，然后再同时拟合。

根据分析，我们没有在 1991~1992 年的 CCD 数据（总数据量的 20%）中发现候选透镜事件。对于这些数据，如果银晕整体上均由范围在 $10^{-7}M_\odot < M < 10^{-5}M_\odot$ 之间的暗天体组成，那么我们预期发现大约 3 个候选透镜事件。

对施密特底片 40% 的数据的初步分析显示，有两个候选事件符合微引力透镜假设。光变曲线如图 1、图 2 所示，相关特征参数列于表 1 中。它们是迄今分析发现仅有的、存在明显光度放大且没有其他变化的光变曲线。（目前没有发现任何一个光变曲线表现出两次或者更多的类微引力透镜现象。）这些曲线和理论曲线一致；考虑测光误差中大约 20% 的不确定性，我们得到了很好的 χ^2。在误差之内，在 10% 的水平上事件不依赖于波长。其放大率接近这类时标下可探测到的事件的预期（放大率）中位值（$\delta m = 1.0$）。在整个观测期间邻近的恒星没有变化。这两颗恒星未发生透镜事件时的星等值接近我们星表中恒星星等的平均值。在颜色-星等图中，候选天体 1 位于主序带和巨星支之间，而候选天体 2 则位于主序带上。只有对更多事件的观测才可以判断颜色-星等图上代表变星现象的区域是否存在事件的积累。

Table 1. Characteristics of the two microlensing candidates

	Candidate 1	Candidate 2
Coordinates of star (J2000)	$\alpha = 5\,h\,26\,m\,36\,s$ $\delta = -70°\,57'37''$	$\alpha = 5\,h\,06\,m\,05\,s$ $\delta = -65°\,58'34''$
b magnitude	19.3 ± 0.2	19.3 ± 0.2
b–r	0.3 ± 0.2	0.0 ± 0.2
Date of maximum amplification	1 February 1992	29 December 1990
Event duration (τ in days)	27 ± 2	30 ± 3
Maximum amplification in magnitudes (blue filter)	1.0 ± 0.1	1.1 ± 0.2
Maximum amplification in magnitudes (red filter)	1.0 ± 0.1	1.3 ± 0.2
Maximum amplification in magnitudes (combined fit)	1.0 ± 0.1	1.2 ± 0.2
χ^2 (combined fit)	192 for 248 d.o.f.	167 for 131 d.o.f.

Errors in the magnitudes include fitting errors as well as systematic uncertainties in the magnitude-plate transparency relation. The χ^2 were calculated using the estimated errors which are known only to an estimated precision of 20%. The timescale τ is the time taken by the dark object to cross an angle corresponding to one "Einstein radius" (ref. 3). This definition differs from the traditional one which is the time the dark object remains within the Einstein ring. The traditional definition is meaningless for lensing events with a minimum impact parameter greater than the Einstein radius.

If the events are interpreted as arising from microlensing, the lensing objects would have a mass between a few $\times\,10^{-2}$ and $1\ M_\odot$. This range is based on simulations with the standard isothermal halo yielding the observed flat rotation curve out to the LMC (refs 2, 6). The range is wide because, for fixed mass, the lensing time varies due to the uncertain distance and speed of the lensing object. The allowed masses include those expected for brown dwarfs and dim main sequence stars. If they are located in the Galactic halo, they would not be detectable. If the halo consists entirely of such objects, we estimate that we would have observed about six events if the dominant mass is $10^{-2}\ M_\odot$ and about one event if it is $1\ M_\odot$, in agreement with the observed number.

Obviously, this interpretation of the events must be confirmed by further observations of the stars in question and, especially, by the discovery of further events, which would permit us to study their statistical properties. In particular, the distribution of amplification magnitudes must be shown to be consistent with the microlensing hypothesis and the microlensed stars must be distributed throughout the observed colour–magnitude diagram and throughout the LMC. Until this is done, it is not possible to rule out the possibility that we are dealing with a new type of variable star. During the preparation of this paper we learned that a similar microlensing event has been observed by the "MACHO" collaboration (C. Alcock, personal communication).

表 1. 两个微引力透镜候选事件的特征

	候选事件 1	候选事件 2
恒星的坐标 (J2000)	$\alpha = 5\,h\,26\,m\,36\,s$ $\delta = -70°\,57'\,37''$	$\alpha = 5\,h\,06\,m\,05\,s$ $\delta = -65°\,58'\,34''$
蓝星等	19.3 ± 0.2	19.3 ± 0.2
蓝星等－红星等	0.3 ± 0.2	0.0 ± 0.2
亮度增益最大的日期	1992 年 2 月 1 日	1990 年 12 月 29 日
现象时标 (τ 以天为单位)	27 ± 2	30 ± 3
星等增益的最大值 (蓝滤光片)	1.0 ± 0.1	1.1 ± 0.2
星等增益的最大值 (红滤光片)	1.0 ± 0.1	1.3 ± 0.2
星等增益的最大值 (综合拟合)	1.0 ± 0.1	1.2 ± 0.2
χ^2 (综合拟合)	192/248 自由度	167/131 自由度

星等误差中既包括拟合误差也包括星等－施密特底片透明度关系的系统不确定性。χ^2 是用估计的误差计算的，估计的误差精度只有 20%。时标 τ 是指暗天体穿过一个"爱因斯坦半径"(参考文献 3) 对应角度所用的时间。这个定义与传统定义不同，传统定义的时标是暗天体处在爱因斯坦环内的时间。对于最小影响参数大于爱因斯坦半径的透镜事件，这一传统的时标没有意义。

如果这些事件被解释为由微引力透镜事件导致，那么可以估计透镜天体的质量在数倍 $10^{-2}M_\odot$ 到 $1\,M_\odot$ 之间。这个质量范围基于标准等温晕模型下的模拟，该模型可以给出银晕外围直到大麦哲伦云范围之内的平坦自转曲线 (参考文献 2、6)。这个范围较宽是因为对于给定透镜质量，透镜现象持续时间会由于距离以及透镜天体速度的不同而不同。这些可能的质量涵盖了褐矮星以及暗弱的主序星。如果它们位于银晕中，那么它们是不可被直接探测到的。假设银晕完全由这种天体组成，我们估计如果主要是质量为 $10^{-2}M_\odot$ 的透镜天体，会发现 6 个事件；如果质量为 $1\,M_\odot$ 的透镜天体主导，会发现 1 个事件，和观测到的数量一致。

显然，这些事情的解释必须由对所研究恒星的进一步观测证实，特别是发现更多的事件，可以让我们研究它们的统计性质。特别地，放大星等的分布应该和微引力透镜假设的理论预言相符合，被引力透镜放大的恒星应该遍布观测到的颜色－星等图以及大麦哲伦云。在做到这一步之前，我们没法排除所研究的天体是一种新型变星的可能性。在准备这篇论文期间，我们得知"MACHO"合作组 (阿尔科克，个人交流) 观测到一个类似的微引力透镜事件。

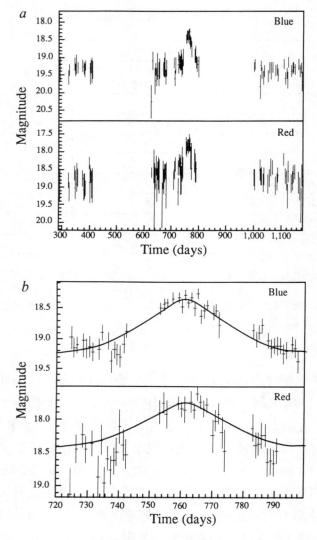

Fig. 1. *a*, The measured magnitudes for candidate 1 as a function of time. The time is counted from 1 January 1990. The error bars correspond to the estimated 1σ errors. *b*, The light-curve of candidate 1 on an expanded scale. The curve shows the best fit for the microlensing hypothesis. The parameters of the best fit are shown in Table 1.

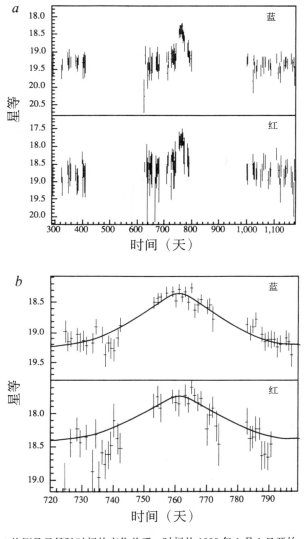

图 1. *a*，候选事件 1 的测量星等随时间的变化关系。时间从 1990 年 1 月 1 日开始。误差棒是估算得到的 1σ 误差值。*b*，在扩展刻度坐标下的候选事件 1 的光变曲线。该曲线显示观测结果与微引力透镜假说吻合得很好。最佳拟合的参数列于表 1 中。

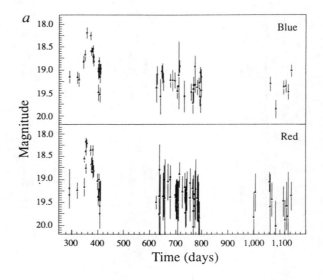

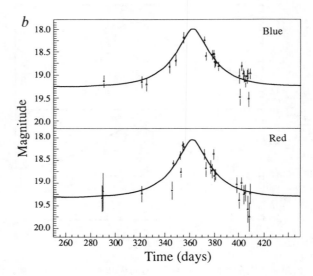

Fig. 2. As Fig. 1, for candidate 2

The EROS collaboration is continuing to collect and analyse data and it is expected that further results will be presented within a year's time.

Note added in proof: We have located in our data the star involved in the candidate microlensing presented by the MACHO collaboration (C. Alcock *et al.*, this issue). Because the star is very faint in the blue band, we have reliable measurements only in the red. (This fact explains the rejection of the event in our analysis.) We confirm in this colour the existence and characteristics of the MACHO event. No other significant luminosity variations are seen in the 1990–91 and 1991–92 seasons, reinforcing the microlensing interpretation of the event.

(**365**, 623-625; 1993)

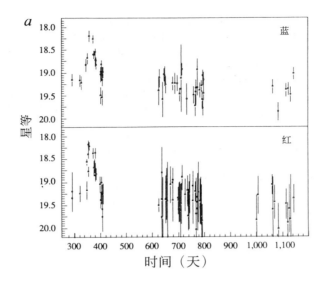

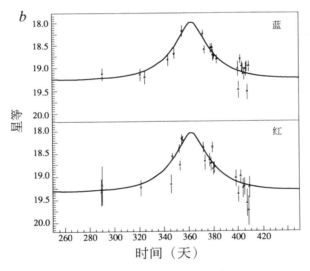

图 2. 对应于图 1，观测对象为候选事件 2

EROS 合作组将继续收集和分析数据，预计一年之内将会有更多新的结果。

附加说明： 在我们的数据中找到了上文中提到的 MACHO 合作组（阿尔科克等人，请见本刊中另一篇文章）提供的候选微引力透镜天体。因为这颗恒星在蓝波段非常暗，我们只能在红波段得到可靠的测量结果。（这就是我们在分析时没有筛选出该事件的原因。）我们在该颜色下验证了 MACHO 所产生的透镜事件的存在性和特征。在 1990~1991 年和 1991~1992 年期间，并未发现该目标恒星存在其他明显的光度变化，这也进一步证明了可以用微引力透镜事件解释该例子。

（冯翀 翻译；臧伟呈 毛淑德 审稿）

E. Aubourg[*], **P. Bareyre**[*], **S. Bréhin**[*], **M. Gros**[*], **M. Lachièze-Rey**[*], **B. Laurent**[*], **E. Lesquoy**[*], **C. Magneville**[*], **A. Milsztajn**[*], **L. Moscoso**[*], **F. Queinnec**[*], **J. Rich**[*], **M. Spiro**[*], **L. Vigroux**[*], **S. Zylberajch**[*], **R. Ansari**[†], **F. Cavalier**[†], **M. Moniez**[†], **J.-P. Beaulieu**[‡], **R. Ferlet**[‡], **Ph. Grison**[‡], **A. Vidal-Madjar**[‡], **J. Guibert**[§], **O. Moreau**[§], **F. Tajahmady**[§], **E. Maurice**[||], **L. Prévôt**[||] & **C. Gry**[¶]

[*] DAPNIA, Centre d'Études de Saclay, 91191 Gif-sur-Yvette, France

[†] Laboratoire de l'Accélérateur Linéaire, Centre d'Orsay, 91405 Orsay, France

[‡] Institut d'Astrophysique de Paris, 98 bis Boulevard Arago, 75014 Paris, France

[§] Centre d'Analyse des Images de l'Institut National des Sciences de l'Univers, Observatoire de Paris, 61 Avenue de l'Observatoire, 75014 Paris, France

[||] Observatoire de Marseille, 2 Place Le Verrier, 13248 Marseille 04, France

[¶] Laboratoire d'Astronomie Spatiale de Marseille, Traverse du Siphon, Les Trois Lucs, 13120 Marseille, France

Received 22 September; accepted 30 September 1993.

References:

1. Trimble, V. *A. Rev. Astr. Astrophys.* **25**, 425-472 (1987).

2. Primack, J. R., Seckel, D. & Sadoulet, B. *A. Rev. Nucl. Part. Sci.* **38**, 751-807 (1988).

3. Paczyński, B. *Astrophys. J.* **304**, 1-5 (1986).

4. Aubourg, E. *et al. Messenger* **72**, 20-27 (1993).

5. Aubourg, E. thesis, Univ. Paris (1992).

6. Griest, K. *et al. Astrophys. J.* **372**, L79-82 (1991).

7. Berger, J. *et al. Astr. Astrophys. Suppl. Ser.* **B7**, 389 (1991).

8. Alcock, C. *et al. Nature* **365**, 621-623 (1993).

Acknowledgements. We thank C. Alcock for discussions at the beginning of this project. We thank A. Bijaoui, Ph. Veron, the staff at the Observatoire de Haute Provence, the ESO staff at La Silla, and the technical staff of the collaborating laboratories for their advice and help. We thank D. Bennett of the MACHO collaboration for help and interesting discussions. This work is based on observations at the European Southern Observatory, La Silla, Chile, and is funded by DSM-CEA, IN2P3-CNRS, INSU-CNRS, with support from ESO.

A Search for Life on Earth from the Galileo Spacecraft

C. Sagan *et al.*

Editor's Note

This paper is a canny mixture of prescience and opportunism. By using a planned fly-by of the Earth by NASA's Galileo spacecraft in 1990 to investigate our planet as though it were an unknown, potentially habitable world, Carl Sagan and co-workers set the scene for observations of extrasolar planets in the early twenty-first century. The paper takes the inventive approach of treating the Earth as a hitherto unexplored planetary environment, asking whether, in such a situation, we could identify definitive evidence of life. The researchers use the Galileo observations of the chemistry of Earth's atmosphere, images of the planetary surface, and detection of radio-wave emissions, to infer that the presence of water-based life, probably intelligent, seems highly likely.

In its December 1990 fly-by of Earth, the Galileo spacecraft found evidence of abundant gaseous oxygen, a widely distributed surface pigment with a sharp absorption edge in the red part of the visible spectrum, and atmospheric methane in extreme thermodynamic disequilibrium; together, these are strongly suggestive of life on Earth. Moreover, the presence of narrow-band, pulsed, amplitude-modulated radio transmission seems uniquely attributable to intelligence. These observations constitute a control experiment for the search for extraterrestrial life by modern interplanetary spacecraft.

A T ranges varying from ~100 km to ~100,000 km, spacecraft have now flown by more than 60 planets, satellites, comets and asteroids. They have been equipped variously with imaging systems, photometric and spectrometric instruments extending from ultraviolet to kilometre wavelengths, magnetometers and charged-particle detectors. In none of these encounters has compelling, or even strongly suggestive, evidence for extraterrestrial life been found. For the Moon, Venus and Mars, orbiter and lander observations confirm the conclusion from fly-by spacecraft. Still, extraterrestrial life, if it exists, might be quite unlike the forms of life with which we are familiar, or present only marginally. The most elementary test of these techniques—the detection of life on Earth by such an instrumented fly-by spacecraft—had, until recently, never been attempted.

Galileo is a single-launch Jupiter orbiter and entry probe currently in interplanetary space and scheduled to arrive in the Jupiter system in December 1995. It could not be sent directly to Jupiter; instead, the mission incorporated two close gravitational assists at the

用伽利略木星探测器探测地球生命

萨根等

编者按

本文是预知结果与取巧验证的巧妙结合。通过利用美国国家航空航天局伽利略探测器1990年按计划掠过地球的机会，把我们的行星当成未知的、潜在的宜居世界进行研究，卡尔·萨根与合作者们为二十一世纪早期对太阳系外行星的观测设定了情景。本文将地球当作从未探索过的行星环境，以此创新方法研究在这样的情形下我们是否可以确定地证认生命的存在。这些研究者使用伽利略探测器对地球大气化学、地球表面图像和无线电波辐射进行探测，推断地球存在水基生命，看起来很有可能是有智慧的。

伽利略号探测器在1990年12月从地球掠过时，发现了丰富的气态氧存在的证据：一种广泛分布在地球表面、在可见光谱红端有尖锐吸收边缘的色素，以及大气中CH_4处于极端热力学非平衡态。所有这些都有力地证明地球存在生命。此外，观测到的窄带的、脉冲的、振幅调制的无线电发射信号似乎只能归结为智慧文明。这些观测结果构成了现代行星际探测器探索地球外生命的对照实验。

现在，各种探测器已经在100~100,000 km的距离上掠过了60多颗行星、卫星、彗星和小行星。它们都装备了各种各样从紫外到千米波的成像系统、光度计和光谱仪，以及磁强计和带电粒子探测器。在这些交会中没有发现令人信服的甚或是强有力的生命存在的证据。对于月球、金星和火星，轨道飞行器和着陆器的观测已经证实了飞掠探测器得出的结论。然而，如果有外星生命的话，其形式很可能不是我们熟知的那样，或者是很少量的存在。应用以上这些技术进行最初步的检测——用装备有这些技术设备的飞掠探测器探测地球上的生命——直到最近还从来没有人尝试过。

伽利略号是单向发射的木星轨道飞行器和进入行星际空间的探测器，计划在1995年12月抵达木星系统。它不能直接向木星发射，取而代之的是，它的任务包括两次紧密的引力加速，一次在地球，另一次在金星。这大大延长了转运时间，但

Earth and one at Venus. This greatly lengthened the transit time, but it also permitted close observations of the Earth. The Galileo instruments were not designed for an Earth encounter mission, so an appropriate control experiment has fortuitously been arranged: a search for life on Earth with a typical modern planetary probe.

Closest approach to Earth in the 8 December 1990 encounter was 960 km over the Caribbean Sea. The Earth was approached from its night side, so all data in reflected light were acquired post-encounter. Evidence relevant to the search for life was obtained with the near-infrared mapping spectrometer (NIMS), the ultra-violet spectrometer (UVS), the solid-state imaging system (SSI), and the plasma wave spectrometer (PWS). These instruments are described in refs 1–4, respectively. Because of the high encounter velocity, most NIMS and SSI data were obtained 2 hours to 3.5 days after closest approach.

In what follows, we do not assume properties of life otherwise known on Earth, but instead attempt to derive our conclusions from Galileo data and first principles alone. We compare these conclusions with ground-based and low-altitude measurements that we describe, collectively, as the "ground-truth Earth". A necessary but not sufficient condition for the presence of life is a marked departure from thermodynamic equilibrium[5-8]. Once candidate disequilibria are identified, alternative explanations must be eliminated. Life is the hypothesis of last resort. As an analogy, mountains are in mechanical disequilibrium, given the Earth's erosional environment, but orogenic processes build mountains faster than wind, water and plate tectonics destroy them. Ozone is in substantial thermodynamic disequilibrium in the Earth's atmosphere, but this is driven by solar ultraviolet (UV) photochemistry. Bursts of high-brightness-temperature kilometre-wave radiation occur in the Earth's auroral zones, but are pumped by the interaction of the solar wind with the Earth's magnetosphere. No biological explanations of these disequilibrium phenomena need to be sought. As we will show, however, Galileo found such profound departures from equilibrium that the presence of life seems the most probable cause.

Chemistry

NIMS spectral and radiometric measurements indicate the presence of water in several forms. Spectra of Antarctica[9] show distinctive features due to condensed water, which are broadened and shifted to longer wavelengths compared to gas-phase features. The radiometric temperatures ($\sim -30\,°C$) indicate ice, and analysis of the spectra[9] give snow grain sizes of 50–200 μm. This ice and snow cover occurs on continental scale around the South Pole.

At higher latitudes are extensive areas with higher, nearly uniform temperatures just at, or slightly above, the melting point of water. In particular, the radiometric temperatures measured at 5 μm, uncorrected for atmospheric absorption, are $\sim -3\,°C$ at high southern latitudes, increasing to 8–18 °C at midlatitudes. The average 1 μm albedo of these extensive areas is $\sim 4\%$, much smaller than the albedos of snow, clouds and rocky surfaces, but

同时也让我们得以仔细观测地球。伽利略号探测器并不是为探测地球而设计的，所以临时安排了一个合适的对照试验：利用典型的现代行星探测器搜寻地球上的生命。

1990 年 12 月 8 日的交会中距地球最近时是在加勒比海面上空 960 km 处。探测器进入到地球的夜面，所以所有反射光数据在交会之后获得。搜寻和生命相关的证据分别通过近红外成像光谱仪（NIMS）、紫外光谱仪（UVS）、固体成像系统（SSI）和等离子体波谱仪（PWS）获得。在参考文献 1~4 中分别介绍了这些探测设备。由于交会时速度大，大多数的 NIMS 和 SSI 近地点探测数据在过最近点之后的 2 小时到 3.5 天得到。

接下来，我们不去假设地球上已知生命的特征，相反，我们尝试从伽利略号提供的数据和第一性原理中得出结论。我们将这些结论同我们所描述的以地面状况为基础和对近地表的测量结果——称之为"实况地球"相比较。对于生命的存在而言，一个必要不充分条件就是显著偏离热力学平衡[5-8]。一旦候选体的不平衡被证实，那么其他的解释就必须被排除。有生命是最终才采用的假设。作为类比，考虑到地球的侵蚀性环境，山体处于力学的非平衡态，但是造山过程比风、水和板块构造对山体的破坏快。在地球大气层中，O_3 实际上处于热力学非平衡态，但这是受到太阳紫外线光化学的作用所致。高亮温度的千米波辐射爆发在地球的极光带，但却是受太阳风和地球磁层的相互作用激发的。这些不平衡现象不需要生物学解释。然而正如我们将要展示的，伽利略探测器发现了如此深刻的偏离平衡现象，生命的存在是解释这种现象最可能的原因。

化　学

NIMS 频谱和辐射测量结果说明了水以数种形式存在。南极的频谱[9]显示冷凝水造成的独有的特征，这些冷凝水的频谱相比于它的气相特征，波谱被展宽并且向长波方向移动。辐射温度（约 $-30\ ℃$）表明存在冰，频谱分析[9]还显示存在 $50~200\ \mu m$ 大小的米雪。在规模上，这些冰雪覆盖了南极附近的大陆。

高纬度地区是一片广泛具有更高的、差不多处于或稍稍高于水的熔点的均一温度的地区。特别是，不考虑大气吸收的修正，在南半球高纬度地区测到的 $5\ \mu m$ 处的辐射温度大约是 $-3\ ℃$。这个温度在中纬度地区增加到 $8~18\ ℃$。这些广阔地区 $1\ \mu m$ 处的平均反照率约是 4%，这比雪、云和岩石表面的反照率小得多，但是却和包括

consistent with the low diffuse reflectance of dielectric liquid surfaces, including water. In many of the NIMS images, greatly enhanced specular reflection is observed[10]—implying the existence of large areas that are macroscopically smooth and homogenous (that is, not granular) and most easily explained by the presence of liquid surfaces of oceanic dimensions. Evidence of gas-phase H_2O is found over the entire planet. Representative NIMS infrared spectra in the 0.7–1.0 µm range, and in the 2.4–5.2 µm range, are shown in Fig. 1. They were obtained over a fairly clear area in the eastern Pacific, north of Borneo. Analysis[10] of the vibration–rotation bands of water vapour gives typical abundances of ~1,000 parts per million (p.p.m.) or ~0.6 g cm^{-2}. The observed high humidities, found over most of the planet, along with the preceding discussion, imply that the oceans are composed of liquid water.

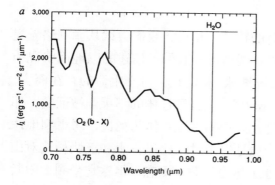

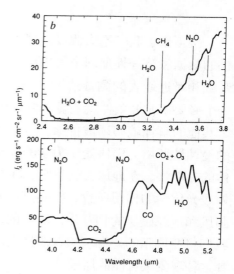

Fig. 1. a, Galileo long-wavelength-visible and near-infrared spectra of the Earth over a relatively cloud-free region of the Pacific Ocean, north of Borneo. The incidence and emission angles are 77° and 57° respectively. The (b$'\Sigma_g^+$–X$^3\Sigma_g^-$) O—O band of O_2 at 0.76 µm is evident, along with a number of H_2O features. Using several cloud-free regions of varying airmass, we estimate an O_2 vertical column density of 1.5 km-amagat ± 25%. b and c, Infrared spectra of the Earth in the 2.4–5.2 µm region. The strong v_3 CO_2 band is seen at the 4.3 µm, and water vapour bands are found, but not indicated, in the 3.0 µm region. The v_3 band of nitrous oxide, N_2O, is apparent at the edge of the CO_2 band near 4.5 µm, and N_2O combination bands are also seen near 4.0 µm. The methane (0010) vibrational transition is evident at 3.31 µm. A crude estimate[10] of the CH_4 and N_2O column abundances is, for both species, of the order of 1 cm-amagate ($\equiv$ 1 cm path at STP).

Spectral data aside, from the albedo and heliocentric distance of the Earth alone it follows that the equilibrium temperature of the planet is only 20 °C or so below the freezing point of water—so that even a modest greenhouse effect would bring temperatures high enough that water, a cosmically abundant molecule, could exist in all three of its phases. Abundant surface liquid water is seen nowhere else in the contemporary Solar System. The dielectric constant, solvation properties, heat capacity, and temperature range of the liquid state are among the nonparochial reasons that water seems an ideal medium for life[11].

水在内的介电液体表面较低的漫反射率一致。在很多的 NIMS 图像中，观测到了大大增强的镜面反射[10]——这表明存在着大面积宏观上平滑且均匀的区域（也就是说，不是颗粒状的），用存在着海洋规模的液体表面来解释这个观测结果是最容易的。在整颗行星的所有地区都能找到气态水存在的证据。图 1 显示了非常具有代表性的 0.7~1.0 μm 波段和 2.4~5.2 μm 波段的 NIMS 近红外光谱。光谱是在婆罗洲北部的东太平洋上非常晴朗的地区获得的。对水蒸气的振动–转动谱带的分析[10] 得出了其丰度的典型值约是 1,000 ppm（ppm：百万分之一）或 0.6 g·cm^{-2}。在地球大部分地区观测到的高湿度，加上之前的讨论，说明海洋是由液态水组成的。

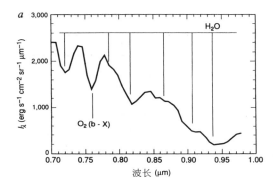
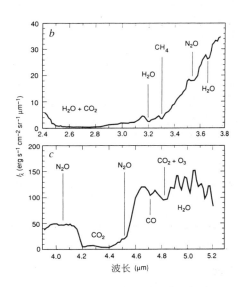

图 1. a，伽利略探测器在婆罗洲北部的太平洋上空相对无云地区探测到地球长波可见光和近红外光谱。入射角和出射角分别是 77° 和 57°。0.76 μm 处 O_2 的 $(b'\sum_g^+ - X^3\sum_g^-)$ O—O 带明显可见，同时伴有一些水的特征线。通过使用几个不同大气质量的无云地区的光谱数据，我们估计了一个 1.5 km 阿马加 ±25% 的 O_2 垂直柱密度。b 和 c，2.4~5.2 μm 波段范围内的地球红外光谱。在 4.3 μm 处观测到强的 CO_2 的 υ_3 带，并且在 3.0 μm 带上发现了水蒸气带，但是没有标明。N_2O 的 υ_3 带位于 CO_2 带边缘，在 4.5 μm 附近出现；N_2O 组合带也在 4.0 μm 附近被发现了。CH_4（0010）的振动跃迁在 3.31 μm 处很明显。CH_4 和 N_2O 柱丰度的粗略估计[10] 都是 1 cm 阿马加（恒等于标准温度和压强下 1 cm 路径）。

不使用频谱数据，单从反照率和地球的日心距就可知道地球的平衡温度只比水的凝固点低 20 ℃ 左右。所以即使是最微弱的温室效应都会让温度升到足够高，以使一种宇宙中丰富的分子——水能够以它的三种相存在。在目前的太阳系中任何其他地方都没有看到如此大量水。液态水的介电常数、溶解特性、热容和温度范围都有力地说明，水看起来是生命理想的媒介[11]。

Figure 1 is notable for the presence of the A band of molecular oxygen at 0.76 μm. This transition is spin-forbidden, and the strength of the feature indicates ~200 g cm^{-2} of O_2 (Table 1). So large an abundance of O_2 is also unique among all the worlds in the Solar System. Oxygen can be generated by the UV photodissociation of water and the subsequent Jeans escape of H to space. But can the accumulation of so much O_2 over geological time be understood?

Table 1. Constituents of the Earth's atmosphere (volume mixing ratios)

Molecule	Standard abundance (ground-truth Earth)	Galileo value*	Thermodynamic equilibrium value	
			Estimate 1†	Estimate 2‡
N_2	0.78		0.78	
O_2	0.21	0.19 ± 0.05	0.21§	
H_2O	0.03–0.001	0.01–0.001	0.03–0.001	
Ar	9×10^{-3}		9×10^{-3}	
CO_2	3.5×10^{-4}	$5 \pm 2.5 \times 10^{-4}$	3.5×10^{-4}	
CH_4	1.6×10^{-6}	$3 \pm 1.5 \times 10^{-6}$	$< 10^{-35}$	10^{-145}
N_2O	3×10^{-7}	$\sim 10^{-6}$	2×10^{-20}	2×10^{-19}
O_3	10^{-7}–10^{-8}	$> 10^{-8}$	6×10^{-32}	3×10^{-30}

* Galileo values for O_2, CH_4 and N_2O from NIMS data; O_3 estimate from UVS data.
† From ref. 16 (P, 1 bar; T, 280 K).
‡ From ref. 17 (P, 1 bar; T, 298 K).
§ The observed value; it is in thermodynamic equilibrium only if the under-oxidized state of the Earth's crust is neglected.

Certainly, Venus and Mars—where atmospheric water vapour is being UV photodissociated—display very low O_2 abundances, < 1 and $\sim 10^{-3}$ p.p.m., respectively[12,13], despite large quantities of water lost through photodissociation and atmospheric escape of H. But a real understanding of the Earth's steady-state O_2 abundance requires at the least knowledge of the oxidation state of the surface, surface erosion rates, and temperatures at the tropopause, the mesopause and the exobase. Galileo did not provide this data set. Even if it had, we could not be confident that present circumstances are typical of Earth history. An upper bound on the UV generation rate of O_2 is set by the photon-limited water photolysis rate, $\sim 10^{13}$ cm^{-2} s^{-1} on the ground-truth Earth[14]—which yields the present O_2 abundance in $< 10^5$ yr. If instead we use the ground-truth present H escape flux[14] (which is H_2O diffusion-limited) and assume that all the H atoms are H_2O-derived, the present O_2 abundance would require several times the age of the Earth to accumulate. If there is substantial oxidation of the crust, these timescales will be longer. But the lack of impact craters in Galileo imagery, and pervasive wind and water on Earth suggest continuing exposure of fresh, oxidizable regolith. Accordingly, oxidation of the Earth's crust should be more extensive than on Venus and Mars, and yet these planets have much less atmospheric O_2. Galileo's observations of O_2 thus at least raise our suspicions about the presence of life. If detailed modelling showed solar UV to be insufficient, a process seems needed whereby the much more abundant, but

在图 1 中可以明显看出在 0.76 μm 处存在着 A 带的氧分子。这种跃迁是自旋禁阻的，这种特性的强度表明存在大约 200 g·cm⁻² 的 O_2（表 1）。如此大量的 O_2 在太阳系的所有行星中也是很独特的。O_2 可以通过水的紫外（UV）光致离解和接下来 H 向太空的金斯逃逸作用而产生。但是在地质时期内积累起这么多的 O_2 能说得通吗？

表 1. 地球大气的组成（体积混合比）

分子	标准丰度（实况地球）	伽利略值 *	热力学平衡值	
			估值 1†	估值 2‡
N_2	0.78		0.78	
O_2	0.21	0.19 ± 0.05	0.21§	
H_2O	0.03~0.001	0.01~0.001	0.03~0.001	
Ar	9×10^{-3}		9×10^{-3}	
CO_2	3.5×10^{-4}	$(5 \pm 2.5) \times 10^{-4}$	3.5×10^{-4}	
CH_4	1.6×10^{-6}	$(3 \pm 1.5) \times 10^{-6}$	$< 10^{-35}$	10^{-145}
N_2O	3×10^{-7}	$\sim 10^{-6}$	2×10^{-20}	2×10^{-19}
O_3	$10^{-7} \sim 10^{-8}$	$> 10^{-8}$	6×10^{-32}	3×10^{-30}

* O_2、CH_4 和 N_2O 的伽利略值来自 NIMS 数据；O_3 的伽利略值由 UVS 数据估计得出。
† 来自参考文献 16（压强为 1 bar，温度为 280 K）。
‡ 来自参考文献 17（压强为 1 bar，温度为 298 K）。
§ 观测值；只有在忽略地壳的氧化状态时才处于热力学平衡。

当然，尽管金星和火星大气中的水蒸气通过紫外光致离解以及 H 逃逸出大气层而大量损失，但仍显示出非常低的 O_2 含量，分别为 < 1 ppm 和约 10^{-3} ppm[12,13]。但对地球的稳态 O_2 丰度的真正理解要求至少了解表面的氧化状态、表面侵蚀率以及对流层顶、中间层顶和外大气层底的温度。伽利略号没有提供这些数据。即使有这些数据，我们也不能确定当前的环境就能代表地球的历史。O_2 的紫外产生速率的上限是由水的光解速率限定的，而水的光分解速率受到光子限制，在实况地球中约为 10^{13} cm⁻²·s⁻¹[14]——按照这样的速率会在小于 10^5 年的时间之内得到当前的 O_2 丰度。相反，如果我们使用实况地球 H 逃逸流量[14]（这受到水扩散的限制），并且假设所有的 H 原子都是 H_2O 生成的，那么就需要用地球年龄很多倍的时间才能积累到目前的 O_2 丰度。如果存在大量的地壳氧化作用，那么时标将会更长。但是在伽利略号获得的影像中缺乏陨击坑，以及地球上普遍存在的风和水表明有新鲜的、可被氧化的土壤持续暴露出来。相应地，地壳的氧化作用比在金星和火星规模更大，然而这些行星上却只有比地球少得多的 O_2。因此伽利略号关于 O_2 的观测至少引起了我们对于生命存在的猜测。如果详细的模拟显示太阳紫外光子对于光致离解过程是不足的，那么就需要一个过

much less energetic visible light photons are used in series for H_2O photodissociation (at least two visible photons would be needed per photodissociation event). Apparently, only biological systems can accomplish this.

In Fig. 1*b* and *c*, the presence of carbon dioxide, methane, nitrous oxide and ozone are indicated. All are greenhouse gasses; together with water vapour, they mainly account for the discrepancy between the equilibrium and measured radiometric temperatures of the Earth's surface.

From straightforward photochemical theory it follows[15] that one consequence of the high oxygen abundance is a stratospheric ozone layer opaque in the middle UV. Even a quick look at the Galileo UVS raw data shows the strong Hartley bands of O_3 at wavelengths greater than 0.21 μm in the spectrum of the Earth but not of Venus. (O_3 absorption is also found in NIMS infrared spectra.) The presence of disequilibrium O_3 is not in itself a sign of life, because UV photochemistry is a disequilibrium process, but the photochemical abundance of O_3 is related approximately logarithmically to the O_2 abundance, so the observed quantity of O_3 does imply a substantial abundance of O_2. Therefore a train of argument may exist[15] from abundant O_3 to abundant O_2 to life. The Hartley bands provide substantial optical depth at wavelengths less than ~0.3 μm, suggesting that in addition to the oceans (where life could be protected at depth from UV radiation), life on the land is also possible provided structural molecular bond strengths exceed ~50 kcal mol^{-1}. In this category fall a large number of organic functional groups, including C—C (70–130 kcal mol^{-1}), C—H (80–110), C—O (~90) and C—N (80–100). Corresponding multiple bonds are even stronger. Of course this is not, by itself, an argument for organic biochemistry on Earth.

The agreement of ground-truth atmospheric abundances with those determined by Galileo is reasonably good (Table 1). Also shown in Table 1 are two independent estimates[16,17], made 25 years apart, of the thermodynamic equilibrium abundances expected of minor constituents in the observed excess of O_2. Such calculations are characteristically performed by minimizing the free energy of the system while simultaneously satisfying the equilibrium constants of all known reactions of all known reactants. This approach is less vulnerable to unknown reaction pathways or erroneous rate constants than is absolute reaction rate kinetics. But it is an idealization at best, because thermodynamic equilibrium may not be achieved in the age of the Solar System, and because there are prominent nonequilibrium processes including photochemistry and biology. Ozone is present at more than 20 orders of magnitude above its thermodynamic expectation value, but, as noted above, this disequilibrium is not considered evidence for life because a UV photochemical pathway from O_2 to this O_3 abundance is well known.

The circumstance of methane is different. It is oxidized quickly to CO_2 and H_2O, and at thermodynamic equilibrium there should not be a single methane molecule in the Earth's atmosphere[16,17]. The disparity between observation and thermodynamic equilibrium is about 140 orders of magnitude. Clearly there is some mechanism that pumps CH_4 into the Earth's atmosphere so rapidly that substantial steady-state abundances accrue before

程，将更多但能量小得多的可见光光子用于一系列水的光致离解过程（每次光致离解事件至少需要两个可见光光子）。很显然，只有生物过程才能满足这个条件。

在图 1b 和 1c 中，显示存在 CO_2、CH_4、N_2O 和 O_3。它们都是温室气体，跟水蒸气混合在一起。它们是导致地球表面平衡温度和实际观测到的辐射温度之间的偏差的主要原因。

直接从光化学理论来看[15]，高氧含量的一个结果是存在对中紫外波段不透明的平流臭氧层。 即使快速浏览一下伽利略号的 UVS 获取的原始数据也能发现地球光谱中波长比 $0.21\ \mu m$ 长的强 O_3 哈脱莱吸收带，这在金星光谱中是不存在的。（NIMS 红外光谱中同样发现了 O_3 的吸收谱线。）O_3 的非平衡态的存在本身不是生命的迹象，因为紫外光化学是一个非平衡过程，但是 O_3 的光化学丰度是与 O_2 丰度近似成对数关系的，所以观测到的 O_3 量确实表明有可观的 O_2 丰度。这样，可能存在一系列从丰富的 O_3 到丰富的 O_2 再到生命的论证[15]。哈脱莱吸收带使得波长小于 $0.3\ \mu m$ 处有相当大的光深，这表明除了海洋（在海洋深处生命可以免受紫外线的侵害），这片土地上的生命也可能提供键能超过 $50\ kcal \cdot mol^{-1}$ 的分子键。在这类分子键中有一大批有机的官能团，包括 $C{-}C$（$70\sim130\ kcal \cdot mol^{-1}$），$C{-}H$（$80\sim110\ kcal \cdot mol^{-1}$），$C{-}O$（约 $90\ kcal \cdot mol^{-1}$）和 $C{-}N$（$80\sim100\ kcal \cdot mol^{-1}$）。相应的多重键更强。当然，就其本身而言，这并不是地球上有机生物化学的论据。

伽利略号测量的值和实况地球大气层的丰度一致性相当好（表 1）。在表 1 中也可以看到两个相隔 25 年、相对独立的、对过量 O_2 中所预期的微量成分的热动力学平衡丰度的估计[16,17]。这样的计算一般是通过在使系统自由能最小并同时满足所有已知反应物的所有已知的反应的平衡常量而进行的。这种方法对未知的反应路径或者错误的速率常数来说，要比绝对的反应速率动力学更稳妥。但是这最多是一个理想化的方法，因为热力学平衡在太阳系的年龄内可能无法实现，还因为事实上存在着包括光化学和生物学在内的明显的不平衡过程。现在的 O_3 丰度要比热动力学预期值高 20 个数量级。但是正如上面所说，这种不平衡并不是生命存在的证据，因为存在一个广为人知的从 O_2 到 O_3 丰度的紫外光化学途径。

CH_4 的情况不同。它能很快被氧化成 CO_2 和 H_2O，而且在热力学平衡态，地球大气层中不应该存在单独的 CH_4 分子[16,17]。观测和热力学平衡值大约差 140 个数量级。很明显，存在着某些机制将 CH_4 快速地注入地球的大气层，以至于在其氧化能够跟上节奏之前就获得巨大的稳态丰度。一直以来就存在一种观点，在富氧环境中

oxidation can keep pace. It has long been suggested that an extreme disequilibrium abundance of a reduced gas such as CH_4 in an O_2-rich atmosphere could be evidence for life on Earth[6-8,16]. The total emission flux of CH_4 into the atmosphere of the ground-truth Earth from all sources[18] required to sustain the steady state abundance is 500 ± 100 Tg yr^{-1} (where 1 Tg is 10^{12}g), or $\sim 10^{-4}$ g cm^{-2} yr^{-1}, an oxidation of all atmospheric CH_4 roughly every decade. Conceivably, methane could be injected into the Earth's atmosphere by other means (for example, the decomposition of prebiological organic matter) but so large a rate of injection, corresponding to ~ 1 bar of CH_4 after only 10^7 yr, seems highly implausible. Oxidation of such organic matter has certainly gone to completion on, for example, Venus. In fact, on the ground-truth Earth the contribution of volcanos, fumaroles, and earthquakes to atmospheric CH_4 is negligible[18]. About half the annual CH_4 injection is thought to arise from natural systems (methane bacteria and so on) and approximately half is anthropogenic; rice cultivation, biomass burning and flatulence from domesticated ruminants are among the principal sources[18]. All these sources are biological, including those deriving from fossil fuels. Thus the disequilibrium abundance of CH_4 in the Earth's oxidizing atmosphere is found by ground-based observations to be indeed caused by biology, as naive consideration of the Galileo data would suggest. It is also evidence that organic chemistry plays some role in life on Earth.

The presence of nitrous oxide (N_2O) in the atmosphere at high disequilibrium abundances is another indicator of biological processes. Nitrous oxide is partly lost to photodissociation, with an atmospheric lifetime[19] of about 50 years. Although there are non-biological mechanisms for producing N_2O (for example lightning), the major source of N_2O on the ground-truth Earth is nitrogen-fixing bacteria and algae that convert soil and oceanic nitrate (NO_3^-) to N_2 and N_2O.

Imaging

A typical Galileo image of the Earth shows continents, oceans, the Antarctic polar cap and a highly time-variable configuration of clouds. The six bands used in SSI global images can be combined in various ways to visualize specific spectral contrasts in the clouds or on the surface. Of the many possibilities, three categories of band combinations prove most informative. First is (RED, GRN, VIO) (equivalent wavelengths 0.670, 0.558 and 0.407 μm respectively), which gives an approximately natural colour view (Fig. 2a). Large expanses of blue ocean and apparent coastlines are present, and close examination of the images shows a region of specular reflection in ocean but not on land. Clouds cover much of the land surface, but in clear areas extreme albedo contrasts are seen. The lighter areas have a colour compatible with mineral soils, while a greenish tint can be perceived in the darkest areas.

类似 CH_4 这种还原气体的极端不平衡丰度可以作为地球上存在生命的证据[6-8,16]。要保持稳态丰度，所有排放源产生的到实况地球大气层的 CH_4 排放总量[18] 需要保持在 500 ± 100 Tg·yr^{-1}（1 Tg 等于 10^{12} g），或者 $\sim 10^{-4}$ g·cm^{-2}·yr^{-1}，这大约是每十年大气层中氧化的 CH_4 总量。可以想象，CH_4 可以通过其他方式注入大气层（比如，通过生命起源前的有机物质的分解），但是仅仅经过 10^7 年就能产生约 1 bar 的 CH_4，这所需要的 CH_4 注入速率是很大的，这似乎非常不可能。这种有机物质的氧化在金星这样的星体上已经结束了。实际上，实况地球上的火山口、喷气孔和地震发生时向大气中喷发出来的 CH_4 是可以忽略的[18]。大约每年一半的 CH_4 的注入量都是通过自然系统增加的（CH_4 细菌等等），还有大概一半是人造的：水稻的种植、生物质的燃烧和驯化的反刍动物的肠胃气都是主要的来源[18]。所有这些来源都是生物的，包括那些化石燃料燃烧产生的。这样，通过地球表面观测到的地球氧化大气层中的 CH_4 丰度的不平衡现象被证实是通过生物产生的，正如对伽利略探测器的数据的简单考虑所示。这也表明有机化学在地球生命中发挥了一定的作用。

大气层中处于高度非平衡丰度的 N_2O 的存在是生物过程的另外一个迹象。在 50 年大气生命周期内[19] N_2O 一部分被光致离解。虽然，存在着生成 N_2O 的非生物学机制（比如闪电），但是实况地球上 N_2O 的主要来源还是能将土壤和海洋中 NO_3^- 转换成 N_2 和 N_2O 的固氮细菌和藻类。

成　　像

一幅典型的伽利略探测器得到的图像显示了大陆、海洋、南极极地冰冠以及时变的云。在 SSI 的全球成像中使用的六个波段可以通过各种方法结合起来，将云层中或者地球表面不同的光谱可视化。在这么多的可能性中，三种波段结合方法被证明最有信息量。首先是（红，绿，紫）（波长分别是 0.670 μm、0.558 μm 和 0.407 μm），这三个波段近似给出了自然色景象（图 2a）。图中呈现了广阔的蓝海和明显的海岸线。仔细检查图像发现了一个海洋中产生镜面反射的区域，但是在陆上没有发现镜面反射的区域。云覆盖了绝大部分陆地，但是在晴朗区域可以观察到极端的星体反照率的反差。浅色区域色彩与矿质土壤一致，同时在颜色最深的区域可以看到绿色色调。

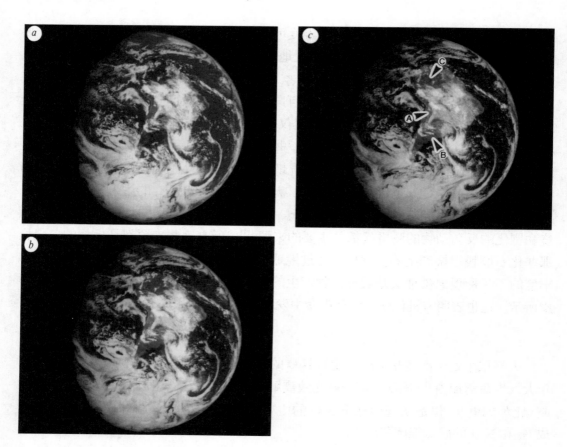

Fig. 2. Three colour-composite versions of a Galileo view of Earth centred over 72° W, 34° S. The SSI bands are identified by the following mnemonics and mean wavelengths in micrometres: VIO (0.407), GRN (0.558), RED (0.670), 0.73 (0.734/N), 0.76 (0.760/N), 0.89 (0.887/N), 1.0 (0.984). N indicates a narrow-band filter (the others are broadband), and effective wavelengths and radiometric calibration for data presented here are for the SSI camera with the clear lens cap on, which was the case for the encounters described here. Of these seven bands, six (all except 0.89) were used for global imaging of the Earth at 20–30 km resolution. (Galileo also imaged Australia and Antarctica at higher resolution (~one to a few km per pixel), but these imaging sequences did not use bands beyond 0.73 μm). a, Approximately natural-colour view constructed from (RED, GRN, VIO) filters; *b*, colour-composite produced from mapping the (1.0 μm, RED, GRN) bands to red, green and blue; c, colour-composite produced from closely spaced (0.76 μm, 0.73 μm, RED) bands, which uniquely separate rock and soil (grey tones) from areas that have unusual, very steep spectral slopes near 0.7 μm, possibly indicative of photosynthetic pigments in autotrophic terrestrial life. Areas whose spectra are shown in Fig. 3 are marked with A, B, C on this composite.

图 2. 伽利略探测器观测到的以西经 72° 和南纬 34° 为中心的三组地球色彩合成视觉图。SSI 不同波段通过以下的助记符号和以微米为单位的平均波长标示：紫 (0.407)、绿 (0.558)、红 (0.670)、0.73 (0.734/N)、0.76 (0.760/N)、0.89 (0.887/N)、1.0 (0.984)。N 代表一个窄带滤光片 (其他代表宽带)，这里呈现的数据的有效波长和辐射定标是针对开启无色的镜头盖的 SSI 成像相机，这就是我们在这里描述的相遇的情形。在这 7 个波段中，有 6 个 (0.89 除外) 是用来以 20~30 km 分辨率拍摄地球全球图像的。(伽利略探测器还以更高的分辨率来拍摄澳大利亚和南极的图像 (每像素一到几千米)，但是这些拍摄结果没有使用超过 0.73 μm 的波段。) a，从 (红，绿，紫) 滤光片合成的接近自然光的视图；b，将 (1.0 μm，红，绿) 波段映射为红、绿和蓝得到的颜色合成；c，由密近排布的 (0.76 μm，0.73 μm，红) 波段得到的颜色合成，这就能区分来自不寻常的、在 0.7 μm 附近有非常陡的谱斜率的区域与岩石和土壤 (灰色调)，这也许就可以表明自养型陆地生命的光合作用的色素。图 3 显示的光谱对应的地区在这张合成图中标注为 A、B、C。

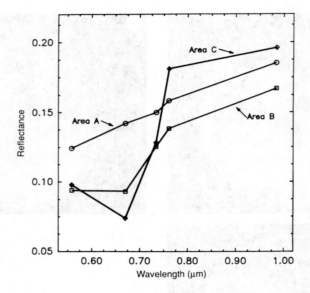

Fig. 3. Representative spectra from three areas on the land surface (see Fig. 2*c*). A gently sloping spectrum (circles, Area A) is consistent with any of several types of rock or soil. An intermediate spectrum (squares, Area B) shows some evidence of an absorption band near 0.67 μm (RED). Substantial areas on the surface have an unusual spectrum (diamonds, Area C) with a strong absorption in the RED band and a steep band edge just beyond 0.7 μm. This spectrum is inconsistent with all likely rock and soil types, and is plausibly associated with photosynthetic pigments (see text).

Second, we may translate (1.0, RED, GRN) (equivalent wavelength of 1.0 is 0.984 μm) bands to red, green and blue, respectively, in a false-colour image (Fig. 2*b*). This version reveals two kinds of sharp spectral contrasts. First, the cyan colour of the bright polar cap is caused by absorption in the 1.0 μm band, which confirms its H_2O-ice composition, and second, some land areas appear bright red, indicating a high albedo at 1.0 μm along with a low albedo in the visible spectrum (especially RED). Even without additional spectral information, a GRN/RED/1.0 signature so extreme is inconsistent with most dry or hydrated rocks or soils that might be expected on the surface of a terrestrial planet.

Using the 0.73 and 0.76 μm bands deepens the mystery. Figure 3 shows average mean spectra for three classes of land surface. (VIO is not plotted because of strong, differential atmospheric scattering corrections that are not fully modelled). The spectrum of area A (circles) has a gentle slope that rises in brightness uniformly from GRN to 1.0 μm, consistent with a variety of dark rock or mineral-soil surfaces. The spectrum of area B, an intermediate-albedo area, shows an absorption centred at RED. Although such areas are common on the surface, no common igneous, altered igneous, or sedimentary rock/soil surface displays such a signature[20]. The spectrum of area C is from a large low-albedo area in the northern part of the continent. Its very unusual spectrum has a strong absorption in the visible spectrum and a very steep spectral slope from 0.67 (RED) to 0.76 μm.

The third category of colour composite uses three closely spaced bands (0.76, 0.73, RED), and emphasizes strong spectral slopes over this narrow wavelength range (0.67–0.76 μm)

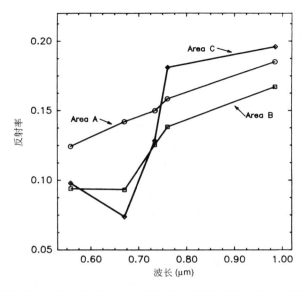

图 3. 地球表面三个地区的代表性光谱（见图 2c）。任何几个类型的岩石或者土壤都跟一条斜率缓和的光谱（圆圈，A 区域）一致。中间的光谱（方形，B 区域）显示 0.67 μm（红色）附近的吸收带的一些证据。地球表面的大量区域具有不寻常的光谱（菱形，C 区域），这条光谱在红端有强吸收带且在超出 0.7 μm 处有较陡的带边缘。这条光谱与所有可能的岩石和土壤都不一致，可能和光合作用的色素有关。

其次，在一幅伪彩色图像中（图 2b）我们可以将（1.0，红，绿）（1.0 对应的等效波长为 0.984 μm）分别转换为红色、绿色和蓝色。这幅图像揭示出了两种截然不同的光谱。第一种，青色代表的闪亮的极盖是由在 1.0 μm 波段吸收引起的，这证实了它的成分就是水结成的冰。第二种，一些陆地地区显示出亮红色，表明 1.0 μm 处的高反照率伴随着可见光光谱（尤其是红端）中的较低的反照率。即使是没有其他的光谱信息，一个如此极端的绿／红／1.0 的特征与预计的类地行星表面的大部分干燥或者含水的岩石或者土壤也不一致。

0.73 μm 和 0.76 μm 波段更加深了这种神秘感。图 3 展示出了地表的三种典型的平均谱。（紫色没有绘制出来，因为其强烈、与众不同的大气散射修正不能完全地建模）。A 区域内的光谱（圆圈）有一条从绿色到 1.0 μm 亮度均匀上升的斜线，这与一些暗色岩石和矿质土表面一致。B 区域是一个中等反照率的区域，其光谱显示出以红端为中心的吸收带。虽然这些区域在地球表面很常见，但是不常见的火成岩、变相的火成岩或者沉积岩／土壤表面却不显示这样的特征[20]。C 区域的光谱来自于北部大陆大片的低反照率地区。它非同寻常的光谱在可见光波段有一个强吸收，且在 0.67 μm（红色）到 0.76 μm 之间有非常陡的光谱斜率。

第三种色彩组合使用了三个紧密分布的波段（0.76，0.73，红），并突出了光谱

281

(Fig. 2c). Areas that have gently sloped spectra consistent with plausible rocks and soils appear grey here, whereas areas dominated by the unusual surface material with a strong absorption edge near 0.7 µm appear in greenish-yellow/orange hues. (The only other substantial contrast are the magenta areas in clouds, due to the 0.73 µm water-vapour band.)

These spectra cannot by uniquely interpreted; however, because they are inconsistent with any known rock or soil types on terrestrial planets of iron silicate surface composition, with or without aqueous alteration[20], unusual materials must be considered. The possibility naturally arises that the strong RED absorption is the signature of a light-harvesting pigment in a photosynthetic system—already suggested, as discussed above, as one possible explanation of the large atmospheric O_2 abundance. Plant life might have to be widespread in order to sustain this O_2 abundance in the face of likely loss by oxidation of the crust. Substantial areas of the surface seem to be covered by this pigment, which on the ground-truth planet is of course chlorophyll a and b. Photosynthesis might also be driven by oceanic microbes and plants, but the strong red-to-infrared absorption of water makes their pigments much more difficult to detect.

Morphology and Topographic Resolution

During this fly-by, Galileo's highest resolution systematic imaging of Earth was obtained at 1–2 km per pixel. A two-part mosaic of the ~2,900 by 4,000 km continent of Australia was produced: the eastern half of the continent was imaged mostly with four-band (VIO, GRN, RED, 0.73) coverage at ~1 km per pixel, and the western half with three-band (VIO, GRN, RED) coverage. A mosaic of Antarctica was also produced in three bands (VIO, GRN, RED) at ~2 km per pixel (at the pole).

A later six-band global imaging sequence at ~26 km per pixel showed Australia to be dominated by large central and western deserts, but with some 1.0 µm-bright areas (presumably plant life) concentrated toward the eastern and northern coasts, while Antarctica was found to be almost entirely covered by H_2O ice (Fig. 2b). In ~1 km per pixel Galileo mosaics of the Australian continent, no reworking of the surface into geometric patterns, or other compelling indications of artefacts of a technical civilization could be discerned. Although we find some large-scale albedo boundaries in Australian coastal regions that can be associated a posteriori with agriculture, in our judgement they are not sufficiently distinctive to be, by themselves, indicative of intelligent life. Kilston et al.[21] have demonstrated from a large array of daytime orbital imagery that very few images of the ground-truth Earth at resolution ~1 km reveal evidence of life.

In a study using daytime satellite imaging at 0.1 km resolution, C.S. and Wallace[22] concluded that the chance of finding convincing artifacts in a random frame was only ~10^{-2}. They further estimated, as a function of resolution, the threshold (in terms of fraction of the ground-truth surface image) for detection of a civilization at the current

（0.67~0.76 μm 这个狭窄波长范围内的）中明显的倾斜（图 2c）。具有缓和斜率的光谱的区域可能是岩石和土壤，在这里表现为灰色，但是那些被不寻常的表面物质覆盖的地区在 0.7 μm 附近有强烈的吸收边缘，在这里表现为青黄色或者橘色。（根据 0.73 μm 处的水蒸气波段，唯一一个有巨大差别的就是洋红色的有云的区域。）

我们无法对这些光谱进行唯一的解读。因为无论是否有水侵，它们都无法与类地行星表面上任何由铁硅酸盐组成的已知的岩石或者是土壤类型相符合[20]，所以应该考虑特殊物质。自然而然地想到，红端强烈的吸收可能是光合系统中集光色素的信号——正如上面所讨论的，这可以作为大气层中大量 O_2 存在的一个可能解释。为了维持这个 O_2 丰度，植被可能需要广泛分布以抵消由于地壳氧化而导致的 O_2 消耗。大量区域的表面似乎被这种色素覆盖着，当然这在地球上就是叶绿素 a 和 b。光合作用很可能也是受到海洋微生物和植物的驱动，但是水在红色到红外范围的强烈吸收使得它们的色素难以被探测到。

地貌和地形的分辨率

在这次飞掠过程中，伽利略号获得了关于地球的每像素 1~2 km 的高分辨率图像。通过拼接方法将两部分拼接起来，约 2,900 km × 4,000 km 的澳大利亚大陆图像就产生了：大陆东部主要用了四个波段（紫，绿，红，0.73），每像素覆盖约 1 km；西部地区用了三个波段（紫，绿，红）。南极地区也用三个波段（紫，绿，红）以每像素约 2 km（在极点）合成了拼接图像。

之后的每像素约 26 km 的六波段全景成像序列显示，澳大利亚中部和西部是大片的沙漠，但是有一些 1.0 μm 亮的地区（可能是植物）主要集中在东部和北部海岸。而几乎整个南极洲都被水冰覆盖着（图 2b）。在澳大利亚大陆的每像素 1 km 的伽利略拼接图像中，没有发现对表面改造形成几何图案，也没有发现技术文明的其他有力证据。虽然我们在澳大利亚海岸地区发现了一些大规模反照边缘，根据后验这跟农业耕作有关，但是根据我们的判断这些东西本身还不足以成为智慧生命活动的指示。基尔斯顿等人[21]已经通过一系列日间轨道成像证明在约 1 km 的分辨率范围内几乎没有什么实况地球的成像能够成为生命存在的证据。

在一个用 0.1 km 分辨率的日间卫星图像研究中，萨根和华莱士[22]得出结论，在一个随机区域内发现人类存在痕迹的可能性只有约 0.01。他们估计了一个阈值（根据实况地球的表面图像部分），这个阈值是关于分辨率的函数，它检测了在目前人类

human level of development (type A) and a hypothetical civilization that reworks its planetary surface to a significantly greater degree (type B). Their Fig. 29 predicts that even with complete surface coverage, detection of a type A civilization would require ~2-km resolution, and type B, ~10-km resolution. Galileo's Australia mosaic represents 2.3% of the whole surface of the Earth imaged at ~1 km per pixel, and the Antarctic mosaic adds another 4% at ~2 km per pixel. Unluckily, these are among the most sparsely settled regions of the ground-truth planet. Imaging about 1% of the surface at this resolution would detect a type B civilization, but imaging nearly all the surface would be required to detect one of type A[22]. A type B civilization is either wholly absent, or present in other continents than Australia and Antarctica. Extensive imaging of the Earth at resolution better than 0.1 km would have readily detected signs of life[23]. The foregoing analysis is based on visible and near-infrared Galileo imaging in reflected sunlight. No usable imaging data were obtained from the night hemisphere of the planet.

Radio Emission

Ground-truth television and radar transmissions are predicted to generate a non-thermal radio emission spectrum so strong and striking as to announce the presence of intelligent life not just over interplanetary, but over interstellar distances[24,25]. With a rough knowledge of the composition and structure of the Earth's atmosphere and the solar UV spectrum, it is a straightforward matter[26] to derive the order of magnitude of N_e, the ionospheric electron density in the E and F layers, yielding a plasma frequency f_p ~1–5 MHz. The higher value is the maximum for the sunlit hemisphere. Radio emissions from a technical civilization at the Earth's surface should be detectable only at $f > f_p$.

During the Galileo fly-by, the plasma wave instrument detected radio signals, plausibly escaping through the nightside ionosphere from ground-based radio transmitters. Of all Galileo science measurements, these signals provide the only indication of intelligent, technological life on Earth. They are illustrated in the PWS frequency–time spectrograms in Fig. 4. The transmitter signals can be seen near the top of the spectrograms in Fig. 4a, starting at about 18:00 UT and extending to about 20:25 UT, shortly before closest approach (C/A). These signals were detected only during the inbound, nightside pass, and not on the outbound, dayside, pass. Also seen in Fig. 4a are a series of Type III solar radio bursts[27] and several bursts of auroral kilometric radiation[28]. The narrow-band emission line labelled f_p is an electrostatic oscillation excited at the local electron plasma frequency by thermal fluctuations in the ionospheric plasma. The sharp peak in f_p near closest approach is caused by the local peak in N_e as the spacecraft passed through the ionosphere at an altitude of ~950 km.

技术水平条件下的文明（A 类）和一个假想的很大程度上可以重塑行星表面的文明（B 类）。他们的图 29 预测，即使表面完全被覆盖，探测 A 类文明也需要约 2 km 的分辨率，探测 B 类文明需要 ~10 km 的分辨率。伽利略探测器对澳大利亚的拼接图像每像素 1 km，仅代表着地球表面图像的 2.3%，而南极的拼接图像增加了 4% 的地球表面图像，分辨率为每像素 2 km。非常不幸的是，这两个地区都是这个星球上最人烟稀少的地区之一。用这种方法对表面的 1% 进行成像就会探测到 B 类文明的存在，但是要探测一个 A 类文明需要对全部表面进行成像 [22]。B 类文明或者是完全不存在的，或者是在除了澳大利亚和南极以外的大陆存在。比 0.1 km 分辨率更高的大面积成像方法将会更容易探测到生命的迹象 [23]。前述的分析建立在反射太阳光的可见光和近红外的伽利略图像基础上。未获得这颗行星的夜半球可用的成像数据。

无线电辐射

我们预测实况地球电视和雷达传输可以产生强烈的非热无线电辐射，这足以证明生命不仅仅存在于行星际的距离上也存在于恒星际的距离上 [24,25]。通过对地球大气层和太阳紫外光谱组成和结构的粗略了解，可以直接 [26] 得到在 E 层和 F 层的电离层的电子密度 N_e 的数量级，对应大约 1~5 MHz 的等离子体频率。较大的 N_e 值是日照半球的最大值。地球表面技术文明产生的无线电辐射只有在 $f > f_p$ 范围内才能被探测到。

在伽利略号飞掠期间，等离子体波谱仪探测到了无线电信号，可能是从夜面地面无线电发射器发射出来的。在所有伽利略号科学测量中，这些信号是唯一表明了地球上存在着智慧技术生命的指标。它们在图 4 中用等离子体波谱仪（PWS）频率－时间谱图表示。发射器的信号可以在图 4a 谱图的顶部看见，大约从 18:00 UT 到 20:25 UT，仅仅稍微早于最接近时刻（C/A）。这些信号只在经过夜面时探测到，在日间离开时没有探测到。在这张图中我们还可以看到一系列 Ⅲ 型太阳射电暴 [27] 以及几次极光千米波辐射暴发 [28]。标记为 f_p 的窄带发射线是电离层等离子体的热涨落以局域电子－等离子体频率激发的静电振荡。在最接近时刻附近的 f_p 处的峰是由探测器在大约 950 km 高度穿过电离层时的当地 N_e 的峰值导致的。

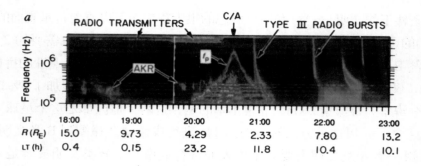

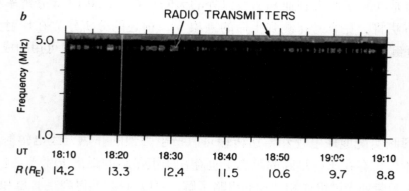

Fig. 4. A frequency–time spectrogram of the radio signals detected by the Galileo plasma wave instrument. The intensities are coded in the sequence blue–green–yellow–red, with blue lowest and red highest. Several natural sources of radio emission are shown in *a*, including auroral kilometric radiation (AKR). Modulated emission at $f > 4\,\mathrm{MHz}$ is shown with an expanded time scale in *b*. Modulated patterns of this type are characteristic of the transmission of information, and would be highly unusual for a naturally occurring radio source. (UT, universal time; *R* is distance of Galileo from Earth in units of Earth's radius, R_E; LT, local time.)

The identification of the narrow-band emissions near 4–5 MHz as ground-based radio transmitters is based on studies by LaBelle *et al.*[29] and Keller[30] of the ground-truth planet; satellite observations clearly showed the signals originating from surface transmitters. That a similar conclusion could be drawn from the aforementioned Galileo fly-by data alone, without any previous knowledge of the existence of radio transmitters on Earth, is plausible but not beyond doubt. The rapid increase in the signal strength as the spacecraft approaches the Earth clearly indicates a near-Earth origin. The fact that the signals are only observed on the nightside inbound pass, where the ionosphere propagation cutoff frequency is sufficiently low to allow the signals to escape through the ionosphere, but not on the dayside where the cutoff prevents escape, strongly indicates a source beneath the ionosphere. Taking into account the expected exponential decrease in ionospheric N_e with increasing altitude, the theoretical maximum $f_p \sim 5\,\mathrm{MHz}$ is in good agreement with the peak local plasma frequency ($\sim 2\,\mathrm{MHz}$) observed at C/A, which was over the sunlit hemisphere at 16:30 LT. (These data might also be consistent with a class of nocturnal transmitting stations orbiting the Earth above the ionosphere, but the conclusion of intelligent life would be unchanged.)

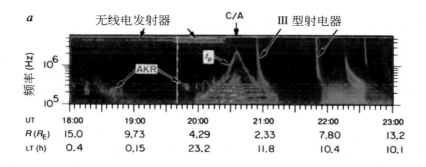

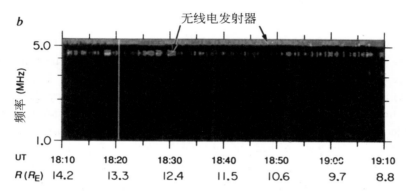

图 4. 伽利略号等离子体波谱仪捕捉到的无线电信号的频率–时间谱图。强度用蓝–绿–黄–红来表示。蓝色最低，红色最高。图 a 中显示了几种自然源的无线电发射情况，其中包括极光千米波辐射（AKR）。图 b 中显示了一个扩展的时间段内 $f > 4\,MHz$ 的调制辐射。这种类型的调制波形是信息传递的特征体现，对一个自然发生的电磁波资源来说是非常罕见的。（UT 代表世界时间；R 代表以地球半径（R_E）为单位计算的伽利略探测器距离地球的距离；LT 代表地方时）。

对 $4\sim5\,MHz$ 附近的地面无线电发射器的窄带发射的识别是基于拉贝尔等人[29]和凯勒[30]关于行星表面实况的研究。卫星观测清晰地展示了由地面发射器发射的信号。在没有关于地球无线电发射器存在的任何先验知识的情况下，从前面提到的伽利略号数据中可以总结出一个类似的结论，它看似合理却不是毋庸置疑的。当探测器接近地球的时候，信号强度的快速增长清晰地表明这个信号是源自于近地地区。事实是信号仅仅在经过夜面时在电离层的传播截止频率足够低到让信号逃离电离层时才能被观察到，而不是在太阳照射的截止频率让信号无法逃脱的日面，这有力地表明在电离层下有一个发射源。考虑到在电离层中 N_e 随着高度的增加而指数降低，f_p 的理论最大值（约 $5\,MHz$）和 16:30 LT 的日照半球上 C/A 处观测到的等离子体频率峰值（约 $2\,MHz$）是一致的。（这些数据可能和在电离层之上绕地球旋转的夜间传输站的数据一致，但是智慧生命存在的结论可能不会改变。）

More difficult to estimate from first principles is the nightside f_p, because it depends on various losses and secondary ionization processes that cannot easily be evaluated from Galileo data alone. But because the primary (UV) ionization source is absent on the nightside, it is clear that N_e there will be much lower than on the dayside. From remote observations of Venus and Mars, it is entirely plausible that the nightside f_p should be depressed by factors of three to ten, relative to dayside values, permitting the escape of radio signals through the nightside ionosphere at 4–5 MHz, and providing a consistent overall interpretation of the day–night asymmetry in the observed radio signal. Ground-truth measurements of the night-time ionosphere show that $f_p < 4$ MHz is quite common, particularly at high latitudes[31].

The signals are confined mainly to two or three distinct channels near the top of the spectrogram (Fig. 4). The fact that the central frequencies of these signals remain constant over periods of hours strongly suggests an artificial origin. Naturally generated radio emissions almost always display significant long-term frequency drifts. Even more definitive is the existence of pulse-like amplitude modulation. When the spectrum in Fig. 4a is expanded (Fig. 4b), the individual narrow-band components can be seen to have a complex modulation pattern. Although the time resolution of the instrument (18.67 s) is inadequate to decode the modulation, such modulation patterns are never observed for naturally occurring radio emissions and implies the transmission of information. On the basis of these observations, a strong case can be made that the signals are generated by an intelligent form of life on Earth.

Conclusions

From the Galileo fly-by, an observer otherwise unfamiliar with the Earth would be able to draw the following conclusions: The planet is covered with large amounts of water present as vapour, as snow and ice, and as oceans. If any biota exists, it is plausibly water-based. There is so much O_2 in the atmosphere as to cast doubt on the proposition that UV photodissociation of water vapour and the escape of hydrogen provide an adequate source. An alternative explanation is biologically mediated photodissociation of water by visible light as the first step in photosynthesis. An unusual red-absorbing pigment that may serve this purpose, corresponding to no plausible mineral, is found widely on land. Methane is detected at ~1 p.p.m., some 140 orders of magnitude higher than the thermodynamic equilibrium value in this oxygen-rich atmosphere. Only biological processes are likely to generate so large a disparity. But how plausible a world covered with carbon-fixing photosynthetic organism, using H_2O as the electron donor and generating a massive (and poisonous) O_2 atmosphere, might be to observers from a very different world is an open question.

Several per cent of the land surface was imaged at a resolution of a few kilometres—entirely in Australia and Antarctica. No unambiguous sign of technological geometrization was found. Narrow-band pulsed amplitude-modulated radio transmission above the

从第一性原理上更难估计的是夜面的 f_p，因为它依赖于各种各样的损失和二次电离过程，它们不能简单地仅仅从伽利略数据中推算出来。但是因为主要的(紫外，UV)电离源不在夜面，所以很清楚地知道夜面的 N_e 比日面要低很多。从对金星和火星的远距离观测可知，完全可信的是夜面的 f_p 为日面值的 $\frac{1}{10} \sim \frac{1}{3}$，以允许无线信号通过夜面电离层以 4~5 MHz 逃逸，并且提供一致的、完整的关于日面和夜面观测到的无线信号不对称的解释。夜间电离层地面实况测量表明 $f_p < 4$ MHz 是非常常见的情况，特别是在高纬度 [31]。

信号主要被限制在谱图顶部附近的两、三个不同的通道之内(图 4)。这些信号的中心频率保持几个小时不变的事实表明存在一个人工源。自然产生的无线电辐射几乎总是呈现明显的长期的频率漂移。更具决定性的是存在着像脉冲信号的调幅。当图 4a 中的频谱被扩展(图 4b)，可以看到单个窄带成分都有一个复杂的调制模式。尽管该仪器的时间分辨率(18.67 s)不足以解调，但这种调制方式从未在自然产生的无线电辐射中看到过，这暗示了信息的传输。在这些观测的基础上，可以做出这样一个结论：信号是由地球上一种智慧生命形式产生的。

结　　论

从伽利略号飞掠可知，不熟悉地球的观察者将会得出如下的结论：这颗行星是由大量水覆盖的，这些水以水蒸气、雪、冰和海洋等形式存在。如果有任何生物群存在，那么它们几乎都是水基的。在大气中有太多的 O_2，这使我们对水蒸气紫外光致离解和 H 的逃逸提供足够氧气源的观点提出了疑问。一个可能的解释是通过生物调控的可见光光解水作为光合作用的第一步。一种不同寻常的吸收红光的色素广泛地存在于陆地上，它可能满足这一要求，与此一致的是没有发现合理的矿物。探测到的 CH_4 浓度约为百万分之一，在这样一个 O_2 丰富的大气层中，这个值比热力学平衡值高出大约 140 个数量级。只有生物过程能够产生如此大的差异。但是从一个完全不同的世界来观察，一个由固碳的光合生物覆盖，将 H_2O 作为电子给体，并产生大量的(有毒的)O_2 层的世界有多大的可能性，这是一个开放的问题。

有部分陆地表面是以几千米的分辨率成像的——这部分陆地都是在澳大利亚和南极洲。没有发现关于技术导致的几何图形的清晰特征。在等离子体频率之上的窄

plasma frequency strongly suggests the presence of a technological civilization. Most of the evidence uncovered by Galileo would have been discovered by a similar fly-by spacecraft as long ago as about 2 billion (10^9) years. In contrast, modulated narrow-band radio transmissions could not have been detected before this century.

The identification of molecules profoundly out of thermodynamic equilibrium, unexplained by any non-biological process; widespread pigments that cannot be understood by geochemical processes; and modulated radio emission are together evidence of life on Earth without any *a priori* assumptions about its chemistry; 200 g cm^{-2} O_2 is at least suggestive of biology. Negative results in spacecraft exploration of other planets have thus much wider application than merely to "life as we know it". Of course putative ecosystems that are only weakly coupled to the surface environment (for example, subsurface[32,33]) are not excluded by such observations.

Surface oceans of liquid water are unique in the Solar System; conceivably this is part of the reason that Earth is the only planet in the Solar System with abundant surface life. Similar spectroscopic methods, although without resolution of the disk, may be useful in examining planets of other stars for indigenous life, as has been suggested for O_2 by Owen[34]. Large filled-aperture or interferometric telescopes intended for investigating extrasolar planets, especially those of terrestrial mass, might incorporate into their design the wavelength range and spectral resolution that has proved useful in the present work. In the radio search for extraterrestrial intelligence (SETI), optimum transmission through interstellar space and plausible planetary atmospheres lies in the 1–3 GHz range, not the MHz range used here.

The Galileo mission constitutes an apparently unique control experiment on the ability of fly-by spacecraft to detect life at various stages of evolutionary development on other worlds in the Solar System. Although a similar opportunity arises in the summer 1999 Earth fly-by of the ESA/NASA Cassini spacecraft on its way to Saturn, there are, because of funding constraints, no plans to observe the Earth with Cassini. Although a great deal more exploration remains to be done before such conclusions can be considered secure, our results are consistent with the hypothesis that widespread biological activity now exists, of all the worlds in this Solar System, only on Earth.

(**365**, 715-721; 1993)

Carl Sagan[*], W. Reid Thompson[*], Robert Carlson[†], Donald Gurnett[‡] & Charles Hord[§]

[*] Laboratory for Planetary Studies, Cornell University, Ithaca, New York 14853, USA

[†] Atmospheric and Cometary Sciences Section, Jet Propulsion Laboratory, Pasadena, California 91109, USA

[‡] Department of Physics and Astronomy, University of Iowa, Iowa City, Iowa 52242-1479, USA

[§] Laboratory for Atmospheric and Space Physics, University of Colorado, Boulder, Colorado 80309, USA

Received 17 February; accepted 14 September 1993.

带脉冲调制的无线电传输强烈暗示存在一个技术文明。大部分伽利略号发现的证据可能已经在大约 20 亿年前被一个类似的飞掠探测器发现了。相反，调制的窄带无线电传输在这个世纪之前未探测到。

对热力学极度不平衡且无法用非生物过程解释的分子的认证、无法用地球化学过程理解的广泛分布的色素以及调制的无线电辐射，这些都是在没有任何有关其化学过程的先验假设时在地球上存在生命的证据。$200 \ g \cdot cm^{-2}$ 的 O_2 是适合生物生存的最低标准。在探测器探索其他星球时否定的研究结果具有更广阔的应用空间而不仅仅是应用于"我们所知道的生命形式"。当然，这样的观察并没有排除公认的与地表环境弱耦合的生态系统（比如，地下[32,33]）。

在太阳系的各层次天体中液态水海洋的表面是独特的。可以相信，这是地球是太阳系中唯一一个表面有丰富生命的行星的原因。虽然还没有行星盘的分辨率，但相似的光谱学方法在检验其他行星是否具有原住生命时具有参考价值，就像曾经由欧文[34] 对 O_2 的建议那样。为搜索系外行星特别是和地球质量类似的行星而使用连续孔径或者干涉望远镜时，应该将对于当前研究有用的波长范围和谱分辨率包含在内。在用无线电进行地外文明探索时，适宜在星际空间或者是可能存在的行星大气层传播的无线电的频率在 $1\sim3 \ GHz$ 波段，而不是在这里所用的 MHz 波段。

伽利略探测器任务构成了一个独特的对于飞掠型探测器探测太阳系中其他世界各种不同的演化阶段的对照实验。虽然在 1999 年的夏季，由 ESA/NASA 从地球发射的卡西尼号土星探测器在它去往土星的旅程中有一个类似的机会。但因为预算的限制，没有为卡西尼号土星探测器安排观测地球的计划。尽管在保证结论准确无误之前还需进行更多的探索，但我们的结果仍然和假设一致，那就是在太阳系中大范围的生物活动只存在于地球上。

（刘霞 翻译；欧阳自远 审稿）

References:

1. Carlson, R. W. *et al. Space Sci. Rev.* **60**, 457-502 (1992).

2. Hord, C. W. *et al. Space Sci. Rev.* **60**, 503-530 (1992).

3. Belton, M. J. S. *et al. Space Sci. Rev.* **60**, 413-455 (1992).

4. Gurnett, D. A. *et al. Space Sci. Rev.* **60**, 341-355 (1992).

5. Lederberg, J. *Nature* **207**, 9-13 (1965).

6. Lovelock, J. *Nature* **207**, 568-570 (1965).

7. Lovelock, J. E. *Proc. R. Soc.* B**189**, 167-181 (1975).

8. Sagan, C. *Proc. R. Soc.* B**189**, 143-166 (1975).

9. Carlson, R. W., Arakelian, T. & Smythe, W. D. *Antarct. J. U.S.* (in the press).

10. Drossart, P. J. *et al. Planet. Space Sci.* (submitted).

11. Henderson, L. J. *The Fitness of the Environment: An Inquiry into the Biological Significance of the Properties of Matter* (Peter Smith, Gloucester, Mass., 1913).

12. von Zahn, U., Kumar, R. S., Neimann, H. & Prinn, R. in *Venus* Ch. 13 (eds Hunten, D. M., Colin, L., Donahue, T. M. & Moroz, V. I.) (Univ. of Arizona Press, Tucson, 1983).

13. Owen, T. in *Mars* Ch. 25 (eds Keiffer, H. H., Jakosky, B. M., Snyder, C. W. & Matthews, M. S.) (Univ. of Arizona Press, Tucson, 1992).

14. Walker, J. G. C. *Evolution of the Atmosphere* (Macmillan, New York, 1977).

15. Léger, A., Pirre, M. & Marceau, F. J. *Astr. Astrophys.* (in the press).

16. Lippincott, E. R., Eck, R. V., Dayhoff, M. O. & Sagan, C. *Astrophys. J.* **147**, 753-764 (1967).

17. Chameides, W. L. & Davis, D. D. *Chem. Engng. News* **60**, 38-52 (1992).

18. Hogan, K. B., Hoffman, J. S. & Thompson, A. M. *Nature* **354**, 181-182 (1991).

19. Lewis, J. S. & Prinn, R. G. *Planets and Their Atmospheres* (Academic, New York, 1984).

20. Bowker, D. E., Davis, R. E., Myrick, D. L., Stacy, K. & Jones, W. T. Ref. Publ. No. 1139 (NASA, Washington, 1985).

21. Kilston, S. D., Drummond, R. R. & Sagan, C. *Icarus* **5**, 79-98 (1966).

22. Sagan, C. & Wallace, D. *Icarus* **15**, 515-554 (1971).

23. Sagan, C. *et al.* in *Biology and the Exploration of Mars* Ch. 9 (eds Pittendrigh, C. S., Vishniac, W. & Pearman, J. P. T.) (Natl. Acad. Sci. Washington, 1966).

24. Shklovskii, I. S. & Sagan, C. *Intelligent Life in the Universe* (Holden Day, San Francisco, 1966).

25. Sullivan, W. T., Brown, S. & Wetherill, C. *Science* **199**, 377-388 (1978).

26. Chapman, S. *Proc. Phys. Soc.* **43**, 483-501 (1931).

27. Fainberg, J. & Stone, R. G. *Space Sci. Rev.* **16**, 145-188 (1974).

28. Gurnett, D. A. *J. Geophys. Res.* **79**, 4227-4238 (1974).

29. LaBeile, J., Trumann, R. A., Boehm, M. H. & Gewecke, K. *Radio Sci.* **24**, 725-737 (1989).

30. Keller, A. thesis, Univ. Iowa (1990).

31. Hines, C. O., Paghis, I., Hartz, T. R. & Fejer, J. A. *Physics of the Earth's Upper Atmosphere* (Prentice Hall, Englewood Cliffs, 1965).

32. Lederberg, J. & Sagan, C. *Proc. Natl. Acad. Sci. U.S.A.* **48**, 1473-1475 (1962).

33. Gold, T. *Proc. Natl. Acad. Sci. U.S.A.* **89**, 6045-6049 (1992).

34. Owen, T. in *Strategies for the Search for Life in the Universe* (ed. Papagiannis, M.) 177-185 (Reidel, Dordrecht, 1980).

Acknowledgements. We are grateful to W. O'Neil, F. Fanale, T. Johnson, C. Chapman, M. Belton and other Galileo colleagues, as well as W. Sullivan, for encouragement and support; and to J. Lederberg, A. Léger, J. Lovelock, A. McEwen, T. Owen and J. Tarter for comments. This research was supported by the Galileo Project Office, Jet Propulsion Laboratory, NASA and by a grant from NASA's Exobiology Program.

Total Synthesis of Taxol

K. C. Nicolaou *et al.*

Editor's Note

The anticancer drug taxol was a prime target for synthetic organic chemistry ever since its molecular structure was revealed in 1971. It is extracted for clinical use from the bark of the Pacific yew tree—an expensive process that kills the tree. Synthesizing the molecule from widely available raw ingredients promised the prospect of cheaper and more ecological supplies. Here K. C. Nicolaou of the Scripps Research Institute and his co-workers report a "total synthesis" of taxol, beginning from relatively simple starting materials. The report was more or less coincident with a paper describing an alternative synthetic route, published in the *Journal of the American Chemical Society* by Robert Holton and co-workers of Florida State University.

Taxol[1-4], a substance originally isolated from the Pacific yew tree (*Taxus brevifolia*) more than two decades ago, has recently been approved for the clinical treatment of cancer patients. Hailed as having provided one of the most significant advances in cancer therapy[5], this molecule exerts its anticancer activity by inhibiting mitosis through enhancement of the polymerization of tubulin and consequent stabilization of microtubules[6]. The scarcity of taxol and the ecological impact of harvesting it have prompted extensive searches for alternative sources including semisynthesis, cellular culture production and chemical synthesis[2,3]. The latter has been attempted for almost two decades, but these attempts have been thwarted by the magnitude of the synthetic challenge. Here we report the total synthesis of taxol by a convergent strategy, which opens a chemical pathway for the production of both the natural product itself and a variety of designed taxoids.

THE strategy for the present synthesis of taxol (**1**, Fig. 1*a*) was based on a retrosynthetic analysis involving the bond disconnections[7] shown in Fig. 1*b*. Thus, in the synthetic direction the following key operations were proposed: (1) two fragments, representing precursors to rings A and C (see Fig. 1*a*), were to be coupled by a Shapiro reaction[8] and a McMurry coupling[9] to assemble the ABC ring skeleton; (2) instalment of the oxetane ring; (3) addition[10] of the various substituents around the peripheries of rings B and C; (4) oxygenation[10] at C-13; and (5) esterification to attach the side chain[11].

294

紫杉醇的全合成

尼科拉乌等

编者按

自从 1971 年发表了紫杉醇的分子结构以来，这种抗癌药物就成为有机合成化学的首要目标分子。它是从太平洋紫杉的树皮中提取得到，并应用于临床研究。但砍伐树木耗资巨大。因此，利用可广泛获得的原材料人工合成该分子具有价格经济和支持生态保护的广阔前景。本文中，斯克里普斯研究所的尼科拉乌及其同事们从相对简单的初始原料出发，实现了紫杉醇的"全合成"。这项研究与佛罗里达州立大学的罗伯特·霍尔顿及其同事们在《美国化学会志》上发表的另一条合成路线的文章或多或少有些巧合。

紫杉醇[1-4]最初是在二十多年前从太平洋紫杉(*Taxus brevifolia*)中分离出来的一种物质，最近已被批准用于癌症患者的临床治疗。这种被认为是实现了癌症治疗中最重要进展之一[5]的分子是通过增强微管蛋白聚合和由此产生的微管稳定性来抑制有丝分裂，从而实现其抗癌活性的[6]。紫杉醇的稀缺和大量提取对生态环境造成的影响促进了寻找替代源的进一步研究，其中包括半合成、细胞培育生产和化学合成[2,3]。后一种方式的尝试已有近二十年，但是这些努力都被合成的困难程度所阻挠。这里我们要报道一种采用汇聚式合成策略制备紫杉醇的全合成方法，该方法为天然紫杉醇和一系列人工改造的紫杉烷类产物的合成开辟了一种化学途径。

目前的紫杉醇(1，图 1*a*)合成策略所依据的是涉及图 1*b* 中所示的断键过程[7]的逆合成分析。因此，在合成方向上提出下列关键操作:(1)代表环 A 和环 C(见图 1*a*)前体的两个片段，要借助夏皮罗反应[8]和麦克默里偶联[9]来装配成 ABC 环骨架;(2)氧杂环丁烷环的形成;(3)环 B 和环 C 周边各种取代基的添加[10];(4)C-13 位的氧化[10];以及(5)侧链上的酯化反应[11]。

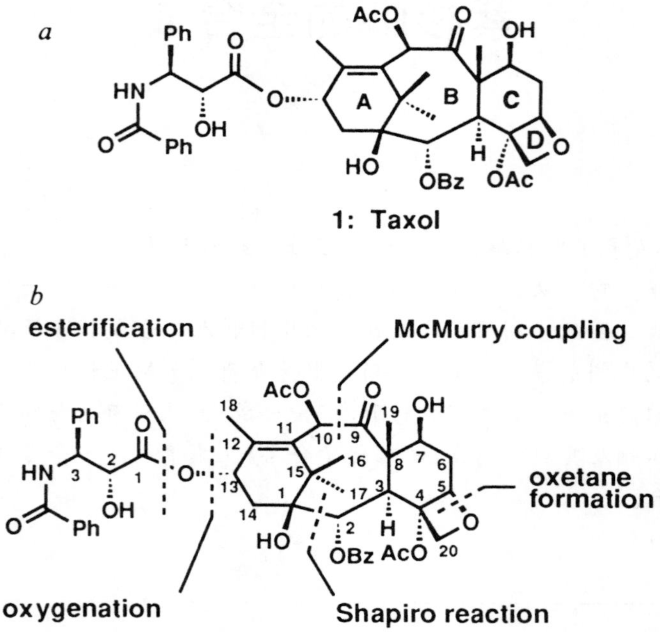

Fig. 1. Structure (*a*) and strategic bond disconnections of taxol (*b*). Abbreviations for chemical groups (see also Figs 2, 3 and 5): Ph, phenyl; OBz, benzoyl; OAc, acetyl.

The previously reported intermediates **2** (ref. 12) (Fig. 2) and **8** (refs 7, 13) (Fig. 3) served as the starting points for the convergent synthesis of taxol reported here. Figure 2 presents the construction of the requisite C-ring aldehyde **7** from **2**. Protection of both hydroxyl groups in **2** with TBS groups (95%) (for abbreviations see figure legend) followed by selective reduction of the ester group with LiAlH₄ at 0 °C, furnished primary alcohol **3** (94% yield). Acid-catalysed deprotection of the secondary alcohol in **3** proceeded in a highly selective manner to give the corresponding diol (90% yield), which was then selectively protected with a TPS group at the primary position and a benzyl group at the secondary to afford compound **4** in 80% overall yield. The γ-lactone in **4** was then reductively opened with concomitant desilylation at the tertiary position using LiAlH₄ at 25 °C to produce triol **5** in 80% yield. Finally, acetonide formation followed by TPAP[14] oxidation in the presence of NMO resulted in the formation of the targeted aldehyde **7** in 80% overall yield.

1: 紫杉醇

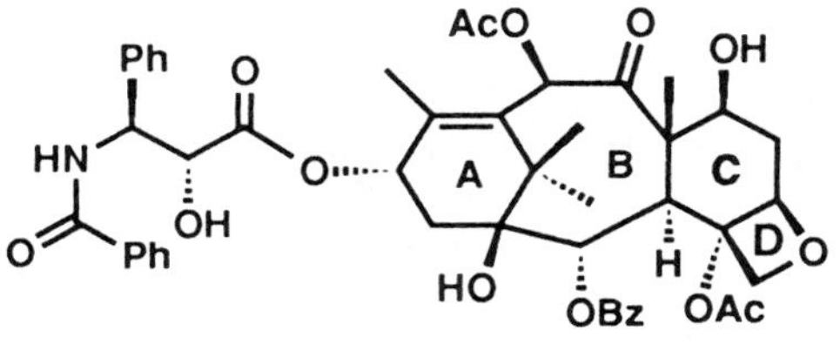

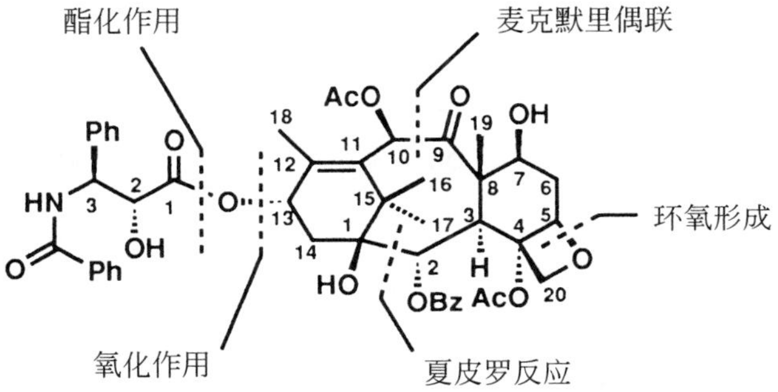

图 1. 紫杉醇的结构(*a*)和断键策略(*b*)。化学基团的缩写(另见图 2、图 3 和图 5)：Ph，苯基；OBz，苯甲酰基；OAc，乙酰基。

　　这里报道的紫杉醇汇聚式合成是以从前报道的中间体 **2**（参考文献 12）（图 2）和 **8**（参考文献 7，参考文献 13）（图 3）为起点进行的。图 2 显示了从 **2** 生成必不可少的 C-环醛 **7** 的过程。**2** 中的两个羟基都用 TBS 基团(缩写，结构见图例)保护起来 (95%)，接着用 LiAlH$_4$ 在 0 ℃ 对酯基进行选择性还原，得到伯醇 **3**（产率 94%）。酸催化条件下，以高选择性将 **3** 中的仲醇去保护，得到相应的二醇（产率 90%），继而用 TPS 基团对伯羟基以及用苄基对仲羟基进行选择性保护，得到化合物 **4**，总产率 80%。接着用 LiAlH$_4$ 在 25 ℃ 时进行还原开环，打开 **4** 中的 γ-内酯，并伴随着叔羟基上的脱硅保护基，产生了三醇 **5**，产率 80%。最后，与丙酮形成缩酮化合物后，在 NMO 存在下用 TPAP[14] 氧化，形成目标化合物醛 **7**，总产率 80%。

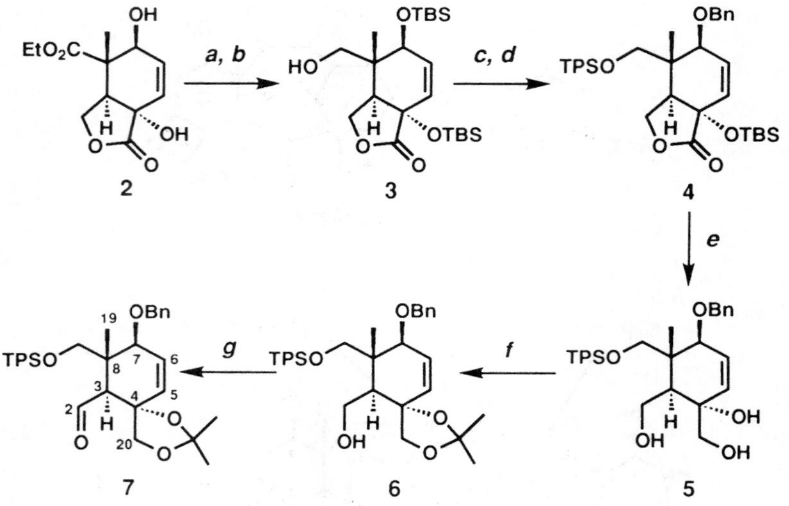

Fig. 2. Construction of C-ring system **7**. Reagents and conditions. (*a*) *t*-BuMe₂SiOTf (4 equivalents(eq.)), 2,6-lutidine (4 eq.), 4-DMAP (0.01 eq.), CH₂Cl₂, 0 °C, 4 h, 95%; (*b*) LiAlH₄ (1.1 eq.), Et₂O, 0 °C, 1 h, 94%; (*c*) (1) CSA (0.05 eq.), MeOH, CH₂Cl₂, 25 °C, 1 h, 90%; (2) *t*-BuPh₂SiCl (1.5 eq.), imidazole (1.6 eq.), DMF, 25 °C, 6 h, 92%; (*d*) KH (1.2 eq.), Et₂O, *n*-Bu₄NI(cat.), BnBr (1.2 eq.), 25 °C, 2 h, 87%; (*e*) LiAlH₄ (3 eq.), Et₂O, 25 °C, 12 h, 80%; (*f*) 2,2-dimethoxypropane (5 eq.), CSA (0.1 eq.), CH₂Cl₂, 25 °C, 7 h 82%; (*g*) TPAP (0.05 eq.), NMO (1.5 eq.), CH₃CN, 25 °C, 2 h, 95%. (Bn = CH₂Ph; CSA = (±)-camphorsulphonic acid; 4-DMAP = 4-dimethylaminopyridine; DMF = N,N-dimethylformamide; NMO = N-methylmorpholine-N-oxide; TBS = *t*-BuMe₂Si; TPAP = tetra-*n*-propylammonium perruthenate; TPS = *t*-BuPh₂Si.) Selected physical data for compound **7**: ¹H NMR (500 MHz, CDCl₃, taxol numbering): δ 9.98 p.p.m. (d, *J* = 3.5 Hz, 1 H, 2-H), 7.65–7.12 (m, 15 H, aromatic), 5.84 (dd, *J* = 10.5, 1.5 Hz, 1 H, 6-H), 5.71(dd, *J* = 10.5, 2.0 Hz, 1 H, 5-H), 4.50 (d, *J* = 11.5 Hz, 1 H, OCH₂Ph), 4.22 (d, *J* = 11.5 Hz, 1 H, OCH₂Ph), 4.20 (d, *J* = 9.5 Hz, 1 H, 20-H), 4.10 (dd, *J* = 2.0, 1.5 Hz, 1 H, 7-H), 3.84 (d, *J* = 9.5 Hz, 1 H, 20-H), 3.72 (d, *J* = 10.0 Hz, 1 H, 9-H), 3.70 (d, *J* = 10.0 Hz, 1 H, 9-H), 3.18 (d, *J* = 3.5 Hz, 1 H, 3-H), 1.42 (s, 3 H, CH₃-acetonide), 1.39 (s, 3 H, CH₃-acetonide), 1.09 (s, 9 H, (CH₃)₃ CSi), 1.04 (s, 3 H, 19-CH₃); ¹³C NMR (125 MHz, CDCl₃): δ 202.3, 138.1, 135.8, 135.6, 133.0, 132.9, 131.1, 129.7, 129.4, 129.5, 128.8, 128.2, 127.6, 127.4, 127.4, 127.2, 127.2, 127.1, 108.6, 80.6, 75.4, 71.8, 70.0, 65.7, 57.6, 44.9, 26.9, 26.8, 26.5, 19.3, 13.6; infrared (pure compound): ν_max 2,931.4, 2,857.0, 1,720.4, 1,111.5 cm⁻¹; high resolution mass spectrometry (fast atom bombardment) (HRMS (FAB)): calcd for C₃₆H₄₄O₅Si(M⁺+Cs) mass-to-charge ratio *m*/*z* = 607.2856 atomic mass units (a.m.u.), found 607.2865 a.m.u.

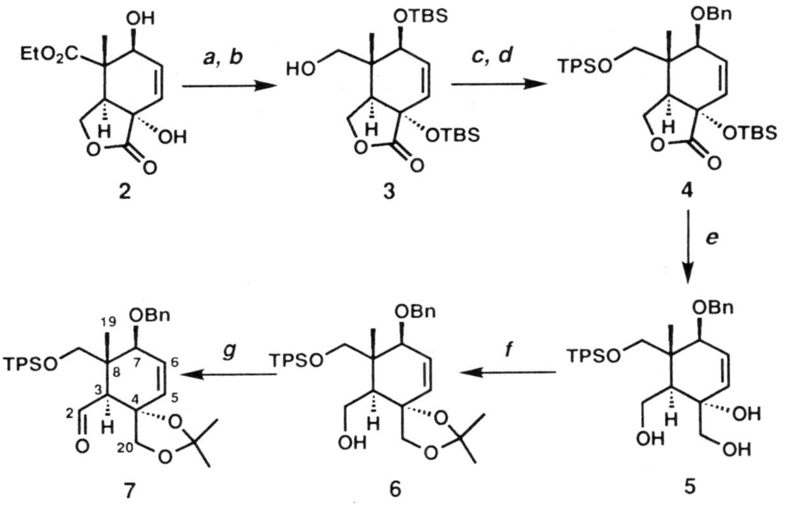

图 2. C–环体系 **7** 的构造过程。试剂和条件。(a)t-BuMe₂SiOTf(4 当量 (eq.))，2,6–二甲基吡啶(4 eq.)，
4-DMAP(0.01 eq.)，CH₂Cl₂，0 ℃，4 小时，95%；(b)LiAlH₄ (1.1 eq.)，Et₂O，0 ℃，1 小时，94%；(c)(1)
CSA(0.05 eq.)，MeOH，CH₂Cl₂，25 ℃，1小时，90%；(2)t-BuPh₂SiCl(1.5 eq.)，咪唑 (1.6 eq.)，DMF，
25 ℃，6 小时，92%；(d)KH(1.2 eq.)，Et₂O，n-Bu₄NI(催化量)，BnBr(1.2 eq.)，25 ℃，2 小时，87%；
(e)LiAlH₄ (3 eq.)，Et₂O，25 ℃，12 小时，80%；(f)2,2–二甲氧基丙烷(5 eq.)，CSA(0.1 eq.)，CH₂Cl₂，
25 ℃，7小时，82%；(g)TPAP(0.05 eq.)，NMO(1.5 eq.)，CH₃CN，25 ℃，2 小时，95%。(Bn = CH₂Ph；
CSA = (±)–樟脑磺酸；4-DMAP = 4–二甲氨基吡啶；DMF = N,N–二甲基甲酰胺；NMO = N–甲基吗
啉–N–氧化物；TBS = t-BuMe₂Si；TPAP = 过钌酸四(n–丙基)铵盐；TPS = t-BuPh₂Si。)化合物 **7** 的重要
物理数据如下：¹H NMR(500 MHz，CDCl₃，按紫杉醇编号)：δ 9.98 ppm (d，J = 3.5 Hz，1 H，2-H)，
7.65~7.12 (m，15 H，芳香氢)，5.84 (dd，J = 10.5，1.5 Hz，1 H，6-H)，5.71 (dd，J = 10.5，2.0 Hz，1 H，
5-H)，4.50 (d，J = 11.5 Hz，1 H，OCH₂Ph)，4.22 (d，J = 11.5 Hz，1 H，OCH₂Ph)，4.20 (d，J = 9.5
Hz，1 H，20-H)，4.10 (dd，J = 2.0，1.5 Hz，1 H，7-H)，3.84 (d，J = 9.5 Hz，1 H，20-H)，3.72 (d，
J = 10.0 Hz，1 H，9-H)，3.70 (d，J = 10.0 Hz，1 H，9-H)，3.18 (d，J = 3.5 Hz，1 H，3-H)，1.42 (s，3 H，
CH₃–丙酮缩酮)，1.39 (s，3 H，CH₃–丙酮缩酮)，1.09 (s，9 H，(CH₃)₃CSi)，1.04 (s，3 H，19-CH₃)；
¹³C NMR(125 MHz，CDCl₃)：δ 202.3，138.1，135.8，135.6，133.0，132.9，131.1，129.7，129.4，
129.5，128.8，128.2，127.6，127.4，127.4，127.2，127.2，127.1，108.6，80.6，75.4，71.8，70.0，
65.7，57.6，44.9，26.9，26.8，26.5，19.3，13.6；红外 (纯物质)：ν_max 2,931.4，2,857.0，1,720.4，1,111.5 cm⁻¹；
高分辨质谱 (快原子轰击)(HRMS(FAB))：C₃₆H₄₄O₅Si(M⁺+Cs) 计算值质荷比 m/z = 607.2856 amu(原子
质量单位)，测定值为 607.2865 amu。

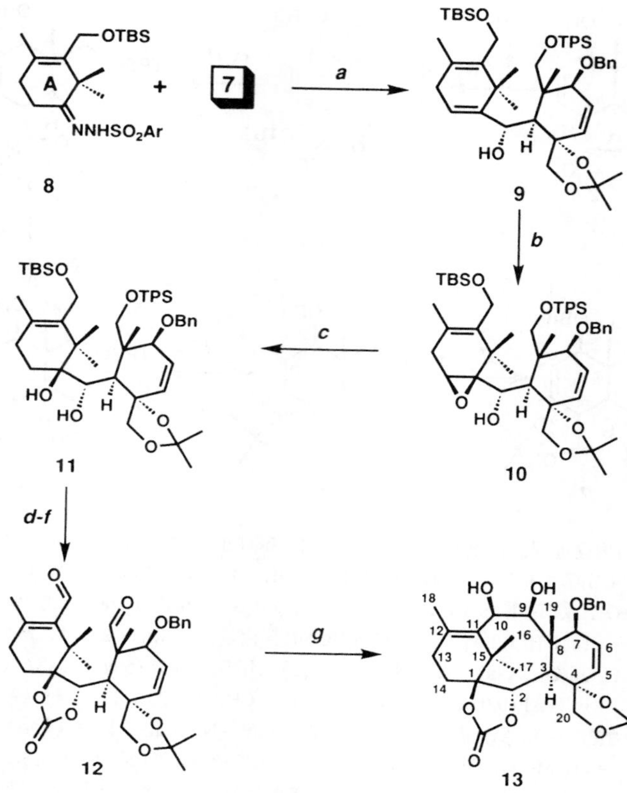

Fig. 3. Construction of ABC ring system **13**. Reagents and conditions. (*a*) (1) **8**, *n*-BuLi (2.05 eq.), THF, −78 °C → 25 °C, cool to 0 °C and add **7** (1.0 eq. in THF), 0.5 h, 82%; (*b*) VO(acac)$_2$ (0.03 eq.), *t*-BuOOH (3 eq.), 4-Å molecular sieve (cat.), benzene, 25 °C, 12 h, 87%; (*c*) LiAlH$_4$ (3 eq.), Et$_2$O, 25 °C, 7 h, 76%; (*d*) KH (3 eq.), HMPA/Et$_2$O (30/70), COCl$_2$ (20% in benzene, 2 eq.), 25 °C, 2 h, 48%; (*e*) TBAF (10 eq.), THF, 25 °C, 7 h, 80%; (*f*) TPAP (0.05 eq.), NMO (3 eq.), CH$_3$CN/CH$_2$Cl$_2$ (2:1), 25 °C, 2 h, 82%; (*g*) (TiCl$_3$)$_2$–(DME)$_3$ (10 eq.), Zn–Cu (20 eq.), DME, 70 °C, 1 h, 23%. Ar = 2,4,6-triisopropylbenzene sulphonyl; HMPA = hexamethyl-phosphoric triamide; NMO = 4-methylmorpholine-N-oxide; TBAF = tetra-*n*-butylammonium fluoride; TBS = *t*-BuMe$_2$Si; TPAP = tetra-*n*-propylammonium perruthenate. Selected physical data for compound **13**: ^{1}H NMR (500 MHz, CDCl$_3$ taxol numbering): δ 7.42–7.31 (m, 5 H, aromatic), 5.97 (dd, *J* = 10.0, 1.5 Hz, 1 H, 5-H), 5.63 (dd, *J* = 10.0, 1.5 Hz, 1 H, 6-H), 5.46 (d, *J* = 5.0 Hz, 1 H, 2-H), 4.77 (d, *J* = 12.0 Hz, 1 H, OCH$_2$Ph), 4.49 (d, *J* = 8.5 Hz, 1 H, 20-H), 4.39 (d, *J* = 12.0 Hz, 1 H, OCH$_2$Ph), 4.29 (d, *J* = 5.5 Hz, 1 H, 10-H), 4.24 (d, *J* = 5.5 Hz, 1 H, 9-H), 3.80 (d, *J* = 8.5 Hz, 1 H, 20-H), 3.58 (b, 1 H, 7-H), 2.75–2.71 (m, 1 H, 13-H), 2.61–2.50 (m, 1 H, 13-H), 2.34 (d, *J* = 5.0 Hz, 1 H, 3-H), 1.98–1.92 (m, 1 H, 14-H), 1.83–1.74 (m, 1 H, 14-H), 1.58 (s, 3 H, 18-CH$_3$), 1.45 (s, 3 H, 19-CH$_3$), 1.42 (s, 3 H, CH$_3$-acetonide), 1.41 (s, 3 H, CH$_3$-acetonide), 1.19 (s, 3 H, 16-CH$_3$), 1.08 (s, 3 H, 17-CH$_3$); ^{13}C NMR (125 MHz, CDCl$_3$): δ 153.9, 139.4, 137.3, 136.1, 135.6, 128.7, 128.5, 128.3, 122.0, 108.2, 93.4, 82.4, 77.9, 75.7, 74.2, 71.2, 70.4, 69.3, 46.3, 44.3, 40.0, 31.2, 29.6, 28.9, 27.9, 26.8, 23.6, 21.7, 21.3, 16.0; infrafred (pure compound): ν_{max} 2,970.3, 1,789.1, 1,455.6, 1,100.3 cm^{-1}; HRMS (FAB) calcd for C$_{31}$H$_{40}$O$_8$ (M$^+$+Cs), *m/z* = 673.1778 a.m.u., found 673.1782 a.m.u.

图 3. ABC 环体系 **13** 的构造。试剂和条件。(*a*)(1)**8**，*n*-BuLi(2.05 eq.)，THF，−78 ℃ → 25 ℃，冷却到 0 ℃ 并加入 **7**(1.0 eq. 的 THF 溶液)，0.5 小时，82%；(*b*)VO(acac)₂(0.03 eq.)，*t*-BuOOH(3 eq.)，4 Å 分子筛(催化量)，苯，25 ℃，12 小时，87%；(*c*)LiAlH₄(3 eq.)，Et₂O，25 ℃，7 小时，76%；(*d*)KH(3 eq.)，HMPA/Et₂O(30/70)，COCl₂(20% 的苯溶液，2 eq.)，25 ℃，2 小时，48%；(*e*) TBAF(10 eq.)，THF，25 ℃，7 小时，80%；(*f*)TPAP(0.05 eq.)，NMO(3 eq.)，CH₃CN/CH₂Cl₂(2∶1)，25 ℃，2 小时，82%；(*g*)(TiCl₃)₂–(DME)₃(10 eq.)，Zn–Cu(20 eq.)，DME，70 ℃，1 小时，23%。Ar = 2,4,6–三异丙基苯磺酰基；HMPA = 六甲基磷酸三酰胺；NMO = 4–甲基吗啉–N–氧化物；TBAF = 氟化四(*n*–丁基)铵；TBS = *t*-BuMe₂Si；TPAP = 过钌酸四(*n*–丙基)铵。化合物 **13** 的重要物理数据如下：^{1}H NMR(500 MHz, CDCl₃，按紫杉醇编号)：δ 7.42~7.31(m，5 H，芳香氢)，5.97(dd，*J* = 10.0, 1.5 Hz，1 H，5-H)，5.63(dd，*J* = 10.0, 1.5 Hz，1 H，6-H)，5.46(d，*J* = 5.0 Hz，1 H，2-H)，4.77(d，*J* = 12.0 Hz，1 H，OCH₂Ph)，4.49(d，*J* = 8.5 Hz，1 H，20-H)，4.39(d，*J* = 12.0 Hz，1 H，OCH₂Ph)，4.29(d，*J* = 5.5 Hz，1 H，10-H)，4.24(d，*J* = 5.5 Hz，1 H，9-H)，3.80(d，*J* = 8.5 Hz，1 H，20-H)，3.58(b，1 H，7-H)，2.75~2.71(m，1 H，13-H)，2.61~2.50(m，1 H，13-H)，2.34(d，*J* = 5.0 Hz，1 H，3-H)，1.98~1.92(m，1 H，14-H)，1.83~1.74(m，1 H，14-H)，1.58(s，3 H，18-CH₃)，1.45(s，3 H，19-CH₃)，1.42(s，3 H，CH₃–丙酮缩酮)，1.41(s，3 H，CH₃–丙酮缩酮)，1.19(s，3 H，16-CH₃)，1.08(s，3 H，17-CH₃)；^{13}C NMR(125 MHz, CDCl₃)：δ 153.9, 139.4, 137.3, 136.1, 135.6, 128.7, 128.5, 128.3, 122.0, 108.2, 93.4, 82.4, 77.9, 75.7, 74.2, 71.2, 70.4, 69.3, 46.3, 44.3, 40.0, 31.2, 29.6, 28.9, 27.9, 26.8, 23.6, 21.7, 21.3, 16.0；红外(纯物质)：ν_{max} 2,970.3, 1,789.1, 1,455.6, 1,100.3 cm^{-1}；HRMS(FAB)：C₃₁H₄₀O₈(M⁺+Cs)计算值 *m/z* = 673.1778 amu，测定值为 673.1782 amu。

301

Figure 3 summarizes the coupling of intermediates **7** and **8** and elaboration of the coupling product to give the requisite tricyclic system **13**. When the vinyl lithium reagent derived from aryl hydrazone **8** and n-C$_4$H$_9$Li (refs 8, 13) was reacted with aldehyde **7** at $-78\,^{\circ}$C, a single diastereoisomer of hydroxycompound **9** was obtained in 82% yield. Directed epoxidation of the C1–C14 double bond in **9** was realized, in 87% yield, using t-C$_4$H$_9$OOH in the presence of VO(acac)$_2$ (ref. 15), leading selectively to epoxide **10** which was regioselectively opened with LiAlH$_4$ to give the 1,2-diol **11** (76% yield). X-ray crystallographic analysis of this compound (**11**) confirmed the designated stereochemistry for intermediates **9–11** and their relatives (Fig. 4a). To prepare the molecule for closure of the 8-membered B ring, and in order to create subsequent opportunities for the introduction of the benzoate functionality at C-2, diol **11** was converted to its cyclic carbonate by exposure to phosgene in the presence of KH, furnishing dialdehyde **12**, after desilylation (n-(C$_4$H$_9$)$_4$NF) and oxidation (TPAP-NMO)[14] in 32% overall yield. The suitably preorganized dialdehyde **12** was then subjected to a McMurry-type[9,13] cyclization to afford the taxoid ABC ring system **13** in 23% yield (stereochemistry at the newly generated centres assigned by X-ray crystallographic analysis of a subsequent intermediate, **13′**; see below and Fig. 4c).

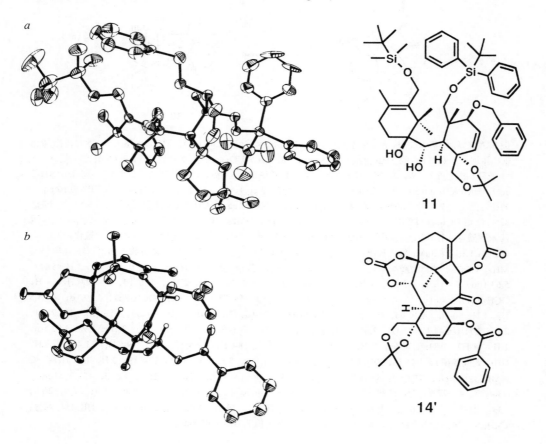

11

14′

图 3 概括了中间产物 **7** 和 **8** 的偶联，及其产物进一步偶联得到必需的三环体系 **13** 的详细过程。将用芳基腙 **8** 和 n-C₄H₉Li(参考文献 8，参考文献 13)制备的烯基锂与醛类物质 **7** 在 -78 ℃ 反应，得到羟基化合物 **9** 的单一非对映异构体，产率 82%。在 VO(acac)₂ (参考文献 15)存在下用 t-C₄H₉OOH 实现 **9** 中 C1–C14 双键定向环氧化，以 87% 的产率，选择性地得到环氧化物 **10**，后者在 LiAlH₄ 作用下区域选择性地开环，得到 1,2– 二醇 **11** (产率 76%)。对化合物(**11**)的 X 射线晶体学分析确证了中间产物 **9**~**11** 具有指定的立体化学构型和彼此的相互关系(图 4a)。为制备能闭合成八元 B 环的分子，并为了随后在 C–2 位上引入苯甲酸酯官能团创造机会，将二醇 **11** 在有 KH 存在的条件下暴露于光气之中，使之转变为环状碳酸酯，经脱硅保护基(n-(C₄H₉)₄NF) 和氧化反应(TPAP–NMO)[14] 之后，产生二醛 **12**，总产率为 32%。于是，经过适当构建的二醛 **12** 就可以发生麦克默里类型[9,13] 的成环反应，生成紫杉类 ABC 环体系 **13**，产率为 23%(利用 X 射线晶体学分析后继中间产物 **13′** 确认了其新生成的手性中心的立体化学构型；见下面和图 4c)。

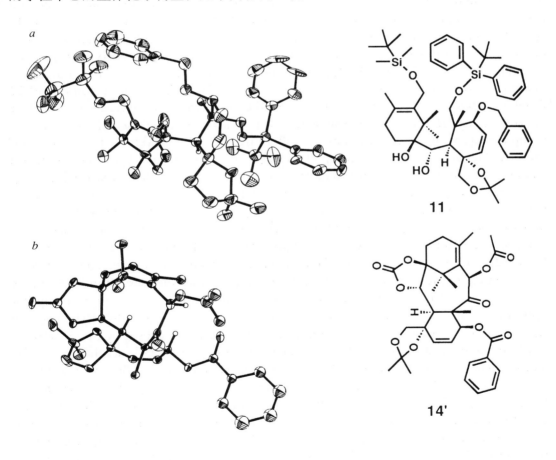

11

14′

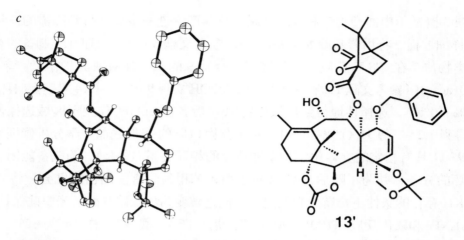

13'

Fig. 4. ORTEP drawings of compounds **11** (*a*), **14'** (*b*) and **13'** (*c*). (ORTEP, Oregon national thermal ellipsoid program.)

The next important intermediate in the synthesis was **19**, a compound that was reached from **13** as outlined in Fig. 5. Monoacetylation of **13** followed by oxidation with TPAP-NMO[14] furnished, regioselectively in 88% overall yield, ketoacetate **14**. The stereochemistry of the acetate group at C-10 was confirmed through conversion of **14** to the crystalline benzoate **14'** (PCC, NaO(CO)CH₃, celite, benzene, heat) and X-ray crystallographic analysis on the latter (see ORTEP drawing, Fig. 4*b*). Hydroboration of compound **14** followed by basic hydrogen peroxide treatment led to a mixture of two regioisomeric alcohols (55%, ~3:1 by ¹H NMR) which was subjected to acid-induced removal of the acetonide group and chromatographic separation to afford triol **15** (33% yield from **14**) as the major product. The primary hydroxyl group in **15** was then selectively acetylated under standard conditions, furnishing compound **16** in 95% yield. At this stage the benzyl protecting group on the C-7 oxygen was replaced by a triethyl silyl group (TES) for reasons arising from later stages of the synthesis, and the resulting compound was selectively monodeacetylated under mildly basic conditions (K₂CO₃-CH₃OH) leading to triol **17** (78% overall yield). The oxetane ring was finally constructed by sequential monosilylation with TMSCl (primary OH), triflate formation (secondary OH) and mild acid treatment to afford, after acetylation of the remaining tertiary hydroxyl group, the targeted intermediate **19** in 38% overall yield[16]. Racemic **19**, obtained from this sequence, was identical in all respects (except for optical rotation) with an authentic sample generated from taxol (**1**) or 10-deacetyl baccatin III (ref. 17) as described elsewhere[10]. Optically active **19** was obtained by the same route using enantiomerically pure diol **13** secured by resolution with l(S)-(−)-camphanic chloride. Thus, reaction of racemic **13** with l(S)-(−)-camphanic chloride gave, in 86% total yield, two diastereoisomers (**13'** and **13''**) which were chromatographically separated and characterized by X-ray crystallographic analysis on one of them (more polar isomer, silica gel, 15% C₂H₅O(CO)CH₃ in benzene, $R_F = 0.21$) (see ORTEP drawing for **13'**, antipode to desired enantiomer; Fig. 4*c*). Optically pure **13** ($[\alpha]_D^{22} + 187°$(CHCl₃, *c* 0.5)) was then generated from the correct diastereoisomer (**13''**, less polar, silica gel, 15% C₂H₅O(CO)CH₃ in benzene, $R_F = 0.26$) by exposure to methanolic K₂CO₃ (90% yield).

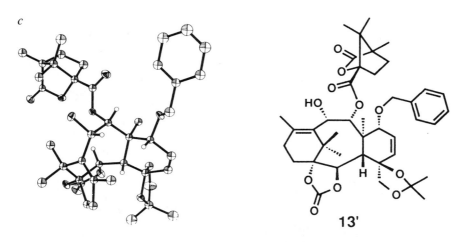

图 4. 化合物 **11** (*a*)、**14′**(*b*) 和 **13′**(*c*) 的 ORTEP 图。(ORTEP, 美国橡树岭国家实验室晶体结构可视化——热椭圆体绘图程序。)

　　合成中下一个重要的中间产物是 **19**。它是从 **13** 得到的一种化合物, 如图 5 所示。将 **13** 单乙酰化后再用 TPAP–NMO[14] 氧化, 区域选择性地得到酮乙酸酯 **14**, 总产率为 88%。通过将 **14** 转变为结晶的苯甲酸酯 **14′**(PCC, NaO(CO)CH₃, 硅藻土, 苯, 加热)并对后者进行 X 射线晶体学分析(见 ORTEP, 图 4*b*), 确认了 C–10 处乙酸酯基的立体化学特性。将化合物 **14** 硼氢化, 再用碱性过氧化氢处理, 得到两种区域异构体醇类物质的混合物(55%, 约 3:1, 由 ¹H NMR 测得), 后者先通过酸诱导反应使丙酮基团离去, 再进行色谱分离, 得到的主要产物为三醇 **15** (从 **14** 计算的产率为 33%)。接着在标准条件下将 **15** 中的伯羟基选择性地乙酰化, 生成化合物 **16**, 产率为 95%。在这一步, C–7 氧上的苄基保护基被三乙基硅基(TES)取代, 这是基于对后续合成步骤的考虑; 将所得化合物在温和条件下(K₂CO₃–CH₃OH)选择性地脱去单乙酰保护基, 得到三醇 **17** (总产率 78%)。最后构造氧杂环丁烷环, 要连续地通过用 TMSCl(伯 OH) 进行的单硅烷基化、三氟甲磺酸酯的形成(仲 OH)和温和的酸处理以获得(在将余下的叔羟基进行乙酰化之后)目标中间产物 **19**, 总产率 38%[16]。经过这一系列反应而得到的外消旋的 **19** 与由紫杉醇(**1**)或其他地方报道的 10–去乙酰基浆果赤霉素 III (参考文献 17)所生成的标准样品相比, 除了旋光性之外, 其他数据都是一样的[10]。在用 1 (S)–(–)–莰烷酸酰氯拆分得到的对映体纯的二醇 **13** 做保证的条件下, 以同样的步骤得到光学活性的 **19**。外消旋的 **13** 与 1 (S)–(–)–莰烷酸酰氯反应, 得到两种非对映异构体(**13′** 和 **13″**), 总产率 86%。将其进行色谱分离并用 X 射线晶体学分析鉴定其中之一(极性较大的异构体, 硅胶, 15% C₂H₅O(CO)CH₃ 的苯溶液, $R_F = 0.21$)(见 **13′** 的 ORTEP 图, 其与所需的对映体正好相反; 图 4*c*)。接着将正确的非对映异构体(**13″**, 极化较小的, 硅胶, 15% C₂H₅O(CO)CH₃ 的苯溶液, $R_F = 0.26$)置于 K₂CO₃ 的甲醇溶液中, 生成光学纯的 **13** ($[\alpha]_D^{22} +187°$ (CHCl₃, *c* 0.5))(产率 90%)。

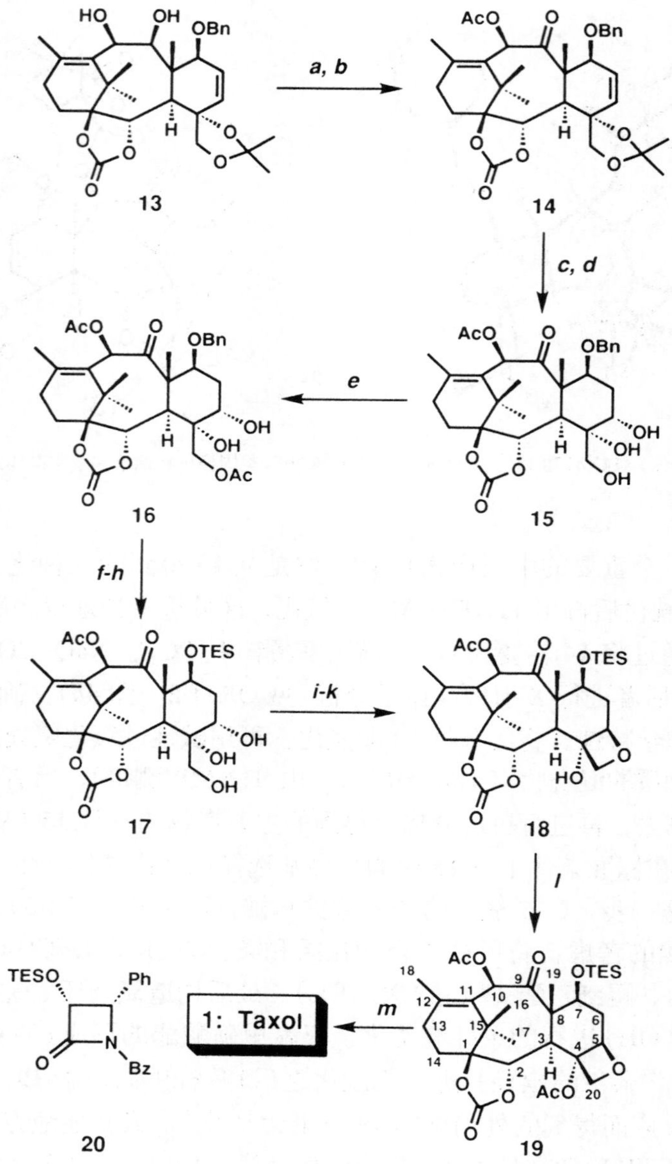

Fig. 5. Total synthesis of ABCD ring system **19** and taxol (**1**). Reagents and conditions. (*a*) Ac₂O (1.5 eq.), 4-DMAP (1.5 eq.), CH₂Cl₂, 25 °C, 2 h, 95%; (*b*) TPAP (0.1 eq.), NMO (3 eq.), CH₃CN, 25 °C, 2 h, 93%; (*c*) BH₃–THF (5.0 eq.), THF, 0 °C, 2 h then H₂O₂, aqueous NaHCO₃, 0.5 h, 55% (~3:1 mixture of C5–C6 regioisomers by ¹H NMR); (*d*) conc. HCl, MeOH, H₂O, 25 °C, 5 h 80%; (*e*) Ac₂O (1.5 eq.), 4-DMAP (1.5 eq.), CH₂Cl₂, 25 °C, 0.5 h, 95%; (*f*) H₂, 10% Pd(OH)₂(C), EtOAc, 25 °C, 0.5 h, 97%; (*g*) Et₃SiCl (25 eq.), pyridine, 25 °C, 12 h, 85%; (*h*) K₂CO₃ (10 eq.), MeOH, 0 °C, 15 min., 95%; (*i*) Me₃SiCl (10 eq.), pyridine (30 eq.), CH₂Cl₂, 0 °C, 15 min., 96%; (*j*) Tf₂O (15 eq.), *i*-Pr₂NEt (30 eq.), CH₂Cl₂, 25 °C, 0.5 h, 70%; (*k*) CSA (cat.), MeOH, 25 °C, 10 min., then silica gel, CH₂Cl₂, 25 °C, 4 h, 60%; (*l*) Ac₂O (10 eq.), 4-DMAP (20 eq.), CH₂Cl₂, 25 °C, 4 h, 94%; (*m*) (1) PhLi (5 eq.), THF, −78 °C, 10 min., 80%; (2) PCC (30 eq.), NaOAc, celite, benzene, reflux, 1 h, 75%; (3) NaBH₄ (10 eq.), MeOH, 25 °C, 5 h, 83%; (4) NaN(SiMe₃)₂ (3.5 eq.), β-lactam **20**,

图 5. ABCD 环体系 **19** 和紫杉醇 (**1**) 的全合成。试剂和条件。(*a*)Ac₂O(1.5 eq.)，4-DMAP(1.5 eq.)，CH₂Cl₂，25 ℃，2 小时，95%；(*b*)TPAP(0.1 eq.)，NMO(3 eq.)，CH₃CN，25 ℃，2 小时，93%；(*c*)BH₃–THF(5.0 eq.)，THF，0 ℃，2 小时，接着用 H₂O₂、NaHCO₃ 水溶液，0.5 小时，55%(约 3∶1 的 C5–C6 区域异构体的混合物，由 ¹H NMR 测得)；(*d*)浓盐酸，MeOH，H₂O，25 ℃，5 小时，80%；(*e*)Ac₂O(1.5 eq.)，4-DMAP (1.5 eq.)，CH₂Cl₂，25 ℃，0.5 小时，95%；(*f*)H₂，10% Pd(OH)₂(C)，EtOAc，25 ℃，0.5 小时，97%；(*g*)Et₃SiCl(25 eq.)，吡啶，25 ℃，12 小时，85%；(*h*)K₂CO₃ (10 eq.)，MeOH，0 ℃，15 分钟，95%；(*i*) Me₃SiCl(10 eq.)，吡啶(30 eq.)，CH₂Cl₂，0 ℃，15 分钟，96%；(*j*)Tf₂O(15 eq.)，*i*-Pr₂NEt(30 eq.)，CH₂Cl₂，25 ℃，0.5 小时，70%；(*k*)CSA(催化)，MeOH，25 ℃，10 分钟，接着用硅胶，CH₂Cl₂，25 ℃，4 小时，60%；(*l*)Ac₂O(10 eq.)，4-DMAP(20 eq.)，CH₂Cl₂，25 ℃，4 小时，94%；(*m*)(1)PhLi(5 eq.)，THF，−78 ℃，10 分钟，80%；(2)PCC(30 eq.)，NaOAc，硅藻土，苯，回流 1 小时，75%；(3)NaBH₄ (10

THF, 0 °C, 87%, based on 90% conversion; (5) HF-pyridine, THF, 25 °C, 1.5 h, 80%. (CSA = (±)-camphorsulphonic acid; 4-DMAP = N-dimethylaminopyridine; NMO = 4-methylmorpholine-N-oxide; TPAP = tetra-n-propylammonium perruthenate.) Selected physical data for compound **19**: ^{1}H NMR (500 MHz, CDCl$_3$, taxol numbering): δ 6.40 (s, 1 H, 10-H), 4.95 (d, J = 9.0 Hz, 1 H, 5-H), 4.60 (d, J = 9.0 Hz, 1 H, 20-H), 4.47 (d, J = 9.0 Hz, 1 H, 20-H), 4.43 (dd, J = 10.0, 7.5 Hz, 1 H, 7-H), 4.39 (d, J = 5.5 Hz, 1 H, 2-H), 3.36 (d, J = 5.5 Hz, 1 H, 3-H), 2.71 (m, 1 H, 13α-H), 2.56 (m, 1 H, 6-H), 2.17 (s, 3 H, OAc), 2.15 (s, 3 H, OAc), 2.12 (m, 1 H, CH$_2$), 2.07 (s, 3 H, 18-CH$_3$), 1.97 (m, 1 H, CH$_2$), 1.88 (m, 2 H, CH$_2$), 1.78 (s, 3 H, 19-CH$_3$), 1.23 (s, 3 H, 16-CH$_3$), 1.17 (s, 3 H, 17-CH$_3$), 0.88 (t, J = 7.5 Hz, 9 H, Si (CH$_2$CH$_3$)$_3$), 0.55 (dq, J = 8.0, 3.0 Hz, 6 H, Si(CH$_2$CH$_3$)$_3$); ^{13}C NMR (125 MHz, CDCl$_3$): δ 202.6, 170.3, 169.2, 153.1, 144.0, 130.7, 92.8, 84.0, 80.3, 80.0, 76.4, 76.1, 60.3, 43.5, 38.0, 29.7, 29.4, 25.5, 23.1, 21.9, 21.1, 19.1, 9.8, 6.7, 5.2; infrared (pure compound) ν_{max} 2,924, 1,814, 1,728, 1,461, 1,372, 1,238 cm^{-1}; HRMS (FAB) calcd for C$_{31}$H$_{46}$O$_{10}$Si(M$^+$+ Cs) m/z = 739.1915 a.m.u., found 739.1929 a.m.u.

The conversion of enantiomerically pure **19** to taxol (**1**) followed the sequence[10]: (1) excess C$_6$H$_5$Li, −78 °C to regioselectively open the carbonate ring and afford the desired hydroxybenzoate functionality (80%); (2) PCC-NaO(CO)CH$_3$, benzene, reflux to introduce a carbonyl group at C-13 (75%); (3) excess NaBH$_4$-CH$_3$OH to stereospecifically generate the C-13 hydroxyl group (83%); (4) NaN(Si(CH$_3$)$_3$)$_2$ then Ojima's β-lactam (**20**)[11], 0 °C, to attach the side chain (87% yield based on 90% conversion); and (5) HF–pyridine, to remove the silyl groups (80%). Synthetic taxol was found to be identical in all respects with naturally occurring taxol, including spectroscopic characteristics (^{1}H and ^{13}C NMR, infrared spectroscopy, mass spectra, $[\alpha]_D^{22}$) and biological activity (microtubule stabilization and cytotoxicity against Molt-4 leukaemia cells).

The chemistry described here not only offers a solution to a formidable synthetic challenge but also opens a completely chemical avenue to taxol, other naturally occurring taxoids and synthetic, designed taxoid derivatives.

(**367**, 630-634; 1994)

K. C. Nicolaou[*†], Z. Yang[*], J. J. Liu[*], H. Ueno[*], P. G. Nantermet[*], R. K. Guy[*], C. F. Claiborne[*], J. Renaud[*], E. A. Couladouros[*], K. Paulvannan[*] & E. J. Sorensen[*†]

[*] Department of Chemistry, The Scripps Research Institute, 10666 North Torrey Pines Road, La Jolla, California 92037, USA

[†] Department of Chemistry, University of California, San Diego, 9500 Gilman Drive, La Jolla, California 92093, USA

Received 24 January; accepted 31 January 1994.

References:

1. Wani, M. C., Taylor, H. L., Wall, M. E., Coggon, P. & McPhail, A. T. *J. Am. Chem. Soc.* **93**, 2325-2327 (1971).

2. Nicolaou, K. C., Dai, W.-M. & Guy, R. K. *Angew. Chem. Int. Ed. Engl.* **33**, 15-44 (1994).

3. Guenard, D., Gueritte-Voegelein, F. & Poitier, P. *Acct Chem. Res.* **26**, 160-167 (1993).

4. Rowinksy, E. K., Cazenave, L. A. & Donehower, R. C. *J. Natl. Cancer Inst.* **82**, 1247-1259 (1990).

5. *Paclitaxel (Taxol) Investigations Workshop Semin. Oncol.* **20** (4, Suppl. 3), 1-60 (1993).

6. Schiff, P. B., Fant, J. & Horwitz, S. B. *Nature* **277**, 665-667 (1979).

eq.)，MeOH，25 ℃，5 小时，83%；(4)NaN(SiMe₃)₂ (3.5 eq.)，β– 内酰胺 **20**，THF，0 ℃，87%，基于 90% 转化率；(5)HF–吡啶，THF，25 ℃，1.5 小时，80%。(CSA =（±）–樟脑磺酸，4-DMAP = N–二甲氨基吡啶；NMO = 4–甲基吗啉–N–氧化物；TPAP = 过钌酸四(n–丙基)铵。)化合物 **19** 的重要物理数据如下：¹H NMR(500 MHz，CDCl₃，紫杉醇编号)：δ 6.40 (s，1 H，10-H)，4.95 (d，J = 9.0 Hz，1 H，5-H)，4.60 (d，J = 9.0 Hz，1 H，20-H)，4.47 (d，J = 9.0 Hz，1 H，20-H)，4.43 (dd，J = 10.0 Hz，7.5 Hz，1 H，7-H)，4.39 (d，J = 5.5 Hz，1 H，2-H)，3.36 (d，J = 5.5 Hz，1 H，3-H)，2.71 (m，1 H，13α-H)，2.56 (m，1 H，6-H)，2.17 (s，3 H，OAc)，2.15 (s，3 H，OAc)，2.12 (m，1 H，CH₂)，2.07 (s，3 H，18-CH₃)，1.97 (m，1 H，CH₂)，1.88 (m，2 H，CH₂)，1.78 (s，3 H，19-CH₃)，1.23 (s，3 H，16-CH₃)，1.17 (s，3 H，17-CH₃)，0.88 (t，J = 7.5 Hz，9 H，Si(CH₂CH₃)₃)，0.55 (dq，J = 8.0，3.0 Hz，6 H，Si(CH₂CH₃)₃)；¹³C NMR(125 MHz，CDCl₃)：δ 202.6，170.3，169.2，153.1，144.0，130.7，92.8，84.0，80.3，80.0，76.4，76.1，60.3，43.5，38.0，29.7，29.4，25.5，23.1，21.9，21.1，19.1，9.8，6.7，5.2；红外(纯物质)：ν_max 2,924，1,814，1,728，1,416，1,372，1,238 cm⁻¹；HRMS(FAB)：C₃₁H₄₆O₁₀Si(M⁺+Cs) 计算值 m/z = 739.1915 amu，测定值为 739.1929 amu。

从对映异构体纯 **19** 到紫杉醇(**1**)的转化遵循下列步骤 [10]：(1) 用过量 C₆H₅Li 在 −78 ℃ 区域选择性地打开碳酸酯环，形成所需的羟基苯甲酸酯官能团(80%)；(2)PCC–NaO(CO)CH₃，苯，回流，在 C–13 位引入一个羰基(75%)；(3) 过量 NaBH₄–CH₃OH，立体专一性生成 C–13 位的羟基(83%)；(4)NaN(Si(CH₃)₃)₂，小岛的 β– 内酰胺(**20**)[11]，0 ℃，引入侧链(基于 90% 转化率的产率为 87%)；(5) 用 HF–吡啶脱除硅烷保护基(80%)。发现合成的紫杉醇与天然生成的紫杉醇在各个方面都是一致的，包括光谱特性(¹H 和 ¹³C NMR，红外光谱，质谱，[α]_D²²)和生物学活性(微管稳定作用和对 Molt-4 白血病细胞的细胞毒性)。

这里所描述的化学方法不仅给极度困难的合成提供了一种解答，还为紫杉醇、其他天然紫杉醇类似物以及合成设计紫杉醇衍生物提供了一条完全化学式的途径。

(王耀杨 翻译；许家喜 审稿)

7. Nicolaou, K. C., Hwang, C.-K., Sorensen, E. J. & Claiborne, C. F. *J. Chem. Soc., Chem. Commun.* 1117-1118 (1992).

8. Chamberlin, A. R. & Bloom, S. H. *Org. React.* **39**, 1-83 (1990).

9. McMurry, J. E. *Chem. Rev.* **89**, 1513-1524 (1989).

10. Nicolaou, K. C., Nantermet, P. G., Ueno, H. & Guy, R. K. *J. Chem. Soc., Chem. Commun.* 295-296 (1994).

11. Ojima, I. *et al. Tetrahedron* **48**, 6985-7012 (1992).

12. Nicolaou, K. C., Liu. J. J., Hwang, C.-K, Dai, W.-M. & Guy, R. K. *J. Chem. Soc., Chem. Commun.* 1118-1120 (1992).

13. Nicolaou, K. C., Yang, Z., Sorensen, E. J. & Nakada, M. *J. Chem. Soc., Chem. Commun.* 1024-1026 (1993).

14. Griffith, W. P., Ley, S. V. *Aldrichimica Acta.* **23**, 13-19 (1990).

15. Sharpless, K. B. & Verhoeven, T. R. *Aldrichimica Acta*, **12**, 63-74 (1979).

16. Magee, T. V., Bornmann, W. G., Isaacs, R. C. A. & Danishefsky, S. J. *J. Org. Chem.* **57**, 3274-3276 (1992).

Acknowledgements. We thank I. Ojima for a sample for β-lactam **20**, E. Bombardelli for a gift of 10-deacetyl baccatin III, R. Chadha for the X-ray crystallographic analysis and W. Wrasidlo for the biological assays. This work was supported by the NIH, The Scripps Research Institute, fellowships from Mitsubishi Kasei Corporation (H. U.), Rhone-Poulene Rorer (P. G. N.), The Office of Naval Research (R. K. G.), Glaxo, Inc. (C. F. C.), Mr Richard Staley (C. F. C.), NSERC (J. B. R.), The Agricultural University of Athens (E. A. C.), R. W. Johnson—ACS Division of Organic Chemistry (E. J. S.), and grants from Merck Sharp and Dohme, Pfizer, Inc. and Schering Plough. Z. Y. and J. J. L. contributed equally to this project.

A Cell Initiating Human Acute Myeloid Leukaemia after Transplantation into SCID Mice

T. Lapidot *et al.*

Editor's Note

This paper by Canadian cell biologist John E. Dick and colleagues marks a significant shift in cancer biology. Dick isolated putative stem cells from blood samples of patients with acute myeloid leukaemia (AML) and injected them into mice with deficient immune systems, causing the animals to develop leukaemia. The experiment suggested that these rare cancer stem cells cause AML, and offered a potential explanation for why chemotherapy, which targets fast-growing cancer cells rather than slow-growing stem cells, sometimes fails. Reaction was guarded: many researchers thought that leukaemia, a cancer of the blood, might be an exceptional case. But opinion changed in 2003 when researchers found cancer stem cells in two different solid tumours—human breast cancer and brain cancer.

Most human acute myeloid leukaemia (AML) cells have limited proliferative capacity, suggesting that the leukaemic clone may be maintained by a rare population of stem cells[1-5]. This putative leukaemic stem cell has not been characterized because the available *in vitro* assays can only detect progenitors with limited proliferative and replating potential[4-7]. We have now identified an AML-initiating cell by transplantation into severe combined immune-deficient (SCID) mice. These cells homed to the bone marrow and proliferated extensively in response to *in vivo* cytokine treatment, resulting in a pattern of dissemination and leukaemic cell morphology similar to that seen in the original patients. Limiting dilution analysis showed that the frequency of these leukaemia-initiating cells in the peripheral blood of AML patients was one engraftment unit in 250,000 cells. We fractionated AML cells on the basis of cell-surface-marker expression and found that the leukaemia-initiating cells that could engraft SCID mice to produce large numbers of colony-forming progenitors were $CD34^+CD38^-$; however, the $CD34^+CD38^+$ and $CD34^-$ fractions contained no cells with these properties. This *in vivo* model replicates many aspects of human AML and defines a new leukaemia-initiating cell which is less mature than colony-forming cells.

THE success in transplanting normal human haematopoietic cells[8,9] and acute lymphoid leukaemia cells[10,11] into immuno-deficient SCID mice[12] suggested that this system might be useful for studying human myeloid leukaemias. But previous experiments indicated that primary AML cells could not be grafted into SCID mice after intravenous injection[13-15], and only a few samples grew locally after implantation into the peritoneum

一种植入 SCID 小鼠中引发
人急性髓性白血病的细胞

拉皮多特等

编者按

加拿大细胞生物学家约翰·迪克和同事发表的这篇文章标志着肿瘤生物学研究的一个重大转变。迪克从急性髓性白血病患者的血液样品中分离得到了假定的干细胞，并将它们注入免疫系统缺陷的小鼠，使后者患上白血病。实验表明少数的癌症干细胞即能引起急性髓性白血病，这也解释了为什么以快速生长的肿瘤细胞而不是生长缓慢的干细胞为靶点的化学疗法有时候会失败。一开始人们的反应比较谨慎，许多研究者认为白血病作为一种血液肿瘤发现干细胞可能是一个例外。但是在 2003 年当研究人员在实体瘤——人乳腺肿瘤和脑肿瘤中也发现了癌症干细胞，人们对它的看法才发生了变化。

大多数人急性髓性白血病（AML）细胞的增殖能力有限，这暗示可能存在着数量非常稀少的肿瘤干细胞来维系白血病细胞克隆的存在 [1-5]。由于现有的体外实验只能检测出增殖和替换能力有限的祖细胞，因此人们一直未能鉴定出这种白血病干细胞 [4-7]。本文中，我们通过对重度联合免疫缺陷（SCID）小鼠进行细胞移植实验，发现了一种可以引发 AML 的细胞。这些细胞会归巢于骨髓中，并且在细胞因子的刺激下在体内会快速增殖，产生与初始白血病患者体内形态和模式均相似的白血病细胞。有限稀释实验显示，这些能够引发白血病的细胞在 AML 患者的外周血中的频率为 1/250,000，即每 25 万个外周血淋巴细胞可以通过移植引发一例新的白血病。我们根据细胞表面标志分子的表达对 AML 细胞进行了分选，发现那些能够通过细胞移植引发 SCID 小鼠产生大量集落形成前体细胞的白血病起始细胞的表型是 $CD34^+CD38^-$，而表型为 $CD34^+CD38^+$ 以及 $CD34^-$ 的细胞则不具备这种能力。这个体内实验模型再现了人 AML 的许多特征。利用这一模型，我们发现了一类新的白血病起始细胞。这类细胞在发育上较那些集落形成细胞来说还不够成熟。

在过去的研究中，人们成功地在免疫缺陷的 SCID 小鼠 [12] 体内植入正常的人造血细胞 [8,9] 和急性淋巴细胞白血病细胞 [10,11]，这提示我们可以利用这一模型开展人髓性白血病的研究。不过，以往的实验表明通过静脉注射方式无法将原代 AML 细胞植入 SCID 小鼠中 [13-15]。如果采用腹膜内植入或肾小囊下植入的方式，也只有少部分

or under the renal capsule[13,14]. As AML cells have stringent cytokine requirements *in vitro*[7], we tested the effect of treating SCID mice, transplanted with peripheral blood cells (PBL) from AML patients newly diagnosed according to the French–American–British classification (FAB) as Ml, with cytokine PIXY321 (Fig. 1 legend) and human mast-cell growth factor (MGF). DNA analysis indicated that the bone marrow from mice treated for 30–60 days contained 10–100-fold more human cells than those from untreated control mice (data not shown). We have now examined a large number of samples ($n = 17$) from patients with newly diagnosed AML of different FAB subtypes (AML Ml, M2, M4) for their ability to proliferate in SCID mice. The cell source was either fresh bone marrow, fresh PBL, or banked frozen samples. All transplanted mice were treated with growth factors for the duration of the experiment (30–45 days). DNA and cytological analysis indicated that the bone marrow from 60 of 70 mice (86%) contained 10–100% human cells (Fig. 1), leading to almost complete replacement of murine haematopoiesis. Moreover, AML cells from all of the FAB subtypes (16 of 17 patients) engrafted SCID mice to high levels, indicating high reproducibility of the transplant system.

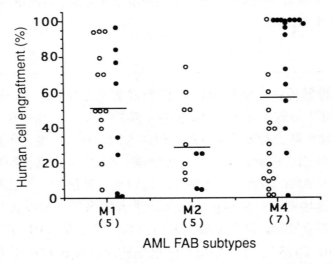

Fig. 1. Summary of human cell engraftment in the bone marrow of SCID mice transplanted with cells from AML patients, FAB subtypes M1, M2 or M4, where: M1 is AML without maturation; M2 is AML with granulocytic maturation; M4, acute myelomonocytic leukaemia; M5, acute monocytic leukaemia[22]. Number of donors is indicated. Engraftment was quantified by DNA analysis (open circles) or by cytology (filled circles) of Wright-stained bone marrow touch preparations 17–45 days post-transplantation. Lines represent mean level of engraftment for each FAB group.

Methods. Bone marrow and peripheral blood were obtained after informed consent according to procedures approved by the Human Experimentation Committee. Fresh or thawed AML cells were enriched by Ficoll-density gradient centrifugation and washed in IMDM medium containing 10% FCS. For transplantation of human cells, cells (1×10^7–4×10^7) were injected into the tail vein of sublethally irradiated (400 cGy, using a ^{137}Cs irradiator) SCID mice according to our established protocols[9]. PIXY321 (a fusion protein of human granulocyte–macrophage colony-stimulating factor with human IL-3) (7 μg) and human mast-cell growth factor (hMGF; c-*kit*-ligand; 10 μg) were administered on alternate days by intraperitoneal injection. Mice were bred and maintained in a defined flora colony (Ontario Cancer Institute). Grafting of human cells was quantified as described[9]. Briefly, 5 μg phenol-extracted DNA was digested with *Eco*RI, blotted onto a nylon membrane (Amersham) and probed with p17H8, a human

细胞可以在植入部位存活 [13,14]。由于人 AML 细胞在体外的生长依赖于细胞因子 [7]，我们对 PIXY321（参见图 1 图注）和人肥大细胞生长因子（MGF）在治疗 SCID 小鼠方面的效果进行了测试。其中，实验用的 SCID 小鼠均植入新诊断的 AML 患者（按照法国 – 美国 – 英国（FAB）分类标准定义为 M1）的外周血细胞（PBL）。DNA 分析显示，经细胞因子处理 30~60 天的小鼠骨髓中，人淋巴细胞的数量是未处理过的小鼠中的数量的 10~100 倍（数据未展示）。我们现已检测了 17 例不同 FAB 分型的 AML 患者（AML M1、M2 和 M4）的淋巴细胞在 SCID 小鼠中的增殖能力。这些细胞有的来源于新鲜骨髓，有的来源于新鲜 PBL，还有的是冷冻的库存样品。实验期间（30~45 天），所有移植后小鼠都使用生长因子处理。DNA 和细胞学分析结果表明，70 只小鼠中的 60 只，即 86% 的骨髓中含有 10%~100% 的人淋巴细胞（图 1），这导致小鼠造血细胞几乎完全被替代了。此外，所有 FAB 亚型的 AML 细胞（17 例中有 16 例）移植到 SCID 小鼠中都会出现高水平扩增，表明这一实验模型具有很高的可重复性。

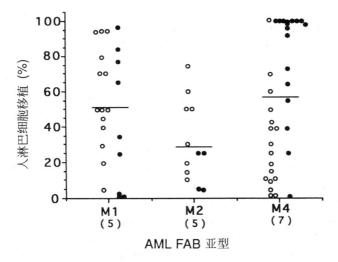

图 1. 不同 FAB 亚型（M1、M2、M4）AML 患者细胞植入 SCID 小鼠后小鼠骨髓中人类细胞的移植概况。M1 为 AML 未分化型；M2 为 AML 部分分化型；M4 为急性粒 – 单核细胞白血病；M5 为急性单核细胞白血病 [22]。供体的数量如图所示。在植入细胞后的 17~45 天中，使用 DNA 分析（图中的空心圆）或使用细胞学（图中的实心圆）分析经瑞氏染色的骨髓印片标本，从而对移植进行量化研究。图中的横线代表各组的平均值。

方法。按照人体试验委员会批准的程序，在获得 AML 患者知情同意后，采集患者的骨髓和外周血样品。使用聚蔗糖密度梯度离心法富集新鲜或解冻的 AML 细胞，然后用含 10% 胎牛血清的 IMDM 培养基洗涤细胞。按照我们先前建立的方法进行人类细胞的移植，将 1×10^7~4×10^7 个细胞通过尾静脉注射到经亚致死剂量（400 cGy，使用 ^{137}Cs 作为放射源）照射的 SCID 小鼠体内 [9]。隔日腹腔注射 7 μg PIXY321（人粒细胞 – 巨噬细胞集落刺激因子和白介素 3 的融合蛋白）和 10 μg 人肥大细胞生长因子（hMGF，c-*kit* 配体）。小鼠在安大略肿瘤研究所饲养。扩散到骨髓中的人淋巴细胞的数量按文献中描述的方法计算 [9]。简单地说，5 μg 使用苯酚抽提的 DNA 经 *Eco*RI 消化后转印到尼龙膜上（安马西亚公司）。然后使用特异性识别人 17 号染色体序列的 α 卫星探针——p17H8 作为探针进行检测 [23]。通过比较样品与人 – 小鼠

α-satellite probe specific for human chromosome-17 sequences[23]. The percentage of human cells present in the mouse tissues was estimated by comparison of the intensity of the characteristic 2.7-kb band with standard human/mouse DNA mixtures (0, 0.1, 1.0, 10 and 50% human DNA).

Many morphological and dissemination features characteristic of the donor's disease were reproduced in the SCID-leukaemia mice. The bone marrow of mice transplanted with AML Ml cells was extensively infiltrated with undifferentiated blast cells (Fig. 2a); Auer rods were also seen in some leukaemic cells (Fig. 2b). SCID mice transplanted with AML M4 cells containing an inversion of chromosome 16 had many characteristically abnormal eosinophils with large basophilic granules (Fig. 2c). Flow cytometric analysis, using CD33 and CD13, of leukaemic cells from the engrafted murine bone marrow indicated that they had an immunophenotype identical to the donor leukaemic cells (data not shown). In addition, leukaemic cells were also present in the peripheral blood of engrafted SCID mice (Fig. 2d). In contrast to mice transplanted with AML M1 and M2, some with AML M4 cells became sick or died as early as 10–20 days post-transplant, with dissemination of leukaemic blasts to the liver (Fig. 2e), lungs, spleen and kidney (data not shown). Clinically, leukaemic blasts from patients with the monocytic subtypes AML M4 and M5 disseminate more extensively to extra-medullary sites than those from patients with AML M1/M2, suggesting that the SCID-leukaemia model accurately reflects biological differences between different AML subtypes.

To determine whether immature leukaemic blast colony-forming units (AML-CFU) were present in the bone marrow of highly engrafted mice, single-cell suspensions of marrow were plated in methylcellulose cultures. AML-CFU were present in mice transplanted with 11 of 11 donor samples, regardless of the FAB classification (Fig. 3a), and no progenitors of normal lineages were detected. Leukaemic cells, before and after transplantation into SCID mice, were plated at limiting dilution to compare the frequencies of AML-CFU. The assay was linear, and similar frequencies were obtained from the patient sample and the mouse bone marrow, 0.9 versus 0.3% respectively (Fig. 3b). Interestingly, the response in culture to interleukin-3 (IL-3) and human MGF of AML-CFU from the patient and the transplanted mouse was identical, indicating that neither the murine environment nor exogenous cytokine treatment selected for clones with altered responses to growth factors (Fig. 3b). Kinetic experiments were done to measure the number of human cells and AML-CFU present in the murine bone marrow over 28 days following transplantation of either 10^6 or 1.3×10^7 cells. At both cell doses, AML-CFU increased by > 100-fold over 14–28 days relative to the number detected in bone marrow one day after transplantation (Fig. 3c). The total number of human cells increased by 1,000-fold over the same period (data not shown). The presence of large numbers of growth-factor-responsive AML-CFU and their extensive expansion in the bone marrow of cytokine-treated mice implied that a leukaemic stem cell more immature than AML-CFU was maintaining the progenitor pool.

DNA 混合标准品 (0、0.1%、1.0%、10% 以及 50% 人 DNA) 中特征性的 2.7 kb 条带的浓度即可估算出人细胞在小鼠组织中的含量。

在 SCID 白血病小鼠中，供体的许多形态学和扩散性疾病特征得以再现。如植入 AML M1 型细胞的小鼠骨髓被未分化的母细胞高度浸润 (图 2a)；在某些白血病细胞中可以观察到 Auer 小体的存在 (图 2b)。植入 16 号染色体倒置的 AML M4 型细胞的 SCID 小鼠体内有明显异常的嗜酸性粒细胞，这些细胞中含有巨大的嗜碱性颗粒 (图 2c)。使用流式细胞仪分析这些小鼠骨髓中白血病细胞表面 CD33 和 CD13 的表达情况时发现，它们具有和供体白血病细胞相同的免疫表型 (数据未展示)。此外，在 SCID 白血病小鼠的外周血中也可以检测到白血病细胞 (图 2d)。与植入 AML M1 型和 M2 型细胞的小鼠相比，一些植入 AML M4 型细胞的小鼠在植入后 10~20 天会由于白血病母细胞扩散到肝脏 (图 2e)、肺部、脾脏和肾脏 (数据未展示) 而开始生病或死去。从临床上来讲，AML M4 和 M5 单核细胞亚型患者体内的白血病母细胞在骨髓外的扩散范围要比 AML M1 和 M2 型患者的更广。这表明 SCID-白血病小鼠模型可以精确地反映出不同 AML 亚型的生物学差异。

为了明确植入细胞的小鼠骨髓中是否存在不成熟的白血病母细胞集落形成单位 (AML-CFU)，我们用甲基纤维素培养基制备了骨髓单细胞悬液。在全部 11 个供体样本中 (不考虑 FAB 分型) 都可以检测到 AML-CFU (图 3a)，而检测不到正常细胞系的祖细胞。为了比较 AML-CFU 的频率，我们对移植前后的白血病细胞进行了有限稀释培养。分析结果表明两者呈线性关系，并且在患者样品和小鼠骨髓中 AML-CFU 出现的频率相近，分别为 0.9% 和 0.3% (图 3b)。有意思的是，在培养基中患者和移植小鼠的 AML-CFU 对白介素 3 和人 MGF 的反应是一致的，表明小鼠体内环境和外源细胞因子的处理都与白血病细胞针对不同生长因素的克隆选择无关 (图 3b)。在 10^6 或 1.3×10^7 个细胞植入小鼠后的 28 天内，我们对小鼠骨髓中人类细胞和 AML-CFU 的数量进行了动力学研究。结果显示，在两种细胞剂量下，骨髓中检测到的 AML-CFU 的数量在细胞植入后 14~28 天内相较于第一天都增加至原来的 100 倍以上 (图 3c)，而人类细胞的数量在相同时期内则增加至原来的 1,000 倍 (数据未展示)。大量生长因子应答型 AML-CFU 的存在及其在细胞因子处理后的小鼠骨髓中广泛的扩增表明，很可能有一种比 AML-CFU 分化程度更低的白血病干细胞存在，从而使得祖细胞的数量得以维持。

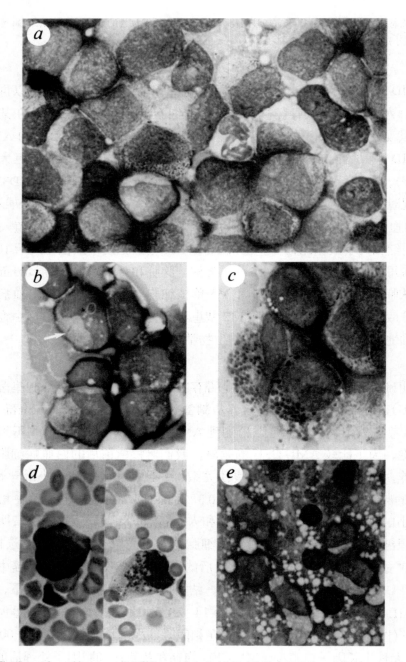

Fig. 2. Histology of cytokine-treated SCID mice injected with AML cells 3–5 weeks post-transplantation. *a*, Bone marrow touch preparation of a mouse highly infiltrated with AML Ml cells. Only one mouse neutrophil with a ring-shaped nucleus is present among the characteristic AML Ml blast cells. *b*, Mouse marrow repopulated with cells from a different AML Ml patient containing an Auer rod (arrow). *c*, Mouse marrow repopulated with cells from an AML M4 (with eosinophils and inversion of chromosome 16) patient containing characteristic eosinophils with large basophilic granules. *d*, Peripheral blood smear of a mouse repopulated with AML M4 cells. Human blast cells (left) and eosinophils (right) were present in the circulation of the mouse. *e*, Liver touch preparation of a mouse engrafted with AML M4 cells. Infiltrating leukaemic blast cells can be seen among mouse hepatocytes.

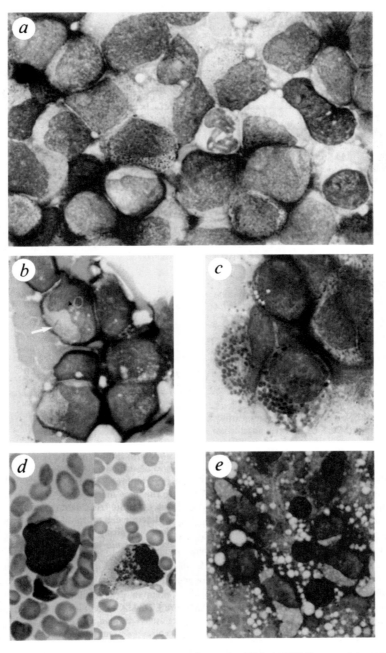

图 2. 经细胞因子处理后的 SCID 小鼠植入 AML 细胞 3~5 周后的组织学图片。*a*，受人 AML M1 细胞高度浸润的小鼠骨髓印片。在 AML M1 母细胞中只有一个小鼠中性粒细胞（环状核）。*b*，另一个 M1 型 AML 患者的细胞在小鼠骨髓中的扩散情况。箭头所指为 Auer 小体。*c*，将 M4 型 AML 患者（含有嗜酸性粒细胞，并且 16 号染色体倒置）的细胞植入小鼠，在骨髓中可以看见含有巨大的嗜碱性颗粒的嗜酸性粒细胞。*d*，植入 M4 型 AML 患者细胞的小鼠外周血涂片。在小鼠的血液循环系统中可以看见人母细胞（左）和嗜酸性粒细胞（右）。*e*，植入 M4 型 AML 患者细胞的小鼠肝脏印片。在小鼠肝细胞周围可以看见渗入的白血病母细胞。

319

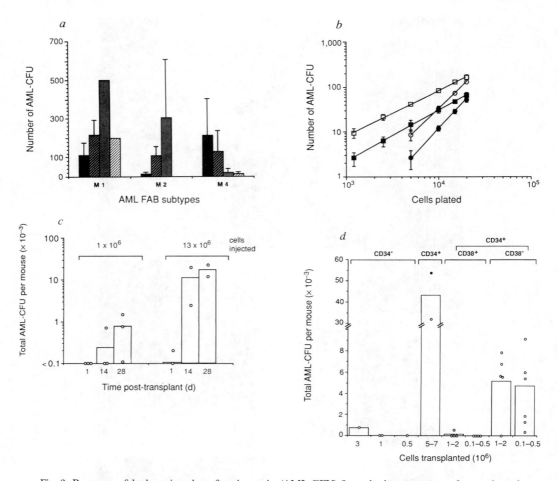

Fig. 3. Recovery of leukaemic colony-forming units (AML-CFU) from the bone marrow of transplanted SCID mice. *a*, Summary of the number of AML-CFU from the bone marrow of SCID mice transplanted with cells from AML M1, M2 or M4 patients and treated with hMGF and PIXY321 for 21 to 45 days. Each bar represents a unique donor sample showing the mean ± s.d. Error bars are shown only for groups containing 3 mice or more. The AML-CFU assay was performed in duplicate by plating 2×10^5 bone marrow cells in 0.9% methylcellulose-containing fetal bovine serum (15%), human plasma (15%), hMGF (50 ng ml^{-1}), PIXY 321 (5 ng ml^{-1}), hGM–CSF (1 U ml^{-1}), hIL-3 (10 U ml^{-1}) and human erythropoietin (2 U ml^{-1}). At day 7, leukaemic blast colonies were scored and their leukaemic identity confirmed by cytology and chromosomal analysis where applicable. No murine colonies were obtained under these selective culture conditions[8,9]. *b*, Frequency of AML-CFU before and after transplantation. Limiting dilution analysis of AML-CFU present in the PBL of an AML M1 patient before (open symbols) and after (filled symbols) transplantation. Cell numbers indicated were plated in methylcellulose culture containing either hIL-3 (1 nM) alone (circles) or in combination with hMGF (323 pM) (squares). Bone marrow from the transplanted mouse was analysed 35 days after transplantation and treatment with hMGF and PIXY321. *c*, Expansion of AML-CFU in the bone marrow of transplanted SCID mice. SCID mice were transplanted with AML M1 cells at the cell numbers indicated and killed at 1, 14 and 28 days post-transplant. The total number of AML-CFU per mouse was determined by multiplying the AML-CFU per 2×10^5 cells plated by the total number of bone marrow cells present in the mouse. The limit of detection was 100 AML-CFU per mouse. *d*, Measurement of AML-CFU from SCID mice transplanted with AML cells fractionated according to CD34 and CD38 expression. Three independent cell-sorting experiments were done on thawed cells containing 75% CD34$^+$ cells from an AML M1 patient; of these 40% were

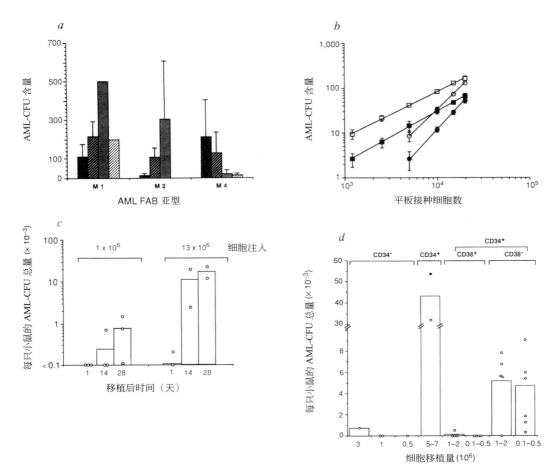

图 3. 从移植后小鼠骨髓中分离的白血病母细胞集落形成单位（AML-CFU）。a，植入 AML M1、M2 和 M4 细胞并且使用 hMGF 和 PIXY321 处理 21~45 天的小鼠骨髓中 AML-CFU 的含量。每个柱代表同一个植入样本在不同小鼠中 AML-CFU 含量的平均值 ± 标准差。只有每组小鼠数量大于等于 3 只时才计算误差。AML-CFU 测定按如下方法重复进行：将 2×10^5 个骨髓细胞接种在含有 15% 胎牛血清、15% 人血浆、50 ng·ml^{-1} 人肥大细胞生长因子、5 ng·ml^{-1} PIXY321、1 U·ml^{-1} 人粒细胞-巨噬细胞集落刺激因子、10 U·ml^{-1} 人白介素 3 和 2 U·ml^{-1} 人促红细胞生成素的 0.9% 甲基纤维素中。在第七天的时候计算白血病母细胞集落数。此时通过细胞学和染色体分析的方法可以鉴别他们的白血病特征。在这种选择培养条件下，没有出现鼠源细胞集落 [8,9]。b，在细胞植入前后，AML-CFU 出现的频率。使用有限稀释法分析 M1 型 AML 患者外周血淋巴细胞中 AML-CFU 的含量。空心符号为植入前，实心符号为植入后。圆圈表示甲基纤维素中含有人白介素 3（1 nM）的实验组，方框为同时含有人白介素 3（1 nM）和人肥大细胞生长因子（323 pM）的实验组。骨髓样品取自植入细胞 35 天后并使用人肥大细胞生长因子和 PIXY321 处理的小鼠。c，AML-CFU 在 SCID 小鼠骨髓中的扩增。向 SCID 小鼠中植入了如图所示数量的 AML M1 细胞，并分别在植入后 1 天、14 天和 28 天处死。每只小鼠的 AML-CFU 总量等于每 2×10^5 个细胞中 AML-CFU 的数量乘以小鼠中总骨髓细胞数。检测的下限是每只小鼠 100 个 AML-CFU。d，植入了不同 CD34 和 CD38 表达分型的 AML 细胞的小鼠中，AML-CFU 数量的测量。我们使用 3 个相互独立的细胞分选实验对来自 M1 型 AML 患者解冻的细胞进行检测，其中 75% 为 CD34$^+$，40% 为 CD38$^+$。分别使用荧光激活细胞分选法（FACStar^{PLUS}，BD 公司）或使用 CD34 亲和层析柱（Cell-Pro 公司，图中为

CD38+. Cells were purified by fluorescence-activated cell sorting (FACStar^{PLUS}; Becton–Dickinson) or using a CD34 affinity column (Cell-Pro) (filled circle). In the first experiment, cells were separated on the basis of CD34 expression; the CD34+ and CD34- populations were each 98% pure; in experiments 2 and 3, respectively, the CD34+/CD38- cells were 88 and 97% pure, and the CD34+/CD38+ cells were 80 and 73% pure, being contaminated with 10 or 15% CD34+/CD38- cells. The CD34+/CD38- and the CD34+/CD38+ fractions from both experiments 2 and 3 contained an average of 6,525 and 8,736 AML-CFU per 2×10^5 cells, respectively. Mice were transplanted with the indicated number of purified cells and treated with cytokines. After 45 days (experiment 1) or 30 days (experiment 2 and 3), the total number of AML-CFU was determined.

Flow-sorting was used to characterize and purify the leukaemia-initiating cells. CD34 is a cell-surface marker normally expressed on a small population of bone marrow cells, including progenitor cells and pluripotent stem cells[16]. Expression of CD38 on CD34+ cells is an important marker for lineage commitment and therefore the CD34+CD38- phenotype defines an immature human cell in normal bone marrow. Although the expression of CD34 and CD38 on AML cells is very heterogeneous[17], the CD34+CD38- phenotype is present on immature AML-CFU[18]. Peripheral blood cells from an AML M1 patient were separated into CD34-positive and -negative fractions and transplanted into SCID mice. Leukaemic cell proliferation and high levels of AML-CFU were observed in the bone marrow of mice transplanted with CD34+ cells, as in mice transplanted with unsorted populations (Fig. 3d). By contrast, four mice transplanted with CD34- cells were poorly engrafted (0–0.1%) and contained no AML-CFU, except for one mouse that had been transplanted with a high cell dose and contained only a few colonies (Fig. 3d). In two further experiments mice were transplanted with CD34+CD38- or CD34+CD38+ cells purified from the same donor. Leukaemia cell proliferation and high levels of AML-CFU were only seen in mice transplanted with CD34+CD38- cells (Fig. 3d). Interestingly, both populations contained comparably high numbers of AML-CFU before injection into SCID mice, providing evidence that at least CD34+CD38+ AML-CFU could not engraft SCID mice. CD34+CD38- cells transplanted into SCID mice did not produce any detectable normal human progenitors; all of the colony-forming cells tested (40/40) contained the same t(2;4) chromosomal translocation found in the patient's leukaemic clone.

We next investigated whether there was a linear relationship between the number of cells injected and leukaemic engraftment, in order to develop a quantitative assay for AML-initiating cells. Peripheral blood cells from AML patients were diluted in a tenfold series from 2×10^7 cells to 2×10^4 cells before transplanting into SCID mice. In a representative experiment, DNA analysis indicated that as few as 2×10^5 cells were sufficient to initiate leukaemic proliferation (Fig. 4). Statistical analysis of the proportion of mice that had leukaemic proliferation at each cell dose, using data from four different donors transplanted into 40 mice, indicated that the frequency of the leukaemia-initiating cell in the PBL of AML-M1 patients was 1 engraftment unit per 2.5×10^5 cells (range: 1 in 1.2×10^5 to 1 in 5.3×10^5); the engraftment followed single-order kinetics as measured by the χ^2 test (95% confidence limit).

实心圆）对细胞进行纯化。在第一个实验中，我们根据 CD34 的表达情况对细胞进行了分离。CD34+ 细胞和 CD34− 细胞的纯度都达到了 98%。在实验二和实验三中，CD34+/CD38− 细胞的纯度分别为 88% 和 97%，CD34+/CD38+ 细胞的纯度分别为 80% 和 73%，其中可能污染了 10% 或 15% 的 CD34+/CD38− 细胞。实验二和实验三中，每 2×10^5 个 CD34+/CD38− 细胞以及 CD34+/CD38+ 细胞中分别含有 6,525 和 8,736 个 AML-CFU。向小鼠植入图中所示数量的纯化细胞并使用细胞因子处理，并在 45 天后（实验一）或 30 天后（实验二和实验三）确定其 AML-CFU 总量。

我们使用流式分选技术对这种白血病起始细胞进行分离纯化。CD34 是一个细胞表面标记，正常情况下仅表达于小部分骨髓细胞中，包括祖细胞和多能干细胞[16]。CD34+ 细胞中 CD38 分子的表达是一个重要的细胞系定型标志。CD34+CD38− 表型是正常骨髓中未成熟细胞的标志。尽管在 AML 细胞中，CD34 和 CD38 的表达差别很大[17]，但 CD34+CD38− 却是未成熟 AML-CFU 细胞的一个特征[18]。我们将 AML M1 型白血病患者的外周血细胞分成 CD34+ 和 CD34− 两部分，并分别把它们植入 SCID 小鼠体内。结果发现，在那些植入 CD34+ 细胞和未分选细胞的小鼠骨髓中，可观察到白血病细胞的增殖和高水平的 AML-CFU（图 3d）。相反，四只植入 CD34− 细胞的 SCID 小鼠中植入成功率很低（0~0.1%），并且不含有 AML-CFU 细胞（除一只植入大剂量细胞且含有少量集落的小鼠外）（图 3d）。在两个后续实验中，我们将来自同一供体纯化的 CD34+CD38− 或 CD34+CD38+ 细胞移植到小鼠体内。结果显示，只有在植入 CD34+CD38− 细胞的小鼠体内能够看到白血病细胞的增殖和高水平的 AML-CFU（图 3d）。有趣的是，这两群细胞在植入 SCID 小鼠之前都包含同等高水平的 AML-CFU。这证明至少 CD34+CD38+ 的 AML-CFU 细胞不能植入 SCID 小鼠。那些 CD34+CD38− 细胞在植入 SCID 小鼠后不能产生可检测的正常人祖细胞，在检测的 40 个集落形成细胞中都含有与患者白血病细胞中一样的染色体易位 t(2; 4)。

接下来，我们研究了接种细胞数与白血病植入数之间是否存在线型关系，以便建立一个 AML 起始细胞的定量分析模型。在向 SCID 小鼠植入细胞前，我们将 AML 患者的外周血细胞进行了 10 倍梯度稀释，从 2×10^7 一直稀释到 2×10^4。在一个代表性实验中，DNA 分析结果显示，最少 2×10^5 个细胞就足以引起白血病细胞的增殖（图 4）。我们利用四个不同患者的细胞植入 40 只小鼠后的数据，针对不同细胞接种剂量中出现白血病细胞增殖的小鼠比例进行了统计学分析，结果发现 AML-M1 患者的外周血中，白血病起始细胞的频率为每 2.5×10^5 个细胞中 1 个植入单位，这一细胞数的波动范围为 1.2×10^5~5.3×10^5。使用卡方检验（χ^2，95% 置信限）发现白血病小鼠的移植变化趋势呈一级动力学曲线。

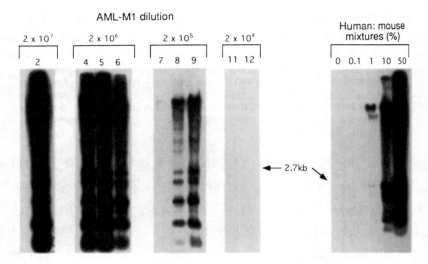

Fig. 4. Determination of the frequency of the SCID leukaemia-initiating cell (SL-IC) engraftment unit by limiting dilution analysis. PBL cells from an AML M1 patient were thawed and different cell doses (2×10^4, 2×10^5, 2×10^6 and 2×10^7 cells) were transplanted into groups of 3 or 4 mice. Mice were treated with hMGF and PIXY321 for 1 month, after which DNA from the bone marrow was analysed for human cells as described for Fig. 1. The Southern blot is representative of four experiments with four different donors. SCID mice containing > 5% leukaemic cells in the bone marrow were considered positive for the statistical analysis used to determine the frequency of SL-IC by the method of Porter and Barry[24]. The negative mice contained from 0.1% to undetectable human cells. Ethidium bromide staining indicated that equal amounts of DNA were loaded in each gel lane.

We have identified an AML-initiating cell on the basis of its ability to establish human leukaemia in SCID mice (the SCID leukaemia-initiating cell, or SL-IC). Three pieces of evidence suggest that there may be a hierarchy of leukaemic stem cells in human AML, where SL-IC are more immature than AML-CFU. First, the frequency of SL-IC in the PBL of AML M1 patients is at least 1,000-fold lower than the frequency of AML-CFU. Second, only mice transplanted with CD34$^+$CD38$^-$ cells developed leukaemia whereas CD34$^+$CD38$^+$ mice did not, despite the fact that similar numbers of AML-CFU were present in both populations before transplantation. Third, based on the low proliferative capacity of AML-CFU in liquid or long-term cultures[4,19,20] even with maximal growth-factor stimulation, it is likely that their large expansion in SCID mice for > 45 days post-transplantation is due to the proliferation and differentiation of SL-IC. In future, autologous transplantation with purged cells may address the relationship between SL-IC and the leukaemic stem cell that maintains the disease in patients. But the fact that SL-IC shares a CD34$^+$CD38$^-$ expression pattern similar to normal stem cells indicates that purging strategies may be difficult to develop. It will also be possible to create complementary DNA libraries[21] from single cells to characterize genes that are expressed in SL-IC and compare them with those from normal stem cells and the more differentiated AML-CFU. Finally, a SCID-leukaemia model that reproduces many features of human AML should help us to understand the processes governing the transformation and progression of leukaemic stem cells and to test new therapeutic strategies.

(**367**, 645-648; 1994)

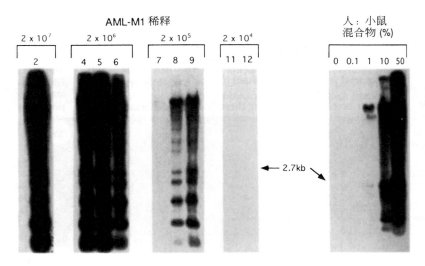

图 4. 利用有限稀释法计算 SCID 白血病起始细胞（SL-IC）扩散的频率。将解冻后不同细胞剂量的 M1 型 AML 患者的外周血淋巴细胞（2×10^4、2×10^5、2×10^6 和 2×10^7）分别植入各组小鼠中（每组含 3 或 4 只 小鼠），使用人肥大细胞生长因子和 PIXY321 处理一个月，然后从小鼠骨髓中提取 DNA 并采用图 1 中 提及的方法计算人细胞的含量。图中所示的是四个不同供体的 DNA 印迹结果。采用波特和巴里的方 法 [24] 确定 SL-IC 的频率时，从统计学分析来讲骨髓中白血病细胞含量超过 5% 即视为阳性。而人细 胞含量在 0.1% 以下或无法检测则视为阴性。使用溴化乙锭染色可以看到每个孔中总 DNA 的上样量 是一致的。

通过衡量细胞在 SCID 小鼠中引发人白血病的能力，我们鉴定了一类 AML 起 始细胞（称为 SCID 白血病起始细胞或 SL-IC）。有三方面的证据表明在人 AML 中 可能存在白血病干细胞群体，并且在这个群体中 SL-IC 比 AML-CFU 分化程度更 低。第一，在 AML M1 型患者的外周血中 AML-CFU 的频率至少是 SL-IC 的 1,000 倍。第二，虽然在移植前 CD34$^+$CD38$^+$ 和 CD34$^+$CD38$^-$ 两种细胞中都含有大致相等 的 AML-CFU，但是只有 CD34$^+$CD38$^-$ 细胞可以在 SCID 小鼠中引发白血病。第三， 即使使用最大剂量的生长因子刺激，AML-CFU 在液体或长期培养中的增殖能力都 很低 [4,19,20]。在植入细胞超过 45 天后，SCID 小鼠中 AML-CFU 的大幅扩增看起来 更像是由于 SL-IC 细胞的增殖和分化。在将来，使用净化的细胞进行自体移植实验 或许可以揭示 SL-IC 和维持病人生病状态的白血病干细胞之间的关系。不过，由于 SL-IC 和大多数干细胞一样也是 CD34$^+$CD38$^-$ 型的，这使得将其与干细胞区分开来 变得很困难。人们有可能通过从单个细胞中建立 cDNA 文库 [21] 的方法来比较 SL-IC 与正常干细胞和 AML-CFU 中基因表达的差异。最后，这样一个再现了许多人 AML 特点的 SCID 白血病小鼠模型对于我们理解白血病干细胞分化的过程和试验新的治 疗方案具有很大的帮助。

（张锦彬 翻译；秦志海 审稿）

325

Tsvee Lapidot, Christian Sirard, Josef Vormoor, Barbara Murdoch, Trang Hoang[*], Julio Caceres-Cortes[*], Mark Minden[†], Bruce Paterson[‡], Michael A. Caligiuri[§] & John E. Dick[‖]

Department of Genetics, Research Institute, Hospital for Sick Children and Department of Molecular and Medical Genetics, University of Toronto, 555 University Avenue, Toronto, Ontario M5G 1X8, Canada

[*] Clinical Research Institute, Montreal, Quebec H2W 1R7, Canada

[†] Department of Medicine and [‡] Department of Oncologic Pathology, Princess Margaret Hospital, Toronto, Ontario M4X 1K9, Canada

[§] Department of Medicine, Roswell Park Cancer Institute, Buffalo, New York 14263-0001, USA

Received 30 September; accepted 29 November 1993.

References:

1. Sawyers, C., Denny, C. & Witte, O. *Cell* 64, 337-350 (1991).

2. Fearon, E., Burke, P., Schiffer, C., Zehnbauer, B. & Vogelstein, B. *New Engl. J. Med.* 315, 15-24 (1986).

3. Keinänen, M., Griffin, J., Bloomfield, C., Machnicki, J. & de la Chapelle, A. *New Engl. J. Med.* 318,1153-1158 (1988).

4. Griffin, J. & Löwenberg, B. *Blood* 68, 1185-1195 (1986).

5. Grier, H. & Civin, C. in *Hematology of Infancy and Childhood* (eds Nathan, D. G. & Oski, F. A.) 1288-1318 (Saunders, Philadelphia, 1993).

6. McCulloch, E., Izaguirre, C., Chang, L. & Smith, L. *J. Cell. Physiol. Suppl.* 1,103-111 (1982).

7. Löwenberg, B. & Touw, I. *Blood* 81, 281-292 (1993).

8. Kamel-Reid, S. & Dick, J. E. *Science* 242, 1706-1709 (1988).

9. Lapidot, T. *et al. Science* 255, 1137-1141 (1992).

10. Kamel-Reid, S. *et al. Science* 246, 1597-1600 (1991).

11. Kamel-Reid, S. *et al. Blood* 78, 2973-2981 (1991).

12. Dick, J., Lapidot, T. & Pflumio, F. *Immun. Rev.* 124, 25-43 (1991).

13. Cesano, A. *et al. Oncogene* 7, 827-836 (1992).

14. Sawyers, C., Gishizky, M., Quan, S. Golde. D. & Witte, O. *Blood* 79, 2089-2098 (1992).

15. De Lord, C. *et al. Expl Hemat.* 19, 991-993 (1991).

16. Civin, C. *et al. J. Immun.* 133, 157-165 (1984).

17. Terstappen, L. *et al. Leukemia* 6, 993-1000 (1992).

18. Terstappen, L., Huang, S., Safford, M., Lansdorp, P. & Loken, M. *Blood* 77, 1218-1227 (1991).

19. Coulombel, L., Eaves, C., Kalousek, D., Gupta, C. & Eaves, A. *J. Clin. Invest.* 75, 961-969 (1985).

20. Schiró, R. *et al. Blut* 61, 267-270 (1990).

21. Brady, G., Barbara, M. & Iscove, N. *Meth. Molec. Cell. Biol.* 2, 17-25 (1990).

22. Bennett, J. *et al. Br. J. Haemat.* 33, 451-458 (1976).

23. Waye, S. & Willard, H. *Molec. Cell. Biol.* 6, 3156-3165 (1986).

24. Porter, E. & Berry, R. *Brit. J. Cancer* 17, 583-595 (1964).

Acknowledgments. We thank F. Pflumio, R. A. Phillips, A. Bernstein, N. Iscove and M. Buchwald for reviewing the manuscript; D. Williams (Immunex) for growth factors; and P. Laraya, D. Brown and L. Harton for assistance. Supported by grants from the MRC of Canada, the National Cancer Institute of Canada (NCIC), with funds from the Canadian Cancer Society, the NIH (M.A.C.), Coleman Leukemia Research Fund (M.A.C.), a studentship award (Hospital for Sick Children) (C.S.), postdoctoral fellowships from the NCIC (T.L.) and the Deutsche Forschungsgemeinschaft (J.V.), and a Research Scientist award from the NCIC (J.E.D.). T.L. and C.S. contributed equally to this work.

2.2 Mb of Contiguous Nucleotide Sequence from Chromosome III of *C. elegans*

R. Wilson *et al.*

Editor's Note

The collaborative effort to sequence the genome of the nematode worm *Caenorhabditis elegans* having been underway for three years, British biologist John Sulston and colleagues provide a progress update. Nearly 2.2 million base pairs out of the total 100 million base pairs had been sequenced, confirming the previously reported high gene density and yielding several intriguing features. Putative gene duplications and other repeats raised potential evolutionary implications, and the complete *C. elegans* gene catalogue was already valuable to those using the model organism to study development, behaviour and gene function. The project also suggested that megabase-scale DNA sequencing at a reasonable cost was possible. An essentially complete version of the genome was published, on schedule, in 1998.

As part of our effort to sequence the 100-megabase (Mb) genome of the nematode *Caenorhabditis elegans*, we have completed the nucleotide sequence of a contiguous 2,181,032 base pairs in the central gene cluster of chromosome III. Analysis of the finished sequence has indicated an average density of about one gene per five kilobases; comparison with the public sequence databases reveals similarities to previously known genes for about one gene in three. In addition, the genomic sequence contains several intriguing features, including putative gene duplications and a variety of other repeats with potential evolutionary implications.

THE free-living nematode *Caenorhabditis elegans* is an excellent model organism for the study of development and behaviour, and its small size and short life cycle greatly facilitate genetic analysis[1,2]. Because a nearly complete clonal physical reconstruction of the genome is available[3-5], and 1,200 genetic loci have been identified, the nematode is also a good candidate for complete DNA sequence analysis. The haploid genome of *C. elegans* contains approximately 100 Mb (megabases) distributed on six chromosomes[2]. Many of the genes required for normal development and behaviour in the nematode have extensive similarity to their mammalian counterparts. However, compared with mammalian genes, genes in *C. elegans* typically have smaller and fewer introns[2,6], thus simplifying the identification of previously uncharacterized genes. Many of these newly identified genes may in turn be used to probe for as-yet unidentified mammalian genes.

As previously reported[6], we have embarked on a collaborative project to sequence the

秀丽隐杆线虫 3 号染色体上的 2.2 Mb 连续核苷酸序列

威尔逊等

编者按

秀丽隐杆线虫基因组序列的测定工作已经进行了三年，英国生物学家约翰·萨尔斯顿和他的同事们不断更新进展。一亿个碱基对中有近 220 万碱基对已完成测序，证实了前期关于其高基因密度的报道并且发现了几个非常有趣的特征。推断的基因重复和其他序列重提高了其潜在的进化意义，并且完整的秀丽隐杆线虫基因目录对于用模式生物研究发育、行为和基因功能发挥了重要作用。这个项目也表明以合理的花费进行兆碱基规模 DNA 测序是可行的。一个基本完整的基因组在 1998 年如期发表。

对线虫纲秀丽隐杆线虫 100 兆碱基（Mb）的基因组进行测序是我们研究的一部分，我们已经完成了秀丽隐杆线虫 3 号染色体的重要基因簇上连续 2,181,032 个碱基对的测序。对完成测序的序列的分析表明基因的平均密度为每五千个碱基含一个基因；与公开序列数据库的比较显示，这与已知基因的密度（每三千个碱基含一个基因）相似。此外，基因组序列包含几个有趣的特征，包括具有潜在进化意义的推断的基因重复和各种其他重复。

自由生活的线虫纲秀丽隐杆线虫是研究发育和行为极好的模式生物。它个体小，生命周期短，大大方便了遗传分析 [1,2]。因为基因组克隆序列重建几乎已经完成 [3-5]，并已鉴定了 1,200 个遗传基因座，所以线虫也是很好的分析完整 DNA 序列的候选者。秀丽隐杆线虫单倍体基因组约为 100 Mb，分布在六条染色体上 [2]。线虫正常发育和行为所必需的许多基因与哺乳动物对应基因有广泛的相似性。然而，与哺乳动物基因相比，秀丽隐杆线虫基因的内含子较小且较少 [2,6]，因此简化了之前未知基因的鉴定。许多新鉴定的基因反过来可作为探针寻找目前还未鉴定的哺乳动物基因。

正如以前报道的那样 [6]，我们早就着手秀丽隐杆线虫全基因组测序的合作项目。

entire genome of *C. elegans*. Here we report some of the results from the first three years of the pilot phase, a point at which each laboratory has completed one contiguous megabase of genomic sequence. The combined data represent a sequence spanning more than 2.1 Mb. Most of the sequence derives from cosmid clones that were mapped to chromosome III by restriction fingerprinting[3]. At this physical map location, there are two large cosmid contigs, each more than 1 Mb long and bridged by a yeast artificial chromosome (YAC) clone. A small cosmid contig of 92 kilobases (kb) lies near the centre of the YAC bridge. Our genomic sequence analysis of this large region of chromosome III has confirmed the high gene density that we found in the first three sequenced cosmids[6], and has resulted in the identification of many more genes and other interesting sequence features.

Sequencing Strategy

At the start of the pilot phase, we experimented with a primer-directed or "walking" strategy in which site-specific oligonucleotide primers were used to extend sequences sequentially from a limited number of starting points[7]. This was initially done using cosmid DNA as template for the sequencing reactions. However, because cosmid DNA proved difficult to purify in sufficient quantities and was troublesome because of the presence of repeated sequences, we used random phagemid and Ml3 subclones as templates for the walking strategy[8,9]. During this work, we found that a combination of small insert (1–2 kb) and large insert (6–9 kb) subclones provided representative coverage for a typical cosmid. Even with subclones, primer-directed sequencing was occasionally problematic because of the presence of repeated sequences. Thus, our strategy has evolved to the point where most sequence data come from the initial readings of 600–800 random subclones. As the use of automated fluorescent DNA sequencing machines for data collection provides high-throughput sample processing[10,11], this approach is efficient and cost-effective. This random or "shotgun" phase not only provides much of the final sequence, but also maps the subclones needed for closing gaps and completing the complementary strand. At this point, a walking strategy can be successfully exploited for completion, as most repeated sequences in the cosmid insert can be identified and selectively avoided. Many of the details of our sequencing strategy have been reported elsewhere[6,12-23].

Sequences were considered to be finished when every base had been determined on both strands and all ambiguities had been resolved. At this point, the finished sequence was compared with the public sequence databases using the BLASTX program for protein similarities and BLASTN for nucleotide similarities[24]. When similarity searches were complete, likely genes were identified using GENEFINDER (P.G. and L.H., unpublished), and in some cases interactively edited using ACEDB (R.D. and J.T.-M., unpublished). Finished sequences were annotated with regard to likely genes, homologies, *trans*-spliced leaders[26], complementary DNA matches[27,28] and other features, such as structural RNA genes and transposons, and submitted to the GenBank and EMBL databases. Also, to present genomic sequence data in the context of the physical and genetic maps of the nematode, all sequences are deposited in the *C. elegans* database ACEDB, which is available to the research community.

在这里，我们公布试验期第一个三年的一些结果，至此各个实验室已经完成了连续的一兆碱基的基因组序列。汇总的数据代表了长度大于 2.1 Mb 的序列。大部分序列来自利用限制性指纹识别的定位于 3 号染色体上的黏粒克隆 [3]。在这个物理图谱上有两个大的黏粒重叠群，每个长度都大于 1 Mb，并由一个酵母人工染色体（YAC）克隆连接。有一个 92 kb 的小黏粒重叠群邻近 YAC 桥中心。对 3 号染色体上这个大区域的基因组序列的分析证实了我们在前三个完成测序的黏粒中发现的高基因密度 [6]，并鉴定了更多基因和其他有趣的序列特征。

测 序 策 略

试验阶段开始时，我们使用引物引导或"步移"策略，用位置特异的寡核苷酸引物从有限的起始点顺序扩展序列 [7]。最初用黏粒 DNA 做模板进行测序反应。然而，因为黏粒 DNA 很难纯化到足够的量，并且由于存在重复序列而非常棘手，所以我们用随机噬菌粒和 M13 亚克隆做模板进行步移 [8,9]。在此工作期间，我们发现一个小插入（1~2 kb）亚克隆和大插入（6~9 kb）亚克隆的组合代表性地覆盖了一个典型的黏粒。因为重复序列的存在，即使采用亚克隆，引物引导的测序偶尔也会出现问题。因此，我们的策略已经发展到从最初解读的 600~800 个随机亚克隆中获得多数序列数据的程度。由于使用自动荧光 DNA 测序仪收集数据可以高通量地处理样品 [10,11]，所以这个方法经济有效。这个随机或"鸟枪"时期不仅提供了大量最终的序列，也为封闭缺口和完成互补链所需的亚克隆进行了作图。至此，步移策略得以成功运用，黏粒插入的大多数重复序列可被鉴定和选择性避免。我们测序策略的很多细节也已在别处报道过 [6,12-23]。

当两条链上的所有碱基都已确定，所有不明确都已解决时就认为序列已经完成。这时，用 BLASTX 软件比较最终序列与公开序列数据库的蛋白相似性，用 BLASTN 比较核酸相似性 [24]。完成相似性查找后，用 GENEFINDER（格林和希利尔，未发表）鉴定可能的基因，有些情况下交互使用 ACEDB（德宾和蒂埃里－米格，未发表）进行编辑。对最终序列上的可能基因、同源物、反式剪接前导序列 [26]、互补 DNA 匹配物 [27,28] 和其他特征（如结构 RNA 基因和转座子）进行注释，并提交到 GenBank 和 EMBL 数据库。而且，将基因组序列数据绘制到线虫基因组物理和遗传图谱中，所有数据都放入线虫数据库 ACEDB 中，这些数据可供研究团体使用。

Sequences

Table 1 gives the cosmid clones that were sequenced, along with their database accession numbers and lengths. Most of the redundant overlapping data have been omitted from the database entries, although neighbouring sequences typically contain a small number of overlapping bases to facilitate joining or to keep a gene intact. The total non-overlapping sequence assembled from all of the clones in Table 1 spans 2.181 Mb. A map of this region showing the sites of predicted genes and previously known loci is presented in Fig. 1. Several additional cosmids which extend the sequence more than 2,000 kb to the left and 500 kb to the right are in various stages of completion.

Table 1. Sequences submitted to the GenBank and EMBL databases

Cosmid name	Locus name	Acc. no.	Length (bp)	Cosmid name	Locus name	Acc. no.	Length (bp)
ZK112	CELZK112	L14324	38,269	K02D10	CELK02D10	L14710	18,683
ZC97	CELZC97	L14714	4,166	F54F2	CELF54F2	L23645	39,573
ZK686	CELZK686	L17337	11,435	F44E2	CELF44E2	L23646	33,651
C08C3	CELC08C3	L15201	44,025	pAR3	CELPAR3	U00026	4,590
C27D11	CELC27D11	L23650	9,973	K01F9	CEK01F9	Z22175	19,834
ZK652	CELZK652	L14429	36,052	ZK637	CE1	Z11115	40,699
C02C2	CELC02C2	L23649	20,495	ZK638	CEZK638	Z12018	1,762
ZK688	CELZK688	L16621	36,977	ZK643	CEZK643	Z11126	39,534
C29E4	CELC29E4	L23651	40,050	R08D7	CER08D7	Z12017	27,368
F54H12	CELF54H12	L25599	19,168	F59B2	CEF59B2	Z11505	43,782
C06G4	CELC06G4	L25598	29,122	R107	CER107	Z14092	40,970
F44B9	CELF44B9	L23648	36,327	F02A9	CEF02A9	Z19555	26,242
K12H4	CELK12H4	L14331	38,582	ZK507	CEZK507	Z29116	13,501
K06H7	CELK06H7	L15314	22,073	ZK512	CEZK512	Z22177	36,997
C14B9	CELC14B9	L15188	43,492	F54G8	CEF54G8	Z19155	31,613
D2007	CELD2007	L16560	13,651	ZC84	CEZC84	Z19157	38,955
C50C3	CELC50C3	L14433	44,733	T23G5	CET23G5	Z19158	26,926
C30A5	CELC30A5	L10990	27,743	T02C1	CET02C1	Z19156	10,308
C02F5	CELC02F5	L14745	22,333	M01A8	CEM01A8	Z27081	19,001
F09G8	CELF09G8	L11247	41,449	K01B6	CEK01B6	Z22174	34,002
F10E9	CELF10E9	L10986	32,733	C40H1	CEC40H1	Z19154	27,271
ZC262	CELZC262	L23647	4,166	K04H4	CEK04H4	Z27078	33,930
R05D3	CELR05D3	L07144	38,810	C38C10	CEC38C10	Z19153	34,193
ZK353	CELZK353	L15313	24,916	T26G10	CET26G10	Z29115	30,251
ZK1236	CELZK1236	L13200	28,878	F54C8	CEF54C8	Z22178	23,000

序 列

表 1 给出已经测序的黏粒克隆及它们的数据库编号和长度。虽然相邻序列间经常包含促进连接处结合或保持基因完整的少量重叠碱基，但大部分冗余重叠数据已从数据库条目中去除。从表 1 的所有克隆中收集的非重叠序列横跨 2.181 Mb。图 1 是显示这个区域预测基因位置和已知基因座的图。使序列向左延伸 2,000 kb、向右延伸 500 kb 的多个黏粒处在测序的不同阶段。

表 1. 提交到 GenBank 和 EMBL 数据库的序列

黏粒名称	基因座名称	编号	长度 (bp)	黏粒名称	基因座名称	编号	长度 (bp)
ZK112	CELZK112	L14324	38,269	K02D10	CELK02D10	L14710	18,683
ZC97	CELZC97	L14714	4,166	F54F2	CELF54F2	L23645	39,573
ZK686	CELZK686	L17337	11,435	F44E2	CELF44E2	L23646	33,651
C08C3	CELC08C3	L15201	44,025	pAR3	CELPAR3	U00026	4,590
C27D11	CELC27D11	L23650	9,973	K01F9	CEK01F9	Z22175	19,834
ZK652	CELZK652	L14429	36,052	ZK637	CE1	Z11115	40,699
C02C2	CELC02C2	L23649	20,495	ZK638	CEZK638	Z12018	1,762
ZK688	CELZK688	L16621	36,977	ZK643	CEZK643	Z11126	39,534
C29E4	CELC29E4	L23651	40,050	R08D7	CER08D7	Z12017	27,368
F54H12	CELF54H12	L25599	19,168	F59B2	CEF59B2	Z11505	43,782
C06G4	CELC06G4	L25598	29,122	R107	CER107	Z14092	40,970
F44B9	CELF44B9	L23648	36,327	F02A9	CEF02A9	Z19555	26,242
K12H4	CELK12H4	L14331	38,582	ZK507	CEZK507	Z29116	13,501
K06H7	CELK06H7	L15314	22,073	ZK512	CEZK512	Z22177	36,997
C14B9	CELC14B9	L15188	43,492	F54G8	CEF54G8	Z19155	31,613
D2007	CELD2007	L16560	13,651	ZC84	CEZC84	Z19157	38,955
C50C3	CELC50C3	L14433	44,733	T23G5	CET23G5	Z19158	26,926
C30A5	CELC30A5	L10990	27,743	T02C1	CET02C1	Z19156	10,308
C02F5	CELC02F5	L14745	22,333	M01A8	CEM01A8	Z27081	19,001
F09G8	CELF09G8	L11247	41,449	K01B6	CEK01B6	Z22174	34,002
F10E9	CELF10E9	L10986	32,733	C40H1	CEC40H1	Z19154	27,271
ZC262	CELZC262	L23647	4,166	K04H4	CEK04H4	Z27078	33,930
R05D3	CELR05D3	L07144	38,810	C38C10	CEC38C10	Z19153	34,193
ZK353	CELZK353	L15313	24,916	T26G10	CET26G10	Z29115	30,251
ZK1236	CELZK1236	L13200	28,878	F54C8	CEF54C8	Z22178	23,000

Continued

Cosmid name	Locus name	Acc. no.	Length (bp)	Cosmid name	Locus name	Acc. no.	Length (bp)
C30C11	CELC30C11	L09634	30,865	B0464	CEB0464	Z19152	40,090
F42H10	CELF42H10	L08403	28,687	F55H2	CEF55H2	Z27080	22,950
C04D8	CELC04D8	L16687	10,433	ZK1098	CEZK1098	Z22176	37,310
ZC21	CELZC21	L16685	36,087	C48B4	CEC48B4	Z29117	35,000
K10C7 (C02D5)	CELC02D5	L16622	28,735	F58A4	CEF58A4	Z22179	38,000
C06E1/F43A9	CELC06E1	L16560	40,216	C15H7	CEC15H7	Z22173	28,000
C13G5	CELC13G5	L14730	10,883	C07A9/C40D10	CEC07A9	Z29094	66,004
F22B7	CELF22B7	L12018	40,222	T05G5	CET05G5	Z27079	36,180
B0523	CELB0523	L07143	14,334	R10E11	CER10E11	Z29095	32,254
B0303	CELB0303	M77697	41,071	ZK632	CEZK632	Z22181	36,000
ZK370	CELZK370	M98552	37,675	K11H3	CEK11H3	Z22180	33,000
pAR2	CELPAR2	U00025	12,721	ZK757	CEZK757	Z29121	31,000

The most striking result from genomic DNA sequencing is the continued high number of predicted genes in the region. In the 2.181 Mb of genomic sequence reported here, 483 putative genes were identified by similarity searches and GENEFINDER analysis. Start points for these candidate genes are indicated for both strands of the genomic sequence in Fig. 1. Generally, genes seem to be dispersed evenly throughout the region, with only a few examples of apparent clustering. One of the most gene-dense regions is contained in cosmids C30A5, C02F5 and F09G8 (Fig. 1, 492–553 kb). Here a 61-kb region contains 141 exons (in 24 putative genes), which account for 47% of the sequence. When the introns are also considered, more than 80% of the bases in this region are within predicted genes. Also in a 69.5-kb stretch of genomic DNA (F55H2, ZK1098; Fig. 1, 1,770–1,840 kb), 109 exons (in 19 putative genes) are predicted, with 40% of this region representing coding sequence and a total of 65% contained in genes. The longest stretch of genomic sequence that does not contain a likely gene is ~25 kb (pAR3, K01F9; Fig. 1, 1,145–1,170 kb). By comparison, the entire 2.181-Mb region is 29% coding sequence, with a total of 48% representing putative exons and introns. In our analysis of the first 0.1% of the genome, genes were found every 3–4 kb on average[6]. With more than 2% of the genomic DNA sequence now completed, the density is one gene every 4.5 kb. Because the region is expected to be relatively gene-rich[2], we cannot use this density to extrapolate the total gene number. However, an estimate independent of gene density can be made using the number of tagged cDNAs which hit candidate genes in the sequence[27]. Because 125 of the 4,615 *C. elegans* cDNA tags match predicted genes in the sequence, we can now estimate that the genome contains about 17,800 genes (483 × 4615 / 125) for an average density of one gene every 5.6 kb.

There are no clear examples of genes that overlap, either on the same or on complementary strands. Several cases of orphan open reading frames that have high GENEFINDER scores and that overlap or are contained within candidate genes were observed, although

黏粒名称	基因座名称	编号	长度(bp)	黏粒名称	基因座名称	编号	长度(bp)
C30C11	CELC30C11	L09634	30,865	B0464	CEB0464	Z19152	40,090
F42H10	CELF42H10	L08403	28,687	F55H2	CEF55H2	Z27080	22,950
C04D8	CELC04D8	L16687	10,433	ZK1098	CEZK1098	Z22176	37,310
ZC21	CELZC21	L16685	36,087	C48B4	CEC48B4	Z29117	35,000
K10C7 (C02D5)	CELC02D5	L16622	28,735	F58A4	CEF58A4	Z22179	38,000
C06E1/F43A9	CELC06E1	L16560	40,216	C15H7	CEC15H7	Z22173	28,000
C13G5	CELC13G5	L14730	10,883	C07A9/C40D10	CEC07A9	Z29094	66,004
F22B7	CELF22B7	L12018	40,222	T05G5	CET05G5	Z27079	36,180
B0523	CELB0523	L07143	14,334	R10E11	CER10E11	Z29095	32,254
B0303	CELB0303	M77697	41,071	ZK632	CEZK632	Z22181	36,000
ZK370	CELZK370	M98552	37,675	K11H3	CEK11H3	Z22180	33,000
pAR2	CELPAR2	U00025	12,721	ZK757	CEZK757	Z29121	31,000

　　基因组 DNA 测序最引人注目的结果是这个区域内有连续的大量预测基因。这里报道的 2.181 Mb 基因组序列中，通过相似性查找和 GENEFINDER 分析鉴定了 483 个假定基因。图 1 表明了这些候选基因在基因组序列两条链中的起始点。总体上，基因好像均匀地分散在整个区域，只有少数出现明显的簇集。基因密度最大的一个区域包含在黏粒 C30A5、C02F5 和 F09G8 中（图 1，492~553 kb）。有一个 61 kb 的区域包含 141 个外显子（在 24 个假定基因中），占这个序列的 47%。当考虑内含子时，这个区域 80% 以上的碱基都在预测基因上。在一段 69.5 kb 的基因组 DNA 内（F55H2、ZK1098；图 1，1,770~1,840 kb），预测了 109 个外显子（在 19 个假定基因中），这个区域 40% 的序列代表编码序列，总共 65% 包含在基因中。不包含可能基因的最长基因组序列片段约为 25 kb（pAR3、K01F9；图 1，1,145~1,170 kb）。经过比较，整个 2.181 Mb 区域中 29% 是编码序列，48% 代表预测的外显子和内含子。在我们分析的前 0.1% 基因组中，平均每 3~4 kb 发现一个基因[6]。现在完成了多于 2% 的基因组 DNA 序列测序，基因的密度为每 4.5 kb 含一个基因。因为预测这个区域相对富含基因[2]，所以我们不能用这个密度推断总的基因数目。然而，可以不依赖基因密度而是用击中序列中候选基因的标记 cDNA 数目估算总的基因数目[27]。因为 4,615 个秀丽隐杆线虫 cDNA 标记中有 125 个与这段序列中的预测基因匹配，所以我们估算整个基因组包含 17,800 个基因（483 × 4615/125），平均 5.6 kb 含一个基因。

　　在相同或互补链上都没有基因重叠的明显例子。我们观察到几个有高 GENEFINDER 值的单独开放阅读框，它们重叠或包含在候选基因中，但没有数据表

there are no data to indicate that any of these is expressed. When the translated sequence is used in all six reading frames to search the public databases using the program BLAST, approximately one-third of the genes find significant matches to proteins from organisms other than *C. elegans,* with several very highly conserved genes indicated (Table 2). As can be seen in Table 2, a wide variety of different functions are represented, and with the exception of a homeobox cluster (see below), there is no obvious clustering of genes with related function. Most of the matches represent cross-phylum matches, for very little sequence from other nematodes is present in the databases. The fraction of genes with cross-phylum matches will increase as more genes from other organisms are entered into the database, but our previous analysis of these ancient conserved regions indicates that it is unlikely to rise above 40%, as most ancient conserved regions are already represented in the databases[29]. Although the data are inconclusive, preliminary evidence suggests that the fraction of matches to vertebrate proteins will be similar to this for any non-vertebrate genome.

Table 2. Gene candidates showing significant similarity to existing protein sequences

Gene name	Closest DB hit, Acc. no.	Closest block	Description
ZK112.2	TVMSBF, A40951	—	Kinase-related transforming protein
ZK112.7	A41087	BL00232	Tumour suppressor
ZK686.2	DB73_DROME, P26802	BL00039	ATP-dependent RNA helicase
ZK686.8	A24148	—	*N*-acetyllactosamine synthetase
C08C3.1	HM11_CAEEL, P17486	BL00027	*C. elegans* Hox protein egl-5 (ceh-11) gene
C08C3.3	HMMA_CAEEL, P10038	BL00027	*C. elegans* Hox protein mab-5
ZK652.4	R5RT35, A34571	BL00579	60S ribosomal protein L35
ZK652.5	A34218	BL00027	Distal-less homeotic protein
ZK652.6	S29962	—	ref (2) P protein, Zn-finger region
ZK652.8	C35815	—	Myosin heavy chain-3
C02C2.1	TYRO_STRGA, P06845	BL00497	Tyrosinase
C02C2.3	ACHG_RAT, P18916	BL00236	Acetylcholine receptor
C02C2.4	S27951	—	Sodium/phosphate transport protein
ZK688.8	A24148	—	*N*-acetyllactosamine synthase
C29E4.3	RNA1_YEAST, P11745	—	RNA production/processing
C29E4.7	S16267	—	Auxin-induced protein
C29E4.8	JS0422, JS0422	BL00113	Adenylate kinase
F54H12.1	ACON_YEAST, P19414	BL00450	Aconitate hydratase
F54H12.6	EF1B_BOMMO, P29522	—	Elongation factor 1β
C06G4.2	CAP3_RAT, P16259	—	Calpain
C06G4.5	SSR3_MOUSE, P30935	BL00237	Somatostatin receptor
F44B9.1	ACPH_RAT, P13676	BL00708	Acylamino-acid-releasing enzyme

明它们表达。用所有六个阅读框的翻译序列通过 BLAST 程序搜索公开数据库，发现约三分之一的基因与秀丽隐杆线虫以外的生物蛋白显著匹配，并发现了几个保守性很高的基因（表 2）。如表 2 中看到的，预测基因代表了种类广泛的不同的功能，并且除了同源框基因簇以外（见下文）没有相关功能基因的明显集合。因为只有很少其他线虫序列出现在数据库中，所以大多数匹配代表跨门匹配。随着其他生物的更多基因录入到数据库中，跨门匹配的基因比例会增加，但我们以前对这些古老保守区域的分析表明基因跨门匹配的比例不可能上升到 40% 以上，因为大多数古老的保守区域已经存在于数据库中了[29]。虽然数据还不确定，但初步证据表明对于任何非脊椎动物而言，与脊椎动物蛋白匹配的比例都是相近的。

表 2. 候选基因与已有蛋白序列间有明显的相似性

基因名称	最接近的数据库检索编号	最接近的序列块	描述
ZK112.2	TVMSBF, A40951	—	激酶相关转化蛋白
ZK112.7	A41087	BL00232	肿瘤抑制蛋白
ZK686.2	DB73_DROME, P26802	BL00039	依赖 ATP 的 RNA 解旋酶
ZK686.8	A24148	—	N–乙酰氨基乳糖合成酶
C08C3.1	HM11_CAEEL, P17486	BL00027	秀丽隐杆线虫同源框蛋白 egl-5 (ceh-11) 基因
C08C3.3	HMMA_CAEEL, P10038	BL00027	秀丽隐杆线虫同源框蛋白 mab-5
ZK652.4	R5RT35, A34571	BL00579	60S 核糖体蛋白 L35
ZK652.5	A34218	BL00027	Distal-less 同源异型蛋白
ZK652.6	S29962	—	参考文献 (2)P 蛋白，锌指域
ZK652.8	C35815	—	肌球蛋白重链 3
C02C2.1	TYRO_STRGA, P06845	BL00497	酪氨酸酶
C02C2.3	ACHG_RAT, P18916	BL00236	乙酰胆碱受体
C02C2.4	S27951	—	钠 / 磷酸盐转运蛋白
ZK688.8	A24148	—	N–乙酰氨基乳糖合成酶
C29E4.3	RNA1_YEAST, P11745	—	RNA 产物 / 加工
C29E4.7	S16267	—	植物生长素诱导蛋白
C29E4.8	JS0422,JS0422	BL00113	腺苷酸激酶
F54H12.1	ACON_YEAST, P19414	BL00450	乌头酸水合酶
F54H12.6	EF1B_BOMMO, P29522	—	延伸因子 1β
C06G4.2	CAP3_RAT, P16259	—	钙蛋白酶
C06G4.5	SSR3_MOUSE, P30935	BL00237	生长抑素受体
F44B9.1	ACPH_RAT, P13676	BL00708	酰基氨基酸释放酶

Continued

Gene name	Closest DB hit, Acc. no.	Closest block	Description
F44B9.8	A45253	—	Replication factor C
F44B9.9	PARB12, S11060	BL00125	Protein phosphatase
K12H4.1	JQ1397	—	*Drosophila melanogaster* Prospero
K12H4.4	SPC2_CHICK, P28687	—	Signal peptidase
K12H4.8	DEAD_ECOLI, P23304	BL00039	ATP-dependent RNA helicase dead
K06H7.1	S22127	BL00107	Protein kinase
K06H7.3	IPPI_YEAST, P15496	—	Isopentenyl-diphosphate δ-isomerase
K06H7.4	S24168	—	Sec7
K06H7.8	YCK1_YEAST, P23291	—	Casein kinase I
C14B9.1	CRAB_HUMAN, P02511	—	α-B-crystallin
C14B9.2	ER72_MOUSE, P08003	BL00194	Deoxycytidine kinase
C14B9.4	S22127, S22127	BL00098	Protein kinase
C14B9.7	R5RT21, A33295	—	Ribosomal protein L21
C14B9.8	S24109	—	Phosphorylase kinase
D2007.5	KERB_AVIER, P00535	—	ERB-B tyrosine kinase
C50C3.3	SPCN_CHICK, P07751	BL00545	Spectrin α-chain
C50C3.5	TPC1_BALNU, P21797	BL00018	Calmodulin
C50C3.7	OCRL_HUMAN, Q01986	—	Inositol polyphosphate-5-phosphatase
C50C3.11	JH0565	—	Calcium channel α-2b chain
C30A5.1	GRR1_YEAST, P24814	—	GRR1 protein (same as C02F5.7)
C30A5.3	S30854	BL00125	Phosphoprotein phosphatase
C30A5.4	SYB_DROME, P18489	BL00417	Synaptobrevin
C30A5.6	UN86_CAEEL, P13528	BL00035	Unc-86 alternate protein
C30A5.7	UN86_CAEEL, P13528	BL00035	Unc-86 protein
C02F5.3	JC1349	—	GTP-binding protein
C02F5.7	GRR1_YEAST, P24814	—	Glucose-induced repressor (GRR1)
C02F5.9	PRC5_HUMAN,P20618	BL00631	Proteasome component C5
F09G8.3	RS9_BACST, P07842	BL00360	Ribosomal protein S9
F09G8.6	A37122	—	Cuticle collagen
ZC262.3	A43425	—	N-CAM Ig domain
ZC262.5	ATPE_ BOVIN, P05632	—	ATP synthase ε-chain
R05D3.1	TOPB_HUMAN, Q02880	BL00177	DNA topoisomerase II homologue
R05D3.3	ZG44_XENLA, P18721	—	Gastrula zinc-finger protein
R05D3.6	ATPE_BOVIN, P05632	—	ATP synthase ε-chain
R05D3.7	KINH_LOLPE, P21613	BL00411	Kinesin heavy chain
ZK353.6	AMPA_RICPR, P27888	BL00631	Aminopeptidase

续表

基因名称	最接近的数据库检索编号	最接近的序列块	描述
F44B9.8	A45253	—	复制因子 C
F44B9.9	PARB12, S11060	BL00125	蛋白磷酸酶
K12H4.1	JQ1397	—	黑腹果蝇 Prospero 蛋白
K12H4.4	SPC2_CHICK, P28687	—	信号肽酶
K12H4.8	DEAD_ECOLI, P23304	BL00039	依赖 ATP 的 RNA 解旋酶 dead
K06H7.1	S22127	BL00107	蛋白激酶
K06H7.3	lPPl_YEAST, P15496	—	异戊烯二磷酸 δ 异构酶
K06H7.4	S24168	—	Sec7
K06H7.8	YCK1_YEAST, P23291	—	酪蛋白激酶 I
C14B9.1	CRAB_HUMAN, P02511	—	α-B 晶体蛋白
C14B9.2	ER72_MOUSE, P08003	BL00194	脱氧胞苷激酶
C14B9.4	S22127, S22127	BL00098	蛋白激酶
C14B9.7	R5RT21, A33295	—	核糖体蛋白 L21
C14B9.8	S24109	—	磷酸化酶激酶
D2007.5	KERB_AVIER, P00535	—	ERB-B 酪氨酸激酶
C50C3.3	SPCN_CHICK, P07751	BL00545	血影蛋白 α 链
C50C3.5	TPC1_BALNU, P21797	BL00018	钙调蛋白
C50C3.7	OCRL_HUMAN, Q01986	—	肌醇多磷酸 −5− 磷酸酶
C50C3.11	JH0565	—	钙通道 α-2b 链
C30A5.1	GRR1_YEAST, P24814	—	GRR1 蛋白（同 C02F5.7）
C30A5.3	S30854	BL00125	磷蛋白磷酸酶
C30A5.4	SYB_DROME, P18489	BL00417	小突触小泡蛋白
C30A5.6	UN86_CAEEL, P13528	BL00035	Unc-86 替代蛋白
C30A5.7	UN86_CAEEL, P13528	BL00035	Unc-86 蛋白
C02F5.3	JC1349	—	GTP 结合蛋白
C02F5.7	GRR1_YEAST, P24814	—	葡萄糖诱导的阻遏物（GRR1）
C02F5.9	PRC5_HUMAN,P20618	BL00631	蛋白酶体组分 C5
F09G8.3	RS9_BACST, P07842	BL00360	核糖体蛋白 S9
F09G8.6	A37122	—	表皮胶原蛋白
ZC262.3	A43425	—	N-CAM Ig 结构域
ZC262.5	ATPE_BOVIN, P05632	—	ATP 合酶 ε 链
R05D3.1	TOPB_HUMAN, Q02880	BL00177	DNA 拓扑异构酶 II 同源物
R05D3.3	ZG44_XENLA, P18721	—	原肠胚锌指蛋白
R05D3.6	ATPE_BOVIN, P05632	—	ATP 合酶 ε 链
R05D3.7	KINH_LOLPE, P21613	BL00411	驱动蛋白重链
ZK353.6	AMPA_RICPR, P27888	BL00631	氨肽酶

Continued

Gene name	Closest DB hit, Acc. no.	Closest block	Description
ZK1236.1	LEPA_ECOLI, P07682	BL00301	LepA
ZK1236.2	NUCL_RAT, P13383	—	Nucleolin
C30C11.2	DXA2_MOUSE, P14685	—	Diphenol oxidase
C30C11.4	S30788	BL00297	HSP Msi3p
F42H10.4	GYRTI, A03270	—	Cysteine-rich intestinal protein
C04D8.1	SPCB_DROME, Q00963	—	Spectrin β-chain
ZC21.2	JH0588	—	Trp protein
ZC21.3	S14548	—	Dual bar protein
ZC21.4	S29956	—	Breakpoint cluster region (Bcr) protein
C02D5.1	ACDL_RAT, P15650	BL00072	Acyl-CoA dehydrogenase
C06E1.10	S22609, S22609	BL00690	Hypothetical protein
C06E1.4	B40171	—	Glutamate receptor
C06E1.8	B60191	—	Zn-finger
C06E1.9	A31922	—	ATP-dependent RNA helicase
C13G5.1	F34510	BL00027	Engrailed homeotic protein
F22B7.4	S18345	—	Environmental stress protein
F22B7.5	DNAJ_ECOLI, P08622	BL00636	DnaJ
F22B7.6	MUCB_ECOLI, P07375	—	Mucb protein
F22B7.7	S09048	—	Potassium channel protein Hak-6
B0523.1	S00904	BL00239	Tyrosine kinase
B0523.5	GELS_MOUSE, P13020	—	Gelsolin (flightless-1)
B0303.1	CYYA_YEAST, P08678	—	Adenylate cyclase
B0303.2	PNMT_BOVIN, P10938	—	Phenylethanolamine-*N*-methyltransferase
B0303.3	THIL_RAT, P17764	BL00098	Acetyl-CoA acetyltransferase
B0303.5	YT31_CAEEL, P03934	—	Tc3
B0303.7	NCF2_HUMAN, P19878	—	SH3 domain
B0303.9	SLP1_YEAST, P20795	—	SLP-1
ZK370.3	TALI_MOUSE, P26039	—	Talin
ZK370.4	KAPR_DICDI, P05987	—	Cyclic AMP-dependent protein kinase
ZK370.5	BCKD_RAT, Q00972	—	3-Methyl-2-oxobutanoate dehydrogenase
K02D10.1	S16088, S16088	—	4-Nitrophenylphosphatase
K02D10.5	S07258, S07258	—	*Escherichia coli* plasmid *RK2* gene for P116
F54F2.1	ITAP_DROME, P12080	BL00242	Vitronectin receptor α-subunit
F54F2.2	A44067	—	109K basic protein H
F44E2.1	S08405	—	Protease
F44E2.3	S28589	—	DnaJ

续表

基因名称	最接近的数据库检索编号	最接近的序列块	描述
ZK1236.1	LEPA_ECOLI, P07682	BL00301	LepA
ZK1236.2	NUCL_RAT, P13383	—	核仁蛋白
C30C11.2	DXA2_MOUSE, P14685	—	二酚氧化酶
C30C11.4	S30788	BL00297	HSP Msi3p
F42H10.4	GYRTI, A03270	—	富半胱氨酸肠蛋白
C04D8.1	SPCB_DROME, Q00963	—	血影蛋白 β 链
ZC21.2	JH0588	—	Trp 蛋白
ZC21.3	S14548	—	双杆蛋白
ZC21.4	S29956	—	裂点簇区（Bcr）蛋白
C02D5.1	ACDL_RAT, P15650	BL00072	脂酰辅酶 A 脱氢酶
C06E1.10	S22609, S22609	BL00690	假定蛋白
C06E1.4	B40171	—	谷氨酸受体
C06E1.8	B60191	—	锌指
C06E1.9	A31922	—	依赖 ATP 的 RNA 解旋酶
C13G5.1	F34510	BL00027	Engrailed 同源异型蛋白
F22B7.4	S18345	—	环境应激蛋白
F22B7.5	DNAJ_ECOLI, P08622	BL00636	DnaJ
F22B7.6	MUCB_ECOLI, P07375	—	Mucb 蛋白
F22B7.7	S09048	—	钾通道蛋白 Hak-6
B0523.1	S00904	BL00239	酪氨酸激酶
B0523.5	GELS_MOUSE, P13020	—	凝溶胶蛋白（flightless-1）
B0303.1	CYYA_YEAST, P08678	—	腺苷酸环化酶
B0303.2	PNMT_BOVIN, P10938	—	苯基乙醇胺 –N– 甲基转移酶
B0303.3	THIL_RAT, P17764	BL00098	乙酰辅酶 A 乙酰转移酶
B0303.5	YT31_CAEEL, P03934	—	Tc3
B0303.7	NCF2_HUMAN, P19878	—	SH3 结构域
B0303.9	SLP1_YEAST, P20795	—	SLP-1
ZK370.3	TALI_MOUSE, P26039	—	踝蛋白
ZK370.4	KAPR_DICDI, P05987	—	依赖 cAMP 的蛋白激酶
ZK370.5	BCKD_RAT, Q00972	—	3– 甲基 –2– 氧桥丁酸脱氢酶
K02D10.1	S16088, S16088	—	4– 硝基苯磷酸酶
K02D10.5	S07258, S07258	—	P116 的大肠杆菌质粒 RK2 基因
F54F2.1	ITAP_DROME, P12080	BL00242	玻连蛋白受体 α 亚基
F54F2.2	A44067	—	109K 碱性蛋白质 H
F44E2.1	S08405	—	蛋白酶
F44E2.3	S28589	—	DnaJ

Continued

Gene name	Closest DB hit, Acc. no.	Closest block	Description
F44E2.4	S03430	–	LDL receptor
F44E2.6	PILB_NEIGO, P14930	–	PILB protein
F44E2.7	CALD_CHICK, P12957	–	Caldesmon
ZK637.1	STP1_ARATH, P23586	–	Sugar transporter
ZK637.10	GSHR_HUMAN, P00390	BL00076	Glutathione reductase
ZK637.11	CC25_SCHPO, P06652	–	CDC25
ZK637.13	GLBH_TRICO, P27613	–	Globin
ZK637.14	PICO_HSV11, P08393	BL00518	Transactivator ICPO (motif 1)
ZK637.5	ARSA_ECOLI, P08690	–	ArsA
ZK637.8	VPP1_RAT, P25286	–	Proton pump
ZK643.2	DCTD_BPT2, P00814	–	DCMP deaminase
ZK643.3	CALR_PIG, P25117	BL00649	G-protein-coupled receptor
R08D7.5	CATR_CHLRE, P05434	BL00018	Calcium-binding protein
R08D7.6	CNAG_BOVIN, P14099	BL00126	Cyclic GMP phosphodiesterase
F59B2.3	NAGA_ECOLI, P15300	–	*N*-acetyl-glucosamine-6-phosphate deacetylase
F59B2.7	RAB6_HUMAN, P20340	–	Rab6 (Ras protein)
R107.7	GTP_CAEEL, P10299	–	Glutathione S-transferase P subunit
LIN12A.cds	LI12_CAEEL, P14585	BL00022	Lin-12/Notch, EGF and ankyrin repeats
F02A9.5	PCCB_RAT, P07633	–	Propionyl-CoA carboxylase
GLP1A.cds	GLP1_CAEEL, P13508	BL00022	Lin-12/Notch, EGF and ankyrin repeats
ZK507.1	HR25_YEAST, P29295	BL00107	HRR25 protein kinase
ZK507.6	CG2A_PATVU, P24861	BL00292	G2/M cyclin A
ZK512.2	SPB4_YEAST, P25808	BL00039	RNA helicase
ZK512.4	SRP9_CANFA, P21262	–	Signal recognition particle 9K protein
F54G8.2	KDGL_PIG, P20192	BL00479	Diacylglycerol kinase
F54G8.3	ITA3_CRISP, P17852	BL00242	Integrin α-chain
F54G8.4	KRET_HUMAN, P07949	BL00518	Ret zinc-finger region
ZC84.1	LACI_RABIT, P19761	BL00280	Serine protease inhibitor
ZC84.2	CNGC_RAT, Q00195	–	Cyclic nucleotide gated olfactory channel
ZC84.4	GASR_RAT, P30553	BL00237	G-protein-coupled receptor
T23G5.1	RIR1_HUMAN, P23921	BL0089	Ribonucleoside-disphosphate reductase Ig chain
T23G5.2	SC14_KLULA, P24859	–	SEC14 (yeast)
T23G5.5	NTTN_HUMAN, P23975	BL00610	Neurotransmitter transporter
T02C1.1	RA18_YEAST, P10862	BL00518	RAD-18 DNA-binding protein
M01A8.4	BIK1_YEAST, P11709	–	Nuclear fusion protein
C40H1.1	S24577	–	Ovarian protein (*D. melanogaster*)

基因名称	最接近的数据库检索编号	最接近的序列块	描述
F44E2.4	S03430	—	LDL 受体
F44E2.6	PILB_NEIGO, P14930	—	PILB 蛋白
F44E2.7	CALD_CHICK, P12957	—	钙调蛋白结合蛋白
ZK637.1	STP1_ARATH, P23586	—	糖转运蛋白
ZK637.10	GSHR_HUMAN, P00390	BL00076	谷胱甘肽还原酶
ZK637.11	CC25_SCHPO, P06652	—	CDC25
ZK637.13	GLBH_TRICO, P27613	—	珠蛋白
ZK637.14	PICO_HSV11, P08393	BL00518	反式激活蛋白 ICPO(motif 1)
ZK637.5	ARSA_ECOLI, P08690	—	ArsA
ZK637.8	VPP1_RAT, P25286	—	质子泵
ZK643.2	DCTD_BPT2, P00814	—	DCMP 脱氨酶
ZK643.3	CALR_PIG, P25117	BL00649	G 蛋白偶联受体
R08D7.5	CATR_CHLRE, P05434	BL00018	钙结合蛋白
R08D7.6	CNAG_BOVIN, P14099	BL00126	cGMP 磷酸二酯酶
F59B2.3	NAGA_ECOLI, P15300	—	$N-$乙酰葡糖胺$-6-$磷酸脱乙酰酶
F59B2.7	RAB6_HUMAN, P20340	—	Rab6(Ras 蛋白)
R107.7	GTP_CAEEL, P10299	—	谷胱甘肽 S-转移酶 P 亚基
LIN12A.cds	LI12_CAEEL, P14585	BL00022	Lin-12/Notch,EGF 和锚蛋白重复序列
F02A9.5	PCCB_RAT, P07633	—	丙酰辅酶 A 羧化酶
GLPlA.cds	GLP1_CAEEL, P13508	BL00022	Lin-12/Notch,EGF 和锚蛋白重复序列
ZK507.1	HR25_YEAST, P29295	BL00107	HRR25 蛋白激酶
ZK507.6	CG2A_PATVU, P24861	BL00292	G2/M 细胞周期蛋白 A
ZK512.2	SPB4_YEAST, P25808	BL00039	RNA 解旋酶
ZK512.4	SRP9_CANFA, P21262	—	信号识别颗粒 9K 蛋白
F54G8.2	KDGL_PIG, P20192	BL00479	二酰甘油激酶
F54G8.3	ITA3_CRISP, P17852	BL00242	整联蛋白 α 链
F54G8.4	KRET_HUMAN, P07949	BL00518	Ret 锌指区
ZC84.1	LACI_RABIT, P19761	BL00280	丝氨酸蛋白酶抑制蛋白
ZC84.2	CNGC_RAT, Q00195	—	环核苷酸控制的嗅觉通道
ZC84.4	GASR_RAT, P30553	BL00237	G 蛋白偶联受体
T23G5.1	RIR1_HUMAN, P23921	BL0089	核苷二磷酸还原酶 Ig 链
T23G5.2	SC14_KLULA, P24859	—	SEC14(酵母)
T23G5.5	NTTN_HUMAN, P23975	BL00610	神经递质转运体
T02C1.1	RA18_YEAST, P10862	BL00518	RAD-18 DNA 结合蛋白
M01A8.4	BIK1_YEAST, P11709	—	核融合蛋白
C40H1.1	S24577	—	卵巢蛋白(黑腹果蝇)

Continued

Gene name	Closest DB hit, Acc. no.	Closest block	Description
C40H1.4	YCS4_YEAST, P25358	BL00030	Yeast hypothetical protein
K04H4.1	CA14_CAEEL, P17139	—	Collagen
C38C10.1	NK3R_RAT, P16177	BL00237	G-protein-coupled receptor
C38C10.5	RGR1_YEAST, P19263	—	Glucose repression regulatory protein RGR1
T26G10.1	DEAD_ECOLI, P23304	BL00039	RNA helicase
T26G10.3	RS24_HUMAN, P16632	BL00529	Ribosomal protein S24
F54C8.1	HCDH_PIG, P00348	BL00067	3-hydroxyacyl-CoA dehydrogenase
F54C8.2	H31_SCHPO, P09988	BL00322	Histone H3
F54C8.4	Y19K_NPVAC, P24656	—	ACMNPV hypothetical protein
F54C8.5	RAS_LENED, P28775	—	Ras family
B0464.1	SYD2_HUMAN, P14868	BL00179	Aspartyl--tRNA synthetase
B0464.5	KCLK_MOUSE, P22518	BL00107	Serine/threonine kinase
F55H2.1	SODC_BOVIN, P00442	BL00087	Superoxide dismutase
F55H2.2	MTPG_SULAC, P22721	—	Membrane-associated ATPase γ-chain
F55H2.5	C561_BOVIN, P10897	—	Cytochrome b$_{561}$
ZK1098.10	TPMX_RAT, P18342	—	Coiled-coil protein
ZK1098.4	GCN3_YEAST, P14741	—	GCN3 (yeast transcription activator)
C48B4.1	CA01_RAT, P07872	BL00072	Acyl-CoA oxidase I
C48B4.2	RHOM_DROME, P20350	—	Rhomboid (*D. melanogaster*)
C48B4.4	NODI_RHILO, P23703	BL00211	ATP-binding transport protein
C48B4.5	LIVG_SALTY, P30293	BL00211	ATP-binding transport protein
F58A4.10	UBC7_WHEAT, P25868	BL00183	Ubiquitin-conjugating enzyme
F58A4.3	H3_VOLCA, P08437	BL00322	Histone H3
F58A4.4	PRI1_MOUSE, P20664	—	DNA primase 49K subunit
F58A4.5	RTJK_DROME, P21328	—	Mobile element Jockey-rev. transcriptase
F58A4.7	A36394	BL00038	Transcription factor AP-4
F58A4.8	TBG_XENLA, P23330	BL00227	γ-Tubulin
F58A4.9	RPC9_YEAST, P28000	—	RNA Pol I/Ⅲ 16K polypeptide
C15H7.2	KFPS_DROME, P18106	BL00790	Tyrosine kinase
C15H7.3	TCPT_HUMAN, P17706	—	Protein tyrosine phosphatase
C07A9.2	G10_XENLA, P12805	—	G10 protein
C07A9.3	KRAC_HUMAN, P31749	BL00107	Ser/Thr kinase
C07A9.4	S20969	BL00470	Na/Ca, K antiporter
C07A9.5	SPCA_DROME, P13395	BL00018	Spectrin α-chain
C07A9.6	UDP2_RAT, P09875	BL00375	UDP-glucuronosyltransferase
T05G5.3	CC2_HUMAN, P06493	BL00107	CDC2 kinase

基因名称	最接近的数据库检索编号	最接近的序列块	描述
C40H1.4	YCS4_YEAST, P25358	BL00030	酵母假定蛋白
K04H4.1	CA14_CAEEL, P17139	—	胶原蛋白
C38C10.1	NK3R_RAT, P16177	BL00237	G 蛋白偶联受体
C38C10.5	RGR1_YEAST, P19263	—	葡糖阻遏调节蛋白 RGR1
T26G10.1	DEAD_ECOLI, P23304	BL00039	RNA 解旋酶
T26G10.3	RS24_HUMAN, P16632	BL00529	核糖体蛋白 S24
F54C8.1	HCDH_PIG, P00348	BL00067	3−羟脂酰辅酶 A 脱氢酶
F54C8.2	H31_SCHPO, P09988	BL00322	组蛋白 H3
F54C8.4	Y19K_NPVAC, P24656	—	ACMNPV 假定蛋白
F54C8.5	RAS_LENED, P28775	—	Ras 家族
B0464.1	SYD2_HUMAN, P14868	BL00179	天冬氨酰 tRNA 合成酶
B0464.5	KCLK_MOUSE, P22518	BL00107	丝氨酸／苏氨酸激酶
F55H2.1	SODC_BOVIN, P00442	BL00087	超氧化物歧化酶
F55H2.2	MTPG_SULAC, P22721	—	膜结合 ATP 酶 γ 链
F55H2.5	C561_BOVIN, P10897	—	细胞色素 b_{561}
ZK1098.10	TPMX_RAT, P18342	—	卷曲螺旋蛋白质
ZK1098.4	GCN3_YEAST, P14741	—	GCN3（酵母转录激活因子）
C48B4.1	CA01_RAT, P07872	BL00072	脂酰辅酶 A 氧化酶 I
C48B4.2	RHOM_DROME, P20350	—	Rhombiod（黑腹果蝇）
C48B4.4	NODI_RHILO, P23703	BL00211	ATP 结合转运蛋白
C48B4.5	LIVG_SALTY, P30293	BL00211	ATP 结合转运蛋白
F58A4.10	UBC7_WHEAT, P25868	BL00183	泛素缀合酶
F58A4.3	H3_VOLCA, P08437	BL00322	组蛋白 H3
F58A4.4	PRI1_MOUSE, P20664	—	DNA 引发酶 49K 亚基
F58A4.5	RTJK_DROME, P21328	—	可动元件 Jockey-rev. 转录酶
F58A4.7	A36394	BL00038	转录因子 AP-4
F58A4.8	TBG_XENLA, P23330	BL00227	γ 微管蛋白
F58A4.9	RPC9_YEAST, P28000	—	RNA 聚合酶 I/III 16K 多肽
C15H7.2	KFPS_DROME, P18106	BL00790	酪氨酸激酶
C15H7.3	TCPT_HUMAN, P17706	—	蛋白酪氨酸磷酸酶
C07A9.2	G10_XENLA, P12805	—	G10 蛋白
C07A9.3	KRAC_HUMAN, P31749	BL00107	丝氨酸／苏氨酸激酶
C07A9.4	S20969	BL00470	Na/Ca, K 反向转运体
C07A9.5	SPCA_DROME, P13395	BL00018	血影蛋白 α 链
C07A9.6	UDP2_RAT, P09875	BL00375	UDP 葡糖醛酸转移酶
T05G5.3	CC2_HUMAN, P06493	BL00107	CDC2 激酶

Continued

Gene name	Closest DB hit, Acc. no.	Closest block	Description
T05G5.5	S27735	—	Hypothetical protein A (*Thermus aquaticus*)
T05G5.6	ECHM_RAT, P14604	BL00166	Enoyl-CoA hydratase
T05G5.10	IF5A_HUMAN, P10159	—	Initiation factor 5A
R10E11.1	FSH_DROME, P13709	BL00633	Bromodomain
R10E11.2	VATL_DROME, P23380	BL00605	Vacuolar ATP synthase subunit
R10E11.3	UBP2_YEAST, Q01476	—	Ubiquitin-specific processing protease
R10E11.4	NALS_MOUSE, P15535	—	Galactosyltransferase
ZK632.1	MCM3_YEAST, P24279	—	Mcm 2/3
ZK632.3	S26727	—	Hypothetical protein 186 (*Thermoplasma acidophilum*)
ZK632.4	MANA_ECOLI, P00946	—	Mannose 6-phosphate isomerase
ZK632.6	CALX_HUMAN, P27824	BL00803	Calnexin
ZK632.8	ARF2_YEAST, P19146	—	ADP-ribosylation factor
K11H3.1	GPDA_DROVI, P07735	—	Glycerol-3-phosphate dehydrogenase
K11H3.3	UCP_HUMAN, P25874	BL00215	Mitochondrial carrier family
ZK757.2	TPCL_HUMAN, P28562	—	Protein tyrosine phosphatase

Known Genes

Several interesting genes had been positioned in this region before our sequence analysis. The first 120 kb of the sequence reported here is part of the HOM homeobox gene complex which extends an additional 150 kb to the left[30-33]. The region is centred around the *Antennapedia*-like gene *mab-5*, which is responsible for pattern formation in a posterior body region[31]. GENEFINDER predicted a gene candidate with sequence identity to the *mab-5* cDNA sequence (GenBank M22751) on the complementary strand of the cosmid clone C08C3 (annotated as C08C3.3). Approximately 30 kb to the right of *mab-5*, the *abdominal-B*-like gene *egl-5(ceh-11)*[31,32], which is required for normal development of several cell types in the tail region, was located (C08C3.1). Interestingly, the *mab-5* and *egl-5* genes are encoded in opposite orientation. A third homeobox gene, *ceh-23*, lies 23 kb to the right of *egl-5* (ZK652.5). The *ceh-23* gene, which is similar to the *Drosophila* genes *Distal-less* and *empty spiracles*, was located by identity to a cDNA clone[32]. Two additional homeobox genes, *lin-39(ceh-15)* and *ceh-13*, lie approximately 200 kb to the left of *mab-5*. Preliminary sequence data indicate that the order of these two genes relative to *mab-5* is *lin-39*, *ceh-13*, and not *ceh-13*, *lin-39* as originally reported[32,33]. An unrelated gene, *egl-45*, with no similarity to any known *Drosophila* genes, maps between the *egl-5* and *ceh-23* genes (tentatively correlated to gene candidate *C27D11.1*), and several other putative genes are contained within the HOM region.

Other genes previously mapped to the region were correlated to distinct loci (shown in

346

基因名称	最接近的数据库检索编号	最接近的序列块	描述
T05G5.5	S27735	—	假定蛋白 A(栖热水生菌)
T05G5.6	ECHM_RAT, P14604	BL00166	烯酰辅酶 A 水合酶
T05G5.10	IF5_HAUMAN, P10159	—	起始因子 5A
R10E11.1	FSH_DROME, P13709	BL00633	布罗莫结构域
R10E11.2	VATL_DROME, P23380	BL00605	液泡 ATP 合酶亚基
R10E11.3	UBP2_YEAST, Q01476	—	泛素特异性加工蛋白酶
R10E11.4	NALS_MOUSE, P15535	—	半乳糖基转移酶
ZK632.1	MCM3_YEAST, P24279	—	Mcm2/3
ZK632.3	S26727	—	假定蛋白 186 (嗜酸热原体)
ZK632.4	MANA_ECOLI, P00946	—	甘露糖 6- 磷酸异构酶
ZK632.6	CALX_HUMAN, P27824	BL00803	钙连蛋白
ZK632.8	ARF2_YEAST, P19146	—	ADP 核糖基化因子
K11H3.1	GPDA_DROVI, P07735	—	甘油 -3- 磷酸脱氢酶
K11H3.3	UCP_HUMAN, P25874	BL00215	线粒体载体家族
ZK757.2	TPCL_HUMAN, P28562	—	蛋白酪氨酸磷酸酶

已 知 基 因

在我们进行序列分析前，已经有几个有趣的基因定位在这个区域了。这里报道的第一个 120 kb 序列是 HOM 同源框基因复合体的一部分，HOM 同源框基因复合体额外往左延伸 150 kb[30-33]。这个区域以 *Antennapedia* 类似基因 *mab-5* 附近为中心，*mab-5* 控制身体后部区域模式的形成 [31]。GENEFINDER 在黏粒克隆 C08C3（注释为 C08C3.3）的互补链上预测到一个与 *mab-5* cDNA 序列（GenBank M22751）具有序列一致性的候选基因。*abdominal-B* 类似基因 *egl-5* (*ceh-11*)[31,32] 定位于 *mab-5* 右侧约 30 kb 处（C08C3.1），它是尾部几个细胞类型正常发育所必需的。有趣的是，*mab-5* 和 *egl-5* 两个基因的编码方向相反。第三个同源框基因 *ceh-23* 基因，位于 *egl-5* (ZK652.5) 右侧 23 kb 处。*ceh-23* 基因与果蝇基因 *Distal-less* 和 *empty spiracles* 相似，通过一致性定位到一个 cDNA 克隆上 [32]。另外两个同源框基因，*lin-39* (*ceh-15*) 和 *ceh-13* 大约定位于 *mab-5* 左侧 200 kb 处。初始序列数据表明这两个基因相对 *mab-5* 的顺序依次是 *lin-39*、*ceh-13*，而不是最初报道的 *ceh-13*、*lin-39*[32,33]。一个与任何已知果蝇基因都无相似性的无关基因——*egl-45*，定位在 *egl-5* 和 *ceh-23* 基因（暂时与候选基因 *C27D11.1* 相关）之间，HOM 区域还包含其他几个假定基因。

通过基因组 DNA 测序，我们将之前定位在这个区域的其他基因与特定的基因

parentheses) by genomic DNA sequencing. These include *egl-45* (tentatively C27D11.1), *lin-36* (F44B9.6), *unc-36* (C50C3.1l), *unc-86* (C30A5.7), *mig-10* (tentatively F10E9.6), *unc-116* (R05D3.7), *ceh-16* (C13G5.1), *dpy-19* (F22B7.10), *sup-5* (B0523.5), *unc-32* (ZK637.10), *lin-9* (ZK637.7), *gst-1* (R107.7), *lin-12* (LIN12A in cosmid R107), *glp-1* (GLP1A in cosmid F02A9), *emb-9* (K04H4.1), *tbg-1* (F58A4.8) and *ncc-1* (T05G5.3). The *unc-86* and *emb-9* genes and part of the *ceh-16* gene has been sequenced previously[34-36]. In the cases of *egl-45* (M. Basson and H. R. Horvitz, personal communication), *lin-36* (J. Thomas and H. R. Horvitz, personal communication), *unc-36* (L. Loebel and H. R. Horvitz, personal communication), *unc-116* (ref. 37), *lin-9* (G. Beitel and H. R. Horvitz, personal communication), *gst-1* (ref. 38), *lin-12* (ref. 39) and *glp-1* (ref. 40), cDNA sequences provided by researchers within the *C. elegans* community enabled gene assignments to be made. For *tbg-1* and *ncc-1*, cDNAs from the consortium tag-sequencing project[27] allowed assignment to genomic loci. For *mig-10*, *dpy-19* and *unc-32*, transgenic rescue experiments with mutant phenotypes localized the genes to a particular restriction fragment (J. Manser; S. Colloms; D. Thierry-Mieg, personal communications). In some cases, availability of the genomic sequence facilitated this type of analysis.

A few kilobases of genomic DNA sequence which included *sup-5* had been reported previously[41]. However, additional genomic sequencing revealed that the *sup-5* locus, a gene for transfer RNA^{Trp}, lies within an intron in the same transcriptional orientation as a homologue of *Drosophila melanogaster flightless I* (ref. 42) (B0303.1). As the *sup-5* mutation has been shown to suppress specific alleles of many unrelated genes[43], it is known to be a functional tRNA gene. Further, the *C. elegans fl I* homologue is expressed and spliced as predicted (ref. 42, and R. Wilson, unpublished data).

tRNA Genes

The haploid genome of *C. elegans* has been estimated to contain about 300 tRNA genes[44]. Thus, we would expect to find an average of three tRNA genes per megabase of genomic sequence. However, using tRNAscan[45], in the 2.181 Mb of the sequence reported here, at least 14 tRNA genes were identified. These are indicated in Fig. 1. Strikingly, two cosmid clones, C14B9 and F22B7, contain seven of these tRNA genes. Like the *sup-5* tRNA gene, a $tRNA^{Ser}$ and two $tRNA^{Phe}$ genes lie within introns of likely genes.

Repeats

Several types of repeated sequence are present in the 2.181-Mb region. Figure 1 indicates the locations of the larger and more complex repeats. Detailed analysis of three major types of repeated sequences (inverted, tandem and interspersed) reveals several interesting features.

Inverted repeats, in which a segment of genomic sequence lies within a few to several

座（括号中显示）一一对应。这些基因包括 *egl-45*（暂定 C27D11.1）、*lin-36*（F44B9.6）、*unc-36*（C50C3.11）、*unc-86*（C30A5.7）、*mig-10*（暂定 F10E9.6）、*unc-116*（R05D3.7）、*ceh-16*（C13G5.1）、*dpy-19*（F22B7.10）、*sup-5*（B0523.5）、*unc-32*（ZK637.10）、*lin-9*（ZK637.7）、*gst-1*（R107.7）、*lin-12*（黏粒 R107 中的 LIN12A）、*glp-1*（黏粒 F02A9 中的 GLP1A）、*emb-9*（K04H4.1）、*tbg-1*（F58A4.8） 和 *ncc-1*（T05G5.3）。*unc-86* 和 *emb-9* 基因及部分 *ceh-16* 基因以前已测过序[34-36]。秀丽隐杆线虫群落的研究者提供 cDNA 序列帮助我们确定基因 *egl-45*（巴松和霍维茨，个人交流）、*lin-36*（托马斯和霍维茨，个人交流）、*unc-36*（勒贝尔和霍维茨，个人交流）、*unc-116*（参考文献 37）、*lin-9*（比特尔和霍维茨，个人交流）、*gst-1*（参考文献 38）、*lin-12*（参考文献 39）、*glp-1*（参考文献 40）的排布。进行标签测序项目[27]的团队提供的 cDNA 允许我们将 *tbg-1* 和 *ncc-1* 定位到基因组基因座上。通过突变表型的转基因拯救实验将基因 *mig-10*、*dpy-19* 和 *unc-32* 定位到一个特定的限制性片段上（曼瑟、科洛姆斯、蒂埃里 – 米格，个人交流）。在一些情况下，利用基因组序列能方便这类分析。

包含 *sup-5* 在内的几千个碱基的基因组 DNA 序列以前已经报道过[41]。然而，额外的基因组测序反映了 *sup-5* 基因座（一个 tRNA^{Trp} 基因）位于一个内含子内，并且作为黑腹果蝇 *flightless I*（参考文献 42）（B0303.1）的同源物转录方向与其相同。因为 *sup-5* 突变表现出对许多无关基因的特异等位基因的抑制[43]，所以它被认为是有功能的 tRNA 基因。此外秀丽隐杆线虫 *fl I* 同源物和预测一样进行表达和剪接（参考文献 42 和威尔逊的未发表数据）。

tRNA 基 因

经估计秀丽隐杆线虫的单倍体基因组约包含 300 个 tRNA 基因[44]。因此，我们期望基因组序列中平均每兆碱基发现 3 个 tRNA 基因。然而，在这报道的 2.181 Mb 序列中，用 tRNAscan[45] 鉴定了至少 14 个 tRNA 基因。这些 tRNA 基因表示在图 1 中。令人惊奇的是，C14B9 和 F22B7 这两个黏粒克隆，包含了其中的 7 个 tRNA 基因。像 *sup-5* tRNA 基因一样，一个 tRNA^{Ser} 和两个 tRNA^{Phe} 基因位于可能基因的内含子中。

重 复 序 列

这 2.181 Mb 区域中出现了几类重复序列。图 1 表明较大和较复杂的重复序列的定位。对三种主要重复序列类型的详细分析（反向的，串联的和散在的）反映了几个有趣的特征。

在反向重复序列中，一段基因组序列位于它反向拷贝的几个到几百个碱基之内。

hundred bases of an inverted copy of itself, are the most common type of repeat that we have found. Considering only those inverted repeats of up to 1 kb end to end, with at least 70% identity, on average an inverted repeat is found every 5.5 kb. Most of these are quite small, with an average segment length of 70 base pairs (bp) and an average loop size of 164 bp. A relatively high proportion of these repeats (43%) occur in introns, which represent only 20% of the genome. Most inverted repeats fall into families and may be remnants of mobile elements. In particular, there were examples of inverted repeat elements from known transposons Tc3 (ref. 46) and Tc4 (ref. 47).

Tandem repeats, in which a segment of genomic sequence lies adjacent to one or more copies of itself, occur on average every 10 kb. As with inverted repeats, most of these are small, with an average segment length of 17 bp and an average copy number of 14. Interestingly, only 17% of tandem repeats were found in introns, whereas 63% occurred between genes. The most common category of tandem repeats were triplets, some of which were found in predicted exons. One of the most complex tandem repeats found was a 95-bp sequence which was repeated more than 30 times in the clone pAR3 (Fig. 1; 1,144–1,150 kb). This region, which was missing from the cosmid map, had to be recovered from the YAC clone Y53B1 by targeted gap rescue in yeast. Also a large (7.9 kb) tandem repeat, flanked by more complex short repeats, was found in cosmid ZC262 (Fig. 1; 595–633 kb). Sequence assembly for these repeat regions was accomplished with very stringent parameters and, in some cases, aided by map information.

There are several examples of short repetitive sequences that are scattered throughout the genome, including the 94-bp consensus of the repeat element from most common inverted repeat families, previously observed in *lin-12* and *glp-1* introns[39,40]. These elements are widely dispersed, with an average of 14 copies every 100 kb at varying levels of conservation. Often, the repeat elements of inverted repeat families are also found in singleton or tandem arrangements. For example, a tandem pair of degenerate elements (69% identical over 77 bp) flanks part of the predicted gene *F58A4.2*. As discussed below, this seems to have been duplicated from a region 200 kb away.

Gene Duplications

In addition to the short interspersed repeats discussed above, there are sequences that are repeated tens or hundreds of kilobases apart, with up to 98% similarity. In some cases, these apparent duplications have a complex structure wherein several segments from one region are repeated in a second location, but with different spacings and orientations. Many of these long-range repeats involve coding regions. In particular, there seems to be a recent gene duplication involving *F22B7.5* and *C38C10.4*, which are approximately 750 kb apart but more than 95% similar. The predicted genes *C38C10.3* and *F58A4.2*, mentioned above, are more than 200 kb apart but share a 1.4-kb region that is 98% similar. Two predicted exons are contained within the repeat. If the GENEFINDER predictions are correct, this would be an example of exon shuffling. Perhaps more likely, the *F58A4.2*

反向重复是我们发现的最普遍的重复序列类型。只考虑那些端到端达到 1 kb 且至少有 70% 相似性的反向重复序列，平均每 5.5 kb 发现一个反向重复序列。重复序列大多数都很小，平均片段长度 70 bp，平均环大小为 164 bp。占基因组 20% 的内含子中出现这些重复的比率相对较高（43%）。大多数反向重复序列属于家族，可能是可动元件的残迹。尤其是，有例子表明有的反向重复元件来自已知的转座子 Tc3（参考文献 46）和 Tc4（参考文献 47）。

在串联重复中，一段基因组序列与它自身的一个或多个拷贝相连。平均每 10 kb 含一个串联重复。与反向重复一样，大多数串联重复很小，平均片段长度为 17 bp，平均拷贝数为 14。有趣的是，只有 17% 的串联重复存在于内含子中，而 63% 的串联重复存在于基因间。最普遍的串联重复是三拷贝串联，其中一些在预测的外显子中发现。发现的最复杂的串联重复之一是一个 95 bp 的序列，它在 pAR3 克隆中重复了三十多次（图 1；1,144~1,150 kb）。这个区域从黏粒图中缺失了，必须通过目标间隔拯救从酵母 YAC 克隆 Y53B1 中恢复。在黏粒 ZC262 中也发现了一个大的（7.9 kb）串联重复，它两侧有更复杂的短重复（图 1；595~633 kb）。借助严格的参数，有时辅以图谱信息，完成了这些重复区域的序列组装。

有几个短重复序列分散在基因组中，其中包括一个以前在 lin-12 和 glp-1 内含子中发现的来自最常见反向重复家族的重复元件的 94 bp 共有序列[39,40]。这些元件分散广泛，保守程度不同，平均每 100 kb 含 14 个拷贝。反向重复家族的重复元件也经常以单独或串联的形式被发现。例如，一个简并元件的串联对（69% 相似性超过 77 bp）在部分预测基因 F58A4.2 的两侧。如下文讨论的那样，这好像是从 200 kb 以外的区域复制过来的。

基 因 重 复

除了上面讨论的短散在重复，还有长度达几万或几十万碱基的重复序列，相似性高达 98%。有些例子中，这些明显的重复有一个复杂结构，其中一个区域的几个片段在第二个位置重复，但重复的间隔和方向都不同。许多大范围重复涉及编码区。特别是 F22B7.5 和 C38C10.4 好像发生了较新的基因重复，二者相距约 750 kb 但相似性高于 95%。上面提到的预测基因 C38C10.3 和 F58A4.2 之间距离大于 200 kb，但共享一个相似性为 98% 的 1.4 kb 的区域。这个重复中包含两个预测的外显子。如果 GENEFINDER 预测正确的话，这可能是一个外显子混编的例子。F58A4.2 中那重复的部分或许更可能是 C38C10.3 中一个功能基因的一部分的非转录拷贝。上述黏粒

version is a non-transcribed copy of part of a functional gene in *C38C10.3*. The 7.9-kb repeats in cosmid ZC262 described above contain segments of three different gene candidates, including a kinesin heavy-chain locus which was identified as *unc-116* (ref. 37). The *unc-116* gene begins outside the second copy of the repeat, with the last two exons present in the 7.9-kb. The same two exons in the first copy of the repeat are predicted to splice to a different exon in the second copy of the repeat. In addition to these recent gene duplications, we have identified similarities between other genes in the region. However, the degree of similarity suggests that these are more ancient in origin and may be examples of new gene families in *C. elegans*.

Prospects

The sequence reported here is already proving useful. In the very narrow sense, several genes previously under study have been sequenced, speeding the analysis and further study of these genes. The full sequence of the homeobox region will clarify its relationship to the *Drosophila Antennapedia* complex. More importantly, the 483 genes identified through genomic sequencing, together with the 1,194 genes discovered in the cDNA tagging project[27], are providing new and fruitful avenues for *C. elegans* research.

Furthermore, our experience in the pilot phase indicates that megabase-scale DNA sequencing at a reasonable cost is feasible with current methods and technology[6,48]. At the same time we feel that significant improvements are possible at almost every step. For example, we have developed an automated DNA template preparation capable of producing 400 Ml3 templates daily[18]. Initial plaque picking can also be done robotically[49], and instruments are under development that can perform large numbers of small-volume sequencing reactions automatically. Longer read lengths and greater sample capacity for the present generation of fluorescent gel readers are being developed, and more powerful instruments are being designed. Further improvements in the software will soon eliminate much of the sequence editing, which is currently a tedious task. Software tools are already available which simplify the selection of templates and oligonucleotides for directed sequencing (R.S., L.H. and S.D., unpublished). With these improvements and some increase in the scale of effort, production of more than 10 megabases of finished sequence per site per annum seems feasible. With this capacity in both halves of the consortium, the *C. elegans* genome sequence should be essentially completed before the end of 1998. In addition, both laboratories are contributing resources to speed the completion of the *S. cerevisiae* genome sequence. The complete genome sequences of these two organisms will provide insight into the genes that are likely to be common to all eukaryotes, and those specific to metazoans.

ZC262 中 7.9 kb 的重复序列包含三个不同候选基因的片段，包括一个鉴定为 *unc-116*（参考文献 37）的驱动蛋白重链基因座。*unc-116* 基因起始于这个重复第二个拷贝的外侧，且最后两个外显子在这个 7.9 kb 重复序列内。在这个重复的第一个拷贝中同样的两个外显子预测会剪接到该重复第二个拷贝的另一个外显子上。除这些最近的基因重复外，我们也鉴定了这个区域其他基因间的相似性。然而，相似性的水平表明它们的起源更古老，而且有可能是秀丽隐杆线虫的新基因家族的例子。

前　　景

实践已经证明本文报道的序列是有用的。从狭义上讲，完成了几个以前研究的基因的测序，加快了对这些基因的分析和进一步研究。同源框区域的所有序列会阐明它与果蝇 *Antennapedia* 复合体的相互关系。更重要的是，通过基因组测序鉴定的 483 个基因与 cDNA 标记项目 [27] 中发现的 1,194 个基因，一同为秀丽隐杆线虫的研究提供了新的富有成效的途径。

此外，我们在试验阶段的经验表明，用目前的方法和技术，在合理的花费下进行兆碱基规模的 DNA 测序是可行的 [6,48]。同时，我们感到几乎每一步都可能有明显的改进。例如，我们已经发展了一种自动的 DNA 模板制备方法，每天制备 400 个 M13 模板 [18]。最初的噬菌斑挑取现在也可以用机器完成 [49]，并且可自动进行大量小体积测序反应的仪器也在开发中。有更长的读取长度和更大的样品容量的荧光凝胶显示仪正在开发，更有效的机器也正在设计。序列编辑目前是一个乏味的工作，进一步地改善软件可以消除大量的序列编辑工作。软件工具的使用简化了定向测序的模板和寡聚核苷酸的选择（施塔登、希利尔和迪尔，未发表）。随着这些进步和更大范围的努力，每个单位每年产生 10 多兆碱基的最终序列似乎是可行的。以这样的速度，团队双方在 1998 年年底之前一定可以完成秀丽隐杆线虫基因组的测序。此外，双方实验室正为加快完成酿酒酵母基因组的测序贡献资源。这两个生物完整的基因组序列可以帮助大家了解可能所有真核生物中都普遍存在的基因，及后生动物特异的基因。

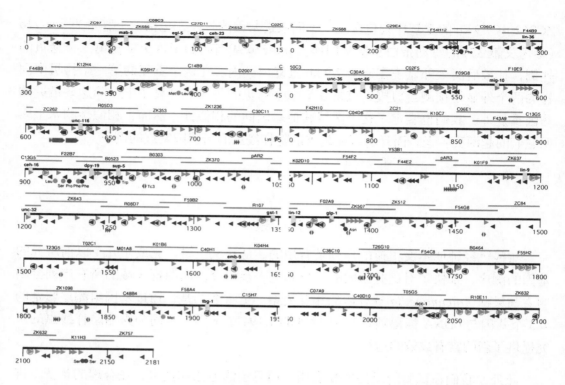

Fig. 1. The region of chromosome Ⅲ described here. Each line represents 300 kb, with cosmid clones indicated by blue bars; a magenta bar indicates the YAC clone Y53B1. Red and blue arrowheads indicate the approximate starting points of gene candidates for both strands. Circled arrowheads indicate cDNA hits. Red or blue circles indicate the positions of tRNA genes. Green arrowheads indicate the position and type of major repeats. Genetic markers previously mapped to the region and assigned to genomic loci after DNA sequencing are indicated by vertical yellow bars.

Methods. Subclone libraries were prepared and sequencing reactions performed as previously described[6,12,14]. For data collection, automated fluorescent DNA sequencers were used. Both the Applied Biosystems 373A and Pharmacia ALF instruments were initially tested, although the 373A was preferred for the shotgun phase because of its greater sample capacity. Both laboratories currently complete two daily runs of each sequencer with 36 lane gels. Thus, with only four of these sequencing instruments, typically more than 1,700 samples are processed per week. After subtracting for failures and contaminating vector sequences, this is sufficient for yearly production of more than 20 Mb of raw sequence data. Two additional sequencing instruments are available for directed sequencing to close gaps and complete the complementary strand. At the conclusion of each sequencer run, the ABI trace files were transferred from the host Macintosh to UNIX workstations for all further work. During the shotgun phase all processing on the UNIX systems is fully automated using a single script. This includes reformatting the trace files using MAKESCF (S.D., unpublished), selection of the quality data from each reading using AUTOTED (L.H., unpublished), clipping off cosmid and sequencing vector sequences using VEP (R.S., unpublished), and assembly using BAP[13]. After the shotgun phase, XBAP[13], which includes the oligo selection engine of OSP[22], is used to edit and finish each project. GENEFINDER and COP (S.D., unpublished) were used to check the finished sequence for errors. GENEFINDER is useful for identifying insertions and deletions in regions containing predicted genes, and COP, which compares the final sequence back to the raw data from which it was produced, is useful for identifying editing errors. We and others have previously described an evaluation of the accuracy of raw data from automated fluorescent DNA sequencers[6,25].

(**368**, 32-38; 1994)

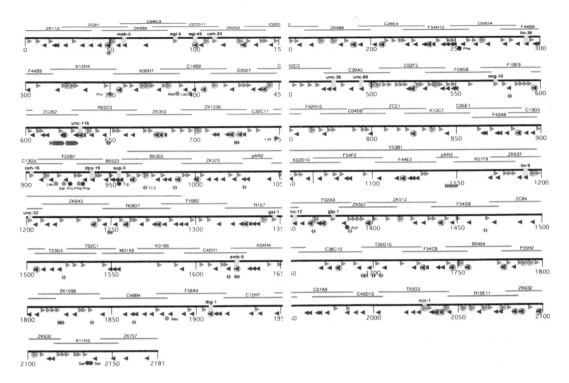

图 1. 本文描述的 3 号染色体的区域。每条线代表 300 kb，蓝色线段代表黏粒克隆；紫红色线段表示 YAC 克隆 Y53B1。红色和蓝色箭头指示候选基因在两条链的大致起点。带圈箭头指示 cDNA 位点。红色或蓝色的圈指示 tRNA 基因的位置。绿色箭头代表主要重复的位置和类型。用垂直的黄色线条表示之前定位到这个区域的遗传标记和 DNA 测序后确定到基因组基因座的遗传标记。

方法。 按以前描述的方法制备亚克隆文库，进行测序反应 [6,12,14]。用自动荧光 DNA 测序仪收集数据。美国应用生物系统公司的 373A 和法玛西亚的 ALF 仪器最初都进行过测试，但 373A 因为其样品容量大所以是鸟枪时期更倾向使用的仪器。现在双方实验室每台测序仪每天可运行 36 泳道凝胶两次。因此只用四个测序设备每周可处理 1,700 多个样品。减去失败和污染的载体序列后，每年足以产生 20 多兆碱基的原始序列数据。另外两个测序仪器可用来定向测序以闭合间隙及完成互补链序列。每台测序仪完成测序后，从 Macintosh 主机将 ABI 跟踪文件转到 UNIX 工作站进行下一步处理。鸟枪时期 UNIX 系统所做的所有处理是完全自动化的，并使用单一脚本。这包括用 MAKESCF 改变追踪文件格式（迪尔，未发表），用 AUTOTED 从每个读取数据中选择质量好的数据（希利尔，未发表），用 VEP 剪掉黏粒和测序载体序列（施塔登，未发表），以及用 BAP 组装序列 [13]。鸟枪时期以后，用包含 OSP[22] 寡核苷酸选择机器的 XBAP[13] 进行编辑并完成每个项目。用 GENEFINDER 和 COP（迪尔，未发表）检查完成序列的错误。GENEFINDER 对鉴定含有预测基因的区域中的插入和缺失很有用；COP 用来比较最终数据和原始数据，对鉴定编辑错误很有用。我们和其他人都已经评价过自动荧光 DNA 测序仪所得原始数据的准确性 [6,25]。

（李梅 翻译；杨崇林 审稿）

355

R. Wilson[*], R. Ainscough[†], K. Anderson[*], C. Baynes[†], M. Berks[†], J. Bonfield[†], J. Burton[†], M. Connell[*], T. Copsey[†], J. Cooper[*], A. Coulson[†], M. Craxton[†], S. Dear[†], Z. Du[*], R. Durbin[†], A. Favello[*], A. Fraser[†], L. Fulton[*], A. Gardner[†], P. Green[*], T. Hawkins[†], L. Hillier[*], M. Jier[*], L. Johnston[*], M. Jones[†], J. Kershaw[†], J. Kirsten[*], N. Laisster[†], P. Latreille[†], J. Lightning[†], C. Lloyd[†], B. Mortimore[†], M. O'Callaghan[†], J. Parsons[*], C. Percy[†], L. Rifken[*], A. Roopra[*], D. Saunders[†], R. Shownkeen[†], M. Sims[†], N. Smaldon[†], A. Smith[†], M. Smith[†], E. Sonnhammer[†], R. Staden[†], J. Sulston[*], J. Thierry-Mieg[‡], K. Thomas[†], M. Vaudin[*], K. Vaughan[*], R. Waterston[*], A. Watson[†], L. Weinstock[*], J. Wilkinson-Sproat[†] & P. Wohldman[*]

[*] Department of Genetics and Genome Sequencing Center, Washington University School of Medicine, St Louis, Missouri 63110, USA

[†] MRC Laboratory of Molecular Biology and Sanger Center, Hinxton Hall, Cambridge CB10 IRQ, UK

[‡] CNRS-CRBM et Physique-Mathematique, Montpellier 34033, France

Received 15 November 1993; accepted 5 January 1994.

References:

1. Brenner, S. *Genetics* 77, 71-94 (1974).

2. Wood, W. B. *et al. The Nematode* Caenorhabditis elegans (Cold Spring Harbor Laboratory Press, New York, 1988).

3. Coulson, A. R., Sulston, J. E., Brenner, S. & Karn, J. *Proc. Natl. Acad. Sci. U.S.A.* 83, 7821-7825 (1986).

4. Coulson, A., Waterston, R., Kliff, J., Sulston, J. & Kohara, Y. *Nature* 335, 184-186 (1988).

5. Coulson, A. *et al. Bioessays* 13, 413-417 (1991).

6. Sulston, J. *et al. Nature* 356, 37-41 (1992).

7. Strauss, E. C., Kobori, J. A., Siu, G. & Hood, L. E. *Analyt. Biochem.* 154, 353-360 (1986).

8. Deininger, P. *Analyt. Biochem.* 129, 216-223 (1983).

9. Bankier, A. T. & Barrell, B. G. *Tech. Nucleic Acid Biochem.* B5, 1-34 (1983).

10. Smith, L. M. *et al. Nature* 321, 674-679 (1986).

11. Connell, C. R. *et al. BioTechniques* 5, 342-348 (1987).

12. Craxton, M. *Methods: A Comparison to Methods in Enzymology* Vol. 3 (ed. Roe, B.) 20-26 (Academic, San Diego, 1991).

13. Dear, S. & Staden, R. *Nucleic Acids Res.* 19, 3907-3911 (1991).

14. Halloran, N., Du, Z. & Wilson, R. K. in *Methods in Molecular Biology* Vol. 10: *DNA Sequencing: Laboratory Protocols,* (eds Griffin, H. G. & Griffin, A. M.) 297-316 (Humana, Clifton, New Jersey, 1992).

15. Schriefer, L., Gebauer, B. K., Qiu, L. Q. Q., Waterson, R. H. & Wilson, R. K. *Nucleic Acids Res.* 18, 7455-7456 (1990).

16. Lee, L. *et al. Nucleic Acids Res.* 20, 2471-2483 (1992).

17. Hawkins, T. L., Du, Z., Halloran, N. D. & Wilson, R. K. *Electrophoresis* 13, 552-559 (1992).

18. Watson, A., Smaldon, N., Lucke, R. & Hawkins, T. *Nature* 362, 569-570 (1993).

19. Du, Z., Hood, L. & Wilson, R. K. *Meth. Enzym.* 218, 104-121 (1993).

20. Gleeson, T. & Hillier, L. *Nucleic Acids Res.* 19, 6481-6483 (1991).

21. Gleeson, T. J. & Staden, R. *Comput. Appl. Biosci.* 7, 398 (1991).

22. Hillier, L. & Green, P. *PCR Meth. Appl.* 1, 124-128 (1991).

23. Dear, S. & Staden, R. *DNA Sequence* 3, 107-110 (1992).

24. Alschul, S. F., Gish, W., Miller, W., Myers, E. W. & Lipman, D. J. *J. Molec. Biol.* 215, 403-410 (1990).

25. Koop, B. F., Rowan, L., Chen, W.-Q., Deshpande, P., Lee, H. & Hood, L. *BioTechniques* 14, 442-447 (1993).

26. Krause, M. & Hirsh, D. *Cell* 49, 753-761 (1987).

27. Waterston. R. *et al. Nature Genet.* 1, 114-123 (1992).

28. McCombie, W. R. *et al. Nature Genet.* 1, 124-131 (1992).

29. Green, P. *et al. Science* 259, 1711-1716 (1993).

30. Burglin, T. R. *et al. Nature* 351, 703 (1991).

31. Chisholm, A. *Development* 111, 921-932 (1991).

32. Wang, B. B. *et al. Cell* 74, 29-42 (1993).

33. Clark, S., Chisholm, A. & Horvitz, H. R. *Cell* 74, 43-55 (1993).

34. Finney, M., Ruvkun, G. & Horvitz, H. R. *Cell* 55, 757-769 (1988).

35. Guo, X., Johnson, J. J. & Kramer, J. M. *Nature* 349, 707-709 (1991).

36. Naito, M., Kohara, Y. & Kurosawa, Y. *Nucleic Acids Res.* 20, 2967-2969 (1992).

37. Patel, N., Thierry-Mieg, D. & Mancillas, J. R. *Proc. Natl. Acad. Sci. U.S.A.* 90, 9181-9185 (1993).

38. Weston, K., Yochem, J. & Greenwald, I. *Nucleic Acids Res.* 17, 2138 (1989).

39. Yochem, J., Weston, K. & Greenwald, I. *Nature* **335**, 547-550 (1988).

40. Yochem, J. & Greenwaid, I. *Cell* **58**, 553-563 (1989).

41. Waterston, R. H. GenBank locus CESUP5 (Acc. no. X54122) (1990).

42. Campbell, H. D. *et al. Proc. Natl. Acad. Sci. U.S.A.* **90**, 11386-11390 (1993).

43. Waterston, R. H. & Brenner, S. *Nature* **275**, 715-719 (1978).

44. Sulston, J. E. & Brenner, S. *Genetics* **77**, 95-104 (1974).

45. Fichant, G. & Burks, C. *J. Molec. Biol.* **220**, 659-671 (1991).

46. Collins, J., Forbes, E. & Anderson, P. *Genetics* **121**, 47-55 (1989).

47. Yuan, J., Finney, M., Tsung, N. & Horvitz, H. R. *Proc. Natl. Acad. Sci. U.SA.* **88**, 3334- 3338 (1991).

48. Sulston, J. *Nature* **357**, 106 (1992).

49. Uber, D. C., Jaklevic, J. M., Theil, E. H., Lishanskaya, A. & McNeely, M. R. *BioTechniques* **11**, 642-647 (1991).

Acknowledgements. We thank T. Schedl for critical reading of the manuscript, P. Kassos and J. Rogers for administrative support, and other members of the *C. elegans* Genome Consortium for technical support. Database searches with St Louis sequences were done remotely using the NCBI BLAST server. ACEDB is available by anonymous ftp from cele.mrc-lmb.cam.ac.uk and from ncbi.nlm.nih.gov. This work was supported by the NIH National Center for Human Genome Research and the MRC Human Genome Mapping Project.

357

The First Skull and Other New Discoveries of *Australopithecus afarensis* at Hadar, Ethiopia

W. H. Kimbel *et al.*

Editor's Note

Almost 300 specimens of the primitive hominid *Australopithecus afarensis* had been found at Hadar in Ethiopia, the most famous being the skeleton known as Lucy. A frustrating absence was a skull, without which many questions remained unanswered—such as whether *A. afarensis* constituted a single, sexually dimorphic species, or two distinct species. This report, of a skull from Hadar, solved many riddles. Although the dentition marked it unequivocally as *afarensis*, it was bigger than any *Australopithecus* skull ever reported: evidence for sexual dimorphism in a single species. At three million years old, it was also one of the latest-known *afarensis* specimens. With the oldest at 3.9 million, Kimbel and colleagues claimed stasis as the rule in this species' 900,000-year tenure.

The Hadar Formation in Ethiopia is a prolific source of Pliocene Hominidae attributed to the species *Australopithecus afarensis*[1]. Since 1990, three seasons of field work have contributed 53 new specimens to the hominid inventory from Hadar, including the first fairly complete adult skull. Ranging from 3.0 to 3.4 million years in age (Fig.1)[2-4], the new specimens bear on key debates in hominid palaeontology, including the taxonomic implications of sample variation and the reconstruction of locomotor behaviour. They confirm the taxonomic unity of *A. afarensis* and constitute the largest body of evidence for about 0.9 million years of stasis in the earliest known hominid species.

THE Hadar site yielded nearly 250 hominid fossils during the 1970s, including 40% of a female skeleton, A.L. 288-1 ("Lucy", ~3.18 million years), and the partial remains of at least 13 individuals from A.L. 333 (~3.20 Myr). Subsequent study of this collection and the sample from Laetoli, Tanzania, led to the recognition of the craniodentally primitive, bipedal species *Australopithecus afarensis*[5]. Morphological and metric variation in the *A. afarensis* hypodigm were initially explained as intraspecific, partly because of sexual dimorphism[6]. An alternative view attributed the differences to species-level taxonomic variation[7]. Debate was fuelled by the absence of a complete skull[8-10]. Similarly, although some interpreted the postcranial anatomy as indicating a complete adaptation to terrestrial bipedality[11,12], others saw evidence of a significant arboreal component in the locomotor repertoire of the species[13,14]. The new Hadar discoveries address both of these issues.

在埃塞俄比亚的哈达尔发现的第一例南方古猿阿法种的头骨和其他新发现

金贝尔等

编者按

在埃塞俄比亚的哈达尔地点发现了大约 300 块原始人类——南方古猿阿法种的标本，其中最著名的化石标本被称为露西骨架。令人遗憾的是这具标本缺乏头盖骨化石，而这令许多的问题仍然没有答案——例如，南方古猿阿法种是否是单一的、具有性二形性的物种，或是两个不同的物种。这份哈达尔头盖骨的报告解决了许多此前未能解释的谜题。虽然本文发现的头盖骨齿系明确地将之标记为南猿阿法种，但是它的头盖骨大于曾经发现报道过的所有南猿属：是同一物种性二形性的证据。在近 300 万年的历史中，这是最新发现的南猿阿法种标本之一。最古老的是在 390 万年前，金贝尔和他的同事断言此物种存在 90 万年的停滞期。

埃塞俄比亚的哈达尔组出土了丰富的上新世人科化石，这些化石标本都属于南方古猿阿法种[1]。自 1990 年以来，对哈达尔进行的三个季度的野外挖掘工作已经为原始人类化石记录贡献了 53 个新标本，包括第一例非常完整的成年头骨。新标本的年代在距今 300 万年到 340 万年之间（图 1）[2-4]，这些新标本导致了古人类学中的一些重要争议，包括样本变异的分类学意义及其行动方式的重建等。他们确认了南方古猿阿法种可作为单独的分类学单元存在，并构成了证明已知的最早原始人类物种存在约 90 万年停滞期的最大证据。

哈达尔地点在 20 世纪 70 年代出土了将近 250 件原始人类化石，包括一具雌性骨架的 40%、AL 288-1（"露西"，约 318 万年前）和来自 AL 333（约 320 万年前）的至少 13 个个体的部分残骸。对这些化石和来自坦桑尼亚莱托里地点的样本进行的后续研究使得在颅骨和牙齿上表现出原始性的两足直立行走物种——南方古猿阿法种得以辨别出来[5]。南方古猿阿法种种型群的形态和测量变异最初被解释成种间差异，部分是因为性二形性[6]。另一种观点将这种差异归结为物种水平的分类学差异[7]。由于缺少完整的头骨，所以这方面的争议较大[8-10]。相似地，尽管有些人将颅后骨骼特征解释为对陆地直立行走的完全适应[11,12]，但是其他人将其视为该物种的行动方式中树栖行为占重要地位的证据[13,14]。在哈达尔地点新发现的标本可以解决这两个问题。

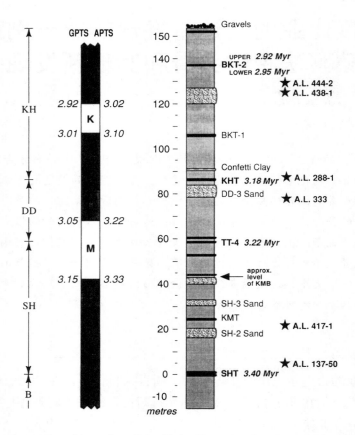

Fig. 1. Composite stratigraphic section of the Hadar Formation, based on revisions by R. C. Walter and J. L. Aronson through the 1993 field season, with positions of hominid specimens discussed in the text indicated. Single-crystal laser fusion (SCLF) $^{40}Ar/^{39}Ar$ ages for the SHT (3.40 ± 0.03 Myr), TT-4 (3.22 ± 0.01 Myr), KHT (3.18 ± 0.01 Myr) and BKT-2 (2.92–2.95 Myr) confirm that no Hadar hominid is older than 3.40 Myr, and establish ages of ~3.18 Myr for the A.L. 288-1 ("Lucy") skeleton and ~3.20 Myr for the A.L. 333 hominid assemblage[2,3]. The Kadada Moumou basalt (KMB) does not occur in the type-area, but its relative stratigraphic position has been correlated into the type-section in the field. A whole-rock $^{40}Ar/^{39}Ar$ plateau age of 3.28 ± 0.04 Myr has been obtained for the KMB (ref. 4). New specimens from A.L. 438 and 444 represent the first Hadar hominid discoveries stratigraphically above A.L. 288-1 ("Lucy"), extending the temporal range of *A. afarensis* at Hadar from ~3.4 to ~3.0 Myr. At left are shown the stratigraphic ranges of Basal (B), Sidi Hakoma (SH), Denen Dora (DD) and Kada Hadar (KH) Members of the Hadar Formation. Also depicted is the composite magnetostratigraphic section with the global polarity time scale (GPTS) and the astronomical polarity time scale (APTS); the new $^{40}Ar/^{39}Ar$ and magnetostratigraphic data support the APTS calibration of the Mammoth (M) and Kaena (K) reversed subchrons[3,4].

The new skull A.L. 444-2, from the middle Kada Hadar (KH) Mb. (~3.0 Myr), is clearly that of an adult male (Fig. 2). It has large canines and, with a biasterionic breadth of 106 mm, it is the largest *Australopithecus* cranium on record. Although the maxillary postcanine teeth are larger than any of those in the limited Hadar + Laetoli sample from the 1970s, relative to canine size they are not unusual[15,16]. The mandibular corpus is quite large, but its robusticity index falls below the Hadar mean (Table 1). The specimen's attribution to *A. afarensis* is warranted by its primitive constellation of mandibular, facial and calvarial

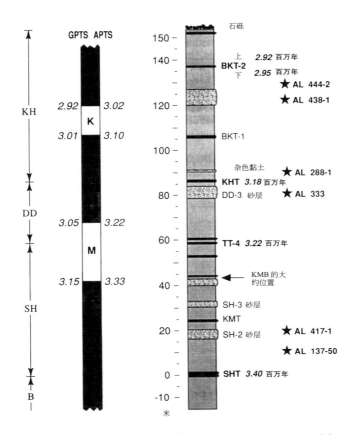

图 1. 哈达尔组剖面合成图，基于沃尔特和阿伦森 1993 野外工作进行的修正，图中标出了本文所指并讨论的原始人类标本的位置。SHT (340 万 ± 3 万年)、TT-4 (322 万 ± 1 万年)、KHT(318 万 ± 1 万年) 和 BKT-2 (292 万至 295 万年) 的单晶体激光核聚变 (SCLF) ^{40}Ar/^{39}Ar 年代证实了哈达尔原始人类的年代早于 340 万年前，确立了 AL 288-1 ("露西") 骨架的年代约为 318 万年前，而 AL 333 原始人类系列的年代约为 320 万年前 [2,3]。在该类型区域没有发现卡达达穆穆玄武岩 (KMB)，但是其相对地层位置与该野外典型剖面相关联。一块 KMB 整岩的 ^{40}Ar/^{39}Ar 坪年龄为 328 万 ± 4 万年 (参考文献 4)。来自 AL 438 和 AL 444 的新标本代表了在地层上位于 AL 288-1 ("露西") 之上发现的第一例哈达尔原始人类，将哈达尔南方古猿阿法种的时间范围从约 340 万年前扩展到了约 300 万年前。左侧给出了哈达尔组的底部 (B)、西迪哈克玛 (SH)、德嫩多拉 (DD) 和卡达哈达尔 (KH) 段的地层学范围。图中也描述了考虑了地球极性时间表 (GPTS) 和天文极性时间表 (APTS) 的复合地磁地层学剖面；新的 ^{40}Ar/^{39}Ar 和地磁地层学数据支持猛犸 (M) 和凯纳 (K) 反向亚时事件的 APTS 校正 [3,4]。

在卡达哈达尔 (KH) 段中部新发现的 AL 444-2 新头骨 (约 300 万年前) 明显属于一个成年雄性个体 (图 2)。此例标本具有大的犬齿，星点间宽为 106 毫米，是可考的最大的南方古猿头盖骨。尽管该上颌前臼齿比发现于 20 世纪 70 年代的有限的哈达尔和莱托里样本的都要大，但是相对于犬齿尺寸而言，它们的大小还算正常 [15,16]。该样本的下颌体相当大，但是其粗壮指数低于哈达尔样本的均值 (表 1)。通过与其他

361

characters relative to that of other *Australopithecus* species[15-20]. Its morphology is consistent with that of Hadar specimens from A.L. 333 that comprise the major components of the composite reconstruction of a male *A. afarensis* skull based on the 1970s collection[18,21,22]. The new Hadar skull refutes suggestions that the reconstruction incorporated facial and calvarial remains from two contemporaneous hominid species[9,10], and supports the interpretation of Hadar hominid cranial variation as intraspecific.

Table 1. Mandible corpus measurements

	Breadth (mm)	Height (mm)	Robusticity (%)
A.L. 417-1a (left)	18.0	36.0	50.0
A.L. 444-2b (right)	22.0	43.2	50.9
1970s Hadar sample	$\bar{x} = 18.5$	$\bar{x} = 33.6$	$\bar{x} = 55.1$
	$n = 12$	$n = 10$	$n = 10$
	$\sigma = 2.1$	$\sigma = 4.1$	$\sigma = 6.4$
	range = 15.6–22.4	range = 28.0–40.5	range = 45.5–63.8

Mandible corpus measurements of A.L. 417-la, compared with those of A.L. 444-2b and the 1970s Hadar sample[26]. All measurements recorded here are for P4/M1 position, since measurements at M1 on A.L. 444-2b are not possible without further reconstruction of the corpus.

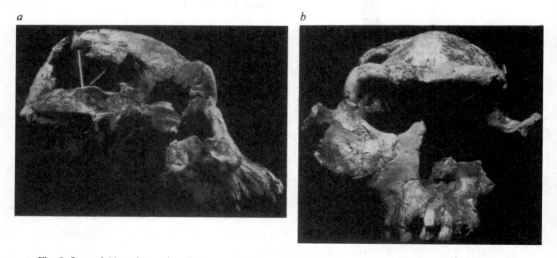

a *b*

Fig. 2. Lateral (*a*) and anterior (*b*) views of Hadar skull A.L. 444-2, preliminary reconstruction, 47.5% natural size. Thirteen major pieces and many small fragments were clustered together in a small gully on a steep surface of Kada Hadar Member silts. Excavation failed to reveal additional hominid remains, but *in situ* mammal bone fragments with patina and preservation identical to that of the hominid were recovered upslope from the skull in a stratigraphic level 10.5 m below marker tuff BKT-2 (Lower). We believe this level to be the source horizon of the skull (Fig.1). It comprises the right mandible and symphysis (not shown) with fragmentary left and right incisors, partial right C and damaged P4–M1, the maxilla with right I¹, C, P⁴–M³ and left I¹, C, P³–M³, the right zygomatic, most of the nasal bones (not shown), most of the frontal with attached anteromedial segments of the parietals, the left parietal, the occipital with attached posterior right parietal, and both temporals. The anterior cranial base is missing, as are most of both temporal squames. Although there are no contacts between the frontal,

南方古猿物种的下颌骨、面部和头盖骨等特征的对比，将该标本划分为南方古猿[15-20]。其形态学特征与来自 AL 333 的哈达尔标本一致，研究人员根据这些 20 世纪 70 年代出土的标本综合重建出了一个雄性南方古猿阿法种头骨的主要部分[18,21,22]。新发现的哈达尔头骨驳斥了重建结果是两个同时代的原始人类物种的面部和头盖骨特征的拼接[9,10]的看法，而支持哈达尔原始人类头盖骨变异是种内变异的观点。

表 1. 下颌体的测量值

	宽度（毫米）	高度（毫米）	粗壮指数（%）
AL 417-1a（左）	18.0	36.0	50.0
AL 444-2b（右）	22.0	43.2	50.9
20 世纪 70 年代的哈达尔样本	$\bar{x} = 18.5$	$\bar{x} = 33.6$	$\bar{x} = 55.1$
	$n = 12$	$n = 10$	$n = 10$
	$\sigma = 2.1$	$\sigma = 4.1$	$\sigma = 6.4$
	范围 $= 15.6 \sim 22.4$	范围 $= 28.0 \sim 40.5$	范围 $= 45.5 \sim 63.8$

AL 417-1a 的下颌体测量值与 AL 444-2b 的那些样本和 20 世纪 70 年代的哈达尔样本的测量值进行比较[26]。这里记录的所有测量值都是在 P4/M1 位置测得的，因为 AL 444-2b 的下颌体没有得到进一步的重建，所以不可能测量其 M1 位置处的尺寸。

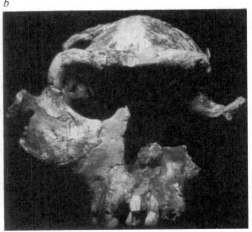

图 2. 哈达尔头骨 AL 444-2 初步重建结果的侧面视图（a）和前面视图（b），相当于自然尺寸的 47.5%。13 个大碎片和许多小碎片都聚集在卡达哈达尔地层淤泥陡面上的一个小峡谷中。挖掘工作中没有发现其他的原始人类遗迹，但是在发现该头骨的标志性凝灰岩 BKT-2（下层）之下 10.5 米的地层学水平向上，挖掘出了一些原位埋藏的保存状况与原始人类相同的生有绿锈的哺乳动物骨骼碎片。我们相信该水平是该头骨的来源地层（图 1）。该头骨由右侧下颌骨和正中联合部位（没有展示）、上颌骨、右颧骨、大部分鼻骨（没有展示）、大部分额骨（上面连有附着的顶骨的前正中部分）、左顶骨、附着右后顶骨的枕骨和两块颞骨构成。下颌骨上有成碎片了的左、右门齿，部分右 C 和损坏的 $P_4 \sim M_1$；上颌骨上带有右 I^1、C、$P^4 \sim M^3$ 和左 I^1、C、$P^3 \sim M^3$。颅底前部和两块颞骨鳞部的大部分都没有保存下来。尽管在额骨、上颌骨和颧骨之间没有任何衔接，但是保存下来的部分足以提供他们彼此之间和相对于脑颅位置的初步信息。

the maxilla and the zygomatic, there is sufficient preserved to provide a preliminary idea of their positions relative to one another and to the calvaria. Post-depositional deformation has compressed the palate along the midline, uplifted the right side of the frontoparietal fragment and supraorbital, twisted the left and elevated the right zygomatic arch, and pushed the nuchal plane of the occipital into the cranial cavity. The *A. afarensis* character complex present in A.L. 444-2 comprises a higher number of hominid symplesiomorphies than in any other species of the genus (including those attributed by some to *Paranthropus*). These primitive characters include strong prognathism relative to both the calvaria and the P^4/M^1 take-off of the zygomatic process of the maxilla, marked projection of sagittally and transversely convex premaxilla anterior to bicanine plane, horizontally inclined nasoalveolar clivus, procumbent maxillary incisors, extensive intranasal component of premaxilla with step-down to nasal cavity floor, sharp lateral nasal aperture margins, canine fossae, curved zygomaticoalveolar crests, anteriorly flat palate, $I^2/\underline{C}+\overline{C}/P_3$ diastemata, posteriorly convergent temporal lines with low, probably bifid, posterior sagittal crest, compound temporal/nuchal crest, asterionic notch sutural pattern, massive mastoid processes inflected beneath the cranial base with tips independent of occipitomastoid crests, shallow mandibular fossae, tubular tympanic plates that sit completely posterior to large postglenoid processes, weak petrous crest of tympanics, and coexistent transverse-sigmoid and occipital-marginal venous drainage systems (the polarity of this last character is indeterminate). Estimation of cranial capacity should be possible, but awaits final reconstruction of the calvaria. Measurements of the better-preserved maxillary teeth are (in mm, buccolingual breadth × mesiodistal length, the latter corrected for interproximal wear): Right C: 11.5 × 10.4; Left P4: 14.5 × 10.6, LM1: 15.0 × 13.7, LM2: 15.8 × 14.2, LM3: 16.2 × 14.9.

The frontal is a taxonomically important cranial region under-represented in the previous sample of *A. afarensis*. In A.L. 444-2 the supraorbital torus is vertically thick laterally and the very low squama has neither a chimpanzee-like supratoral sulcus nor a frontal trigone such as is found in "robust" *Australopithecus* crania. The distance across the postorbital constriction in A.L. 444-2 is large compared to that of other *Australopithecus* species, both absolutely (77 mm) and relative to facial breadth (frontobiorbital breadth index ~80%)[18]. These features are shared with the ~3.9 Myr Belohdelie frontal BEL-VP-1/1 (ref. 23), confirming the previously tentative attribution of the latter specimen to *A. afarensis*[24].

Maxilla A.L. 417-ld from the middle Sidi Hakoma (SH) Mb. (~3.25 Myr), associated with a partial mandible and cranial base fragments, constitutes the first relatively intact face of an *A. afarensis* female (Fig. 3a–d). It features small canines and less prognathism than A.L. 444-2, consistent with the great ape model of intraspecific sexual dimorphism[18,25], and otherwise demonstrates the same morphological pattern as do larger *A. afarensis* faces[17]. The mandible conforms to the *A. afarensis* plan[26]. Its low corpus robusticity index is identical to that of the A.L. 444-2 male mandible (Table 1). The P_3 lacks a lingual cusp, as in other *A. afarensis* females (A.L. 128-23, 288-1i) and some males (A.L. 277-1), but another new female jaw, A.L. 315-22, has a bicuspid P_3, confirming that P_3 polymorphism cuts across the size range of Hadar mandibles.

The A.L. 438-1 partial upper limb skeleton from middle KH Mb. (~3.0 Myr) includes the most complete *Australopithecus* ulna known (Fig. 3e, f); based on the associated mandible (corpus height at P_4/M_1 = 42.5 mm) and frontal fragment, it is almost certainly a male. Maximum ulnar length (excluding styloid process) of 268 mm is 22% greater than our length estimate for the A.L. 288-1 female ulna (220 mm). The size disparity between

沉积后的变形将上颚沿中线压缩了，将顶骨碎片和眶上部分的右侧提高了，左颧弓扭曲，右颧弓抬高，而枕骨的顶平面则被推进了颅腔。AL 444-2 中存在众多南方古猿阿法种的复合特征，其原始人类共同祖征（包括被某些人归属到傍人属中的那些特征）比该属其他任何物种都要多。这些原始特征包括相对于顶骨和上颌骨颧突（P⁴/M¹ 上方）而言强烈的凸颌、位于犬齿平面前的颌骨在矢状和横向方向明显突出、水平倾斜的鼻槽斜坡、平伏的上颌门齿、较大的下降到鼻腔底的前上颌骨的鼻内部分、锐利的梨状孔边缘、犬齿窝、弯曲的颧骨齿槽脊、前面坦平的上颚、I²/C̲+C̄/P₃ 间隙裂、低的可能分叉的后矢状脊、颞线后方收敛、复合的颞骨／项脊、星点切迹缝形状、弯曲的位于颅底下的具有独立于枕乳脊的尖端的巨大乳突、浅的下颌窝、完全位于大型下颌窝后突之后的管状鼓板、鼓室的微弱岩脊以及同时存在乙状窦沟和枕边缘窦沟（最后这一特征的极性还不确定）。对颅容量的估计应该是可能的，但是还需等待对头盖骨的最终重建。保存较好的上颌牙齿的测量尺寸如下（单位：毫米，颊舌宽度 × 近远中长度，后者根据牙间磨损进行了修正）：右 C：11.5×10.4；左 P4：14.5×10.6，LM1：15.0×13.7，LM2：15.8×14.2，LM3：16.2×14.9。

额骨在分类学上是一个很重要的颅骨区域，此前的南方古猿阿法种样本中并没有相应的代表。在 AL 444-2 中，眶上圆枕两侧在垂直方向厚，鳞部很低，既没有像黑猩猩一样的圆枕上沟，也没有在"粗壮"南方古猿的头盖骨中观察到的额三角。与其他南方古猿物种比起来，AL 444-2 的眶后缩窄绝对值（77 毫米）和相对于面部宽度的相对值（额眶宽指数约为 80%）[18] 都较大。这些特征在大约 390 万年前的贝洛德利样本的额区 BEL-VP-1/1（参考文献 23）中也存在，证实了以前将后者归为南方古猿阿法种这一暂时决定的正确性 [24]。

来自西迪哈克玛（SH）段中部的上颌骨 AL 417-1d（约 325 万年前），与部分下颌骨和颅底碎片连在一起，构成了第一例相对完整的雌性南方古猿阿法种的面部（图 3a~d）。其特征是犬齿较小，凸颌程度比 AL 444-2 低，这与大型猿类的种内性二形模式是一致的 [18,25]，另外，证实了其与较大型南方古猿阿法种的面部具有同样的形态学模式 [17]。下颌骨与南方古猿阿法种相符 [26]。其下颌体的粗壮指数较低，这与 AL 444-2 雄性下颌骨一致（表 1）。P₃ 缺少舌侧牙尖，这与其他南方古猿阿法种雌性（AL 128-23，AL 288-li）和一些雄性（AL 277-1）是一样的，但是另一个新发现的雌性下颌骨 AL 315-22 的 P₃ 有两个牙尖，证实了 P₃ 在哈达尔下颌骨中就有不一致性。

来自 KH 段中部的 AL 438-1 的部分上肢骨骼（约 300 万年前）包括已知的最完整的南方古猿尺骨（图 3e 和 f）；参照与之相关联的下颌骨（下颌体高度 P₄/M₁ = 42.5 毫米）和额部碎片，几乎可以肯定该样本是一个雄性。尺骨最大长（不算茎状突）是 268 毫米，比 AL 288-1 雌性尺骨的长度估计值（220 毫米）大 22%。这两个哈达尔尺骨之间的尺寸差异与 AL 333x-5 和 AL 333w-36 的尺骨差异一样大。可以看出其前后的

these two Hadar ulnae is equalled by proximal ulnae A.L. 333x-5 and 333w-36. With anteroposterior shaft curvature visibly less than in chimpanzees, a tall olecranon process, and an anteriorly oriented trochlear notch, the A.L. 438-1 ulna diverges from the modern African ape condition and matches the human morphology of other Hadar hominid ulnae[27,28].

The large, presumably male, humerus A.L. 137-50 from the lower SH Mb. (Fig. 3e, f) is a remarkably close match for the recently reported Maka humerus MAK-VP-1/3, with which it is penecontemporaneous (~3.4 Myr)[23], as well as for Hadar proximal humerus A.L. 333-107 (~3.2 Myr)[28]. The new Hadar specimen has a retroflexed shaft and appears to be very robust relative to length, with thick cortical bone, pronounced deltoid and humeral adductor insertion sites, and a strong lateral supracondylar crest.

Fig. 3. Lateral (*a*) and anterior (*b*) views of A.L. 417-1d maxilla; lateral (*c*) and occlusal (*d*) views of A.L. 417-1a mandible, 50% natural size. Diagnostic *A.afarensis* morphology combined in the specimen is primitive relative to that of other *Australopithecus* species and includes: mandible corpus hollowed laterally, mental foramen positioned below midcorpus and opens anterosuperiorly, extramolar sulcus high and narrow, postcanine tooth row slightly concave buccally, low corpus robusticity, flat, vertical infraorbital bone plate, sagittally and transversely convex premaxilla that protrudes in front of the bicanine plane, and sharp lateral nasal aperture margin. Measurements of the dentition are (recorded as described in Fig. 2 legend): *Maxilla*, RC: 9.9 × 9.4, RP3: 11.7 × 8.3, RP4: 12.2 × 8.9, RM1: 13.4 × 12.3, RM2: 14.7 × 13.2, RM3: 14.8 × 13.0; *Mandible*, LP3: 10.8 × 8.9, LP4: 11.2 × 8.6, LM1: 11.6 × 12.4, LM2: 13.1 × 13.0, RM3: 13.3 × 14.9. *e*, Anterior view of right humerus A.L. 137-50; *f*, lateral view of left ulna A.L. 438-1a,

骨干曲率比黑猩猩的小，AL 438-1 中高的鹰嘴突出和向前的滑车切迹都与现代非洲猿类的情况不同，而与其他的哈达尔原始人类尺骨的人类形态学相一致[27,28]。

来自下 SH 段的较大的、推测是男性的肱骨 AL 137-50（图 3e 和 f）与近期报道的马卡肱骨 MAK-VP-1/3 具有非常密切的一致性，是几乎同时期的（约 340 万年前）[23]，哈达尔近端肱骨 AL 333-107（约 320 万年前）[28] 也是这样。新发现的哈达尔标本骨干呈翻转状，其相对长度似乎很粗壮，具有厚的皮质、突出的三角肌和肱骨内收肌附着处以及强壮的外侧髁上脊。

图 3. AL 417-1d 上颌骨的侧面（a）和前面（b）视图；AL 417-1a 下颌骨的侧面（c）和咬合面（d）视图，相当于自然尺寸的 50%。该标本中整合的南方古猿阿法种决定性的形态学特征相对于其他南方古猿物种来说比较原始，包括：侧面凹陷的下颌体、位于下颌体中部下向前上方开口的颏孔、高而窄的臼齿后沟、颊侧稍微凹陷的前臼齿、下颌骨体粗壮度较低、平而垂直的眶下骨板、在双侧犬齿平面沿纵向和横向突出的前颌骨以及锐利的梨状孔边缘。齿系的尺寸如下（按图 2 图注的描述记录）：上颌骨，RC：9.9×9.4，RP3：11.7×8.3，RP4：12.2×8.9，RM1：13.4×12.3，RM2：14.7×13.2，RM3：14.8×13.0；下颌骨，LP3：10.8×8.9，LP4：11.2×8.6，LM1：11.6×12.4，LM2：13.1×13.0，RM3：13.3×14.9。e，右肱骨 AL 137-50 的前面视图；f，左尺骨 AL 438-1a 的侧面视图，都相当于自然尺寸的 50%。AL 438 尺骨与

both 50% natural size. The A.L. 438 ulna is associated with a partial mandible, a frontal fragment, three metacarpals, as well as shaft portions of the right ulna, left and right radii and right humerus. Two fragments of the complete ulna were recovered *in situ* in a KH Member sand unit, 12 m below marker tuff BKT-2 (Lower) (Fig. 1).

Our preliminary estimate of humeral length for A.L. 137-50 is 295 mm, ~24% greater than that of A.L. 288-1 (238 mm, ref. 27). Using the A.L. 438-1 ulna as a counterpart to A.L. 137-50 yields an ulna/humerus length index of ~91%. The index for the A.L. 288-1 female is ~92.5%. If it is true that in *A. afarensis* humerus length is roughly that expected in a modern human of comparable body size[29], then these figures indicate relatively long ulnae (and, presumably, forearms) for the Hadar hominids, distinctly closer to the relative ulnar length of chimpanzees ($\bar{x} = 95\%$, $\sigma = 3\%$, $r = 88–101\%$, $n = 20$) than to that of modern humans ($\bar{x} = 80\%$, $\sigma = 3\%$, $r = 74–88\%$, $n = 20$). The combination of a relatively short, but robust, humerus and a long forearm is unlikely to resolve the debate about locomotion in *A. afarensis*—which has been concerned as much with incompatible evolutionary models for the interpretation of functional morphology as with divergent interpretations of the fossils themselves[11,12,30].

The new Hadar fossils support the taxonomic unity of *A. afarensis*. A single hominid species is now well documented in all three fossiliferous members of the Hadar Formation, spanning 0.4 Myr. The new discoveries for the first time extend the *A. afarensis* stratigraphic range well up into the Kada Hadar Member, by which time in the Hadar Fm. a variety of other macromammal clades had gone through taxonomic turnover[31]. Furthermore, with ages of ~3.0 Myr for the A.L. 444-2 skull and ~3.9 Myr for the Belohdelie frontal, the 0.9 Myr temporal range of *A. afarensis* is bracketed by specimens of high diagnostic value. The Hadar sample forms nearly all of the post-3.4 Myr portion of the *A. afarensis* hypodigm and, at close to 300 specimens, it is the most persuasive body of evidence for prolonged stasis within the oldest known hominid species[6,23]

(**368**, 449-451; 1994)

William H. Kimbel*, Donald C. Johanson* & Yoel Rak*†
* Institute of Human Origins, 2453 Ridge Road, Berkeley, California 94709, USA
† Department of Anatomy, Sackler School of Medicine, Tel Aviv University, Tel Aviv, Israel

Received 10 January; accepted 22 February 1994.

References:

1. Johanson, D. C., Taieb, M. & Coppens, Y. *Am. J. Phys. Anthrop.* **57**, 373-402 (1982).

2. Walter, R. C. & Aronson, J. L *J. Hum. Evol.* **25**, 229-240 (1993).

3. Walter, R. C. *Geology* **22**, 6-10 (1994).

4. Renne, P., Walter, R., Verosub, K., Sweitzer, M. & Aronson, J. *Geophys. Res. Lett.* **20**, 1067-1070 (1993).

5. Johanson, D. C., White, T. D. & Coppens, Y. *Kirtlandia* **28**, 1-14 (1978).

6. Johanson, D. C. & White, T. D. *Science* **203**, 321-329 (1979).

7. Olson, T. R. in *Ancestors: The Hard Evidence* (ed. Delson, E.) 102-119 (Liss, New York, 1985).

8. Leakey, R. E. & Walker, A.C. *Science* **207**, 1103 (1980).

部分下颌骨、一个额骨碎片、三块掌骨以及右尺骨的骨干部分、左右桡骨和右肱骨连在一起。完整尺骨的两块碎片是在位于标志性凝灰岩 BKT-2（下层）之下 12 米的 KH 段的沙质单元原位出土的（图 1）。

　　我们对 AL 137-50 的肱骨长度的初步估计是 295 毫米，比 AL 288-1 的肱骨（238 毫米，参考文献 27）约长 24%。如果将 AL 438-1 作为 AL 137-50 的对照，可以得出尺骨／肱骨长度指数约为 91%。AL 288-1 雌性样本的该指数约为 92.5%。如果南方古猿阿法种的肱骨长度大体上与身体大小相当的现代人一样[29]，那么这些数字就说明哈达尔原始人类具有相对较长的尺骨（前臂可能也相应较长）；与现代人的（$\bar{x}=80\%$，$\sigma=3\%$，$r=74\%\sim88\%$，$n=20$）相比，它与黑猩猩的尺骨相对长度（$\bar{x}=95\%$，$\sigma=3\%$，$r=88\%\sim101\%$，$n=20$）更接近。一个相对较短但粗壮的肱骨和一个较长前臂的组合不太可能解决关于南方古猿阿法种行动方式的争议——这个问题不但与对功能形态学解释（引出的）不相容的进化模式有关，还与化石本身的不同解释有关[11,12,30]。

　　新发现的哈达尔化石支持南方古猿阿法种这一分类单元。一个单一的原始人类物种得到了很好的保存，分散在哈达尔组的三个化石层中，前后共跨越了 40 万年。这些新发现第一次将南方古猿阿法种的地层学范围扩展到了卡达哈达尔段，哈达尔组的许多其他的巨型哺乳动物进化枝都经历了分类学的颠覆[31]。另外，AL 444-2 头骨的年代距今约为 300 万年，贝洛德利额骨的年代距今约为 390 万年，可靠的标本将南方古猿阿法种 90 万年的时间范围框定起来。哈达尔样本组成了过去的 340 万年中几乎所有的南方古猿阿法种种型群，有将近 300 个标本，这是证明在已知的最古老的原始人类物种中存在长期停滞的最具有说服力的证据[6,23]。

（刘皓芳 翻译；崔娅铭 审稿）

9. Shipman, P. *Discover* 7, 87-93 (1986).

10. McKee, J. K. *Am. J. Phys. Anthrop.* 80, 1-9 (1989).

11. Lovejoy, C. O. *Sci. Am.* 256, 118-125 (1988).

12. Latimer, B. M. in *Origine(s) de la Bipédie chez les Hominidés* (eds Coppens, Y. & Senut, B.) 169-176 (CNRS, Paris, 1991).

13. Susman, R. L., Stern, J. T. & Jungers, W. L. *Folia Primatol.* 43, 113-156 (1984).

14. Stern, J. T. & Susman, R. L. *Am. J. Phys. Anthrop.* 60, 279-318 (1983).

15. White, T. D., Johanson, D. C. & Kimbel, W. H. S. *Afr. J. Sci.* 77, 445-470 (1981).

16. Kimbel, W. H., White, T. D. & Johanson, D. C. in *Ancestors: The Hard Evidence* (ed. Delson, E.) 122-137 (Liss, New York, 1985).

17. Rak, Y. *The Australopithecine Face* 1-169 (Academic, New York, 1983).

18. Kimbel, W. H., White, T. D. & Johanson, D. C. *Am. J. Phys. Anthrop.* 64, 337-388 (1984).

19. Kimbel, W. H. & Rak, Y. *Am. J. Phys. Anthrop.* 66, 31-54 (1985).

20. Ward, S. C. & Kimbel, W. H. *Am. J. Phys. Anthrop.* 61, 157-171 (1983).

21. Kimbel, W. H., Johanson, D. C. & Coppens, Y. *Am. J. Phys. Anthrop.* 57, 453-499 (1982).

22. Kimbel, W. H. & White, T. D. *J. Hum. Evol.* 17, 545-550 (1988).

23. White, T. D. *et al. Nature* 366, 261-265 (1993).

24. Asfaw, B. *J. Hum. Evol.* 16, 611-624 (1987).

25. Wood, B. A., Yu, L. & Willoughby, C. *J. Anat.* 174, 185-205 (1991).

26. White, T. D. & Johanson, D. C. *Am. J. Phys. Anthrop.* 57, 501-544 (1982).

27. Johanson, D. C. *et al. Am. J. Phys. Anthrop.* 57, 403-451 (1982).

28. Lovejoy, C. O., Johanson, D. C. & Coppens, Y. *Am. J. Phys. Anthrop.* 57, 637-650 (1982).

29. Jungers, W. L. & Stern, J. T. *J. Hum. Evol.* 12, 673-684 (1983).

30. Stern, J. T. & Susman, R. L. in *Origine(s) de la Bipédie chez les Hominidés* (eds Coppens, Y. & Senut, B.) 99-111 (CNRS, Paris, 1991).

31. White, T. D., Moore, R. V. & Suwa, G. *J. Vert. Paleont.* 4, 575-583 (1984).

Acknowledgements. We thank the Center for Research and Conservation of Cultural Heritage (Ethiopian Ministry of Culture and Sports Affairs) and the National Museum of Ethiopia for permission to conduct field work and for logistical support. Field work was funded by grants from the National Science Foundation, the National Geographic Society, the L. S. B. Leakey Foundation and Lufthansa Airlines. We thank R. Walter, chief geologist and project co-leader, J. Aronson, R. Bernor, M. Black, G. Eck, J. Harris, E. Hovers, N. Kahn, P. Renne, S. Semaw, C. Vondra and T. Yemane for scientific contributions to the project, T. White for the discovery of A.L. 137-50 during his visit to Hadar in 1990, B. Latimer and L. Jellema for human and chimpanzee data from the Hamann-Todd Osteological Collection, Cleveland Museum of Natural History and our Ethiopian colleagues T. Asebwork, A. Asfaw, Z. Assefa, H. Bolku, M. Fesseha, T. Hagos, M. Kassa, M. Tesfaye, S. Teshome, T. Wodajo and the Afar people of Eloha village without whose assistance our field work would not have been possible.

Deuterium Abundance and Background Radiation Temperature in High-redshift Primordial Clouds

A. Songaila *et al.*

Editor's Note

Atoms of deuterium (heavy hydrogen) contain one proton and one neutron. Deuterium is depleted in our Milky Way galaxy, as it has been burned in stars whose gas is then returned to the interstellar medium. Here Antoinette Songaila and colleagues measure the deuterium abundance in a cloud of gas at a redshift of about 3.3, meaning that it is being seen only about 2 billion years after the Big Bang. They found that deuterium in this cloud is much more abundant than it is today in the Milky Way. This is consistent with current models of element formation (nucleosynthesis) associated with the first few minutes after the Big Bang, and so acts to verify our understanding of that process.

Measurements of the deuterium abundance in the early Universe provide a sensitive test of the "standard" Big Bang cosmology. The probable detection of deuterium absorption by a gas cloud between us and a distant quasar suggests an abundance much greater than estimated from observations in the Milky Way, and consistent with the amount of presently observed luminous matter comprising all the baryons in the Universe. The same spectra imply a cosmic background temperature for the early Universe which is consistent with our expectations from standard Big Bang cosmology.

THE primary observational supports of Big Bang cosmology are the spectrum and isotropy of the cosmic microwave background radiation (CMBR)[1-4] and the measurement of light-element abundances predicted by standard Big Bang nucleosynthesis (SBBN)[5-10]. Given a present-day CMBR temperature, SBBN predicts the composition of material emerging from the first few minutes of the Big Bang as a function of the universal density of baryons. Measurements of the relative primordial abundances of H, D, ^{3}He, ^{4}He, and ^{7}Li test the consistency of SBBN—whether there is any value of the baryon density for which the theory predicts all of these abundances correctly. They also provide a measurement of the baryon density, $\Omega_b h^2$ (in units where the cosmic critical density $\Omega = 1$ and the Hubble constant $H_0 = 100h$ km s^{-1} Mpc^{-1}), which can be compared with other data—the density of stars, gas and mass in the Universe.

Of the light elements, only H and ^{4}He have been measured outside the Galaxy. ^{7}Li has been measured in Galactic metal-poor old halo stars, yielding what is presumed to be a

高红移原初气体云中的氘丰度
和背景辐射温度

桑盖拉等

编者按

氘原子（重氢）包含一个质子和一个中子。在我们的银河系中，氘几乎消耗殆尽，这是由于在恒星核反应中会发生氘燃烧，而其产生的气体则会回到星际介质当中去。这里安托瓦内特·桑盖拉和同事们在一个红移大约 3.3 左右，也就是大爆炸仅仅 20 亿年之后的气体云中测量了氘丰度。他们发现该气体云中的氘丰度远高于今天银河系的氘丰度。这个结果与当前描述大爆炸后几分钟之内元素形成（核合成）的模型十分吻合，因此这也进一步证实了我们对这一过程的理解。

对早期宇宙中氘丰度的测量可以很灵敏地检验"标准"大爆炸宇宙论。对遥远类星体和我们之间的一块气体云进行观测，我们探测到可能的氘吸收线，这表明气体云中的氘丰度远高于从银河系观测所得到的估计值，并且与目前观测得到的包含宇宙中所有重子发光物质的含量一致。相同的光谱还暗示早期宇宙的背景温度与标准大爆炸宇宙论的预言一致。

支持大爆炸宇宙论的主要观测证据包括宇宙微波背景辐射（CMBR）[1-4] 的光谱和各向同性，以及标准大爆炸核合成模型（SBBN）[5-10] 预言的轻元素丰度测量。给定一个现在的宇宙微波背景辐射温度，标准大爆炸核合成理论可以预言出大爆炸之初的几分钟内合成的物质组分随宇宙重子密度的变化关系。测量氢（H）、氘（D）、氦 3（^{3}He）、氦 4（^{4}He）以及锂 7（^{7}Li）的相对原始丰度可以检验大爆炸核合成理论的自洽性——是否存在一个使得所有丰度预言都正确的重子密度。这些相对丰度还可以用于测量宇宙重子密度，$\Omega_b h^2$（以宇宙临界密度 $\Omega = 1$，哈勃常数 $H_0 = 100h\ \mathrm{km \cdot s^{-1} \cdot Mpc^{-1}}$ 为单位），这个量可以与其他观测数据相比较——比如，宇宙中恒星密度、气体密度和质量密度。

在所有的轻元素中，只有 H 和 ^{4}He 的丰度在银河系以外被测量过。人们在银河系内年老的贫金属晕族星中也对 ^{7}Li 的丰度进行了测量，这样测得的丰度据推测接近

nearly primordial abundance, although this interpretation has been questioned[10]. As yet, deuterium and ^{3}He have been observed only within the highly evolved and chemically active disk of our Galaxy. Moreover, because D is the most fragile of isotopes, it is easily destroyed in stars, where some of it is converted into ^{3}He and heavier elements, and only some of these daughter products are returned to the interstellar medium. The primordial abundances of these elements have been estimated by modelling the chemical evolution of the Galaxy, a complex process involving the cycling of interstellar gas through generations of stars[11]. Therefore, in practice the use of these elements in testing the SBBN model has been limited by the need to use evolutionary corrections to the observed abundances. Here we aim at a precise measurement of the ratio of the abundance of deuterium to hydrogen (D/H) in a chemically unevolved environment, bypassing the need for such corrections. The measurement is also confirmation of the predicted universality of the abundances over great distances—a new test of the cosmological principle. Among the light elements, only the ^{4}He/H ratio has previously been measured in more than one galaxy, and no ratios have been measured at cosmological distances.

This measurement also affects the SBBN estimate of Ω_b. The most precisely and reliably known primordial abundance is the helium mass fraction, estimated[12] from seven nearby metal-poor galaxies to be $Y_p = 0.228 \pm 0.005$. The baryon density implied by this estimate alone is rather low, $\Omega_b h^2 = 0.005$, barely more than the number of baryons we know to be present in luminous stars[13,14] or high-redshift quasar absorbers[15] ($\Omega_b \approx 2.9 \pm 0.6 \times 10^{-3}$). With such a low value for $\Omega_b h^2$ however, SBBN predicts a very high value for deuterium, $D/H \approx 2 \times 10^{-4}$, ~10 times the value of D/H observed in the interstellar medium. Chemical evolution models predict that with such a high D/H, the presolar nebula should be much more enriched in ^{3}He than allowed by observations of the solar wind[11]. The best chemical evolution model fits, and the constraint of the (D+^{3}He)/H abundance from Solar System measurements, both suggest a primordial D/H in the range $1.9 \times 10^{-5} < D/H < 6.8 \times 10^{-5}$ (for example, ref. 11).

For this reason, the preferred canonical range of baryon density believed[9-11] to yield the best consistency with all the light elements is $\Omega_b h^2 \approx 0.010$–$0.015$. Although this formally predicts Y_p between 2σ and 3σ (where σ is standard deviation) above the observed value, systematic uncertainties in the Y_p determination may be large enough to overpower the formal errors[13]. If the true value of $\Omega_b h^2$ does lie in this range, most of the baryons are in some dark, as yet unobserved, form.

Truly primordial abundances can be measured by studying the absorption spectra of high-redshift quasars. Light from quasars encounters many foreground gas clouds at various redshifts, leading to absorption lines of a variety of species which provide a sensitive probe of cloud composition. This technique offers an opportunity to discover directly the value of D/H in a variety of very distant and fairly chemically unevolved environments, where much less time has elapsed since the Big Bang and where one can verify that little stellar enrichment has occurred, hence little deuterium destruction. Furthermore, some high-column-density quasar absorption clouds—certain of the so-called "Lyman limit

原始丰度，尽管有人对这一解释表示怀疑[10]。迄今，我们也只在高度演化且化学活跃的银盘内对氘和 ^{3}He 进行过观测。不仅如此，由于氘是氢最不稳定的同位素，因此它在恒星中很容易被破坏，变成 ^{3}He 或者更重的元素，然后这些产物中只有一部分回到星际介质中。这些元素的原始丰度可以利用星系化学演化模型来进行估算，但须考虑星际气体在各代恒星间复杂的循环过程[11]。因此，实际利用这些元素对标准大爆炸核合成模型进行的检验受限于必须考虑对观测丰度做演化修正。在这里我们的目标是在无化学演化环境中对氘氢丰度比(D/H)进行精确测量，无需这些修正。这个测量还可以用来确认丰度值在很大距离范围内的普适性——这是一种对宇宙学原理的新检验。在所有轻元素中，只有 ^{4}He/H 比在不止一个星系中被测量过，但从未在宇宙学尺度上被测量过。

另外，这个测量的结果还会影响标准大爆炸核合成理论对 Ω_b 的估计。原始丰度的研究中最精确和可信的测量来自对邻近七个贫金属星系的氦丰度测量[12]，$Y_p = 0.228 \pm 0.005$。由此估算的重子密度很低，$\Omega_b h^2 = 0.005$，只比目前已知的在高光度恒星[13,14] 或者高红移类星体吸收天体[15] 中的重子含量($\Omega_b \approx (2.9 \pm 0.6) \times 10^{-3}$) 稍高一点。然而在如此低的重子密度的情况下，标准大爆炸核合成理论却能预言出非常高的氘丰度，$D/H \approx 2 \times 10^{-4}$，大约是星际介质中 D/H 观测结果的 10 倍。化学演化模型预言，在如此高的 D/H 值下，太阳前星云中 ^{3}He 的含量要比太阳风允许的观测结果高得多[11]。最好的化学演化模型的拟合结果以及太阳系内 $(D + ^3He)/H$ 丰度测量结果的限制，都倾向于 D/H 值在 $1.9 \times 10^{-5} < D/H < 6.8 \times 10^{-5}$ 的范围内(例如，参考文献 11)。

由于这个原因，人们普遍相信重子密度的范围[9-11]是 $\Omega_b h^2 \approx 0.010 \sim 0.015$，这样与所有轻元素丰度观测一致性最好。尽管这样预言的 Y_p 会在 2σ 到 3σ 水平上高于观测值(σ 是标准差)，但是 Y_p 的系统误差可能大到超过前者的误差[13]。如果重子密度的真实值确实处在这个范围之内，那么大部分重子必然是以某种暗的、尚未被观测到的形式存在。

事实上，真实的原始丰度可以通过观测高红移类星体的吸收光谱来进行测量。高红移类星体的光线在传播过程中会穿过位于不同红移处的前景气体云，在光谱的不同位置产生对应不同元素的大量吸收线，因此这些吸收线可以用来精确探测气体云的具体元素组成。这种技术给了我们一个直接观测那些遥远的、在基本未发生化学演化环境中的 D/H 值的机会，这些环境处于大爆炸之后很短的时间内，且可以证实其所对应的恒星元素增丰效应还很不显著，因此氘也几乎未被破坏。不仅如此，有些高柱密度的类星体吸收云，即所谓的莱曼系限系统(LLS)，它们对于氢原子的

systems" (LLS), which are optically thick to photoelectric absorption by hydrogen—are nearly ideal sites for measuring D/H accurately[16]. The H column density of a cloud can be measured quite precisely from the optical depth at the Lyman continuum limit or from line profile fitting of multiple lines of the series. A simple model of a multicomponent gas cloud, consisting of a series of velocity components, each one characterized by a velocity, a column density and spectral "b-parameter" ($b \equiv (2kT/m)^{1/2}$ where m is the atomic mass and T the temperature) can thereby be overconstrained by simultaneously fitting many lines of the Lyman series. Deuterium is measured by its isotopically shifted absorption lines, displaced towards the blue from the hydrogen lines by an apparent velocity $v = cm_e/2m_p = 82\,\mathrm{km\,s^{-1}}$ (where m_e and m_p are the masses of the electron and proton, respectively). The much smaller D column density is nevertheless detectable and accurately measured in the lowest-order lines.

This important programme has been attempted for years by us and others on 4-m class telescopes without notable success, because the faintness of the high-redshift quasars (that is, high enough redshift to see the Lyman series from the ground) makes high signal-to-noise spectroscopy too difficult at the required resolution $\sim 10\,\mathrm{km\,s^{-1}}$—to constrain the cloud model reliably. In addition, a certain amount of good fortune is required to locate suitably clean absorbers where the deuterium line is not contaminated by other intervening hydrogen lines.

We have now finally obtained data of the required quality, using the recently introduced high spectral resolution spectrograph on the Keck 10-m telescope (Mauna Kea, Hawaii), and report here the result of the first measurements, based on one night of data. We find absorption consistent with a detection D/H $\approx (1.9\text{–}2.5) \times 10^{-4}$ in a chemically unevolved cloud in the line of sight to the quasar Q0014+813; because in any single instance we cannot rule out the possibility of a chance H contamination at exactly the D velocity offset, this result should be considered as an upper limit until further observations of other systems are made. As more measurements are made, we would expect to see a consistent minimum value of D/H emerging as the true, primordial value.

The same spectra also allow a test of another fundamental prediction of relativistic cosmology—namely, that the temperature of the cosmic microwave background radiation T_{CMBR} should evolve with redshift, z, as $T_{CMBR} \propto (1+z)$—which is a more direct constraint than other arguments[17] against alternative models for the origin of the background radiation. Recent experiments have provided extraordinarily precise confirmation of the isotropy of the cosmic microwave background radiation and of its black-body spectrum; the current value of T_{CMBR} is now extremely accurately measured, at 2.73 K, both directly[1,2] and from cyanogen excitation in the interstellar medium[18]. The value of T_{CMBR} at high z can similarly be measured through fine-structure splitting of atomic carbon lines in high-z quasar absorption line systems[19,20]. Although attempts have been made to use this technique on C II and C I lines[20,21], the results have again been limited by the difficulty of obtaining very high signal-to-noise spectra on these very faint ($V = 16\text{–}17$, where V is visual magnitude) quasars. We present below such a measurement of C II 1,334 Å in the Lyman limit absorber in quasar

光电吸收是光学厚的，是精确测量 D/H 值近乎完美的理想场所 [16]。从莱曼连续谱系限的光深，或者通过莱曼系多条吸收线的轮廓拟合，我们可以精确测量气体云中氢元素的柱密度。对于一个包含了多种速度组成、简单的多成分气体云模型，我们可以用速度、柱密度和谱参数 $b(b \equiv (2kT/m)^{1/2})$ 来描述其中的各个成分，其中 m 是原子质量，T 是温度，这些量均可以通过同时拟合多条吸收线来进行很好的限制。对氘的测量是通过其由于同位素效应而移动的谱线进行的，该谱线比氢线稍朝蓝端移动，相应的视速度为 $v = cm_e/2m_p = 82 \ \mathrm{km \cdot s^{-1}}$（其中 m_e 和 m_p 分别是电子和质子质量）。虽然氘的柱密度很小，但还是可观测的，人们已经通过最低阶的谱线对其进行了精确的测量。

多年来我们和其他人都曾经用 4 米级的望远镜尝试进行这个重要的项目，但是并没有取得明显的成功。这是因为暗淡的高红移类星体（其红移需高到足以利用地面望远镜接收莱曼系光子），在所需的分辨率下（约为 $10 \ \mathrm{km \cdot s^{-1}}$）很难得到高信噪比的光谱，即很难可靠地限制气体云模型。另外当然还需要一点好运气，这样才能找到不受其他氢吸收线污染的干净的氘吸收线。

使用 10 米凯克望远镜（夏威夷冒纳凯阿火山）上最新引进的高分辨率光谱仪，我们最终获得了所需分辨率的数据。在这里我们报告基于一个晚上观测数据所得到的首次测量结果。我们在类星体 Q0014+813 的视线方向上一个无化学演化的气体云中发现了对应 $D/H \approx (1.9 \sim 2.5) \times 10^{-4}$ 的吸收线。因为对任何一个单独的事例我们都不能排除正好在对应于氘谱线速度的地方存在氢污染的可能性，我们观测到其他系统之前，这个值应该被理解为一个上限。随着更多观测的进行，我们期待可以得到自洽的 D/H 的最小值，这将给出真正的原始丰度。

这些光谱还可以用来检验另一个相对论宇宙学的基本预言——宇宙微波背景辐射的温度 T_{CMBR} 随红移 z 的演化规律，即满足 $T_{CMBR} \propto (1+z)$——相对于其他论证方法 [17] 来说，该检验可以对不同微波背景辐射起源理论给出更直接的限制。最近的实验以极高的精度确认了宇宙微波背景辐射的各向同性和黑体谱特征，且通过直接观测 [1,2] 或者从星际介质中的氰激发 [18] 得到了迄今为止对微波背景辐射温度最准确的测量结果，T_{CMBR} 约为 2.73 K。而高红移处的 T_{CMBR} 也可以类似地通过高红移类星体吸收线系统中因碳原子精细结构而导致的谱线分裂来进行测量 [19,20]。尽管此前已有人利用 C II 和 C I 线进行相关尝试 [20,21]，但是结果依旧受限于难以获得这些暗淡类星体高信噪比的光谱（$V = 16 \sim 17$，V 为目视星等）。下面，我们给出对类星体 Q0636+68 莱曼系限吸收体中的 C II 1,334 Å 谱线的测量结果。这个结果对 $z = 2.9092$

Q0636+68, which places a new tighter limit of 13.5 K on T_{CMBR} at $z = 2.9092$, corresponding to a redshifted value $T_{CMBR}/(1+z) < 3.5$ K measured at wavelength $611/(1+z)$ µm.

Abundance Measurements

Observations of the two quasars, Q0636+68 ($V = 16.5$) and Q0014+813 ($V = 16.9$), were made on 11 November 1993 with the Keck 10-m telescope, as four 40-min exposures and one 50-min exposure for Q0636+68 (3.5 h total), and six 40-min exposures for Q0014+813 (4.0 h total). A $1.2'' \times 3.8''$ slit was used. Each observation covered the range 3,500–5,900 Å at a resolution $R = 36,000$ and, at the longer wavelengths of interest here, sky- and read-noise and detector dark current were negligible, so that the signal-to-noise ratio was determined only by source counts.

The two quasars have strong LLS, at $z = 2.909$ in Q0636, and $z = 2.813$ in Q0014 (ref. 22). Both are metal-line systems and have very complex structure, stretching over several hundred kilometres per second in velocity. In particular, there is contamination by high-negative-velocity hydrogen at the expected position of deuterium, making measurement of D/H essentially impossible. In this they resemble certain interstellar lines of sight[23] which are too complicated to be useful for D/H measurement.

Q0014 also has a much weaker LLS at $z = 3.3201$ corresponding to the modestly high hydrogen atom column density ($N_H \approx 10^{17}$ atoms cm^{-2}) metal-poor cloud extensively studied by Chaffee and collaborators[24,25]. This cloud may contain some elements heavier than helium, as indicated by the possible presence of Si III 1,206 Å and C III 977 Å absorption lines. Although the lines occur at the proper wavelengths, they lie in a region with many Lyman-α absorption lines, and Chaffee et al.[25] argue that these cannot be attributed to Si and C because the line strengths are not consistent with the expected intensities. Irrespective of this point, the metallicity in the Chaffee cloud is very low. Even in the unlikely case that the cloud were predominantly neutral, the C II and C I line limits ($< 10^{12}$ cm^{-2} from our data) would place the metallicity at less than one-fortieth of the solar value, whereas if C III or C IV were the dominant ionization state, the hydrogen would be highly ionized, whether the cloud were photoionized or collisionally ionized[25,26] and in this case both Chaffee et al.[25] and Donahue and Shull[27] concluded that the metallicity was less than, or about, $10^{-3.5}$ of solar.

Chaffee et al. found that the neutral hydrogen in this cloud was well fitted by two components, each with $N_H \approx 5 \times 10^{16}$ cm^{-2} and $b \sim 28$ km s^{-1}, and with a separation of N_H 110 km s^{-1}. With our higher signal-to-noise, higher resolution data, we have reanalysed the neutral hydrogen model, using the Lyman break at a wavelength of 3,939 Å (Fig. 1) to obtain the combined neutral hydrogen column density. We compared the flux in the 40 Å below the break to that between 3,960 Å and 4,000 Å, and evaluated the ratio of the maximum peaks (0.58), the fifth maximum peaks (0.55), the medians (0.58) and the means (0.60). The maximum peak

的宇宙微波背景辐射温度给出了更好的限制，其温度约为 13.5 K，对应在波长为 $611/(1+z)$ μm 处测得 $T_{CMBR}/(1+z) < 3.5$ K。

丰 度 测 量

我们在 1993 年 11 月 11 日使用凯克 10 米望远镜对两个类星体 Q0636+68 ($V = 16.5$) 和 Q0014+813 ($V = 16.9$) 进行了观测，其中包括对 Q0636+68 的 4 段 40 分钟和 1 段 50 分钟的曝光（总共 3.5 小时），对 Q0014+813 的 6 段 40 分钟的曝光（总共 4 小时）。在整个观测过程中，我们使用了 $1.2'' \times 3.8''$ 的光缝。每一次观测覆盖的波长为 3,500~5,900 Å，分辨率为 $R = 36,000$。同时，在感兴趣的较长波段区间，由于天空噪声、读噪声和探测器暗流噪声均可以忽略，因此信噪比仅取决于源计数。

这两个类星体都有很强的莱曼系限系统，其中 Q0636 的莱曼系限系统出现在红移为 $z = 2.909$ 处，而 Q0014 的莱曼系限系统则出现在红移为 $z = 2.813$ 处（参考文献 22）。这两者都是金属谱线系统，并具有很复杂的结构，其速度展宽可以超过每秒几百千米。特别的是，在预期氘谱线的位置上存在高负速度氢所带来的污染，这使得对 D/H 的精确测量几乎变得不可能。这与某些视线方向的星际介质 [23] 相似，太复杂以至于无法用于对 D/H 的测量。

Q0014 在红移 $z = 3.3201$ 处还有一个弱得多的莱曼系限系统，对应一个具有中等高氢原子柱密度（每平方厘米约 10^{17} 个原子）的贫金属气体云。该气体云已被查菲及其合作者们广泛地研究过 [24,25]。从可能存在的 Si III 1,206 Å 和 C III 977 Å 吸收线的迹象判断，这块气体云可能包含比氢更重的元素。尽管这些吸收线出现在相应的位置，但是它们所在的波长范围内还存在很多莱曼 α 吸收线。并且由于这些吸收线的强度与预期的强度不符，查菲等人 [25] 认为这些并不是碳和硅的吸收线。不考虑这一点，这块查菲气体云的金属丰度很低。即便这块气体云处于不太可能的中性状态，C II 和 C I 线给出的限制（我们的数据显示 $< 10^{12}$ cm^{-2}）也表明该气体云的金属丰度小于太阳的四十分之一。然而如果电离的 C III 和 C IV 是主要的状态，那么不管气体云是光致电离还是碰撞电离 [25,26]，氢都将是高度电离的。在这种情况下查菲等人 [25]、多纳休和沙尔 [27] 都推测该气体云的金属丰度大约仅为太阳的 $10^{-3.5}$ 或更低。

查菲等人发现这块气体云中的中性氢可以用两部分来进行很好的拟合，每一部分对应：$N_H \approx 5 \times 10^{16}$ cm^{-2}，$b \sim 28$ km·s^{-1}，两部分 N_H 之间相差 110 km·s^{-1}。利用所得的高信噪比、高分辨率的数据我们重新分析这个中性氢模型，用波长为 3,939 Å 处的莱曼断裂（图 1）去计算整体的中性氢柱密度。我们比较了莱曼断裂波长以下 40 Å 处以及 3,960 Å 到 4,000 Å 处的流量，并计算了最高峰 (0.58)、第五最高峰 (0.55)、中位数 (0.58) 和平均值 (0.60) 之间的比值。这里最高峰的比值给出了氢柱密度的最

ratios constitute the best estimate, with the mean serving as an upper bound as it is raised by the presence of the Lyman series in the upper wavelength range. Together they give an optical depth $\tau = 0.55 \pm 0.05$, corresponding to $N_H = 9.5 \times 10^{16} \pm 0.8 \times 10^{16}\,\mathrm{cm}^{-2}$.

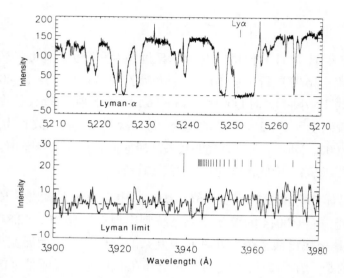

Fig. 1. The region of Lyman-α (5,250 Å; top) and the Lyman break (3,939 Å; bottom) in the $z = 3.32$ Lyman limit system (LLS) in the quasar Q0014+813. Six CCD (charge-coupled device) frames were flat-fielded with a quartz lamp exposure, spatially registered and added with a filter to remove cosmic rays; one-dimensional spectra were formed by subtracting a heavily smoothed sky and then summing the spatial points along the slit corresponding to a particular spectral pixel. The spatial summation included all points where the flux exceeded 10% of the maximum on the source. The spectra were precisely wavelength-calibrated using a Th–Ar lamp and approximately flux-calibrated (F_v) using observations of the white dwarf star Feige 110. The resulting signal-to-noise ratio was ~87 per resolution element at Lyman-α and much less (~15 per resolution element) at the Lyman break, because of the rapid drop-off in both detector efficiency and the cross-disperser blaze function at and below 4,000 Å. The positions of Ly-α(top) and Lyman 9 to Lyman 30 and the Lyman break (bottom) are shown as vertical lines. The dashed lines indicate the median values below and above the Lyman break.

To determine the b-values and relative strengths of the strongest components, which are the key to measuring D/H, it is desirable to work with the unsaturated very-high-order Lyman series lines. The structure of this region is, however, complex, being deep in the Lyman forest, and fitting of individual lines is somewhat subjective (compare Fig. 1). To alleviate this problem we formed the medians in velocity space of the lines Lyman 7 to Lyman 13, and Lyman 14 to Lyman 20 (Fig. 2). This eliminated contaminating lines, leaving only the relatively invariant Lyman lines themselves. In the Lyman 14–20 composite, only the strong component at $-17.5\,\mathrm{km\,s}^{-1}$ is clearly seen. The uncertainty in the central velocity is ~5 km s^{-1}. Fitting this with a single cloud, we find a b-value of 21 km s^{-1} with an acceptable range of 18–28 km s^{-1}. If we assume that the line approximates Lyman 17, because the oscillator strengths vary only slowly in the high Lyman series, we find $N_H = 5.5 \times 10^{16}\,\mathrm{cm}^{-2}$. The primary uncertainty in N_H is the placement of the continuum, and the value could range from $8.7 \times 10^{16}\,\mathrm{cm}^{-2}$ to $4.0 \times 10^{16}\,\mathrm{cm}^{-2}$. The second component at 80 km s^{-1} shows up clearly in the Lyman 7–13 composite. This component is best fitted with two clouds, each

380

佳估计，而考虑到莱曼系出现在波长范围的长波段，平均值的比值可作为上限。最终结果表明，光深 $\tau = 0.55 \pm 0.05$，对应 $N_{\mathrm{H}} = 9.5 \times 10^{16} \pm 0.8 \times 10^{16}\ \mathrm{cm}^{-2}$。

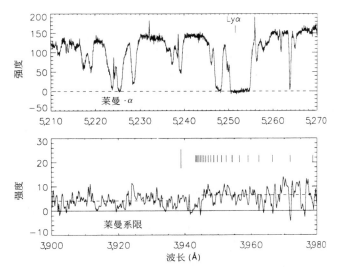

图 1. 类星体 Q0014+813 在 $z = 3.32$ 处莱曼系限系统中对应的莱曼 α(5,250 Å，上图) 和莱曼断裂(3,939 Å，下图) 的光谱。六幅 CCD(电荷耦合器件) 观测图像，通过石英灯进行平场校正、并进行空间校正后，使用一定的滤波函数滤去宇宙线干扰。减去高度平滑的天空背景后，沿着光缝将对应于某一光谱像素的空间点相叠加后得出一维光谱。空间叠加包含了所有超过源最大值 10% 的点。利用钍–氩灯，我们对光谱的波长进行了精确定标，并用白矮星 Feige 110 的观测进行近似流量定标(F_ν)。最终得到莱曼 α 处单位可分辨单元的信噪比约为 87，而莱曼断裂处的信噪比要低很多(对应单位可分辨单元的信噪比约为 15)，这是因为在 4,000 Å 及以下，传感器效率和横向色散器闪耀函数都将迅速降低。莱曼 α(上图)，莱曼 9 到莱曼 30 和莱曼断裂(下图) 的位置均已用竖线标出。而虚线则标出高于或低于莱曼断裂的中值。

　　为了确定 b 值以及最强成分的相对强度这些测量 D/H 的关键量，我们必须处理未饱和的很高阶的莱曼系谱线。这些谱线所对应的区域处在莱曼森林中，结构非常复杂，因此要拟合单一谱线就多少受主观因素影响(比较图 1)。为了解决这个问题，我们在速度空间上画出莱曼 7 到莱曼 13，和莱曼 14 到莱曼 20 的中值(图 2)。这样做可以排除掉干扰的谱线，只留下相对不变的莱曼线系。对于莱曼 14~20 的合成谱，只有在 $-17.5\ \mathrm{km} \cdot \mathrm{s}^{-1}$ 的强成分可以清晰地被辨认。中心速度的误差为 $5\ \mathrm{km} \cdot \mathrm{s}^{-1}$。若用单一气体云模型来拟合，我们发现 b 值为 $21\ \mathrm{km} \cdot \mathrm{s}^{-1}$，可接受的范围是 $18\sim28\ \mathrm{km} \cdot \mathrm{s}^{-1}$。如果我们假设这条谱线近似是莱曼 17，考虑到振子强度在高阶莱曼系的变化非常缓慢，我们可以得到 $N_{\mathrm{H}} = 5.5 \times 10^{16}\ \mathrm{cm}^{-2}$。这里 N_{H} 的主要误差来源是连续谱的精确定位，因此 N_{H} 的可取值范围为 $8.7 \times 10^{16}\ \mathrm{cm}^{-2}$ 到 $4.0 \times 10^{16}\ \mathrm{cm}^{-2}$。在莱曼 7~13 的成分中，我们还清晰地发现了 $80\ \mathrm{km} \cdot \mathrm{s}^{-1}$ 处的第二个成分。这个成

with $b = 16\,\text{km s}^{-1}$ and velocities of $80\,\text{km s}^{-1}$ and $113\,\text{km s}^{-1}$. The cloud column densities are $N_{\text{H}} = 1.5 \times 10^{16}\ \text{cm}^{-2}$ and $5.5 \times 10^{15}\ \text{cm}^{-2}$ if we adopt a fit with the oscillator strength of Lyman 10. As we move up the Lyman series, weaker components with $N_{\text{H}} \sim 10^{15}\text{cm}^{-2}$ are seen, also with b-values around $21\,\text{km s}^{-1}$. The final cloud model is summarized in Table 1 and the fit to the Lyman series is shown in Fig. 2. The total column density of the model fit is $7.9 \times 10^{16}\ \text{cm}^{-2}$, which is slightly lower than the value we have estimated from the Lyman break. This could reflect the uncertainty in the strongest component caused by the continuum fit, or possibly some additional material not well described by static thermal slabs; either way, the near agreement argues against significant systematic errors in estimating N_{H}. For the purposes of estimating D/H, we shall assume that cloud 1 has N_{H} in the range $(5.5\text{–}7.3) \times 10^{16}\ \text{cm}^{-2}$. This is consistent with the range of $N_{\text{H}} = (2.3\text{–}8.7) \times 10^{16}$ cm^{-2} found by Chaffee et al.[24].

The Chaffee cloud is very well suited for a determination of the D/H abundance ratio because the high-column-density component lies at the blue end of the complex. In Fig. 3 we show the predictions of the cloud model of Table 1 for Dα as a function of the value of D/H assuming that $b_{\text{deuterium}} = b_{\text{hydrogen}}/\sqrt{2}$ —that is, thermal broadening. The feature seen in the blue wing of Lyman-α is precisely at the expected position of deuterium and, if interpreted as deuterium, gives a best fit of $\text{D/H} = 2.5 \times 10^{-4}$ for $N_{\text{H}} = 5.5 \times 10^{16}\ \text{cm}^{-2}$. If the larger value of N_{H} obtained from fitting the break were used, this becomes 1.9×10^{-4}.

Table 1. Best cloud model ($z = 3.32015$)

v (km s^{-1})	b (km s^{-1})	N (cm^{-2})
−17.5	21.0	5.5×10^{16}
13.5	24.0	1.8×10^{15}
80.0	16.0	1.5×10^{16}
113.0	16.0	5.5×10^{15}
155.0	21.5	6.5×10^{14}

v, Central velocity; b, Doppler parameter; N, column density.

分用两块气体云模型拟合得最好，每块气体云都有 $b = 16\ km \cdot s^{-1}$，且速度分别为 $80\ km \cdot s^{-1}$ 和 $113\ km \cdot s^{-1}$。如果用莱曼 10 的振子强度来进行拟合，那么气体云的柱密度分别为 $1.5 \times 10^{16}\ cm^{-2}$ 和 $5.5 \times 10^{15}\ cm^{-2}$。如果我们转向更高阶的莱曼线，将可以看到柱密度 N_H 约为 $10^{15}\ cm^{-2}$ 的相对更弱的成分，同样对应 b 值约为 $21\ km \cdot s^{-1}$。在表 1 中我们总结了最终的气体云模型，并把对莱曼线系的拟合结果显示在图 2 中。最终模型拟合得到的总柱密度为 $7.9 \times 10^{16}\ cm^{-2}$，这比直接用莱曼断裂所估计的值稍小。这可能是因为连续谱拟合带来最强成分的不确定性，也可能还存在一些不能用静态热板块模型进行很好描述的因素。但无论如何，这个接近吻合的数值表明在估计 N_H 时并没有明显的系统误差。为了估计 D/H，我们将假设第一块气体云的柱密度为 $(5.5 \sim 7.3) \times 10^{16}\ cm^{-2}$，这和查菲等人的结果 $(2.3 \sim 8.7) \times 10^{16}\ cm^{-2}$ 相吻合[24]。

查菲气体云非常适合用来计算 D/H 丰度比，因为其中的高柱密度成分处于复合体的蓝端。在图 3 中，假设热致宽 $b_D = b_H / \sqrt{2}$，我们基于表 1 中给出的气体云模型预言给出了 Dα 随 D/H 变化的函数关系。可以看到，莱曼 α 的蓝端刚好位于氘的位置，如果解释为氘，那么在 $N_H = 5.5 \times 10^{16}\ cm^{-2}$ 的条件下，有最佳拟合值 $D/H = 2.5 \times 10^{-4}$。如果换成使用拟合莱曼断裂所得到的更大的 N_H 时，D/H 的最佳拟合值变为 1.9×10^{-4}。

表 1. 最佳气体云模型 ($z = 3.32015$)

$v(km \cdot s^{-1})$	$b(km \cdot s^{-1})$	$N(cm^{-2})$
−17.5	21.0	5.5×10^{16}
13.5	24.0	1.8×10^{15}
80.0	16.0	1.5×10^{16}
113.0	16.0	5.5×10^{15}
155.0	21.5	6.5×10^{14}

v，中心速度；b，多普勒参数；N，柱密度。

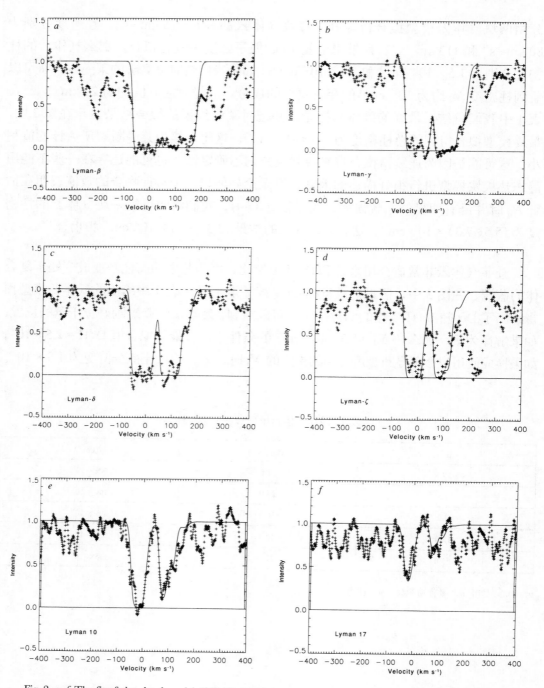

Fig. 2. *a–f*, The fit of the cloud model of Table 1 to Lyman series lines (identified lower left of each panel) of the $z = 3.32015$ LLS in Q0014+813. The profile labelled "Lyman 10" is a median in velocity space of the Lyman 7 to Lyman 13 profiles, and "Lyman 17" is a composite of Lyman 14 to Lyman 20. Crosses mark the data values and the solid line the model fit.

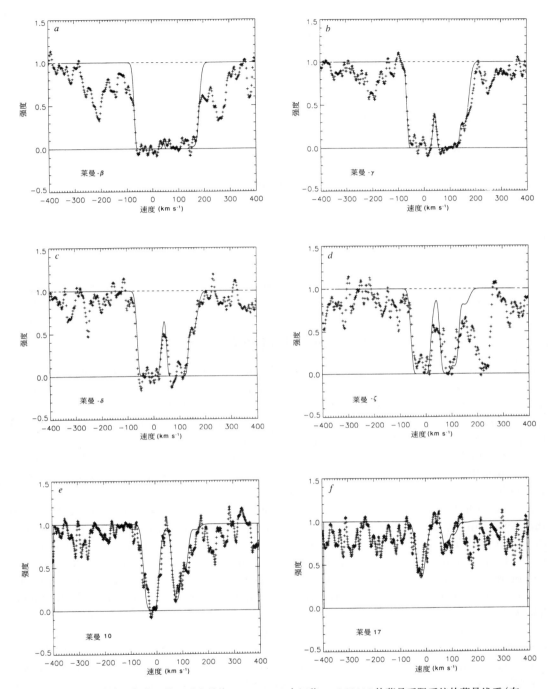

图 2. a~f, 采用表 1 气体云模型对类星体 Q0014+813 中红移 z = 3.32015 的莱曼系限系统的莱曼线系 (在每张小图左下注明) 所得到的拟合结果。标注 "莱曼 10" 的轮廓线是莱曼 7 到莱曼 13 轮廓线速度空间的中值, 标注 "莱曼 17" 的轮廓线是莱曼 14 到莱曼 20 的合成谱。十字是数据点, 实线是模型拟合。

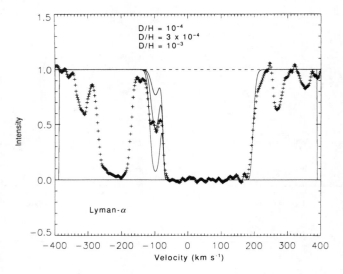

Fig. 3. The prediction of the cloud model of Table 1 for deuterium-α absorption in Q0014+813. Crosses mark data values, and the three solid lines show model fits for D/H = 10^{-4} (top), 3×10^{-4} (middle) and 10^{-3} (bottom).

Implications for the Big Bang

In the case of a single absorber, we cannot rule out the possibility that an errant hydrogen cloud, with a column density 2.5×10^{-4} that of the main cloud, happens to be floating at the velocity shift where we expect to find deuterium; note in particular that the signal to noise is insufficient to distinguish the narrower thermal broadening expected for D ($b_{\text{deuterium}} = b_{\text{hydrogen}} / \sqrt{2}$). But we can place limits on the likelihood of such a chance interpolation. The redshift of the Chaffee cloud lies close to the redshift of the quasar (3.41) and the number density of Lyman-α forest lines increases steeply with decreasing wavelength in this region. The Ly-α line lies at the red end of echelle order 68, where there are 12 Ly-α forest lines in the observed 75 Å which would be strong enough to contaminate the deuterium region, whereas in order 67, which is 80 Å to the red, the number has dropped to 4 in 75 Å. A rate of 12 lines per 75 Å would amount to a probability of 3% that a Ly-α line might be observed at random within ± 5 km s^{-1} of the deuterium position. Although this is quite small, until similar abundances are regularly found in other absorbers, it is necessary to regard our measurement as an upper limit on the deuterium abundance. Viewed in this light, the limit is encouragingly close to the values of D/H predicted from Galactic chemical evolution models, and suggests that, as further clouds are studied, we will be able to refine the measurement of D/H to significantly constrain SBBN and chemical evolution models. The quality of the data is sufficient to detect even much lower abundances, so that a small statistical survey of similar absorbers should remove the current ambiguity due to possible contamination.

It is also possible that this might prove to be the best measurement to date of the primordial D/H, and as such it is interesting to examine its potential consequences for cosmological theory. A value of D/H as high as 2.5×10^{-4} is acceptable within SBBN, is just consistent

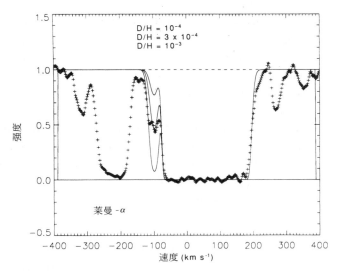

图 3. 表 1 气体云模型对类星体 Q0014+813 中的氘-α 吸收所做的预言。十字是数据点，三条实线是对 D/H 比分别为 10^{-4}（上）、3×10^{-4}（中）和 10^{-3}（下）的模型拟合。

大爆炸的含义

在只观测到一个吸收体的情况下，我们不能排除这是一块柱密度为主气体云的 2.5×10^{-4} 倍漂浮的氢气体云且正好以产生我们期望观测到氘线的速度在漂移的可能性。特别值得注意的是，（这一数据的）信噪比还不足以有效地区分具有较窄热致宽的氘（$b_D = b_H / \sqrt{2}$）。但是我们可以对产生这种现象的概率加以限制。查菲气体云红移和类星体红移 (3.41) 很接近，而莱曼 α 森林谱线的数密度在这个区域随着波长的减小而迅速增长。莱曼 α 谱线位于中阶梯光栅第 68 级的红端，在观测的 75 Å 波长内有 12 条莱曼 α 森林谱线，可以强到足以污染氘的区域。而在第 67 级，也就是距红端大约 80 Å 处，莱曼 α 谱线的数目在 75 Å 内下降到 4 条。每 75 Å 内的 12 条谱线造成莱曼 α 谱线随机出现在氘线附近 5 km·s^{-1} 内的可能性是 3%。尽管很小，但在更多的吸收体中发现相似的结果前，我们还是应该把我们测得的氘丰度仅仅视为是一个上限。这样看来，这个极限很接近星系化学演化模型预言的 D/H 值。这表明，随着更多的气体云研究，我们将可以不断改进 D/H 测量的精度，并用来更好地限制标准大爆炸核合成和化学演化模型。数据的质量将足以用来探测更低的丰度，因此一个小的寻找类似吸收体的统计巡天观测应该可以很好地排除目前可能的污染所造成的不确定性。

与此同时，这可能也是迄今为止对原初 D/H 值的最佳测量，因此很有必要进一步讨论该结果对宇宙学理论的潜在影响。首先，高达 2.5×10^{-4} 的 D/H 值在标准大爆炸核合成理论中是可接受的，且这个值与 ^{7}Li 的结果相吻合 [10]，甚至与 ^{4}He 符合

with ^{7}Li measurements[10], and is even favoured by ^{4}He (ref. 28). It has the consequence of reducing Ω_b a factor of three below its canonical value, to $0.005h^{-2}$ (refs 9, 10), which roughly agrees[13-15] with the inventory of luminous and gaseous matter in the Universe. Because evolution after the Big Bang is a net destroyer of deuterium, it is not surprising to find relatively high D/H in a relatively unevolved primordial cloud.

There are however difficulties reconciling such a high value of D/H with the much lower values found in the interstellar medium[29] (of the order of 10^{-5}), and especially with the Solar System abundance of ^{3}He. Although ^{3}He can be both created and destroyed in different types of stars, models including a normal mix of stars predict[11] that Galactic chemical evolution leads to at best only a slight decrease with time in the sum $(D+^3He)/H$, so that the $^3He/^4He$ ratio measured locally in the solar wind seems to imply a low presolar value of $(D+^3He)/H \approx 4 \times 10^{-5}$, contradicting our D/H measurement. It is of course possible that the chemical evolution models are inadequate; for example, it could be that the presolar nebula at the time of its formation contained abundance atypical of the Galaxy. (The possibility of such spatial fluctuations in $^3He/H$ is suggested by interstellar measurements of $^3He/H$ using hyperfine transitions[30], which show a range of values for $^3He/H$ from $\lesssim 1 \times 10^{-5}$ to 15×10^{-5}.) These uncertainties make the use of local ^{3}He observations ambiguous for cosmological arguments, and motivate further measurements of D/H at high redshift, which should give a much cleaner test of SBBN.

Demonstration of a low value of Ω_b would have a wide impact on other aspects of cosmological theory. For example, many models of galaxy formation predict that the baryon mass fraction in galaxy clusters ought to be Ω_b, and a low value of Ω_b exacerbates their conflict with the observed high baryon fraction ($> 0.05h^{-3/2}$) of the Coma cluster[31]. A low baryon density would also conflict with massive spiral galaxy halos being made primarily of baryonic objects, a prediction which can be tested by gravitational microlensing experiments[32,33]. If we are indeed seeing almost all of the baryons already, dynamical evidence points even more strongly to halos made of non-baryonic dark matter.

Cosmic Background Temperature

The evolution of the microwave background temperature with redshift is a little-doubted prediction of relativistic cosmology which is nevertheless worth testing precisely. For example, this test complements other arguments[17,34] constraining alternatives to the Big Bang origin of the background radiation. At the redshifts of our absorbers, we can observe transitions from the ground state of singly ionized atomic carbon C II, as well as from the fine structure split state C II* which lies 64 cm^{-1} above the ground state. At these redshifts, the frequency difference is only about three times the peak frequency of the CMBR, so C II* is predicted to have a non-negligible population just due to the presence of the microwave background. We measure the relative populations of C II and C II* from the strengths of ultra-violet absorption lines from the two states.

得更好（参考文献28）。但是该结果却可以使 Ω_b 减小到人们公认值的三分之一，约 $0.005h^{-2}$（参考文献9，10），这与宇宙中发光物质和气体物质的总量大致相当[13-15]。由于大爆炸结束后氘就只消耗而不产生，因此在一个无演化的原初气体云中发现较高的 D/H 值并不奇怪。

然而，要调和这一高 D/H 值与在星际介质中测得的低得多的值 [29]（约 10^{-5}）之间的矛盾，尤其是与太阳系中 ^{3}He 丰度间的矛盾却非常困难。尽管 ^{3}He 在不同的恒星中既可以产生也可以减少，但是具有正常的恒星组合的模型预言[11]，星系的化学演化最多只能造成 $(D+^3He)/H$ 随时间缓慢减少，因此在太阳风中测得的 ^{3}He/^{4}He 暗示原始太阳可能具有较小的 $(D+^3He)/H$ 值，约 4×10^{-5}，这与我们测得的 D/H 值矛盾。当然也有可能是星系化学演化模型不完善导致的，例如，太阳前星云在它诞生之时包含的丰度不是银河系典型的星系丰度。（用超精细跃迁 [30] 测得的星际 ^{3}He/H 值揭示了 ^{3}He/H 值的这种空间涨落的可能性，对应值的范围是 $\leqslant 1\times10^{-5}$ 到 15×10^{-5}。）这使得我们利用本地测得的 ^{3}He 值讨论宇宙学问题时存在不确定性，因此我们需要观测得到高红移的 D/H 值，这样可以给出对标准大爆炸核合成更准确的检验。

如果低的 Ω_b 被证实，那将对于宇宙学很多其他方面产生重要的影响。例如，很多星系形成模型预言星系团中的重子质量百分比应该就是 Ω_b，而较小的 Ω_b 将加剧它们与观测的后发星系团中高重子比例（$>0.05h^{-3/2}$）之间的矛盾[31]。低重子密度也和大质量旋涡星系晕主要由重子物质构成的预言相矛盾，这个预言可以用微引力透镜实验进行检验[32,33]。如果我们确实已经看到了所有的重子物质，那么动力学证据则更加强烈地证明星系晕是由非重子暗物质组成。

宇宙背景温度

虽然宇宙微波背景温度随红移的演化是相对论宇宙学的一个很少被怀疑的预言，然而精确的检验还是非常有必要的。例如，这个检验可以与其他研究手段一起用于限制关于背景辐射的各种非大爆炸起源的模型 [17,34]。在我们研究的吸收体的红移处，我们可以观测到一次电离碳原子 CⅡ 的基态跃迁，也可以看到在基态之上 64 cm^{-1} 的精细结构分裂状态 CⅡ* 的跃迁。在这些红移处，这个频率差仅仅是宇宙微波背景辐射峰值频率的 3 倍，因此正因为存在微波背景，模型预言存在不可忽略数量的 CⅡ*。我们利用这两个态的紫外吸收线强度测量了 CⅡ 和 CⅡ* 的相对数。

We have observed the C II line at 1,334.532 Å corresponding to the LLS at $z = 2.909$ found by Sargent *el al.*[22] in the quasar Q0636+68. The C I multiplets are too weak in this system to be useful for this test while N II lies within the Lyman forest. As Fig. 4 shows, the C II line consists of three strong, and a number of weaker, components stretching over more than ± 100 km s^{-1}, the strongest of which has a redshift, $z = 2.9034$ which we have chosen to be the zero velocity. Comparison with other lines such as Si II leaves no doubt that all the components seen are C II lines, and confirms the accuracy of the wavelength scale.

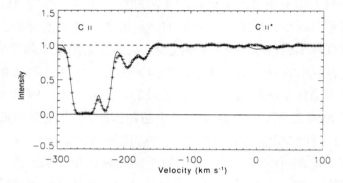

Fig. 4. C II 1,334.532 Å and C II* 1,335.708 Å absorption in the $z = 2.9034$ LLS in Q0636+68. Crosses show the data values and the positions of C II and C II* are labelled. The solid line shows a model in which the column density of C II* is 1% of C II, to show where C II* would appear if it were present. The rest equivalent width of the three strongest C II components is 248 mÅ, corresponding to a minimum column density $N_{(C II)} = 1.5 \times 10^{14}$ cm^{-2}. More precisely, profile-fitting gives $N_{(C II)} = 4.6 \times 10^{14}$ cm^{-2}. The equivalent width of C II* for all three main components is ≤ 0.4 mÅ ± 0.6 mÅ, corresponding to a 2σ upper limit of 10^{12} cm^{-2} in this line.

Profile-fitting the three strongest components gives a column density, $N_{(C II)} = 4.6 \times 10^{14}$ cm^{-2}. Considerable additional material could be hidden in strongly saturated components, but this is the minimum value needed to give an accurate fit. By contrast, we do not see the line at 1,335.708 Å from the excited fine-structure level C II*. We have determined the noise level in this region empirically by fitting the column densities at random positions at neighbouring ("wrong") wavelengths and find that the equivalent width of C II* for all three main components is 0.4 mÅ ± 0.6 mÅ, corresponding to a 2σ upper limit of 10^{12} cm^{-2} in this line. The relative populations of the two states then imply a 2σ limit, $T_{CMBR} < 13.5$ K, which should be compared with the prediction of 10.66 K at this redshift; or, representing the temperature as $T_{CMBR} = T_0(1+z)^\alpha$, we find that the 2σ upper limit on α is 1.15. This is a firm upper bound: saturation effects could only raise the column density of the C II (and so lower the temperature limit) as would any additional excitation of the C II* line, other than the CMBR. This is the tightest limit to date on T_{CMBR} at high redshift; the previous best limit of Meyer *et al.*[21] gave $T_{CMBR} < 16$ K at $z = 1.776$, or $\alpha < 1.73$.

It seems that the fine-structure lines will provide a sensitive new test of relativistic cosmology. The extremely weak excitation of the fine structure levels in this absorber suggests that the population of C II* is dominated just by the cosmic background, so that we are likely to be able to actually determine T_{CMBR} with improved observations. Because the dependence

在类星体 Q0636+68 的吸收线系统中，我们观测到对应 1,334.532 Å 的 C II 线，这将对应在 $z = 2.909$ 处萨金特等人发现的莱曼系限系统[22]。CI 的多重线因强度太弱无法用于检验，而 N II 则位于莱曼森林内。如图 4 所示，C II 线包含了 3 个强的和一些弱的成分，速度展宽大于 $\pm 100\ \mathrm{km \cdot s^{-1}}$，其中最强的成分在红移 $z = 2.9034$ 处，我们将其取为零速度。通过和 Si II 等其他线进行比较，结果证实这些吸收线毫无疑问是 C II 线，这也进一步确定了波长尺度的准确性。

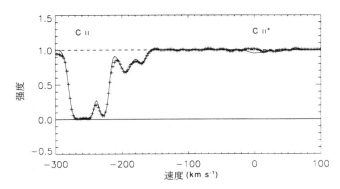

图 4. 类星体 Q0636+68 中对红移 $z = 2.9034$ 的莱曼系限系统中的 C II 1,334.532 Å 与 C II*1,335.708 Å 吸收线的观测。十字是数据点，C II 与 C II* 的位置标在图上。实线是 C II* 柱密度为 C II 的 1% 的模型，这是为了显示如果 C II* 存在的话它应该存在的位置。三条最强的 C II 谱线成分的静止等值宽度为 248 mÅ，对应于最小柱密度 $N_{(CII)} = 1.5 \times 10^{14}\ \mathrm{cm^{-2}}$，轮廓拟合给出了更精确的柱密度 $N_{(CII)} = 4.6 \times 10^{14}\ \mathrm{cm^{-2}}$。C II* 三个主要成分的等值宽度 $\leqslant 0.4\ \mathrm{mÅ} \pm 0.6\ \mathrm{mÅ}$，对应于这条线柱密度 $10^{12}\ \mathrm{cm^{-2}}$ 的 2σ 上限。

对三个最强成分的轮廓进行拟合，结果表明其柱密度 $N_{(CII)} = 4.6 \times 10^{14}\ \mathrm{cm^{-2}}$。当然，在强饱和的成分中可能还藏有相当多的额外物质，但这个数值是给出准确拟合的下限。相对而言，我们没有看到 1,335.708 Å 的处于激发态的 C II* 的谱线。我们通过拟合附近（"错误"）波长的随机位置的柱密度来估算噪声水平，结果发现三个主要成分的 C II* 的等值宽度为 $0.4\ \mathrm{mÅ} \pm 0.6\ \mathrm{mÅ}$，在 2σ 水平上对应于一个上限为 $10^{12}\ \mathrm{cm^{-2}}$ 的柱密度。这两个状态的相对数量比表明在 2σ 水平上，$T_{CMBR} < 13.5\ \mathrm{K}$，而对应理论给出该红移处的预言为 10.66 K。如果将温度写成 $T_{CMBR} = T_0\ (1+z)^\alpha$ 的形式，我们发现 α 的 2σ 上限是 1.15。这是一个很可靠的上限：因为饱和效应只会提供不同于宇宙微波背景辐射的额外激发机制来产生更多的激发态 C II* 线，从而只能提高 C II 的柱密度（而降低温度上限）。这是迄今为止对高红移 T_{CMBR} 的最强限制；之前由迈尔等人做出的限制[21]给出在 $z = 1.776$，或者说 $\alpha < 1.73$ 时，$T_{CMBR} < 16\ \mathrm{K}$。

看上去精细结构谱线可以提供一个精确检验相对论宇宙学的新方法。吸收体中处于精细结构能级激发态的数量非常少，这表明 C II* 的量主要由微波背景辐射决定，因此可以通过改进对 C II* 的观测精度来更好地测量 T_{CMBR}。因为等值宽度对温度的依

of equivalent width on temperature is only logarithmic, rather precise measurements of the temperature should be obtainable. In the present case, an increase in signal-to-noise ratio of a factor of 5 (less would be needed at higher redshift) must result in a significant detection of $C\,II^*$ if the relativistic prediction is correct. Note that systems at different redshifts yield measurements of the background at various present-day frequencies $64/(1+z)\,cm^{-1}$, and so also constrain the shape of the spectrum. Because this technique for measuring the temperature always yields an upper limit, a single well-constrained measurement lower than predicted would have catastrophic repercussions for standard Big Bang theory, whereas a firm measurement of the temperature at the expected level would rule out other possible explanations for the background radiation.

(**368**, 599-604; 1994)

A. Songaila[*†], L. L. Cowie[*†], C. J. Hogan[‡] & M. Rugers[‡]

[*] Institute for Astronomy, University of Hawaii, 2680 Woodlawn Drive, Honolulu, Hawaii 96822, USA
[‡] Department of Astronomy, University of Washington, Seattle, Washington 98195, USA

Received 12 January; accepted 10 March 1994.

References:

1. Mather, J. C. *et al. Astrophys. J.* **354**, L37-L40 (1990).
2. Mather, J. C. *et al. Astrophys. J.* **420**, 439-444 (1994).
3. Smoot, G. F. *et al. Astrophys. J.* **396**, L1-L5 (1992).
4. White, M., Scott, D. & Silk, J. *A. Rev. Ast. Astrophys.* (in the press).
5. Peebles, P. J. E. *Astrophys. J.* **146**, 542-552 (1966).
6. Wagoner, R., Fowler, W. & Hoyle, F. *Astrophys. J.* **148**, 3-49 (1967).
7. Reeves, H., Audouze, J., Fowler, W. & Schramm, D. N. *Astrophys. J.* **179**, 909-930 (1973).
8. Epstein, R., Lattimer, J. & Schramm, D. N. *Nature* **263**, 198-202 (1976).
9. Walker, T. P., Steigman, G., Schramm, D. N., Olive, K. A. & Kang, H. S. *Astrophys. J.* **376**, 51-69 (1991).
10. Smith, M. S., Kawano, L. H. & Malaney, R. A. *Astrophys. J. Suppl. Ser.* **85**, 219-247 (1993).
11. Steigman, G. & Tosi, M. *Astrophys. J.* **401**, 150-156 (1992).
12. Pagel, B. E. J., Simonson, E. A., Terlevich, R. J. & Edmunds, M. G. *Mon. Not. R. astr. Soc.* **255**, 325-345 (1992).
13. Pagel, B. E. J. *Phys. Scripta* **T36**, 7-15 (1991).
14. Binney, J. & Tremaine, S. *Galactic Dynamics* (Princeton Univ. Press, 1987).
15. Wolfe, A. M. *Ann. N.Y. Acad. Sci.* **688**, 281-296 (1993).
16. Webb, J. K., Carswell, R. F., Irwin, M. J. & Penston, M. V. *Mon. Not. R. astr. Soc.* **250**, 657-665 (1991).
17. Peebles, P. J. E., Schramm, D. N., Turner, E. I. & Kron, R. G. *Nature* **352**, 769-776 (1991).
18. Roth, K. C., Meyer, D. M. & Hawkins, I. *Astrophys. J.* **413**, L67-L71 (1993).
19. Bahcall, J. N. & Wolf, R. A. *Astrophys. J.* **152**, 701-729 (1968).
20. Bahcall, J. N., Joss, P. C. & Lynds, R. *Astrophys. J.* **182**, L95-L98 (1973).
21. Meyer, D. M., Black, J. H., Chaffee, F. H., Foltz, C. & York, D. G. *Astrophys. J.* **308**, L37-L41 (1986).
22. Sargent, W. L. W., Steidel, C. C. & Boksenberg, A. *Astrophys. J. Suppl. Ser.* **69**, 703-761 (1989).
23. Cowie, L. L., Laurent, C., Vidal-Madjar, A. & York, D. G. *Astrophys. J.* **229**, L81-L85 (1979).
24. Chaffee, F. H., Foltz, C. B., Röser, H.-J., Weymann, R. J. & Latham, D. W. *Astrophys. J.* **292**, 362-370 (1985).
25. Chaffee, F. H., Foltz, C. B., Bechtold, J. & Weymann, R. J. *Astrophys. J.* **301**, 116-123 (1986).
26. Shapiro, P. R. & Moore, R. T. *Astrophys. J.* **207**, 460-483 (1976).
27. Donahue, M. & Shull, J. M. *Astrophys. J.* **383**, 511-523 (1991).
28. Vangioni-Flam, E. & Audouze, J. *Astr. Astrophys.* **193**, 81-86 (1988).
29. Linsky, J. L. *et al. Astrophys. J.* **402**, 694-709 (1993).
30. Bania, T. M., Rood, R. T. & Wilson, T. L. *Astrophys. J.* **323**, 30-43 (1987).

赖满足对数关系，因此可以期待得到更加精确的温度测量结果。以目前的情况为例，如果相对论的预言是正确的，那么增加至 5 倍的信噪比将足以探测到显著的 C II* 吸收（在更高红移处则并不要求这么高的信噪比）。注意到测量不同红移处的系统对应的是今天光谱中不同的频率，$64/(1+z)\,\mathrm{cm^{-1}}$，因此通过对这些系统的观测将可以用来限制谱的形状。因为这种对温度的测量总是给出上限，如果探测到的数值低于预言的结果，那么将对标准大爆炸理论带来灾难性的后果。然而，如果确定温度在所预期的区间内则可排除对背景辐射起源的其他解释。

(周杰 翻译；张华伟 审稿)

31. White, S. D. M., Navarro, J. F., Evrard, A. E. & Frenk, C. S. *Nature* **366**, 429-433 (1993).

32. Alcock, C. *et al. Nature* **365**, 621-623 (1993).

33. Aubourg, E. *et al.* **365**, 623-625 (1993).

34. Wright, E. L. *et al. Astrophys. J.* **420**, 450-456 (1994).

Acknowledgements. We are grateful to the designers and builders of the Keck 10-m telescope and of HIRES. We particularly thank M. Keane and B. Shaeffer for their help in obtaining the observations. This work was supported at the University of Hawaii by the State of Hawaii and by NASA, and at the University of Washington by the US NSF and NASA.

A Diverse New Primate Fauna from Middle Eocene Fissure-fillings in Southeastern China

K. C. Beard *et al.*

Editor's Note

The Eocene epoch (56–34 million years ago) was a golden age for mammalian evolution, particularly primates. However, until the mid-1990s, knowledge of Eocene primates was biased towards Europe and North America, and most consisted of two extinct groups—the adapids and omomyids—whose relationships with later forms was obscure. Barely a handful of fragmentary Eocene primates were known from Asia. This paper changed all that. Eocene deposits from Shanghuang in Jiangsu, China, offered a wealth of adapids and omomyids, a tarsier, and that most elusive of Eocene primates—a simian, *Eosimias sinensis*, then the earliest-known representative of the lineage which would eventually lead to monkeys, apes and man.

We report the discovery of a fauna of primates from Eocene (~45 Myr) deposits in China having a diversity greater than in European and North American localities of similar antiquity. From the many forms that will illuminate questions of primate phylogeny comes evidence for a basal radiation of primitive simians.

AT present, the fossil record of early primate evolution is strongly biased geographically, with the stratigraphically dense and intensively studied samples of Eocene primates from North America and Europe standing in sharp contrast to the paucity of similar data for Africa and Asia[1,2]. For example, only eight species of Eocene primates have been described from Asia[3-10], and most of these are represented by fragmentary or unique fossils. As a result, the phylogenetic affinities of Eocene Asian primates are controversial[1,11-14], and little is known about how this Asian record relates to those of other continents[15].

Since January 1992 we have worked on richly fossiliferous fissure-fillings located near the village of Shanghuang, in southern Jiangsu Province in the People's Republic of China (PRC) (Fig. 1 has been omitted in this edited version). These are the first such fillings of Eocene age to be discovered in Asia. The fissures have yielded a large and varied mammalian fauna[16], of which the diversity of Eocene primates is greater than that of the rest of Asia combined.

中国东南部中始新世裂隙堆积中新发现的一个多样化灵长类动物群

比尔德等

编者按

始新世（5,600 万 ~ 3,400 万年前）是哺乳动物演化的一个黄金时代，特别是灵长类动物。然而，直到 20 世纪 90 年代中期，对始新世灵长类动物的认知都来自欧洲和北美洲，大部分由两个灭绝的类群——兔猴类和鼩猴类组成，他们与后来的类型之间的关系是模糊不清的。在亚洲已知的仅仅是少数零星破碎的始新世灵长类化石。本文改写了这一切。中国江苏省上黄村的始新世堆积物中发现了丰富的兔猴类和鼩猴类、一种跗猴以及最难捉摸的始新世灵长类——中华曙猿（一种真猴类）。在当时，中华曙猿是最终分化出猴、猿和人这一谱系的已知最早代表。

我们报道了从中国的始新世（约 4,500 万年前）堆积物中发现的灵长类动物群，该动物群的多样性比欧洲和北美洲年代相仿地点的更为丰富。这些为灵长类系统发育关系问题带来光明的众多类型，也为原始真猴类的基群辐射带来了证据。

现在，早期灵长类演化的化石记录在地理位置上存在严重的偏向，地层中分布密集且研究比较集中的北美洲和欧洲的始新世灵长类化石样本与非洲和亚洲相似化石材料的缺乏形成鲜明对比 [1,2]。例如，亚洲到目前为止只描述过 8 种始新世时期的灵长类 [3-10]，其中大部分只有破碎的或唯一的化石材料。因此，始新世时期亚洲灵长类的系统发育亲缘关系就存在争议 [1,11-14]，而且关于这一亚洲记录与其他大陆发现的灵长类的关系如何还知之甚少 [15]。

自 1992 年 1 月以来，我们一直致力于几处含有丰富化石的裂隙堆积物的野外发掘工作，它们位于中国江苏省南部的上黄村附近（图 1；该图显示上黄裂隙堆积物的地理位置，此版本中省略）。这是亚洲首次发现始新世时期的这种堆积物。从这些裂隙中得到了一个多样的大型哺乳动物群 [16]，其中始新世灵长类的多样性比亚洲其余地方发现的总和还要丰富。

Like many Eocene localities in North America and Europe, the primate fauna from the Shanghuang fissures includes both adapiforms and omomyids. But the fillings have also yielded distinctive fossil primates that are not found elsewhere: these include the first Eocene tarsier and fossils that we interpret as basal simians (anthropoids or "higher primates"). This co-occurrence of adapiforms, omomyids, tarsiids and basal simians is unique, and provides fresh insight into primate phylogeny in general and the biogeographic role of Asia during early phases of primate evolution in particular.

Age and Geological Setting

The Shanghuang fissure-fillings were formed as middle Eocene karstic infillings into surrounding Triassic carbonates. So far, four fossiliferous fissure-fillings (IVPP locality 93006 A–D) of Eocene age have been sampled. All are exposed in an active commercial quarry near Shanghuang, where the Triassic carbonates are being mined for cement production. Available evidence indicates that the fissure-fillings span only a short interval (probably 1–2 Myr) of middle Eocene time, with the fauna from fissure D being slightly older than the others.

Biostratigraphically, the mammalian faunas from the fissures appear to represent the Irdinmanhan and early Sharamurunian Land Mammal Ages (LMAs), on the basis of taxa such as the lagomorph *Lushilagus lohoensis*[16], the carnivore *Miacis lushiensis*[16], the brontothere *Microtitan,* and the cricetid rodent *Pappocricetodon.* Unfortunately, direct radiometric dating of middle Eocene LMAs in Asia has not yet proven possible. However, the Irdinmanhan LMA can be correlated with the Bridgerian and early Uintan LMAs of North America on the basis of a major episode of intercontinental mammalian dispersal[17]. In North America the Bridgerian/Uintan boundary occurs at about 46 Myr[18]. As a rough appraisal based on these considerations, we estimate the age of the Shanghuang fissures to be about 45 Myr.

Shanghuang Adapiforms

Adapiforms[1] are lemur-like early Cenozoic primates that seem to be closely related to living strepsirhines[19]. At least two species are known from the Shanghuang fissures (Fig. 2), where they are most abundant in fissure D.

像北美洲和欧洲的许多始新世时期的化石地点一样，来自上黄裂隙的灵长类动物群既包括兔猴型类，也有鼩猴类（已经灭绝的鼩猴科的成员）。该堆积物也出产了没有在其他地方发现过的独特的灵长类化石，这些化石包括第一种始新世的跗猴化石和我们认为是基底真猴类（类人猿或"高等灵长类"）的化石。兔猴型类、鼩猴类、跗猴类（或称眼镜猴类）和基底真猴类的同时出现是独一无二的。这提供了对灵长类的总体系统发育关系，尤其是对灵长类早期演化过程中亚洲的生物地理作用的一些新见解。

年代和地质概况

上黄裂隙堆积物是由中始新世时期的喀斯特填充物堆积到三叠纪碳酸盐围岩裂隙中形成的。到现在为止，已经发掘了四处始新世时期的含化石的裂隙堆积（IVPP地点编号93006 A~D）。所有裂隙堆积都暴露在上黄附近的一处活跃的商业采石场里，那里的三叠纪碳酸盐岩被开采出来进行水泥生产。现在得到的证据显示这些裂隙堆积的形成只横跨了中始新世一个短暂的年代区间（约100万年到200万年）。从裂隙D得到的动物群要比其余裂隙的稍微古老一些。

从生物地层方面来看，根据兔形类——洛河卢氏兔[16]、食肉类——卢氏小古猫[16]、王雷兽类——小雷兽和仓鼠类——祖仓鼠等类群判断，从这些裂隙发掘出来的哺乳动物群应该代表了陆地哺乳动物期（LMAs）中的伊尔丁曼哈期和沙拉木伦早期。不幸的是，现在想对亚洲中始新世时期的LMA进行直接的同位素年代测定还是不可能的。然而，基于各大陆间哺乳动物扩散的主要时期，伊尔丁曼哈期LMA可以与北美洲的布里杰期和早尤因塔期的LMA相对比[17]。在北美洲，布里杰期/尤因塔期的界线大约是在4,600万年前[18]。根据这些考虑粗略地评估了一下，我们估计上黄裂隙的年代约为4,500万年前。

上黄兔猴型类

兔猴型类[1]是类似狐猴的早新生代时期的灵长类动物，它们似乎与现生的曲鼻猴类具有亲密的关系[19]。来自上黄裂隙的兔猴型类现在已知的至少有两种（图2），所有上黄裂隙中，它们在裂隙D的化石最为丰富。

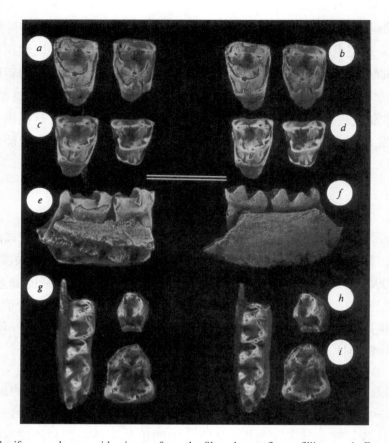

Fig. 2. Adapiform and omomyid primates from the Shanghuang fissure-fillings. *a, b, Europolemur*-like adapiform: IVPP V11019 (*a*), and IVPP V11020 (*b*), each consisting of an isolated left M^1 or M^2 from fissure D, occlusal view. *c–g, Adapoides troglodytes*: IVPP V11021 (*c*), isolated right M^1 or M^2 from fissure D, occlusal view; IVPP V11022 (*d*), isolated right deciduous P^4 from fissure D, occlusal view; *e–g*, IVPP V11023, right mandible fragment with M_{2-3} from fissure B, holotype of *Adapoides troglodytes*, in buccal (*e*), lingual (*f*) and occlusal (*g*) views. *h, i, Macrotarsius macrorhysis*: IVPP V11025 (*h*), isolated right P_4 from fissure D, holotype of *Macrotarsius macrorhysis*, occlusal view; IVPP V11024 (*i*), isolated left M_1 from fissure D, occlusal view. Occlusal views are stereopairs. Scale bar, 5 mm.

Aside from several isolated teeth from the Kuldana Formation of Pakistan[9], the Shanghuang adapiforms comprise the only unequivocal evidence for adapiforms in Asia during the Eocene.

A relatively primitive adapiform is represented by isolated teeth from fissure D. Cheek teeth of this species resemble those of *Europolemur*, an adapiform from the middle Eocene of Europe[1,20]. In particular, upper molars from Shanghuang resemble those of *E. koenigswaldi* from Messel, Germany[20], in that they lack a hypocone. However, absence of a hypocone in these two species is a shared primitive feature, and thus does not reflect a special relationship between them. The Shanghuang species is smaller than any previously named species of *Europolemur*, but further specimens will be required to ascertain whether it represents the first Asian record of this genus.

400

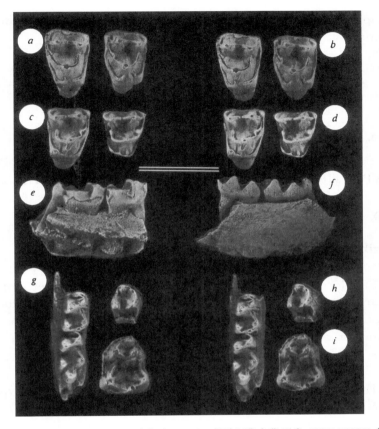

图 2. 来自上黄裂隙堆积的兔猴型类和鼩猴类。*a*, *b*, 似欧狐猴兔猴型类: IVPP V11019 (*a*) 和 IVPP V11020 (*b*), 每个都包括一颗来自裂隙 D 的游离左 M^1 或 M^2, 咬合面视图。*c~g*, 穴居似兔猴: IVPP V11021 (*c*), 来自裂隙 D 的游离右 M^1 或 M^2, 咬合面视图; IVPP V11022 (*d*), 来自裂隙 D 的游离右 dP^4, 咬合面视图; *e~g*, IVPP V11023, 来自裂隙 B 的带有 M_{2-3} 的右下颌体残段, 穴居似兔猴正模标本, 颊面 (*e*)、舌面 (*f*) 和咬合面 (*g*) 视图。*h*, *i*, 扬子大跗猴: IVPP V11025 (*h*), 来自裂隙 D 的游离右 P_4, 扬子大跗猴的正模标本, 咬合面视图; IVPP V11024 (*i*), 来自裂隙 D 的游离左 M_1, 咬合面视图。咬合面视图是立体像对。比例尺, 5 毫米。

除了巴基斯坦的库尔达纳组地层 [9] 中的几颗游离牙齿以外, 上黄兔猴型类提供了始新世时期唯一一个确凿的亚洲兔猴型类的证据。

来自裂隙 D 的几颗游离牙齿代表了一种相对原始的兔猴型类。这一种类的颊齿与欧狐猴属的相似, 后者是一种欧洲中始新世时期的兔猴型类 [1,20]。尤其是, 上黄的上臼齿与在德国梅瑟尔发现的孔氏欧狐猴的很相似 [20], 因为它们缺少一个次尖。然而, 这两个种类中次尖的缺失是一个共有的原始特征, 因此并不能反映出它们之间具有特别的关系。上黄的种类比其他之前已命名的欧狐猴属内的种类都要小, 但是还需要更多的标本才能确定它是否代表了该属在亚洲的首次记录。

A second adapiform is represented by more nearly complete fossils, which permit its description here.

Order Primates Linnaeus, 1758
Suborder Strepsirhini Geoffroy, 1812
Family Adapidae Trouessart, 1879
Subtribe Adapina Trouessart, 1879
Adapoides troglodytes, new genus and species

Holotype. IVPP V11023, right mandibular fragment preserving M_{2-3} (Fig. 2).

Type locality. IVPP 93006, fissure B.

Known distribution. Middle Eocene of Jiangsu Province, PRC.

Diagnosis. Smaller than *Adapis*, *Cryptadapis* and *Leptadapis*. Lower molars relatively longer and narrower than in *Leptadapis*. Lower molars without metastylids, in contrast to *Cryptadapis*, *A. parisiensis* and *L. magnus*. Lower molars with high, continuous crest between protoconid and metaconid and deep talonid notch, in contrast to *Microadapis* and *Leptadapis*.

Etymology. From the generic name *Adapis* + Greek suffix *-oides* (like). Trivial name from Greek *troglodytes* (inhabitant of caves).

Description. *Adapoides troglodytes* is a small adapinan, with lower molars (M_2L: 2.65 mm, M_2W: 1.90 mm; M_3L: 3.55 mm, M_3W: 1.80 mm) similar in size to those of *Microadapis sciureus*. The lower molars are primitive in lacking metastylids but derived in having a deep talonid notch and a strong crest uniting protoconid and metaconid. Referred upper molars show most of the derived features typical of adapinans (buccal crests form a single mesiodistally oriented shearing surface, metaconule weak or absent, occlusal outline of crown mesiodistally longer and transversely narrower than in *Europolemur* and its close relatives), but primitively lack well-developed hypocones.

Discovery of the Shanghuang adapiforms illuminates two abiding questions about adapiform evolution and biogeography. First, the controversial adapiform *Mahgarita stevensi*, known only from the Duchesnean (late Eocene) of western Texas[21-23], has been suggested to be an immigrant from Asia[24]. Previously, however, there were no Asian adapiforms of suitable morphology to represent a close relative of *Mahgarita*, the affinities of which lie near *Europolemur*[1,21]. Discovery of a *Europolemur*-like species at Shanghuang provides the first direct evidence that adapiforms of suitable morphology to represent the ancestral stock for *Mahgarita* inhabited Asia during the Eocene, thus corroborating the hypothesis of an Asian origin for this enigmatic genus.

另一种兔猴型类由更加接近完整的化石材料所代表，我们在此对其进行描述。

灵长目 Primates Linnaeus, 1758
曲鼻猴亚目 Strepsirhini Geoffroy, 1812
兔猴科 Adapidae Trouessart, 1879
兔猴亚族 Adapina Trouessart, 1879

穴居似兔猴（新属、新种）*Adapoides troglodytes*, n. gen. et sp.

正模标本。IVPP V11023，保存有 M_{2-3} 的右下颌体残段（图 2）。

产地。IVPP 93006，裂隙 B。

分布。中华人民共和国江苏省，中始新世。

特征。比兔猴属、隐兔猴属和丽兔猴属小。下臼齿与丽兔猴属相比，相对较长且狭窄。与隐兔猴属、巴黎兔猴和硕丽兔猴不同，下臼齿没有下后附尖。与倭兔猴和丽兔猴不同，下臼齿在下原尖和下后尖之间有高而连续的脊，并且有很深的下跟座缺。

词源。来源于属名 *Adapis*（兔猴）＋希腊语后缀 *-oides*（类似）。种名取自希腊语 *troglodytes*（穴居者）。

描述。穴居似兔猴是一种小型兔猴亚族成员，其下臼齿（M_2L：2.65 毫米，M_2W：1.90 毫米；M_3L：3.55 毫米，M_3W：1.80 毫米）的尺寸与松鼠倭兔猴的相似。下臼齿比较原始，缺少下后附尖，但是具有深的下跟座缺和非常发育的将下原尖和下后尖联结在一起的脊。归入的上臼齿显示出大多数兔猴亚族成员的典型衍生特征（颊脊形成单一的近远中方向的剪切面，后小尖发育弱或缺失，齿冠咬合面轮廓在近远中方向上比欧狐猴属及其近缘属更长，横向则更窄），但是比较原始的特征是缺少发达的次尖。

上黄兔猴型类的发现为探讨兔猴型类演化和生物地理这两个长久以来一直存在的问题带来了光明。首先，存在争议的兔猴型类玛氏兔猴仅发现于得克萨斯州西部的杜申阶（晚始新世）地层 [21-23]，有人认为其是从亚洲迁移过来的 [24]。但是，之前并没有具有适当形态学特征的亚洲兔猴型类可以代表玛氏兔猴属的亲缘属，因此一直认为它们的亲缘关系与欧狐猴属接近 [1,21]。在上黄发现的这种似欧狐猴属样的种类首次提供了直接证据，表明代表玛氏兔猴的祖先类群并具有相应形态学特征的兔猴型类于始新世期间生活在亚洲，因此证实了这一神秘属的亚洲起源假说。

Second, Shanghuang adapiforms also shed light on the phylogeny and biogeography of the subtribe Adapina (including *Adapis*, *Leptadapis*, *Cryptadapis*[1,25] and *Adapoides*). Anatomically, the Adapina are among the best known Eocene primates, being represented by well-preserved skulls, jaws and numerous postcranial elements[1,26-28]. However, the phylogenetic and geographic origin of the group has been obscure because the fossil record of these animals was previously limited to Europe, where they appeared suddenly at the beginning of the Robiacian LMA (late Eocene)[20,29]. Discovery of the small, anatomically primitive adapinan *Adapoides troglodytes* in the middle Eocene of China suggests that adapinans immigrated into Europe from Asia rather than Africa, as had been thought[20].

The Shanghuang adapiforms show no special resemblances to the enigmatic Sivaladapinae from the Miocene of India, Pakistan and Yunnan Province, PRC[30,31].

Shanghuang Tarsiiforms

Both omomyid and tarsiid primates have been recovered from Shanghuang (Figs 2, 3). Omomyids are usually considered to be primitive tarsiiforms[1,15,32], although this has been disputed[2]. Remains of omomyids are the rarest primate fossils recovered to date from Shanghuang, where only two isolated teeth have been found in fissure D. Despite their rarity, they are of great interest because they represent a new species of *Macrotarsius*, a genus otherwise known only from western North America[1,33,34].

Infraorder Tarsiiformes Gregory, 1915
Family Omomyidae Trouessart, 1879
Macrotarsius macrorhysis, new species

Holotype. IVPP V11025, isolated right P_4 (P_4L, 2.65 mm; P_4W, 2.05 mm) (Fig. 2).

Type locality. IVPP 93006, fissure D.

Known distribution. Middle Eocene of Jiangsu Province, PRC.

Diagnosis. P_4 smaller, relatively narrower and with simpler talonid than in other species of *Macrotarsius*. M_1 smaller than in *M. montanus* and *M. siegerti* and without complete ectocingulid, in contrast to *M. roederi*.

Etymology. Trivial name from Greek *makros* (long)+Greek *rhysis* (river), in allusion to the Yangtze River.

Description. *Macrotarsius macrorhysis* closely resembles North American species of *Macrotarsius* in comparable aspects of anatomy: P_4 is mesiodistally short and bears a strongly molarized trigonid, and a well developed crest unites the metaconid and entoconid

其次，上黄兔猴型类也对兔猴亚族（包括兔猴属、丽兔猴属、隐兔猴属[1,25]和似兔猴属）的系统发育关系和生物地理有所启示。从解剖学上说，兔猴亚族属于了解得最为清楚的始新世灵长类，已经发现保存很好的头骨、下颌和大量头后骨骼[1,26-28]。但是，该类群的系统发育和地理上的起源一直都很模糊，因为这些动物的化石记录之前都只局限在欧洲，在那里他们是在 LMA 罗比亚克期（晚始新世）的初期突然出现的[20,29]。在中国的中始新世时期发现这种小型的、解剖学特征原始的兔猴亚族成员——穴居似兔猴，表明兔猴亚族是从亚洲迁移到欧洲的，而非以前所认为的是从非洲迁移过去的[20]。

上黄兔猴型类没有显示出与印度、巴基斯坦和中国云南省中新世的神秘的西瓦兔猴亚科有特别的相似之处[30,31]。

上黄跗猴型类

鼩猴类和跗猴类这两类灵长类在上黄都有发现（图 2，图 3）。鼩猴类通常被认为是原始的跗猴型类[1,15,32]，尽管这一点一直都争议不断[2]。鼩猴类的化石是到现在为止从上黄发掘到的灵长类化石中最为稀少的，只从裂隙 D 中发现了两颗游离的牙齿。尽管它们的化石很稀少，但是它们仍具有重大意义，因为它们代表了一个大跗猴属的新种类，而大跗猴属之前仅在北美洲西部被发现过[1,33,34]。

跗猴型下目 Tarsiiformes Gregory, 1915

始镜猴科 Omomyidae Trouessart, 1879

扬子大跗猴（新种）*Macrotarsius macrorhysis*，n. sp.

正模标本。IVPP V11025，游离右 P_4（P_4L：2.65 毫米；P_4W：2.05 毫米）（图 2）。

产地。IVPP 93006，裂隙 D。

分布。中华人民共和国江苏省，中始新世。

特征。与大跗猴属的其他种相比，P_4 较小，相对较窄，并且下跟座较简单。M_1 比蒙大拿长跗猴和西氏长跗猴的小，没有完整的下外齿带，与罗氏长跗猴正好相反。

词源。种名取自希腊语 *makros*（长）+ 希腊语 *rhysis*（河），暗指长江。

描述。扬子大跗猴在相应的解剖学特征方面，与大跗猴属中北美洲的种类很像：P_4 近远中方向短，具有臼齿化强烈的下齿座，一条发达的脊将 M_1 的下后尖和下外

on M_1. In terms of size and crown structure, M_1 in *M. macrorhysis* is practically indistinguishable from that in *M. jepseni*, known from the early Uintan (middle Eocene), Uinta Basin, Utah[33].

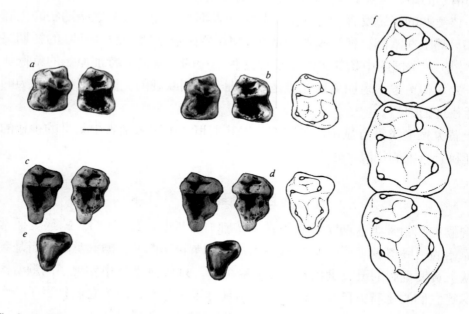

Fig. 3. *a–e, Tarsius eocaenus* from the Shanghuang fissure-fillings: IVPP V11026, isolated left M_1 from fissure A, occlusal view (*a*); IVPP V11030, isolated right M_1 from fissure C, holotype of *Tarsius eocaenus*, occlusal view (*b*); IVPP V11027, isolated right M_3 from fissure A, occlusal view (*c*); IVPP V11031, isolated right M_3 from fissure C, occlusal view (*d*); IVPP V11029, isolated left P^3 from fissure C, occlusal view (*e*). All views are stereopairs; scale equals 1 mm. (*f*), Dental morphology of *Tarsius eocaenus* (IVPP V11030 and IVPP V11027) compared with that of living *Tarsius bancanus* (USNM 300917), drawn to same scale.

Family Tarsiidae Gray, 1825
Tarsius eocaenus, new species

Holotype. IVPP V11030, isolated right M_1 (M_1L, 1.65 mm; M_1W, 1.55 mm) (Fig. 3).

Type locality. IVPP 93006, fissure C.

Known distribution. Middle Eocene of Jiangsu Province, PRC.

Diagnosis. Smaller than other species of *Tarsius*.

Etymology. Trivial name recognizes the Eocene age of this species.

Description. Isolated cheek teeth from fissures A and C attributed to *T. eocaenus* are virtually identical to those of living *Tarsius* in terms of crown structure (Fig. 3). Several aspects of dental anatomy distinguish *T. eocaenus* from omomyids and *Afrotarsius*[35]. For

尖联结在一起。从尺寸和牙冠结构方面看，扬子大跗猴的 M_1 与犹他州尤因塔盆地早尤因塔期（中始新世）的杰氏长跗猴的几乎没有区别[33]。

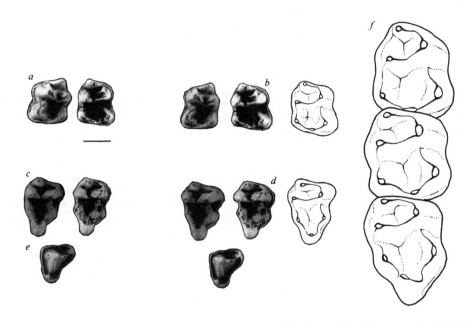

图 3. a~e，来自上黄裂隙堆积的始新跗猴：IVPP V11026，来自裂隙 A 的游离左 M_1，咬合面视图（a）；IVPP V11030，来自裂隙 C 的游离右 M_1，始新跗猴的正模标本，咬合面视图（b）；IVPP V11027，来自裂隙 A 的游离右 M_3，咬合面视图（c）；IVPP V11031，来自裂隙 C 的游离右 M_3，咬合面视图（d）；IVPP V11029，来自裂隙 C 的游离左 P^3，咬合面视图（e）。所有视图都是立体像对，比例尺是 1 毫米。（f），始新跗猴（IVPP V11030 和 IVPP V11027）与现生马来跗猴（USNM 300917）的牙齿形态学对比，绘图的比例相同。

跗猴科 Tarsiidae Gray, 1825

始新跗猴（新种）*Tarsius eocaenus*，n. sp.

正模标本。IVPP V11030，游离右 M_1（M_1L：1.65 毫米；M_1W：1.55 毫米）（图 3）。

产地。IVPP 93006，裂隙 C。

分布。中华人民共和国江苏省，中始新世。

特征。比跗猴属的其他种小。

词源。其种名指示该种年代是始新世。

描述。从裂隙 A 和 C 发掘出来的游离颊齿虽然被归入始新跗猴，但是这些颊齿在齿冠结构上与现生的跗猴属实际上是一样的（图 3）。牙齿的解剖学特征可从几个

example, the lower molars of *T. eocaenus* possess shelf-like paraconids situated near the lingual margin of the trigonid; a well developed entocristid uniting the entoconid and metaconid; entoconid positioned near the base of the trigonid, so that the talonid is short on M_1 and the entoconid is mesial to the level of the hypoconid on M_3 (M_2 is unknown); an angular, robust hypoconid; M_3 with a simple, unicuspid, distally projecting hypoconulid lobe. Cheek teeth of *T. eocaenus* are uniformly smaller than those of living species of *Tarsius*, including *T. pumilus*[36].

The tarsiiform primates from Shanghuang demonstrate for the first time that tarsiids and omomyids were virtually, if not certainly, sympatric during the middle Eocene in southeastern China. Discovery of *Macrotarsius* in Asia confirms previous predictions[15] regarding the feasibility of omomyid dispersal between North America and Asia during the middle Eocene. More dramatically, *Tarsius eocaenus* nearly triples the palaeontologically documented antiquity of tarsiers via a stratigraphic range extension from the Miocene[37] down to the middle Eocene. This brings the fossil record for Tarsiidae into much greater concordance with predictions based on cladistic reconstructions of the phylogenetic position of this group[2,32,38].

Basal Simians

The most diverse group of primates from the Shanghuang fissures, represented by at least four species, belongs to a further radiation of Eocene primates, interpreted here as basal simians. This radiation has been poorly sampled in the fossil record until now. Although the retention of several primitive features distinguishes these animals from more advanced simian taxa, such a combination of primitive and derived traits is not unexpected in basal simians[39-42]. Available evidence does not allow us to determine whether the basal simian taxa sampled to date from Shanghuang constitute a monophyletic or paraphyletic assemblage. Here we describe the basal simian from Shanghuang that is best represented in our current sample.

Suborder Anthropoidea Mivart, 1864
Eosimiidae, new family

Type genus. *Eosimias*, n. gen.

Diagnosis. Differs from Strepsirhini and Tarsiiformes in having the following combination of characters: lower dental formula 2-1-3-3; I_{1-2} small and vertically implanted; C_1 larger than I_{1-2} and P_2; P_2 single-rooted; P_{3-4} mesiodistally short and obliquely oriented with respect to tooth row (mesial root more labial than distal root); M_{1-2} with cuspidate paraconid, metaconid widely separated from enlarged protoconid, entoconid situated mesial to level of hypoconid, and distally-projecting hypoconulid.

方面将始新跗猴与鼩猴类和非洲跗猴区分开来 [35]。例如，始新跗猴的下臼齿具有搁板状的位于下齿座舌侧边缘附近的下前尖；具有发达的将下内尖和下后尖联结在一起的下内脊；其下内尖位于下齿座基部附近，所以 M_1 的下跟座很短，而下内尖在 M_3 上的位置较下次尖更靠近中侧（M_2 的情况尚不知道）；具有一个尖锐的、粗壮的下次尖；其 M_3 有一个简单的、单尖的、远端突出的下次小尖叶。始新跗猴的颊齿比现生的包括小跗猴在内的跗猴属内的种类都要小 [36]。

来自上黄的跗猴型类第一次从实际上（即使不确切）呈现了跗猴类和鼩猴类在中始新世的中国东南部的分布区是重叠的。在亚洲发现大跗猴属化石证实了之前对于中始新世期间鼩猴类在北美洲和亚洲之间扩散的可能性的预测 [15]。更引人注目的是，始新跗猴将跗猴的地层分布下限从中新世 [37] 向下扩展至中始新世，使跗猴在古生物上记录到的年代范围向前延伸了两倍。这使得跗猴科的化石记录与建立在该类群系统位置的支序系统重建基础上的预测更加一致了 [2,32,38]。

基底真猴类

来自上黄裂隙的最具多样性的灵长类类群至少代表了四个种类，它们属于始新世灵长类一次进一步辐射的产物，这里将其解释为基底真猴类。直到现在，化石记录中对这次辐射的记载都很不完善。尽管几种原始特征的保留将这些动物与更进步的真猴类类群区别了开来，但是这种原始特征与衍生特征的结合在基底真猴类中并不意外 [39-42]。我们还无法根据现有证据确定目前为止从上黄采集的基底真猴类是构成了单系还是并系类群。这里我们描述了来自上黄的现有标本中最具有代表性的基底真猴类。

类人猿亚目 Anthropoidea Mivart, 1864
曙猿科（新科）Eosimiidae，n. fam.

模式属。*Eosimias*，n. gen.

特征。在如下几个特征方面不同于曲鼻猴亚目和跗猴型下目：下齿式为 2-1-3-3；I_{1-2} 小，垂直嵌入；C_1 比 I_{1-2} 和 P_2 大；P_2 单根；P_{3-4} 近远中方向短，就齿列而言是斜向的（近中根比远中根更靠近唇侧）；M_{1-2} 具有多尖的下前尖，下后尖与膨大的下原尖完全分离开了，下内尖位于下次尖近中侧，下次尖向远中突出。

Differs from other simians (except possibly *Catopithecus*[41], *Proteopithecus*[41], *Serapia*[42], *Arsinoea*[42] and *Afrotarsius*[35,37,40]) in retaining an unfused mandibular symphysis and prominent paraconids on M_{1-2}. Differs from simians except Parapithecidae, *Arsinoea* and possibly *Afrotarsius* in having P_4 metaconid situated well distal and inferior to protoconid, without strong transverse crest uniting these cusps. Differs from Platyrrhini and *Afrotarsius* in having prominent, distally-projecting hypoconulids on M_{1-2}. Differs from Old World simians except *Afrotarsius*, *Amphipithecus* and *Pondaungia* in lacking twinned entoconid and hypoconulid cusps on M_{1-2}.

Eosimias sinensis, new genus and species

Holotype. IVPP V10591, right mandible preserving P_4–M_2 and roots or alveoli for C_1, P_{2-3}, and M_3 (Fig. 4).

Type locality. IVPP 93006, fissure B.

Known distribution. Middle Eocene of Jiangsu Province, PRC.

Diagnosis. As for the family (currently monotypic).

Etymology. Greek *eos* (dawn, early) and Latin *simia* (ape). Trivial name refers to geographic provenance of this species.

Description. Aspects of the anterior lower dentition can be inferred from IVPP V10592, a referred specimen from fissure A (Fig. 4). Alveoli for I_{1-2} preserved in this specimen are diminutive. In contrast, the C_1 alveolus is relatively enormous, being much larger than those for I_{1-2} and P_2. The relative proportions of I_1–P_2 in eosimiids are plausibly interpreted as primitive for primates, since they resemble the conditions in other Paleogene simians, adapiforms[24] and certain omomyids (e.g., *Washakius*)[43]. Both IVPP V10591 and V10592 possess an unfused mandibular symphysis (more completely preserved in IVPP V10592). In contrast to adapiforms and omomyids, the symphyseal region of the mandible is dorsoventrally deep rather than strongly procumbent. In this derived feature, *Eosimias* resembles simians.

The crown of P_3 is unknown. Its alveoli, like those of P_4, are obliquely oriented with respect to the tooth row, the mesial alveolus being situated labial to the distal alveolus. This derived condition does not occur among Eocene adapiforms and omomyids, but is common among Fayum simians (e.g., *Qatrania*)[44]. A similar condition exists in *Amphipithecus* from the Eocene of Burma, a genus widely[5,12] but not universally[1] considered to be a primitive simian.

在保留未融合的下颌联合部以及 M_{1-2} 上的突出的下前尖方面，与其他真猴类（可能除了下猿属[41]、锋猿属[41]、塞拉皮斯猿属[42]、阿尔西诺伊猿属[42]和非洲跗猴属[35,37,40]）不同。与除副猿科、阿尔西诺伊猿属、可能还有非洲跗猴属之外的真猴类也都有所不同，其 P_4 上下后尖位置比下原尖更靠近远中并比下原尖矮，没有发达的横脊将这些齿尖联结在一起。在 M_{1-2} 上具有显著的、向远中方向突出的下次小尖方面，与阔鼻猴小目和非洲跗猴属不同。在 M_{1-2} 缺乏成对下内尖和下次小尖方面，与除非洲跗猴、半猿、蓬当猿以外的旧世界真猴类不同。

中华曙猿（新种）*Eosimias sinensis*，n. sp.

正模标本。IVPP V10591，保存了 $P_4 \sim M_2$ 以及 C_1、P_{2-3} 和 M_3 的齿根或齿槽的右下颌骨（图 4）。

产地。IVPP 93006，裂隙 B。

分布。中华人民共和国江苏省，中始新世。

特征。与该科的特征一致（目前是单型属）。

词源。希腊语 *eos*（黎明，早的）和拉丁文 *simia*（猿）。其种名是指该种的地理产地。

描述。前下齿列的特征可以在 IVPP V10592 上观察到，这是一个来自裂隙 A 的标本（图 4）。该标本保存下来的 I_{1-2} 的齿槽都是小型的。相比之下，C_1 的齿槽相对庞大，比 I_{1-2} 和 P_2 的要大得多。曙猿中 $I_1 \sim P_2$ 的相对比例似乎可以理解为对灵长类而言是原始的，因为它们与其他古近纪真猴类、兔猴型类[24]和某些鼩猴类（例如，华谢基猴属）的形态相似[43]。IVPP V10591 和 V10592 都拥有一个未融合的下颌联合部（IVPP V10592 中保存得更完整）。与兔猴型类和鼩猴类不同，该下颌骨的联合部在背腹方向上很深，并不是非常平伏。对于该衍生特征，曙猿属与真猴类相像。

P_3 的齿冠形态还是未知的。其齿槽与 P_4 的一样，相对于齿列来说是斜向的，近中侧的齿槽位于远中侧齿槽的唇侧。这种衍生状态在始新世兔猴型类和鼩猴类中并没出现，但是在法尤姆的真猴类中很常见（例如，夸特拉尼猿属）[44]。来自缅甸始新世的半猿中也存在类似的情况，这是一个广泛[5,12]但不是普遍[1]被认为是原始真猴类的属。

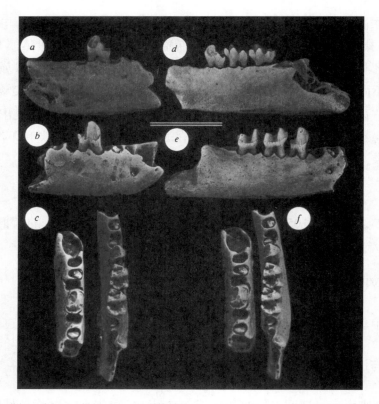

Fig. 4. Eosimiid partial mandibles from the Shanghuang fissure-fillings. *a–c*, IVPP 10592, right mandible fragment with P₄ and alveoli for anterior teeth from fissure A, in *a*, lingual; *b*, labial; and *c*, occlusal views. *d–f*, IVPP 10591, right mandible fragment with P₄–M₂ and alveoli for C₁–P₃ and M₃ from fissure B, holotype of *Eosimias sinensis*, in *d*, lingual; *e*, labial; and *f*, occlusal views. Occlusal views are stereopairs. Scale bar, 5 mm.

P_4 in the holotype is mesiodistally short (1.45 mm) and buccolingually wide (1.25 mm), a derived condition by comparison with such primitive, early Eocene primates as *Cantius* and *Steinius*[45] (Fig. 5). The moderately exodaenodont (labially bulging) crown is dominated by the protoconid. A weak metaconid occurs distal and well inferior to the protoconid. This position resembles that in parapithecids and *Arsinoea* but contrasts with the condition in other simians, in which the protoconid and metaconid are transversely aligned and united by a strong crest[40]. Neither a distinct paraconid nor an entoconid is present. The short talonid is open distolingually but is bounded labially by the hypoconid and cristid obliqua. A weak cingulid is discernible labially.

M_1 (length, 1.85 mm; width, 1.40 mm) bears a cuspidate paraconid. Despite this primitive retention, the M_1 trigonid shares derived characters with simians that are not found among Eocene adapiforms and omomyids (Fig. 5). In *Eosimias* the protoconid is enlarged relative to the metaconid and these two cusps are widely separated, as is typical for simians. Among Eocene adapiforms and omomyids these cusps are similar in size and more closely spaced[1,45]. A premetacristid, also typically absent among Eocene

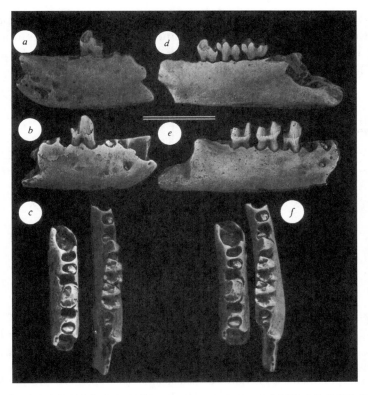

图 4. 来自上黄裂隙堆积的曙猿的残破下颌骨。$a \sim c$，IVPP 10592，来自裂隙 A 的带有 P_4 和前齿齿槽的右下颌骨残段。a，舌面视图；b，唇面视图；c，咬合面视图。$d \sim f$，IVPP 10591，来自裂隙 B 的带有 $P_4 \sim M_2$ 以及 $C_1 \sim P_3$ 齿槽和 M_3 齿槽的右下颌骨残段，中华曙猿的正模标本。d，舌面视图；e，唇面视图；f，咬合面视图。咬合面视图是立体像对。比例尺，5 毫米。

正模标本的 P_4 近远中方向上很短（1.45 毫米），颊舌方向很宽（1.25 毫米），与肯特猴和斯氏猴 [45] 等原始的早始新世灵长类相比，其为衍生特征（图 5）。胖边形齿（唇侧隆起）齿冠发育程度中等，并主要由下原尖占据。在下原尖远中侧有一个不发达并且明显比其矮的下后尖。该位置与副猿类和阿尔西诺伊猿属的情况相像，但与其他真猴类的情况相反，后者的下原尖和下后尖横向排列，由一个强脊将它们联结起来 [40]。不存在明显的下前尖和下内尖。短小的下跟座是向远中舌侧开放的，但在唇侧以下次尖和下斜脊为界。可以辨别出唇侧有一个不发达的下齿带。

M_1（长度为 1.85 毫米，宽度为 1.40 毫米）具有一个多尖的下前尖。尽管这是一种原始特征的保留，但是 M_1 的下齿座与真猴类共有某些衍生特征，这些特征在始新世兔猴型类和鼩猴类中都没有观察到过（图 5）。曙猿属中，下原尖相对于下后尖来说扩大了，而且这两个齿尖被远远隔开，这是真猴类的典型特征。始新世兔猴型类和鼩猴类中，这些齿尖在大小上接近，彼此间距更加紧密 [1,45]。始新世兔猴型类和

adapiforms and omomyids[1,45], unites the metaconid with the base of the paraconid. The talonid, which is wider than the trigonid, is unusual in having the entoconid situated farther mesial than the hypoconid and in possessing a prominent, distally projecting hypoconulid. The buccal cingulid is weak.

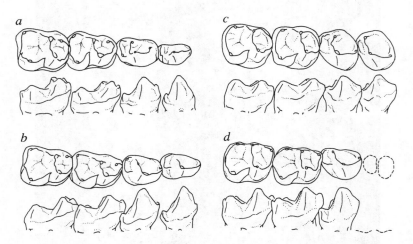

Fig. 5. Comparative schematic drawings of P_3–M_2 in selected fossil primates (not to same scale). In each pair of drawings, the upper view is occlusal and the lower view is buccal. *a*, The early Eocene adapiform *Cantius frugivorus* (CM 37448); *b*, the early Eocene omomyid *Steinius vespertinus* (USGS 25027); *c*, the middle Miocene simian *Neosaimiri fieldsi* (UCMP 39205); *d*, the middle Eocene simian *Eosimias sinensis* (IVPP V10591; crowns of P_4–M_2 only). Note obliquely oriented and mesiodistally short P_{3-4} and similar molar morphology in the simians, in contrast to conditions in *Cantius* and *Steinius*. See text for further discussion.

M_2 (length, 1.85 mm; width 1.55 mm) is very similar to M_1, from which it differs in being relatively wider and having a less distally projecting hypoconulid. The paraconid is conspicuous and widely separated mesially from the metaconid. Among Eocene adapiforms and omomyids that retain paraconids on M_2, this cusp is typically much more connate with the metaconid[1,45].

Despite its retention of such primitive characters as diminutive body size (mean estimates based on regressions of body size against M_1 area in living primates[46] range from 67–137 g), an unfused mandibular symphysis and prominent paraconids on M_{1-2}, *Eosimias* appears to be a primitive simian based on its possession of the following dental synapomorphies: lower dental formula 2-1-3-3; P_2 single-rooted; mesiodistally short, obliquely oriented, and moderately exodaenodont P_{3-4}; M_{1-2} with enlarged protoconid widely separated from metaconid, premetacristid present, and mesially situated entoconid.

Recent palaeontological discoveries[41,42] have revealed that the dentitions of early simians retained many primitive features, including lower molar paraconids. These symplesiomorphies complicate attempts to reconstruct phylogenetic relationships among early simians and their relatives, particularly on the basis of dental and jaw anatomy

齁猴类 [1,45] 通常所不具备的下后尖前脊，将下后尖与下前尖基部联结起来。下跟座比下齿座更宽，具有位置比下次尖更靠近近中侧的下内尖以及显著的向远中突出的下次小尖，这些特征都是不同寻常的。颊侧齿带微弱。

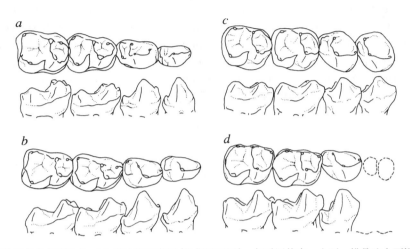

图 5. 相关灵长类化石的 $P_3 \sim M_2$ 的比较示意图（比例尺不同）。每对图片中，上面一排是咬合面视图，下面一排是颊面视图。a，早始新世兔猴型类——食果肯特猴（CM 37448）；b，早始新世齁猴类——夜斯氏猴（USGS 25027）；c，中新世中期的真猴类——菲氏新松鼠猴（UCMP 39205）；d，中始新世的真猴类——中华曙猿（IVPP V10591；只有 $P_4 \sim M_2$ 的齿冠）。请注意，真猴类中斜向的、近远中方向短的 P_{3-4} 和相似的白齿形态学特征与肯特猴属和斯氏猴属的情况正好相反。见正文中的进一步讨论。

M_2（长度为 1.85 毫米，宽度为 1.55 毫米）与 M_1 非常相似，但前者相对较宽并且下次小尖向远中侧突出程度弱于后者。下前尖明显，在近中部与下后尖远远隔开。M_2 上保留了下前尖的始新世兔猴型类和齁猴类中，该齿尖通常与下后尖融合在一起 [1,45]。

尽管曙猿属保留了一些原始特征，例如体型极小（根据现生灵长类 [46] 的 M_1 面积对身体大小进行的回归分析估计出来的平均值范围在 67~137 g 之间）、未融合的下颌联合部以及 M_{1-2} 显著的下前尖等，但从曙猿属拥有如下牙齿的共有裔征来看，其应是一种原始真猴类：下齿式为 2-1-3-3；P_2 单根；近远中方向短、斜向、中度胖边形齿的 P_{3-4}；M_{1-2} 具有膨大的下原尖并与下后尖远远隔开，下后尖前脊存在以及下内尖位置靠近近中侧。

最近的古生物学发现 [41,42] 揭示出早期真猴类的齿列保留了许多原始特征，包括下白齿的下前尖。这些共有祖征使得尝试重建早期真猴类与其亲缘类群的系统发育关系变得更加复杂，尤其是只根据牙齿和下颌骨的解剖学特征来重建的时候。然而，

alone. Nevertheless, the combination of characters listed above for *Eosimias* and many early simians is absent in adapiforms and omomyids, suggesting that they are best interpreted as simian synapomorphies. Derived features of *Eosimias* consistently point toward simian affinities, whereas we know of no derived characters for *Eosimias* that suggest an alternative phylogenetic position. Moreover, the specifically simian-like mode of dental reduction and premolar compaction in *Eosimias* differs from that found in certain omomyids (in which this usually occurs in conjunction with hypertrophy of I_1) and adapiforms (none of which evolved obliquely oriented lower premolars as a means of compressing the antemolar dentition)[1]. Within Anthropoidea, *Eosimias* appears to occupy a very basal phylogenetic position, certainly before the diversification of Parapithecidae, Oligopithecinae, Platyrrhini and Catarrhini (Fig. 6).

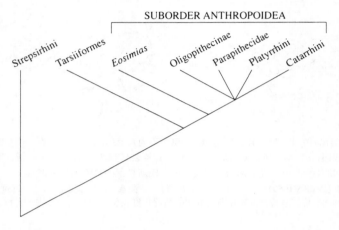

Fig. 6. Cladogram illustrating basal position of *Eosimias* with respect to the evolutionary radiation of simians. Relationships among more advanced simian clades are left unresolved, reflecting the lack of consensus regarding the phylogenetic resolution of this node[40,41,50].

Given this position, *Eosimias* yields new insight into the phylogenetic relationships of simians with respect to other primates. One hypothesis holds that early simians evolved from Eocene adapiforms[23,24,47,48]. The age and anatomy of *Eosimias* cast doubt on this idea. *Eosimias* is smaller than all known adapiforms except the specialized and temporally late *Anchomomys*. Hence, one must postulate an episode of phyletic dwarfing, which is rare among mammals, to derive *Eosimias* from adapiforms other than *Anchomomys*. Moreover, derivation of *Eosimias* from adapiforms such as *Mahgarita* (recently cited[23] as a possible close relative of early simians) would entail at least two implausible character reversals: loss of mandibular symphyseal fusion and neomorphic reacquisition of lower molar paraconids. Rather, *Eosimias* and other recent finds[32,41,42,48-50] suggest that Anthropoidea is a very ancient clade that did not evolve from either Eocene adapiforms or omomyids. This is consistent with the monophyly of either Haplorhini (Anthropoidea+Tarsiiformes) or Prosimii (Strepsirhini+Tarsiiformes), but runs counter to a monophyletic Simiolemuriformes (Strepsirhini+Anthropoidea). A wide body of evidence supports the monophyly of Haplorhini among living primates[1,2], and we prefer this phylogenetic hypothesis at present (Fig. 6).

上面列出的曙猿属和许多早期真猴类的特征组合在兔猴型类和蝹猴类中都不存在，表明对它们最好的解释就是真猴类共有裔征。曙猿属的衍生特征一致地指明其与真猴类的亲缘关系，但是我们知道曙猿属没有那些指示其具有其他系统发育位置的衍生特征。此外，曙猿属中与真猴类相似的牙齿减少和前臼齿紧缩的模式与某些蝹猴类（蝹猴类中这种情况通常是与 I_1 的过度增大一起出现的）和兔猴型类（该类群中没有任何种类进化出斜向的下前臼齿以压缩臼前齿齿列）中观察到的情况不同[1]。类人猿亚目中，曙猿属肯定在副猿科、渐新猿亚科、阔鼻猴小目和狭鼻猴小目发生分化之前，就已经占据了一个非常基底的系统发育位置（图 6）。

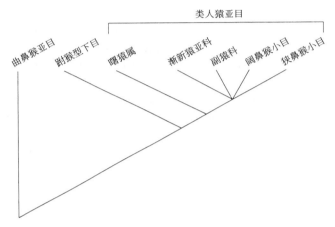

图 6. 从真猴类的演化辐射角度描述了曙猿属基底位置的支序图。更高级的真猴类演化分支间的相互关系还没有得到解决，这反映了对于该结点的系统发育关系问题的解决还缺乏一致意见[40,41,50]。

鉴于曙猿属的这个系统发育位置，其提供了真猴类系统发育关系的新见解。其中一个假说认为早期真猴类是从始新世兔猴型类进化而来的[23,24,47,48]。曙猿属的年代和解剖学特征使人们对这种假说产生了怀疑。除了特化的、在年代上稍晚的近蝹猴属以外，曙猿属比所有已知的兔猴型类都要小。因此，人们肯定会假定存在一个系统发育过程中的矮小化时期，这一现象在哺乳动物中很罕见，这一过程使曙猿属从兔猴型类衍生出来而非从近蝹猴属。此外，果真曙猿从诸如玛氏兔猴属（最近被引用[23]为早期真猴类的一种可能的关系密切的亲属）之类的兔猴型类衍生出来的话，将必须假定至少两个难以置信的特征逆向演化：下颌联合部的融合的丢弃以及下臼齿下前尖这一新生性状的重新获得。但更确切地说，曙猿属和其他最近的发现[32,41,42,48-50]显示类人猿亚目是一个非常古老的演化分支，它们既不是从始新世兔猴型类进化而来的，也不是从蝹猴类进化而来的。这与直鼻猴类（类人猿亚目 + 跗猴型下目）或原猴类（曲鼻猴亚目 + 跗猴型下目）的单系性是一致的，但是与类人猿狐猴型亚目（曲鼻猴亚目 + 类人猿亚目）的单系性却是背道而驰的。大量证据支持现生灵长类中直鼻猴类具有单系性[1,2]，我们现在更倾向于接受这种系统发育假说（图 6）。

The discovery of *Eosimias* also bears on hypotheses concerning the biogeographic centre of origin for higher primates. Recent discoveries of Eocene simians in Africa[41,42,48-50] have emphasized the antiquity of higher primates there, leading some to suggest that simians may have originated on that continent[40,49,50]. The primitive nature and great age of *Eosimias* suggest, at least, that southeastern Asia was also an important theatre of early simian evolution. The possibility that simians originated in Asia rather than Africa[11,12] cannot be rejected without further palaeontological evidence from both continents.

If *Eosimias* and related taxa from Shanghuang are basal simians as we suggest, they may help clarify a longstanding controversy concerning the younger Asian primates *Amphipithecus*, *Pondaungia* and *Hoanghonius*. All of these taxa have been compared favourably with early simians[1,2,47], and several workers have suggested that some or all of them represent early Asian higher primates[3,5,11,12,39]. The affinities of these taxa cannot be resolved here, but we note substantive similarities between *Eosimias* and *Amphipithecus*, particularly in the morphology of the lower premolars. These suggest that *Amphipithecus*, and possibly *Pondaungia* and/or *Hoanghonius*, may be younger, more derived members of the basal simian radiation sampled at Shanghuang. If so, the simian affinities of the entire radiation may be better documented by the Shanghuang primates, because of the acquisition of uniquely specialized features through time in the younger *Amphipithecus*, *Pondaungia* and *Hoanghonius*.

Discussion

The Shanghuang primates show surprisingly varied biogeographic affinities, reflecting the complex role played by Asia during early primate evolution. Both Shanghuang adapiforms exhibit clear affinities with European taxa, although the *Europolemur*-like species may be related to North American *Mahgarita* as well. *Macrotarsius* from Shanghuang, like *Asiomomys changbaicus* from Jilin Province, PRC[15], is closely related to North American omomyids. The tarsiid is endemic. The basal simian radiation sampled at Shanghuang, although probably related to younger Asian taxa such as *Amphipithecus* and *Hoanghonius*, may also indicate an ancient (?Palaeocene) biogeographic link with Africa, where early Cenozoic simians are becoming increasingly well known. Although these findings demonstrate that the Eocene primate fauna of Asia interacted with those of other continents through dispersal, many factors underlying the different dispersal patterns of individual taxa remain unknown.

(**368**, 604-609; 1994)

K. Christopher Beard[*], Tao Qi[†], Mary R. Dawson[*], Banyue Wang[†] & Chuankuei Li[†]

[*] Section of Vertebrate Paleontology, Carnegie Museum of Natural History, 4400 Forbes Avenue, Pittsburgh, Pennsylvania 15213, USA

[†] Institute of Vertebrate Paleontology and Paleoanthropology (IVPP), Academia Sinica, Beijing 100044, People's Republic of China

曙猿属的发现也对高等灵长类起源的生物地理中心方面的假说产生了影响。最近在非洲发现的始新世真猴类 [41,42,48-50] 强调了那里的高等灵长类的古老性，这使得有些人认为真猴类可能是在非洲大陆上起源的 [40,49,50]。至少曙猿属的原始特征和古老年代显示了亚洲东南部也是早期真猴类演化的一个重要舞台。如果亚洲和非洲这两块大陆不能找到进一步的古生物学证据的话，那么真猴类是从亚洲而非非洲起源的 [11,12] 这种可能性就不能排除。

如果正如我们所提出的，来自上黄的曙猿属及相关类群是基底真猴类的话，那么它们可能有助于澄清长久以来一直存在争议的关于比较年轻的亚洲灵长类——半猿属、蓬当猿属和黄河猴属的问题。所有这些类群都被倾向性地认为可与早期真猴类对比 [1,2,47]，有些学者提出这些灵长类中的部分或者全部都代表了早期的亚洲高等灵长类 [3,5,11,12,39]。这些类群的亲缘关系在这里还不能得以解决，但是我们注意到，曙猿属和半猿属之间存在着实质性的相似性，尤其是下前臼齿的形态特征方面。这些意味着半猿属，还可能包括蓬当猿属和(或)黄河猴属，可能是上黄基底真猴类演化辐射的更年轻的、更进步的成员。如果是这样的话，那么整个真猴类辐射的亲缘关系就可能通过上黄灵长类得到了更好的记录，因为更年轻的半猿属、蓬当猿属和黄河猴属经过岁月的长河获得了独特且特化的特征。

讨 论

上黄灵长类显示出了令人惊奇的多样的生物地理亲缘关系，反映了亚洲在早期灵长类演化过程中所扮演的复杂角色。尽管似欧狐猴的种类可能也与北美洲玛氏兔猴属有关，但是两种上黄兔猴型类都展示出与欧洲类群清晰的亲缘关系。来自上黄的大趾猴属就像来自中国吉林省的长白亚洲鼩猴 [15] 一样，与北美洲鼩猴类具有密切的关系。鼩猴类具有地方性。在上黄记录到的基底真猴类辐射，尽管可能与诸如半猿属和黄河猴属等年轻亚洲类群有关，但是也可能暗示着一种与非洲古老的(? 古新世)生物地理联系，我们对那里的早新生代的真猴类的了解正在变得越来越清楚。尽管这些发现展现了亚洲的始新世灵长类动物群通过扩散与其他大陆的那些灵长类相互影响，但是关于各个类群的不同扩散模式的许多潜在因素，我们仍然不清楚。

(刘皓芳 翻译；张颖奇 审稿)

Received 29 December 1993; accepted 8 February 1994.

References:

1. Szalay, F. S. & Delson, E. *Evolutionary History of the Primates* (Academic, New York, 1979).

2. Martin, R. D. *Nature* **363**, 223-234 (1993).

3. Pilgrim, G. E. *Mem. Geol. Surv. India* **14**, 1-26 (1927).

4. Zdansky, O. *Palaeontol. Sinica* **6**, 1-87 (1930).

5. Colbert, E. H. *Am. Mus. Novitates* **951**, 1-18 (1937).

6. Chow, M. *Vert. PalAsiatica* **5**, 1-5 (1961).

7. Dashzeveg, D. & McKenna, M. C. *Acta Palaeontol. Polonica* **22**, 119-137 (1977).

8. Russell, D. E. & Gingerich, P. D. *C. R. Acad. Sci., Paris* (Sér. D) **291**, 621-624 (1980).

9. Russell, D. E. & Gingerich, P. D. *C. R. Acad. Sci., Paris* (Sér. II) **304**, 209-214 (1987).

10. Wang, B. & Li, C. *Vert. PalAsiatica* **28**, 165-205 (1990).

11. Maw, B., Ciochon, R. L. & Savage, D. E. *Nature* **282**, 65-67 (1979).

12. Ciochon, R. L., Savage, D. E., Tint, T. & Maw, B. *Science* **229**, 756-759 (1985).

13. Rose, K. D. & Krause, D. W. *J. Mamm.* **65**, 721-726 (1984).

14. Gingerich, P. D., Dashzeveg, D. & Russell, D. E. *Geobios* **24**, 637-646 (1991).

15. Beard, K. C. & Wang, B. *Am. J. Phys. Anthrop.* **85**, 159-166 (1991).

16. Qi, T., Zong, G.-F. & Wang, Y.-Q. *Vert. PalAsiatica* **29**, 59-63 (1991).

17. Russell, D. E. & Zhai, R.-J. *Mém. Mus. Natl. Hist. Nat.* (Sér. C) **52**, 1-488 (1987).

18. Prothero, D. R. & Swisher, C. C. in *Eocene-Oligocene Climatic and Biotic Evolution* (eds Prothero, D. R. & Berggren, W. A.) 46-73 (Princeton Univ. Press, Princeton, 1992).

19. Beard, K. C., Dagosto, M., Gebo, D. L. & Godinot, M. *Nature* **331**, 712-714 (1988).

20. Franzen, J. L. *Cour. Forsch.-Inst. Senckenberg* **91**, 151-187 (1987).

21. Wilson, J. A. & Szalay, F. S. *Folia Primatol.* **25**, 294-312 (1976).

22. Wilson, J. A. & Stevens, M. S. *Univ. Wyoming Contrib. Geol. Spec. Pap.* **3**, 221-235 (1986).

23. Rasmussen, D. T. *Int. J. Primatol.* **11**, 439-469 (1990).

24. Gingerich, P. D. in *Evolutionary Biology of the New World Monkeys and Continental Drift* (eds Ciochon, R. L. & Chiarelli, A. B.) 123-138 (Plenum, New York, 1980).

25. Godinot, M. *C. R. Acad. Sci., Paris* (Sér. II) **299**, 1291-1296 (1984).

26. Gingerich, P. D. & Martin, R. D. *Am. J. Phys. Anthrop.* **56**, 235-257 (1981).

27. Dagosto, M. *Folia Primatol.* **41**, 49-101 (1983).

28. Godinot, M. & Jouffroy, F. K. in *Actes du Symposium Paléontologique Georges Cuvier* (eds Buffetaut, E., Mazin, J. M. & Salmon, E.) 221-242 (Le Serpentaire, Montbeliard, 1984).

29. Franzen, J. L. & Haubold, H. *Mod. Geol.* **10**, 159-170 (1986).

30. Gingerich, P. D. & Sahni, A. *Int. J. Primatol.* **5**, 63-79 (1984).

31. Pan, Y. *J. Hum. Evol.* **17**, 359-366 (1988).

32. Beard, K. C., Krishtalka, L. & Stucky, R. K. *Nature* **349**, 64-67 (1991).

33. Krishtalka, L. *Ann. Carnegie Mus.* **47**, 335-360 (1978).

34. Kelly, T. S. *Nat. Hist. Mus. Los Angeles County, Contrib. Sci.* **419**, 1-42 (1990).

35. Simons, E. L. & Bown, T. M. *Nature* **313**, 475-477 (1985).

36. Musser, G. G. & Dagosto, M. *Am. Mus. Novitates* **2867**, 1-53 (1987).

37. Ginsburg, L. & Mein, P. *C. R. Acad. Sci., Paris* (Sér. II) **304**, 1213-1215 (1987).

38. Norell, M. A. & Novacek, M. J. *Science* **255**, 1690-1693 (1992).

39. Deison, E. & Rosenberger, A. L. in *Evolutionary Biology of the New World Monkeys and Continental Drift* (eds Ciochon, R. L. & Chiarelli, A. B.) 445-458 (Plenum, New York, 1980).

40. Fleagle, J. G. & Kay, R. F. *J. Hum. Evol.* **16**, 483-532 (1987).

41. Simons, E. L. *Proc. Natl. Acad. Sci. U.S.A.* **86**, 9956-9960 (1989).

42. Simons, E. L. *Proc. Natl. Acad. Sci. U.S.A.* **89**, 10743-10747 (1992).

43. Covert, H. H. & Williams, B. A. *J. Hum. Evol.* **21**, 463-467 (1991).

44. Simons, E. L. & Kay, R. F. *Am. J. Primatol.* **15**, 337-347 (1988).

45. Rose, K. D. & Bown, T. M. *Proc. Natl. Acad. Sci. U.S.A.* **88**, 98-101 (1991).

46. Conroy, G. C. *Int. J. Primatol.* **8**, 115-137 (1987).

47. Rasmussen, D. T. & Simons, E. L. *Folia Primatol.* **51**, 182-208 (1988).

48. Simons, E. L. *Science* **247**, 1567-1569 (1990).

49. de Bonis, L., Jaeger, J.-J., Coiffat, B. & Coiffat, P.-E. *C. R. Acad. Sci., Paris* (Sér. II) **306**, 929-934 (1988).

50. Godinot, M. & Mahboubi, M. *Nature* **357**, 324-326 (1992).

Acknowledgements. We thank J. L. Carter for help with photography and A. D. Redline for artwork. Invaluable help in the field was provided by Wang Qingqing and Di Fubao of the Liyang Cultural Museum. This research was supported by the US NSF, the Chinese NSF, and M. Graham Netting and O'Neil Research Funds (Carnegie Museum of Natural History).

Chemical Self-replication of Palindromic Duplex DNA

T. Li and K. C. Nicolaou

Editor's Note

The replication of DNA happens in cells with the assistance of several enzymes. But it is widely thought that the earliest replicating molecular systems on the young Earth may have been nucleic-acid-like entities that produced copies of themselves in the absence of catalytic proteins. This prompts the question of whether DNA can itself replicate without enzymes. Here K. C. Nicolaou and Tianhu Li of the Scripps Research Institute demonstrate how that can happen. In cells replication involves the separation of double-helical strands, each of which can provide a template for the assembly of a strand with the complementary sequence of bases. Nicolaou and Li use DNA strands that are palindromic and thus self-complementary, and show how they can copy themselves by transferring information via a triple-helical complex.

Molecular replication, a fundamental process of life, has in recent years been the subject of laboratory investigations using simple chemical systems[1-10]. Whereas the work of Rebek's group[4,5] has focused on molecular architectures not known in living systems, self-replicating and template-based self-assembling systems based on nucleotides[6-8] are regarded as potential models for exploring the evolution of replicating systems on the early Earth. Previous replicating oligonucleotides have been of the single-stranded, self-complementary type: small oligonucleotide fragments are assembled on a pre-existing template and linked to form an exact copy of the template. This process cannot easily be reiterated, however, because of the strong binding of the newly formed strand to the original template. Furthermore, DNA replication in living systems operates by complementarity rather than self-complementarity—each newly assembled strand is complementary to, rather than identical to, its template—and the replication process starts and finishes with double helices. Here we report the self-replication of palindromic (symmetrical) duplex DNA-like oligonucleotides, 24 monomers long, in the absence of enzymes by means of a cycle that transfers information from template to copy and is potentially capable of extension to include non-symmetrical sequences, selection and mutation. Replication proceeds by a chemical process involving the formation of an intermediate triplex structure, and is sequence-selective in the sense that mismatches impair its efficiency. These results indicate that DNA-like double-helical molecules can replicate without assistance from proteins, a finding that may be relevant both to the appearance of replicating systems on the early Earth and to the development of new approaches to DNA amplification.

FIGURE 1a depicts the self-replication cycle that we have designed, which is based on the well-known principles of triple-strand[10,11] (Watson–Crick–Hoogsteen) and double-strand (Watson–Crick) DNA formation. It was anticipated that the relatively weaker

回文双链 DNA 的化学自我复制

李天虎（音译），尼科拉乌

编者按

在几种酶的帮助下，DNA 在细胞中进行复制，但人们普遍认为在早期地球上最早的分子复制系统可能是核酸样的物质，它可以在无催化蛋白的情况下自我复制。这就提出了疑问：DNA 可否在没有酶的存在下自我复制。这里斯克里普斯研究所的尼科拉乌和李天虎（音译）揭示了这种复制是如何发生的。在细胞中 DNA 复制时会发生双链的分离，在碱基互补配对的原则下，每条单链都可作为组装另一条链的模板。尼科拉乌和李天虎使用具有回文结构的自我互补的 DNA 链来展示它们如何通过三螺旋复合体来传递信息以实现自我复制。

分子复制是生命的一个基本过程，近年来成为实验室利用简单化学系统进行研究的主题 [1-10]，赖拜克团队 [4,5] 的工作集中在生命系统中未知的分子构建上。对于探究早期地球上复制系统的进化，自我复制系统和基于核苷酸的以模板为基础的自我装配系统 [6-8] 被认为是有潜力模型。先前复制的寡核苷酸都是单链的、自我互补的类型：小的寡核苷酸片段被装配到一个事先存在的模板上并连在一起，以形成模板的精确拷贝。然而，这个过程很难延续，因为新形成的链与初始模板有力地结合在一起。此外，在生命系统中 DNA 的复制是通过与模板互补而不是自我互补实现的——每条新组装的链与其模板互补而非相同——并且这个复制过程开始并结束于双螺旋。在这篇文章里我们将报道回文（对称）双链 DNA 样寡核苷酸（长度为 24 碱基对）的自我复制，在没有酶参与的情况下通过一个循环可以将其携带的信息从模板转移到拷贝上，此方法还有可能扩展到非对称序列并具有选择和突变的能力。此化学复制的过程利用了核酸三链结构作为中间态。从错配会降低复制效率方面讲，这个过程具有序列选择性。这些结果说明 DNA 样双螺旋分子可以在没有蛋白质的帮助下复制，这一发现可能既与早期地球上复制系统的出现有关，也将有助于发展 DNA 扩增的新方法。

图 1a 描述了我们基于已知的三链 [10,11]（沃森 – 克里克 – 霍赫斯滕）和双链（沃森 – 克里克）DNA 形成原则设计的自我复制循环。由于三螺旋中涉及的霍赫斯滕结

Hoogsteen binding involved in triple helices would allow release of the newly generated strand from a double helical template[12], thus ensuring, in combination with double-strand formation, continuous production of new copies. According to this scheme, duplex DNA serves, at an appropriately acidic pH, as a template to attract complementary single-strand DNA fragments, pre-organizing them along its major groove and orienting them in the right direction for ligation (1→2, Fig. 1a)[13]. A suitable chemical reagent then brings about P—O bond formation[13] thus forming a new strand, identical with one of the two strands of the original duplex (2→3). Raising the pH (pH driven) or adding an excess of oligonucleotides complementary to the newly formed strand drives the equilibrium away from the triplex structure, releasing the single strand (3→4), thus allowing it to serve as a template for duplex formation in the presence of complementary single-strand DNA fragments (4→5)[14-18]. Finally, a chemical reagent causing P—O bond formation[18] completes the cycle by generating a new strand identical to the second strand of the original DNA in an overall process that accomplishes replication of the original duplex (5→1, 6). This scheme, of course, requires symmetrical sequences, otherwise the product of the cycle is of the retro-sense. In the latter case (non-palindromic sequences) a second cycle and appropriate substrate fragments will be required to produce an identical copy of the original template. It should also be noted that the present triplex replication scheme requires at least one of the strands to be an all-purine sequence.

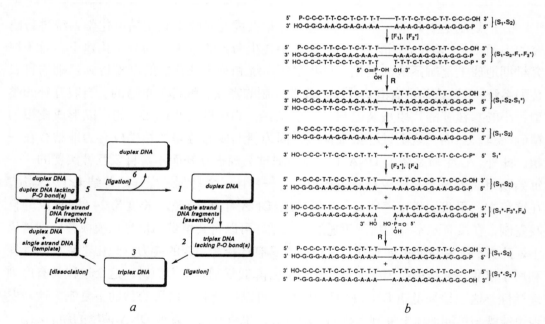

Fig. 1. *a*, General schematic representation of chemical self-replication of a palindromic duplex DNA cycle by triple- and double-helix formation. *b*, Replication of duplex DNA as a result of sequential triple- and double-helix formation. Sequences of oligodeoxyribonucleotides used: F_1 is 5' P-TTTCTCCTTCCC-OH 3'; F_2 is 5' P*-CCCTTCCTCTTT-OH 3'; F_3 is 5' P*-GGGAAGGAGAAA-OH 3'; F_4 is 5' P-AAAGAGGAAGGG-OH 3'. The asterisk designates radiolabelled (^{32}P) 5' phosphorus (unlabelled:labeled ≈100). R is the reagent N-cyanoimidazole. Oligonucleotides were purchased from Operon Technologies. For details of experimental conditions, see text and legends to Figs 2–4.

合相对较弱，可以使新生成的链易于从双螺旋模板上释放出来 [12]，从而实现双链模板的重复利用，继续产生新拷贝。根据这个方案，在适当的酸性 pH 条件下，双链 DNA 作为模板通过霍赫斯滕配对将单链 DNA 片段按照正确的、方便进行连接的方向沿着其大沟进行排列（1→2，图 1a）[13]。随后加入合适的化学试剂引起 P—O 键的形成，从而形成一条新链 [13]，这条新链与最初双链的两条链中的一条相同（2→3）。提高 pH（pH 推动）或加入过量与新形成的链互补的寡核苷酸会推动三链结构解离，释放单链（3→4），再利用此解离出的单链作为模板，与另外能与之互补的单链 DNA 片段形成双链（4→5）[14-18]。最后，由加入的化学试剂引发 P—O 键形成 [18] 使循环结束，从而产生一条新的、与原 DNA 中另外一条互补链完全相同的新链，完成对原双链的复制（5→1，6）。当然，这个方案需要对称序列，否则循环的产物将没有意义。在后一种情况下（非回文序列），需要在第二个循环中加入合适的底物片段以产生与初始模板相同的拷贝。还需要指出本文中的三链方案需要至少一条链为全嘌呤序列。

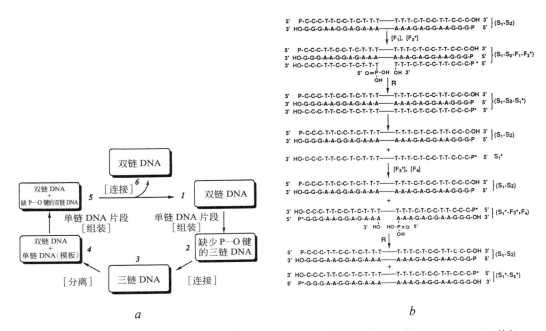

图 1. a，通过形成三螺旋和双螺旋进行的回文双链 DNA 的化学自我复制的总示意图。b，双链 DNA 的复制是连续的三螺旋和双螺旋形成的结果。所用的寡脱氧核苷酸序列为：F_1: 5′ P-TTTCTCCTTCCC-OH 3′；F_2: 5′ P*-CCCTTCCTCTTT-OH 3′；F_3: 5′ P*-GGGAAGGAGAAA-OH 3′；F_4: 5′ P-AAAGAGGAAGGG-OH 3′。星号表示放射性标记(^{32}P)5′ 磷酸基（未标记：标记 ≈100）。R 是试剂氮–氰基咪唑。寡核苷酸购自欧佩伦技术公司。实验的详细条件见正文和图 2~4 图注。

Figure 1b summarizes the experiments leading to replication of a palindromic 24-monomer duplex DNA fragment ($S_1 \cdot S_2$). Fragments F_1 and F_2^* (chosen to be complementary to S_2) were added to the DNA duplex (pre-annealed in the presence of 100 mM NaCl by incubation at 90 °C for 3 min followed by slow cooling to 20 °C over 1 h) in a pH 6.0 buffer solution (imidazole/HCl) to form the triplex ($S_1 \cdot S_2 \cdot F_1$, F_2^*) in which one P—O bond is missing in strand F_1, F_2^*. N-cyanoimidazole[18] (cyanogen bromide[18] also works, but less efficiently) was then added to the mixture, ligating the two fragments of the third strand by P—O bond formation and leading to the complete triple helix ($S_1 \cdot S_2 \cdot S_1^*$).

The products were analysed by denaturing gel electrophoresis. As shown in Fig. 2a (lane 3), a new strand, F_1–F_2^*, which is identical to S_1^*, was formed with high yield (80%). Appropriate control experiments revealed no S_1 strand formation in the absence of ($S_1 \cdot S_2$) template (lane 4, Fig. 2a), or in the presence of S_1 (lane 5, Fig. 2a), but efficient S_1^* strand formation in the presence of S_2 template as expected (lane 6, Fig. 2a). No condensation was apparent in the absence of F_1 (lane 7, Fig. 2a). Furthermore, the requirement for N-cyanoimidazole for the formation of S_1 was confirmed (lane 8, Fig. 2a). The second strand (S_2) of the duplex was replicated in the same reaction mixture at pH 7.0 using the newly generated first strand (F_1–F_2^*) ($\equiv S_1^*$) as a template. Thus, fragments F_3^* and F_4 (complementary to F_1 and F_2^* respectively) were added to form the "disconnected" duplex ($S_1^* \cdot F_3^*$, F_4), which is lacking a P—O bond between F_3^* and F_4. Addition of N-cyanoimidazole (or cyanogen bromide) brought about smooth coupling of the two fragments as expected. Because these sequences are palindromic, the newly formed DNA duplex copy (F_1–$F_2^* \cdot F_3^*$–F_4) ($\equiv S_1^* \cdot S_2^*$) (lane 6, Fig. 2b; 50% yield based on the newly formed template, 40% yield based on the original duplex) is identical with the original duplex ($S_1 \cdot S_2$). The results of appropriate control experiments are shown in Fig. 2b and are in accord with the proposed reactions. Digestion of F_1–F_2^* ($\equiv S_1^*$) and F_3^*–F_4 ($\equiv S_2^*$) with phosphodiesterase I revealed the presence of a 3′, 5′-phosphodiester bond, thus confirming the expected orientation of fragments F_1, F_2, F_3 and F_4 on the templates. It was of interest to note in these experiments several slower moving bands (totaling ~5% of radioactivity and reaching ~30% with increasing amount of N-cyanoimidazole, not shown in gel). These products, assumed to be 36- and higher polymers, are presumed to be formed by ligation at the ends of the triple helices, a phenomenon that may be of special significance in considering elongation of DNA.

图 $1b$ 总结了引导 24 碱基长的回文双链 DNA 片段 ($S_1 \cdot S_2$) 进行复制的实验。将片段 F_1 和 F_2^*（它与 S_2 互补）加入到含有 DNA 双链的、pH 6.0 的咪唑／盐酸缓冲液中（双链结构已经在 100 mM 氯化钠存在下，90 ℃ 温育 3 分钟，然后缓慢冷却退火 1 小时以上，至最终温度 20 ℃）以形成三链 ($S_1 \cdot S_2 \cdot F_1$, F_2^*)，此结构中 F_1、F_2^* 之间没有磷酸二酯键连接。随后，将氮–氰基咪唑[18]（溴化氰[18] 也可，但效率低）加入到混合物中，促使 P—O 键形成使两个片段连接在一起，从而形成完整的三螺旋 ($S_1 \cdot S_2 \cdot S_1^*$)。

通过变性凝胶电泳法分析产物，结果如图 $2a$（泳道 3）所示：与 S_2^* 相同的一条新链 F_1–F_2^* 以很高的产率（80%）形成。合理的对照实验显示没有 ($S_1 \cdot S_2$) 模板存在（泳道 4，图 $2a$）或有 S_1 存在（泳道 5，图 $2a$）时不能形成 S_1 链，但存在 S_2 模板时高效产生了 S_1^*（泳道 6，图 $2a$），符合预期。没有 F_1（泳道 7，图 $2a$）时不发生明显的凝聚作用。同时，实验结果确定了 S_1 形成需要氮–氰基咪唑（泳道 8，图 $2a$）。以新产生的第一条链 (F_1–F_2^*) ($\equiv S_1^*$) 为模板，在 pH 为 7.0 的相同反应混合液中，可以实现双链中的另一条单链 S_2 的复制。加入片段 F_3^* 和 F_4（分别与 F_1 和 F_2^* 互补）形成"不连接的"双链 ($S_1^* \cdot F_3^*$, F_4)，该双链在 F_3^* 和 F_4 之间缺少磷酸二酯键。加入氮–氰基咪唑（或溴化氰）可以使这两个片段按预期顺利连接。因为这些序列是回文的，新形成的 DNA 双链拷贝 (F_1–$F_2^* \cdot F_3^*$–F_4) ($\equiv S_1^* \cdot S_2^*$)（泳道 6，图 $2b$；50% 的产量基于新形成的模板，40% 的产量基于初始双链）与初始双链 ($S_1 \cdot S_2$) 是相同的。合理的对照实验结果（如图 $2b$ 所示）与预期的反应是一致的。F_1–F_2^* ($\equiv S_1^*$) 和 F_3^*–F_4 ($\equiv S_2^*$) 可以被磷酸二酯酶 I 清化 3′, 5′–磷酸二酯键的存在，这证实了片段 F_1、F_2、F_3 和 F_4 在模板上是按照预期方向排列的。有意思的是，我们注意到在这些实验中还有几条移动较慢的带（总共约为放射性活度的 5%，并随氮–氰基咪唑量的增加达到 30% 左右，没有在本凝胶中显示）。我们推测这些产物（36 碱基或更长）是通过三螺旋末端之间的连接形成的，在考虑 DNA 延伸时，这个现象可能具有特定的意义。

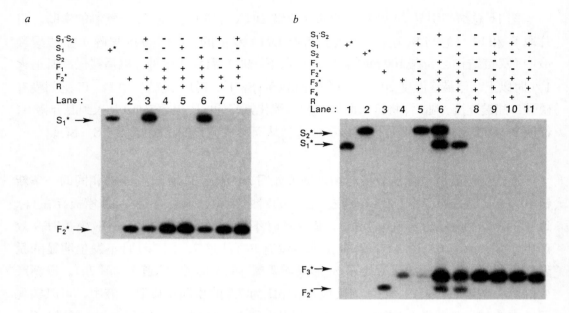

Fig. 2. Replication of duplex oligodeoxyribonucleotide ($S_1 \cdot S_2$) by varying pH (6.0→7.0). Autoradiograms of high-resolution, denaturing 20% polyacrylamide gels. a, First half of the cycle; b, second half of the cycle.

Methods. Radioactive fragments were prepared by phosphorylation of synthetic oligonucleotides at their 5′ end with polynucleotide kinase and [γ-^{32}P]ATP; asterisk indicates radioactivity incorporated to the extent unlabelled : labeled ≈ 100. R is the reagent N-cyanoimidazole. Reactions were processed after termination by cooling in dry ice, evaporation to dryness, dissolving in loading buffer and denaturation. a, First half of the cycle. Demonstration of template ($S_1 \cdot S_2$)-directed formation of copies of S_1 strand from oligodeoxyribonucleotide fragments F_1 and F_2. Lane 1, S_1^*; lane 2, F_2^*. Lanes 3–8 represent reaction mixtures, each of which was obtained by incubation of 100 mM imidazole-HCl (initial pH 6.0), 10 μM ZnCl$_2$, 100 mM NaCl, 40 mM N-cyanoimidazole and oligodeoxyribonucleotides in a total volume of 30 μl at 20 °C for 72 h. Lanes: 3, 10 μM annealed $S_1 \cdot S_2$, 10 μM F_1 and 10 μM F_2^*; 4, 10 μM F_1 and 10 μM F_2^*; 5, 10 μM S_1, 10 μM F_1 and 10 μM F_2^*; 6, 10 μM S_2, 10 μM F_1 and 10 μM F_2^*; 7, 10 μM $S_1 \cdot S_2$ and 10 μM F_2^*; 8, as lane 3, except for the absence of ligating agent N-cyanoimidazole. b, Second half of the cycle. Newly formed copies of S_1 released from template by increasing the pH to 7.0, directed formation of S_2 stand from oligo-deoxyribonucleotides F_3 and F_4. Lane 1, S_1^*; lane 2, S_2^*; lane 3, F_2^*; lane 4, F_3^*. Lanes 5 and 8–11 represent reaction mixtures obtained by incubation of 100 mM imidazole (initial pH 7.0), 10 μM ZnCl$_2$, 100 mM NaCl, 80 mM N-cyanoimidazole and oligodeoxyribonucleotides in a total volume of 30 μl at 20 °C for 72h. Lanes: 5, 5 μM S_1, 5 μM F_3^* and 5 μM F_4; 8, 5 μM F_3^* and 5 μM F_4; 9, 5 μM S_2, 5 μM F_3^* and 5 μM F_4; 10, 5 μM S_1 and 5 μM F_3^*; 11, as in lane 5, except for the absence of ligating agent N-cyanoimidazole. The reaction mixtures of lanes 6 and 7 were prepared from 15 μl of the original solutions represented by lanes 3 and 6 in a (after 72h incubation) and appropriate addition of reagents, bringing the total volume to 30 μl containing 100 mM imidazole-HCl (initial pH 7.0), 10 μM ZnCl$_2$, 100 mM NaCl, 80 mM N-cyanoimidazole and oligonucleotides. After incubation for 72 h at 20 °C, reactions were terminated by cooling in dry ice, samples were lyophilized, dissolved in loading buffer and denatured. Lane 6, 5 μM F_3^*, 5 μM F_4 and 15 μl of solution, corresponding to lane 3 in a; lane 7, 5 μM F_3^*, 5 μM F_4 and 15 μl of solution, corresponding to lane 6 in a.

Self-replication of a palindromic duplex DNA ($S_1 \cdot S_2$) was also demonstrated at the constant pH of 6.15. At this pH, it was anticipated that the equilibrium[12] between the triplex structure and its components would be driven towards dissociation by excess fragments that would strongly bind the released single strand, and that the rate of ligation of the newly assembled duplex would

428

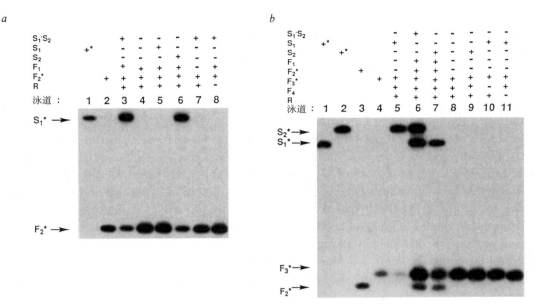

图 2. 通过改变 pH(6.0 → 7.0) 复制双链寡脱氧核糖核苷酸($S_1 \cdot S_2$)。高分辨率的放射自显影，20% 的变性聚丙烯酰胺凝胶。a，前半部分循环；b，后半部分循环。

方法。用多核苷酸激酶和 [γ-^{32}P]ATP 作用于合成的寡核苷酸的 5′ 端，使其磷酸化，从而制备放射性片段；星号表示放射活性掺入程度（未标记：标记 ≈100）。R 是试剂氮−氰基咪唑。反应用干冰冷却终止后对样品进行处理，蒸发干燥，溶于上样缓冲液并变性。a，前半部分循环。说明模板($S_1 \cdot S_2$)指导的从寡脱氧核糖核苷酸片段 F_1 和 F_2 形成 S_1 链的拷贝，泳道 1 为 S_1^*；泳道 2 为 F_2^*；泳道 3~8 代表反应混合物，其中每一个都是通过总体积为 30 μl 的 100 mM 咪唑−HCl(初始 pH 6.0)、10 μM $ZnCl_2$、100 mM NaCl、40 mM 氮−氰基咪唑和寡脱氧核糖核苷酸 20 ℃下温育 72 小时得到的。泳道 3，10 μM 退火的 $S_1 \cdot S_2$、10 μM F_1 和 10 μM F_2^*；泳道 4，10 μM F_1 和 10 μM F_2^*；泳道 5，10 μM S_1、10 μM F_1 和 10 μM F_2^*；泳道 6，10 μM S_2、10 μM F_1 和 10 μM F_2^*；泳道 7，10 μM $S_1 \cdot S_2$ 和 10 μM F_2^*；泳道 8，除没有连接试剂氮−氰基咪唑外与泳道 3 相同。b，后半部分循环。通过将 pH 升高到 7.0 使新形成的 S_1 的拷贝从模板上释放下来，指导寡脱氧核糖核苷酸 F_3 和 F_4 形成 S_2 链。泳道 1，S_1^*；泳道 2，S_2^*；泳道 3，F_2^*；泳道 4，F_3^*。泳道 5 和 8~11 代表通过总体积为 30 μl 的 100 mM 咪唑(初始 pH 7.0)、10 μM $ZnCl_2$、100 mM NaCl、80 mM 氮−氰基咪唑和寡脱氧核糖核苷酸 20 ℃下温育 72 小时得到的。泳道 5，5 μM S_1、5 μM F_3^* 和 5 μM F_4；泳道 8，5 μM F_3^* 和 5 μM F_4；泳道 9，5 μM S_2、5 μM F_3^* 和 5 μM F_4；泳道 10，5 μM S_1 和 5 μM F_3^*；泳道 11，除没有连接试剂氮−氰基咪唑外与泳道 5 相同。泳道 6 和 7 的反应混合物是由 a(温育 72 小时后)中泳道 3 和 6 的 15 μl 初始溶液制备而来的，并适当添加试剂，使其总体积达到 30 μl，包含 100 mM 咪唑−HCl (初始 pH 7.0)、10 μM $ZnCl_2$、100 mM NaCl、80 mM 氮−氰基咪唑和寡脱氧核糖核苷酸。在 20 ℃温育 72 小时后，通过干冰冷却终止反应，将样品冻干，溶于上样缓冲液中并变性。泳道 6，5 μM F_3^*、5 μM F_4 和 15 μl 溶液，对应于 a 中的泳道 3；泳道 7，5 μM F_3^*、5 μM F_4 和 15 μl 溶液，对应 a 中的泳道 6。

回文双链 DNA($S_1 \cdot S_2$)的自我复制也可以在恒定 pH 为 6.15 的条件下实现。在此 pH 下，我们可以预测：过量的片段将强烈结合释放出的单链，从而将三链结构及其组分之间的平衡[12] 朝分离方向推动，并且新组装双链的连接速率将达到最佳[18]。

be optimum[18]. Figure 3 depicts the experimental evidence for this constant-pH cycle. Thus pre-annealed ($S_1 \cdot S_2$) duplex (lacking 5′ phosphates, to avoid end ligation) was incubated with a 1.2-fold excess of F_1^* and F_2 (lacking 5′ phosphate) in the presence of N-cyanoimidazole to produce, in 85% yield, strand F_1^*–F_2($\equiv S_1^*$) (lane 6, Fig. 3). In the presence of F_1, F_2 and a sixfold excess of F_3 (lacking 5′ phosphate), and F_4^*, the same experiment demonstrated the formation of the second strand (F_3–F_4^*) ($\equiv S_2^*$) in 70% overall yield (lane 8, Fig. 3). Appropriate control experiments confirmed the requirement for the template in this process (lanes 5 and 7, Fig. 3). Employing the above conditions, three successive replication cycles were demonstrated starting with 2.0 nmol of template ($S_1 \cdot S_2$) and purifying the duplex DNA between cycles using a centricon concentrator. The total amount of 24-monomer duplex DNA and the overall yield were determined both by counting radioactivity corresponding to incorporated and free fragments after electrophoresis, and by checking absorbance by ultraviolet-visible spectroscopy. The 24-monomer duplex DNA formed contained predominantly replicated template ($S_1 \cdot S_2$) but also small amounts of end ligation products resulting from triple-helix formation as determined by control experiments. There is a roughly fivefold increase in the total amount of 24-monomer duplex DNA over three cycles ($\sim 75\%$ yield for each cycle). Whether this represents exponential growth is not yet clear, however—the precise kinetics and the scope and mechanism of the observed end ligation are under further investigation.

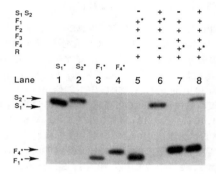

Fig. 3. Replication of duplex oligodeoxyribonucleotide ($S_1 \cdot S_2$) at constant pH 6.15. Autoradiogram of high-resolution, denaturing 20% polyacrylamide gel.

Methods. Radiolabelling and reaction processing were carried out as for Fig. 3. R is the reagent N-cyanoimidazole. Strand sequences were the same as in Fig. 2 apart from the absence of phosphate at the 5′ end of S_1, S_2, F_2 and F_3. Lane 1, S_1^*; lane 2, S_2^*; lane 3, F_1^*; lane 4, F_4^*; lane 6, 100 mM imidazole-HCl, 5 µM ZnCl$_2$, 100 mM NaCl, 20 mM N-cyanoimidazole, 20 µM annealed ($S_1 \cdot S_2$) (2 nmol), 24 µM F_1^* (2.4 nmol) and 24 µM F_2 (2.4 nmol) in a total volume of 100 µl, incubated at 20 °C for 72 h; lane 5, same as in lane 6 apart from the absence of ($S_1 \cdot S_2$). Lane 8, as lane 6 except that only unlabelled F_1 was used in the first half of the cycle; F_3 (12 nmol), F_4^* (12 nmol), buffer and water were added and the mixture was incubated for 10 h at 20 °C before N-cyanoimidazole was added, giving a total volume of 200 µl (pH 6.15) and containing 100 mM imidazole-HCl, 5 µM ZnCl$_2$, 100 mM NaCl, 20 mM N-cyanoimidazole and oligonucleotides. The reaction mixture was incubated at 20 °C for a further 72 h. Lane 7, as lane 8 except for the initial absence of ($S_1 \cdot S_2$) and the use of only 2.4 µM (0.48 nmol) of each F_1^* and F_2. Yield of generated duplex DNA was determined by counting radioactivity of the bands corresponding to S_1^* and F_1^* (lane 6) and S_2^* and F_4^* (lane 8).

We have also examined selection effects and the fidelity of the replication process. Figure 4 summarizes several experiments in which four mismatched F_1 fragments (F_1-mis) were allowed to compete with F_1 and among themselves. As seen from lanes 4–9 (Fig. 4), only F_1 participated

图 3 展示了这个恒定 pH 循环的实验证据。因此，在存在氮－氰基咪唑的情况下用提前退火的 $(S_1 \cdot S_2)$ 双链（缺少 5′ 磷酸盐，以防止末端连接）与 1.2 倍过量的 F_1^* 和 F_2（缺少 5′ 磷酸盐）温育，以 85% 的产率生成链 $F_1^*\text{–}F_2$（$\equiv S_1^*$）（泳道 6，图 3）。在存在 F_1、F_2 和 6 倍过量 F_3（缺少 5′ 磷酸盐）以及 F_4^* 时，相同实验条件下第二条链（$F_3\text{–}F_4^*$）（$\equiv S_2^*$）形成的总产率为 70%（泳道 8，图 3）。合理设置的对照实验证实在这个过程中模板是必需的（泳道 5 和 7，图 3）。我们还采用上面的实验条件，演示了从 2.0 nmol 模板 $(S_1 \cdot S_2)$ 开始的三个连续复制循环，并用微量浓缩离心器对其进行分离纯化。通过测量电泳后整合的和自由片段中的放射活性以及紫外线－可见光谱法，对所生成的全部的 24 碱基对双链 DNA 和所有产物进行定量分析。所形成的 24 碱基对的双链 DNA 包含大量的被复制的模板 $(S_1 \cdot S_2)$ 以及少量的通过对照实验可以证实的三螺旋末端连接产物。结果表明，经过三个循环，24 碱基对长的双链 DNA 的总量大约增加为 5 倍（每个循环产率约为 75%）。目前还不清楚增长是否是指数式的，但是已观察到的末端连接现象的动力学（性质）、范围及发生机制正在进一步研究中。

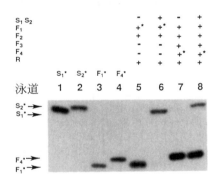

图 3. 在恒定 pH 为 6.15 条件下，双链寡脱氧核糖核苷酸 $(S_1 \cdot S_2)$ 的复制。高分辨率放射自显影照片，20% 的变性聚丙烯酰胺凝胶。

方法。与图 3 有关的放射性标记和反应过程。R 是试剂氮－氰基咪唑。除 S_1、S_2、F_2 和 F_3 的 5′ 端没有磷酸盐外，所有链序列与图 2 相同。泳道 1，S_1^*；泳道 2，S_2^*；泳道 3，F_1^*；泳道 4，F_4^*；泳道 6，100 mM 咪唑–HCl、5 μM $ZnCl_2$、100 mM NaCl、20 mM 氮－氰基咪唑、20 μM 退火的 $S_1 \cdot S_2$（2 nmol）、24 μM F_1^*（2.4 nmol）和 24 μM F_2（2.4 nmol），总体积为 100 μl，20 ℃ 下温育 72 小时；泳道 5，除没有 $S_1 \cdot S_2$ 外与泳道 6 相同；泳道 8，除前半部分循环只使用了未标记的 F_1 外，与泳道 6 相同；加入 F_3（12 nmol）、F_4^*（12 nmol）、缓冲液和水，并在加入氮－氰基咪唑前，将混合物在 20 ℃ 下温育 10 小时，总体积达到 200 μl（pH 6.15）并且包含 100 mM 咪唑–HCl、5 μM $ZnCl_2$、100 mM NaCl、20 mM 氮－氰基咪唑和寡核苷酸。反应混合物在 20 ℃ 下再温育 72 小时；泳道 7，除了最初缺少 $S_1 \cdot S_2$ 和只用了 2.4 μM（0.48 nmol）的 F_1^* 和 F_2 外，与泳道 8 相同。通过计算与 S_1^* 和 F_1^*（泳道 6）以及 S_2^* 和 F_4^*（泳道 8）相对应的条带放射性活度可以确定产生的双链 DNA 的量。

我们还采用 4 个错配的 F_1 片段（$F_1\text{-mis}$）与 F_1 片段共同进行反应以检验复制过程的选择性和精确性。如图 4，泳道 4~9 中所看到的，只有 F_1 片段显著地参与了循环

predominantly in the cycle (lanes 5 and 6 showed small amounts of F_1-mis-1 and F_1-mis-2 incorporation respectively), reflecting lower tendencies of the mismatched sequences to form triple-helical structures with the template ($S_1 \cdot S_2$). It was noted, however, that in the absence of F_1, the sequence with only one mismatch base (F_1-mis-1 $\equiv$ 5'P-TTCCTCCTTCCC 3'; mismatched base in bold) enters the replication cycle successfully (lane 10, Fig. 4). Thus, "mutated" sequences can be replicated, albeit with lower efficiency.

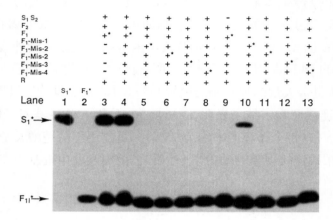

Fig. 4. Selection and mutation in self-replication of duplex oligodeoxyribonucleotide ($S_1 \cdot S_2$). Autoradiogram of high resolution, 20% polyacrylamide denaturing gel.

Methods. Radiolabelling and reaction processing were carried out as described for Fig. 3. R, N-cyanoimidazole. For strand sequences, see Fig. 2 legend. Lane 1, S_1^*; lane 2: F_1^*. Each of the reaction mixtures (pH 6.15) for lanes 3–9 initially contained 100 mM imidazole-HCl, 5 µM $ZnCl_2$, 100 mM NaCl, 10 mM N-cyanoimidazole, 1 µM $S_1 \cdot S_2$ (except for lane 9), 2 µM each of F_2, F_1, F_1-mis-1 [5' P-TTCCTCCTTCCC 3'], F_1-mis-2 [5' P-TTTCCTTCTCCC 3'], F_1-mis-3 [5' P-TTCTTCCTTCCC 3'] and F_1-mis-4[5' P-TCTCTCTTCCTC 3'] in 100 µl. Each reaction mixture contained only one radiolabelled sequence as follows. Lane 4, F_1^*; lane 5, [F_1-mis-1]*; lane 6, [F_1-mis-2]*; lane 7, [F_1-mis-3]*; lane 8, [F_1-mis-4]*; lane 9, F_1^*; lane 3, F_1^* in the absence of mismatch sequences. The reaction mixtures for lanes 10–13 were same as in 5–8, respectively, except for the absence of F_1. The reaction mixtures were incubated for 24 h at 20 °C.

The chemical processes described here demonstrate the viability of proliferation of duplex DNA by relying on the principles of complementarity involved in DNA triple- and double-helix formation and using simple chemical reactions and reagents. In the present example we made use of a template whose complement is identical to the template itself. In principle, however, this system could be extended to non-palindromic templates, provided that the appropriate substrate fragments are supplied to enable replication of both strands of the duplex. The possibility of extending these principles to the synthesis of more sophisticated DNA systems and other important biopolymers, including RNA, proteins and polysaccharides, is intriguing. The simplicity of the process may allow further improvements and automation, and the demonstrated selection and informational nature of the molecules involved may have significant implications for the origins of life on Earth[19-23].

(**369**, 218-221; 1994)

(泳道 5 和泳道 6 分别显示了少量的参与循环的 F_1–mis–1 和 F_1–mis–2），这反映出错配序列与模板（$S_1 \cdot S_2$）形成三螺旋结构的趋势很小。然而需要特别指出的是，在没有 F_1 存在的情况下，只含有一个错配碱基的序列（F_1–mis–1 ≡ 5′ P–TT**C**CTCCTTCCC 3′；错配碱基加粗）可以成功参与复制循环（泳道 10，图 4）。此结果说明，尽管效率较低，但"突变的"序列可以被复制。

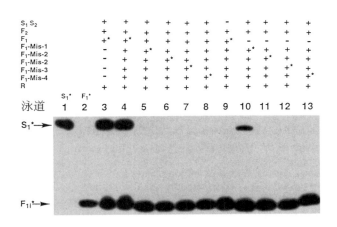

图 4. 双链寡脱氧核糖核苷酸（$S_1 \cdot S_2$）自我复制中的选择与突变。高分辨率的放射自显影照片，20% 的聚丙烯酰胺变性凝胶。

方法。 放射性标记和反应过程按图 3 中的描述进行。R，氮–氰基咪唑。链序列见图 2 的图注。泳道 1，S_1^*；泳道 2，F_1^*。对于泳道 3~9，各反应混合物最初包含 100 mM 咪唑–HCl、5 μM $ZnCl_2$、100 mM NaCl、10 mM 氮–氰基咪唑、1 μM $S_1 \cdot S_2$（除第 9 泳道外），F_2、F_1、F_1–mis–1[5′ P–TT**C**CTCCTTCCC 3′]、F_1–mis–2 [5′ P–TTT**CCTT**CTCCC 3′]、F_1–mis–3 [5′ P–TT**CTT**CCTTCCC 3′] 和 F_1–mis–4 [5′ P–T**C**TCTC**TT**CC**T**C 3′] 各 2 μM，体积是 100 μl。每组反应混合物只包含一个放射性标记的序列，具体如下：泳道 4，F_1^*；泳道 5，[F_1–mis–1]*；泳道 6，[F_1–mis–2]*；泳道 7，[F_1–mis–3]*；泳道 8，[F_1–mis–4]*；泳道 9，F_1^*；泳道 3，没有错配序列的 F_1^*。除了缺少 F_1 外，泳道 10~13 的反应混合物分别与 5~8 中的相同。反应混合物在 20 ℃下温育 24 小时。

本文描述的化学过程证明：基于 DNA 三螺旋和双螺旋的互补配对原则，简单的化学反应和试剂就可以实现双链 DNA 的复制扩增。在本文的例子中我们使用的模板的互补链与模板本身是相同的。然而，在原理上，如果提供合适的底物片段以使双链的两条链都能复制，那么这个系统可以延伸到非回文模板。将这些原理延伸到更复杂的 DNA 系统和其他重要生物多聚物（包括 RNA、蛋白质和多糖）合成的可能性是非常吸引人的。这个过程的简单性允许进一步对其进行改进和自动化，并且所涉及分子的已被证明的选择性和其信息性本质对研究地球上生命的起源有重要的意义[19-23]。

（李梅 翻译；刘冬生 审稿）

T. Li & K. C. Nicolaou*

Department of Chemistry, The Scripps Research Institute, 10666 North Torrey Pines Road, La Jolla, California 92037, USA and Department of Chemistry, University of California, San Diego, 9500 Gilman Drive, La Jolla, California 92093, USA

* To whom correspondence should be addressed.

Received 11 February; accepted 4 March 1994.

References:

1. Orgel, L. E. *Nature* **358**, 203-209 (1992).

2. Joyce, G. F. *Nature* **338**, 217-224 (1989).

3. Hoffmann, S. *Angew. Chem. Int. Ed. Engl.* **31**, 1013-1016 (1992).

4. Tjivikua, T., Ballesten, P. & Rebek, J. Jr *J. Am. Chem. Soc.* **112**, 1249-1250 (1990).

5. Feng, Q., Park, T. K. & Rebek, J. Jr *Science* **256**, 1179-1180 (1992).

6. von Kiedrowski, G. *Angew. Chem. Int. Ed. Engl.* **25**, 932-935 (1986).

7. von Kiedrowski, G., Wlotzka, B. & Helbing, J. *Angew. Chem. Int. Ed. Engl.* **28**, 1235-1237 (1989).

8. von Kiedrowski, G., Wlotzka, B., Helbing, J., Matzen, M. & Jordan, S. *Angew. Chem. Int. Ed. Engl.* **30**, 423-426 (1991).

9. Goodwin, J. T. & Lynn, D. G. *J. Am. Chem. Soc.* **114**, 9197-9198 (1992).

10. Kanavarioti, A. *J. theor. Biol.* **158**, 207-219 (1992).

11. Eschenmoser, A. & Lowewenthal, E. *Chem. Soc. Rev.* **21**, 1-16 (1992).

12. Maher, L. J., Dervan, P. B. & Wold, B. J. *Biochemistry* **29**, 8820-8826 (1990).

13. Leubke, K. J. & Dervan, P. B. *J. Am. Chem. Soc.* **111**, 8733-8735 (1989).

14. Inoue, T. & Orgel, L. E. *Science* **219**, 859-862 (1983).

15. Acevedo, O. L. & Orgel, L. E. *J. Molec. Biol.* **197**, 187-193 (1987).

16. Chen, C. B., Inoue, T. & Orgel, L. E. *J. Molec. Biol.* **181**, 271-279 (1985).

17. Kanavarioti, A., Bernasconi, C. F., Alberas, D. J. & Baird, E. E. *J. Am. Chem. Soc.* **115**, 8537-8546 (1993).

18. Kanaya, E. & Yanagawa, H. *Biochemistry* 7423-7430 (1986).

19. Miller, S. L. in *Cold Spring Harbor Symp. Quant. Biol.* **LII**, 17-27 (1987).

20. Gedulin, B. & Arrhenius, G. in *Early Life on Earth* (ed. Bengston, S.) 91-110 (Nobel. Symp. No. 84, Columbia Univ. Press, New York, 1993).

21. Ferris, J. P. & Ertem, G. *J. Am. Chem. Soc.* **115**, 12270-12275 (1993).

22. Hunziker, J. *et al. Helv. Chim. Acta* **76**, 259-352 (1993).

23. Eschenmoser, A. *Chem. Biol.* Introd. issue iv-v (1994).

Acknowledgements. We thank L. E. Orgel and G. F. Joyce for discussion. This work was supported by The Scripps Research Institute, the US NIH, Pfizer, Inc. and Glaxo Pharmaceuticals, Inc.

Self-replication of Complementary Nucleotide-based Oligomers

D. Sievers and G. von Kiedrowski

Editor's Note

In 1986, German chemist Günter von Kiedrowski showed that short strands of self-complementary nucleic acid—which could pair up with a copy of itself—could serve as templates for self-replication from two fragments without the help of enzymes. This hinted that molecules related to DNA or RNA might have been able to "reproduce" in the prebiotic world without needing proteins, as they do in living cells today. Here von Kiedrowski and colleague Dirk Sievers show how replication can happen for nucleic acids of arbitrary, rather than self-complementary, sequence—more akin to DNA and RNA themselves. The scheme involves two complementary strands that can cross-catalyse each other's replication. A different strategy for enzyme-free DNA self-replication was reported in a companion paper.

The development of non-enzymatic self-replicating systems based on autocatalytic template-directed reactions is a current objective of bioorganic chemistry[1-6]. Typically, a self-complementary template molecule **AB** is synthesized autocatalytically from two complementary template fragments **A** and **B**[7-16]. Natural replication of nucleic acids, however, utilizes complementary rather than self-complementary strands. Here we report on a minimal implementation of this type of replication[17] based on cross-catalytic template-directed syntheses of hexadeoxynucleotide derivatives from aminotrideoxynucleotides. In our experiments, two self-complementary and two complementary templates compete for their combinatorial synthesis from four common trimeric precursors. We provide kinetic evidence that cross-catalytic self-replication of complementary templates can proceed with an efficiency similar to that of autocatalytic self-replication of self-complementary templates. We observe selective stimulation of template synthesis, and thus information transfer, on seeding the reaction mixtures with one of four chemically labelled templates bearing the sequence of the reaction products. Our results bring a stage closer the development of schemes that might explain how replicating systems based on nucleic acids arose on the prebiotic Earth.

A minimal implementation of cross-catalytic self-replication is given by the general reactions (1) and (2) where **A**, **B** and **AA**, **BB** denote complementary template fragments and templates, respectively:

$$\mathbf{A} + \mathbf{A} + \mathbf{BB} \rightleftharpoons \mathbf{A} \cdot \mathbf{A} \cdot \mathbf{BB} \rightarrow \mathbf{AA} \cdot \mathbf{BB} \rightleftharpoons \mathbf{AA} + \mathbf{BB} \qquad (1)$$

互补配对的寡聚核苷酸的自我复制

1986 年，德国化学家金特·冯·凯德罗夫斯基发现自互补的核酸短链——可以与自身的一个拷贝配对——在没有酶的帮助下能够作为模板完成两个片段的自我复制。这暗示着在生命起源之前的地球上，一些与 DNA 或 RNA 有关的分子也许可以在不需要蛋白质参与的情况下进行"复制"，正如它们今天在活细胞中所进行的那样。这里，冯·凯德罗夫斯基和他的同事迪尔克·西弗斯展示了任意的核苷酸序列——而不是自我互补的序列——是如何实现复制的，这与 DNA 和 RNA 本身更加类似。此体系涉及两个可以交叉催化对方复制的互补双链。另一种不需要酶的 DNA 自我复制的策略由本书中另一篇文章报道。

发展基于自催化模板诱导的非酶促自我复制体系是目前生物有机化学的目标之一 [1-6]。一般来讲，一个自我互补模板分子 **AB** 是由两个互补模板片段 **A** 和 **B** 自催化合成的 [7-16]。然而，自然界中核酸的复制利用的是互补链而非自我互补链。在本文中，我们报道了这类复制的一个最小体系 [17]，从氨基三聚脱氧核苷酸基于交叉催化模板诱导合成得到六聚脱氧核苷酸衍生物。在我们的实验中，两个自我互补的模板和两个非自我互补的模板从四种三聚前体中竞争组合式合成。我们提供了互补模板进行交叉催化的自我复制的效率与自我互补模板的自催化的自我复制的效率相似的动力学证据。当向反应混合物中加入化学标记的含有产物序列的四个模板之一时，我们观察到模板合成的选择性刺激，以及由此带来的信息传递。我们的结果进一步推动了体系的发展，这或许能解释以核酸为基础的复制系统在生命起源以前是如何形成的。

通过基本反应（1）和（2），实现了交叉催化的自我复制的一个最小体系，其中 **A**、**B** 和 **AA**、**BB** 分别表示互补的模板片段和模板：

$$\mathbf{A+A+BB} \rightleftharpoons \mathbf{A \cdot A \cdot BB} \rightarrow \mathbf{AA \cdot BB} \rightleftharpoons \mathbf{AA+BB} \tag{1}$$

$$B+B+AA \rightleftharpoons B \cdot B \cdot AA \rightarrow AA \cdot BB \rightleftharpoons AA+BB \qquad (2)$$

The reactions proceed via reversibly formed termolecular complexes ($A \cdot A \cdot BB$ and $B \cdot B \cdot AA$) in which irreversible ligation of template fragments takes place. The resulting template duplex ($AA \cdot BB$) reversibly dissociates to give the template molecules. As long as both templates are formed by the same type of chemistry, conditions that enable cross-catalytic formation of complementary products AA and BB will also allow for the autocatalytic synthesis of self-complementary products AB and BA:

$$A+B+AB \rightleftharpoons A \cdot B \cdot AB \rightarrow AB \cdot AB \rightleftharpoons 2AA \qquad (3)$$
$$B+A+BA \rightleftharpoons B \cdot A \cdot BA \rightarrow BA \cdot BA \rightleftharpoons 2BA \qquad (4)$$

Consequently, reactions (1)–(4) must be equally efficient for best observability of the cross-catalytically coupled reactions (1) and (2). Experiments on the template-directed synthesis of hexadeoxynucleotides from trimeric fragments revealed that the reactions are predominantly controlled by the stacking of nucleotide bases flanking the reaction site in the termolecular complex[18]. Thus in order to approach equal reaction efficiency, all products should have the same base sequence at the newly formed internucleotide link. The above general reaction model is realized in our example where the trideoxynucleotide sequences are CCG (A) and CGG (B).

Figure 1a–c shows the structures, the basic reactions and the template-catalysed condensations of the trimeric constituents chosen for the experiments. Two 5′-protected trideoxynucleotide 3′-phosphates, ^{N_3}CCGp (Ap, N_3 is 5′-azido) and ^{MTM}CGGp (Bp, MTM is 5′-methylthiomethoxy), were reacted with two 5′-aminotrideoxynucleotide 3′-(o-chlorphenyl)-phosphates, nCCGp^{ClPh} (nA) and nCGGp^{ClPh} (nB), in the presence of water-soluble carbodiimide EDC (1-ethyl-3-(3-dimethylaminopropyl)-carbodiimide) as the condensing agent[19]. The formation of the four 3′-5′-phosphoramidate linked hexamers ($ApnA$, $BpnB$, $ApnB$ and $BpnA$, respectively) resulting from combinatorial synthesis was monitored by high-performance liquid chromatography. A typical elution profile showing the composition of the reaction mixture after 1.5 h reaction time is depicted in Fig. 2; the experimental conditions are given in the legend. Figure 3a reflects the time-course of product formation. All four products are formed with comparable rates. In experiments in which similar hexamers (5′-azido-3′-(2-phenylthioethyl)-phosphates) were synthesized separately so that the cross-catalysis could not occur, the 1-h yields of the self-complementary products were five times higher than those of the complementary products.

438

$$B+B+AA \rightleftharpoons B \cdot B \cdot AA \rightarrow AA \cdot BB \rightleftharpoons AA+BB \tag{2}$$

反应以可逆方式形成三分子复合物（$A \cdot A \cdot BB$ 和 $B \cdot B \cdot AA$）来进行，在此过程中发生了模板片段的不可逆连接。产生的模板双链（$AA \cdot BB$）发生可逆分离以提供模板分子。只要两个模板通过相同类型的化学形成，那么能够使交叉催化形成互补产物 **AA** 和 **BB** 的条件也允许自催化合成自我互补的产物 **AB** 和 **BA**：

$$A+B+AB \rightleftharpoons A \cdot B \cdot AB \rightarrow AB \cdot AB \rightleftharpoons 2AA \tag{3}$$

$$B+A+BA \rightleftharpoons B \cdot A \cdot BA \rightarrow BA \cdot BA \rightleftharpoons 2BA \tag{4}$$

因此，为了最好地观测交叉催化的偶联反应（1）和（2），反应（1）~（4）应该具有相等的效率。模板诱导的从三聚体片段合成六聚脱氧核苷酸的实验表明这个反应主要通过三分子复合物中反应位点旁边的核苷酸碱基的堆积来控制[18]。因此，为获得相同的反应效率，所有产物在新形成的核苷酸间连接处应该具有相同的碱基序列。在我们的实验中实现了上述基本的反应模式，其中三脱氧核苷酸序列是 CCG（**A**）和 CGG（**B**）。

图 1a~c 显示了实验中选择的三聚体成分的结构、基本反应和模板催化的缩合反应。在存在水溶性缩合剂[19]碳二亚胺 EDC（1－乙基－3－（3－二甲氨基丙基）－碳二亚胺）的情况下，两个 5′－受保护的三脱氧核苷酸 3′－磷酸盐——^{N_3}CCGP（**Ap**，N_3 是 5′－叠氮基）和 ^{MTM}CGG$_P$（**Bp**，MTM 是 5′－甲基硫代甲氧基）与两个 5′－氨基三脱氧核苷酸 3′－（o－氯苯基）－磷酸盐——nCCGP^{ClPh}（**nA**）和 nCGGP^{ClPh}（**nB**）反应。通过高效液相色谱监测以组合式合成的四个 3′－5′－氨基磷酸酯连接的六聚体（分别是 **ApnA**、**BpnB**、**ApnB** 和 **BpnA**）。如图 2 所示，一个典型的洗脱分布图显示了反应 1.5 小时后反应混合物的成分；图注中给出了实验条件。图 3a 反映了产物形成的时间曲线。所有四种产物形成的速率相当。在实验中，相似的六聚体（5′－叠氮基 3′－（2－苯基巯乙基）－磷酸盐）都是分别合成的，因此不能发生交叉催化，自我互补产物的每小时产量是互补产物的 5 倍。

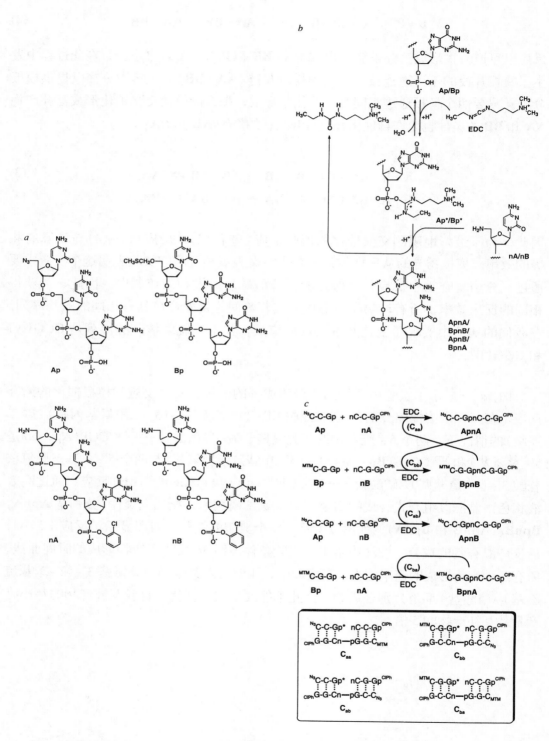

Fig. 1. *a*, Chemical structures of the trideoxynucleotide derivatives **Ap**, **Bp**, **nA** and **nB**. *b*, Basic reactions of **Ap**, **Bp**, **nA** and **nB** in the presence of water-soluble carbodiimide EDC. The 3'-phosphate groups of **Ap** and **Bp** add to the carbodiimide EDC to yield the isourea derivatives **Ap*** and **Bp***, respectively.

图 1. *a*，三聚脱氧核苷酸衍生物 **Ap**、**Bp**、**nA** 和 **nB** 的化学结构；*b*，在水溶性碳二亚胺 EDC 存在的情况下 **Ap**、**Bp**、**nA** 和 **nB** 的基本反应。**Ap** 和 **Bp** 将 3′–磷酸基团加入到碳二亚胺 EDC 中分别产生异尿素衍生物 **Ap*** 和 **Bp***。活化的 3′–磷酸盐水解产生最初的磷酸盐。因此，活化和水解以准可逆反应进行。

The activated 3'-phosphates are hydrolysed to reproduce the original phosphates. Thus, activation and hydrolysis proceed as quasi-reversible reactions. Alternatively, **Ap*** and **Bp*** react with the 5'-aminogroup of **nA** and **nB** to give the four possible hexameric 3'-5'-phosphoramidates **ApnA**, **BpnB**, **ApnB** and **BpnA** by combinatorial synthesis. *c*, The cross-catalytic formation of **ApnA** and **BpnB**, and the autocatalytic synthesis of **ApnB** and **BpnA** proceed via termolecular complexes C_{aa}, C_{bb}, C_{ab} and C_{ba}, respectively. In these complexes, in which the reaction products serve as templates to bind the respective trideoxynucleotide precursors by Watson-Crick base pairing (dots between base symbols), the reactive phosphate- and amino-groups are oriented into close spatial proximity. Terminal groups are written as superscripts if the sequence is to be read in 5'-3'-direction. Subscripted symbols indicate the reverse direction.

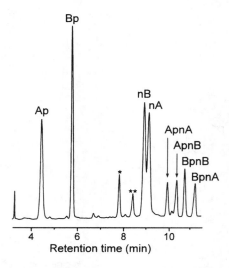

Fig. 2. High-performance liquid chromatography (HPLC) elution profile from the reaction between **Ap**, **Bp**, **nA**, **nB** and EDC after a reaction time of 90 min; $^{\mathrm{N_3}}$CCG and ^{MTM}CGG were used as standards, and are shown as * and ** on the elution profile. Reaction conditions and initial concentrations (indicated by subscript zero) as follows; $T = 30\ ^{\circ}C$, $[\mathbf{Ap}]_0 = [\mathbf{Bp}]_0 = [\mathbf{nA}]_0 = [\mathbf{nB}]_0 = 1$ mM, $[EDC]_0 = 0.2$ M, [HEPES $(Na^+/H^+)] = 0.1M$, pH 7.55.

Methods. HPLC: Column, Nucleosil 120-7 C_{18} (Macherey and Nagel); initial buffer (IB), 0.1 M aqueous NH_4HCO_3; final buffer (FB), acetonitrile/water 3:7 (v/v); flow rate: 1 ml min^{-1}; gradient, 15% to 55% FB within 10 min, 55% to 75% FB within 3 min; detection, simultaneous monitoring of ultraviolet absorbance at wavelengths of 254 nm (above profile) and 273 nm; Equipment (Kontron), two pumps 420, autosampler 460, ultraviolet detector 430, data acquisition using system D450. For all reactions, a batch mixture of the four trideoxynucleotides in equimolar concentrations was prepared. Aliquots of this mixture were lyophilized in Eppendorf tubes using a SpeedVac evaporator (Savant). For experiments with templates, aliquots were co-lyophilized with the hexadeoxynucleotides. The reactions were started by the addition of 10 μl of a freshly prepared solution of EDC in HEPES buffer. The mixtures were then vortexed, centrifuged and drawn into a series of 1-μl precision capillaries (Hirschmann, non-heparinized). During a reaction, the capillaries were stored in small, air-tight containers under a water-saturated atmosphere. After the given interval of time the reaction was quenched by draining the capillaries into 250 μl of IB. HPLC injection volume was 150 μl.

另外一种情况，**Ap*** 和 **Bp*** 与 **nA** 和 **nB** 的 5′–氨基基团通过组合式合成产生四种可能的六聚体 3′–5′–氨基磷酸酯 **ApnA**、**BpnB**、**ApnB** 和 **BpnA**。*c*，交叉催化产生 **ApnA** 和 **BpnB** 以及自催化合成 **ApnB** 和 **BpnA**，分别通过三分子复合物 C_{aa}、C_{bb}、C_{ab} 和 C_{ba} 进行。在这些复合物中，反应产物作为模板通过沃森–克里克碱基配对（碱基符号之间的点）结合各自的三脱氧核苷酸前体，活性磷酸基团和氨基基团在空间上定向靠近。如果序列是从 5′–3′ 方向读取，将末端基团写成上标。下标符号代表反方向。

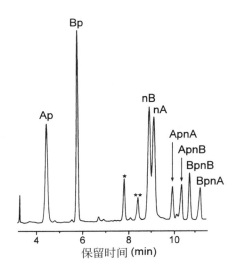

图 2. **Ap**、**Bp**、**nA**、**nB** 和 EDC 反应 90 分钟后的高效液相色谱（HPLC）的洗脱分布图；以 ^{N_3}CCG 和 $^{M^{TM}}$CGG 为标准，并且在洗脱分布图上显示为 * 和 **。反应条件和初始浓度（用下标零表示）如下：$T = 30\ ℃$，$[Ap]_0 = [Bp]_0 = [nA]_0 = [nB]_0 = 1\ mM$，$[EDC]_0 = 0.2\ M$，$[HEPES（羟乙基哌嗪乙磺酸）(Na^+/H^+)] = 0.1\ M$，pH 7.55。

方法。HPLC：柱子为 120–7 C_{18} 反向色谱柱（马赫赖和纳格尔）；初始缓冲液（IB）为 0.1 M NH_4HCO_3 水溶液；最终缓冲液（FB）为乙腈 / 水 3∶7 (v/v)；流速为 1 ml·min^{-1}；梯度，在 10 分钟内将 FB 由 15% 升高到 55%，在 3 分钟内将 FB 由 55% 升高到 75%；检测，同时检测波长在 254 nm（上面的分布图）和 273 nm 处的紫外吸收值；装置（德国控创）：两个泵 420、自动加样仪 460、紫外检测仪 430、数据采集应用系统 D450。对于所有反应，我们都制备了一个批次的等摩尔浓度的四种三脱氧核苷酸混合物。在 SpeedVac 离心浓缩仪（思旺特公司）中将微量离心管内等量的混合物冻干。对于有模板的实验，小份的混合物与六聚脱氧核苷酸一起冻干。加入 10 μl 新制备的 EDC 溶液于 HEPES 缓冲液中，之后反应开始。然后将混合物涡旋、离心并加入至一系列 1 μl 精密毛细管中（德国赫斯施曼公司，非肝素化）。在一个反应过程中，将毛细管放置于一个小的水饱和环境下的密闭容器中。在既定时间间隔之后，通过将毛细管转入 250 μl IB 中来终止反应。HPLC 上样体积为 150 μl。

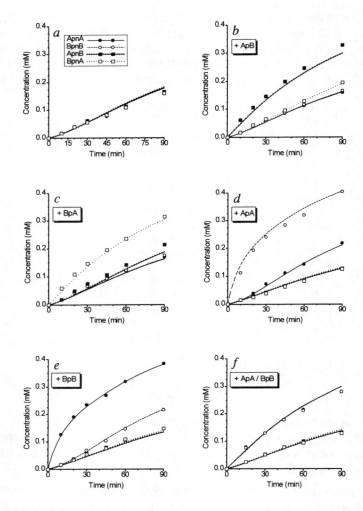

Fig. 3. Experimental points and theoretical curves describing the time courses of the formation of **ApnA**, **BpnB**, **ApnB** and **BpnA** in the absence (*a*), and in the presence of ~0.16 mM concentrations of hexadeoxynucleotide templates **ApB** (*b*), **BpA** (*c*), **ApA** (*d*), **BpB** (*e*) and **ApA**+**BpB** (*f*). In the calculations using the program SimFit, the initial concentrations of the model species were calculated from the respective HPLC peak areas using calibration data for each component. $[\mathbf{AA}]_0$, $[\mathbf{BB}]_0$, $[\mathbf{AB}]_0$ and $[\mathbf{BA}]_0$ were taken from the concentrations of **ApA**, **BpB**, **ApB** and **BpA**, respectively. All duplex concentrations were set to zero. Theoretical species concentrations were calculated by integration of the set of stiff rate equations that were derived from the model using SimFit. Theoretical values for the observable concentrations were calculated using the expressions: $[\mathbf{ApnA}]_{\mathrm{theor}} = [\mathbf{AA}] + [\mathbf{AA} \cdot \mathbf{BB}] - [\mathbf{AA}]_0$; $[\mathbf{BpnB}]_{\mathrm{theor}} = [\mathbf{BB}] + [\mathbf{AA} \cdot \mathbf{BB}] - [\mathbf{BB}]_0$; $[\mathbf{ApnB}]_{\mathrm{theor}} = [\mathbf{AB}] + 2[\mathbf{AB} \cdot \mathbf{AB}] - [\mathbf{AB}]_0$; $[\mathbf{BpnA}]_{\mathrm{theor}} = [\mathbf{BA}] + 2[\mathbf{BA} \cdot \mathbf{BA}] - [\mathbf{BA}]_0$. Nonlinear optimization was based on least-square approximations employing the Newton–Raphson algorithm. The resulting rate constants (see text) and error estimates were $k_a = (2.07 \pm 0.04) \times 10^{-2}\,\mathrm{M^{-1}\,s^{-1}}$, $k_b = (1.68 \pm 0.07) \times 10^3\,\mathrm{M^{-2}\,s^{-1}}$, $k_c = 8.98 \pm 0.81\,\mathrm{s^{-1}}$. The off-diagonal elements of the covariance matrix were; cov $(k_a, k_b) = -0.368$, cov $(k_a, k_c) = +0.219$ and cov $(k_b, k_c) = -0.970$.

The reactions were then followed in the presence of one of the hexadeoxynucleotide templates CCGCCG (**ApA**), CGGCGG (**BpB**), CCGCGG (**ApB**) and CGGCCG (**BpA**). These hexamers, bearing a central 3′-5′-phosphodiester link, can be considered as

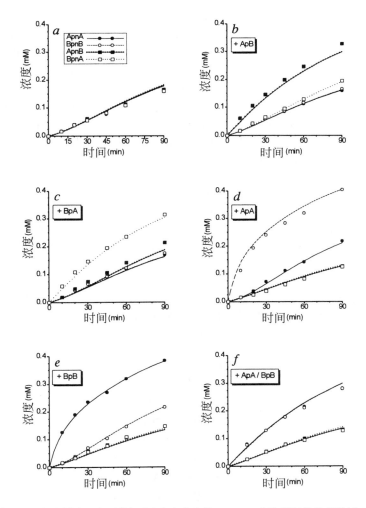

图 3. 实验点和理论曲线描述了在无模板(a)和存在大约 0.16 mM 六聚脱氧核苷酸模板 **ApB**(b)、**BpA** (c)、**ApA**(d)、**BpB**(e)和 **ApA**+**BpB**(f)时 **ApnA**、**BpnB**、**ApnB** 和 **BpnA** 形成的时间过程。在用软件 SimFit 进行计算时，模型种类的初始浓度是分别根据使用的每个组分校准数据的 HPLC 峰面积计算出来的。$[AA]_0$、$[BB]_0$、$[AB]_0$ 和 $[BA]_0$ 分别取自 **ApA**、**BpB**、**ApB** 和 **BpA** 的浓度。所有双链浓度设为零。理论种类的浓度是根据一组刚度率方程积分计算出来的，而刚度率方程是用 SimFit 从模型中得出的。可观测浓度的理论值用如下表达式计算：$[ApnA]_{理论} = [AA]+[AA \cdot BB]-[AA]_0$；$[BpnB]_{理论}$ $= [BB]+[AA \cdot BB]-[BB]_0$；$[ApnB]_{理论} = [AB]+2[AB \cdot AB]-[AB]_0$；$[BpnA]_{理论} = [BA]+2[BA \cdot BA]-[BA]_0$。基于最小平方的近似值进行非线性优化，采用牛顿-拉弗森算法。得出的速率常数（见正文）和误差估计是 $k_a = (2.07 \pm 0.04) \times 10^{-2}$ $M^{-1} \cdot s^{-1}$，$k_b = (1.68 \pm 0.07) \times 10^3$ $M^{-2} \cdot s^{-1}$，$k_c = 8.98 \pm 0.81$ s^{-1}。协方差矩阵的非对角线元素是：$cov(k_a, k_b) = -0.368$，$cov(k_a, k_c) = +0.219$ 和 $cov(k_b, k_c) = -0.970$。

接下来，反应在其中一个六聚脱氧核苷酸模板 CCGCCG（**ApA**）、CGGCGG（**BpB**）、CCGCGG（**ApB**）和 CGGCCG（**BpA**）存在的情况下进行。这些六聚体都由一个中心

445

chemically labelled reaction products. They are eluted at earlier retention times in reversed phase chromatography because they lack lipophilic groups at their 5'- and 3'-ends. The template effects are, however, comparable to the respective products as follows from the results reported here. Figure 3*b–e* provides evidence that each hexamer template stimulates the formation of the one and only reaction product whose sequence is complementary to the respective template sequence. Sequence information is thus transferred from the template to its copy. The effect of a single complementary template, **ApA** or **BpB**, is more pronounced than the effect of a single self-complementary template. When both templates, **ApA** and **BpB**, are present (Fig. 3*f*), the effects are comparable to those of the self-complementary templates. Remarkably, the effects of **ApA** and **BpB** are similar, although the base compositions are different. Base composition proved to be most important in template-directed copolymerizations of nucleoside 5'-phospho-(2-methyl)-imidazolides[20]. In these pioneering attempts at non-enzymatic replication, in which monomers instead of oligomers were employed as informational units, only pyrimidine-rich templates were found to be efficient—purine-rich templates were not.

The experimental data from Fig. 3*a–f* can be rationalized using the following simplified reaction model where **AA**, **BB**, **AB** and **BA** are general species representing both externally added and internally synthesized hexamer templates:

$$\mathbf{Ap+nA \rightarrow AA} \tag{5}$$

$$\mathbf{Bp+nB \rightarrow BB} \tag{6}$$

$$\mathbf{Ap+nB \rightarrow AB} \tag{7}$$

$$\mathbf{Bp+AB \rightarrow BA} \tag{8}$$

$$\mathbf{Ap+nA+BB \rightarrow AA \cdot BB} \tag{9}$$

$$\mathbf{Bp+nB+AA \rightarrow AA \cdot BB} \tag{10}$$

$$\mathbf{Ap+nB+BB \rightarrow AB \cdot AB} \tag{11}$$

$$\mathbf{Bp+nA+BA \rightarrow BA \cdot BA} \tag{12}$$

$$\mathbf{AA+BB \rightleftharpoons AA \cdot BB} \tag{13}$$

$$\mathbf{2AB \rightleftharpoons AA \cdot BB} \tag{14}$$

$$\mathbf{2BA \rightleftharpoons BA \cdot BA} \tag{15}$$

Equations (5)–(8) describe the hexamer-independent (uncatalysed) synthesis of the respective hexamers. Equations (9)–(12) comprise the reversible formation of the respective termolecular complex and the irreversible template-directed synthesis leading to the respective hexamer-duplex. Equations (13)–(15) deal with the reversible association of single-stranded hexamers to give the respective hexamer-duplexes. Activation of the 3'-phosphates **Ap** and **Bp** by EDC and the hydrolysis of the activated species **Ap*** and **Bp*** are not explicitly considered in the model. These processes are known to proceed as fast quasi-reversible reactions establishing the stationary concentration of **Ap*** and **Bp*** within some minutes[19]. Furthermore, as EDC is present in 100-fold excess over the 3'-phosphates, the degree of activation of the latter is assumed to be time-independent over the first 90 min. The rate constants of reactions (5)–(12) are thus apparent constants which depend on the concentration of the carbodiimide.

的 3′–5′–磷酸二酯连接，可以将这些六聚体看作是有化学标记的反应产物。因为它们的 5′–端和 3′–端没有亲脂基团，所以在反相色谱中保留时间短。然而，从本文报道的结果看，模板效应是与各自的产物相匹配的。图 3b~e 表明每个六聚体模板促进了与其互补反应产物的形成。序列信息因此从模板转移到其拷贝中。单个互补模板 **ApA** 或 **BpB** 的效应比单个自我互补模板的效应更显著。当存在两个模板 **ApA** 和 **BpB** 时（图 3f），效应与自我互补模板的效应相当。值得注意的是，虽然 **ApA** 和 **BpB** 的碱基组成不同但二者效应相似。在核苷 5′–磷酸–(2–甲基)–咪唑[20] 的模板指导的共聚合过程中，碱基组成被证明是非常重要的。在这些非酶促复制的探索性尝试中，单体而不是寡聚体被用作信息单元，发现只有富含嘧啶序列的模板是有效的——富含嘌呤的序列的模板则无效。

用以下简化的反应模型可以解释图 3a~f 中的实验数据，其中 **AA**、**BB**、**AB** 和 **BA** 代表了外部加入和内部合成的六聚体模板：

$$Ap+nA \rightarrow AA \tag{5}$$
$$Bp+nB \rightarrow BB \tag{6}$$
$$Ap+nB \rightarrow AB \tag{7}$$
$$Bp+AB \rightarrow BA \tag{8}$$
$$Ap+nA+BB \rightarrow AA \cdot BB \tag{9}$$
$$Bp+nB+AA \rightarrow AA \cdot BB \tag{10}$$
$$Ap+nB+BB \rightarrow AB \cdot AB \tag{11}$$
$$Bp+nA+BA \rightarrow BA \cdot BA \tag{12}$$
$$AA+BB \rightleftharpoons AA \cdot BB \tag{13}$$
$$2AB \rightleftharpoons AA \cdot BB \tag{14}$$
$$2BA \rightleftharpoons BA \cdot BA \tag{15}$$

方程 (5)~(8) 描述了不依赖于模板（非催化）合成各六聚体的过程，方程 (9)~(12) 解释了可逆形成三分子复合物以及不可逆的模板诱导合成产生各六聚体双链的过程。方程 (13)~(15) 论述单链六聚体产生其六聚体双链的可逆结合过程。在此模型中没有明确地考虑 EDC 活化 3′–磷酸 **Ap** 和 **Bp** 以及活化体 **Ap*** 和 **Bp*** 的水解。这些过程被认为是快速的准可逆反应，在几分钟内建立了 **Ap*** 和 **Bp*** 的固定浓度[19]。此外，当 EDC 是 3′–磷酸盐的 100 倍时，前 90 分钟中后者的活化水平假定没有时间依赖性。那么反应 (5)~(12) 的速率常数是表观常数且依赖于碳二亚胺的浓度。

The above model was employed to calculate the theoretical time courses shown in Fig. 3a–f using the computer program SimFit (available from G.v.K. on request). The experimental time-courses of all experiments were evaluated simultaneously to generate a single set of three apparent rate constants k_a, k_b and k_c, from which the theoretical time-courses for all experiments were derived. We assumed, equally efficient uncatalysed reactions (5)–(8) (k_a), equally efficient catalysed reactions (9)–(12) (k_b) and equally efficient duplex dissociations. The latter were characterized by the backward rate constants of reactions (13)–(15) (k_c) providing a symmetry factor of 2 for the self-complementary hexamers. The forward rate constants of reactions (13)–(15) can be chosen arbitrarily, so long as the irreversible reactions remain rate-determining (internal equilibrium). We used a value of $10^6 \, M^{-1} \, s^{-1}$ for all hexamers in our calculation. From the resulting value of k_c it follows that the dissociation constant of the complexes is $\sim 10 \, \mu M$ at $T = 30\,°C$, in good agreement with thermodynamic data on similar hexadeoxynucleotides[18].

Remarkably, although several simplifications were introduced, and although data from six different experiments each with four observables were evaluated simultaneously, the above model (based on only three iterated rate constants) reproduces the experimental time courses quite well. Implicit in the model is that the cross-catalysis between complementary templates occurs with product inhibition as in the case of self-complementary templates. Product inhibition is the rationale for the so-called square-root law of template autocatalysis[6,7] which does not allow for exponential amplification of template concentration; in the best case, growth may be parabolic[6,11].

The evolutionary consequence of parabolic growth is coexistence of competing replicators[21]. They can coexist at stationary concentration levels whose ratio is given by the ratio of the square of the replication rate constants[21]. Non-replicating molecules that compete for their common precursors can reach only levels of concentration whose ratio is determined by the ratio of their formation rate constants, and not by the ratio of their squares[21]. Thus, parabolic growth is expected to enhance selectivity: small differences in reactivity should result in larger concentration differences as compared to those found during synthesis of non-autocatalytic molecules. On the other hand, selection—which is the characteristic outcome of competition between biological species—necessitates exponential growth[22]. In terms of growth laws and their evolutionary consequences, parabolic replicators are thus halfway between chemical and biological systems.

Our results may have important implications for theories of the origin of life, including those that invoke self-organization of complex reaction systems involving collective replication of oligonucleotides[23]. Assuming that pathways for the formation of short random oligonucleotides from monomeric precursors (such as the clay-catalysed pathway[24]) existed on the early Earth, it seems plausible that the first self-replicating systems used oligomers as informational units and operated on the basis of template-

根据上述模型，使用计算机程序 SimFit(可以从冯·凯德罗夫斯基处申请获得)计算了图 $3a\sim f$ 中的理论时间曲线。同时对所有实验的时间曲线进行评价以产生三个表观速率常数 k_a、k_b 和 k_c 的一个单一集合，从中可以得到所有实验的理论时间曲线。我们假设非催化反应(5)~(8)具有同样的反应速率(k_a)、催化反应(9)~(12)具有同样的反应速率(k_b)并且双链分离也都具有同样的速率。对后者的表征是通过反应(13)~(15)(k_c)的反向速率常数来实现的，它为自我互补六聚体提供的对称因子为 2。反应(13)~(15)(k_c)的正向速率常数可以随意选择，只要不可逆反应仍然是速率决定的(内部平衡)。在我们的计算过程中，所有六聚体使用的值均为 10^6 $M^{-1} \cdot s^{-1}$。根据 k_c 的结果值，我们可以得出在 $T = 30$ ℃时复合物的分离常数约为 10 μM，这与相似的六聚脱氧核苷酸的热动力学数据很好地吻合[18]。

值得注意的是，虽然引入了一些简化并同时评价了来自六个不同实验的数据(每一个都有四个观测量)，但上述模型(只基于三个迭代速率常数)能很好地重复实验的时间曲线。模型中隐含着互补模板之间的交叉催化的发生以及自我互补模板情况下的产物抑制。产物抑制是所谓的模板自催化平方根法则的理论基础[6,7]，它阐述了模板浓度不能够指数性增长，在最佳情况下，增长也许是抛物线性的[6,11]。

抛物线性增长的进化意义是相互竞争的复制因子共存[21]。它们可以在稳定浓度水平下共同存在，其浓度水平比率可由复制速率常数平方的比率得出[21]。竞争共同前体的非复制分子浓度能达到的最佳水平的比率是由它们的形成速率常数的比率决定的，而不是由它们平方的比率决定的[21]。因此可以通过抛物线性增长来加强选择性：与非自催化分子合成过程中发现的那些差异相比，反应活性的微小差异将会导致浓度的巨大差异。另一方面，选择性——是生物种类之间竞争的特征性结果——使指数性增长成为必要[22]。根据增长规律及它们的进化意义，抛物线性复制因子是化学系统和生物系统之间的折中方式。

我们的结果可能对生命起源(包括那些涉及寡核苷酸[23]共同复制的复杂反应系统的自我组织)有重要的理论意义。假设早期地球上存在从单体前体到短的随机寡核苷酸的形成途径(比如黏土催化途径[24])，那么最早使用寡聚体作为信息单元和以模板指导的连接为基础运行的自我复制系统似乎是合理的。最近发现双螺旋 DNA 寡

directed ligations. The recent observation of self-replication of double-helical DNA oligomers via the formation of triple-helical intermediates[25] also supports the view that nonenzymatic self-replication of nucleic acids, based on autocatalytic and cross-catalytic ligations, may have been possible on the early Earth.

(**369**, 221-224; 1994)

D. Sievers & G. von Kiedrowski*

Institut für Organische Chemie und Biochemie, Albert-Ludwigs-Universität, Albertstrasse 21, D-79104 Freiburg, Germany

* To whom correspondence should be addressed.

Received 1 March; accepted 24 March 1994.

References:

1. Orgel, L. E. *Nature* **358**, 203-209 (1992).

2. Hoffman, S. *Angew. Chem. Int. Ed. Engl.* **31**, 1013-1016 (1992).

3. Eschenmoser, A. & Loewenthal, E. *Chem. Soc. Rev.* **21**, 1-16 (1992).

4. Bachmann, P. A., Luisi, P. L. & Lang, J. *Nature* **357**, 57-59 (1992).

5. Famulok, J. S., Nowick, J. & Rebek, J. *Acta. Chem. Scand.* **46**, 315-324 (1992).

6. von Kiedrowski, G. *Bioorg. Chem. Front.* **3**, 113-146 (1993).

7. von Kiedrowski, G. *Angew. Chem. Int. Ed. Engl.* **25**, 932-935 (1986).

8. Zielinski, W. S. & Orgel, L. E. *Nature* **327**, 346-347 (1987).

9. von Kiedrowski, G., Wlotzka, B. & Helbing, J. *Angew. Chem. Int. Ed. Engl.* **28**, 1235-1237 (1989).

10. Tjivikua, T., Ballester, P. & Rebek, J. *J. Am. Chem. Soc.* **112**, 1249-1250 (1990).

11. von Kiedrowski, G., Wlotzka, B., Helbing, J., Matzen, M. & Jordan, S. *Angew. Chem. Int. Ed. Engl.* **30**, 423-426 and 892 (1991).

12. Terfort, A. & von Kiedrowski, G. Angew. *Chem. Int. Ed. Engl.* **31**, 654-656 (1992).

13. Hong, J.-I., Feng, O., Rotello, V. & Rebek, J. *Science* **255**, 848-850 (1992).

14. Feng, Q., Park, T. K. & Rebek, J. *Science* **256**, 1179-1180 (1992).

15. Böhler, C., Bannwarth, W. Luisi, P. L. *Helv. Chim.* Acta **76**, 2313-2320 (1993).

16. Achilles, T. & von Kiedrowski, G. *Angew. Chem. Int. Ed. Engl.* **32**, 1198-1201 (1993).

17. Kanavarioti, A. *J. Theor. Biol.* **158**, 207-219 (1992).

18. Wlotzka, B. thesis, Univ. Göttingen (1992).

19. Dolinnaya, N. G., Tsytovich, A. V., Sergeev, V. N., Oretskaya, T. S. & Shabarova, Z. A. *Nucleic Acids Res.* **19**, 3073-3080 (1991).

20. Inoue, T. & Orgel, L. E. *Science* **219**, 859-862 (1983).

21. Szathmáry, E. *Trends Ecol. Evol.* **6**, 366-370 (1991).

22. Eigen, M. & Schuster, P. *The Hypercycle. A Principle of Natural Self-Organization* (Springer, Berlin, 1979).

23. Kauffman, S. A. *The Origins of Order* (Oxford Univ. Press, New York, 1993).

24. Ferris, J. P. & Ertem, G. *J. Am. Chem. Soc.* **115**, 12270-12275 (1993).

25. Li, T. & Nicolaou, K. C. *Nature* **369**, 218-221 (1994).

Acknowledgements. We thank E. Szathmáry and H.-J. Grützmacher for comments and suggestions on the manuscript. This work was supported by Deutsche Forschungsgemeinschaft, Fonds der Chemischen Industrie and NATO.

聚体通过形成三螺旋中间体[25]进行自我复制，这也支持基于自催化和交叉催化连接的核酸非酶促自我复制可能在早期地球上存在的观点。

（李梅 翻译；刘冬生 审稿）

Testing the Iron Hypothesis in Ecosystems of the Equatorial Pacific Ocean

J. H. Martin *et al.*

Editor's Note

The "iron fertilization" hypothesis proposed by oceanographer John Martin in the 1980s suggested that atmospheric concentrations of carbon dioxide might be regulated globally by seeding the ocean with iron, an essential nutrient, to promote the growth of phytoplankton. Iron added to iron-depleted ocean waters did stimulate plankton growth—but would it work on a large scale? This paper describes the results of an experiment in the equatorial Pacific Ocean to examine that question. It shows that the addition of iron does stimulate phytoplankton growth, but concludes that the fertilization effect is transient and limited. Subsequent work has suggested that it might be of little help for engineering climate.

The idea that iron might limit phytoplankton growth in large regions of the ocean has been tested by enriching an area of $64 \, km^2$ in the open equatorial Pacific Ocean with iron. This resulted in a doubling of plant biomass, a threefold increase in chlorophyll and a fourfold increase in plant production. Similar increases were found in a chlorophyll-rich plume downstream of the Galapagos Islands, which was naturally enriched in iron. These findings indicate that iron limitation can control rates of phytoplankton productivity and biomass in the ocean.

OVER 20% of the world's open ocean surface waters are replete with light and the major plant nutrients (nitrate, phosphate and silicate), yet standing stocks of phytoplankton remain low. The factors that limit phytoplankton growth and biomass in these high-nitrate, low-chlorophyll (HNLC) areas have been vigorously debated[1], but not resolved. The suggestion that increased phytoplankton production in HNLC areas could remove significant amounts of carbon dioxide from the atmosphere has renewed interest in this topic[2].

In some HNLC areas, it has been suggested that zooplankton grazing may contribute to the maintenance of low chlorophyll levels[3]. Strong turbulence at high latitudes may also mix phytoplankton below the critical depth, resulting in light-limitation of growth[4,5]. We believe that in addition to these factors, micronutrient elements, such as iron, which are important catalytic components in a wide variety of electron transport and enzymatic systems, have the potential to limit phytoplankton production in HNLC areas[6]. There are several lines of evidence in support of this notion.

在赤道太平洋海域生态系统中
对铁假说的验证

马丁等

编者按

20世纪80年代由海洋学家约翰·马丁提出的"铁施肥/铁加富"假说认为，在大洋中播种基本营养元素铁可以促进浮游植物的生长，从而可能调节全球大气中二氧化碳的浓度。在铁缺乏的海水中加入铁，确实刺激了浮游生物的生长——但该措施能否在大尺度上发生作用？本文介绍了一个在赤道太平洋海域进行的加富实验的结果来审视这个问题。实验表明加入铁确实刺激浮游植物生长，但结论是，施肥效果是短暂而有限的。之后的工作也表明，铁施肥对气候驱动的影响较小。

在赤道附近的太平洋开阔水域中，通过对面积为 64 km² 范围内的海水进行加富实验，对铁限制浮游植物的生长这一观点进行了大范围的验证。结果表明：浮游植物生物量增加了一倍，叶绿素含量增加了两倍，而浮游植物的生产力提高了三倍。相似的情况也发生在加拉帕戈斯群岛下游富含叶绿素的水体中，但这种情况中的铁是自然富集的铁。上述发现说明，铁的限制可以控制大洋中浮游植物的生产力速率以及生物量。

世界开阔大洋中超过 20% 的表层水体光照充足，主植物营养盐（硝酸盐、磷酸盐和硅酸盐）丰富，但浮游植物现存量很低。在这些高硝酸盐、低叶绿素（HNLC）海区，关于限制浮游植物生长和生物量的因素这个问题已存在激烈的争论[1]，但至今仍未找出答案。关于 HNLC 海区浮游植物产量的增加将使大气中二氧化碳含量大大减少的说法又重新引起了人们对这一论题的兴趣[2]。

有学者提出，在有些 HNLC 海区，浮游动物的摄食可能是维持低叶绿素水平的原因所在[3]。高纬度地区，强烈的湍流可能也会导致浮游植物被带到临界深度以下，从而因光照问题限制了它的生长[4,5]。我们认为，除上述原因以外，像铁等作为多种电子传输与酶体系中重要催化剂的微量营养元素可能也是 HNLC 海区浮游植物产量的一个潜在限制因素[6]。关于这一见解我们有几条证据可以支持它。

The development of trace-metal clean sampling techniques over the last two decades has revolutionized our understanding of trace-metal biogeochemistry in the oceans[7]. Open-ocean iron concentrations in surface waters exist at picomolar (10^{-12} M) levels. These concentrations may be insufficient to support high phytoplankton biomass or maximum growth rates[8]. Addition of Fe to uncontaminated seawater samples has been shown to stimulate the growth of phytoplankton, especially diatoms[9-16]. Laboratory experiments have demonstrated that low iron levels may limit phytoplankton growth rates[17-19]. Moreover, techniques such as fast repetition rate (FRR) fluorometry have shown that photochemical energy-conversion efficiency is less than maximal in the equatorial Pacific and can be increased significantly in phytoplankton supplied with nanomolar (10^{-9} M) levels of iron[20,21]. These experiments suggest iron availability may regulate ocean production in HNLC areas.

The extrapolation of results from shipboard and laboratory incubation experiments to whole ecosystems has, however, been strongly criticized[22-24]. Although small-scale experiments may accurately reflect *in situ* processes occurring at the chemical or first trophic level, bottle experiments, by design, do not accurately represent the nature or scale of the community response. Studies of nutrient limitation in lakes have demonstrated that incubations performed on small phytoplankton samples cannot easily be extrapolated to whole ecosystems. Mesocosm experiments with complete communities however, correlated highly with whole-lake responses to nutrient enrichments[25].

We believe that the effects of iron on phytoplankton growth in HNLC areas can be more confidently resolved by mesoscale enrichments of whole ecosystems[26]. Until recently however, enrichment experiments in the open ocean have not been feasible due to the difficulties in tracking a patch over time. The recent development of technology to measure ultra-trace concentrations of the inert gas sulphur hexafluoride, SF_6, has made it possible to mark a patch of sea water and track it for long periods of time[27,28]. Thus, when combined with iron enrichment, the SF_6 tracer provides the potential to assess ecosystem level responses to added iron[29].

The region south of the Galapagos Islands was proposed as the most favourable place for such an iron-enrichment experiment[30]. In this paper, we report the initial results of a mesoscale iron-enrichment experiment performed in this area of the equatorial Pacific. Additionally, the waters both upstream and downstream of the Galapagos Islands were studied to further evaluate the potential role of iron in regulating production. We found substantial and convincing evidence to indicate that iron additions to these HNLC regions increases phytoplankton productivity and biomass.

Open Ocean Iron Fertilization Experiment

In mid-October 1993, the RV *Columbus Iselin* occupied an area approximately 500 km south of the Galapagos Islands to begin the enrichment experiment (Fig. 1A). Ambient

过去 20 年中痕量金属清洁取样技术的发展，已使我们对海洋中痕量金属元素生物地球化学作用的理解产生了革命性的变化[7]。开阔大洋表层水体中铁的浓度一般在皮摩尔（10^{-12} M）的数量级上。该浓度可能不足以维持很高的浮游植物生物量或其最大生长速率[8]。已有研究发现，向未被污染的海水样品中加入额外的 Fe（铁），可促进浮游植物（特别是硅藻）的生长[9-16]。实验室内的研究证明，铁含量低可能会限制浮游植物的生长速率[17-19]。此外，快速重复率（FRR）荧光分析等技术显示，浮游植物的光化学能转化效率低于赤道太平洋海域的最大值，但当加入几个纳摩尔（10^{-9} M）的铁时转化效率就会明显增大[20,21]。上述实验表明，在 HNLC 海区，铁的可用量可能调节海洋生产量。

然而，以船上和实验室的培养实验结果对整个生态系统所作的推断却饱受批评[22-24]。虽然小规模的实验也许能够准确地反映出发生在化学水平或第一营养级上的原位过程，但设计的瓶装实验并不能准确地代表生物群落的响应特征或规模。对湖泊的营养盐限制作用研究证明，小的浮游植物样品的培养实验结果不能轻易地外推到整个生态系统中。而具有完整生物群落的围隔实验结果，与整个湖泊对营养盐富集的响应，具有很好的相关性[25]。

我们相信，利用整个生态系统的中尺度富集实验可以更确切地分析出 HNLC 海区铁元素对浮游植物生长的影响[26]。然而，由于追踪某片海区随时间的变化并非易事，因此直到最近，开阔大洋中的加富实验仍未能实施。近年来，随着对惰性气体六氟化硫（SF₆）超痕量浓度测定技术的发展，标记并长期追踪一片海区已成为可能[27,28]。所以，铁加富实验结合 SF₆ 示踪能够评价区域生态系统对铁施肥的响应[29]。

加拉帕戈斯群岛南部海域被认为是实施铁加富实验的最理想的场所[30]。本文我们将介绍在赤道太平洋的这片海域上进行中尺度铁加富实验得到的最初结果。此外，为了进一步评估铁元素在调节生产量方面的潜在作用，我们对加拉帕戈斯群岛的上游和下游都作了研究。从中我们找到了充分并确凿的证据证明，在 HNLC 海区加入铁可提高浮游植物生产力和生物量。

开阔大洋中的铁施肥实验

1993 年 10 月中旬，哥伦布·艾斯林号调查船对加拉帕戈斯群岛以南约 500 km 的海域开展铁加富实验（图 1A）。该海域周围铁的浓度约为 0.06 nM 量级（参考文献

iron concentrations in this area were of the order of 0.06 nM (ref. 31). An area of about 64 km^2 was enriched with iron to a concentration of ~4 nM. Iron at this level, in bottle experiments, is sufficient to cause large increases in chlorophyll and complete depletion of the available major nutrients within 5 to 7 days. The enriched patch was tracked for 10 days and monitored for changes in biological, chemical and physical parameters.

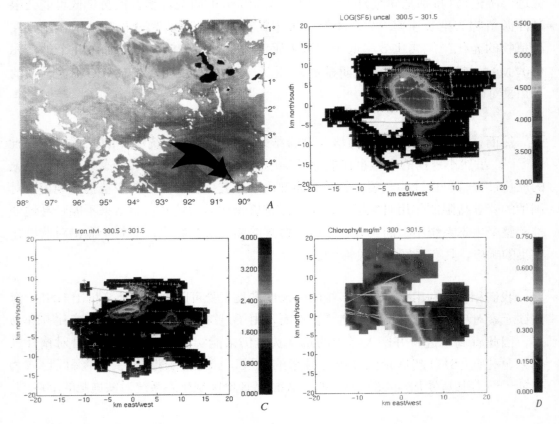

Fig. 1. *A*, False-colour image of the study site from the Coastal Zone Colour Scanner on the Nimbus 7 satellite, October 1983. This image indicates the chlorophyll-rich plume extending west of the Galapagos Islands (red colour indicates higher chlorophyll concentrations; image courtesy of G. Feldman). The arrow indicates the location and relative size of the study site at 5° S. *B–D*, Contour plots of the concentrations of SF$_6$ (*B*) YD 300.5–301.5, iron (*C*) YD 300.5–301.5, and chlorophyll *a* (*D*) YD 300–301. All parameters in *B–D* are plotted relative to the GPS buoy which served as the centre of a lagrangian frame of reference used during the first part of the experiment. A total volume of 15,600 l of the iron solution (8,100 mol or 450 kg Fe) was dispensed. The SF$_6$ solution was prepared by dissolving 0.35 mol of SF$_6$ in sea water in a 2,300-l steel tank before departure from Miami. The SF$_6$ was pumped (1.4 l min^{-1}) together with the iron solution (12 l min^{-1}) into the propellor wash as the ship steamed at ~9 km h^{-1}. The ship's track was updated every 5 min relative to the central GPS buoy (see below) to correct for horizontal advection during the 24-h deployment. This strategy was estimated to produce an increase in the iron concentration within the 35-m mixed layer of 3.8 nM and an SF$_6$ concentration of 180 fM (ref. 51). Horizontal eddy diffusion was predicted to horizontally homogenize the streaks within 1 d of mixing, whereas overturn of the mixed layer would vertically homogenize the iron and SF$_6$ concentrations every evening[36]. The GPS buoy was interrogated every 5 min to determine the location of the ship relative to this central point. In addition, four WOCE drifter buoys equipped with ARGOS position transmitters were deployed at each corner of

31）。实施铁加富的海区面积为 64 km²，铁加富后浓度达 4 nM 左右。瓶装实验显示，该浓度水平的铁足以使叶绿素大幅提高并在 5~7 天内完全耗尽所有主要营养盐。我们对加富海区连续跟踪观测了 10 天，监测了其中各种生物、化学、物理参数的变化。

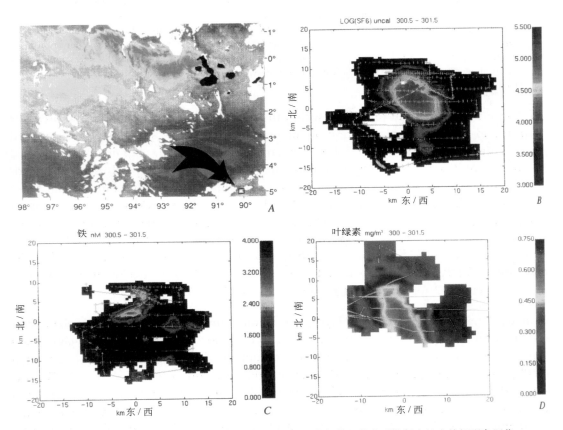

图 1. *A*，1983 年 10 月雨云 (Nimbus)7 卫星上的海岸带彩色扫描仪收集到的研究地点的假彩色图像。此图片显示富叶绿素羽状流延伸到加拉帕戈斯群岛西部 (红色表示较高的叶绿素浓度；图片由费尔德曼提供)。箭头指示研究地点在 5°S 的位置和相对大小。*B~D* 为元素浓度的等值线图：(*B*)YD(Year Days：一年中的天数) 300.5~301.5，SF₆；(*C*)YD 300.5~301.5，铁；以及 (*D*)YD 300~301，叶绿素 *a*。*B~D* 中的所有参数都是相对于 GPS 浮标绘制，该浮标作为第一部分实验使用的拉格朗日参照坐标系的中心。总体积 15,600 升的铁溶液 (8,100 mol 或 450 kg 铁) 被分配。SF₆ 溶液是在从迈阿密出发前，在 2,300 升钢罐中溶解 0.35 mol 的 SF₆ 于海水中配制而成。在以 ~9 km · h⁻¹ 速度行驶的蒸汽船上，分别以 1.4 l·min⁻¹ 和 12 l·min⁻¹ 的泵速将 SF₆ 和铁溶液泵入螺旋桨涡流中。在 24 小时部署过程中，船相对于中心 GPS 浮标的航迹每 5 分钟更新一次 (见下文)，以根据水平平流进行纠正。这种策略估计将在 35 米的混合层中产生 3.8 nM 的铁浓度增加，和 180 fM(fM：飞摩尔，即 10⁻¹⁵ M) 的 SF₆ 浓度增加 (参考文献 51)。据预测，水平涡流扩散将在一天的混合中，使条纹在水平方向均化，而每天晚上混合层的翻转将在垂直方向均化铁和 SF₆ 的浓度 [36]。每 5 分钟审视该 GPS 浮标，以确定船相对这个中心点的位置。此外，配备了 ARGOS 位置发射器的 4 个海洋环流漂流浮标 (WOCE) 配置在该片海区的每个角落。ARGOS 浮标的位置一天更新四次。所有的浮标以 10 米距离连接到洞袜式拖伞，以减少相对该加富海

457

the patch. Updates of the ARGOS buoy positions could be received four times a day. All of the buoys were attached to holey sock drogues set at 10 m to reduce wind slippage relative to the enriched patch. A flow-through pumping system with an intake set at 3 m on the ship's bow was used to sample surface sea water. SF_6 measurements using electron-capture gas chromatography were used to determine the position of the enriched iron patch, relative to the GPS buoy. This information was used daily to correct the central lagrangian reference point based on the GPS buoy (that is, correction for buoy slippage). Surface sea water was supplied for iron analyses via an all-Teflon pumping system also with the intake on the ships' bow. Samples were acidified in-line (pH 3) before analyses resulting in the detection of dissolved iron, freshly precipitated colloidal iron, and much of the aged, colloidal iron (total dissolvable iron, DFe). DFe was analysed continuously using both colorimetric and chemiluminescent techniques (detection limit, 0.3 nM). Chlorophyll depicted in D represents that filtered and extracted from discrete samples taken along the ship's track. Chlorophyll concentrations were quantified using standard fluorescence techniques on board ship.

To ensure that changes in properties within the patch could be attributed to the presence of iron and not to natural variation of the area in general, the study area was surveyed on year days (YD) 295 to YD 297 to determine its biological, chemical and physical heterogeneity. The initial survey, as well as later stations outside the patch, showed mixed-layer plant nutrient concentrations of nitrate, phosphate, silicate and ammonium to be 10.8 ± 0.4 µM, 0.92 ± 0.02 µM, 3.9 ± 0.1 µM and 0.21 ± 0.02 µM respectively, with a chlorophyll concentration of 0.24 ± 0.02 µg l^{-1}. These values are typical of the equatorial HNLC region[32,33]. The low-chlorophyll conditions were substantiated throughout the region by overflights of the NASA airborne oceanographic lidar (AOL) optical laboratory before the experiment (Fig. 2). Iron (450 kg) was added to the patch as a 0.5 M Fe (II) solution in sea water at approximately pH 2, together with 0.35 mol of the inert chemical tracer, SF_6.

Four tracking strategies were employed to maintain contact with the iron enriched area. (1) The iron deployment and initial sampling were performed about a central lagrangian reference point located by a drogued buoy equipped with a Global Positioning System (GPS) receiver interfaced to a VHF packet radio transmitter and receiver. (2) SF_6 was released in constant ratio to the iron injected into the patch. This inert tracer was monitored continuously with detection limits of less than 10^{-16} M. (3) The NASA AOL conducted overflights on YD 298, YD 301, YD 303 and YD 305 to assess the large-scale effects of iron on surface-water chlorophyll in the patch as compared to the surrounding region (Fig. 2). (4) The concentration of iron in the patch was determined continuously throughout the experiment[34,35].

The patch was sampled from YD 298.9 to YD 302.0 using surface pumping systems as the ship steamed through the study area. Each day, one major hydrographic station was occupied within the patch and one outside the patch at a time near local noon. Samples were collected at these stations for analysis of primary productivity, species composition, chlorophyll, FRR fluorescence, pigments (by high-pressure liquid chromatography), nutrients, particulate organic carbon (POC), particulate organic nitrogen (PON), dissolved organic carbon (DOC), dimethylsulphide (DMS), dimethylsulphoniopropionate (DMSP), dissolved and particulate trace metals and halocarbons as well as hydrographic and CO_2 system parameters. The concentration of the SF_6 tracer, together with the ship's position relative to the GPS buoy, were used to distinguish stations inside the patch from those outside.

区的风滑移。一个进水口设定在船头 3 米处的流入式泵系统被用来采集表层海水样品。使用电子捕获气相色谱测量 SF₆ 以确定加富海区相对于 GPS 浮标的位置。基于 GPS 浮标，这些信息被每天用于校正拉格朗日中心参考点（即校正浮标滑移）。用于铁分析的表层海水也是用船头处的进水口通过全特氟隆泵送系统提供。样品在分析之前陆续酸化（pH 为 3），导致可探测到：溶解的铁、新析出的胶体铁以及许多存在时间较长的胶体铁（全部可溶性铁，DFe）。DFe 通过同时使用比色法和化学发光这两种技术（检测限，0.3 nM）进行连续分析。D 图描绘的叶绿素，表示的是通过过滤并提取自沿船舶轨迹采集的分立样品得到的数值。叶绿素浓度在船上使用标准的荧光技术进行量化。

为了确保加富海区内各项特征的变化都能归因于铁的存在而非正常情况下海区的自然变化，我们在一年中的（YD）第 295 天到第 297 天对所研究海区的生物、化学和物理上的不均匀性作了调查。初步调查以及后续的外围海区测站调查显示，混合层中各类植物营养盐的浓度从硝酸盐、磷酸盐、硅酸盐到铵盐分别为 10.8 ± 0.4 μM、0.92 ± 0.02 μM、3.9 ± 0.1 μM 和 0.21 ± 0.02 μM，而叶绿素浓度则为 0.24 ± 0.02 μg·l^{-1}。上述各值在赤道 HNLC 海区非常典型[32,33]。美国国家航空航天局（NASA）的机载海洋雷达（AOL）光学实验室对该海区航空遥感的调查结果证实，铁加富实验之前整个海区一直处于低叶绿素水平（图 2）。铁（450 kg）以 0.5 M、pH 值约为 2 的 Fe(Ⅱ) 溶液的形式加入海水中，同时加入的还有 0.35 mol 的惰性化学示踪剂 SF₆。

实验中采取了四种追踪方法以便更贴近实际的铁加富海区的情况。(1) 铁的释放及最初的取样都是在由装备有全球定位系统（GPS）接收器的锥形浮标定位的拉格朗日中心参考点进行的，其中 GPS 接收器连接在甚高频数据包（VHF packet）无线电发射和接收机上。(2)SF₆ 以与铁恒定的比值注入该加富海区中。对该惰性示踪剂不断监测，仪器检测限小于 10^{-16} M。(3)NASA AOL 分别在第 298 天、第 301 天、第 303 天和第 305 天实施航空飞行，以评估加富海区相对于周围海域，铁对表层水体中叶绿素的大尺度影响（图 2）。(4) 整个实验期间连续测定加富海区中铁的浓度[34,35]。

对加富海区的取样工作是在第 298.9 天到第 302.0 天期间于调查船行经研究区的同时利用水泵获取表层水进行的。每天在接近当地中午时分，加富海区内外各有一个水文站进行该工作。收集以上站位的样品来分析初级生产力、样品组成、叶绿素、FRR 荧光、色素（利用高压液相色谱仪）、营养盐、颗粒态有机碳（POC）、颗粒态有机氮（PON）、溶解有机碳（DOC）、二甲基硫（DMS）、二甲基巯基丙酸（DMSP）、溶解态和颗粒态的痕量金属、卤代烃以及水文学和 CO_2 系统的参数。利用 SF₆ 示踪剂的浓度以及调查船相对于 GPS 浮标的位置可区分加富海区内外的站位。

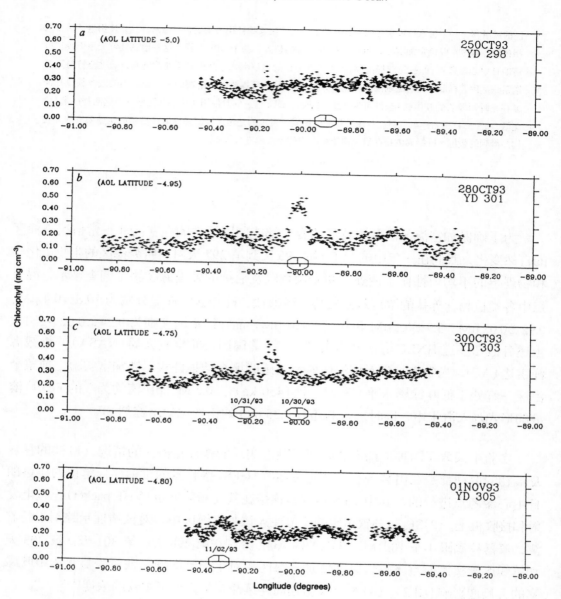

Fig. 2. *a–d*, The NASA airborne oceanographic LIDAR flown in a P-3 Orion aircraft (from Goddard Space Flight Center/Wallops Flight Facility) provided pigment measurements determined by laser-induced chlorophyll fluorescence on YD 298 (*a*), YD 301 (*b*), YD 303 (*c*) and YD 305 (*d*). For each mission day a single representative east–west flightline was selected from numerous lines flown over the patch. The latitude of the horizontal flightline is given in each panel. The longitude of the most contemporaneous central buoy position is indicated by the circle and date at the bottom of each panel. The flight legs were ~180 km long and were flown in a star pattern centred on the GPS buoy[52]. The surface manifestation of the patch was seen at (or very near) the buoy positions on each day after the initial deployment on YD 298. Fluorescence signals showed a rapid initial response followed by a decay in signal strength as the experiment progressed. This result is consistent with the measurements of iron and photochemical energy conversion efficiency[42].

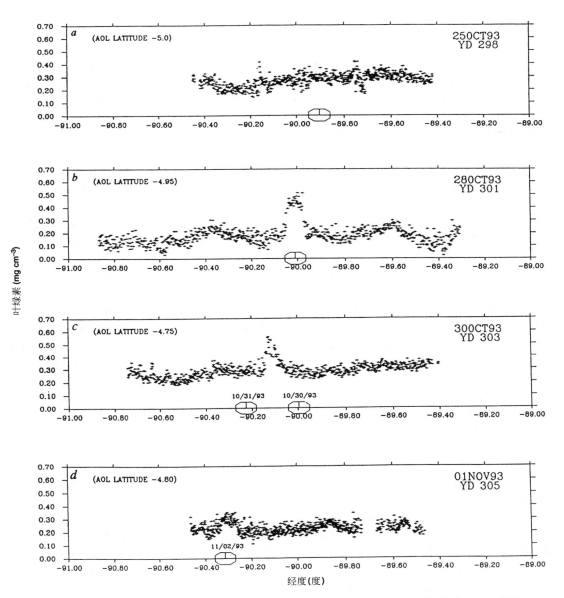

图 2. a~d，跟随 P-3 猎户座飞行器（来自戈达德航天飞行中心／沃洛普斯飞行中心）飞行的 NASA 机载海洋雷达采用激光诱导叶绿素荧光方法进行色素测量，分别在一年中的第 298 天 (a)，第 301 天 (b)，第 303 天 (c) 和第 305 天 (d) 测量得到。每一个测试日都从飞越该加富海区的多条路线中选择一条有代表性的从东至西的飞行路线。水平飞行线的纬度在每个子图中都作了标注。与飞行日时间上最接近的中央浮标位置的经度，在每个子图的底部通过圆和日期指示。航段约 180 km 长并且以 GPS 浮标为中心沿一个星形图案飞行 [52]。在第 298 天最初的部署之后的每日，加富海区的表面表现可在浮标的位置（或非常接近的位置）显现。荧光信号表现出一个快速的初始响应，接下来，随着实验的进行信号强度减弱。这个结果和对铁以及光化学能转化效率的测量结果 [42] 是一致的。

Physical behaviour of the patch. The physical coherence of the patch was one of the greatest concerns in performing the experiment. One potential problem was that as the patch spread by turbulent diffusion, it would disperse into long streaks as it crossed eddy or frontal boundaries. It was, however, remarkably stable. As predicted, the added iron and SF_6 were distributed rapidly throughout the mixed layer by horizontal eddy diffusion and convective overturn. The patch remained as an intact unit from YD 298 to at least YD 302, expanding to become a rectangle of approximately 8×12 km.

Late on YD 302 the core of the patch was subducted beneath a low-salinity front to a depth of 30–35 m, where it was confined in a 5–10 m layer at the top of the thermocline. The patch was still detectable after its subduction by the SF_6 signal, the distinct salinity and low light transmission[36]. SF_6 concentrations did not decrease after subduction. The highest values of SF_6 found each day were a constant 40–50 fM (femtomolar, 10^{-15} M) over the entire 9-day duration of the experiment. The constancy of the SF_6 concentration suggests that unfertilized waters did not penetrate into the core of the patch even after subduction.

Iron chemistry. Dissolvable iron concentrations (DFe) as high as 6.2 nM were measured in the core of the patch within 4 hours of fertilization. DFe decreased rapidly on the first day due to night-time convective mixing of the water column, with the highest values on the subsequent day being 3.6 nM, in good agreement with predicted concentrations (3.8 nM Fe). Concentrations of DFe in the core of the patch decreased ~15% each day. Despite this decrease, contour plots of iron and SF_6 in the surface layer were still in good spatial agreement on YD 301, 3 days after fertilization (Fig. 1B, C). Iron dropped below our detection limit (0.3 nM) in the subducted layer by YD 303.

Previous studies indicate that three distinct pools of iron were formed on injection: dissolved Fe(III), colloidal Fe(III) and cellular Fe. Most of the Fe(II) injected into the patch was oxidized within minutes to Fe(III)[37] and colloidal iron oxyhydroxides should have precipitated with a first-order rate constant of 0.1 h^{-1} (ref. 16). Biological uptake of the dissolved Fe(III) proceeded rapidly (see below). Of the three iron forms, colloidal Fe(III), especially when aged, is not thought to be bioavailable. Laboratory experiments, however, indicate that these colloids would remain suspended in the surface waters (K.H.C. *et al.*, unpublished observations) where they could be photoreduced and rendered bioavailable[16,38]. A computer model of iron photochemistry[16] suggests that once the patch was subducted, there would be insufficient light to maintain the bioavailable pool of dissolved Fe(III) at concentrations above our shipboard detection limits.

Chemical response. Nutrient measurements indicated little or no systematic difference in nitrate, phosphate and silicate concentrations within the mixed layer between inside and outside stations. The ratio of nitrate uptake to chlorophyll production in Fe incubation experiments is approximately 1 mol NO_3 per g chlorophyll (ref. 6). Thus a chlorophyll increase of 0.5 µg l^{-1} should have been accompanied by a 0.5 µM decrease in nitrate. Because initial nitrate concentrations were 10.8 µM and the day-to-day variance in the nitrate measurements was 0.4 µM (1σ) a 0.5 µM decrease would have been at our limit of

462

加富水体的物理特征。加富水体的物理连贯性，是实验实施中考虑的最重要的一点。一个潜在的问题就是，由于加富水体在湍流扩散作用下发生扩散，当它穿过涡旋或锋面边缘时会分散成条状。虽然有这些因素的影响，但是所研究海区的物理过程相当稳定。正如我们之前的预测，在水平涡流扩散和对流翻转的作用下，加入的铁和 SF_6 很快就在整个混合层中分散开来。至少在第 298 天到第 302 天期间浮游植物团块状结构仍保持为一个完整的单元，只是其形状扩展为一个约 8 km × 12 km 的长方形。

在第 302 天晚些时候，团块的核心部分下沉到了一个深 30~35 m 的低盐度锋之下，进而被限制在温跃层顶部 5~10 m 的层内。利用 SF_6 信号、盐度差异以及低透光率特征仍能探测到下沉以后的加富水体[36]。水体下沉后 SF_6 的浓度并未降低。在全部为期 9 天的实验中，每天所能测到的 SF_6 的最高值均稳定在 40~50 fM（fM：飞摩尔，即 10^{-15} M）之间。SF_6 浓度的稳定性表明，即使加富水体发生下沉后，未加富的水体也并未渗透到其中心部分。

铁的化学作用。实施加富后 4 个小时内，在中心区域测得的可溶性铁的浓度（DFe）高达 6.2 nM。由于夜间水体对流混合作用的增强，第一天 DFe 会迅速下降，到第二天时最高值变为 3.6 nM，该值与预测浓度（3.8 nM Fe）一致。中心区域的 DFe 每天下降约 15%。除该值的下降以外，表层水体中铁和 SF_6 的等值线图到第 301 天，即到实施加富后的第 3 天时，仍具有良好的空间一致性（图 1B 和 C）。到第 303 天时已下沉水层中铁的浓度降至我们的检测限（0.3 nM）以下。

前人研究显示，加富海区中铁有三种不同存在形式，即溶解 Fe(Ⅲ)、胶体 Fe(Ⅲ) 和细胞内的 Fe。加入海水中的大部分 Fe(Ⅱ) 在几分钟内就被氧化为 Fe(Ⅲ)[37]，而呈胶态的铁的氢氧化物则以 0.1 h^{-1} 的一级速率常数沉淀下来（参考文献 16）。生物对溶解的 Fe(Ⅲ) 摄取非常迅速（见下文）。上述三种存在形态中，胶体 Fe，特别是存在时间较长的胶体 Fe，很难被生物利用。不过，实验室研究表明，这些胶体仍会悬浮于表层水体中（科尔等，未发表的观察结果），被光降解后即可被生物利用[16,38]。铁的光化学作用计算机模型[16]显示，一旦加富水体下沉，由于光照不足，无法使可被生物利用的溶解 Fe(Ⅲ) 的浓度继续维持在船载设备的检测限之上。

化学响应。营养盐测定结果显示，海区内外测站的混合层中硝酸盐、磷酸盐和硅酸盐的浓度系统差异很小，甚至没有。在 Fe 的培养实验中，硝酸盐摄取量相对叶绿素生产力的比值大致为每克叶绿素对应 1 mol NO_3（参考文献 6）。因此，当叶绿浓度增加 0.5 μg·l^{-1} 时，硝酸盐将相应减小 0.5 μM。由于初始的硝酸盐浓度为 10.8 μM，而硝酸盐测定结果的日变化为 0.4 μM（1σ），因此所下降的 0.5 μM 应该在

detection. Phosphate and silicate also showed no definitive change over this time period inside the patch.

Ammonium, however, showed a consistent difference between inside and outside stations. After fertilization, the mean ammonium concentrations measured inside the patch from YD 299 to YD 302 were $0.10 \pm 0.07 \,\mu M$ (95% confidence interval) lower than the values observed outside the patch. An ammonium maximum with values near $0.45 \,\mu M$ was regularly found near the base of the mixed layer outside the patch. This maximum decreased within the fertilized patch and, with one exception, no ammonium concentrations higher than $0.12 \,\mu M$ were found inside the patch. Preferential uptake of ammonium[39] (especially by the picoplankton, the primary ammonium utilizers) would be expected as physiological rates increased.

The measurements of CO_2 fugacity and total CO_2 in the patch were significantly lower than those observed outside the patch[40]. These changes were apparent within 2 days of the iron release and are lower than expected, but consistent with the drawdown in major plant nutrients. Particulate DMSP, integrated throughout the water column, showed a significant increase (50–80%) in the fertilized patch. DMSP is produced by phytoplankton and decays to produce DMS[41]. There were no clear changes in DMS concentration in surface waters ($2.5 \,nM \pm 0.4$), which is not surprising considering the duration of the study compared to the time needed to degrade DMSP to DMS. Preliminary analysis of low-molecular-weight halocarbon data suggests that there was some increase in the concentration of methyl iodide inside the patch relative to outside stations.

Biological response. Biological parameters measured outside the patch during the course of the experiment remained similar to those measured within the patch region before the addition of Fe. Photosynthetic energy conversion efficiency (relative fluorescence) was the first biological response detected[42] after Fe addition. Relative fluorescence dramatically increased by the first sampling transect through the patch, indicating a large physiological response within the first 24 hours (the period required to fertilize the patch)[42].

Maximum primary production values in the mixed layer were initially $10-15 \,\mu g \, Cl^{-1} \, d^{-1}$ (R.B., personal communication). After fertilization, productivity increased monotonically to values of $48 \,\mu g \, Cl^{-1} \, d^{-1}$ on YD 301 (Fig. 3A). This 3–4 times increase in productivity was observed in all size fractions indicating an overall enhancement of rates in both small and large phytoplankton. Chlorophyll increased nearly three-fold by YD 301 from $0.24 \,\mu g \, l^{-1}$ to maxima consistently over $0.65 \,\mu g \, l^{-1}$ (Figs 2, 3B). NASA overflights confirmed the increase in chlorophyll using Lidar laser fluorescence measurements of the surface layer (Fig. 2).

Preliminary microscopic examination of water collected within the patch indicated an increase in biomass in all classes counted (cyanobacteria and protists). Total autotrophic biomass (excluding Prochlorophytes) calculated from cell numbers and volumes[43-45], increased from 16 to $33 \,\mu g \, Cl^{-1}$. The largest contributors to the plankton biomass were *Synechococcus*, red fluorescing picoplankton and autotrophic dinoflagellates. Diatoms were a small fraction of the total plankton biomass (17%) yet showed increases similar to other groups.

我们的检测限范围内。在此实验期间，加富海区内部磷酸盐和硅酸盐也未发生明显变化。

但是，内外测站的铵盐却显示出一致性差异。铁加富实施后，从第 299 天到第 302 天加富海区内测得的铵盐的平均浓度要比加富海区外低 0.10 ± 0.07 μM（置信区间为 95%）。铵盐浓度的最大值接近 0.45 μM，通常见于加富海区外的混合层底部。而在加富海区内该最大值则有所降低，且其中仅有一个铵盐浓度的测值高于 0.12 μM。随着生理速率的提高，铵盐将会优先被摄取[39]（特别是对作为铵盐初级消费者的超微浮游生物）。

加富海区中 CO_2 的逸度及 CO_2 总量的测定结果显著低于未加富海区[40]。这些变化在铁释放后的前两天非常明显，且低于预期值，不过这一点与主要植物营养盐的下降是一致的。在整个水柱中都能形成的颗粒态 DMSP 在加富海区中有显著升高（50%~80%）。DMSP 是由浮游植物产生的，分解后可形成 DMS[41]。表层水体中 DMS 的浓度无明显变化（2.5 nM $\pm$ 0.4），考虑到本研究的持续时间与 DMSP 降解为 DMS 所需的时间相差甚远，这样的结果并不奇怪。对低分子量的卤代烃数据的初步分析显示，加富海区中碘甲烷的浓度相对于外围海区略有升高。

生物响应。实验期间测得的外围未加富海区的生物参数与所研究水体在未加 Fe 之前基本相同。光合作用能量转换效率（相对荧光强度）是 Fe 加入以后测到[42]的第一个生物响应。在加富海区的第一个取样横断面上相对荧光强度显著提高，说明最初 24 小时内（即对水体加富完成所需的时间）就出现明显的生理响应[42]。

混合层中的最大初级生产力值开始时为 10~15 $μg \cdot Cl^{-1} \cdot d^{-1}$（比迪加雷，个人交流）。加富后，至第 301 天时生产力已单调递增至 48 $μg \cdot Cl^{-1} \cdot d^{-1}$（图 3A）。生产力这种 2~3 倍的提高在各个粒级中都曾观测到，说明所有大小浮游植物的生长速率整体增强。到第 301 天叶绿素的浓度提高到近 3 倍，即由 0.24 $μg \cdot l^{-1}$ 升高至 0.65 $μg \cdot l^{-1}$ 以上（图 2 和 3B）。NASA 利用激光雷达航空遥感得到的激光荧光测定结果证实了表层水体中叶绿素含量的升高（图 2）。

对采自加富区的水体进行的初步显微镜检测显示，所研究的各级生物量都有所增加（蓝藻和原生生物）。根据细胞数和体积计算出的自养生物量（不包含原核绿藻）[43-45] 由 16 $μg \cdot Cl^{-1}$ 增加至 33 $μg \cdot Cl^{-1}$。对浮游植物生物量贡献最大的是聚球藻、红色荧光超微浮游生物以及自养甲藻类。硅藻在浮游植物生物量中仅占一小部分（17%），不过其增速与其他类群相似。异养生物量由 4.7 $μg \cdot Cl^{-1}$ 增加至 7.3 $μg \cdot Cl^{-1}$，

Heterotrophic biomass increased from 4.7 to 7.3 µg Cl⁻¹ and was dominated by heterotrophic dinoflagellates and ciliates. Prochlorophytes were not counted microscopically but preliminary flow cytometric analyses indicate little difference in cell numbers between stations inside and outside the patch.

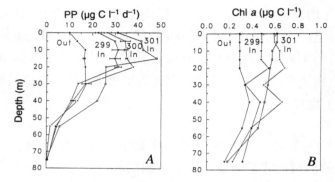

Fig. 3. Vertical profiles, for the 3 days following fertilization, of primary production, PP, (*A*) chlorophyll *a* concentrations, Chl *a*, (*B*) as a function of time inside and outside the patch. Outside values are depicted for YD 299. Primary production was measured using H¹⁴CO₃⁻ uptake determined at various light levels, in incubations on board the ship. Chlorophyll was determined from filtered and extracted samples as in Fig. 1*D*. The errors associated with the chlorophyll analyses are generally < 0.02 µg Cl⁻¹. The depth to which the water column was enriched was ~35 m up to YD 301 (just before subduction). It is in the upper 35 m that the differences are most pronounced. Productivity and chlorophyll both converge by 75 m.

Galapagos Plume Study

Satellite imagery collected with the Coastal Zone Colour Scanner on the Nimbus 7 satellite shows a plume of high-chlorophyll water that is found regularly to the west of the Galapagos Islands in association with the nutrient-rich, westerly flowing, south equatorial current[46] (Fig. 1*A*). Hydrographic surveys also have shown anomalously high chlorophyll concentrations and depleted nitrate concentrations over the Galapagos platform and downstream (westward) of the islands[47]. It has been suggested that these elevated chlorophyll levels are the result of iron derived from the island platform[47], but metal distributions in the Galapagos region are unknown. A series of stations were, therefore, occupied both upstream (to the east) and downstream (to the west) of the Galapagos Islands. Detailed trace-metal profiles were determined, as well as onboard analyses of the same parameters measured in the patch study. Surface-water iron, nitrate, CO_2 fugacity and fluorescence were also measured on transits between stations. The purpose of this sampling strategy was to determine if detectable anomalies of iron were present and, if so, their relationship to increased levels of chlorophyll and primary production in the downstream plume.

Survey results. The Galapagos Islands lie near a sharp equatorial front that separates low-nutrient, oligotrophic waters to the north from high-nutrient waters to the south. There are strong horizontal gradients as a result. Waters immediately around the Islands, during our survey, had nitrate concentrations greater than 10 µM at the surface. Chlorophyll

并且以异养甲藻和纤毛虫类为主。原核绿藻并未在显微镜下计数，不过流式细胞仪初步分析显示，加富海区内外测站之间的细胞数目差异很小。

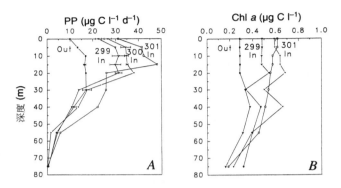

图 3. 施肥后 3 天，加富水体内外随时间变化的垂直剖面数据：(A)初级生产力，PP；(B)叶绿素 a 的浓度，Chl a。加富水体外所用曲线数值取自第 299 天。初级生产力通过在船上的培养过程中，由不同光照水平的 $H^{14}CO_3^-$ 摄取量测量得到。叶绿素的含量通过同图 1D 所用的过滤和提取样品来确定。叶绿素分析相关的误差一般 < 0.02 μg·Cl⁻¹。直到第 301 天（在水体刚要下沉之前），加富的深度约 35 m。在上层 35 m 差异最明显。生产力值和叶绿素值都在 75 m 处汇聚。

加拉帕戈斯羽状流研究

利用雨云(Nimbus)7 号卫星上的海岸带彩色扫描仪收集的卫星图像显示，在加拉帕戈斯群岛西部有一个高叶绿素含量的羽状流水体，可能与营养盐富集的、西向流动的南赤道洋流有关[46]（图 1A）。水文调查结果亦表明，加拉帕戈斯群岛地台及下游(向西)叶绿素浓度异常高而硝酸盐浓度极低[47]。有学者认为，叶绿素浓度的升高是来自岛屿台地的铁所致[47]，但加拉帕戈斯地区的金属分布情况尚不清楚。因此，我们在加拉帕戈斯群岛的上游(向东)和下游(向西)布置了一系列测站，测得了详细的痕量金属剖面，并在船上现场分析了加富水体研究中所测的各项参数，同时还测定了各站位之间过渡带上表层水体中的铁、硝酸盐、CO_2 逸度和荧光强度。选择该取样策略的目的是为了确定是否存在可测的铁异常，倘若果真存在，它们与下行羽状流中叶绿素浓度和初级生产力的升高之间又有何关系。

调查结果。 加拉帕戈斯群岛位于一个陡峭的赤道锋上，它是北部低营养盐的贫营养水体与南部高营养盐水体的分界线。因此这里的水平梯度很大。在我们的调

concentrations and rates of primary production were significantly elevated at stations downstream, when compared to upstream (eastward, Fig. 4).

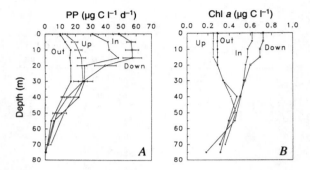

Fig. 4. Comparison of vertical profiles of primary production (*A*) and chlorophyll *a* concentrations (*B*) for stations inside and outside the fertilized patch, and stations upstream (westward) of the Galapagos Islands and downstream (eastward) of the Galapagos Islands.

Surface-water iron concentrations were about 0.06 nM upstream of the Islands. Iron concentrations as high as 1.3 nM were detected on a transect across the downstream plume, from 1° 30′ S to 0° along 91° 45′ W (Fig. 5). These high concentrations appeared to be associated with upwelled water that was in contact with the shelf and has higher salinity and lower temperature than the surrounding surface water masses. Elevated chlorophyll fluorescence signals were also associated with the high iron concentrations (Fig. 5). The highest iron concentrations (3 nM) were found between the islands of Isabella and Fernandina. These concentrations were associated with chlorophyll levels in excess of 13 µg l⁻¹, near-maximum relative fluorescence and nearly complete depletion of nitrate.

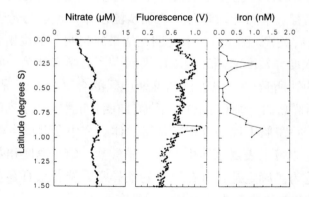

Fig. 5. Nitrate concentration, fluorescence intensity and iron concentrations as a function of latitude on a surface-water transect, along 91° 45′ W, from 1° 30′ S to the Equator.

Extracted surface chlorophyll concentrations in the downstream plume were typically near 0.7 µg l⁻¹, which is about 3 times higher than in the upstream water mass (Fig. 4*B*). However, large increases in chlorophyll fluorescence signals, which are indicative of even higher chlorophyll concentrations, were recorded by the shipboard fluorometer and the aircraft Lidar

查期间，群岛周围的水体表层硝酸盐浓度大于 10 μM。下游站位上的叶绿素浓度及初级生产率明显高于上游（向东，图 4）。

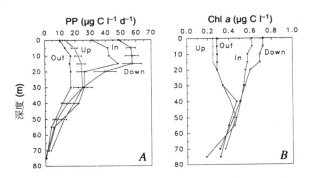

图 4. 加富水体内外测站，以及加拉帕戈斯群岛上游（向西）和下游（向东）测站的（A）初级生产力和（B）叶绿素 a 浓度的垂直剖面数据对比。

群岛上游方向表层水体中铁的浓度约为 0.06 nM。而在下行羽状流的一个横断面上（沿 91°45′ W 由 1°30′ S 到 0°）测到的铁浓度则高达 1.3 nM（图 5）。这种高浓度的出现可能与大陆架接触的上升流水体有关，相对于周围表层水体来说具有高盐、低温的特点。叶绿素荧光强度信号的增强也伴随着高的铁浓度（图 5）。铁的最大浓度（3 nM）见于伊莎贝拉和费尔南迪纳岛之间，在这样高的铁浓度下叶绿素水平超过 13 μg·l⁻¹，几乎到了最大相对荧光值和硝酸盐消耗殆尽的程度。

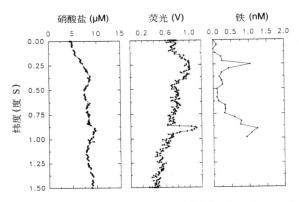

图 5. 硝酸盐浓度、荧光强度和铁浓度随表面水体横切面的纬度变化，沿 91°45′ W 由 1°30′ S 到赤道（0°）。

在下行羽状流中提取出的表层水体的叶绿素浓度一般在 0.7 μg·l⁻¹ 左右，该浓度值约为上游水体浓度的三倍左右（图 4B）。不过船载荧光计和航空雷达系统在下行羽状流的南北断面上记录到了叶绿素荧光强度信号的大幅增加，这说明叶绿素浓度

system on the downstream meridional transects through the plume[38,48]. These high fluorescence signals were regularly associated with frontal features characterized by lower temperatures, higher salinities and higher nitrate concentrations. The highest fluorescence signals always occurred at the interface between these upwelled water masses and the surrounding water. Particulate DMSP and DMSO levels were also significantly higher in the plume than at stations upstream, whereas differences in DMS levels were small.

Discussion

Our results demonstrate a direct and unequivocal biological response of the equatorial Pacific ecosystem to added iron. The response observed in the fertilization experiment was similar in magnitude and character to the increased production and chlorophyll found in the Galapagos plume. Until this study, there were no measured differences in chemical constituents which could explain higher biomass west of the islands. The presence of elevated concentrations of iron in the downstream plume is consistent with the hypothesis that the high chlorophyll concentrations are supported by iron, originating from the Galapagos platform.

Concentrations of chlorophyll as well as rates of primary productivity were up to a factor of 3–4 higher in both the patch and the downstream plume compared to outside the patch and upstream of the islands. The rapid increases in photosynthetic energy conversion efficiency in all size classes of phytoplankton in the patch confirm that at least some members of the natural phytoplankton populations are physiologically limited by lack of available iron[42]. Chlorophyll-specific rates of primary production showed a smaller change. These rates of primary production are less sensitive to iron availability because the carbon/chlorophyll ratio changes on the addition of iron. Moreover, laboratory studies show a three-fold increase in the carbon/chlorophyll ratio as cells become Fe-limited[20]. Carbon/chlorophyll ratios (wt/wt) in the patch decreased from an initial value of 54 to 38 by YD 300. Productivity on a per unit carbon basis, as determined by estimates of cell biovolume, indicate an initial doubling time of 1.0 d^{-1}. By YD 301 the doubling time was 1.5 d^{-1}, a 50% increase. This indicates that the cells grow faster on a per unit carbon basis when iron is present.

Dimethylsulphoniopropionate in the particulate phase also increased within the patch relative to waters outside the patch. This compound serves an osmoregulatory function (or possibly as a cryoprotectant) in certain classes of phytoplankton. It degrades to DMS, a volatile sulphur-containing gas that contributes to non-seasalt sulphur in the atmosphere. The production of these compounds in the iron-enriched patch is consistent with the ice-core record, which links greater iron availability to increased phytoplankton production during glacial times[49].

There was evidence for increased grazing within the fertilized patch. Microscopic examination of samples collected inside and outside the patch indicate that microheterotrophic biomass

可能还要更高[38,48]。高的荧光强度信号通常与以低温、高盐且硝酸盐浓度也很高为特征的锋面结构有关。荧光信号的最高值通常出现在上升流水体与周围水体的分界面上。羽状流中颗粒态 DMSP 和 DMSO 的浓度也明显高于上游站位，不过 DMS 的浓度差异并不大。

讨　　论

本文研究结果直接确切地证明了赤道太平洋生态系统对铁加富的生物响应。加富实验中观测到的响应在量级和特征上均与加拉帕戈斯羽状流中见到的生产力和叶绿素的增加相似。在本研究之前，没有可测得的化学组成差异可以解释岛屿西侧生物量较高的原因。下行羽状流中存在较高的铁浓度与理论假说——来自加拉帕戈斯地台的铁是支撑高叶绿素浓度的原因所在—— 一致。

在加富海区以及群岛下行羽状流中，叶绿素浓度以及初级生产率均为未加富海区和群岛上游的 3~4 倍。加富海区中各级浮游生物的光合作用能量转换效率均快速增加，证明在自然浮游植物群中至少有一部分在生理上受铁缺乏的限制[42]。基于叶绿素的初级生产速率则变化较小。这些初级生产速率对能够获得的铁不敏感，因为铁增加后碳与叶绿素的比值会发生变化。此外，实验室研究显示，在细胞中 Fe 元素有限的情况下碳与叶绿素的比值可提高为 3 倍[20]。加富海区中碳与叶绿素的比值（wt/wt）由开始的 54 下降到第 300 天时的 38。根据估算的细胞生物量，得出的以每单位碳为基础的生产力值显示，最初的倍增速率为 1.0 d⁻¹。到第 301 天时倍增速率变为 1.5 d⁻¹，提高了 50%。这说明，当有铁存在时，每单位碳的细胞生长得更快。

加富海区中颗粒相 DMSP 相对于海区外也有所增加。化合物 DMSP 在某些种类浮游植物中起渗透调节功能（或者很可能是种低温保护剂）。它可降解为 DMS，DMS 是一种挥发性含硫气体，可形成大气中的非海盐硫化物。在铁加富海区中上述化合物的产量与冰芯记录——冰期时更多可利用的铁与提高的浮游植物产量的相关关系[49]———致。

有证据表明加富海区的摄食压力也随之增大。对采自加富海区内外的样本的显微

increased by ~50% over the course of the patch experiment. This increase was rapid and appeared to level off quickly. The corresponding average increase in grazing pressure (assuming grazing rate (μg C d^{-1}) = 2.5 × heterotrophic biomass; F.C. and K.B., personal communication), was approximately 4.5 μg Cl^{-1} d^{-1}.

The biomass increase (excluding Prochlorophytes), estimated from microscopic counts of cell numbers and volumes, was 16.4 μg Cl^{-1} (a doubling). If the pool of inorganic carbon decreased by an equivalent amount, then the fugacity of CO_2 in the mixed layer should have decreased by about 3 μatm in the fertilized patch. This finding is low but consistent with the measurements of Watson and co-workers, indicating that some carbon may have been exported or converted to DOC[40]. When the increased effects of grazing are considered, the gross biomass increase must have been about 60 μg Cl^{-1}. Most of this increase (43 μg Cl^{-1}) was consumed over the 9-day experiment by grazers. These values are conservative in that they exclude consideration of mesozooplankton grazing. Qualitative observations of filters and plankton tows suggest that the mesozooplankton also increased, which presumably occurred when vertically migrating plankton encountered the high biomass in the patch and remained there to feed.

All biological indicators confirmed an increased rate of phytoplankton production in response to the addition of iron. The geochemical effect of iron enrichment was, however, small in both studies relative to the biogeochemical effect that could have been achieved if all the major nutrients were consumed. Nonetheless, the similarity in chlorophyll and productivity profiles measured between the fertilized patch and the downstream Galapagos plume suggests that similar mechanisms control the ecosystem response to added iron. There are several hypotheses that could explain why nutrients were not completely consumed and chlorophyll did not increase more dramatically. (1) Although iron did stimulate initial growth, the depletion of another micronutrient prevented further growth. (2) Grazing increased in the patch and plume environments as a result of increased production and the systems rapidly reached steady state. (3) Iron was lost from the system due to colloidal aggregation and/or sinking of larger particles containing iron.

First, we do not think that the limitation of the response to added iron results from the depletion of another trace nutrient. If that were the case, trace-metal clean shipboard incubations would not result in complete consumption of the major nutrients, but they do. Although there is no significant difference in dissolved Zn, Cu, Ni, Co or Cd between inside and outside stations, we cannot rule out the possibility that *in situ* growth resulted in the limitation of phytoplankton growth by other bioactive trace metals due to biological uptake and re-partitioning of these resources. This possibility seems unlikely over these short timescales and the magnitude of the biological response.

Second, increased grazing pressure must have exerted some control on the rate of biomass increase. Yet grazing does not seem to be a likely mechanism for preventing phytoplankton from completely consuming the available major nutrients in the patch and downstream of the Galapagos Islands. Other investigators have also seen large depletions of major nutrients

观察显示，在整个实验过程中异养微生物的生物量提高了约 50%，其提高过程非常迅速并很快稳定下来。对应的摄食压力平均增加速率（假定摄食速率（$\mu g \cdot C \cdot d^{-1}$）= 2.5 × 异养生物量，查韦斯和巴克，个人交流）约为 4.5 $\mu g \cdot Cl^{-1} \cdot d^{-1}$。

根据显微镜下数出的细胞数量和体积，生物量的增加速率（不包括原核绿藻）约为 16.4 $\mu g \cdot Cl^{-1}$（翻倍）。倘若无机碳含量也降低相同的量，那么在加富海区混合层中 CO_2 的逸度将降低 3 μatm。该值较低但与沃森和其同事的测定结果是一致的，这说明有些碳可能已被转化为溶解有机碳（DOC）[40]。将摄食效应的提高考虑在内后，总生物量的增加应该在 60 $\mu g \cdot Cl^{-1}$ 左右。在为期 9 天的实验中，所增加的大部分生物量（43 $\mu g \cdot Cl^{-1}$）均由于被摄食而消耗。由于我们并未考虑中型浮游动物的摄食，这些值是比较保守的。大量的过滤器和浮游生物拖网观察表明，中型浮游动物的量也有所增加，很可能是这些浮游生物在垂直迁移时遇到高生物量的加富水体并在此停留和摄食的结果。

所有生物指标均证实，浮游植物产率提高是对铁加富的响应。然而，相对于主要营养盐均消耗掉后所能达到的生物地球化学效应来说，在两种研究中铁加富带来的地球化学效应则都比较弱。不管怎样，在加富海区和加拉帕戈斯下行羽状流中分别测得的叶绿素和生产力剖面的相似性说明，相似的机制控制着生态系统对附加铁的响应。有多种假说可以解释为何营养盐未完全耗尽且叶绿素的增加未能更加显著。(1)虽然最初铁确实可以刺激生物的生长，但海区中另一种微量营养盐的缺乏限制了进一步的生长作用。(2)加富海区和羽状流环境中由于生产力提高导致的摄食压力的增大，进而使得系统快速稳定下来。(3)由于胶体的聚集和（或）含铁的较大颗粒的沉淀，系统中的铁丢失。

第一，我们并不认为浮游植物对铁的有限响应是由于另一种痕量营养盐的缺乏所致。倘使如此，在不含痕量金属的船载培养实验中，各主要营养盐就不可能完全消耗掉，而事实上确实消耗尽了。虽然加富海区内外的站位上溶解 Zn、Cu、Ni、Co 和 Cd 的浓度并无明显差异，我们并不能排除由于原位生物生长对上述资源的摄取和再分配，导致了其他生物活性痕量金属元素限制了浮游植物的生长这种可能性。但在如此短的时间内，从生物响应的数量级上来看似乎这种可能性不会发生。

第二，摄食压力的增加必定对生物量的增加速率产生影响。然而，在加富海区和加拉帕戈斯群岛下游海域，摄食作用似乎并非阻碍浮游植物将可利用的营养盐完

at stations over other regions of the Galapagos platform[47]. Although reduced grazing in bottle experiments is likely, there is no reason to expect an equivalent reduction in grazing pressure, especially by microheterotrophs, over shelf regions where high chlorophyll concentrations were observed.

Third, the available data suggest that nutrient consumption and phytoplankton growth is limited in the patch and downstream of the Galapagos Islands because of a loss term that occurs in open waters but not in bottles or in shallow shelf regions. This loss term might be sinking of larger phytoplankton. If sinking keeps the diatom population low, then the absolute rates of nutrient uptake will be limited because phytoplankton growth is a first-order process. Iron would also be lost much more rapidly from open ocean systems than from bottles or shallow waters. In shallow waters, sinking iron is trapped in a nepheloid layer near the bottom. Concentrations in the nepheloid layer along continental margins can be greater than 10 nM (ref. 8). Upwelling of iron-enriched water from a shallow nephloid layer will continually resupply the euphotic zone with iron. The biological similarity of shipboard iron enrichment experiments and stations over the Galapagos platform and Bolivar canal suggest that it is the elimination of the loss term for iron (that is, continuous supply of iron) that may be responsible for complete utilization of nutrients.

Vertical profiles of iron in the equatorial Pacific show a nutrient-like distribution with concentrations increasing at greater depth. However, the highest dissolved-iron values found in the equatorial Pacific (3° S, 140° W) are 0.55 nM at depths of 2,400 m (ref. 31). The depth of the source for upwelled water that reaches the surface along the equator is less than 150 m (ref. 50). Iron concentrations at this depth are less than 0.2 nM. Upwelling of water from the Equatorial undercurrent could not produce the large iron concentrations that we observed in the meridional transect and at the Bolivar canal, unless it is dramatically enriched by contact with the island platform. This must account for the iron concentrations greater than 1 nM observed near the Islands, and ocean currents are, therefore, the most plausible mechanism for the transport of island derived materials to the plume.

The residence time of bioavailable iron added to surface waters must be very short. Iron disappeared rapidly from the patch and was also not detected far from the presumed source downstream of the islands. This indicates that, within a given parcel of water, both the patch and plume systems reflect a transient addition of iron rather than a sustained addition, characteristic of bottle enrichments and shallow shelf stations. With a transient addition, only a few cell divisions are possible before the iron is removed from the system. Continual supply must occur to sustain production. This probably accounts for the low plateau that was reached in the biological response to the iron-addition experiment and the relaxation in relative fluorescence within the fertilized patch[42], but we cannot yet definitively rule out other factors.

We have shown that it is possible to enrich an area of the open ocean with iron and track it for many days. This capability can be used to conduct refined experiments that will address issues of grazing and iron loss, which will be coupled to continuous or semicontinuous

全消耗掉的可能机制。其他研究者在加拉帕戈斯地台其他部分海域的站位上，也见到了主要营养盐的大量消耗[47]。虽然在瓶装实验中摄食压力很可能降低，但我们没有理由认为陆架地区的摄食压力会有相同程度的降低，特别是对于异养微生物来说，因为在这里叶绿素的浓度非常高。

第三，已有数据显示，在加富海区和加拉帕戈斯群岛下游海域，营养盐的消耗和浮游植物的生长受到限制，因为在开阔水体中有一个亏损项，而在瓶装实验和浅海陆架区则没有。这个损失项可能是较大型浮游植物的下沉。倘若这种下沉作用使得硅藻数量保持在较低水平上，则营养盐摄取的绝对速率将受到限制，因为浮游植物的生长是第一级的过程。在开阔大洋系统中，铁元素的消耗应该也会大大快于瓶装实验和浅海水体中的消耗。在浅水中，沉降的铁元素通常会被底部附近的雾状层捕获。沿大陆架边缘，雾状层中铁的浓度要高于 10 nM(参考文献 8)。富铁水体由浅海雾状层上涌将可再次为真光层提供铁。船载铁加富实验与加拉帕戈斯地台和玻利瓦尔运河地区各站位上的铁加富实验具有生物相似性，这说明，铁的亏损项的消除(即铁的持续供给)可能是导致营养盐完全耗尽的原因所在。

赤道太平洋中铁的垂直剖面与营养盐的分布相似，其浓度随深度的增加而增大。不过，赤道太平洋中(3°S，140°W)溶解铁的最高值为 0.55 nM，出现在 2,400 m 深处(参考文献 31)。沿赤道附近到达表层的上升水体的来源深度不到 150 m(参考文献 50)。该深度上铁的浓度小于 0.2 nM。由赤道潜流上升而来的水体并不能使铁的浓度达到我们在南北断面和玻利瓦尔运河中观测到的高值，除非通过与岛屿台地接触而导致铁显著富集。在岛屿附近观测到的大于 1 nM 的铁浓度值可能就来源于此。因而，洋流应该是最有可能将来源于岛屿的物质搬运至羽状流的机制。

加入表层水体的生物可利用的铁的滞留时间必定很短。铁元素迅速从加富海区中消失，并且在距岛屿下游理论源区很远的地方也未能探测到。这表明，在特定的某块水体中，加富水体和羽状流体系均反映了铁的瞬时增加，而不是像瓶装实验和浅海陆架站位上那样持续增加。在瞬时增加条件下，仅能有很少的细胞可以在铁被转移走之前分裂。而持续的供给则能带来持续的生产力。这很可能是导致生物对铁加富实验响应中出现低平台期以及加富海区相对荧光强度降低的原因[42]，但我们尚无法明确排除其他影响因素。

我们已经证明，在开阔大洋中对某片海区实施铁加富并同时追踪数天是可行的。这种实验能力可用于进一步完善实验，从而解决摄食压力和铁的亏损问题，而这又

enrichment experiments. Given the relatively cohesive nature of the patch that was produced, it seems possible to create and track even smaller patches and instrument these patches to obtain better estimates of carbon export. Open-ocean manipulative experiments are, therefore, possible and ecological studies in the open ocean are no longer limited to passive observations and bottle experiments. This, we feel, may change significantly the way geochemical and ecological studies are performed in the ocean.

Finally, we wish to make it clear that the purpose of these experiments is to understand the nature of the controls on productivity and ecosystem function in HNLC waters. Such experiments are not intended as preliminary steps to climate manipulation. We also emphasize the transient nature of these experiments which indicate that the impact of these manipulations is erased in a very short time, because of the short residence time of iron and the rapid food web response.

(**371**, 123-129; 1994)

J. H. Martin[*], K. H. Coale[††‡], K. S. Johnson[†**], S. E. Fitzwater[†], R. M. Gordon[†], S. J. Tanner[†], C. N. Hunter[†], V. A. Elrod[†], J. L. Nowicki[†], T. L. Coley[†], R. T. Barber[§], S. Lindley[§], A. J. Watson[‖], K. Van Scoy[‖], C. S. Law[‖], M. I. Liddicoat[‖], R. Ling[‖], T. Stanton[¶], J. Stockel[¶], C. Collins[¶], A. Anderson[¶], R. Bidigare[#], M. Ondrusek[#], M. Latasa[#], F. J. Millero[☆], K. Lee[☆], W. Yao[☆], J. Z. Zhang[☆], G. Friederich[**], C. Sakamoto[**], F. Chavez[**], K. Buck[**], Z. Kolber[††], R. Greene[††], P. Falkowski[††], S. W. Chisholm[‡‡], F. Hoge[§§], R. Swift[§§], J. Yungel[§§], S. Turner[‖‖], P. Nightingale[‖‖], A. Hatton[‖‖], P. Liss[‖‖] & N. W. Tindale[¶¶]

[†] Moss Landing Marine Laboratories, PO Box 450, Moss Landing, California 95039-0450, USA
[§] Duke University Marine Laboratory, Beaufort, North Carolina 28516, USA
[‖] Plymouth Marine Laboratory, Prospect Place, Plymouth PL1 3DH, UK
[¶] Naval Postgraduate School, Monterey, California 93943-5000, USA
[#] Department of Oceanography, University of Hawaii, 1000 Pope Road, Honolulu, Hawaii 96822, USA
[☆] Rosenstiel School of Marine and Atmospheric Sciences, University of Miami, 4600 Rickenbacker Causeway, Miami, Florida 33149-1098, USA
[**] Monterey Bay Aquarium Research Institute, 160 Central Avenue, Pacific Grove, California 93950, USA
[††] Oceanic and Atmospheric Sciences Division, Brookhaven National Laboratories, Upton, New York 11973, USA
[‡‡] Ralph Parsons Laboratory, Department of Civil and Environmental Engineering, Massachusetts Institute of Technology, Cambridge, Massachusetts 02139, USA
[§§] NASA/GFSC, Wallops Flight Facility, Building N-159, Wallops Island, Virginia 23337, USA
[‖‖] School of Environmental Sciences, University of East Anglia, Norwich NR4 7TJ, UK
[¶¶] Department of Meteorology, Texas A&M University, College Station, Texas 77843-3150, USA
[*] Deceased.
[‡] To whom correspondence should be addressed.

Received 11 April; accepted 1 August 1994.

References:

1. Chisholm, S. W. & Morel, F. M. M. (eds) *Limnol. Oceanogr.* **36** (1991).
2. Martin, J. H. *Paleoceanography* **5**, 1-13 (1990).
3. Frost, B. W. *Mar. Ecol. Prog. Ser.* **39**, 49-68 (1987).
4. El-Sayed, S. Z. *Comp. Biochem. Physiol.* **90B**, 489-498 (1988).
5. Mitchell, B. G., Brody, E. A., Holm-Hansen, O., McClain, C. & Bishop, J. *Limnol. Oceanogr.* **36**, 1662-1677 (1991).
6. Martin, J. H. & Fitzwater, S. E. *Nature* **331**, 341-343 (1989).
7. Bruland, K. W., Franks, R. P., Knauer, G. A. & Martin, J. H. *Anal. Chim. Acta* **105**, 223-245 (1979).
8. Martin, J. H. & Gordon, R. M. *Deep-Sea Res.* **35**, 177-196 (1988).

可与连续或半连续的加富实验相对应。鉴于所形成的加富水域中浮游植物斑块凝聚性较好，应该也能够形成更小片的斑块并加以追踪，同时还可以利用仪器设备对这些斑块进行观测，以更好地评估碳的输出情况。因此，开阔大洋人工控制实验是可行的，而对开阔大洋的生态研究已不再局限于被动观测和瓶装实验。我们认为，这将大大改变海洋中的地球化学和生态学研究方法。

最后，我们希望声明一点，上述实验的目的是为了更好地理解 HNLC 水体中控制生产力和生态系统功能的各因素的本质。此类实验并不能作为气候操控的预备步骤。我们还要强调的是，此类实验的瞬时特性说明这种操作的影响在极短的时间内就会消失，这是因为铁的滞留时间极短而且食物网的响应亦非常迅速。

（齐红艳 翻译；孙松 审稿）

9. Martin, J. H., Fitzwater, S. E. & Gordon, R. M. *Globl. Biogeochem. Cycles* 4, 5-12 (1990).

10. Martin, J. H., Gordon, R. M. & Fitzwater, S. E. *Limnol. Oceanogr.* 36, 1793-1802 (1991).

11. Coale, K. H. *Limnol. Oceanogr.* 36, 1851-1864 (1991).

12. De Baar, H. J. W. *et al. Mar. Ecol. Prog. Ser.* 65, 34-44 (1990).

13. Price, N. M., Anderson, L. F. & Morel, F. M. M. *Deep-Sea Res.* 38, 1361-1378 (1991).

14. Ditullio, G. R., Hutchins, D. A. & Bruland, K. W. *Limnol. Oceanogr.* 38, 495-508 (1993).

15. Hutchins, D. A., Ditullio, G. R. & Bruland, K. W. *Limnol. Oceanogr.* 38, 1242-1255 (1993).

16. Johnson, K. S., Coale, K. H., Elrod, V. E. & Tindale, N. W. *Mar. Chem.* 46, 319-334 (1994).

17. Sunda, W. G., Swift, D. G. & Huntstman, S. *Nature* 351, 55-57 (1991).

18. Brand, L. E. *Limnol. Oceanogr.* 36, 1756-1772 (1991).

19. Hudson, J. M. & Morel, F. M. M. *Limnol. Oceanogr.* 35, 1002-1020 (1990).

20. Greene, R. M., Geider, R. J. & Falkowski, P. G. *Limnol. Oceanogr.* 36, 1772-1782 (1991).

21. Greene, R. M., Kobler, Z. S., Swift, D. G., Tindale, N. W. & Falkowski, P. G. *Limnol. Oceanogr.* (in the press).

22. Banse, K. *Limnol. Oceanogr.* 35, 772-775 (1990).

23. Dugdale, R. C. & Wilkerson, F. P. *Globl Biogeochem. Cycles* 4, 13-19 (1990).

24. Frost, B. W. *Limnol. Oceanogr.* 36, 1616-1630 (1991).

25. Hecky, R. E. & Kilham, P. *Limnol. Oceanogr.* 33, 796-822 (1988).

26. Roberts, L. *Science* 253, 1490-1491 (1991).

27. Upstill-Goddard, R. C., Watson, A. J., Wood, J. & Liddicot, M. I. *Anal. Chim. Acta* 249, 555-562 (1991).

28. Ledwell, J. R., Watson, A. J. & Law, C. S. *Nature* 364, 701-703 (1993).

29. Watson, A. J., Liss, P. & Duce, R. *Limnol. Oceanogr.* 36, 1960-1965 (1991).

30. Martin, J. & Chisholm, P. (eds) *US JGOFS Planning Report No.* 15 (US JGOFS Planning Off, Woods Hole Oceanographic Inst., Woods Hole, 1992).

31. Gordon, R. M., Coale, K. H. & Johnson, K. *EOS* 75, 114, Abstr. (1994).

32. Chavez, F. P. & Barber, R. *Deep-Sea Res.* 34, 1229-1243 (1987).

33. Fiedler, P. C., Philbrick, V. & Chavez, F. P. *Limnol. Oceanogr.* 36, 1834-1850 (1991).

34. Elrod, V. A., Johnson, K. S. & Coale, K. H. *Analyt. Chem.* 63, 893-898 (1991).

35. Coale, K. H., Blain, S. P., Fitzwater, S. E., Coley, T. L. & Johnson, K. S. *Deep-Sea Res.* (submitted).

36. Stanton, T. P. & Watson, A. J. *EOS* 75, 134, Abstr. (1994).

37. Millero, F. J. & Sotolongo, S. *Geochim. Cosmochim. Acta* 53, 1867-1873 (1988).

38. Wells, M. L. & Mayer, L. M. *Deep-Sea Res.* 38, 1379-1395 (1991).

39. Raymont, J. E. G. *Phytoplankton* (Pergamon, Oxford, 1980).

40. Watson, A. J. *et al. Nature* 371, 143-145 (1994).

41. Keller, M. D., Bellows, W. K. & Guillard, R. R. L. in *Biogenic Sulfur in the Environment* (eds Saltzman, E. S. & Cooper, W. J.) 167-182 (Am. Chem. Society, Washington DC, 1989).

42. Kolber, Z. *et al. Nature* 371, 145-149 (1994). (this issue: update)

43. Waterbury, J., Watson, S., Valois, F. & Franks, D. *Can. Bull. Fish. Aquat. Sci.* 214, 71-120 (1985).

44. Eppley, R., Reid, F. & Strickland, J. *Bull. Scripps Inst. Oceanogr.* 17, 33-42 (1970).

45. Beers, J. & Stewart, G. *Bull. Scripps Inst. Oceanogr.* 17, 67-87 (1970).

46. Feldman, G. C. in *Tidal Mixing and Plankton Dynamics: Notes on Costal and Estuarine Studies* (eds Brown, J., Yentsch, M. & Peterson, W. T.) 77-106 (Springer, Berlin, 1986).

47. Chavez, F. P. & Brusca, R. C. in *Galapagos Marine Invertebrates* (ed. James, M. J.) 9-33 (Plenum, New York, 1991).

48. Sakamoto, C. M. & Friederich, G. *EOS* 75, 150, Abstr. (1994).

49. Roger, T. & Wilson, S. *Atmos. Envir.* 22, 2637-2638 (1988).

50. Gargett, H. E. *Limnol. Oceanogr.* 36, 1527-1545 (1991).

51. Fitzwater, S. E. *et al. EOS* 75, 150, Abstr. (1994).

52. Hoge, F. *et al. EOS* 75, 134, Abstr. (1994).

Acknowledgements. K. Coale would like to acknowledge the leadership of Dr John H. Martin, whose vision and perseverance has forged this hypothesis and whose presence and humour we all miss dearly. He would have loved to see this project through. We thank M. Wells for his comments. This work was supported by the US Office of Naval Research and the US National Science Foundation.

Iron Limitation of Phytoplankton Photosynthesis in the Equatorial Pacific Ocean

Z. S. Kolber *et al.*

Editor's Note

A proposal for reducing the atmospheric content of carbon dioxide by stimulating phytoplankton growth in the oceans through the addition of iron, an essential nutrient, was tested in a large-scale experiment in the equatorial Pacific Ocean in 1993. The idea was that enhancing this plant growth would draw down the carbon dioxide from the air and fix it in organic matter that ends up as sea-floor sediment. The experiment, of which this paper reports one component, established that "iron fertilization" worked, but insufficiently to offer a viable strategy for mitigating climate change. Here Zbigniew Kolber and co-workers establish the mechanism of the fertilization effect, showing that added iron increases the efficiency with which solar energy is captured for photosynthesis.

The surface waters of the equatorial Pacific have unusually high nitrate and phosphate concentrations, but relatively low phytoplankton biomass[1-3]. This "high nitrate, low chlorophyll" (HNLC)[4] phenomenon has been ascribed to "top-down" grazing pressure by herbivores, which prevent the phytoplankton from fully utilizing the available nutrients[5]. In the late 1980s, however, Martin and co-workers proposed that iron, which is delivered to the remote open ocean in aeolian dust[6], is the key factor limiting the standing crop of phytoplankton in HNLC areas[7,8]. Using a sensitive fluorescence method[9], we have followed changes in photochemical energy conversion efficiency[9,10] of the natural phytoplankton community both before and after artificial enrichment with iron of a small area (7.5×7.5 km) of the equatorial Pacific Ocean[11]. Our results show that iron limits phytoplankton photosynthesis in all size classes in this region by impairing intrinsic photochemical energy conversion, thereby supporting the hypothesis of physiological ("bottom up") limitation by this element.

FOLLOWING the iron enrichment (described in detail by Martin *et al.*[11]), we continuously measured changes in photochemical energy conversion efficiency with a fast repetition rate (FRR) fluorometer as the ship steamed. The instrument operated in a flow-through mode using a non-toxic (PVC) plumbing system which sampled from 3 m below the surface. The FRR fluorometer measures the change in quantum yield of *in vivo* chlorophyll fluorescence resulting from exciting photosystem II (PS II) with a train of 32 subsaturating flashes each of ~1 μs duration, each separated by 5 μs. The cumulative stimulation of PS II by the fast-repetition-rate flashes induces a saturation profile of chlorophyll

赤道太平洋海域铁对浮游植物光合作用的限制

克尔贝尔等

编者按

1993 年在赤道太平洋的一个大规模实验检验了这样一个假设：通过添加一种必需的营养素铁，刺激海洋浮游植物的生长，从而减少二氧化碳在大气中的含量。当时的想法是，更多这种植物的生长将消耗空气中的二氧化碳，并将之固定在有机物中最终成为海底沉积物。实验证实，"铁施肥"是有效的，但并不足以作为减缓气候变化的一个可行的策略，这篇论文只报道了上述实验的一个部分。本文中的兹比格涅夫·克尔贝尔和同事们通过开展铁施肥提高捕获太阳能进行光合作用的效率，从而证实了施肥作用的机制。

赤道太平洋的表层水体具有异于寻常的高硝酸盐和磷酸盐浓度，但浮游植物生物量却相对较低 [1-3]。这种"高硝酸盐、低叶绿素"(HNLC)[4] 现象被认为是由于浮游动物对浮游植物的摄食压力导致的"下行控制"所致，因为这阻碍了浮游植物对营养盐的充分利用 [5]。然而，20 世纪 80 年代晚期，马丁及其同事们却提出，在 HNLC 海区，导致 HNLC 现象的关键因素——铁元素——限制了浮游植物的现存量 [7,8]，通常铁是通过风蚀尘埃输送到远海中的 [6]。我们利用灵敏的荧光分析法 [9]，研究了赤道太平洋地区的一小片海区 (7.5 km × 7.5 km) 在实施人工铁加富之前和之后 [11] 自然浮游植物群落的光化学能转化效率的变化 [9,10]。结果显示，在该海区，通过削弱内在光化学能转化效率，使各级浮游植物光合作用都受到铁含量的限制，进而支持了本文提出的铁元素生理限制（"上行控制"）假说。

按照铁加富方法（马丁等 [11] 已作详细介绍），我们利用快速重复率 (FRR) 荧光计在调查船行驶过程中连续测得了光化学能转换效率的变化。该设备用一个由无毒的 (PVC) 抽水系统在流通模式下运行，取样位置位于表层以下 3 m。FRR 荧光计根据一列由 32 个持续时间分别为 1 μs 左右、间隔 5 μs 的亚饱和闪光，测定了由受激的光系统 II(PS II) 引起的浮游植物体内叶绿素荧光量子产率的变化。FRR 闪光对 PS II 的累积刺激产生一条位于 685 nm 处的叶绿素荧光饱和曲线，在 100 μs 内就达到稳定阶段（克尔贝尔和法尔科夫斯基，稿件准备中）。饱和曲线的振幅与 PS II 的量子

fluorescence at 685 nm which plateaus within 100 μs (Z.S.K. and P.G.F., manuscript in preparation). The amplitude of the saturation profile is quantitatively proportional to the quantum efficiency of PS II[12-14], and the saturation rate is quantitatively proportional to the functional photon absorption cross-section of the PS II reaction centre, σ_{PSII} (refs 15–17). This cross-section is a quantitative measure of the effective biophysical target size of the antenna serving PS II; the product of σ_{PSII} and incident spectral irradiance gives the average rate of photon delivery to the reaction centres. The FRR technique is extremely sensitive and the precision of the measurements is $>5\%$. To determine the effect of iron enrichment on specific phytoplankton size fractions, additional discrete samples (obtained from selected depths with trace-metal clean sampling techniques[18]) were size-fractionated by selective filtration and measured with the FRR fluorometer.

We previously established that, in laboratory cultures of phytoplankton, iron limitation leads to a marked decrease in the quantum efficiency of photochemistry in PS II[19,20]. This effect, which can be conveniently and sensitively measured in real time from changes in the quantum yield of variable fluorescence[9,14,21,22], is independent of phytoplankton biomass loss processes, such as grazing. Thus, if iron limitation affects phytoplankton photosynthetic physiology in HNLC waters as it does in laboratory cultures, the enrichment should lead to an increase in the quantum efficiency of PS II. If, on the other hand, grazing pressure is the sole factor limiting the accumulation of phytoplankton biomass, little or no effect of iron on the quantum efficiency would be expected.

In the FRR protocol, the quantum yield of fluorescence rises from an initial, low level, F_0, to a maximum value, F_m. The change in the quantum yield of variable fluorescence $(F_v = F_m - F_0)$, normalized to the maximum fluorescence yield (F_v/F_m), is highly constrained in phytoplankton, reaching a value of ~0.65 under optimal growth conditions when cells are nutrient-replete[15,16]. F_v/F_m is a quantitative measure of the quantum efficiency of PS II for an ensemble of reaction centres. We found high values of F_v/F_m in natural phytoplankton communities in high-nutrient waters of upwelling areas and continental margins[16], including regions downstream of the Galapagos Islands, where currents suspend iron-rich sediments from the Galapagos platform and entrain them into nutrient-rich surface waters[11]. In the nutrient-rich, iron-deficient equatorial Pacific, however, F_v/F_m values average ~0.3, indicating a significant ($>50\%$) inactivation of PS II reaction centres and a corresponding decrease in photosynthetic energy conversion efficiency[14,17]. Within 1 day following the addition of iron, F_v/F_m increased by $\sim70\%$ to 0.54, and reached a peak in the centre of the enriched patch after 2 days, at a level of 0.63 (Figs 1 and 2). The increase in F_v/F_m was primarily due to decreases in the initial fluorescence (F_0) values (Fig. 1c), strongly suggesting that the iron enrichment led to an increase in the fraction of functional PS II reaction centres, and a corresponding increase in the utilization of absorbed excitation energy for photochemistry[13,23].

效率定量成正比[12-14]。而饱和率则定量正比于 PS Ⅱ 反应中心的功能光子吸收截面 $\sigma_{PSⅡ}$（参考文献 15~17）。该截面是对作为 PS Ⅱ 的天线的有效生物物理目标尺寸的定量测定结果，$\sigma_{PSⅡ}$ 与入射光谱辐射的乘积给出了光子到达反应中心的平均速度。该测量方法中 FRR 技术极其灵敏，其精确度 > 5%。为了确定铁加富作用对特定级别浮游植物组分的影响，我们还选取了额外的离散样品（利用痕量金属清洁技术[18]取自特定深度层），利用选择性过滤装置对样品作了尺寸分选后，以 FRR 荧光计进行测量。

我们之前已经确定，在浮游植物的实验室培养过程中，铁的限制作用导致 PS Ⅱ 中光化学量子效率明显降低[19,20]。该效应可通过可变荧光的量子产率的变化实时、方便、灵敏地测出[9,14,21,22]，它与浮游植物生物量的减少过程（如摄食等）无关。因此，倘若如实验室培养时一样，铁的缺乏会影响 HNLC 水体中浮游植物的光合生理作用，那么铁加富作用将使 PS Ⅱ 的量子效率得到提高。另一方面，如果摄食压力是限制浮游植物生物量增加的唯一因素，则铁的增加对量子效率的影响将很小甚至没有。

在 FRR 方法中，荧光量子产率由初始时的低水平 F_0 上升至最大值 F_m。可变荧光量子产率的变化（$F_v = F_m - F_0$），将其归一化至最大荧光量子产率后（F_v/F_m），在浮游植物生长中这个值是高度受限的，当营养盐充足，处于最佳生长环境时，该值能够达到 0.65 左右[15,16]。F_v/F_m 是 PS Ⅱ 全体反应中心量子效率的一个定量衡量标准。我们发现自然浮游植物群落的高 F_v/F_m 值可见于上升流区和大陆边缘的高营养盐水体[16]，包含加拉帕戈斯群岛下游，在这里，洋流从加拉帕戈斯台地上带来大量富含铁的悬浮沉积物，输送至富含营养盐的表层水体中[11]。然而，在富营养盐而贫铁的赤道太平洋中，F_v/F_m 的平均值则仅为 0.3 左右，这说明 PS Ⅱ 反应中心明显失活（> 50%），相应的光合能量转换效率也随之下降[14,17]。在加入了额外的铁以后的第一天 F_v/F_m 值就升高了约 70%，达到 0.54，并于第二天在加富海区中心达高值 0.63（图 1 和 2）。F_v/F_m 值的升高主要是由于初始荧光值（F_0）的降低（图 1c），这充分说明，铁加富作用增加了 PS Ⅱ 功能反应中心这一组分，同时伴随着光化学作用中对已经吸收的激发态能量利用率的提高[13,23]。

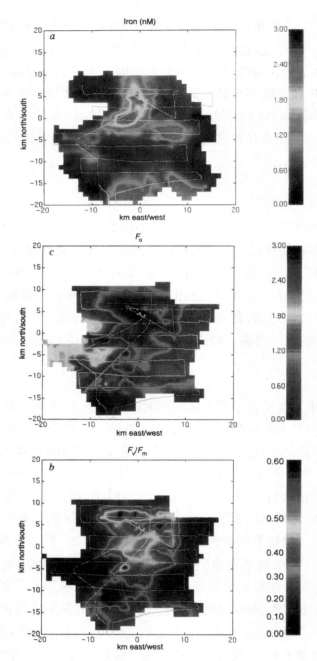

Fig. 1. *a*, Spatial distributions of soluble iron in the iron-enriched area at year day 300–301(27–28 October, 1993)[1]. The ship track is shown as a yellow line. The enriched area is seen as an orange-red feature in the centre of the panel. *b*, The corresponding variations in photochemical energy conversion efficiency (F_v/F_m) measured at 3 m below the sea surface with an onboard FRR fluorometer automatically logging data every 2 min. F_v/F_m values are spatially correlated with the iron enrichment in *a*. *c*, The corresponding spatial distribution of the minimum fluorescence yield, F_0. This parameter is markedly decreased in the iron-enriched area, implying a redistribution of absorbed excitation energy towards photochemistry in the photosynthetic apparatus of the phytoplankton.

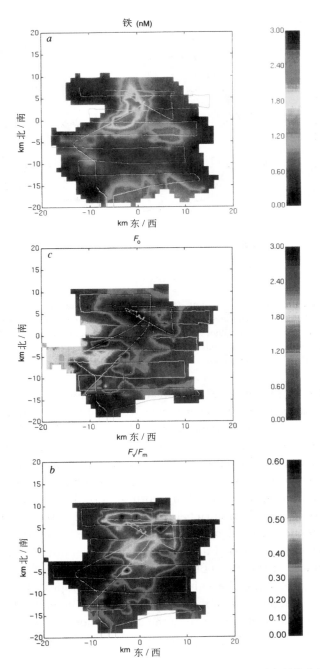

图 1. a，在一年的第 300~301 天（1993 年 10 月 27~28 日）[1]中富铁海区溶解铁的空间分布。黄色线为
调查船的航线。可以看到，图中央的橘红色部分代表富铁海区。b，光化学能转换效率（F_v/F_m）的相应
变化是利用船载 FRR 荧光计在水深 3 m 处测得的，仪器每两分钟读数一次。F_v/F_m 值与图 a 中铁的富
集程度具有空间相关性。c，对应的最低荧光产率 F_0 的空间分布。在铁富集海区，该参数明显减小，这
说明浮游植物的光合反应器吸收的激发能通过光化学转换作用被重新分配。

485

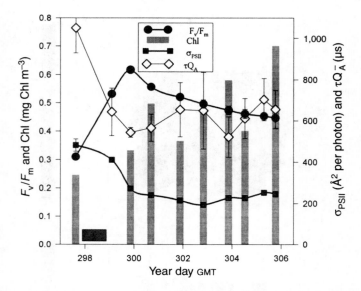

Fig. 2. The time series of changes in chlorophyll a (Chl), F_v/F_m, the functional absorption cross-section of PS II (σ_{PSII}), and the time constant for the oxidation of Q_A^- (τQ_A^-) following the addition of iron on year day 298 (25 October, 1993). These values are taken from the maximum of F_v/F_m in the upper 30 m of the water column. Two days following the start of the enrichment (day 300), F_v/F_m values peaked and subsequently declined with an e-folding time of ~6 d.

The plateau in photosynthetic energy conversion efficiency in the iron-enriched area on year day 300 (2 days after fertilization) was followed by a relaxation in F_v/F_m values (Fig. 2). The half-time for the relaxation in F_v/F_m was ~4 days. During the relaxation period, iron concentrations decreased from 3 nM to < 0.5 nM 4 days after the iron addition. The amplitude and kinetics of iron-stimulated F_v/F_m changes were paralleled by changes in photosynthetic parameters obtained from short-term incubations with $H^{14}CO_3^-$. Based on an analysis of 34 photosynthesis–irradiance curves, the initial slopes were 19% higher inside the iron-enriched area compared with outside, while the light-saturated photosynthetic rates, normalized to chlorophyll a, increased ~35%. An analysis of covariance (ANCOVA) revealed that the difference in both of these parameters was statistically significant at the $P = 0.0001$ level. Moreover, based on measured optical absorption cross-sections and the values of the initial slopes of the photosynthesis–irradiance curves, the maximum quantum yield calculated for carbon fixation was 60–70% higher in the iron-enriched patch relative to the area outside the patch[24]. Both the elevated F_v/F_m signals and enhanced photosynthetic rates were limited to the iron-enriched patch.

In addition to changes in F_v/F_m, iron affects the functional absorption cross-section of PS II[20,25] and the rate of oxidation of the primary electron acceptor in PS II, Q_A^-, in model algal systems[20]. Following the addition of iron to the waters in the equatorial Pacific, the functional absorption cross-section of PS II decreased by a factor of two, suggesting that more reaction centres became functional for a given pool of antenna pigments. Moreover, the oxidation rate of Q_A^- (which was deduced from the kinetics of the decay of variable fluorescence in the 1-ms time domain[15,20,25]) increased by 60% within the first 2 days, suggesting an increase

486

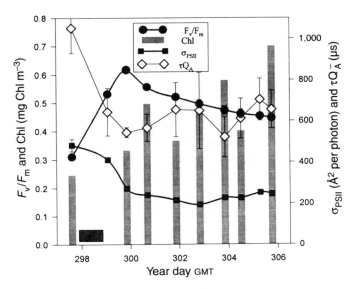

图 2. 在一年的第 298 天（1993 年 10 月 25 日）实施铁加富以后，叶绿素 a(Chl)、F_v/F_m、PS II 的功能性吸收作用截面（σ_{PSII}）以及 Q_A^- 氧化作用的时间常数（τQ_A^-）随时间的变化。上述值均取自 F_v/F_m 值最大的上层 30 m 水柱。实施加富的两天之后（第 300 天）F_v/F_m 达到峰值，随后开始下降，在约 6 天的时间里成指数倍数衰减。

在铁加富海区，光合能量转换效率在该年的第 300 天（实施铁加富的两天之后）达到最高值后，F_v/F_m 值就开始放缓（图 2）。F_v/F_m 值的半弛豫时间约为 4 天。在弛豫期内，铁加富后的 4 天里，铁的浓度由 3 nM 降低至 0.5 nM 以下。由铁引起的 F_v/F_m 值的变化的振幅及其动力学特征均与用 $H^{14}CO_3^-$ 短期培养后获得的光合作用参数的变化一致。根据 34 条光合作用－辐照曲线的分析结果，与外部相比，在铁加富海区内部其起始斜率要高出 19%，而光饱和条件下的光合作用速率（标准化到叶绿素 a）则增加了 35% 左右。协方差分析（ANCOVA）显示，上述两种参数的差异在 $P = 0.0001$ 时具有统计学意义。此外，根据测得的光吸收截面和光合作用－辐照曲线的初始斜率值计算得出：在铁加富海区中，固碳作用的最大量子产率相对于未加富海区要高出 60%~70%[24]。F_v/F_m 信号的升高和光合作用速率的增强都仅限于铁加富海区。

除了 F_v/F_m 值的变化以外，藻类模拟系统[20]显示，铁还影响 PS II 的功能性吸收作用截面[20,25]以及 PS II、Q_A^- 中初始电子受体的氧化作用速率。对赤道太平洋水体实施铁加富以后，PS II 的功能性吸收作用截面下降了一半，这说明，在给定的天线色素池中有更多的反应中心开始起作用。同时，在前两天里 Q_A^- 的氧化速率（它是由可变荧光在 1 ms 的时间域内衰减的动力学推导得到的[15,20,25]）提高了 60%，这意味着

in intersystem electron-transfer efficiency between PS II and PSI[26]. Similar effects of iron on PS II have been reported in phytoplankton cultures[20]. The increase in electron-transfer rates on the acceptor side of PS II reduces the possibility of back reactions within the photosystem, leading to both an increase in the overall photosynthetic energy conversion efficiency and a reduction in the potential of photoinhibition at supraoptimal photon fluence rates.

Measurements of F_v/F_m in four size fractions spanning from > 10 μm to < 1.0 μm, revealed that outside the iron-enriched area, all size fractions of phytoplankton had low photochemical energy-conversion efficiency; average values of F_v/F_m ranged from 0.2 to 0.3 (Fig. 3a). The vast majority of phytoplankton chlorophyll biomass ($> 90\%$) was contained in small cells (< 5 μm) which mainly included pico-eukaryotes, cyanobacteria and Prochlorophytes (Fig. 3b). Within 24 hours of the addition of iron, all size fractions displayed a marked increase in F_v/F_m (Fig. 3a).

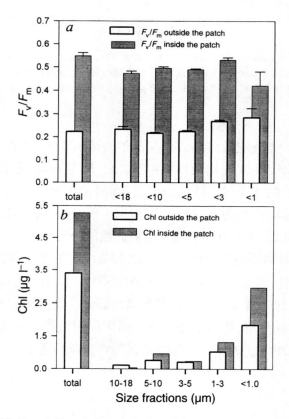

Fig. 3. Changes in F_v/F_m (a) and chlorophyll concentrations (b) in 4 size fractions inside and outside the iron-enriched patch on year day 300 (27 October, 1993), 2 days after the beginning of the iron enrichment. Note the relatively large and statistically significant increases in F_v/F_m in all size fractions in the iron-enriched waters, indicating ubiquitous physiological limitation of photosynthetic energy-conversion efficiency.

Picoplankton, with their high surface-area to volume ratio, are thought to have a competitive advantage in terms of iron transport[27,28]. Moreover, some oceanic picoplankton may have exceedingly low iron requirements per unit cell volume[29]. The observed rapid changes

PS Ⅱ和PS Ⅰ系统间电子传递效率提高[26]。在浮游植物培养中铁对PS Ⅱ的类似影响也已有报道[20]。PS Ⅱ中受体侧电子传递速率的升高降低了光系统内逆反应发生的可能性，从而提升总光合能量转换效率的同时，降低在最适光子通量率时光抑制发生的可能性。

在 >10 μm 到 <1.0 μm 之间分四个粒级组分测的 F_v/F_m 比值显示，在铁加富区域以外，所有粒级组分的浮游植物的光化学能转换效率都较低，F_v/F_m 的平均值在 0.2~0.3 之间（图 3a）。占浮游植物叶绿素总量比例最高（$>90\%$）的是小细胞（<5 μm），主要包括微型真核生物、蓝藻以及原核绿藻（图 3b）。在铁加富 24 小时内，各粒级组分中 F_v/F_m 值都明显升高（图 3a）。

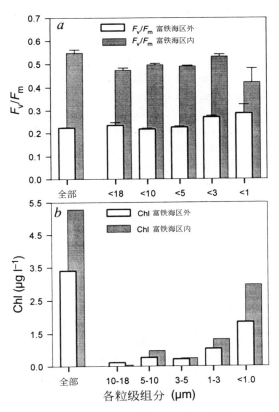

图 3. 铁加富实施的两天之后，即第 300 天（1993 年 10 月 27 日），在富铁海区内外四组大小不同粒级的 F_v/F_m 值（a）和叶绿素浓度（b）的变化情况。注意，在富铁水体中所有粒级的 F_v/F_m 值都相对较高并具有统计学意义，说明光合作用能量转换效率普遍受到了生理限制。

超微型浮游生物的表面积与体积之比很高，在对铁的输送方面有独特的竞争优势[27,28]。此外，有些海洋超微型浮游生物中每单位细胞体积的铁需求量可能极低[29]。

in photosynthetic parameters reflect molecular alterations and/or modification of the photosynthetic apparatus and electron-transfer pathways within PS II reaction centres. That these occur in the picoplankton as well as within larger cells, implies that any refuge afforded by a high surface-to-volume ratio[30] is marginal in the HNLC waters of the equatorial Pacific.

The photosynthetic apparatus contains numerous loci for iron[31]. In PS II there are two iron atoms, one in the haem of cytochrome *b*-559, and a non-haem iron coordinated between the two reaction-centre proteins, D1 and D2[32]. In laboratory studies with iron-limited cells, fluorescence lifetimes measured in the picosecond time domain are dramatically altered by iron availability. The relative amplitudes of the two shorter lifetimes, at 155 and 530 ps, which correspond to excitation trapping and primary charge separation, respectively[33,34] are markedly lower in iron-deficient cells compared with iron-replete cells[35]. In contrast, a long-lived fluorescence component at 1,200 ps, which corresponds to excitation energy loss within the pigment bed[34], is markedly increased. These results reveal that in iron-limited cells, there is a marked probability that excitation energy absorbed by the light-harvesting chlorophyll antenna complexes will not be trapped by the reaction centre, but rather, will be radiatively dissipated in the antenna. Western blots of photosynthetic proteins reveal large deficiencies in D1, and the two core chlorophyll antenna complexes, CP43 and CP47 relative to the light-harvesting antenna in iron-limited cells (I. R. Vassiliev, Z.S.K., D. Mauzerall, K. Wyman and P.G.F., manuscript in preparation). Addition of iron leads to an enhancement in functional PS II reaction centres, a corresponding decrease in F_0 and an increase in variable fluorescence, as more of the excitation energy is used in photosynthesis. Because of the changes in the fluorescence lifetimes, the intrinsic quantum efficiency of chlorophyll fluorescence in the phytoplankton of the equatorial Pacific is three times higher than that in non-iron-limited waters of the subtropical Pacific gyre[17]. Therefore, changes in fluorescence properties following iron enrichment strongly imply that iron limitation in the equatorial Pacific fundamentally affects the intrinsic molecular structure of the photosynthetic apparatus in natural phytoplankton communities.

The results presented here demonstrate that phytoplankton photosynthesis in HNLC waters of the equatorial Pacific is impaired by lack of iron, resulting in a marked reduction in the efficiency with which light is photochemically converted to stored chemical energy. The iron enrichment did not lead to a large increase in phytoplankton biomass or a correspondingly large reduction in nutrient concentrations[11]. The latter observation might be construed to suggest that grazing maintained a low standing stock of phytoplankton. We note, however, that 2 days following the iron enrichment, photosynthetic energy conversion efficiency began to decline, suggesting that either the iron enrichment was not sufficient to sustain long-term growth, or that another trace element subsequently became physiologically limiting. Whatever the reasons for the decline, the initial increase in both the quantum efficiency of PS II and cellular chlorophyll indicate that before the iron enrichment, cells were not growing at maximum rates[15,22]. Hence the growth of phytoplankton in the equatorial Pacific is physiologically limited by iron rather than by extrinsic factors such as grazing.

(**371**, 145-149; 1994)

我们所观察到的光合作用参数的快速变化反映了分子的交换作用和(或)PS II 反应中心内部光合反应器和电子传递通道的改进。该过程发生在超微型浮游生物和较大细胞内部，这表明在赤道太平洋 HNLC 水体中高的表面积体积比[30]对该过程的影响是非常有限的。

光合反应器中含有许多铁的位点[31]。在 PS II 中有两个铁原子，一个位于细胞色素的血红素细胞 b-559 中，另一个非血红素铁配位于两个反应中心蛋白质 D1 和 D2 之间[32]。对铁限制细胞的实验室研究显示，可用铁的量对在皮秒的时间域内测定的荧光寿命影响显著。两次寿命较短的荧光各持续了 155 ps 和 530 ps，分别对应着激发捕获与初级电荷分离作用[33,34]，与富铁的细胞相比，在贫铁细胞中它们的相对振幅明显低得多[35]。相反，与色素床中激发能的减少相对应[34]的寿命长达 1,200 ps 的荧光组分则显著增加。上述结果说明，在铁含量受限制的细胞中，具有集光作用的叶绿素天线复合体所吸收的激发能不会被反应中心捕获而能通过天线辐射发散掉的几率大大提高了。光合作用蛋白的 Western 印迹（译者注：一种免疫印迹实验）说明，在铁限制细胞中，相对于集光天线来说，D1 以及两条核心叶绿素复合体天线 CP43 和 CP47 存在很大缺陷（瓦西列夫、克尔贝尔、莫泽罗尔、怀曼和法尔科夫斯基，稿件准备中）。在铁加富作用下，由于光合作用中消耗的激发能增多，导致功能性 PS II 反应中心增加，相应地 F_0 下降而可变荧光提高。由于荧光寿命的变化，赤道太平洋海域的浮游植物中叶绿素荧光的本征量子效率为不贫铁的副热带太平洋环流水体中的三倍[17]。因此，铁加富后荧光性质的变化充分说明在赤道太平洋海域铁的缺乏从根本上影响着自然浮游植物群落中光合反应器的内在分子结构。

本文介绍的结果证明，赤道太平洋的 HNLC 水体中浮游植物的光合作用由于缺少铁元素而减弱，从而降低了光能通过光化学转换作用储存为化学能的效率。铁加富作用并未使浮游植物生物量大幅增加或营养盐浓度大幅降低[11]。后一个观测结果可以解释为，摄食使浮游植物维持在一个低的生物现存量。不过我们注意到，实施铁加富作用的两天之后，光合作用能量转换效率开始降低，这说明铁加富不足以维持长期的生长作用，或者还有另一种痕量元素随后变成生理限制因子。不论是何种原因导致了降低，最初时 PS II 的量子效率的增加以及细胞叶绿素的增加已表明，在铁加富之前，细胞并不是以最大速率生长的[15,22]。所以，在赤道太平洋海域，从生理上限制浮游植物生长的是铁而非摄食等其他外部因素。

（齐红艳 翻译；孙松 审稿）

Zbigniew S. Kolber[*], **Richard T. Barber**[†], **Kenneth H. Coale**[‡], **Steve E. Fitzwater**[‡], **Richard M. Greene**[*], **Kenneth S. Johnson**[‡§], **Steven Lindley**[†] **& Paul G. Falkowski**[*]

[*] Oceanographic and Atmospheric Sciences Division, Brookhaven National Laboratory, Upton, New York 11973, USA

[†] Duke University Marine Laboratory, Beaufort, North Carolina 28516, USA

[‡] Moss Landing Marine Laboratory, PO Box 450, Moss Landing, California 95039, USA

[§] Monterey Bay Aquarium Research Institute, Pacific Grove, California 93950, USA

Received 14 April; accepted 1 August 1994.

References:

1. Sverdrup, H. U. *J. Cons. Perm. Int. Explor. Mer.* **18**, 287-295 (1953).

2. Reid, J. L. Jr, *Limnol. Oceanogr.* **7**, 287-306 (1962).

3. Barber, R. T. & Chavez, F. P. *Limnol. Oceanogr.* **36**, 1803-1815 (1991).

4. Minas, H., Minas, M. & Packard, T. *Limnol. Oceanogr.* **31**, 1182-1206 (1986).

5. Walsh, J. *Limnol. Oceanogr.* **21**, 1-13 (1976).

6. Duce, R. & Tindale, N. *Limnol. Oceanogr.* **36**, 1715-1726 (1991).

7. Martin, J. H. & Fitzwater, S. E. *Nature* **331**, 341-343 (1988).

8. Martin, J. H. in *Primary Productivity and Biogeochemical Cycles in the Sea* (eds Falkowski, P. G. & Woodhead, A. D.) 123-137 (Plenum, New York, 1992).

9. Kolber, Z. & Falkowski, P. G. *Limnol. Oceanogr.* **38**, 1646-1665 (1993).

10. Falkowski, P. G., Greene, R. & Geider, R. *Oceanography* **5**, 84-91 (1992).

11. Martin, J. H. *et al. Nature* **371**, 123-129 (1994).

12. Butler, W. L. *A. Rev. Pl. Physiol.* **29**, 345-378 (1978).

13. Krause, G. H. & Weis, E. *A. Rev. Pl. Physiol.* **42**, 13-349 (1992).

14. Geider, R. J., Greene, R. M., Kolber, Z., MacIntyre, H. L. & Falkowski, P. G. *Deep-Sea Res.* **40**, 1205-1224 (1993).

15. Kolber, Z., Zehr, J. & Falkowski, P. G. *Pl. Physiol.* **88**, 72-79 (1988).

16. Falkowski, P. G. *Photosyn. Res.* **39**, 235-238 (1994).

17. Greene, R. M., Kolber, Z. S., Swift, D. G., Tindale, N. W. & Falkowski, P. G. *Limnol. Oceanogr.* (in the press).

18. Hunter, C., Gordon, M., Fitzwater, S. & Johnson, K. *EOS* 5150 (1994).

19. Greene, R. M., Geider, R. J. & Falkowski, P. G. *Limnol. Oceanogr.* **36**, 1772-1782 (1991).

20. Greene, R. M., Geider, R. J., Kolber, Z. & Falkowski, P. G. *Pl. Physiol.* **100**, 565-575 (1992).

21. Falkowski, P. G., Ziemann, D., Kolber, Z. & Bienfang, P. K. *Nature* **352**, 55-58 (1991).

22. Falkowski, P. G. in *Primary Productivity and Biogeochemical Cycles in the Sea* (eds Falkowski, P. G. & Woodhead, A. D.) 47-67 (Plenum, New York, 1992).

23. Kitajima, M. & Butler, W. L. *Biochem. Biophys. Acta* **376**, 105-115 (1975).

24. Lindley, S. T. thesis, Duke Univ. (1994).

25. Mauzerall, D. & Greenbaum, N. L. *Biochim. Biophys. Acta* **974**, 119-140 (1989).

26. Falkowski, P. G., Wyman, K., Ley, A. C. & Mauzerall, D. *Biochim. Biophys. Acta* **849**, 183-192 (1986).

27. Morel, F. M. M., Reuter, J. G. & Price, N. M. *Oceanography* **4**, 56-61 (1991).

28. Hudson, R. J. M. & Morel, F. M. M. *Limnol. Oceanogr.* **35**, 1002-1020 (1990).

29. Sunda, W. G., Swift, D. & Huntsman, S. A. *Nature* **351**, 55-58 (1991).

30. Brand, L. E. *Limnol. Oceanogr.* **36**, 1756-1771 (1991).

31. Raven, J. *New Phytol.* **109**, 279-287 (1988).

32. Barber, J. (ed.) *The Photosystems: Structure Function and Molecular Biology (Topics in Photosynthesis* Vol. 11) (Elsevier, Amsterdam, 1992).

33. Roelofs, T. A., Gilbert, M., Schuvalov, V. A. & Holzwarth, A. R. *Biochim. Biophys. Acta* **1060**, 237-244 (1991).

34. Holzwarth, A. R. *Photochem. Photobiol.* **43**, 707-725 (1986).

35. Falkowski, P. G., Kolber, Z. & Mauzerall, D. *Biophys. J.* **66**, 923-925 (1994).

Acknowledgements. We thank H. Walker and E. Green for helping to arrange this collaborative effort, Z. Johnson, P. Chisholm, J. Berges and D. Wallace for constructive suggestions in preparation of the manuscript, and T. Stanton for help with the colour graphics. This research was supported by the US DoE, the US EPA, NASA and the US Office of Naval Research.

Australopithecus ramidus, a New Species of Early Hominid from Aramis, Ethiopia

T. D. White *et al.*

Editor's Note

The further one travels back in time, the scarcer the fossil evidence of human antiquity becomes. It is sparse enough beyond four million years; beyond five, it almost disappears completely (or did so until recent discoveries such as *Sahelanthropus* and *Orrorin*). Hence the significance of this announcement of a collection of extremely primitive fragments from Ethiopia, dated at 4.4 million years. With only a small number of dental features marking it out as hominid, *Australopithecus ramidus* had some claim to be close to the root of the divergence between the chimp and human lineages. In fact, White and colleagues later considered the form to be too primitive even for *Australopithecus*, and re-named it *Ardipithecus*.

Seventeen hominoid fossils recovered from Pliocene strata at Aramis, Middle Awash, Ethiopia make up a series comprising dental, cranial and postcranial specimens dated to around 4.4 million years ago. When compared with *Australopithecus afarensis* and with modern and fossil apes the Aramis fossil hominids are recognized as a new species of *Australopithecus*—*A. ramidus* sp. nov. The antiquity and primitive morphology of *A. ramidus* suggests that it represents a long-sought potential root species for the Hominidae.

WORK in southern Africa established *Australopithecus* as a human ancestor and revealed specific diversity within that genus. Subsequent work in eastern Africa extended the known geographical and temporal distribution of the genus. Until now, the earliest hominid species known was *Australopithecus afarensis*, dated to between 3 and 4 Myr. *A. afarensis* narrowed the temporal and morphological gap between Miocene hominoids and other early hominids[1]. Its primitive craniodental anatomy offered some support for molecular work[2] which had suggested a late Miocene or early Pliocene age for the common ancestor of hominids and African apes. Because details of the ape and human divergence are poorly understood[3-9], taxonomically diagnostic hominoid fossil evidence antedating the existing record of *A. afarensis* has been eagerly anticipated.

494

在埃塞俄比亚的阿拉米斯发现的一种新型的早期原始人类物种——南方古猿始祖种

怀特等

编者按

当我们向过去回溯的时间越古老，古人类的化石证据就越稀少。当超过四百万年时，这类化石是非常稀少的；超过五百万年后，这类化石几乎完全消失了（直到最近发现的托麦人属（乍得撒海尔人）和千禧人属）。因此本篇文章的意义在于在埃塞俄比亚收集到的一批非常原始的化石碎片，年代在 440 万年前。由于只有少量的牙齿特征标记出化石属于原始人类，有些人声称南方古猿始祖种接近于黑猩猩和人类谱系之间的分歧的根部。实际上，怀特和他的同事们后来经过考虑认为这一标本即使是相对于南方古猿属来说也过于原始，于是将其重命名为地猿属。

从埃塞俄比亚中阿瓦什阿拉米斯的上新世地层中挖掘到了 17 个人科动物化石，包括牙齿、颅骨和颅后骨骼的系列标本，年代可以追溯到约 440 万年前。通过与南方古猿阿法种及现代猿和化石猿相比，阿拉米斯原始人类化石被认为是南方古猿的一个新种——南方古猿始祖种（*A. ramidus* sp. nov.）（"sp. nov." 是 "species nova" 的缩写，即 "新种" 之意）。南方古猿始祖种的古老型和原始形态特征都提示它可能是人们长久以来寻找的人科祖根物种。

南部非洲的工作将南方古猿确立为人类的祖先之一，并且揭示了南方古猿属内的多样性。接下来在东非的工作扩展了该属已知的地理和时间分布。迄今为止，已知最早的人类是南方古猿阿法种，其可追溯到距今 300 万到 400 万年前。南方古猿阿法种将中新世人猿超科与其他早期人类之间[1]时间和形态学缺口缩窄了。其原始的颅骨牙齿解剖学特征为分子学研究提供了支持[2]，分子工作提示原始人类和非洲猿的共同祖先生活的年代是晚中新世或早上新世。由于对猿类和人类的分化细节理解得还不够[3-9]，所以人们热切渴望能够找到具有分类学鉴别意义的比现存的南方古猿阿法种记录更早的人科动物化石证据。

Description of *A. ramidus*

Order Primates Linnaeus 1758
Suborder Anthropoidea Mivart 1864
Superfamily Hominoidea Gray 1825

Australopithecus DART 1925

Australopithecus ramidus sp. nov.

Etymology. In recognition of the Afar people who occupy the Middle Awash study area and contribute to fieldwork there. The name is from the Afar language. "Ramid" means "root" and it applies to both people and plants.

Holotype. ARA-VP-6/1 (Fig. 1a) is an associated set of teeth from one individual that includes: upper left I^1, $\underline{C}$, P^3, P^4, right I^1, $\underline{C}$ (broken), P^4, M^2; and lower right P_3 and P_4. Found by Gada Hamed on Wednesday, 29 December 1993. Holotype and paratype series housed at the National Museum of Ethiopia, Addis Ababa.

Paratypes. Table 1 lists the holotype and paratype series, all from Aramis. Included are associated postcranial elements, two partial cranial bases, a child's mandible, associated and isolated teeth.

Locality. Aramis localities 1–7 are in the headwaters of the Aramis and Adgantoli drainages, west of the Awash river in the Middle Awash palaeoanthropological study area, Afar depression, Ethiopia[10]. Aramis VP Locality 6 is at 10° 28.74′ north latitude; 40° 26.26′ east longitude; ~625 m elevation.

Horizon and associations. All hominid specimens were surface finds located in the section within 3 m of the Daam Aatu Basaltic Tuff. The immediately underlying Gàala Vitric Tuff Complex is dated at 4.39 ± 0.03 Myr (ref. 10).

Diagnosis. *A. ramidus* is a species of *Australopithecus* distinguished from other hominid species, including *A. afarensis*, by the following: upper and lower canines larger relative to the postcanine teeth; lower first deciduous molar narrow and obliquely elongate, with large protoconid, small and distally placed metaconid, no anterior fovea, and small, low talonid with minimal cuspule development; temporomandibular joint without definable articular eminence; absolutely and relatively thinner canine and molar enamel; lower third premolar more strongly asymmetrical, with dominant, tall buccal cusp and steep, posterolingually directed transverse crest; upper third premolar more strongly asymmetric, with relatively larger, taller, more dominant buccal cusp.

南方古猿始祖种的描述

灵长目，林奈，1758 年
类人猿亚目，米瓦特，1864 年
人猿总科，格雷，1825 年

南方古猿属，达特，1925 年

南方古猿始祖种，新种

词源。按照居住在中阿瓦什研究地区并对那里的野外工作作出贡献的阿法尔人民的叫法而来。该名字来源于阿法尔语言。"Ramid"意思是"根"，既适用于人类也适用于植物。

正模标本。ARA-VP-6/1（图 1a）是来自同一个体的一套牙齿，包括：左上 I^1、C、P^3、P^4，右上 I^1、C(断裂)、P^4、M^2，以及右下 P_3 和 P_4。嘎达·哈米德于 1993 年 12 月 29 日星期三发现该样本。正模标本和副模标本系列都存放在位于亚的斯亚贝巴的埃塞俄比亚国家博物馆中。

副模标本。表 1 列出了正模标本和副模标本系列，它们都来自阿拉米斯。表中列出的标本包括相关联的颅后骨骼、两块头盖骨基底部分、一块儿童下颌骨，还有相关但游离的牙齿。

产地。阿拉米斯 1~7 地点位于阿瓦什河西边，在阿拉米斯与阿德甘托利流域的上游源头处，该地在埃塞俄比亚阿法尔凹地的中阿瓦什古人类学研究区[10]。阿拉米斯 VP 地点 6 的地理坐标是北纬 10°28.74′，东经 40°26.26′；海拔约 625 米。

相关地层。所有原始人类标本都是在地表发现的，地层位于达阿姆–阿图玄武岩凝灰岩层 3 米内的剖面，其下覆的伽拉玻璃凝灰岩复合体地层年代为 439 万 ± 3 万年（参考文献 10）。

种征。南方古猿始祖种是南方古猿属中的一个种，它与包括南方古猿阿法种在内的其他原始人类物种有以下不同：相对于颊齿来说，上、下犬齿较大；下颌第一乳白齿窄而斜向延长，有大的下原尖，小而分开很远的下后尖，没有前凹，小而低的跟座，小牙尖不发达；颞下颌关节没有可确定的关节界限；绝对及相对较薄的犬齿和白齿釉质；下颌第三前白齿非常不对称，具有突出的、高的颊侧牙尖，陡峭的后舌侧方向的横脊；上颌第三前白齿更加不对称，具有相对较大、较高、较占优势的颊侧牙尖。

Table 1. Aramis fossil hominid specimens

Specimen number	Collection year	Element	Discoverer	Dental dimensions
ARA-VP-1/1	1992	RM^3	G. Suwa	RM^3: 10.2MD, 12.3BL
ARA-VP-1/2	1992	RI^1	A. Asfaw	RI^1: 8.2LL
ARA-VP-1/3	1992	L$_c$ frag.	G. Suwa	
ARA-VP-1/4	1992	Right humerus, full shaft	S. Simpson	
ARA-VP-1/125	1992	Left temporal	S. Simpson	
ARA-VP-1/127	1992	L^c, RM^1, worn roots of incisors, canine and premolar	T. White	
ARA-VP-1/128	1992	Associated teeth	T. Assebework	L$_c$: 11.0LL; RP$_3$: 7.5Mn, (9.8)Mx; LP$_3$: 7.5 Mn, (9.9)Mx; RP$_4$: 7.3 (7.5)MD, 9.5BL; LP$_4$: 7.3 (7.5)MD; RM$_1$: 10.9 (11.2)MD, (10.3)BL; LM$_1$: 10.6 (11.0)MD, (10.1)BL; LM$_2$: 12.8 (13.0)MD, 11.9BL; RM$_3$: 12.7(MD),11.0(BL)
ARA-VP-1/129	1992	Right mandible (I$_1$, dm$_1$)	A. Asfaw	RI$_1$: 6.0MD; Rdm$_1$: 7.3MD, 4.9BL
ARA-VP-1/182	1992	RM3 fragment	Group	
ARA-VP-1/183	1992	UC fragment	Group	
ARA-VP-1/200	1993	LM$_1$	A. Ademassu	LM$_1$: 11.0MD, 10.3BL
ARA-VP-1/300	1993	R^c	Y. Haile-Selassie	R^c: (11.2)MD, 11.1LL, 14.3CH
ARA-VP-1/400	1993	LM^2	Y. Beyene	LM^2: (11.3–12.3)MD, (15.0)BL
ARA-VP-1/401	1993	LM$_3$ fragment	M. Feseha	
ARA-VP-1/500	1993	R.+L. temp.+occ.	T. White	
ARA-VP-6/1	1993	Associated teeth	G. Hamed	LI^1: 9.6 (10.0)MD, 7.5LL, 12.5swCH; R^c: 11.6LL, 14.5CH; L^c: 11.7LL, 14.6CH, 11.5MD; LP^3: 7.7MD, 8.4MxMD; 12.5BL; RP^4: 8.4MD, (11.3)BL; RM^2: 11.8MD, (14.1)BL; RP$_3$: (8.2) MnMD; (11.5)MxBL; RP$_4$: 8.9MD, 9.7BL
ARA-VP-7/2	1993	Left humerus, radius, ulna	A. Asfaw	

Fossil hominid specimens recovered from Aramis between December 1992 and December 1993. Dental dimensions are standard, estimates for breakage or interproximal attrition are shown in parentheses. BL, Buccolingual; LL, labiolingual; MD, mesiodistal; CH, distance from buccal enamel line to apex (canine height); Mn, minimum diameter; Mx, maximum diameter; sw, slightly worn. All measurements were taken on original specimens by the authors.

498

表 1. 阿拉米斯原始人类化石标本

标本号	采集年份	标本	发现者	牙齿尺寸
ARA-VP-1/1	1992	RM³	谙访	RM³: 10.2MD, 12.3BL
ARA-VP-1/2	1992	RI¹	阿斯富	RI¹: 8.2LL
ARA-VP-1/3	1992	L_c 碎片	谙访	
ARA-VP-1/4	1992	右侧肱骨，全骨干	辛普森	
ARA-VP-1/125	1992	左侧颞	辛普森	
ARA-VP-1/127	1992	L_c, RM¹，切牙、尖牙和前磨牙的破损根	怀特	
ARA-VP-1/128	1992	相关的牙齿	阿塞贝沃克	L_c: 11.0LL; RP_3: 7.5Mn,(9.8)Mx; LP_3: 7.5 Mn,(9.9)Mx; RP_4: 7.3 (7.5)MD, 9.5BL; LP_4: 7.3 (7.5)MD; RM_1: 10.9 (11.2)MD,(10.3)BL; LM_1: 10.6 (11.0)MD,(10.1)BL; LM_2: 12.8 (13.0)MD, 11.9BL; RM_3: 12.7 (MD),11.0 (BL)
ARA-VP-1/129	1992	右下颌骨 (I_1, dm_1)	阿斯富	RI_1: 6.0MD; Rdm_1: 7.3MD, 4.9BL
ARA-VP-1/182	1992	RM3 碎片	团队	
ARA-VP-1/183	1992	UC 碎片	团队	
ARA-VP-1/200	1993	LM_1	阿德马苏	LM_1: 11.0MD, 10.3BL
ARA-VP-1/300	1993	R^c	海尔塞拉西	R^c:(11.2)MD, 11.1LL, 14.3CH
ARA-VP-1/400	1993	LM²	贝耶内	LM²:(11.3~12.3)MD,(15.0)BL
ARA-VP-1/401	1993	LM_3 碎片	费塞哈	
ARA-VP-1/500	1993	R.+L. temp.+occ.	怀特	
ARA-VP-6/1	1993	相关的牙齿	弗拉梅德	LI¹: 9.6 (10.0)MD, 7.5LL, 12.5swCH; R^c: 11.6LL, 14.5CH; L^c: 11.7LL, 14.6CH, 11.5MD; LP³: 7.7MD, 8.4MxMD; 12.5BL; RP⁴: 8.4MD,(11.3)BL; RM²: 11.8MD,(14.1)BL; RP_3:(8.2) MnMD;(11.5)MxBL; RP_4: 8.9MD, 9.7BL
ARA-VP-7/2	1993	左侧肱骨，桡骨，尺骨	阿斯富	

于 1992 年 12 月至 1993 年 12 月之间从阿拉米斯挖掘到的原始人类化石标本。牙齿尺寸标准，对破裂或磨损牙齿的估计值在圆括号中标明。BL，颊舌径；LL，唇舌径；MD，近中–远中径；CH，颊侧釉质线到牙尖点的距离（犬齿高度）；Mn，最小径；Mx，最大径；sw，轻微磨损。所有测量尺寸都是作者对原始标本测量而得。

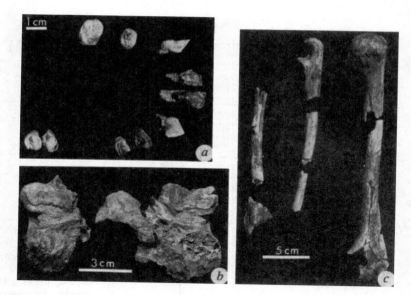

Fig. 1. *a*, Holotype specimen, ARA-VP-6/1 upper and lower dentition from a single individual; *b*, partial adult basicranium, ARA-VP-1/500; *c*, associated adult arm elements, ARA-VP-7/2. All alignments approximate. See text for descriptions.

A. ramidus is distinguished as a hominid from modern great apes and known elements of *Sivapithecus, Kenyapithecus, Ouranopithecus, Lufengpithecus* and *Dryopithecus* by the following: canine morphology more incisiform, crowns less projecting, with relatively higher crown shoulders; cupped distal wear pattern on lower canine; mandibular P_3 with weaker mesiobuccal projection of the crown base and without functional honing facet; modally relatively smaller mandibular P_3; modally relatively broader lower molars; foramen magnum anteriorly placed relative to carotid foramen; hypoglossal canal anteriorly placed relative to internal auditory meatus; carotid foramen placed posteromedial to tympanic angle.

A. ramidus is further distinguished from both *Pan* and *Gorilla* by the following: upper canine not mesiodistally elongate.

A. ramidus is further distinguished from *Pan troglodytes* and *Pan paniscus* by the following: upper central incisors small relative to postcanine teeth; lower third molars elongate and larger relative to other molars; molars not as crenulated, occlusal foveae not as broad.

A. ramidus is further distinguished from *Gorilla* by the following : smaller absolute tooth and upper limb size; flatter temporomandibular joint; lack of strong molar cusp relief; less sectorial first deciduous molar, dm_1.

500

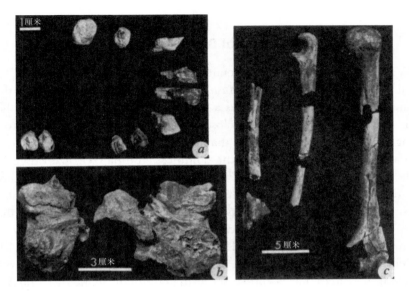

图 1. a，正模标本，来自同一个体的 ARA-VP-6/1 上、下齿系；b，部分成年颅底部，ARA-VP-1/500；c，相关的成年手臂部分，ARA-VP-7/2。所有比对都接近。描述见正文。

南方古猿始祖种被视为一种原始人类，与现代的大型猿类和已知的西瓦古猿、肯尼亚古猿、欧兰诺古猿、禄丰古猿和森林古猿在如下方面有所不同：犬齿门齿化，牙冠不太突出，具有相对较高的牙冠台肩；下颌犬齿是凹陷的远端磨损模式；下颌 P_3 在牙冠基部具有微弱的近中颊侧突出、没有功能性的研磨面；下颌 P_3 相对较小；下颌臼齿相对较宽；枕骨大孔相对于颈动脉孔的位置更靠前；舌下神经管相对于内耳道的位置更靠前；颈动脉孔位于鼓室倾角的中后部。

南方古猿始祖种还在如下方面与黑猩猩属和大猩猩属都不同：上颌犬齿不是在近中–远中方向上延伸。

南方古猿始祖种在如下方面与黑猩猩和倭黑猩猩都不同：相对于颊齿来说，上中门牙较小；下颌第三臼齿延伸，且相对于其他臼齿较大；臼齿皱纹少，咬合面凹也不宽。

南方古猿始祖种与大猩猩属还在如下方面有所不同：牙齿和上肢的绝对尺寸较小；颞下颌关节较平；缺乏强壮的臼齿齿尖突出；第一乳臼齿 dm_1 不太像扇形。

Dental Description

The ARA-VP-1/129 child's mandible retains a first deciduous molar (dm_1). The dm_1 has been crucially important in studies of *Australopithecus* since the discovery of the genus 70 years ago, and has been used frequently as a key character for sorting apes and hominids[11-13]. The Aramis dm_1 is morphologically far closer to that of a chimpanzee than to any known hominid (Fig. 2). It is very small—more than 4 s.d. units below the combined *A. afarensis/ africanus* mean. It is at the low end of the common chimpanzee size range ($n = 29$) and comparable to the bonobo mean ($n = 21$) (Table 2). The apelike Aramis dm_1 lacks the apparently derived hominid features of buccolingual crown expansion, mesiolingually prominent metaconid, well-defined anterior fovea, and large talonid with well differentiated cusps. The only probable hominid derived feature shared with *A. afarensis* is an occlusally and mesiobuccally reduced protoconid, possibly associated with a loss of deciduous canine honing. The relative size of the talonid, whether judged by relative protoconid length or actual area ratios, lies at the chimpanzee means. The Aramis tooth stands farther in this feature from *A. afarensis* than *A. afarensis* is separated from robust *Australopithecus* homologues. The crown length to breadth ratio (1.49) shows a very narrow dm_1, surpassed in mean values only by the common chimpanzee (mean = 1.58) among fossil hominids and modern hominoids. The ratio between labiolingual breadth of the deciduous canine root and the square root of the computed dm_1 area shows a relatively large Aramis canine, nearly matching the *Pan paniscus* ratio mean and exceeding the *P. troglodytes* average and the *G. gorilla* range *(n = 20)*. The only measurable *A. afarensis* specimen (L.H.-2) lies closer to the most extreme *A. boisei* condition (KNM-ER 1477) than it does to Aramis in this ratio.

Table 2. Lower first deciduous molar (dm_1) measurements

	Mesiodistal (MD) length	Buccolingual (BL) breadth	MD × BL area	Protoconid length	MD Length + protoconid length
Aramis ($n = 1$)	7.3	4.9	35.8	5.2	1.4
A. afarensis					
n	4	4	4	4	4
min	8.5	7.6	68.0	4.3	1.7
max	9.6	8.4	80.6	5.6	2.0
mean	**9.2**	**7.9**	**72.5**	**5.1**	**1.8**
s.d.	0.5	0.4	5.7	0.6	0.1
A. africanus					
n	7	5	5	3	3
min	8.4	7.1	59.6	5.2	1.6
max	9.1	8.1	73.7	5.3	1.7
mean	**8.8**	**7.6**	**66.6**	**5.2**	**1.7**
s.d.	0.2	0.4	5.5	0.1	0.1

牙 齿 描 述

ARA-VP-1/129 儿童下颌骨保留一颗第一乳臼齿(dm₁)。自从 70 年前发现该属以来，该牙对于研究南方古猿属一直都意义重大，经常作为对猿类和原始人类进行分类的关键特征[11-13]。阿拉米斯 dm₁ 在形态学上与黑猩猩的相似性比与其他已知原始人类的都更大(图 2)。这颗牙非常小——比南方古猿阿法种 / 非洲种的平均值要小 4 个标准偏差单位以上。该值处于普通黑猩猩尺寸范围的下限(n = 29)，与倭黑猩猩的均值(n = 21)相当(表 2)。似猿的阿拉米斯 dm₁ 明显缺少人类的以下衍生特征：颊舌径扩展，近中舌侧突出的下后尖，界线明确的前凹以及具有分化良好的牙尖的大跟座。唯一与南方古猿阿法种可能共有的人类衍生特征就是下原尖在咬合面和近中颊侧减小，这可能与乳犬齿咬合功能缺失有关。无论是相对于下原尖长度还是面积，跟座的相对大小都与黑猩猩的均值相当。阿拉米斯牙齿在这个特征上与南方古猿阿法种的差别比南方古猿阿法种与同源的南方古猿粗壮种的差别更大。牙冠的长宽比(1.49)表明这是一个很窄的 dm₁，比化石人类和现代其他类人猿都大，仅低于普通黑猩猩的均值(均值 = 1.58)。乳犬齿牙根的唇舌宽度与 dm₁ 牙根面积的平方根值相比，表明阿拉米斯的犬齿相对较大，几乎与倭黑猩猩的比值均值相匹配，而超过了黑猩猩的均值和大猩猩的范围(n = 20)。与阿拉米斯样本的相比，唯一可测量的南方古猿阿法种标本(LH-2)的这一比值与南方古猿鲍氏种的极端情况(KNM-ER 1477)更接近。

表 2. 下颌第一乳臼齿(dm₁)的测量值

	近中－远中(MD)长度	颊舌(BL)宽度	MD × BL 面积	下原尖长度	MD 长度 + 下原尖长度
阿拉米斯样本 (n = 1)	7.3	4.9	35.8	5.2	1.4
南方古猿阿法种					
n	4	4	4	4	4
最小值	8.5	7.6	68.0	4.3	1.7
最大值	9.6	8.4	80.6	5.6	2.0
均值	**9.2**	**7.9**	**72.5**	**5.1**	**1.8**
标准差	0.5	0.4	5.7	0.6	0.1
南方古猿非洲种					
n	7	5	5	3	3
最小值	8.4	7.1	59.6	5.2	1.6
最大值	9.1	8.1	73.7	5.3	1.7
均值	**8.8**	**7.6**	**66.6**	**5.2**	**1.7**
标准差	0.2	0.4	5.5	0.1	0.1

Continued

	Mesiodistal (MD) length	Buccolingual (BL) breadth	MD × BL area	Protoconid length	MD Length+protoconid length
A. robustus					
n	8	8	8	8	8
min	9.0	7.7	71.0	4.3	1.8
max	10.8	9.7	101.9	5.8	2.3
mean	**10.1**	**8.3**	**83.7**	**4.9**	**2.1**
s.d.	0.5	0.6	9.5	0.5	0.1
P. paniscus					
n	21	21	21	20	20
min	6.3	4.4	27.7	4.3	1.3
max	8.8	5.5	48.4	6.0	1.6
mean	**7.4**	**5.1**	**37.6**	**5.0**	**1.5**
s.d.	0.6	0.31	4.7	0.5	0.1
P. troglodytes					
n	29	29	29	29	29
min	7.0	4.6	32.9	5.0	1.3
max	9.4	5.8	54.5	6.7	1.6
mean	**8.1**	**5.2**	**42.2**	**5.8**	**1.4**
s.d.	0.6	0.4	5.2	0.5	0.1
G. gorilla					
n	20	20	20	20	20
min	9.8	6.7	71.4	6.7	1.3
max	12.2	8.9	108.6	9.0	1.6
mean	**11.0**	**7.5**	**82.3**	**7.8**	**1.4**
s.d.	0.7	0.6	10.7	0.6	0.1
P. pygmaeus					
n	6	6	6	6	6
min	8.4	6.4	53.8	5.8	1.3
max	10.2	8.1	82.6	8.1	1.5
mean	**9.2**	**7.1**	**66.2**	**6.7**	**1.4**
s.d.	0.7	0.6	10.3	0.8	0.1
H. sapiens					
n	21	21	21	21	21
min	7.4	6.4	47.4	4.0	1.4
max	9.2	8.1	69.9	5.7	2.1
mean	**8.4**	**7.2**	**60.4**	**4.9**	**1.7**
s.d.	0.5	0.4	6.1	0.5	0.2

Comparative metrics on deciduous lower first molars (dm_1) of various hominoid taxa. Abbreviations and conventions as in Table 1.

	近中－远中（MD）长度	颊舌（BL）宽度	MD × BL 面积	下原尖长度	MD 长度 + 下原尖长度
南方古猿粗壮种					
n	8	8	8	8	8
最小值	9.0	7.7	71.0	4.3	1.8
最大值	10.8	9.7	101.9	5.8	2.3
均值	**10.1**	**8.3**	**83.7**	**4.9**	**2.1**
标准差	0.5	0.6	9.5	0.5	0.1
倭黑猩猩					
n	21	21	21	20	20
最小值	6.3	4.4	27.7	4.3	1.3
最大值	8.8	5.5	48.4	6.0	1.6
均值	**7.4**	**5.1**	**37.6**	**5.0**	**1.5**
标准差	0.6	0.31	4.7	0.5	0.1
黑猩猩					
n	29	29	29	29	29
最小值	7.0	4.6	32.9	5.0	1.3
最大值	9.4	5.8	54.5	6.7	1.6
均值	**8.1**	**5.2**	**42.2**	**5.8**	**1.4**
标准差	0.6	0.4	5.2	0.5	0.1
银背大猩猩					
n	20	20	20	20	20
最小值	9.8	6.7	71.4	6.7	1.3
最大值	12.2	8.9	108.6	9.0	1.6
均值	**11.0**	**7.5**	**82.3**	**7.8**	**1.4**
标准差	0.7	0.6	10.7	0.6	0.1
婆罗洲猩猩					
n	6	6	6	6	6
最小值	8.4	6.4	53.8	5.8	1.3
最大值	10.2	8.1	82.6	8.1	1.5
均值	**9.2**	**7.1**	**66.2**	**6.7**	**1.4**
标准差	0.7	0.6	10.3	0.8	0.1
智人					
n	21	21	21	21	21
最小值	7.4	6.4	47.4	4.0	1.4
最大值	9.2	8.1	69.9	5.7	2.1
均值	**8.4**	**7.2**	**60.4**	**4.9**	**1.7**
标准差	0.5	0.4	6.1	0.5	0.2

对各种人科动物类群的下颌第一乳臼齿（dm_1）的测量尺寸进行的比较。缩写及惯例同表 1。

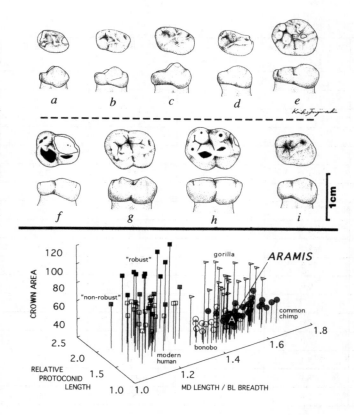

Fig. 2. Deciduous first molar comparisons. Metric and morphological comparisons show a wide separation between the dm₁ of Aramis and those of other early hominid species. *a, Dryopithecus* (IPS 42/1784); *b, Pan paniscus* (T-26992); *c, Pan troglodytes* (PRI 1372); *d, Australopithecus ramidus* (ARA-VP-1/129); *e, A. afarensis* (A.L. 333-43B); *f, A. africanus* (Taung); *g, A. robustus* (TM 1601); *h, A. boisei* (KNM ER-1477); *i, Homo sapiens* (modern). The three-dimensional plot shows dm₁ crown area (buccolingual (BL) multiplied by mesiodistal (MD)) in square mm on the vertical axis. MD length divided by total protoconid length is shown on the left depth axis. The third axis represents a measure of tooth crown narrowness, the MD length divided by the BL breadth. Individual specimens are shown. The "robust" sample includes *A. robustus, A. aethiopicus* (L704) and *A. boisei*. The "non-robust" sample includes *A. africanus, A. afarensis* and early *Homo* (KNM ER-1507; Omo 222). The new species *A. ramidus* is centred in the chimpanzee ranges for these measures. It represents a good ancestral morphotype for all later hominid species.

The *A. ramidus* permanent dentition is represented at most positions (Fig. 3; Table 3). Upper and lower incisors do not exhibit the large size typical of extant *Pan*. Upper and lower central incisor size relative to postcanine teeth is comparable to Miocene hominoids and gorillas. Of the five individuals for whom canine size is determinable, all five have crowns at or larger than the *A. afarensis* mean. Upper and lower canines are also large relative to postcanine teeth. ARA-VP-1/128 is over 5 s.d. units above the *A. afarensis* mean in measures of relative canine size within known individuals ($C \div P_4$; $C \div M_1$; and $C \div M_3$ ratios of maximum labiolingual canine crown breadth ÷ square root of computed molar or premolar crown area). In ARA-VP-6/1 relative canine crown area is comparable to the female great ape condition. Morphology of the known Aramis canines, however, diverges from that of known apes (Fig. 3). The upper canines are slightly less incisiform than homologues of

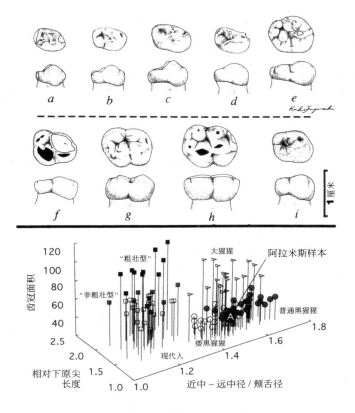

图 2. 第一乳臼齿的比较。度量及形态学比较表明阿拉米斯样本的 dm₁ 和其他早期原始人类物种的 dm₁ 之间具有很大的区别。a，森林古猿属 (IPS 42/1784)；b，倭黑猩猩 (T-26992)；c，黑猩猩 (PRI 1372)；d，南方古猿始祖种 (ARA-VP-1/129)；e，南方古猿阿法种 (A.L. 333-43B)；f，南方古猿非洲种 (汤恩)；g，南方古猿粗壮种 (TM 1601)；h，南方古猿鲍氏种 (KNM ER-1477)；i，智人 (现代)。三维图的纵轴显示了以平方毫米表示的 dm₁ 的牙冠面积 (颊舌径 (BL) 乘以近中–远中径 (MD))。MD 长度除以下原尖的全长的结果在左侧的深度轴线上表示出来了。第三条轴表示牙冠狭窄度的测量值，即 MD 长度除以 BL 宽度。各个标本都有显示。"粗壮"样本包括南方古猿粗壮种、南方古猿埃塞俄比亚种 (L704) 和南方古猿鲍氏种。"非粗壮"样本包括南方古猿非洲种、南方古猿阿法种和早期人属 (KNM ER-1507；奥莫 222)。新物种——南方古猿始祖种的这些尺寸都集中在黑猩猩的范围内。其代表了一种较好的后来所有的原始人类物种的祖先形态型。

　　南方古猿始祖种的恒牙系在大部分位置都有出现 (图 3；表 3)。上、下门齿没有显示出现存黑猩猩属所具有的典型的巨大尺寸。上、下中门齿相对于颊齿的大小与中新世人科动物和大猩猩的具有可比性。在可以确定犬齿尺寸的五个个体中，所有这五个样本的牙冠都与南方古猿阿法种的均值相同或更大。上、下犬齿相对于颊齿来说也较大。在已知的个体中，ARA-VP-1/128 犬齿相对大小的测量值超过南方古猿阿法种的均值 5 个标准偏差单位以上 (C÷P₄、C÷M₁ 和 C÷M₃ 最大唇舌犬齿牙冠宽度÷臼齿或前臼齿牙冠面积的平方根的比值)。ARA-VP-6/1 中，犬齿牙冠的相对面积与雌性大型猿类的情况相当。然而，已知的阿拉米斯犬齿形态学与已知猿类

A. afarensis but more incisiform than any ape counterpart, with occlusally placed terminations of the mesial and distal apical crests (Fig. 3g). The visual result of apically placed crown shoulders is a low, blunt canine tooth relative to more projecting ape canines, a morphological condition which may have important evolutionary implications. The Aramis upper canine is large buccolingually, forming a further contrast with mesiodistally elongate African ape canines. Wear pattern also differs significantly from the ape condition. Mandibular canine wear does not show the pattern typical of great apes. Some worn female *Pan* canines are superficially similar, but still lack the distal crown cupping seen on Aramis. Instead, they feature planar wear surfaces from contact with the upper canine, even on individuals with rounding (not honing) of the buccal P_3 face.

Table 3. Comparative dental metrics for permanent dentition

	a, Upper dentition													
	Mesiodistal					Labio/buccolingual					Crown area (MD × BL)			
	n	Min	Max	Mean	s.d.	*n*	Min	Max	Mean	s.d.	*n*	Min	Max	Mean	s.d.
I¹															
A. afarensis	3	10.8	11.8	11.2	0.6	5	7.1	8.6	8.20	0.6	3	90.5	99.1	94.2	4.5
Aramis	1	—	—	(10.0)	—	2	7.5	8.2	—	—	1	—	—	(75.0)	—
C															
A. afarensis	9	8.9	11.6	10.0	0.8	10	9.3	12.5	10.9	1.1	9	82.8	145.0	109.9	18.9
Aramis	2	(11.2)	(11.5)	—	—	2	11.1	11.7	—	—	2	(124.3)	(134.5)	—	—
P³															
A. afarensis	9	7.5	9.3	8.7	0.5	8	11.3	13.4	12.4	0.6	8	84.7	120.9	108	11.0
Aramis	1	—	—	7.7	—	1	—	—	12.5	_	1	—	—	96.3	—
P⁴															
A. afarensis	10	7.6	9.7	9.0	0.6	6	11.1	12.6	12.1	0.6	6	84.4	119.7	106.8	12.6
Aramis	1	—	—	8.4	—	1	—	—	(11.3)	—	1	—	—	(94.9)	—
M²															
A. afarensis	5	12.1	13.5	12.8	0.5	6	13.4	15.1	14.7	0.6	5	162.1	199.8	187.5	14.6
Aramis	2	(11.8)	11.8	—	—	2	(14.1)	(15.0)	—	—	2	(166.4)	(177.0)	—	—
M³															
A. afarensis	8	10.5	14.3	11.9	1.4	8	13.0	15.5	13.8	1.0	8	136.5	215.9	165.1	30.9
Aramis	1	—	—	10.2	—	1	—	—	12.3	—	1	—	—	125.5	—
	b, Lower dentition														
	Mesiodistal					Labio/buccolingual					Crown area (MD × BL)			
	n	Min	Max	Mean	s.d.	*n*	Min	Max	Mean	s.d.	*n*	Min	Max	Mean	s.d.
I₁															
A. afarensis	2	6.2	8.0	—	—	—	—	—	—	—	—	—	—	—	—
Aramis	1	—	—	6.0	—	—	—	—	—	—	—	—	—	—	—

的不同（图 3）。上颌犬齿的门齿化程度较同源的南方古猿阿法种低些，但是比其他猿类更明显，近中脊和远中脊顶点末端位于咬合面（图 3g）。可见的犬齿牙冠肩台现象说明它相比突出的猿类犬齿来说显得更低而钝，其形态学特征可能具有重要的进化含义。阿拉米斯上颌犬齿颊舌径较大，与近中–远中延伸的非洲猿的犬齿形成进一步的对比。磨耗模式也与猿的情况非常不同。下颌犬齿磨损情况并没表现出大型猿类的典型模式。有些雌性黑猩猩属犬齿表面的磨耗很相似，但是仍然缺乏在阿拉米斯标本中见到的杯状的远端牙冠。它们的特征性平面在与上颌犬齿的接触中相互磨损，甚至在 P_3 颊面圆滑（而非咬合式磨损）的个体中也是如此。

表 3. 恒齿系的牙齿测量尺寸的比较

a, 上牙														
	近中–远中					唇舌 / 下原尖					牙冠面积（MD × BL）			
	n	最小值	最大值	均值	标准差	n	最小值	最大值	均值	标准差	n	最小值	最大值	均值	标准差
I^1															
南方古猿阿法种	3	10.8	11.8	11.2	0.6	5	7.1	8.6	8.20	0.6	3	90.5	99.1	94.2	4.5
阿拉米斯样本	1	—	—	(10.0)	—	2	7.5	8.2	—	—	1	—	—	(75.0)	—
C															
南方古猿阿法种	9	8.9	11.6	10.0	0.8	10	9.3	12.5	10.9	1.1	9	82.8	145.0	109.9	18.9
阿拉米斯样本	2	(11.2)	(11.5)	—	—	2	11.1	11.7	—	—	2	(124.3)	(134.5)	—	—
P^3															
南方古猿阿法种	9	7.5	9.3	8.7	0.5	8	11.3	13.4	12.4	0.6	8	84.7	120.9	108	11.0
阿拉米斯样本	1	—	—	7.7	—	1	—	—	12.5	—	1	—	—	96.3	—
P^4															
南方古猿阿法种	10	7.6	9.7	9.0	0.6	6	11.1	12.6	12.1	0.6	6	84.4	119.7	106.8	12.6
阿拉米斯样本	1	—	—	8.4	—	1	—	—	(11.3)	—	1	—	—	(94.9)	—
M^2															
南方古猿阿法种	5	12.1	13.5	12.8	0.5	6	13.4	15.1	14.7	0.6	5	162.1	199.8	187.5	14.6
阿拉米斯样本	2	(11.8)	11.8	—	—	2	(14.1)	(15.0)	—	—	2	(166.4)	(177.0)	—	—
M^3															
南方古猿阿法种	8	10.5	14.3	11.9	1.4	8	13.0	15.5	13.8	1.0	8	136.5	215.9	165.1	30.9
阿拉米斯样本	1	—	—	10.2	—	1	—	—	12.3	—	1	—	—	125.5	—
b, 下牙															
	近中–远中					唇舌 / 下原尖					牙冠面积（MD × BL）			
	n	最小值	最大值	均值	标准差	n	最小值	最大值	均值	标准差	n	最小值	最大值	均值	标准差
I_1															
南方古猿阿法种	2	6.2	8.0	—	—	—	—	—	—	—	—	—	—	—	—
阿拉米斯样本	1	—	—	6.0	—	—	—	—	—	—	—	—	—	—	—

509

Continued

						b, Lower dentition								
	Mesiodistal					Labio/buccolingual					Crown area (MD × BL)			
	n	Min	Max	Mean	s.d.	*n*	Min	Max	Mean	s.d.	*n*	Min	Max	Mean	s.d.
C															
A. afarenis						13	8.8	12.4	10.4	1.1	—	—	—	—	—
Aramis	—	—	—	—	—	1	—	—	11.0	—	—	—	—	—	—
P₃ (min/max)															
A. afarensis	19	6.5	9.8	8.6	1.1	19	9.7	13.3	11.6	1.1	19	63.1	127.7	99.7	20.4
Aramis	2	7.5	(8.2)	—	—	2	(9.9)	(11.5)	—	—	2	(74.2)	(94.3)	—	—
P₄															
A. afarensis	15	7.7	11.1	9.7	1.0	14	9.8	12.8	10.9	0.8	14	77.0	129.7	106.5	16.8
Aramis	2	7.5	8.9	—	—	2	9.5	9.7	—	—	2	71.2	86.3	—	—
M₁															
A. afarensis	17	11.2	14.0	13.0	0.6	16	11.0	13.9	12.6	0.8	16	124.3	194.6	164.9	17.1
Aramis	2	11.0	11.1	—	—	2	(10.2)	10.3	—	—	2	(113.2)	113.3	—	—
M₂															
A. afarensis	23	12.4	16.2	14.3	1.0	22	12.1	15.2	13.5	0.9	22	152.5	234.1	193.3	24.3
Aramis	1	—	—	(13.0)	—	1	—	—	11.9	—	1	—	—	(154.7)	—
M₃															
A. afarensis	14	13.7	16.3	14.8	0.8	14	12.1	14.9	13.3	0.8	13	172.0	231.5	195.7	17.7
Aramis	1	—	—	12.7	—	1	—	—	11.0	—	1	—	—	139.7	—

Comparative metrics for the permanent teeth of *A. afarensis* (comprises the Hadar pre-1990 sample and the full Laetoli and Maka samples) and *A. ramidus* (from Table 1). Data are shown only for tooth positions represented in both species. Measurements are standard and were taken by the authors on original specimens with conventions and abbreviations as in Table 1. There is considerable overlap between the known species ranges, as there is among other species in the genus. As documented in the text and illustrations, however, proportional differences within individual dentitions combine with other morphological considerations to warrant the recognition of *A. ramidus* as a species distinct from *A. afarensis.*

The broken canines and lower P_3 in ARA-VP-1/128 and -6/1 exhibit thin enamel distinct from previously known hominid conditions. Canine enamel thickness approximates the chimpanzee condition, with a lack of apical thickening we observe in other hominids. The 1.0 mm buccal enamel thickness of the ARA-VP-6/1 broken upper right canine slightly exceeds the 0.9 mm maximum recorded in our small sample of broken female *P. troglodytes* upper canines *(n = 6)* and is approximately 2.4 s.d. units above our combined-sex chimpanzee mean of 0.65 mm (*n* = 14). The broadly constant enamel thickness of the Aramis maxillary canine above the midcrown height level contrasts with the *A. afarensis* condition in which buccal enamel thickens towards the apex, commonly reaching ~1.5 mm. The significance of maxillary canine enamel thickness can be evaluated in the light of proposed wear mechanics of the $\underline{C}/P_3$ complex[14]. The relatively thin enamel and large size

b, 下牙															
	近中—远中					唇舌 / 下原尖					牙冠面积(MD × BL)				
	n	最小值	最大值	均值	标准差	*n*	最小值	最大值	均值	标准差	*n*	最小值	最大值	均值	标准差
C															
南方古猿阿法种						13	8.8	12.4	10.4	1.1					
阿拉米斯样本	—	—	—	—	—	1	—	—	11.0						
P_3 (最小值 / 最大值)															
南方古猿阿法种	19	6.5	9.8	8.6	1.1	19	9.7	13.3	11.6	1.1	19	63.1	127.7	99.7	20.4
阿拉米斯样本	2	7.5	(8.2)	—	—	2	(9.9)	(11.5)	—	—	2	(74.2)	(94.3)	—	—
P_4															
南方古猿阿法种	15	7.7	11.1	9.7	1.0	14	9.8	12.8	10.9	0.8	14	77.0	129.7	106.5	16.8
阿拉米斯样本	2	7.5	8.9	—	—	2	9.5	9.7	—	—	2	71.2	86.3	—	—
M_1															
南方古猿阿法种	17	11.2	14.0	13.0	0.6	16	11.0	13.9	12.6	0.8	16	124.3	194.6	164.9	17.1
阿拉米斯样本	2	11.0	11.1	—	—	2	(10.2)	10.3	—	—	2	(113.2)	113.3	—	—
M_2															
南方古猿阿法种	23	12.4	16.2	14.3	1.0	22	12.1	15.2	13.5	0.9	22	152.5	234.1	193.3	24.3
阿拉米斯样本	1	—	—	(13.0)	—	1	—	—	11.9	—	1	—	—	(154.7)	—
M_3															
南方古猿阿法种	14	13.7	16.3	14.8	0.8	14	12.1	14.9	13.3	0.8	13	172.0	231.5	195.7	17.7
阿拉米斯样本	1	—	—	12.7	—	1	—	—	11.0	—	1	—	—	139.7	—

对南方古猿阿法种(由哈达尔 1990 年之前发现的样本和所有莱托里与马卡的样本构成)和南方古猿始祖种(来自表 1)的恒齿的测量尺寸进行的比较。表中数据仅展示了两个物种都保存了的牙位。测量尺寸标准，是作者遵守与表 1 相同的惯例与缩写对原始标本进行测量得到的。已知的物种范围间存在相当大的重叠区，正如该属中的其他物种一样。但是，就像正文及插图中所说明的，个体齿系内的比例差异与其他形态学因素共同证实南方古猿始祖种是与南方古猿阿法种不同的种。

ARA-VP-1/128 和 ARA-VP-6/1 破裂的犬齿和下颌 P_3 展示出了与之前所知原始人类情况不同的薄型牙釉质。犬齿牙釉质的厚度接近于黑猩猩，同时缺少我们在其他原始人类中观察到的犬齿尖点加厚的现象。ARA-VP-6/1 断裂的上颌右侧犬齿的牙釉质颊侧厚度为 1.0 毫米，稍微超过了我们的小型样本——雌性黑猩猩断裂的上颌犬齿所记录的最大值 0.9 毫米($n = 6$)，两种性别的黑猩猩的均值为 0.65 毫米，所以 ARA-VP-6/1 大约超过了黑猩猩均值 2.4 个标准差单位($n = 14$)。阿拉米斯上颌犬齿在牙冠中部之上的牙釉质厚度的恒定与南方古猿阿法种的情况形成了对比，后者颊侧到牙尖点的牙釉质厚度增加，通常约为 1.5 毫米。上颌犬齿牙釉质厚度的意义可

of the Aramis canine, together with its primitive P₃ morphology, suggest a C̲/P₃ complex morphologically and functionally only slightly removed from the presumed ancestral ape condition.

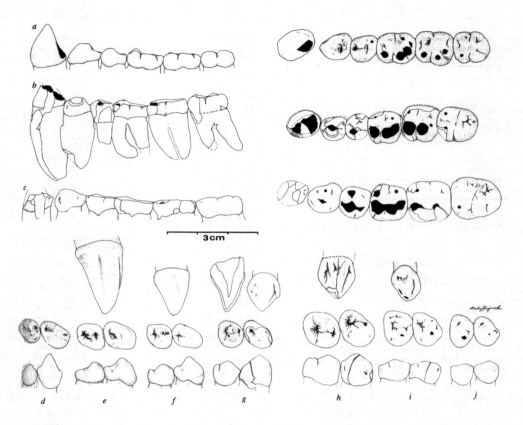

Fig. 3. Comparisons of upper canine/lower premolar complexes and tooth rows. Top three rows, Occlusal and lateral views of the lower tooth rows of: *a, Pan troglodytes* female (CMNH B1770); *b, A. ramidus* (ARA-VP-1/128); *c, A. afarensis* holotype (Laetoli Hominid 4). Bottom three rows, lingual views of upper canines and occlusal and buccal views of lower third and fourth premolars of: *d, Dryopithecus* (MNHNP); *e, Pan troglodytes* male (CMNH B1882); *f, P. troglodytes* female (CMNH B1721); *g, A. ramidus* holotype (ARA-VP-6/1; split right canine on the left); *h, A. afarensis* (LH-3); *i, A. afarensis* (A.L. 400); *j, A. afarensis* (A.L. 288-1, "Lucy"). *a, c* and *h* reversed for comparison.

The ARA-VP-6/1 P₃ is markedly more apelike than any *A. afarensis* homologue in its high protoconid with extensive buccal face and steep, distolingually directed transverse crest (Fig. 3g). In these features it is indistinguishable from ape homologues. The strong mesiobuccal protrusion of its crown base is also outside the known *A. afarensis* range. The Aramis P₃ deviates toward the *A. afarensis* condition in some details. These include a more occlusal termination of the mesial protoconid crest, weaker mesiobuccal protrusion of the crown base (especially ARA-VP-1/128), and a smaller size relative to P₄–M₃ although rare individual *Pan* specimens do approximate the Aramis condition in these features. The worn ARA-VP-1/128 P₃ lacks a honing facet but exhibits steep mesial and distal wear

以从 C/P₃ 复合体的磨损机制中解读[14]。阿拉米斯相对薄的犬齿牙釉质和较大尺寸以及其 P₃ 的原始形态，提示该 C/P₃ 复合体在形态和功能上都仅仅能勉强将其从假定的祖先猿类中分离出来。

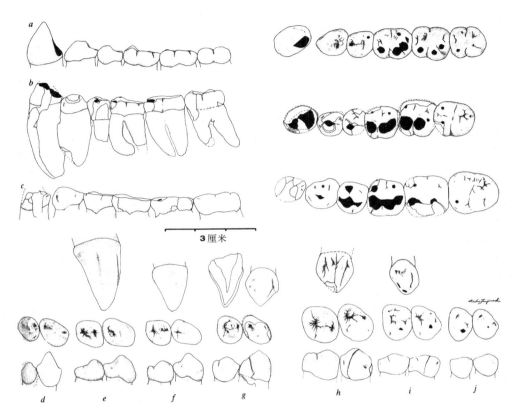

图 3. 上颌犬齿 / 下颌前臼齿复合体及齿列的比较。上面三排为如下物种的下颌齿列的咬合面和侧面视图：a，雌性黑猩猩（CMNH B1770）；b，南方古猿始祖种（ARA-VP-1/128）；c，南方古猿阿法种正模标本（莱托里原始人类 4）。下面三排为如下物种的上颌犬齿的舌面视图以及下颌第三和第四前臼齿的咬合面和颊面视图：d，森林古猿（MNHNP）；e，雄性黑猩猩（CMNH B1882）；f，雌性黑猩猩（CMNH B1721）；g，南方古猿始祖种正模标本（ARA-VP-6/1；左侧是有裂口的右犬齿）；h，南方古猿阿法种（LH-3）；i，南方古猿阿法种（A.L. 400）；j，南方古猿阿法种（A.L. 288-1，"露西"）。a、c 和 h 是反转后进行的比较。

高高的下原尖具有广阔的颊面和陡峭的远中舌侧方向的横脊，在这一点上，ARA-VP-6/1 的 P₃ 比任何同源的南方古猿阿法种都更加像猿类（图 3g）。在这些特征上，难以将该样本与猿类的同源物种区别开来。牙冠基底强壮的近中颊侧突出也不属于已知的南方古猿阿法种的范围。阿拉米斯的 P₃ 在某些细节方面偏离了南方古猿阿法种。这些细节包括近中下原尖脊的终端更加靠近咬合面、牙冠基底更微弱的近中颊侧突出（尤其是 ARA-VP-1/128）以及相对于 P₄~M₃ 更小的尺寸，但是也很少有黑猩猩属的标本个体在这些特征上与阿拉米斯样本的情况接近。ARA-VP-1/128 的磨损的 P₃ 缺少研磨面，但是展示出陡峭的近中和远中磨损斜面，这与南方古猿阿法

slopes not matched in *A. afarensis.*

The P^3 is distinctly primitive in its tall and mesiodistally elongate paracone. Both P^3 and P^4 exhibit a prominent anterior transverse crest. In the P^3 this crest defines an anteriorly facing triangular portion of the occlusal surface, as in apes. The lower P_4 exhibits a prominent transverse crest and minimal talonid development. The P4s from two known individuals are both single rooted.

Molar morphology resembles the *A. afarensis* condition, but lacks the extreme buccolingual breadth relative to mesiodistal length common in that species (Fig. *3a–e).* The "serrate" root pattern and deep dentine wear on the buccal cusps described in *A. afarensis,* Tabarin, and Lothagam[15-17] also occur in Aramis specimens. All molars lack the extensive crenulation and broad occlusal foveae characteristic of modern chimpanzees, or the high cusp topography of gorillas. The Aramis lower third molar is rounded distally, like *A. afarensis* and Miocene hominoids. A great size discrepancy between M_1 and M_2 is seen in ARA-VP-1/128.

A distinct difference from known hominids occurs in molar enamel thickness. Maximum radial enamel thickness of crown faces can be measured in three fractured Aramis specimens and it ranges from 1.1 to 1.2 mm buccally, at or near the unworn cusp apex, perpendicular to the enamel–dentine junction. These values are comparable to the uppermost range of our homologous enamel thickness values measured on broken *P. troglodytes* molars ($n = 22$; M_1 through to M_3). Equivalent measures in *A. afarensis* range from 1.4 to 2.0 mm ($n = 5$). In one case (the ARA-VP-1/128 third molar) Aramis radial enamel thickness at the buccal protoconid face can be evaluated relative to cervical breadth. A comparison of this ratio of enamel thickness suggests that *A. ramidus* may be characterized as intermediate between the chimpanzee and the *A. afarensis/africanus/* early *Homo* conditions.

In postcanine size, the range of the available Aramis sample includes specimens smaller than known *A. afarensis* homologues (the two known M_1 teeth are both more than 3 s.d. units below the mean). Of the seven Aramis individuals for whom postcanine tooth size is determinable, all have crown sizes smaller than the *A. afarensis* mean. We interpret the limited morphology and metrical data available as indicating a single species with a postcanine dentition significantly smaller than in *A. afarensis.*

The postcanine mandibular row can be reconstructed for ARA-VP-1/128 by juxtaposing interproximal facets (Fig. *3a–c).* This shows that the C to M_2 dental row is weakly concave buccally, as in modern and fossil apes and some *A. afarensis* specimens. The P_3 axis is less oblique than in most apes. The canine is positioned directly in line with the mesiodistal axis of the postcanine tooth row rather than being set mesiolingually to the postcanine axis as in the case for most *A. afarensis.* This is a more primitive arrangement shared with modern and Miocene great apes, and may suggest that the mesial part of the lower canine was not functionally incorporated into the incisal row as seen in *A. afarensis*[17].

种不相同。

P^3 非常原始，具有高的、近中－远中端延伸的上前尖。P^3 和 P^4 都展示出突出的前横脊。P^3 中，该脊决定了咬合面前部呈三角形，就像猿类一样。下 P_4 呈现出一条突出的横脊和不发达的跟座。两个已知个体的 P4 都是单牙根。

臼齿形态与南方古猿阿法种的情形相像，但是缺少后者常见的相对于近中－远中长度极端的颊舌宽度（图 3a~e）。在描述南方古猿阿法种、塔巴林样本和洛萨加姆标本 [15-17] 时提到的"锯齿状"牙根模式和颊侧牙尖上深的牙本质磨损在阿拉米斯标本中也有出现。所有臼齿都缺少现代黑猩猩特征性的广泛褶皱和宽阔的咬合窝，或者缺少大猩猩特征性的高牙尖形态。阿拉米斯的下颌第三下臼齿远端呈圆弧状，就像南方古猿阿法种和中新世人科动物的一样。ARA-VP-1/128 的 M_1 和 M_2 有很大的尺寸差异。

与已知原始人类的显著差异是在臼齿牙釉质厚度上。牙冠最大釉质辐射厚度可以在三个断裂的阿拉米斯标本中进行测量，其颊侧范围在 1.1 毫米到 1.2 毫米不等，测量位置位于或接近未磨损的牙尖顶点到牙釉质－牙本质结合处垂直位置。这些数值与我们得到的黑猩猩断裂的臼齿（$n = 22$；M_1 到 M_3）牙釉质厚度的最高范围相当。相应的南方古猿阿法种釉质厚度范围是从 1.4 毫米到 2.0 毫米（$n = 5$）。在一个例子中（ARA-VP-1/128 的第三臼齿），能估计阿拉米斯样本颊侧下原尖面的牙釉质辐射厚度相对于牙颈宽度的比值。这一牙釉质厚度比值的比较，提示南方古猿始祖种的特点介于黑猩猩和南方古猿阿法种／非洲种／早期人属之间。

在颊齿的大小方面，可用的阿拉米斯样本的分布范围包括比已知的同源的南方古猿阿法种小的标本（已知的两颗 M_1 牙齿都比平均值小了 3 个标准差单位以上）。在可以确定颊齿大小的 7 个阿拉米斯标本中，所有牙冠大小都比南方古猿阿法种的平均值还小。我们得到的有限的形态学和测量数据可认为它是比南方古猿阿法种的颊齿小得多的单一物种。

ARA-VP-1/128 的下颌颊齿列可以通过齿间接触面得以重建（图 3a~c）。重建结果表明该标本 C 到 M_2 的齿列在颊侧稍微凹陷些，正如在现代猿和化石猿以及一些南方古猿阿法种标本中看到的情况一样。P_3 轴线没有大部分猿类中的那么倾斜。犬齿的位置刚好与颊齿列的近中－远中轴线一致，而不是像大部分南方古猿阿法种那样位于颊齿轴线的近中舌侧。这是一种与现代和中新世的大型猿类相似的更加原始的排列方式，可能提示该个体下颌犬齿近中部在功能上没有并入门牙系统，这与南方古猿阿法种不同 [17]。

Cranial Description

The ARA-VP-1/125 and -1/500 specimens represent adult temporal and occipital regions (Fig. 1*b*). Both are smaller than their *A. afarensis* counterparts, but no female temporal is known for that species. The Aramis cranial fossils evince a strikingly chimpanzee-like morphology that includes marked pneumatization of the temporal squama which even invades the root of the zygoma. The occipital condyle is small, measuring 16 × 7.5 mm. The anterior border of the foramen magnum (basion) is intersected by a bicarotid chord connecting the centres of right and carotid foramina, and the endocranial opening of the hypoglossal canal is placed more anteriorly relative to the internal auditory meatus than in great apes. This condition, as in other fossil hominid taxa, reflects a shortened basioccipital component of the cranial base relative to modern African ape crania. The temporomandibular joint is very flat, with virtually no articular eminence and weak inferior projection of the entoglenoid process. The tympanic is tubular, bounded anteriorly and posteriorly by deep furrows, and the tube extends to the lateral edge of the postglenoid process in one individual and beyond it in the second. The mastoid process is a blunt eminence rather than the inflated, inflected pyramidal structure diagnostic of the chimpanzee. The digastric groove is distinctly deeper than in the chimpanzee.

Postcranial Description

The ARA-VP-7/2 specimen (Fig. 1*c*) is a rare association of all three bones from the left arm of a single individual. In size the specimen indicates a hominid larger than the A.L. 288-1 *A. afarensis* from Hadar and smaller than other individuals of this species. Fracture of the specimen currently precludes length estimates for the three elements, but the humeral head is approximately 30% larger than the smallest (A.L. 288-1) *A. afarensis* specimen (breadth: Aramis = 34.6, A.L. 288-1 = 27.0; height: Aramis = 36.5, A.L. 288-1 = 28.1). The arm displays a mosaic of characters usually attributed to hominids and/or great apes. From proximal to distal, probable derived characters shared with other hominids include an elliptical humeral head; a blunt, proximally extended ulnar olecranon process surmounting a straight dorsal upper shaft profile; an anteriorly oriented trochlear notch; and, an anteriorly facing ulnar brachialis insertion. The specimen also shows a host of characters usually associated with modern apes, including a strong angulation of the distal radial articular surface due to a large styloid process, a strong lateral trochlear ridge on the distal humerus (also seen in some *A. afarensis*), and an elongate, superoposteriorly extended lateral humeral epicondyle. The Aramis arm diverges from the African ape condition in other features. The proximal humerus lacks the deep, tunnel-like bicipital groove often seen on African apes. Further studies will unravel the functional and phylogenetic significance (polarities) of these and other postcranial characters.

头 骨 描 述

ARA-VP-1/125 和 ARA-VP-1/500 标本代表了成年个体的颞骨和枕骨区（图 1b）。二者相应地都比南方古猿阿法种要小，但是该物种没有发现任何雌性颞骨。阿拉米斯的头盖骨化石表明其具有明显似黑猩猩的形态，这些形态包括颞骨鳞部明显的气腔，该气腔甚至侵入到了颧骨根部。枕（骨）髁小，测量值为 16 毫米 × 7.5 毫米。枕骨大孔（颅底点）的前缘是颈动脉索相互交叉处，后者衔接着右边颈动脉孔，舌下神经管的颅内开口相对于中耳道的位置比大型猿类的更靠前。这种情况与其他原始人类类群化石一样，反映出相对于现代非洲猿类头盖骨，其颅底枕骨底部部分有所缩短。颞下颌关节很平坦，实际上并没有关节隆起，下颌窝内突出的下部突不明显。鼓室呈管状，前后以深沟为界，一个个体中的管状结构延伸至下颌窝后突出的侧边缘，另一个个体的则延伸至边缘之外。乳突是一个钝的突出而非黑猩猩特征性的膨胀的、弯曲的锥形结构。二腹肌沟比黑猩猩的要深得多。

颅后部分的描述

ARA-VP-7/2 标本（图 1c）是稀有的来自同一个体左臂的三块骨头。从大小上看，该标本比哈达尔 A.L. 288-1 南方古猿阿法种更大、而比该物种的其他个体小。由于标本的破碎，目前无法对三件标本的长度进行测量，但是肱骨头部比最小的（A.L. 288-1）南方古猿阿法种要大将近 30%（宽度：阿拉米斯 = 34.6，A.L. 288-1 = 27.0；高度：阿拉米斯 = 36.5，A.L. 288-1 = 28.1）。上臂显示出人类和（或）大型猿类的镶嵌特征。从近端到远端，可能与其他原始人类存在共同的衍生特征，包括椭圆形的肱骨头，一个钝的、近端延伸的尺骨鹰嘴（指肘部的骨性隆起）越过一个直的背侧骨干，向前的滑车切迹，朝前的尺骨肱肌附着部位。同时也显示出许多现代猿类通常具有的特征，包括因大的茎突而产生的尺骨远端关节面较大的角度，肱骨远端强壮的侧滑车脊（有些南方古猿阿法种中也见到过这种特征）和一个延伸的、向后上扩展的肱骨侧上髁。阿拉米斯标本的上肢与非洲猿在其他特征上有所区别。其近端肱骨缺少深的、管状的二头肌沟，而在非洲猿类中经常见到这种特征。进一步的研究将阐明这些特征和其他颅后特征的功能意义和系统发育意义（极性）。

Comparisons and Remarks

The pre-5 Myr record of hominid evolution is sparse. Although the Lothagam fragment has been attributed to *A.* cf. *afarensis*[18-20] this assignment was made mostly on the basis of primitive characters and in the absence of associated cranial, anterior dental or postcranial remains. Hominid remains from the period between 4 and 5 Myr are also few and poor, comprising a proximal humerus and jaw fragment from Baringo[16,19-22], and a distal humerus from Kanapoi of more uncertain age. These and the slightly younger Kubi Algi[23,24] and Fejej[25] specimens have all been attributed to *A. afarensis.*

To our knowledge, no fossils predating 4 Myr have been identified as representing taxa other than *Australopithecus afarensis* and *Australopithecus africanus*[16,19,20,23-26]. Assignment of the limited available > 4 Myr sample to *A. afarensis* was warranted for the comparatively undiagnostic Lothagam, Baringo, Kanapoi and Tabarin specimens from Kenya[16]. The discovery of more complete, more diagnostic specimens at Aramis allows a recognition of characters which distinguish them at (minimally) the species level from Hadar, Maka and Laetoli hominid fossils. The limited preserved morphology in the Lothagam, Tabarin and Baringo specimens broadly matches both the Aramis sample and *A. afarensis.* The discovery of the Aramis hominids demonstrates, however, that some of the suggested differences between Lothagam and *A. afarensis* (for example, enamel thickness[15]) are likely to be substantiated. However, the preserved anatomy of these Kenyan specimens may well reflect primitive character states for the basal hominid (and perhaps ancestral hominoids). Nothing available for these Kenyan specimens validates inclusion in the new Ethiopian taxon before the recovery of more diagnostic body parts.

We note that Ferguson, referring to casts and literature, has invented a plethora of new names for early African hominids (for instance, he divides *A. afarensis* into three species; an alleged dryopithecine ape[27], a diminutive early human[28], and a subspecies of *A. africanus*[29]). His invalid naming of the A.L. 288 specimen as "Homo antiquus" (in which he includes KNM-ER 1813)[28] was followed by his 1989 placement of the Baringo Tabarin specimen (which he incorrectly identified as "KNM-ER TI 13150") into a subspecies ("praegens") of that species[30]. Because of these problems, because Ferguson's diagnosis of that specimen did not differentiate it from *A. afarensis*, and because it lacks any characters that differentiate it from the latter species or unequivocally link it to the Aramis species[16], we consider Ferguson's subspecific nomen *"praegens"* to be a *nomen dubium* and propose that it be suppressed even in the event that the Tabarin specimen be shown conspecific with the Aramis series.

The 1992/93 Aramis hominids share a wide array of traits with *A. afarensis* but also depart anatomically from this species in lacking some of the key traits it possesses and which are shared exclusively among all later hominids. Because of relationships indicated by molecular studies, and because terminal Miocene to Pleistocene fossil African apes are

比较与总结

500 万年以前的人类进化记录只是零星的一点。尽管洛萨加姆碎块被归到南方古猿阿法种 [18-20]，但是这主要是根据原始特征，而缺少相关的头盖骨、前牙或颅后遗骸标本。距今 400 万至 500 万年前的原始人类遗迹也很少，保存状况很差，包括来自巴林戈的一块近端肱骨和一块颌骨碎块 [16,19-22] 以及来自卡纳波伊的年代更加不确定的一块远端肱骨。这些标本以及稍微年轻点的库比阿尔及 [23,24] 和菲耶济 [25] 标本都被划分到了南方古猿阿法种中。

据我们所知，400 万年前的化石还没有被鉴定为代表南方古猿阿法种和南方古猿非洲种之外的种类 [16,19,20,23-26]。有限可得的 400 万年以上的标本划分到南方古猿阿法种的是来自肯尼亚的相对无鉴别特征的洛萨加姆、巴林戈、卡纳波伊和塔巴林的标本 [16]。在阿拉米斯发现的更加完整的、更加具有鉴别特征的标本能够在（至少）物种水平上与来自哈达尔、马卡和莱托里的原始人类化石区分开来。洛萨加姆、塔巴林和巴林戈的标本中保存下来的有限的形态学特征与阿拉米斯样本和南方古猿阿法种都能够匹配上。但是，阿拉米斯原始人类的发现表明洛萨加姆和南方古猿非洲种之间有些潜在的差异（例如，釉质厚度 [15]）有可能得到证实。然而，这些肯尼亚标本的解剖学特征可能很好地反映了基底原始人类（可能是人科动物祖先）的原始特征状态。在发现更多具有鉴别性的身体骨骼标本之前，还没有证据可以证实这些肯尼亚标本属于埃塞俄比亚新类群。

我们注意到弗格森参考模型和文献发明了对早期非洲原始人类新命名的新模型（例如，他将南方古猿阿法种划分成了三个物种：所谓的森林古猿 [27]、早期小型人类 [28] 和南方古猿非洲种的亚种 [29]）。他将 AL 288 标本命名为"古人"（其中将 KNM-ER 1813 也包含了进去）[28]，这是一个无效的命名，后来他在 1989 年把巴林戈塔巴林标本（他误认为是"KNM-ER TI 13150"）放进了该物种的一个亚种（"普拉根"）[30] 中。但是弗格森对那个标本的判断没有将其与南方古猿阿法种区别开来，并且它缺少可以将其与后一物种区分开来的任何特征或缺少将其与阿拉米斯物种清晰关联起来的特征 [16]，基于这些问题，我们认为弗格森的亚种名字"普拉根"是一个疑难学名，并且提议，即使在塔巴林标本显示出与阿拉米斯系列属于同一物种的情况下，这个名字也应该被禁止使用。

1992/1993 的阿拉米斯原始人类与南方古猿阿法种具有许多相同的特征，但是在解剖学上也有所区别，例如缺少一些后者所具有的、与所有后来的原始人类共有的关键特征。由于分子学研究所暗示的关系，以及因为中新世末期到更新世时期的

unknown, comparison of the Aramis hominids and modern African apes is warranted. The Aramis remains evince significant cranial, dental and postcranial similarities to the chimpanzee condition, but some or all of these features may be primitive retentions. Only further discoveries and comparisons may elucidate which features actually define the chimp-human and/or African ape-human clades. Meanwhile, the modern African apes arc distinct in many dental features from both Aramis and middle to late Miocene hominoids, and thus probably do not represent the ancestral condition[8,9]. At the same time, the relatively thin Aramis molar enamel suggests that a simple "hard object feeder" model[7] is likely to be inaccurate for the ancestral African ape/hominid stock.

We have taken a conservative position here regarding placement of the Aramis fossils at the family and genus levels. The major anatomical/behavioural threshold between known great apes and Hominidae is widely recognized to be bipedality and its anatomical correlates. The two derived craniodental characters shared among all hominids are anterior placement of the occipital condyle/foramen magnum and a more incisiform canine with reduced sexual dimorphism. Acquisition of these states at Aramis may correlate with bipedality[31,32] although this remains to be demonstrated. The postcranial evidence available for *A. ramidus* is not definitive on the issue of locomotor pattern.

The anticipated recovery at Aramis of additional postcranial remains, particularly those of the lower limb and hip, may result in reassessment of these fossils at the genus and family level. Meanwhile, characters such as the modified C/P3 complex, an anterior foramen magnum, and proximal ulnar morphology (shared with later *Australopithecus* species) suggest that the Aramis fossils belong to the hominid clade. Similarity to the *A. afarensis* hypodigm warrants the inclusion of the Aramis fossils in the genus *Australopithecus*. At the same time, *A. ramidus* is the most apelike hominid ancestor known, and its remains suggest that modern apes are probably derived in many characters relative to the last common ancestor of apes and humans. More work at Aramis should further elucidate the sexual dimorphism, locomotion, diet and habitat of this species. The fossils already available indicate that a long-sought link in the evolutionary chain of species between humans and their African ape ancestors occupied the Horn of Africa during the early Pliocene.

(**371**, 306-312; 1994)

Tim D. White[*], **Gen Suwa**[†] & **Berhane Asfaw**[‡]

[*] Laboratory for Human Evolutionary Studies, University of California, Berkeley, California 94720, USA

[†] Department of Anthropology, University of Tokyo, Bunkyo-Ku, Hongo, Tokyo 113, Japan

[‡] Ethiopian Ministry of Culture and Sports Affairs, Paleoanthropology Laboratory, PO Box 5717, Addis Ababa, Ethiopia

Received 10 June; accepted 17 August 1994.

References:

1. Johanson, D. C. & White, T. D. *Science* **202**, 321-330 (1979).

2. Sarich, V. M. & Wilson, A. C. *Science* **158**, 1200-1203 (1967).

3. Hasegawa, M., Kishino, H. & Yano, T. *J. Molec. Evol.* **22**, 160-174 (1985).

非洲猿类化石都是未知的，所以其与阿拉米斯原始人类和现代非洲猿类的比较能够得以保证。阿拉米斯标本表明其与黑猩猩在头骨、牙齿和颅后骨骼方面具有显著的相似性，但是这些特征中有些或者全部可能都是原始特征的保留。只有进一步的发现和比较才可能解释清楚哪些特征可以最终确定黑猩猩 – 人类和（或）非洲猿 – 人类进化枝。同时，现代非洲猿在牙齿的许多特征上都与阿拉米斯样本、中新世中期到晚期的人科动物不同，因此可能并不代表祖先的情况 [8,9]。与此同时，相对薄的阿拉米斯臼齿釉质提示：对非洲猿 / 原始人类祖先库来说，一种简单的"坚硬食物"模型 [7] 可能是不准确的。

对于在科和属水平将阿拉米斯化石置于何种地位，我们在这里采取了一个保守态度。已知的大型猿类和人科之间的主要解剖学 / 行为学界线被广泛认为是两足行走及其相关解剖学特征。所有原始人类共有的这两种衍生的颅骨、牙齿特征包括枕（骨）髁 / 枕骨大孔的前置以及具有减弱的两性异形的门齿化的犬齿。尽管还没有得到证实，不过阿拉米斯标本中这些性状的获得可能与两足行走有关 [31,32]。可得到的南方古猿始祖种的颅后证据还不能确定行动模式这一问题。

我们期望在阿拉米斯发现其余颅后残骸，尤其是下肢和髋部遗骸，这样就可能在属和科的水平上重新对这些化石进行评价。同时，有些特征，例如改进的 C/P3 复合体、前置枕骨大孔和近侧尺骨形态学（后来的南方古猿样本也有此特征）提示阿拉米斯化石属于原始人类进化枝。与南方古猿阿法种的相似性证明了阿拉米斯化石是属于南方古猿属的。与此同时，南方古猿始祖种是已知的最像猿类的原始人类祖先，其遗迹提示现代猿类可能衍生了许多与猿类和人类的最终共同祖先相关的特征。在阿拉米斯进行的其他工作应该能进一步阐明该物种的两性异形、行动方式、食性和栖息环境等问题。已经得到的这些化石暗示：长久以来一直在寻找的人类与其非洲猿类祖先之间的进化链物种在早上新世时期生活在非洲好望角。

（刘皓芳 翻译；赵凌霞 审稿）

4. Pilbeam, D. R. *Am. Anthrop.* **88**, 295-312 (1986).

5. Sarich, V. M., Schmid, C. W. & Marks, J. *Cladistics* **5**, 3-32 (1989).

6. Andrews, P. & Martin, L. *Phil. Trans. R. Soc. Lond.* **334**, 199-209 (1991).

7. Andrews, P. *Nature* **360**, 641-646 (1992).

8. Begun, D. R. *Science* **257**, 1929-1933 (1992).

9. Dean, D. & Delson, E. *Nature* **359**, 676-677 (1992).

10. WoldeGabriel, G. *et al. Nature* **371**, 330-333 (1994).

11. Dart, R. A. *Fol. Anat. Jap.* **12**, 207-221 (1934).

12. Robinson, J. T. *Transv. Mus. Mem.* **9**, 1-179 (1956).

13. Le Gros Clark, W. E. *Q. J. Geol. Soc.* **105**, 225-264 (1950).

14. Walker, A. C. *Am. J. Phys. Anthrop.* **65**, 47-60 (1984).

15. White, T. D. *Anthropos* (Brno) **23**, 79-90 (1986).

16. Ward, S. C. & Hill, A. *Am. J. Phys. Anthrop.* **72**, 21-37 (1987).

17. White, T. D. *et al. Nature* **366**, 261-265 (1993).

18. Kramer, A. *Am. J. Phys. Anthrop.* **70**, 457-473 (1986).

19. Hill, A. & Ward, S. *Yearb. Phys. Anthropol.* **31**, 49-83 (1988).

20. Hill, A., Ward, S. & Brown, B. *J. Hum. Evol.* **22**, 439-451 (1992).

21. Hill, A. *Nature* **315**, 222-224 (1985).

22. Pickford, M., Johanson, D. C., Lovejoy, C. O., White, T. D. & Aronson, J. L. *Am. J. Phys. Anthrop.* **60**, 337-346 (1983).

23. Coffing, K., Feibel, C., Leakey, M. & Walker, A. *Am. J. Phys. Anthrop.* **93**, 55-65 (1994).

24. Heinrich, R. E., Rose, M. D., Leakey, R. E. & Walker, A. C. *Am. J. Phys. Anthrop.* **92**, 139- 148 (1993).

25. Fleagle, J. G., Rasmussen, D. T., Yirga, S., Bown, T. M. & Grine, F. E. *J. Hum. Evol.* **21**,145- 152 (1991).

26. Patterson, B., Beherensmeyer, A. K. & Sill, W. D. *Nature* **226**, 918-921 (1970).

27. Ferguson, W. W. *Primates* **24**, 397-409 (1983).

28. Ferguson, W. W. *Primates* **25**, 519-529 (1984).

29. Ferguson, W. W. *Primates* **28**, 258-265 (1987).

30. Ferguson, W. W. *Primates* **30**, 383-387 (1989).

31. Lovejoy, C. O. *Science* **211**, 341-350 (1981).

32. Lovejoy, C. O, in *The Origin and Evolution of Humans and Humanness* (ed. Rasmussen, D. T.) 1-28 (Jones and Bartlett, Boston, 1993).

Acknowledgements. We thank the Anthropology and Archaeometry programmes of the National Science Foundation, the University of California Collaborative Research Program of the Institute of Geophysics and Planetary Physics at Los Alamos National Laboratory, and the National Geographic Society for funding. This research was made possible by the Centre for Research and Conservation of the Cultural Heritage and the National Museum of Ethiopia in the Ethiopian Ministry of Culture and Sports Affairs, the Ethiopian Embassy to the USA, the Afar people, the American Embassy in Addis Ababa, and the Cleveland Museum of Natural History. Special thanks to L-S. Temamo, H. Ali-Mirah, M. Tahiro, Rep. N. Pelosi and M. Starr. K. Coffing, A. C. Walker and D. Begun showed us casts of East Turkana hominids and Miocene hominoids; Lyman Jellema facilitated comparative research on the Hamman-Todd collection. Thanks to Keiko Fujimaki for scientific illustrations. O. Lovejoy and B. Latimer provided assistance in postcranial interpretation and F. C. Howell provided comments, E. Kanazawa, H. Yamada and H. Ishida provided access to equipment and comparative collections in their care. Thanks to our colleagues in Middle Awash project geology and palaeontology for elucidating the environmental and chronostratigraphic placement of this new hominid species. A. Ademassu, A. Almquist, A. Asfaw, M. Asnake, Y. Beyene, J. D. Clark, M. Fisseha, A. Getty, Y. H.-Selassie, B. Latimer, K. Schick, S. Simpson, M. Tesfaye and S. Teshome contributed to the fieldwork. B. Wood, P. Andrews, E. Delson and F. C. Howell provided comments on the manuscript, Thanks to J. Desmond Clark for inviting us to participate in the Middle Awash research and for inspiring us in the search for human origins.

Evidence from Gravity and Topography Data for Folding of Tibet

Yu Jin *et al.*

Editor's Note

The Tibetan Plateau was formed by the collision of the Eurasian and Indian continental plates. Earth scientists had long wondered how the collision uplifted such a large area of crust to such a high elevation. Was the plateau merely compressed and thickened between the plates, or was it "jacked up" by intrusion of the Indian crust underneath? Here Yu Jin and Marcia McNutt of MIT, with colleague Yongsheng Zhu based in China, begin to distinguish between possible models by observing that, although the crust is thickened on the plateau, it has also been warped and folded into shorter (about 150 km) folds than the corresponding undulations (about 500 km) in the upper mantle beneath. This implies that the Tibetan crust and mantle are to some extent delaminated.

Bouguer gravity and topography data from Tibet suggest that the surface of the plateau and the subsurface density interfaces are warped into two series of ridges and troughs trending parallel to the collision zone with wavelengths of 150 and 500 km. These folds are superimposed on an overall state of isostatic compensation owing to crustal thickening. Such folding is predicted from models of compressional shortening of a rheologically layered plate. The results thus suggest the presence of a weak decoupling zone between the Tibetan crust and upper mantle.

THE Tibetan Plateau is the most conspicuous feature of continental topography on Earth, and considerable effort has been devoted to understanding the cause and timing of its uplift for the purpose of understanding its influence on the tectonics of Asia[1], the development of the Indian monsoons[2] and long-term climate patterns[3]. All models for the formation of this broad plateau begin with the assumption that the crustal thickness beneath the plateau has been approximately doubled in response to the collision of India with Asia, beginning about 45 million years ago[4], but differ in the details of how this doubling is accomplished. One of the earliest proposals[5,6] involved simple underplating of the Tibetan crust by the Indian crust. A more recent update of this model conserves mass beneath the crust by proposing subduction of the Asian mantle lithosphere beneath northern Tibet, and involves more realistic compressional shortening as well as overthrusting of Indian crust[7] (Fig. 1*a*). The "rigid indenter" models[8-10] assume that the entire continental lithosphere behaves as a viscous fluid that has been shortened by a factor of two, and thus thickened, by the northward advance of India (Fig. 1*b*). This model predicts thickening of the lithospheric upper mantle as well as the crust, although in a variation on this theme by England and Houseman[11], some portion of the thickened

青藏高原的褶皱作用：来自重力和地形资料的证据

金煜等

编者按

青藏高原是由欧亚大陆板块和印度大陆板块碰撞形成的。然而这个碰撞是如何将如此大范围的地壳隆升至如此高的高度？地球科学家们在很长的一段时间里都对此感到十分好奇。高原的形成仅仅是因为两个板块互相挤压，然后在挤压处变厚？还是因为印度地壳冲入高原的下方，从而将它顶起？本文中，麻省理工学院的金煜和马西娅·麦克纳特及中方合作者朱永盛通过观测将几种可能的模型做了区分。他们观测到，青藏高原的地壳虽然有所加厚，但对应下方上地幔岩石圈约 500 km 的起伏，上地壳岩石圈同时也被挤压成较短波长（约 150 km）的褶皱。这也暗示出，青藏高原的地壳和地幔在一定程度还存在着去耦合。

青藏高原布格重力与高程相关谱分离的特征提示高原与其地下密度界面形成了两个波长截然不同的起伏，波长分别为 150 km 和 500 km，并平行于青藏高原碰撞带的走向。这些褶皱叠加于高原因地壳宏观加厚达到的均衡补偿之上。此类褶皱可通过具有不同流变组构层的板块的挤压缩短状态加以预测。以上结论表明青藏高原上地壳与上地幔岩石圈之间存在一软弱的解耦带。

青藏高原是地球表面地形起伏最为引人注目的特殊现象。为了弄清青藏高原隆升的时间和机制以及隆升对亚洲大地构造 [1]、印度季风 [2] 及地球长期气候格局 [3] 的影响，地球科学家们作出了无数的努力。关于青藏高原形成的所有理论模型都假设大约 4,500 万年前 [4] 由于印度次大陆与欧亚大陆碰撞使青藏高原下的地壳厚度变为原来的两倍，但各种模型对地壳厚度如何加倍的细节认识不同。早期的一个模型假设 [5,6] 地壳厚度加倍是由于印度地壳插入青藏高原的地壳之下引起的。该模型最近的一个翻版是根据质量守恒假设：亚洲地幔岩石圈由北侧俯冲青藏高原而印度地壳逆冲欧亚板块从而产生更合理的青藏高原地壳挤压形变 [7]（图 1a）。另一种"刚性的挤压地块"模型 [8-10] 假设由于印度向北推进，整个青藏岩石圈像一个高塑性物质增厚加倍（图 1b）。增厚不仅是地壳还有上地幔岩石圈。英格兰和豪斯曼的模拟 [11] 与此类似，只是假设过去的 1,100 万年当中，又厚又致密的上地幔岩石圈部分脱落，造

and dense upper mantle detached within the past 11 Myr, leading to rapid uplift of the plateau. Alternatively, Zhao and Morgan[12] have proposed injection of the Indian crust into the weak Tibetan lower crust, leading to plateau uplift in the manner of a hydraulic jack. The fate of the Indian mantle lithosphere is unspecified; one might assume that, stripped of its buoyant continental crust, the Indian upper mantle would subduct into the asthenosphere.

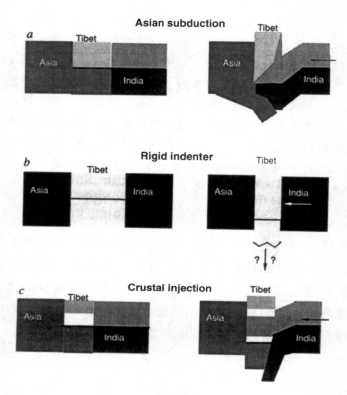

Fig. 1. Three models for the formation of the Tibetan Plateau. Asia, Tibet and India are each represented as blocks in cross-section. The left and right panels for each model show the crustal structure before (left) and after (right) collision with India. Darker shading indicates relatively more rigid blocks. The black line shows the location of the crust–mantle boundary for Tibet and India. The Asian subduction model (a) thickens the Tibetan crust by thrusting Indian crust and mantle beneath the Tibetan crust. The Asian upper mantle is subducted. The rigid indenter model (b) thickens the Tibetan crust and upper mantle by shortening a uniformly weak block. The crustal injection model (c) intrudes the Indian crust into the soft Tibetan lower crust and subducts Indian upper mantle.

The models discussed above differ in their predictions for both the strain field and the strength profile of the Tibetan block. For example, the indenter model (Fig. 1b) requires high (~50%) strain and low strength at all depths. In contrast, the Asian subduction and crustal injection models (Fig. 1a and c, respectively) require low strength only in the decoupling zone in the midcrust (where Indian crust is either underthrust or injected) and subduction rather than north–south shortening in the upper mantle beneath Tibet. These latter two models do differ in whether the upper mantle beneath Tibet is Indian

成青藏高原迅速隆升。还有一种假设出自赵吴玲（音译）和摩根[12]，他们假设印度地壳如同液压千斤顶的原理一样被注入熔融的青藏地壳，从而使高原隆起。印度地幔岩石圈的命运如何尚不确定。我们可假设失去浮力较大的大陆地壳后，剩下的印度地幔岩石圈将俯冲入软流圈。

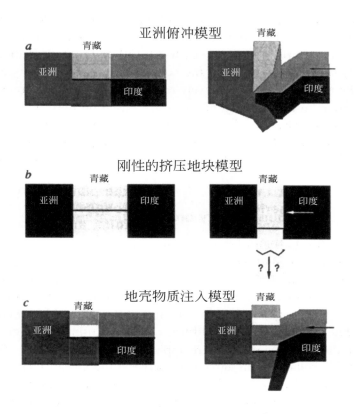

图 1. 形成青藏高原的 3 个模型。其中亚洲、青藏、印度用剖面上的各块体代表。图左及图右分别代表印度与欧亚大陆碰撞之前和之后。颜色深浅代表地块的强弱。黑线为印度和青藏区域地壳与地幔的分界线。亚洲俯冲模型（图 1a）通过印度地壳和地幔俯冲到青藏地壳之下使青藏地壳加厚。其结果是亚洲地幔岩石圈俯冲入地幔。刚性的挤压地块模型（图 1b）是将假设无强度的青藏地块横向挤压变短而使得纵向变厚。地壳物质注入模型（图 1c）是将印度地壳注入熔融的青藏下地壳而印度地幔岩石圈俯冲入地幔。

以上讨论的各种模型预测不同的青藏高原隆升所产生的应变及强度剖面。比如纯横向推进模型（图 1b）需青藏高原被压缩约 50% 而岩石圈强度在各深度上都较弱。与其相反，模型 1a 与模型 1c 只要求被分离的中地壳强度弱从而使印度地壳可下冲入或被注入其中，而地幔岩石圈俯冲至软流圈，从而避免中地壳南北向被挤压后缩短。然而后两者在青藏高原地幔岩石圈来自印度（图 1a）还是本身原有（图 1b）的

upper mantle (Fig. 1a) or the original Tibetan upper mantle (Fig. 1b), but it may be difficult to distinguish the two possibilities on the basis of rheological inferences because the cold, stiff upper mantle beneath the Indian plate[13,14] could be weakened and reheated in the process of underthrusting such that it is indistinguishable from the younger upper mantle beneath the Mesozoic Tibetan block.

Here we present high-resolution gravity data from the Tibetan Plateau that allow us to estimate both its strain and its strength profile. The development of two scales of folds in the surface and subsurface at wavelengths of 150 and 500 km demonstrate that the crust has clearly shortened. However, the coherence between gravity and topography indicates that the upper mantle is relatively rigid beneath Tibet and resists compression, thus lending support to the subduction scenario[7]. Based on both the observation of the development of two wavelengths of folding and results from the experimental deformation of rocks, we propose that Tibet contains two distinct strong regions: one in the upper crust and the other in the uppermost mantle, separated by a lower-crustal decoupling layer.

Bouguer Gravity and Topography Data

The Bouguer gravity data and land elevation information we use was compiled by Ocean University of Qingdao, People's Republic of China. The original point gravity measurements were based on the Potsdam standard within the geographical reference of the Beijing coordinate system and the Yellow Sea elevation system. Data were reduced using the Helmert normal gravity formula for gravity on the spheroid and converted to free air anomalies. The Bouguer gravity field was calculated using a topographic density of 2,670 kg m^{-3}, and terrain corrections were applied out to a distance of 166.7 km (ref. 15). Through a scientific collaboration agreement between the Ocean University of Qingdao and the Massachusetts Institute of Technology, the gravity and topography data were interpolated for us onto a 10-km grid. The original point measurements were uniformly distributed over the plateau, but the lower limit on the wavelengths resolved is closer to 25 than 10 km, except in a few well-sampled areas. The cumulative error in the Bouguer gravity field, including errors in elevation, is estimated to be 1.5 mGal (ref. 15), although uncertainty in the Bouguer reduction density is not included in this value. The validity of the topographic data was verified by E. Fielding at Cornell University by comparing our values over a $2° × 2°$ area with an independent, even higher-resolution, digital elevation model[16]. Although there is a small discrepancy in the registration of the two topographic data sets, the average differences are less than 10 m.

As shown in Fig. 2, the land elevation in our study area consists of east–west trending undulations about a mean plateau elevation of 5 km. Except near the edges of the plateau, the relief rarely departs by more than 1 km from the mean value. This uniform elevation despite the large amount of crustal thickening beneath the plateau has been one of the principal arguments in favour of a weak crust that flows laterally to even out any thickness irregularities imposed during the crustal thickening process[17].

问题上有区别。但是从流变学的角度上区别二者却很困难。因为较冷且坚硬的印度地幔岩石圈[13,14]可在俯冲时变弱变软，从而难以将其与中生代较年轻的青藏地幔岩石圈区分开。

本文我们使用高分辨率的重力数据来估算青藏高原的应变及强度剖面。我们所得到的岩石圈在地表和地下分别存在波长为 150 km 和 500 km 的大尺度褶皱说明地壳的确受挤压变短。然而，重力与高程相关谱显示青藏高原地幔岩石圈强度相对较大，可反抗挤压，从而支持地幔岩石圈俯冲的模型[7]。根据观测到的双波长褶皱，及岩石形变的实验，我们推断青藏高原岩石圈存在两个高强度层，即上地壳和上地幔岩石圈，二者被其中的下地壳软弱的解耦层所分开。

布格重力和高程数据

本文的重力数据和陆地高程信息由中华人民共和国青岛海洋大学（译者注：青岛海洋大学，现名中国海洋大学）整理。原始重力数据的测量是基于波茨坦标准，北京地理坐标参考系和黄海平均海拔高程系统进行的。正常场改正用的是针对球体重力的赫尔默特正常场重力公式，并进行了自由空气异常改正。布格重力场所用的地改密度为 2,670 kg·m⁻³，地改半径为 166.7 km（参考文献 15）。根据青岛海洋大学和麻省理工学院的科研合作协议，重力和高程数据被插值成 10 km×10 km 的网格。原始数据均匀地分布于青藏高原之上，分辨率接近 25 km，少数地区可达到 10 km。包括高程影响的布格重力场的累积误差为 1.5 毫伽（参考文献 15），但布格改正的密度影响不包括在内。美国康奈尔大学菲尔丁把我们 2°×2° 面积上的数值与他们独立得到且分辨率更高的数字高程模型[16]进行了比较，从而证实了高程数据是有效的。虽然两种数据在储存中存在微小不同，但平均差异小于 10 m。

如图 2 所示，所研究区域的高程在平均海拔 5 km 上下存在两个东西向的起伏。除在高原边界附近外，起伏幅度很少偏离平均值超过 1 km。尽管地壳如此变厚，但高程如此均匀，从而从一个方面说明，下地壳很弱，可流向四方，使地壳加厚过程的不规则性均匀化[17]。

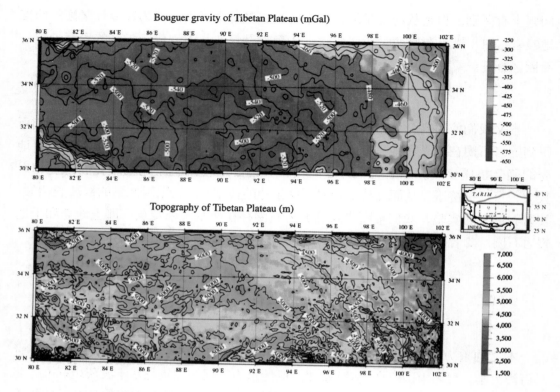

Fig. 2. Main figure, Bouguer gravity and topography over the Tibetan Plateau. Inset, location of grids within China as well as the locations of the three sub-regions, Qiangtang (Q), Bayanhar (B) and Lhasa (L), for which coherence was independently estimated in Fig. 4.

Modelling of the gravity and topography data measured along cross-sections perpendicular to the Himalayan thrust front (Fig. 3) confirms that, to first order, the Bouguer data are fitted by local (Airy) isostatic compensation (solid lines, Fig. 3). Therefore, the overall high elevation of the plateau is buoyed up by a thickened crust with no apparent contribution from any thermal anomalies in the upper mantle. The most notable departures from the predicted Airy model occur just north and south of the plateau's margins, where the more negative Bouguer anomalies reflect the development of foredeep basins on bordering plates with appreciable flexural strength. In addition, there is noticeable signal in the Bouguer gravity at shorter wavelengths undulating across the entire plateau this is not predicted by local compensation, indicating that there must be uncompensated topographic features and/or buried mass anomalies with no corresponding topographic expression. This simple observation suggests that some strong zone must exist within or beneath the crust to support short-wavelength topographic features and prevent buried loads from achieving local isostatic balance by deforming the surface.

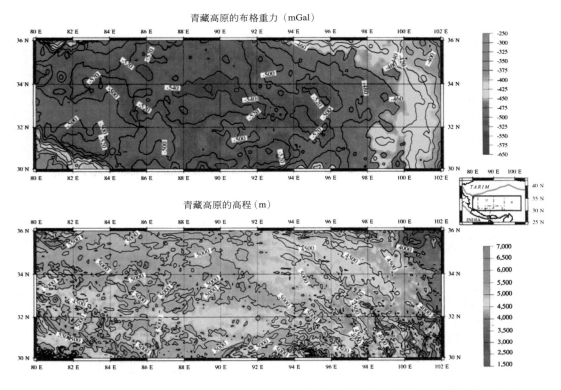

图 2. 主图：青藏高原上的布格重力和高程。插图：中国境内的区域位置及羌塘（Q），巴颜喀拉（B）和拉萨（L）三个子区域的位置。这三个子区域的协函数在图 4 中都进行了独立的估算。

在与喜马拉雅逆冲前沿垂直的剖面上（图 3）对重力和高程的模拟从一级近似上证实布格数据与局部艾里均衡补偿吻合（图 3 中实线）。因此，整个高原在一级近似上由地壳加厚所产生的浮力所支撑，而并无明显的上地幔热效应所产生的结果。与艾里均衡有显著差异的是高原的南北端，在此负布格异常反映的是板块边界发育的具有明显挠曲的山前盆地。另外，还有横跨整个高原的较短波长的、非局部补偿的重力异常。此异常显示，一定存在未被补偿的高程和（或）埋在地下的、未被高程反映的质量异常。这一简单的观测暗示地壳中或地壳下存在刚性层来支撑短波长的高程特征，从而使下部负载无法通过地表形变达到局部均衡。

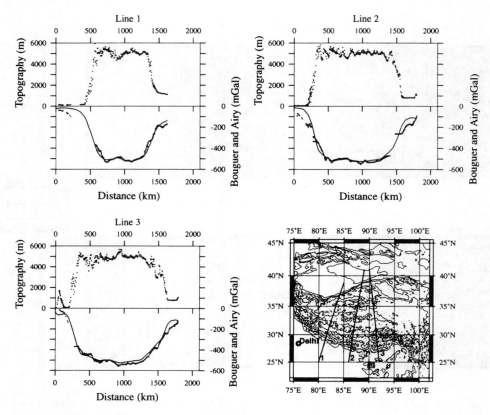

Fig. 3. Graph panels, profiles of topography and Bouguer gravity (dots) along three cross-sections oriented perpendicular to the Himalayan thrust front spanning the plateau from the Indian plate on the south (left) to the Tarim Basin on the north (right). Solid lines show the predicted Bouguer gravity assuming an Airy model of local isostatic compensation (no elastic rigidity) with a crustal thickness of 60 km, crustal density of 2,670 kg m^{-3} and mantle density of 3,300 kg m^{-3}. Map panel, locations of the cross-sections superimposed on a topographic map of the region around Tibet.

Coherence between Gravity and Topography

Forsyth[18] pioneered the technique of using the coherence between Bouguer gravity and topography to estimate the effective elastic thickness in continental regions containing both surface and subsurface loads on the lithosphere. If ΔG and H are the Fourier transforms of the Bouguer gravity field and topography, respectively, then coherence γ^2 is defined as

$$\gamma^2 = \frac{\langle \Delta G \cdot H^* \rangle \langle \Delta G \cdot H^* \rangle}{\langle H \cdot H^* \rangle \langle \Delta G \cdot \Delta G^* \rangle} \tag{1}$$

in which the asterisk denotes complex conjugation and the angle brackets represent averaging in bands of constant wavenumber modulus k. The essence of Forsyth's argument is that if a plate has no elastic strength, then all surface loads will produce corre- sponding crustal thickness variations at the Moho to obtain local isostatic equilibrium, and all

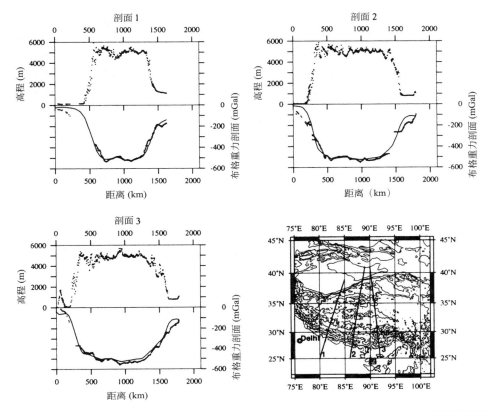

图 3. 前三个子图为 3 条与喜马拉雅逆冲前沿垂直的高程和布格重力剖面（点），剖面由南面印度洋板块（左）到北面塔里木盆地（右）。实线为局部均衡补偿的艾里模型所预测的布格重力（无刚性板块），其中假设地壳厚 60 km，地壳密度 2,670 kg·m⁻³，地幔密度 3,300 kg·m⁻³。最后一个子图：在青藏高原周围高程上叠加了这 3 条剖面的位置。

重力与高程之间归一化的相关函数谱

福赛思[18] 发明了用重力与高程之间归一化的相关函数谱（以后简称协函数谱）来估算具有地表和地下负载的大陆岩石圈的有效弹性厚度。如果 ΔG 和 H 分别为布格重力场和高程的傅里叶变换，那么协函数谱 γ^2 定义为：

$$\gamma^2 = \frac{\langle \Delta G \cdot H^* \rangle \langle \Delta G \cdot H^* \rangle}{\langle H \cdot H^* \rangle \langle \Delta G \cdot \Delta G^* \rangle} \tag{1}$$

其中，星号代表复共轭，尖括号代表在波数模量 k 分段为常数内的平均。福赛思的推断是，如果板块无弹性强度，那么所有地表负载将在莫霍面产生相应的地壳厚度变化以达到局部均衡。并且，所有地壳厚度的变化将会产生相应的地形。此时，对

imposed crustal thickness variations will produce corresponding topography. The Bouguer gravity anomaly, which is sensitive to those undulations at the Moho, will correlate at all wavelengths with the topography and the coherence will be uniformly high. In the other extreme, if the lithosphere is perfectly rigid, surface loads will produce no flexure at the Moho, and loads buried within the plate will produce no topography. The topography will be a perfect measure of the surface load and the Bouguer gravity will reflect only the subsurface load. If the surface and subsurface loads are uncorrelated, the coherence between Bouguer gravity and topography will be small at all wavelengths. Any realistic case for a plate with finite elastic strength will fall somewhere between these two extremes, and the wavelength at which the coherence drops from values approaching unity at long wavelengths to values approaching zero at short wavelengths is a measure of the rigidity of the elastic plate.

For the case in which the subsurface load is applied at the Moho, the theoretical coherence for an elastic plate is given by

$$\gamma^2 = \frac{(1+f)^2}{(1+Y^{-2}f)(1+Y^2f)} \tag{2}$$

$$Y = \left[1 + \frac{(2\pi k)^4 D}{\Delta\rho g}\right]^{-1} \tag{3}$$

where f is the ratio of the power in the subsurface load spectrum to that of the surface load, D is the flexural rigidity of the plate, $\Delta\rho$ is the density contrast at the Moho, and g is the acceleration due to gravity. D is related to the elastic thickness T_e by $D = ET_e^3 / 12(1-v^2)$ where E is Young's modulus (10^{11} N m^{-2}) and v is Poisson's ratio (0.25).

Figure 4 compares the observed coherence calculated for the entire Tibetan Plateau (filled circles) to the predicted coherence if the surface and subsurface loads are supported elastically (solid lines). The drop in the coherence from high values at long wavelengths to low values at short wavelengths begins at wavelengths greater than 500 km, as would be predicted if the elastic plate supporting the plateau's topography is at least 40 km thick. However, the observed coherence does not drop to zero as rapidly as predicted by the theoretical models, and displays an anomalous peak at wavelengths of 100–200 km. Bechtel et al.[19] have suggested that this behaviour might be caused by averaging together in the analysis geological provinces with different elastic rigidities, for example, in this case, between 10 and 40 km elastic thickness. But this does not seem to be the explanation here; even when we subdivide the plateau into three sub-regions (Fig. 2 inset) representing geologically homogeneous provinces, the observed coherence points (diamonds, triangles, and squares in Fig. 4) are similar for each one. Clearly the support for the plateau is not simply described by compensation of uncorrelated loads on and within a single elastic lithosphere.

534

莫霍面起伏敏感的布格重力异常将与所有地形波长相关，协函数谱呈均匀高值。在另一个极端，如果岩石圈充分强硬，地表负载将在莫霍面不产生任何挠曲。同样，板块内部负载将不产生任何地形。高程是地表负载的最佳量度，而布格重力只反映下部负载的影响。如果地上负载与地下负载不相关，则高程与布格重力间的相关函数谱在所有波长都很小。在任何实际情况中，对于具有有限弹性强度的板块来说，其相关函数谱落于以上两极限之间。相关函数谱由长波长接近 1 的情况降到短波长为 0 时所对应的波长描述了弹性板的强度。

对于下部负载位于莫霍面的情况，弹性板的理论协函数为

$$\gamma^2 = \frac{(1+f)^2}{(1+Y^{-2}f)(1+Y^2f)} \tag{2}$$

$$Y = \left[1 + \frac{(2\pi k)^4 D}{\Delta\rho g} \right]^{-1} \tag{3}$$

其中 f 为地下负载功率谱与地上负载功率谱的比值，D 为板块的挠曲刚度，$\Delta\rho$ 为莫霍面的密度差，g 为重力加速度。D 与弹性板厚度 T_e 的关系为：$D = ET_e^3/12\,(1-v^2)$，其中 E 是杨氏模量（$10^{11}\,\mathrm{N \cdot m^{-2}}$），$v$ 是泊松比（0.25）。

图 4 为整个青藏高原观测的协函数（实心圆圈）与理论值（实线）的比较，其中假设地表负载与地下负载由弹性板支撑。观测协函数由长波长的高值向短波长的低值的衰减出现在 500 km，在支撑青藏高原高程的弹性板的弹性厚度至少为 40 km 的条件下，这一观测现象可以理论预测出来。然而，观测的协函数并未像理论模型预测的那样迅速衰减为零，而在波长为 100~200 km 处出现又一异常峰值。贝克特尔等[19]曾假设此谱峰分裂现象可能是由于对一组弹性强度不同的地质单元进行平均的结果，比如此例为对弹性厚度为 10 km 和 40 km 的平均。但是这种解释在这里似乎并不成立。即使我们将高原一分为三（图 2 插图），每个单元地质性质均匀，然而，各个单元得到的协函数是相似的（图 4 中的菱形，三角形和方形）。显然，青藏高原并不是简单地由一个上下负载不相关的弹性岩石圈来补偿的。

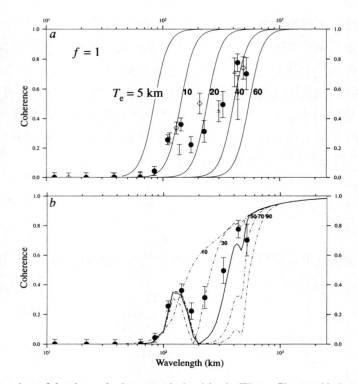

Fig. 4. *a*, Comparison of the observed coherence calculated for the Tibetan Plateau with that corresponding to theoretical elastic plate models as a function of wavelength in kilometres. The solid circles give the coherence for the entire Tibetan Plateau, whereas the triangles, squares and diamonds represent coherence for the Qiangtang, Lhasa and Bayanhar sub-regions (Fig. 2 inset), respectively. The solid lines correspond to theoretical curves for five different values of the elastic plate thickness, T_e, assuming uncorrelated surface and subsurface loads and a single subsurface density discontinuity at the Moho. For the case of a subsurface loading only at the Moho, the theoretical coherence is relatively insensitive to the value for f, the ratio of subsurface to surface loads, here assumed to be 1. *b*, Comparison of the observed coherence data for the entire Tibetan Plateau with theoretical coherence as a function of wavelength in kilometres allowing for the correlation of loads on the surface and in the subsurface. Subsurface loading is allowed at the Conrad discontinuity at 13 km and at the Moho at 60 km. Folding of a rheologically layered plate is simulated by allowing a 60% positive correlation between surface and Conrad loads in the two wavelength bands for folding at 150 and 500 km. A 60% negative correlation between surface and Moho loads is used in the 500-km band. For a layered plate, the curves are more sensitive to f. For these curves, we assumed $f = 3$ for both the Conrad and Moho loads.

Further investigation of the gravity spectrum and its relationship to the topography spectrum suggests that one reason for the failure of the simple model to fit the coherence data is that Tibet is layered in both its density and its rheological structure. The slope of the logarithm of the gravity power spectrum[13,20] (Fig. 5*a*) implies that at wavelengths greater than 100 km, the Bouguer gravity signal is caused by undulations of density interfaces at about 13 km (a midcrustal discontinuity we refer to as the "Conrad") and at about 60 km (the Moho). The two-dimensional coherency γ (Fig. 5*b*) and admittance Q (Fig. 5*c*) between gravity and topography, defined as

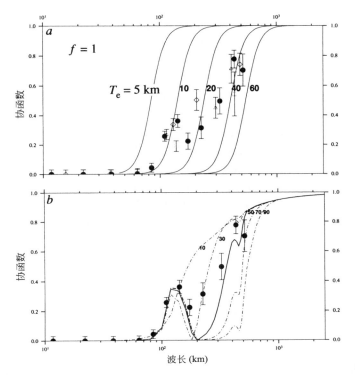

图 4. (a) 青藏高原观测的协函数与理论弹性板的协函数随波长变化的对比，波长单位为千米。实心圆圈为整个高原的协函数，其中三角、方块和菱形分别代表羌塘、拉萨和巴颜喀拉地区的协函数（参考图 2 中的插图）。实线代表 5 个不同弹性板厚度 T_e 的理论曲线，其中假设地表负载与地下负载不相关，且在莫霍面上只有一个密度不连续界面，对于只有莫霍面有下部负载的情况，理论协函数对负载系数（地下与地表负载之比为 f）不敏感，假设 f 为 1。(b) 青藏高原观测协函数与理论协函数的比较，协函数是波长（单位：km）的函数，并假设地表负载与地下负载可相关。地下负载假设来自 13 km 深的康氏面和 60 km 深的莫霍面。运用多层流变介质模拟褶皱的最佳结果是地下康氏面的负载与地表负载为 60% 正相关，主控波长为 150 km 和 500 km。地表和莫霍面为 60% 负相关，波长为 500 km。对于多层板块，理论曲线对负载系数 f 更敏感。为此，我们假设对于康氏和莫霍面的负载，f 为 3。

　　对重力谱与高程谱相互关系的进一步研究表明，用单一模型无法拟合协函数的原因是青藏高原的密度和岩石力学的组构特征都具有成层结构。图 5a 的重力功率谱的斜率 [13,20] 显示波长大于 100 km 的布格重力异常是由 13 km 左右深的密度界面（中地壳的密度界面，我们称为"康拉德"界面），和 60 km 左右的密度界面（莫霍面）的波动所产生的。重力与高程间的二维协函数的根 γ（图 5b）和响应函数 Q（图 5c）定义为：

$$\gamma = \frac{\langle \Delta G \cdot H^* \rangle}{\langle H \cdot H^* \rangle^{1/2} \langle \Delta G \cdot \Delta G^* \rangle^{1/2}} \tag{4}$$

$$Q = \frac{\langle \Delta G \cdot H^* \rangle}{\langle H \cdot H^* \rangle} \tag{5}$$

both show an unexpected positive correlation between Bouguer gravity and topography at wavelengths of 150–200 km which is not predicted by any conventional model of isostatic compensation. One-dimensional cross-spectra $\langle \Delta G \cdot H^* \rangle$ (Fig. 5d–f) computed from the profiles in Fig. 3 similarly display a weak positive peak in the correlation at 150–200 km, as well as a strong negative peak at 500–700 km. We interpret these peaks in the cross-correlation spectrum as evidence for the development of folds[21] in the Tibetan plate by the collision with India, just as the sea floor south of the Bay of Bengal has been folded by this collision[22], with the two distinct wavelengths arising from the expected multi-layered rheology of continental crust[23-25].

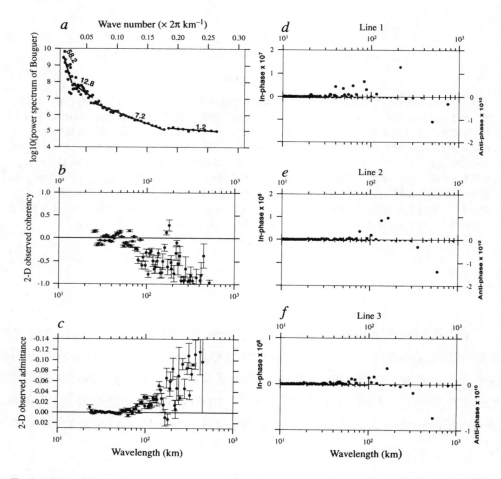

Fig. 5. *a*, $\log_{10}$ of the power in the Bouguer gravity spectrum as a function of wavenumber (2π/wavelength). Straight lines fitted piecewise to the slope of the spectrum provide an estimate of the depth to the density

$$\gamma = \frac{\langle \Delta G \cdot H^* \rangle}{\langle H \cdot H^* \rangle^{1/2} \langle \Delta G \cdot \Delta G^* \rangle^{1/2}} \qquad (4)$$

$$Q = \frac{\langle \Delta G \cdot H^* \rangle}{\langle H \cdot H^* \rangle} \qquad (5)$$

二者同时显示在波长 150~200 km 的布格重力与高程之间出乎意料地为正相关，此现象无法用传统的均衡模型预测。由图 3 剖面中计算的一维重力与高程的互相关谱 $\langle \Delta G \cdot H^* \rangle$（图 5d~f）同样地显示在 150~200 km 处有一个较弱的正峰值，而且在 500~700 km 处一个强负峰值。我们将以上互相关谱的峰值解释为由于印度碰撞青藏而产生的褶皱[21]。这正如印度孟加拉湾南部的海底由此碰撞产生的褶皱一样[22]，波长为截然不同的两组，这与大陆地壳的多层流变学组构结构相关[23-25]。

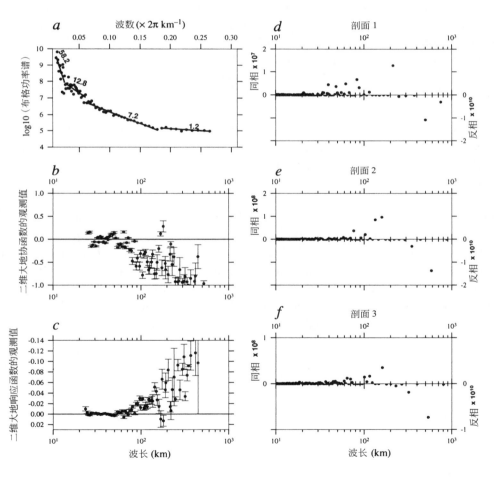

图 5. (a) 布格重力场以 10 为底的 log 功率谱随波数的变化，波数为 2π / 波长。用直线逐段拟合谱线的斜率，估算出造成该段重力谱的不连续密度界面的深度（各段直线上的数字）。(b) 青藏高原上重力与

discontinuity responsible for that portion of the gravity spectrum. Numbers on straight line segments represent the average depth to the density discontinuity presumably responsible for that portion of the gravity spectrum. *b*, Coherency of Bouguer gravity and topography for Tibet. The trend from coherency values near zero at short wavelengths to negative values at long wavelengths as expected for isostatic compensation is interrupted by positive values at 150–200 km. *c*, Admittance of Bouguer gravity and topography for Tibet, *d–f*, One-dimensional cross-correlation of topography and Bouguer gravity for the profiles across the plateau in Fig. 3. Note the large difference in scales for the positive, in-phase, correlation as opposed to the negative, out-of-phase, correlation necessary to highlight the weak positive correlation on all profiles between 150 and 200 km. The prominent negative signal on each profile occurs at 500–700 km wavelength.

Folding of Tibet

Figure 6 shows a strength envelope as inspired by experiments on the deformation of rocks extrapolated to realistic geological pressures, temperatures and strain rates. Strength in the upper part of the plate is controlled by frictional sliding along preexisting faults. The crust becomes increasingly strong with increasing overburden pressure down to depths of about 15 km, at which point ductile creep of diabase becomes the dominant mechanism of failure. Between depths of 25–35 km (depending on the local geotherm) and the base of the crust, a weak ductile channel should exist. In the case of Tibet where the crust is 60-km thick, the ductile channel should be ~30-km thick and well developed. In the uppermost mantle, another relatively strong zone should exist based on the higher strength of olivine. When subjected to the moderate stresses from vertically-directed surface and subsurface loads, the overall mechanical behaviour of the two strong regions separate by a ductile channel has an effective elastic thickness given by $(T_e(\text{upper crust})^3 + T_e(\text{upper mantle})^3)^{1/3}$, which in this case is a little more than the effective elastic thickness of the stronger of the two layers.

However, if subjected to end loads of the order of several hundred megapascals, as might be produced by the collision of India with Tibet, the strength of the upper-crustal layer will be exceeded everywhere. It will fold as a plastic/viscous layer. The stronger layer in the upper mantle will also fold, presumably in an elastic/plastic manner[26]. Zuber[27] has shown that the deformation of two strong layers separated by a weak ductile zone subjected to horizontally-directed compression will be characterized by the growth of folds at two dominant wavelengths, which might explain the signals at 150 and 500 km in the Bouguer gravity data.

高程间的具有正负值的协函数。数值从短波长的近零值向长波长负向的增大表示的是我们期待的均衡补偿，但常规的补偿规律在波长 150 km 至 200 km 处被打断，出现了正值。(c) 青藏高原布格与高程间的大地响应函数。(d) 到 (f) 为图 3 中横跨高原的剖面的高程与重力的一维互相关。请注意图中同相的正相关与反相的负相关的显著区别。较弱的正相关都集中在 150~200 km 波长。而显著的负相关则在 500~700 km 波长。

青藏的褶皱

图 6 表示的是岩石圈的屈服应力场，最初由岩石形变的力学实验推断而来，后外推至实际的地压力、温度和应变率。岩石圈上部强度的大小由脆裂域断层面的摩擦滑动控制。上地壳的强度随地压的加大而增强，但深度超过 15 km 后，岩石屈服以辉绿岩的塑性爬流为主。在 25~35 km 的深度域（根据当地岩石圈地温而定）和地壳底部之间应存在一软流层。就青藏高原而论，其平均地壳厚度约 60 km，塑性层应为 30 km 左右，且发育良好。在地幔最上端，由于更高强度的橄榄岩的存在，形成了又一个强度带。当在垂向受到地面和地下适度的负载应力的影响下，这种两强夹一弱的岩石圈的有效弹性厚度为：$(T_e(上地壳)^3 + T_e(上地幔岩石圈)^3)^{1/3}$，比纯两层的岩石圈的弹性厚度略大。

然而，当受到几百兆帕的横向负载时，比如印度挤压青藏，上地壳就可能全面屈服，形成像塑性体／黏性体一样的褶皱。强硬的上地幔岩石圈也可能以弹性／塑性的方式形成褶皱[26]。朱伯[27] 指出，两强夹一弱的岩石圈结构在水平挤压下易生成双波长褶皱，这解释了青藏高原布格重力异常存在 150 km 和 500 km 波长的特征。

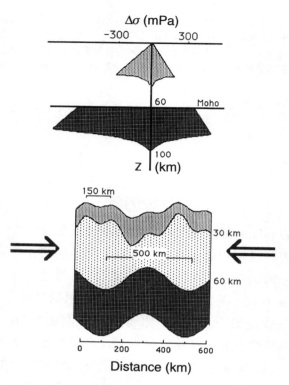

Fig. 6. Top, strength envelope for the crust and lithospheric upper mantle[25]. $\Delta\sigma$ is the difference between the maximum horizontal and vertical stresses in the plate and Z is depth. Strength in the upper part of the crust and uppermost mantle is limited by frictional sliding on faults and increases with overburden pressure. Thermally-activated creep relaxes elastic stresses in the lower crust and below the uppermost mantle. If the stress at any depth in the deformed lithosphere lies within this strength envelope, the stresses will be supported elastically (these regions are denoted by light grey shading for the upper crust and dark grey for the upper mantle). Stresses exceeding the elastic limit will cause failure by frictional sliding or ductile flow. Bottom, cross-section of lithosphere under compression that develops two scales of folding in a rheologically layered plate. The upper plate deforms in a viscous or plastic mode and contains the Conrad discontinuity. Warping of this discontinuity parallel to the surface leads to a Bouguer gravity anomaly and a positive correlation between gravity and topography. The top of the lower elastic plate is bounded by the Moho, the warping of which also leads to Bouguer gravity anomalies. The light and dark shaded regions correspond to the same rheological zones represented in the upper panel.

We can use the coherence data to test the hypothesis that the correlation between Bouguer gravity and topography at 150-km and 500-km wavelengths is caused by the folding of Tibet. The theoretical curves in Fig. 4*b* correspond to the coherence predicted for elastic plates loaded on density interfaces at the surface, a midcrustal discontinuity at 13 km, and at the Moho, as suggested by the gravity spectrum in Fig. 5. The loads at these three interfaces are assumed to be uncorrelated except in narrow wavelength bands centred around 150 and 500 km, where the coherency between the surface and subsurface loads is set at 60% to simulate the effect of folding. In keeping with the folding model shown in Fig. 6, we require that the correlations between the surface and midcrustal loads be positive in both wavelength bands. The correlation between the surface and Moho loads is only non-zero in the 500-km band, where the sign is negative. For large values of the ratio of

542

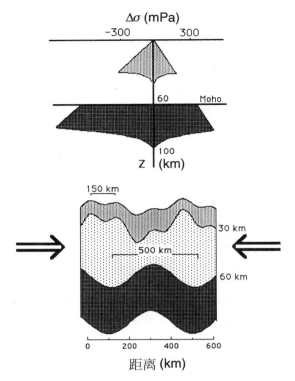

图 6. 上图：地壳和上地幔岩石圈屈服应力场 [25]。$\Delta\sigma$ 为最大水平应力与纵向应力之差，Z 为深度。上地壳与上地幔岩石圈的屈服机制为脆裂并沿断面滑动，且强度随深度增加。在下地壳及上地幔岩石圈之下，温度使弹性应力场屈服并开始蠕变。如果在任何深度应力保持在屈服应力场之内，即岩石圈形变但未屈服，则应力为弹性（未屈服地区在上地壳为浅灰色，地幔岩石圈为深灰）。应力超出屈服范围则出现摩擦滑动或爬流所产生的破坏。下图：受挤压的岩石圈剖面在应力流变的板块上形成了两个尺度的褶皱。板块上层，包括康氏面，以黏性或塑性方式形变。康氏面与地表起伏的一致导致了布格重力的异常及其与高程的正相关。下弹性板的顶部为莫霍面，它的挠曲也产生布格重力异常。浅色与深色的地区所对应的流变区与上图一致。

我们可用描述重力与高程间相关的协函数数据来检验 150 km 和 500 km 波长的特征是由青藏高原岩石圈的褶皱产生的。图 4b 的理论曲线为加载于地表，13 km 中地壳不连续界面及莫霍面的弹性板的协函数（不连续界面见图 5）。三个界面上的负载假设不相关，但在 150 km 和 500 km 的窄波长范围内，地表与地下负载的相关性设置为 60% 以模拟褶皱效应。为了与图 6 的褶皱模型保持一致，我们要求地表与中地壳的负载在两波长上为正相关。地表与莫霍面上的负载只是在 500 km 波长段为负相关，而其他段则为零。中地壳与地表负载之比 f 约为 3 时，理论值与观测值的拟合最佳，此时弹性厚度为 50 km（图 4b）。f 小则弹性板的厚度小（约为 30 km）。然而，

543

midcrustal to surface loads ($f \approx 3$), the best-fitting elastic plate thickness is approximately 50 km (Fig. 4b). Smaller values of f lead to smaller values of elastic plate thickness (~30 km). However, large values for f are required to simulate folding (that is, upwarp of subsurface density discontinuities beneath topographic highs) given a model that produces isostatic compensation (downwarping of density discontinuities beneath topographic highs). The addition of up to 500 MPa (5 kbar) of compression to the plate only modifies the shape of the coherence curves slightly.

Further support for this interpretation comes from laboratory experiments on layered, analogue materials intended to simulate the rheology in Fig. 6. Burg *et al.*[28] report that the initial stages of compression produce periodic buckling at two wavelengths: the longer, first-order wavelength is four times the combined thickness of the two strong layers and their intermediate ductile zone, and the shorter wavelength is four times the thickness of the uppermost layer and involves deformation of that layer alone. Based on the observed scales of folding in Tibet, the predicted thickness for the upper strong layer is 35 km, and the total depth to the base of the strong region in the upper mantle is 125 km, values close to that predicted from the rheological arguments and the best-fitting elastic plate thickness (Fig. 4b). The fact that the 500-km undulations are out of phase with the surface (Fig. 5d–f) suggests that the decoupling in the lower crust is sufficient to lead to an "inverse boudinage" style of folding (Fig. 6).

The total amount of strain is difficult to estimate. If, based on the fit to the coherence data, the upper mantle deforms as a 50-km elastic plate, the amount of shortening obtained by "unfolding" the 500-km wavelength undulations is at most a few percent. In the upper-crustal layer, however, the elastic strength is likely to have been exceeded everywhere, such that it deforms as a viscous or plastic layer. The fact that the coherency at 100–200 km (Fig. 5b) involves both positive and negative correlation between gravity and topography means that folding as well as layer thickening has occurred. Thus the strain in the upper crust could be substantial, as is also the case for the lower-crustal decoupling zone.

Testing Models for Tibet

This interpretation of the Bouguer gravity and topography data for Tibet in terms of folding of layers in the upper crust and uppermost mantle permits a reassessment of the merits of the three simple models presented in Fig. 1. Our layered strength profile with a decoupling zone in the lower crust and a rigid upper mantle is more in keeping with the predictions of the Asian subduction (Fig. 1a, c) models than with that of the rigid indenter model (Fig. 1b), in that the upper mantle appears too strong to shorten by the amount needed to double the thickness of the crust and thus must subduct. Either the Indian plate or the Asian lithosphere might be expected to display an effective elastic thickness of ~40–50 km. Thus our rigidity estimate does not distinguish the different polarities of subduction for the models shown in Fig. 1a and c but does preclude a weak upper mantle as in Fig. 1b. It is intriguing to note, however, that the arcuate gravity low centred at 34° N,

f 大才能模拟褶皱（也即，地下密度的不连续面的起伏与地表一致），而通常的均衡模式是地下起伏与地表反向。即使外加 500 兆帕（5 千大气压）的水平挤压对协函数的改动也不大。

对以上解释的进一步支持来自实验室对成层介质流变学的模拟实验（图 6）。布尔格等 [28] 报道在挤压实验的最初阶段，介质呈双波长的周期性弯曲：其中长波长为两强夹一弱介质总厚度的四倍，而短波长为最上一层厚度的四倍，且短波长只与上层形变相关。根据青藏高原上观测的褶皱尺度，预测的高强度上层厚度为 35 km，而整个岩石圈为 125 km。这结果与实验室流变学预测结果及图 4b 中的最佳拟合得到的弹性板厚度相吻合。事实上，500 km 起伏与地表反相（图 5d~f）说明下地壳的非耦合作用足以形成褶皱理论上的"反香肠"现象（图 6）。

青藏岩石圈的总应变是难以估算的。如果根据协函数的拟合结果，上地幔岩石圈形变为约 50 km 厚的弹性盘，将 500 km 波长的褶皱摊开，总缩短也最多不过百分之几。而对于上地壳，其弹性强度可能已屈服，整个板已呈黏性或塑性形变。事实上，在 100~200 km 波长（图 5b）上的重力和高程的协函数有正有负，说明褶皱及层加厚在同时发生。这样上地壳的应变可以很大，下地壳解耦带也会如此。

对青藏高原成因模型的检验

以上用上地壳及上地幔岩石圈成层结构对青藏高原褶皱的重力和高程数据的解释可帮助我们进一步评估图 1 中有关青藏高原成因的三种简单模型的优劣。我们成层的屈服应力强度剖面（图 6）具有下地壳解耦带和刚性的上地幔岩石圈，这更接近于亚洲俯冲模型（图 1a 和 1c），而差异于纯横向挤压模型（图 1b），也即上地幔岩石圈太硬，无法挤压形变缩短使地壳加倍，而只能向下俯冲。此时，印度板块或亚洲岩石圈都可具有约 40 km 到 50 km 的弹性厚度。因此，我们刚度的估算并无法区分图 1a 和图 1c 中显示的岩石圈俯冲的方向，但确实排除了图 1b 中显示的极弱上地幔岩石圈的存在。有意思的是，位于图 2 中北纬 34 度和东经 90 度的弓形重力低，很像

90° E (Fig. 2) is very similar to the negative gravity anomalies over oceanic trenches. If the oceanic analogue holds, the fact that the low is convex to the north would imply subduction of the Asian mantle as proposed by Willett and Beaumont[7].

(**371**, 669-674; 1994)

Yu Jin[*], Marcia K. McNutt[*] & Yongsheng Zhu[†]

[*] Department of Earth, Atmospheric and Planetary Sciences, Massachusetts Institute of Technology, Cambridge, Massachusetts 02139, USA

[†] Department of Geology, Ocean University of Qingdao, 266003 Qingdao, China

Received 27 December 1993; accepted 25 August 1994.

References:

1. Molnar, P. & Tapponnier, P. *Science* **189**, 419-426 (1975).

2. Prell, W. L. & Kutzbach, J. E. *Nature* **360**, 647-652 (1992).

3. Raymo, M. E., Ruddiman, W. F. & Froelich, P. N. *Geology* **16**, 649-653 (1988).

4. Xu, R. H., Scharer, U. & Allère, C. J. *J. Geol.* **93**, 41-57 (1985).

5. Powell, C. M. & Conaghan, P. J. *Earth Planet. Sci. Lett.* **20**, 1-12 (1973).

6. Barazangi, M. & Ni, J. *Geology* **10**, 179-185 (1982).

7. Willett, S. D. & Beaumont, C. *Nature* **369**, 642-645 (1994).

8. Dewey, J. F. & Burke, K. C. A. *J. Geol.* **81**, 683-692 (1973).

9. England, P. & McKenzie, D. P. *Geophys. J. R. astr. Soc.* **70**, 295-321 (1982).

10. Vilotte, J. P., Daignieres, M. & Madariaga, R. *J. Geophys. Res.* **87**, 10709-10728 (1982).

11. England, P. C. & Houseman, G. A. *J. Geophys. Res.* **94**, 17561-17579 (1989).

12. Zhao, W. & Morgan, W. J. *Tectonics* **4**, 359-369 (1985).

13. Karner, G. D. & Watts, A. B. *J. Geophys. Res.* **88**, 10449-10477 (1983).

14. Lyon-Caen, H. & Molnar, P. *J. Geophys. Res.* **88**, 8171-8192 (1983).

15. Sun, W. *Bouguer Gravity Anomaly Map of the People's Republic of China* (Chinese Academy of Geoexploration, Beijing, 1989).

16. Fielding, E., Isacks, B., Barazangi, M. & Duncan, C. *Geology* **22**, 163-167 (1994).

17. Bird, P. *J. Geophys. Res.* **96**, 10275-10286 (1991).

18. Forsyth, D. W. *J. Geophys. Res.* **90**, 12623-12632 (1985).

19. Bechtel, T. D., Forsyth, D. W., Sharpton, V. L. & Grieve, R. A. *Nature* **343**, 636-638 (1990).

20. Bechtel, T. D., Forsyth, D. W. & Swain, C. J. *Geophys. J. R. astr. Soc.* **90**, 445-465 (1987).

21. Zuber, M. T., Bechtel, T. D. & Forsyth, D. W. *J. Geophys. Res.* **84**, 9353-9367 (1989).

22. Weissel, J. K., Anderson, R. N. & Geller, C. A. *Nature* **287**, 284-291 (1980).

23. McNutt, M. K., Diament, M. & Kogan, M. G. *J. Geophys. Res.* **93**, 8825-8838 (1988).

24. Chen, W.-P. & Molnar, P. *J. Geophys. Res.* **88**, 4183-4214 (1983).

25. Burov, E. B., Lobkovsky, L. I., Cloetingh, S. & Nikishin, A. M. *Tectonophysics* **226**, 73-87 (1993).

26. McAdoo, D. C. & Sandwell, D. T. *J. Geophys. Res.* **90**, 8563-8569 (1985).

27. Zuber, M. *J. Geophys. Res.* **92**, E541-E551 (1987).

28. Burg, J. P., Davy, P. & Martinod, J. *Tectonics* **13**, 475-483 (1994).

Acknowledgements. We thank Y. Zhou for carefully digitizing the gravity and topography data, and L. Royden and S. Willett for insight on the models for the polarity of subduction beneath Tibet. The manuscript benefited from comments and reviews by M. Barazangi, R. Buck, D. Forsyth, P. Molnar, M. Parmentier, C. Ruppel and M. Zuber. This work was supported by NASA.

海沟处的负重力异常。如果真可如此类比，弓背向北突意味着亚洲岩石圈在俯冲，威利特和博蒙特[7]正是这样假设的。

（金煜 翻译；王二七 审稿）

DNA Fingerprinting Dispute Laid to Rest

E. S. Lander and B. Budowle

Editor's Note

After its introduction to the US courts in 1988, DNA fingerprinting was criticized for its poorly defined procedures and inadequate scientific standards. But after hundreds of scientific papers, three sets of guidelines and 150 court decisions, its bad reputation remained difficult to shed, despite having become methodologically rigorous. Here Eric S. Lander, an early critic of the lack of standards, and Bruce Budowle, one of the principal architects of the FBI's DNA typing programme, declare that "the DNA fingerprinting wars are over." There is no scientific reason to doubt the accuracy of forensic DNA typing results, and the major hurdle now, they say, is to persuade the public that the DNA fingerprinting controversy has been resolved.

Two principals in the once-raging debate over forensic DNA typing conclude that the scientific issues have all been resolved.

THE US public, usually indifferent to matters scientific, has suddenly become obsessed with DNA. Nightly newscasts routinely refer to the polymerase chain reaction (PCR) and even the tabloids offer commentary on restriction fragment length polymorphisms (RFLPs). The new-found fascination with nucleic acids does not stem from recent breakthroughs in genetic screening for breast cancer susceptibility or progress in gene therapy—developments which will indeed affect the lives of millions. Rather, it focuses on the murder case against the former US football star, O. J. Simpson.

The Los Angeles trial, starting in November and to be broadcast live by several major television networks, will probably feature the most detailed course in molecular genetics ever taught to the US people. This bold experiment in public education should, in principle, be a cause for rejoicing among scientists. The catch is that the syllabus is being prepared by attorneys whose primary roles are as adversaries; the likely result is confusion. Already, the news weeklies are preparing the ground with warnings that DNA fingerprinting remains "controversial", being plagued by major unresolved scientific issues.

Forensic DNA typing certainly did provoke controversy soon after it was introduced into US courts in 1988. The technology itself represents perhaps the greatest advance in forensic science since the development of ordinary fingerprints in 1892, and is soundly rooted in molecular biology. The problem, however, stemmed from the manner of its introduction. Pioneered by biotech start-up companies with good intentions but no track

DNA 指纹分析争议的平息

兰德，布德沃

编者按

自 1988 年 DNA 指纹分析引入美国法庭以来，就因其缺少明确的步骤和充分的科学标准而饱受批评。虽然已有数百篇相关科学文章、3 组指南和 150 例法院裁决，在方法学上已非常缜密，但这项技术依然难以摆脱坏名声。在这篇文章中埃里克·兰德（早期关注标准缺失的评论家）和布鲁斯·布德沃（美国联邦调查局 DNA 分型项目的主要设计师之一）声称"DNA 指纹战争已经结束了"。他们说，没有科学理由怀疑法医 DNA 分型结果的准确性，现在主要的障碍是说服公众相信 DNA 指纹争议已经解决了。

法医 DNA 分型曾一度引发热议，争论的双方最终达成一致：已经解决所有的科学问题。

通常来说，美国民众对科学问题是漠不关心的，然而，近来他们突然对 DNA 产生了兴趣。晚间新闻广播常常会提及聚合酶链式反应（PCR），甚至连小报也开始出现关于限制性片段长度多态性（RFLP）的评论。这种新发现的对于核酸的痴迷，并非源于乳腺癌易感性遗传筛查方面的新突破，或是可以影响上百万人生命的基因治疗方面的进展，而是源于对美国前橄榄球明星辛普森谋杀案的关注。

多家主要的电视网将对始于 11 月份的洛杉矶审判进行现场直播，这一审判可能成为美国民众学习过的最为详细的分子遗传学课程。一般来说，科学家们应该会对这种公共教育方面的大胆尝试感到欣喜。然而这其中却隐藏着一个不利因素，即教学大纲由辩护律师准备，而律师的首要角色就是反对者，因此这一尝试的结果是很不确定的。在审判之前，新闻周刊就已经预留出了带有警告标语"DNA 指纹分析受困于主要的未解决的科学问题，仍然'存在争议'"的版面。

法医 DNA 分型自 1988 年被引入美国法院后不久便引发了巨大的争议。这项完全基于分子生物学的技术，可能代表了自 1892 年普通指纹技术开始发展以来法庭科学的最大进步。但是，它的引进方式出现了问题。该技术由一些新创的生物技术公司开创，它们拥有不错的目的，然而在法庭科学方面却毫无业绩，并且在早期的几

record in forensic science, DNA typing was marred by several early cases involving poorly defined procedures and interpretation[1]. Standards were lacking for such crucial issues as: declaring a match between patterns; interpreting artefacts on gels; choosing probes; assembling databases; and computing genotype frequencies. There is broad agreement today that many of these early practices were unacceptable, and some indefensible. For its part, the US Federal Bureau of Investigation (FBI) moved much more deliberately in developing procedures, sought public comment and opted for conservative procedures.

As a result of these growing pains, forensic DNA typing was subjected to intense debate and scrutiny. When it first burst on the scene, the supporting scientific literature consisted of a mere handful of papers. By the middle of this year, there had been more than 400 scientific papers, 100 scientific conferences, 3 sets of guidelines from the Technical Working Group on DNA Analysis Methods (TWGDAM), 150 court decisions and, importantly, a 3-year study by a National Research Council (NRC) committee released in 1992 (ref. 2). In the light of this extraordinary scrutiny, it seems appropriate to ask whether there remains any important unresolved issue about DNA typing, or whether it is time to declare the great DNA fingerprinting controversy over.

As co-authors, we can address these questions in an even-handed manner. B.B. was one of the principal architects of the FBI's DNA typing programme, whereas E.S.L. was an early and vigorous critic of the lack of scientific standards, and served on the NRC committee. In a world of soundbites, we are often pegged as, respectively, a "proponent" and an "opponent" of DNA typing. Such labels greatly oversimply matters, but it is fair to say that we represent the range of scientific debate.

We recently discussed the current state of DNA typing, and could identify no remaining problem that should prevent the full use of DNA evidence in any court. What controversy existed seems to have been fully resolved by the NRC report, the TWGDAM guidelines and the extensive scientific literature. The DNA fingerprinting wars are over.

Our goal is to correct the lingering impression to the contrary. Our analysis below represents our unanimous opinions (apart from specific comments about the workings and intent of the NRC committee itself, which necessarily are based on E.S.L.'s recollection). We focus on the subject most often said to remain problematical: population genetics. Our main thesis is that the academic debate that continues to swirl about population genetic issues is rooted in a misunderstanding of the NRC report and is, in any case, of no practical consequence to the courts. We also touch on how the legal and scientific community should cope with the continuing evolution of DNA typing technology. In particular, we question whether a steady succession of *ad hoc* committees, however distinguished, is a wise solution.

例案件中，不明确的流程及解释 [1] 对 DNA 分型技术造成了一定的损害。缺乏标准的关键问题包括：如何判断图谱间相互匹配；如何解释凝胶上的人为假象；如何选择探针；如何整合数据库；如何计算基因型频率。如今，一个被普遍认可的观点是：许多的早期实践是不被认可的，并且有一些是站不住脚的。美国联邦调查局（FBI）方面为优化流程做了大量细致工作，并征求公众意见，最后选择了保守的程序。

作为发展初期必经的困难，法医 DNA 分型经受了激烈的争论和严格的检验。在它第一次出现在人们的面前时，支持性的科学文献是非常少的。到今年年中的时候，已经有 400 多篇科学论文、100 次科学会议、3 组来自 DNA 分析方法技术工作组（TWGDAM）的指南、150 例法院裁决，很重要的是，国家研究委员会（NRC）也在 1992 年发表了一篇用时 3 年的研究结果（参考文献 2）。在这异乎寻常的仔细检查之下，人们对于 DNA 分型是否存在其他未解决的重要问题，或者是否已经到了宣布结束 DNA 指纹争议的时刻的询问，似乎也都是合情合理的。

作为文章的共同作者，我们可以以公平的态度回答这些问题。布鲁斯·布德沃曾是美国联邦调查局 DNA 分型项目的主要设计师之一，而埃里克·兰德早期是一名活跃的关注科学标准缺失的批评家，并供职于国家研究委员会。在一个充满话语片断的世界里，人们通常认为我们分别是 DNA 分型的"支持者"和"反对者"。这样的标签极大地简化了存在的问题，但公平地说，我们确实代表了科学争论的幅度。

最近，我们讨论了 DNA 分型的现状，可以确定没有能阻止 DNA 证据全面应用于法庭的剩余问题。NRC 报告、TWGDAM 指南以及大量的科学文献似乎已经完全解决了存在的争议。这场 DNA 指纹分析战争结束了。

我们的目的是纠正挥之不去的反面印象。下文中的分析阐明了我们一致的观点（除了对于 NRC 委员会的工作内容和目的方面的具体评论，这部分内容必然是基于埃里克·兰德的回忆）。我们所关注的主题是群体遗传学，这也是最常被认为存在问题的方面。我们的主要论点是，围绕群体遗传学问题持续的学术争论是源于对 NRC 报告的错误理解，并且这一争论对于法院来说是没有实际意义的。我们也谈及了法律界和科学界应该如何应对持续发展的 DNA 分型技术。尤其是，我们考虑设立一个连续稳定且杰出的特设委员会是否是一个明智的解决方案。

Comparing autoradiographs from DNA samples at Cellmark Diagnostics.

Laboratory Practices

The initial outcry over DNA typing standards concerned laboratory problems: poorly defined rules for declaring a match; experiments without controls; contaminated probes and samples; and sloppy interpretation of autoradiograms[1]. Although there is no evidence that these technical failings resulted in any wrongful convictions, the lack of standards seemed to be a recipe for trouble. To address these problems, the NRC committee enunciated conservative standards for each laboratory step, based on more than a decade of experience with human DNA analysis. TWGDAM also developed guidelines along similar lines. Today, there is no doubt about the correct laboratory protocols to ensure reliable DNA typing results. Since the NRC report, US courts have unanimously accepted the technical reliability of DNA evidence, both in principle and in practice.

The NRC committee also highlighted the importance of laboratory accreditation, rigorous quality assurance and quality control (QA/QC) programs, and external blind proficiency tests (tests administered by persons outside the testing lab itself). The importance of these practices has been universally acknowledged, and most forensic labs follow TWGDAM's voluntary quality-control guidelines.

Population Genetics

The controversy over population genetics began as a secondary issue. If DNA analysis reveals that two samples match at the loci tested, the final step is to estimate the frequency of the shared genotype in the general population, which indicates the probability that a randomly chosen person would carry this genotype. Such estimates depend on surveys of

在塞尔马克诊断实验室对比 DNA 样品的放射自显影图像。

实验室规范

起初对 DNA 分型标准的强烈抗议是与实验室问题有关的：断定结果相互匹配的标准不明确；实验缺少对照；探针和样品受到污染；以及对于放射自显影图的草率解释[1]。虽然没有证据表明这些技术缺陷会导致错误定罪，但是标准的缺失很可能导致麻烦的产生。为了解决这些问题，NRC 委员会根据十多年对人类 DNA 进行分析的经验，明确阐述了每一项实验室步骤的保守性标准。TWGDAM 也制定了类似的指南。时至今日，这一能确保 DNA 分型结果可靠的正确实验室方案是毋庸置疑的。自 NRC 报告发布以来，美国法院已经在原则上和实践上一致承认 DNA 证据的技术可靠性。

NRC 委员会也强调了实验室认证、严格的质量保证和质量控制（QA/QC）程序，以及外盲水平测试（测试由该测试实验室之外的人执行）的重要性。这些操作的重要性已被广泛认可，并且多数法医实验室遵循了 TWGDAM 的非强制性质量控制指南。

群体遗传学

群体遗传学最初是作为一个次要问题而受争议的。如果 DNA 分析揭示两个样品在所检测的基因座处相互匹配，那么最后的一个步骤就是去评估该共享基因型在人群中的频率，这一结果将表明一个随机选择的个体携带该基因型的概率。然而，

the appropriate population.

In some early cases, the rarity of genotype frequencies was greatly overstated owing to a technical error: the calculations were based on overoptimistic assumptions about the precision with which genotypes could be measured. One commercial lab, for example, reported the astronomical frequency of 1 in 738,000,000,000,000, based on a four-locus match[1]. The NRC committee easily rectified these problems by requiring consistency between the measurement precision used for forensic analysis and for population genetic estimates (a practice that the FBI, in fact, had long followed).

IMAGE
UNAVAILABLE
FOR COPYRIGHT
REASONS

Opting for conservative procedures—FBI serology laboratory in Washington, DC.

A subtler but more challenging issue emerged in later cases, concerning the structure of human populations. The "product rule", used by forensic labs to calculate genotype frequencies, assumed that the individual alleles comprising a genotype could be treated as statistically independent, and their frequencies multiplied[2]. However, some population geneticists asserted that the assumption of independence was appropriate for well-mixed populations (technically, those at Hardy–Weinberg equilibrium and linkage equilibrium), but was not necessarily valid for populations with substructure. According to this argument, the frequency of a common Japanese genotype might be underestimated because the product rule ignored the fact that common Japanese alleles tend to occur together in the US Asian population. Moreover, the frequency of genotypes arising from mixed ethnic ancestry might be understated because the product rule was typically applied to separate racial databases (for the Caucasian, Black and Hispanic populations) and thus did not account for the presence of genotypes involving common alleles from different racial groups. The substructure argument became a *cause célèbre*, pitting such luminaries as Lewontin and Hartl[3] against Chakraborty and Kidd[4]. Both sides conceded that substructure could matter in principle, but many doubted that its effect could be significant in practice (see ref. 5).

这样的评估取决于对适宜人群的调查。

在早期的一些案例中，因为一个技术差错，基因型频率中的罕见情况被过分夸大了：计算结果是基于过于乐观的假设，即其准确性足以估测基因型。例如，一个商业性实验室报告了四个基因座相匹配的频率，得出了 1/738,000,000,000,000 这一天文数字级别的结果 [1]。NRC 委员会则通过要求法医分析和群众遗传评估（事实上是一项 FBI 已经长期遵循的惯例）的测量准确性相一致，从而轻而易举地纠正了这些问题。

因为版权的原因
图像不可用

FBI 在位于华盛顿的血清学实验室选择保守程序。

在后来的一些案例中，浮现出了一个细微但是更具挑战性的问题，即人群的结构。在用于法医实验室计算基因型频率的"乘法定则"中，假设了包含一个基因型的个体等位基因可以被视为在统计学上是独立的，并且其频率是可以相乘的 [2]。然而，一些人口遗传学家坚持认为，独立性的假设对于充分混合的人群而言是合理的（学术上称这些人群处于哈迪－温伯格平衡以及连锁平衡），但对于含有亚结构的人群而言未必成立。根据这一论点，因为乘法定则忽视了常见的日本人等位基因倾向于在美国亚裔人口中同时出现的事实，所以人们可能会低估常见的日本人基因型的频率。此外，由于该乘法定则适用于分离人种的数据库（白种人、黑种人以及西班牙裔美国人），不能解释其他种族的常见等位基因的出现，因此由不同种族混合产生的基因型，其频率可能会被低估。关于亚结构的争论成为了轰动一时的事件，杰出人物们也开始相互辩论，就像路翁亭和哈特尔 [3] 对抗查克拉博蒂和基德 [4] 一样。争辩的双方都承认亚结构在理论上是能够产生影响的，但是许多人质疑其影响在实际操作中的重要性（见参考文献 5）。

The NRC committee at first attempted to settle the issue on its merits. The members agreed that the product rule was probably near the mark, but were hard pressed to say just how close. The committee considered applying formulas from theoretical population genetics based on the empirical measures of the degree of variation and admixture among and within populations. However, it concluded that there were, at the time, too few hard data about the loci used in forensic typing (most classical genetic surveys concerned protein polymorphisms, likely to be strongly influenced by natural selection) and about the precise structure of the US population. It would be too risky to base a recommendation on assumptions that might subsequently turn out to be faulty.

Thomas Caskey (Baylor College) eventually pointed the way out the quagmire when he asked, out of frustration, whether it was possible to ignore population substructure altogether. Taking up the notion, the NRC committee set out to fashion an extremely conservative rule having the virtue that it made virtually no assumptions.

The Ceiling Principle

The solution turned out to be quite simple. Suppose that the US population is descended from a collection of populations P_1, P_2, ..., P_n, each sufficiently old and well mixed to allow the product rule to be safely applied. Regardless of the population substructure, the multiplication rule requires only a slight modification to yield a strict upper bound on the frequency of any genotype G: for each allele in G, the allele frequency should be taken to be the maximum over the component subpopulations. In effect, the approach makes the worst-case assumption that the population may contain individuals who, for example, carry a common Caucasian allele at a locus on chromosome 2 and a common Black allele at a locus on chromosome 17. By assuming the worst, one is guaranteed to be conservative. Because it used the maximum frequency in any subpopulation, the method was dubbed the "ceiling principle"[2].

In practice, it is unnecessary to survey every possible subpopulation. The committee concluded that the likely variation in allele frequencies could be reckoned by conducting modest surveys of 100 individuals from each of 10–15 representative subpopulations spanning the range of ethnic groups represented in the United States—such as English, Germans, Italians, Russians, Navahos, Puerto Ricans, Chinese, Japanese, Vietnamese and west Africans. Each allele frequency could then be taken to be the maximum over these subpopulations, although never less than 5%. (The latter provision was designed to deal with unexamined populations. If an allele was rare in the 10–15 subpopulations surveyed, genetic drift was not likely to have caused its frequency to drift much above 5% in other significant subpopulations.) Even in advance of detailed data about ethnic groups, the committee felt that same principle could be applied to the available racial databases (Caucasian, Black, Hispanic, Asian), although it recommended a 10% floor on allele frequencies to reflect the greater uncertainty about subpopulation variation: this slightly amended form was called the "interim ceiling principle". (The choices of 5% and 10%

556

起初，NRC委员会尝试按照实际情况解决这一问题。委员会成员一致认为该乘法定则基本接近标准，但是很难说究竟有多么接近。委员会考虑过使用理论性群体遗传学公式，这些公式是基于对不同群体间和同一群体内的变异度及混合度的经验测度的。然而，结果表明当时鲜有与法医分型相关的基因座（多数传统遗传学调查与蛋白质多态性有关，很有可能受到自然选择的显著影响）和美国人群精确结构的硬数据。将一项建议建立在可能随即会被证实有误的假设之上，是一件非常冒险的事情。

托马斯·卡斯基（来自贝勒医学院）最终给出了走出这个困境的方法，即是否有可能完全忽视人群亚结构。NRC委员会采纳了这个提议，并开始设计一个非常保守的定则，这个定则的优点是几乎不存在假定条件。

上 限 原 则

结果证明这个解决方法是十分简单的。假设美国人群是由许多不同种群的后代组成（P_1，P_2，$\cdots$，P_n），且每一个种群都足够悠久且充分融合，以至于可以放心运用乘法定则。不考虑人群亚结构，只需要稍稍修改乘法法则就可以获得任何基因型G频率的严格上界：对于基因型G中的每个等位基因而言，其等位基因频率应被视为各亚人群组分中的最大值。实际上，这一方法假设了一个最糟糕的情况，即人群中可能存在2号染色体和17号染色体基因座上分别携带有一个常见的白种人等位基因和一个常见的黑种人等位基因的个体。对这种情况的假设保证了该方法的保守性。由于在任意亚人群中都使用了最大频率，因此该方法被命名为"上限原则"[2]。

事实上，调查每一个可能的亚人群是不必要的。美国种群中有10~15个具有代表性的亚人群，可以通过对来自每一个亚人群的100个个体进行合适的调查，从而估算在等位基因频率方面可能存在的变化，这些亚人群包括英国人、德国人、意大利人、俄罗斯人、纳瓦霍人、波多黎各人、中国人、日本人、越南人和西非人等。尽管这些等位基因频率的数值从未低于5%，但是仍可将每一个等位基因频率视为这些亚人群的最大值。（其中，后一项规定是为处理未被调查的人群而设计的。如果某个等位基因在这10~15个被调查的亚人群中非常少见，那么不可能是遗传漂变导致其频率在其他重要亚人群中发生了明显超过5%的漂变。）甚至在拥有详细的种族群体数据之前，委员会就认为相同的原理可以应用于可获得的种族数据库（白种人、黑种人、西班牙裔美国人以及亚洲人），尽管等位基因频率上10%的最低值被建议用以反映更大的亚人群变化的不确定性：这一微小修正被称为"临时上限原则"。（对

were based on the quantitative effect of genetic drift on the match odds—that is, on the reciprocal of the allele frequency—although none of this reasoning survived into the text of the final report.) The practical effect of these rules was to limit the contribution of any single locus to a factor of 50:1 odds based only on aggregate data for racial classifications and 200:1 odds based on more detailed ethnic surveys.

The ceiling principle was unabashedly conservative. It gave the benefit of every conceivable doubt to the defendant, so that it could withstand attacks from the most stubborn and creative attorneys. Some of the statistical power was sacrificed to neutralize all possible worries about population substructure.

The committee was comfortable with such a lop-sided approach, because even these extreme assumptions did not undermine the practical use of DNA fingerprinting. A four-locus match performed by forensic labs could still provide odds of 6,250,000:1. If this were not enough, two additional loci could increase the odds to more than 15,000,000,000:1.

Finally, the ceiling principle was not intended to be exclusive. Expert witnesses were still free to provide their statistical "best estimate" of genotype frequencies based on the product rule. But if disagreement over such estimates arose, the ceiling principle provided an approach that all parties had to admit was biased to favour a defendant. By all rights, this seemingly solomonic solution should have ended the controversy over population genetics.

Hitting the Ceiling

Surprisingly, attacks came from an unexpected quarter. Some vocal theoretical population geneticists and statisticians concluded that the committee had been too conservative. They argued that the effect of population substructure was slight and that it would best be treated by using formulas from theoretical population genetics. The ceiling principle was accused of being clumsy and scientifically flawed. Suddenly, a new controversy over population genetics seemed to emerge[5-10].

The debate was based on a simple misunderstanding of the NRC Committee report but, with the committee disbanded, there was no easy way to address it. Moreover, the committee members had agreed to let the report speak for itself to avoid the emergence of conflicting gospels according to different members. In retrospect, this was probably an unwise decision because it has allowed a minor academic debate to snowball to the point that it threatens to undermine the use of DNA fingerprinting by suggesting that there is some problem with the use of population-genetic estimates in court.

Six objections have been raised to the ceiling principle, which are worth briefly refuting:

(1) **The ceiling principle is premised on the flawed analysis of Lewontin and Hartl that there is significant population substructure**[8]. On the contrary, the committee

于 5% 和 10% 的选择是根据遗传漂变对匹配概率的定量效应影响而做出的，即对等位基因频率的倒数的影响，虽然这些推论都未出现在最后的报告中。）这些规定的实际作用是限制任意单个基因座的贡献，在仅基于种族分类总数据时，将概率限制在 50 : 1 之内，而当基于更详细的种族调查时，将概率限制在 200 : 1 之内。

上限原则不掩饰自身的保守性。它将每一个可想到的疑点所带来的好处都提供给了被告，以便其能够抵抗来自最固执且富有创造力的律师的攻击。该方法就是通过牺牲一部分统计效能来消除所有关于人群亚结构的可能担忧。

委员会对这种偏向一方的解决方法感到满意，因为即使是这些极端的假设也不能从本质上对 DNA 指纹分析的实际应用产生损害。法医实验室进行了四个基因座的匹配，这一方法仍然可以提供 6,250,000 : 1 的概率。如果这样仍不能满足要求，可以增加两个额外的基因座从而将概率提升至 15,000,000,000 : 1 以上。

最后，上限原则不是排他性的。专家证人仍然可以自由地基于乘法定则，提供关于基因型频率的数据性"最佳估算"。但是，如果对于该估算的反对意见增多，那么上限原则就可以提供一个各方都认可且偏向于被告的解决方法。按理来说，这一看似智慧的解决方法本该结束关于群体遗传学的争议。

对上限原则的冲击

令人惊讶的是，攻击来自于一个出乎意料的群体。一些理论群体遗传学家和统计学家直言不讳地指出委员会过于保守。他们反驳说人群亚结构的作用很微弱，而最佳的选择应该是使用来自理论群体遗传学的公式。上限原则被指责是笨拙并且存在科学性缺陷的。突然之间，似乎出现了一个围绕群体遗传学的新争论 [5-10]。

这一争论起源于对 NRC 委员会报告的误解，然而，随着该委员会的解散，这一问题逐渐变得难以处理。此外，委员会成员已经同意让该报告为它自己正名，从而避免因成员们的不同说法而产生准则间自相矛盾的情况。回顾过去可以发现，这可能不是一个明智的决定，因为这使得一个小的学术争论，通过指出法庭使用群体遗传学评估存在的一些问题而迅速升级到可以威胁 DNA 指纹分析应用的程度。

反对者提出了六条关于上限原则的反对意见，而这些都是值得进行简略反驳的：

（1）**上限原则是以路翁亭和哈特尔提出的、存在重要群体亚结构的缺陷分析为前提的** [8]。事实恰恰相反，虽然委员会非常怀疑亚结构具有的重要影响，但是它仍

was quite dubious that substructure had significant effects, but felt that the possibility needed to be taken seriously rather than dismissed based on theoretical or indirect arguments. The NRC report cites the Lewontin–Hartl article[3] only twice, both times balanced against a longer list of opposing articles.

(2) The ceiling principle is scientifically flawed because it is not used in population genetics[9,10]. Moreover, the plan to sample 10–15 representative populations is statistically unsound[8]. The choice of a statistical method necessarily depends on the dangers of overestimation versus underestimation. In forensics, there is strong agreement on the need to be conservative. By contrast, population geneticists do not need to be conservative in academic studies; they are content to err equally often on the high and low side, and thus ceiling approaches are unnecessary. However, ceiling approaches are common in a closely related genetic pursuit: the mapping of disease genes. To guard against falsely implicating or excluding a chromosomal region, human geneticists often analyse their data under worst-case conditions, such as using an unrealistically low ceiling on the penetrance of a disease gene or an unrealistically high frequency for a marker allele[11,12]. Also, some authors have complained that surveys of 100 individuals do not allow accurate estimates of the frequency of rare alleles[8]. The purpose of the suggested population studies, however, was not to estimate low frequencies, but rather to check that some alleles do not unexpectedly have extremely high frequencies (much more than 5–10%) in certain populations. For this purpose, 100 individuals is quite adequate.

(3) The ceiling principle makes ludicrous assumptions about the possible substructure of a population[9,10]. Although the NRC report called for empirical studies of those groups that made significant contributions to the United States (such as English, Italians and Puerto Ricans), some commentators[9,10] were carried away by hyperbole—asserting that the ceiling principle assumes that "the culprit might be...a Lapp for one allele and a Hottentot for the other". However, if Lapp and Hottentot are replaced by Italians and Puerto Ricans, the assumption is perfectly reasonable. Indeed, it is unreasonable to assume that such genotypes don't occur in the population.

(4) The ceiling principle is so conservative that it hampers the courtroom application of DNA fingerprinting. Despite fears that an ultraconservative standard would clip the wings of the DNA fingerprinting, published analyses by several groups[13,14] agree that the effect is modest: Whereas the product rule typically gives four-locus genotype frequencies of about 10^{-8}–10^{-9}, the ceiling principle pares them back to about 10^{-6}–10^{-7}. That extreme assumptions have so little effect only underscores the power of DNA typing and the wisdom of taking a conservative approach.

(5) The ceiling principle is not actually guaranteed to be conservative. This concern appears in only a single paper[15], in which the authors point out that the conservativeness of the ceiling principle depends on the component populations $P_1, ..., P_n$ being themselves well-mixed. The authors take great pains to construct counterexamples in the event that the populations are themselves substructured. In fact, the NRC committee considered this point

然认为需认真对待这一可能性，而不是根据理论性的或间接的论据而忽视它。NRC 的报告只引用了两次路翁亭－哈特尔的文章 [3]，并且两次都用了更多相反的文章来维持平衡。

（2）**因为上限原则不用于群体遗传学，所以它具有科学性瑕疵 [9,10]。此外，选取 10~15 个代表性群体的计划在统计学上也是不可靠的 [8]。**统计学方法的选择必须基于对高估与低估所导致的危险的比较。法医方面对保守性的需求具有很强的一致性。相比之下，群体遗传学家在学术研究方面并不需要保守性；他们常常满足于在上限和下限同等地犯错，因此上限方法是非必需的。然而，上限方法却常见于与之密切相关的遗传寻踪之中：绘制疾病基因图谱。为了防止错误地引入或排除某个染色体区域，人类遗传学家常常在最坏情况下分析数据，例如将一个不合实际的较低上限值用于某个疾病基因的外显率，或者将一个不合实际的高频率用于某一标记等位基因 [11,12]。与此同时，一些作者抱怨含有 100 个个体的调查并不能对罕见等位基因的基因频率进行精确估算 [8]。但是，对于所建议的群体研究而言，其目的不是为了估算低频率，而是为了验证特定人群中的一些等位基因不具有出乎意料的极高频率（大大超过 5%~10%）。就这一目的而言，100 个个体已经是相当充足的。

（3）**上限原则中关于群体中可能的亚结构的假设是滑稽的 [9,10]。**虽然 NRC 的报告需要那些对美国人群有显著影响的群体（例如英国人、意大利人以及波多黎各人）的经验性研究的支持，但是一些评论员 [9,10] 被夸张的说法冲昏了头脑——他们断言上限原则假定了"罪犯可能……根据一个等位基因而言是拉普人，根据另一个等位基因则是霍屯督人"。但是，如果拉普人和霍屯督人被替换为意大利人和波多黎各人，那么这个假设便变得极其合理了。事实上，假设这样的基因型不会在人群中发生是不合理的。

（4）**上限原则过于保守以至于阻碍了 DNA 指纹分析在法庭上的应用。**尽管对极端保守的标准可能会钳制住 DNA 指纹分析的翅膀的情况存在担忧，但是由多个团队 [13,14] 发表的分析结果表明，该影响是微弱的：乘法定则通常提供的四个基因座基因型频率在 10^{-8}~10^{-9} 左右，然而上限原则将其削减至 10^{-6}~10^{-7} 左右。前面所述的极端假设具有很弱的影响，它仅仅强调了 DNA 分型的效力以及实施保守性方法的智慧。

（5）**事实上，上限原则并未保证其保守性。**这一忧虑仅在一篇论文 [15] 中出现过，作者在文章中指出，上限原则的保守性依赖于自身充分混合的组分人群 P_1，…，P_n。该作者还努力构造了假如人群本身具有亚结构的反例。事实上，NRC 委员会认为，这一点是不证自明的（虽然未能足够清晰地阐述这一点），因为从琐碎的观察中就可

to be self-evident (although failed to state it clearly enough), as can be seen from the trivial observation that the ceiling principle has no effect on genotype frequencies when one combines two identical, but substructured populations. In applying the ceiling principle in practice, the committee was confident that any residual substructure in the component subpopulations could safely be ignored in the context of such a conservative scheme.

(6) The NRC report is causing DNA fingerprinting cases to be thrown out of court[8]. To the contrary, most courts have used the NRC report as strong evidence that, notwithstanding disagreement over the best solution, there is at least one approach that is indisputably conservative. Of the few cases in which DNA evidence has ever been rejected on population-genetic grounds, virtually all involved evidence predating the NRC report. These courts have cited the report solely for its acknowledgement that a controversy existed and was a reason for constituting the committee.

The NRC report, to be sure, has important flaws. The ceiling principle was not elegant solution, but simply a practical way to sidestep a contentious and unproductive debate. The report had more than its share of miswordings, ambiguities and errors, many of which have been corrected by a vigilant commentator[16]. A few poorly worded sentences have been seized upon by lawyers trying to undermine the straightforward calculation of ceiling frequencies (although such arguments have not succeeded). Most important, the report failed to state clearly enough that the ceiling principle was intended as an ultra-conservative calculation, which did not bar experts from providing their own "best estimates" based on the product rule. This failure was responsible for the major misunderstanding of the report. Ironically, it would have been easy to correct.

A Law-enforcement Perspective

Even as academics debated fine points, forensic scientists got on with their business. The FBI and TWGDAM found the ceiling principle to be unnecessarily conservative, but nonetheless promptly adopted precise guidelines for implementing the ceiling principle, correctly clarifying a few ambiguous statements in the NRC report, such as which population databases to include and whether to sum adjacent bins in a frequency distribution. Forensic labs adopted a two-tiered approach, in which experts are prepared to quote both their best estimate and the conservative ceiling bound. As new population-genetic issues arise (such as how to modify or replace the ceiling principle to accommodate the less polymorphic PCR-based systems), the community is preparing to develop further guidelines. Overall, the system meets the spirit and the letter of the NRC report.

Conservative calculations have had no noticeable impact on the use of DNA evidence. In the vast majority of cases, a jury needs to know only that a particular DNA pattern is very rare to weigh it in the context of a case: the distinction between frequencies of 10^{-4}, 10^{-6} and 10^{-8} is irrelevant in the case of suspects identified by other means.

以得知，当一个人群中含有两个相同但具有亚结构的人群时，上限原则对基因型频率是无影响的。在上限原则的实际应用方面，委员会自信地认为基于这种保守性方案的前提可以安全地忽略组分亚人群中任何剩余的亚结构。

(6) NRC 的报告将导致 DNA 指纹分析案件被踢出法庭 [8]。事实恰恰相反，尽管仍然存在对于这项最佳解决方法的异议，大多数法院已经将 NRC 报告作为一个强有力的证据来证明这个方法至少是一个无可争辩的保守性方法。在少数群体遗传学水平上 DNA 证据被弃用的案例中，几乎所有案例都包含在时间上早于 NRC 报告的证据。这些法院已经引用了这个报告，该报告承认争议的存在并以此作为建立该委员会的理由。

诚然，NRC 的报告存在重要的缺陷。虽然上限原则不是绝妙的解决办法，但的确是一个可以避开无休止、无结果的争论的实用方法。这个报告含有的不只是措辞不当、语意含糊以及谬误这些小瑕疵，其中多数不足已经被警惕的评论员修正了 [16]。尝试损害上限频率这种简便计算方法的律师们已经抓住了少数措辞不当的语句（尽管这样的争论还未成功）。最重要的是，该报告未能明确阐述上限原则的目的是作为一个极端保守的计算方法，这一方法没有禁止专家们提出他们自己基于乘法定则的"最佳估算"。这一失误是引起对该报告产生严重误解的原因。讽刺的是，做出改正本应很容易。

执 法 视 角

在学术界辩论细节问题的同时，法医学家继续着他们的工作。FBI 和 TWGDAM 认为上限原则具有的保守性是非必需的，尽管如此，它们也迅速采纳了精确的指南来履行上限原则，正确地阐明了 NRC 报告中的一些模糊表述，例如将哪一个人群数据库包含在内的问题以及是否将频率分布中相邻区间的数据进行相加。法医实验室采取了双层法，即专家们准备引用最佳估算结果以及保守的上限范围。随着新的群体遗传学问题的出现（例如如何修改或替换上限原则以适应基于 PCR 的具有更少多态性的系统），科研团队正准备开发更进一步的指南。总的来说，该系统与 NRC 报告的精神和文字内容相符。

对于 DNA 证据的使用而言，保守性计算的影响已经不再明显。在绝大多数案例中，陪审团只需要了解在一种情况下，某个特定的 DNA 模式很难作为衡量案件的证据，即在用其他方法鉴别出嫌疑人的案件中，10^{-4}、10^{-6} 以及 10^{-8} 这三种频率间的差异是没有意义的 。

The FBI has also rapidly carried out population surveys, as recommended by the NRC committee. FBI scientists have studied more than 25 distinct subpopulations, as well as 50 separate samples from the US population[17-21]. The effort has yielded a remarkable database for examining allele frequency variation among ethnic groups. Reassuringly, the observed variation is modest for the loci used in forensic analysis and random matches are quite rare, supporting the notion that the FBI's implementation of the product rule is a reasonable best estimate. Nonetheless, the FBI has taken the scientifically sound position that it remains wiser to study new loci empirically than to assume that significant variation can never occur.

Most important, the admissibility of such DNA evidence prepared in accordance with the NRC recommendations is firmly established in virtually all US jurisdictions. In a few, the appellate courts have yet to rule formally, but there is little doubt that they will find such evidence acceptable.

Modest Proposals

Although the system ain't broke, there is no shortage of proposals about how to fix it. Some academic commentators advocate a return to the product rule; others propose an approach based on the kinship statistic F_{ST}; and still others recommend an approach involving likelihood ratios that combine gel electrophoresis artefacts and population-genetic considerations into a single statistic[9,10,22-24]. Some seek to determine genotype frequencies exactly, while others prefer conservative estimates. The NRC—at the urging of the National Institute of Justice, representing the academic wing of forensic scientists— has concluded that the best solution is to constitute another *ad hoc* committee on DNA fingerprinting, composed primarily of statisticians and population geneticists.

It is easy to forget that this new debate is purely academic. The most extreme positions range over a mere two orders of magnitude: whether the population frequency of a typical four-locus genotype should be stated, for example, as 10^{-5} or 10^{-7}. The distinction is irrelevant for courtroom use.

Rehashing issues may be a harmless pastime in the academic world, but not so in a legal system that lives by the dictum *stare decisis* (let the decision stand). From the standpoint of law enforcement, it is better to have a settled, if slightly imperfect, rule than ceaselessly to quest after perfection. Already the NRC's intention to re-examine forensic DNA typing has been seized upon by some lawyers as evidence that there remain fundamental problems.

Ad hoc committees typically imagine that they will be able to accomplish their mandate with speed and finality. The original NRC study was anticipated to take one year, but required three. The idea of a second NRC panel was first floated in June 1993 with the optimistic projection that it could report by the end of that year. In fact, the committee has only

就像 NRC 委员会建议的那样，FBI 也已经迅速地进行了群体调查。FBI 的科学家们已经研究了超过 25 个不同的亚人群，以及 50 个来自美国人群的独立样本[17-21]。通过这些努力得到了一个可以检验种群间等位基因频率变化的非凡数据库。可以放心的是，观测到的变化对用于法医分析的基因座而言是轻微的，而且很少发生随机匹配，这一点支持了一个观点，即 FBI 对于乘法定则的应用是一个明智的最佳判断。尽管如此，FBI 已经采取了科学合理的态度，相对于假设从不发生显著变化的情况而言，根据经验研究新基因座仍然更为明智。

最重要的是，按照 NRC 的建议准备的 DNA 证据在几乎所有美国管辖的地区内都被认可了。但在少数地区，还有一些受理上诉的法院未能接受这类证据，但毫无疑问的是，他们终将发现这类证据是值得认可的。

小小的建议

虽然这个系统未被破坏，但是也不缺少关于如何修补它的建议。一些学术评论家主张重新启用乘法定则；另一些则提出了一个基于亲属关系统计值 F_{ST} 的解决方法；还有一些人建议使用涉及似然比的方法，即将凝胶电泳人为假象和群体遗传学方面要考虑的因素组合成一个单个的统计数据[9,10,22-24]。一些人设法精确地确定基因型频率，然而其他人则更倾向于保守性的判断。国家司法研究所是法医学权威的代表，在它的督促下，NRC 最终做出了决定，即最佳的解决方法是建立另一个与 DNA 指纹印分析相关的特设委员会，该委员会主要由统计学家和群体遗传学家组成。

容易遗忘的一点是，这一新辩论是纯学术性的。最极端位置间的差异仅仅超过了两个数量级：例如，一个典型的四个基因座基因型的群体频率是否应被表述为 10^{-5} 或 10^{-7}。这个差异与法庭中的应用并不相干。

在学术界，对于一些问题的重新讨论也许是一种无恶意的娱乐，但是在以遵循先例（维持决议的效力）为信条的司法系统中，情况并非如此。从执法的角度来看，相比于不停地追求一个完美的规则，拥有一个即使存在些许不足的固定规则会更好一些。一些律师已经抓住 NRC 打算重新检查法医 DNA 分型的意图，并将其作为支持 DNA 分型仍然存在严重问题的证据。

特设委员会曾设想自己能够迅速而彻底地完成使命。预期花费一年时间完成的初期 NRC 研究最终用了三年的时间才得以完成。1993 年 6 月，人们首次提出设立第二个 NRC 专家小组的想法，并且乐观地预期它能够在年末发表报告。事实上，委

just begun meeting and will probably not issue a report before late 1995. Even then, any recommendations will take 3 years to ripple through the legal system — guaranteeing that finality will not be achieved on these issues before early 1999. Despite the committee's best efforts, any new report will probably offer new opportunities for misunderstanding that will become apparent only after the panel is disbanded. And, if the new report endorses a different standard, some attorneys are sure to argue, rightly or wrongly, that differences between the reports demonstrate a lack of scientific consensus. These observations are not meant to dissuade the new NRC committee from its mission, but rather to point out the challenge facing any *ad hoc* group.

A Sounder Approach

The real solution is to recognize that forensic DNA typing has become a mature field and requires a more systematic approach. The NRC report anticipated that rapid evolution of technology would pose a steady succession of questions requiring attention. Its most important recommendation was the establishment of a permanent national committee on forensic DNA typing (NCFDT) to address issues as they arose. If such a committee had been appointed in 1992, it could have made short work of the population-genetics issues, by clarifying, changing or discarding the original NRC recommendations.

It is encouraging that this NRC recommendation has recently been adopted. The newly enacted DNA Identification Act of 1994 mandates the FBI to establish a DNA advisory board to recommend standards for laboratory procedures, quality assurance and proficiency testing. The act requires open meetings and broad representation, including molecular and population geneticists not affiliated with forensic laboratories, with board nominations to come from professional organizations including the National Academy of Sciences. Ideally, the panel will provide a forum for weighing important issues, including new laboratory techniques, population genetics and proficiency testing.

Most of all, the public needs to understand that the DNA fingerprinting controversy has been resolved. There is no scientific reason to doubt the accuracy of forensic DNA typing results, provided that the testing laboratory and the specific tests are on a par with currently practiced standards in the field. The scientific debates served a salutary purpose: standards were professionalized and research stimulated. But now it is time to move on.

(**371**, 735-738; 1994)

Eric S. Lander and Bruce Budowle

Eric S. Lander is in the Whitehead Institute for Biomedical Research, Nine Cambridge Center, Cambridge, Massachusetts 02142, USA and the Department of Biology, MIT, Cambridge, Massachusetts 02139, USA.
Bruce Budowle is in the Forensic Science Research and Training Center, FBI Laboratory, FBI Academy, Quantico, Virginia 22135, USA.

员会仅仅是开始进行了会议，并且不太可能在 1995 年年末前发表报告。即使这样，任何建议也都将需要三年的时间才能影响司法系统——确保了这些问题在 1999 年年初前都不会有最终的结果。虽然委员会在不懈努力，但是任何的新报道都有可能给误解的发生提供机会，并且这将在该专家小组解散后显现出来。此外，如果新报告支持一个不同的标准，那么无论正确与否一些律师一定会争辩说这些报告间的差异显示了它们之间缺乏科学共识。这些评论并非旨在劝阻这个新 NRC 委员会完成使命，而是为了指出任何特设委员会会面临的挑战。

一个更合理的方法

真正的解决办法是，认识到法医 DNA 分型已经成为一个成熟的技术领域并且需要一个系统性更强的方法。NRC 的报告做出了预测，技术的迅速发展将导致一连串需要注意的问题的出现。该报告中最重要的建议是建立一个持久的、与法医 DNA 分型相关的国家委员会（NCFDT），以便解决出现的问题。如果在 1992 年就成立了这样的委员会，那么它可能已经通过阐述、改变或弃用最初 NRC 的建议，从而迅速地解决群体遗传学的问题。

令人鼓舞的是，NRC 的这条建议最近已经被采纳了。最新制定的 1994 年 DNA 鉴定相关法案要求 FBI 组建一个 DNA 顾问委员会，用以为实验室程序、质量保证以及水平测试提供标准规范。该法案要求会议公开并且代表具有广泛性，这些代表包括不隶属于法医实验室的分子遗传学家和群体遗传学家，且都是由委员会提名的、来自于包括美国国家科学院在内的专业组织机构。理想状况下，该委员会将提供一个权衡重要问题的平台，这些问题包括新的实验室技术、群体遗传学以及水平测试。

最重要的是，公众需要明白 DNA 指纹分析的争论已经结束。如果测试实验室和特定的测试与当前这一领域的标准规范是一致的，那么就不存在质疑法医 DNA 分型结果的科学理由。这些科学争论是为了一个有益的目的：使标准规范变得专业化并且调查研究能产生促进作用。现在，我们该继续前进了。

（高俊义 翻译；方向东 审稿）

References:

1. Lander, E. S. *Nature* **339**, 501-505 (1989).

2. National Research Council *DNA Technology in Forensic Science* (National Academy Press, 1992).

3. Lewontin, R. C. & Hartl, D. L. *Science* **254**, 1745-1750 (1991).

4. Chakraborty, R. & Kidd, K. K. *Science* **254**, 1735-1739 (1991).

5. *Science* **266**, 201-203 (1994).

6. Weir, B. S. *Proc. Natl. Acad. Sci. U.S.A.* **89**, 11654-11659 (1992).

7. Aldhous, P. *Science* **259**, 755-756 (1993).

8. Devlin, B., Risch, N. & Roeder, K. *Science* **259**, 748-749 (1993).

9. Morton, N. E., Collins, A. & Balasz, I. *Proc. Natl. Acad. Sci. U.S.A.* **90**, 1892-1896 (1993).

10. Morton, N. E. *Genetica* (in the press).

11. Schellenberger, G. D. *et al. Science* **258**, 668 (1992).

12. Terwlliger, J. D. & Ott, J. *Handbook of Human Genetic Linkage* (Johns Hopkins Univ. Press, 1994).

13. Duncan, G. T., Noppinger, K. & Tracy, M. *Genetica* **88**, 51-57 (1993).

14. Krane, D. E. *et al. Proc. Natl. Acad. Sci. U.S.A.* **89**, 10583-10587 (1992).

15. Slimowitz, J. R. & Cohen, J. E. *Am. J. Hum. Genet* **53**, 314-323 (1993).

16. Weir. B. S. *Am. J. Hum. Genet* **52**, 437-440 (1993).

17. Federal Bureau of Investigation *VNTR Population Data: A Worldwide Study* (1993).

18. Budowle, B., Monson, K. L., Giusti, A. M. & Brown. B. L. *J. Forensic Sci.* **39**, 319-352 (1994).

19. Budowle, B., Monson, K. L., Giusti. A. M. & Brown, B. L. *J. Forensic Sci.* **39**, 988-1008 (1994).

20. Budowle, B. *et al. J. Forensic Sci.* (in the press).

21. Huang, N. E. & Budowle, B. *J. Forensic Sci.* (in the press).

22. Morton, N. E. *Proc. Natl. Acad. Sci. U.S.A.* **89**, 2556-2560 (1992).

23. Evett, I. E., Scranage, J. & Pinchin, R. *Am. J. Hum. Genet.* **52**, 498-505 (1993).

24. Balding, D. J. & Nichols, R. A. *Forensic Sci. Int.* **64**, 125-140 (1994).

Distance to the Virgo Cluster Galaxy M100 from Hubble Space Telescope Observations of Cepheids

W. L. Freedman *et al.*

Editor's Note

In astronomy it is essential to know the distance to any object, because only then can the observed brightness at any wavelength be converted to the true luminosity. Variable stars called Cepheids are central to working out this "distance ladder", because their luminosity is closely related to their period and can thus be determined independently. Here Wendy Freedman and colleagues use the Hubble Space Telescope to determine the Cepheid distance to the galaxy M100, and thereby determine an accurate value for the Hubble constant, which measures the expansion rate of the Universe. This was one of the key design goals for the HST. The initial value of $\sim 80\,\mathrm{km\ s^{-1}\ Mpc^{-1}}$ was refined over the following decade.

Accurate distances to galaxies are critical for determining the present expansion rate of the Universe or Hubble constant (H_0). An important step in resolving the current uncertainty in H_0 is the measurement of the distance to the Virgo cluster of galaxies. New observations using the Hubble Space Telescope yield a distance of 17.1 ± 1.8 Mpc to the Virgo cluster galaxy M100. This distance leads to a value of $H_0 = 80 \pm 17\,\mathrm{km\ s^{-1}\ Mpc^{-1}}$. A comparable value of H_0 is also derived from the Coma cluster using independent estimates of its distance ratio relative to the Virgo cluster.

WITHIN the framework of general relativity, the evolution of the Universe can be specified by the Friedmann equation which relates the expansion rate H, to the mean mass density ρ, the curvature k, and a possible additional term, called the cosmological constant Λ (identified with the gravitational effects of the vacuum energy density). In a uniform and isotropic Universe the relative expansion velocity v is proportional to the relative distance r such that $v = H \times r$. Thus a determination of the present-day value of the Hubble constant H_0 determines both the expansion timescale and the size scale of the Universe. The Hubble constant also provides constraints on the density of baryons produced in the Big Bang, the amount of dark matter, and how structure formed in the early Universe[1,2].

Despite 65 years of study, the value of the Hubble constant has remained in dispute. Although the measurement of relative velocities of galaxies is straightforward, the measurement of accurate distances has always been more difficult. For distances out to ~ 5 Mpc, there is now general agreement[3,4] to a level of better than $\sim \pm 10\%$. However, for

由哈勃空间望远镜观测造父变星到室女星系团成员星系 M100 的距离

弗里德曼等

编者按

在天文学中，知道任意天体的距离是重要的，因为只有这样才能将任意波长处观测到的亮度转换为真实的光度。被称作造父变星的变星对得到"距离阶梯"尤为重要，因为它们的光度和它们的光变周期紧密相关，因而它们的光度可以独立地测定。在这篇文章中，温迪·弗里德曼和他的同事们利用哈勃空间望远镜测定到 M100 星系的造父距离，并从而测定哈勃常数（衡量宇宙膨胀率的参数）的精确值。确定哈勃常数是哈勃空间望远镜的主要设计目标之一。它最初的值 $\sim 80 \ \mathrm{km \cdot s^{-1} \cdot Mpc^{-1}}$ 在之后的几十年中得到了修正。

测定到星系的精确距离对于测定目前的宇宙膨胀率或哈勃常数 (H_0) 是至关重要的。解决目前 H_0 不确定性的重要一步是测量到室女星系团的距离。使用哈勃空间望远镜新的观测得到的到室女星系团成员星系 M100 的距离为 $17.1 \pm 1.8 \ \mathrm{Mpc}$。由这一距离得到 $H_0 = 80 \pm 17 \ \mathrm{km \cdot s^{-1} \cdot Mpc^{-1}}$。利用后发星系团相对室女星系团距离比进行独立的测定，也得到了相近的 H_0 值。

在广义相对论的框架内，宇宙的演化可以用弗里德曼方程描述，这一方程将膨胀率 H 与平均质量密度 ρ、曲率 k 以及一个称作宇宙学常数 Λ（等同于真空能量密度的引力作用）的可能的附加项联系起来。在一个均匀且各向同性的宇宙中，相对膨胀速度 v 正比于相对距离 r，即 $v = H \times r$。因此，测定哈勃常数的当前值 H_0 就同时得到了宇宙的膨胀时标和尺度。哈勃常数也对大爆炸时期产生的重子物质密度、暗物质的数量以及宇宙早期结构的形成都具有约束作用 [1,2]。

尽管经过了 65 年的研究，但是哈勃常数的值仍然存在争议。尽管测量星系间的相对速度是直接的，然而测量星系间的精确距离却困难得多。目前普遍认为，对于大约 5 Mpc 的距离的测定，测量的精度高于 $\pm 10\%$ [3,4]。然而，对于像到室女星系团这么遥远的目标的距离，测量结果存在很大的分歧 [5,6]，其测量值大约在 15 Mpc 到

distances as great as the Virgo cluster there is a significant discrepancy[5,6], with quoted values ranging from about 15 to 24 Mpc. Not only is there a range of published distances, but there is a tendency for the values to cluster at the extremes, giving rise to the so-called "short" and "long" distance scales.

The most accurate means of measuring the distances to galaxies has proved to be the application of a relationship between the period and the luminosity for a class of supergiant variable stars known as classical Cepheids. In fact, Cepheids were used by Edwin Hubble to demonstrate the extragalactic nature of the spiral nebulae[7,8]. They are relatively young, massive stars with luminosities $\sim 1,000$ to $100,000$ times brighter than the Sun ($-2 < M_V < -7$ mag). They are well calibrated; they are easy to identify in external galaxies because of their variability and brightness; and they have measured dispersions in the V- and I-band period–luminosity (P–L) relationships amounting to only ± 0.25 and ± 0.20 mag, respectively[3]. In addition, the underlying physical basis for the Cepheid P–L relation is well understood.

Unfortunately, Cepheids are not luminous enough to be observed out to distances where galaxies are participating in the free expansion of the Universe. The motions of individual galaxies can be perturbed by interactions with nearby neighbouring galaxies; in addition, galaxies can participate in large-scale flows[9,10]. Hence, to measure the pure Hubble flow, other (secondary) distance techniques must be used to extend the extragalactic distance scale beyond the observable range of the Cepheids, to recession velocities of a few thousand km s^{-1} where peculiar velocities (which can amount to several hundred km s^{-1}) are small in comparison to the expansion velocity.

The Virgo cluster of galaxies is close enough to be studied in detail; and yet it is far enough away that it is of cosmological interest. It is rich in both spiral and elliptical galaxies and therefore it has played a critical role in the extragalactic distance scale and determination of the Hubble constant. Thus obtaining a Cepheid distance to the Virgo cluster represents a crucial step in resolving the current uncertainty in H_0 and resolving the dichotomy in distance estimates. A variety of other techniques for measuring distances have been applied to the Virgo cluster; hence, an accurate direct measure of the distance to this cluster can be used to calibrate (or set the zero point for) other secondary distance indicators.

The Key Project

The goal of the Hubble Space Telescope Key Project on the extragalactic distance scale is to provide a measure of the Hubble constant accurate to 10%. This aim is non-trivial given that the history of previous attempts to measure the extragalactic distance scale is replete with examples where large systematic errors were eventually revealed. Hence, the determination of accurate distances requires careful attention to eliminating potential sources of systematic error.

24 Mpc 之间。已经发表的距离不仅范围很大，而且到星系团的距离还存在着两种极端趋势，即所谓"短"的和"长"的距离尺度。

已经证实的测量星系团距离最精确的方法是应用被称作经典造父变星的一类超巨星变星的周光关系。事实上，造父变星曾被埃德温·哈勃用来解释旋涡星云位于银河系之外 [7,8]。它们是相对年轻的大质量恒星，其光度是太阳的约 1,000 倍到 10,000 倍（$-2\,\text{mag} < M_V < -7\,\text{mag}$）。它们已经被很好地定标过；由于其光变和亮度，它们很容易在河外星系中被识别出来；它们在 V 波段与 I 波段的周光关系中测量出的弥散度分别只有 $\pm 0.25\,\text{mag}$ 和 $\pm 0.20\,\text{mag}$ [3]。另外，我们对于造父变星周光关系的物理机制也已经有了较好的了解。

遗憾的是，造父变星由于亮度不够，在宇宙自由膨胀的星系中，还不能被观测到。个别星系的运动可能在与邻近星系的相互作用中受到干扰；另外，星系可能参与大尺度的流动 [9,10]。因此，为了测量纯粹的哈勃流，必须使用其他的（次级的）距离测量技术，以便将河外星系的距离尺度扩展到造父变星的可观测范围之外，在这一区域退行速度为每秒几千千米，而本动速度（大小只有每秒几百千米）与宇宙的膨胀速度相比则很小。

室女星系团距离我们足够近，可以详细地加以研究；而且从宇宙学研究的角度来看，它也足够远。该星系团富含旋涡星系和椭圆星系，这使得它在河外星系的距离尺度和哈勃常数测定上都扮演着至关重要的角色。因此，获得室女星系团的造父距离，对于解决当前 H_0 测定的不确定性以及距离估计上的分歧，都是关键的一步。鉴于各种测定距离的其他方法都已经用到了室女星系团；因此，精确地直接测量到这个星系团的距离可以用来定标（或者设置零点）所有其他的次级示距天体。

关 键 项 目

哈勃空间望远镜关于河外距离尺度的关键项目主要目标是将哈勃常数的测量精度提高到 10%。考虑到之前河外距离尺度测量的历史中充斥的许多事例（最终都被证实存在着很大的系统误差），就会发现这一目标是意义非凡的。因此，精确距离的测量要求仔细地去消除潜在的各种系统误差。

The strategy adopted by the Key Project team on the extragalactic distance scale is threefold. The first goal is to discover Cepheids, and thereby measure accurate primary distances to spiral galaxies located in the field and in small groups that are suitable for the calibration of several independent secondary methods. (These secondary methods include: the Tully–Fisher relationship[11,12], the surface-brightness fluctuation method[13], the planetary nebula luminosity function[14], the expanding photosphere method applied to type II supernovae[15,16], and the measurement of the luminosities of type Ia supernovae[6,17-19].) The second objective is to provide a check on potential systematic errors in the Cepheid distance scale through independent distance estimates to the nearby galaxies, M31, M33 and the Large Magellanic Cloud (LMC) and, in addition, to undertake an empirical test of the sensitivity of the zero point of the Cepheid *P–L* relationship to heavy-element abundances. The third and most challenging observational goal is to make Cepheid measurements of distances to three spiral galaxies in the Virgo cluster and two members of the Fornax cluster.

The Distance to M100

Our first observations aimed at finding Cepheids in a Virgo cluster galaxy were made in a two-month period beginning in April 1994 with a sequence of 12 1-hour *V*-band exposures of a field ~2 arcmin east of the nucleus of M100. The observing strategy was designed to provide well-sampled light curves for Cepheids having periods ranging from 10 to 60 days. In addition, *I*-band exposures were taken back-to-back with 4 of the *V* observations. We present here sample light curves for the Cepheids discovered, their *V*-band and *I*-band *P–L* relationships, and a preliminary estimate of the distance to M100. Details of the data reduction and analysis, tabulation of the photometry, and identification of the variables will be presented elsewhere (L.F. *et al.*, manuscript in preparation; R.H. *et al.*, manuscript in preparation). Three independent calibrations of the photometric zero points were made; the final resulting uncertainties in the *V* and *I* zero points amount to ±0.05 and ±0.04 mag, respectively. A description of the sampling strategy used for the optimal discovery of variables, and of the method used for identification of variables, determination of mean magnitudes, reddening, and distance have been published elsewhere[20].

V-band light curves for twelve M100 Cepheids are illustrated in Fig. 1. The total sample of Cepheids has a range of periods from 20 to 65 days, and mean *V* magnitudes ranging from 25.0 to 26.5 mag. It is evident from the small scatter in the light curves that the quality of the photometry being obtained by the Hubble Space Telescope (HST) is excellent. Internal estimates of the random errors for single data points are found to be ±0.14 mag at $V \approx 25$ mag and ±0.17 mag at $V \approx 26$ mag. The errors in the mean magnitudes for the 12 epochs amount to ±0.04 and ±0.05 mag at these same magnitude levels.

关键项目的研究小组在河外距离尺度问题上采取的策略包括三个目标。第一个目标是发现造父变星，在此基础上测量到位于星场中以及位于小星系群内的旋涡星系的精确初级距离，这一结果适合于定标几种相互独立的次级距离测量方法。(这些次级距离测量方法包括：塔利－费希尔关系 [11,12]、面亮度起伏方法 [13]、行星状星云光度函数法 [14]、在 II 型超新星上使用的膨胀光球法 [15,16]，以及 Ia 型超新星光度测量法 [6,17-19]。)第二个目标是通过邻近星系 M31、M33 以及大麦哲伦云(LMC)距离的独立测算检验造父距离的潜在系统误差。此外，还可以经验性地检验造父变星周光关系的零点对重元素丰度的敏感性。第三个也是最具挑战性的观测目标是利用造父变星测量出室女星系团内的三个旋涡星系以及天炉星系团内两个成员星系的距离。

到 M100 的距离

我们的第一个观测目标是寻找室女星系团内的造父变星，通过对 M100 核心区域偏东约 2 arcmin 的视场进行 12 幅为一序列，每幅曝光时间为 1 小时的 V 波段测光，这一观测过程从 1994 年 4 月开始延续了两个月。采取这样的观测策略是为了给光变周期处于 10 天到 60 天的造父变星提供较好的光变曲线采样点。另外，紧接着 4 组 V 波段观测，我们进行了 I 波段的观测。这里，我们给出了所发现的造父变星的样本光变曲线，它们在 V 波段和 I 波段的周光关系，以及初步估计的到 M100 的距离。数据处理与分析的细节，测光列表以及变星的认证将另文发表(温迪·弗里德曼等，稿件准备中；罗伯特·希尔等，稿件准备中)。我们使用了三种独立的测光零点定标；V 波段和 I 波段零点最终结果的不确定性分别为 ±0.05 mag 和 ±0.04 mag。用于最优地发现变星的采样策略，以及认证变星、确定平均星等、红化值以及测量距离的方法都已经在其他地方发表 [20]。

在图 1 中展示了 M100 内 12 颗造父变星在 V 波段的光变曲线。所有造父变星样本的光变周期从 20 天到 65 天，平均 V 星等的范围从 25.0 mag 到 26.5 mag。由光变曲线很小的散射证明哈勃空间望远镜的测光质量是非常好的。单一数据点的随机误差的自身估计在 $V \approx 25$ mag 时为 ±0.14 mag，在 $V \approx 26$ mag 时为 ±0.17 mag。对于 12 次观测得到的平均星等的误差在相同星等条件下分别为 ±0.04 mag 以及 ±0.05 mag。

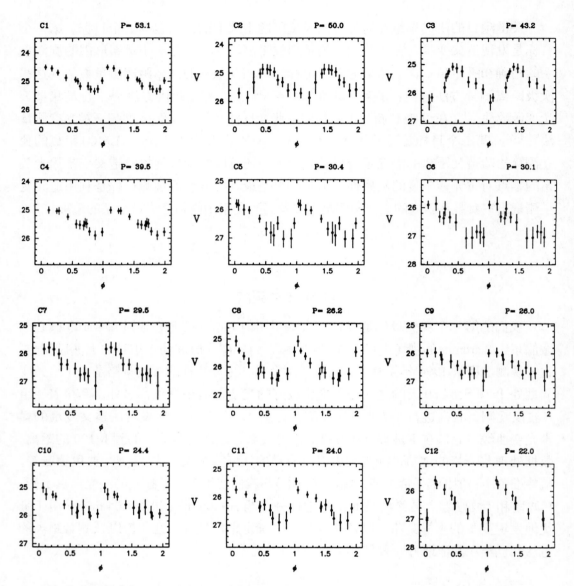

Fig. 1. Sample light curves for twelve Cepheids in M100. The periods of the stars illustrated (~20 to 50 days) are typical of the total sample discovered in M100. In addition to their periods, Cepheids are characterized by their distinctive light curves showing a rapid rise to maximum light, followed by a slower linear decline to minimum light. Cepheids pulsate because their atmospheres are not in hydrostatic equilibrium. The instability occurs as a result of a change in the opacity of a helium ionization zone with temperature. As singly ionized helium becomes doubly ionized, the opacity increases with increasing temperature. This changing opacity acts as a valve so that when the atmosphere is compressed and at higher temperature, it becomes more opaque to radiation, and the thermal energy increases. Subsequently, it expands and cools, becoming more transparent. As the pressure on the atmosphere decreases it then collapses and the cycle repeats.

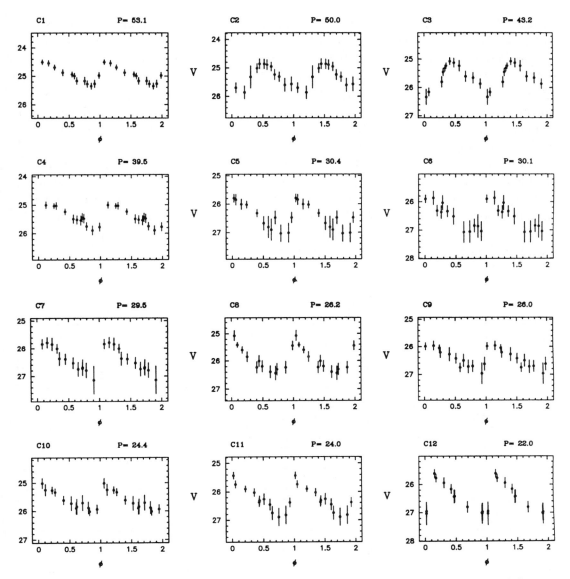

图 1. M100 中 12 颗造父变星光变曲线的示例。图中注明的周期（大约 20 天到 50 天）是 M100 内发现的造父变星总样本中的典型值。除了周期性之外，造父变星的特性主要来自于它们独特的光变曲线：快速增亮到最大光度，然后缓慢、线性地降低到最小光度。造父变星的脉动是由于它们的大气并未处于流体静力平衡状态。当氢电离区的不透明度随着温度变化时不稳定性就会出现。当一次电离的氢被二次电离时，不透明度会随着温度的增加而增加。变化的不透明度的作用就像阀门一样，当大气被压缩并处于更高温度时，它变得对辐射更加不透明，大气的热能增加。接下来，大气开始膨胀并且冷却，变得更加透明。当作用于大气的压力下降时，大气又开始收缩，新的循环又开始。

In Fig. 2, we present the time-averaged, intensity-weighted V-band and I-band P–L relations for 20 Cepheids in M100 (white circles). We compare the brightness of the M100 Cepheids with those in the LMC (black circles) to obtain a distance ratio (M100/LMC). In logarithmic units of magnitudes, the so-called "distance modulus" (μ) is given by $5 \times \log_{10}$ (distance in parsecs) -5.0. A correction for the dimming effect due to interstellar dust is obtained by fitting the apparent V and I moduli to a standard interstellar extinction law. The apparent I-band modulus to M100 is measured to be $\mu_1 = 31.25$ mag; the corresponding V P–L relation for the same sample of Cepheids yields $\mu_V = 31.31$ mag, implying a mean extinction of $A_V = 0.15 \pm 0.17$ for the M100 Cepheid sample. The true (reddening-corrected) distance modulus to M100 is determined to be 31.16 ± 0.20 mag, corresponding to a distance of 17.1 ± 1.8 Mpc. A detailed listing of the errors for this determination is given in Table 1. The random errors in the apparent moduli amount to $< 4\%$ in distance. The uncertainty in the true distance is dominated by systematics due primarily to the adopted LMC distance and correction for reddening, giving a total uncertainty of $\pm 10\%$.

Table 1. Error budget in the M100 distance scale

Source of uncertainty	Type of uncertainty	Error (mag.)	Cumulative error
Distance to M100			
[A] LMC Distance	Independent estimates	± 0.10	
[B] WFPC2 V-band zero point	Ground-based/on-orbit calibration	± 0.05	
[C] WFPC2 I-band zero point	Ground-based/on-orbit calibration	± 0.04	
[D] Extinction-corrected Cepheid modulus	[B] and [C] are uncorrelated	± 0.17	
[E] Charge transfer efficiency	4% across entire chip	± 0.01	
[F] Cepheid V-band modulus	(V-band P–L dispersion) / $\sqrt{N}$	± 0.06	
[G] Cepheid I-band modulus	(I-band P–L dispersion) / $\sqrt{N}$	± 0.07	
[H] Cepheid true modulus	[F] and [G] are correlated	± 0.03	
[I] = [A] + [D] + [E] + [H]	Combined in quadrature		± 0.20
Distance to Virgo			
[J] Velocity of Virgo cluster	± 80 km s^{-1}	± 0.11	
[K] Back-to-front geometry of Virgo	± 3 Mpc	± 0.35	
[L] = [I] + [J] + [K]	Combined in quadrature $H_0 = 82 \pm 17$ km s^{-1} Mpc^{-1}		± 0.42
Distance to Coma			
[M] Velocity of Coma cluster	± 100 km s^{-1}	± 0.02	
[N] Virgo/Coma Relative distance	Secondary indicators	± 0.10	
[O] = [I] + [K] + [M] + [N]	Combined in quadrature $H_0 = 77 \pm 16$ km s^{-1} Mpc^{-1}		± 0.42

A quantitative overview of the propagation of errors associated with our new data set and its application to the extragalactic distance scale. Errors in the photometric zero points and statistical uncertainties associated with the

在图 2 中，我们给出了 M100 内的 20 颗造父变星的时间平均的和强度加权的 V 波段与 I 波段的周光关系（白圆圈）。我们将 M100 内造父变星的亮度与大麦哲伦云内的造父变星（黑圆圈）相比较以得到距离比（M100/LMC）。以星等这种对数性单位，被称作"距离模数"的 μ 可以表述为 $5 \times \log_{10}$（以秒差距为单位的距离）-5.0。通过将 V 波段与 I 波段视星等的模数与标准的星际消光律拟合可以得到由于星际尘埃造成的消光影响的修正量。测量得到的到 M100 的 I 波段视距离模数为 $\mu_I = 31.25$ mag；对于同一造父变星样本，由相应的 V 波段的周光关系求得 $\mu_V = 31.31$ mag，这表明对于 M100 内的造父变星样本，平均消光 $A_V = 0.15 \pm 0.17$。真实的（红化改正的）到 M100 的距离模数为 31.16 ± 0.20 mag，对应的距离为 17.1 ± 1.8 Mpc。表 1 中详尽地列出了这一测定结果的误差来源。视距离模数的随机误差造成了 $< 4\%$ 的距离误差。真实距离的不确定性由所采用的大麦哲伦云的距离以及红化改正主导，其总的不确定性为 $\pm 10\%$。

表 1. M100 距离尺度中的误差估计

误差来源	误差类型	误差（mag）	累计误差
到 M100 的距离			
[A] LMC 距离	独立估计	± 0.10	
[B] WFPC2 V 波段零点	地基／在轨定标	± 0.05	
[C] WFPC2 I 波段零点	地基／在轨定标	± 0.04	
[D] 消光改正的造父变星模数	[B] 和 [C] 不相关	± 0.17	
[E] 电荷转移效率	整个探测器为 4%	± 0.01	
[F] 造父变星 V 波段模数	（V 波段周光关系弥散）$/\sqrt{N}$	± 0.06	
[G] 造父变星 I 波段模数	（I 波段周光关系弥散）$/\sqrt{N}$	± 0.07	
[H] 造父变星真实的模数	[F] 和 [G] 是相关的	± 0.03	
[I] = [A]+[D]+[E]+[H]	正交合成		± 0.20
到室女星系团的距离			
[J] 室女星系团的速度	± 80 km·s^{-1}	± 0.11	
[K] 室女星系团前后的几何形状	± 3 Mpc	± 0.35	
[L] = [I]+[J]+[K]	正交合成 $H_0 = 82 \pm 17$ km·s^{-1}·Mpc^{-1}		± 0.42
到后发星系团的距离			
[M] 后发星系团的速度	± 100 km·s^{-1}	± 0.02	
[N] 室女与后发星系的相对距离	次级示距天体	± 0.10	
[O] = [I]+[K]+[M]+[N]	正交合成 $H_0 = 77 \pm 16$ km·s^{-1}·Mpc^{-1}		± 0.42

与我们新的数据相关的误差传递的定量概述及其在河外星系距离尺度中的应用。测光零点的误差和与平均视距离模数相关的统计不确定性都传递进了真实距离模数的测量当中。就测光定标中的独立误差而言，假设各项是完全不相

mean apparent distance moduli both propagate into the determination of a true distance modulus. In the case of independent errors in the photometric calibration the terms are assumed to be fully uncorrelated giving

$$\varepsilon_{\mu_o}^U = R_{VI} \, (\varepsilon_V^2 + \varepsilon_I^2)^{1/2}$$

where $R_{VI} = A_V / E(V-I) = 2.6$ is the ratio of total-to-selective absorption. For the individual wavelength-dependent moduli the uncertainties are correlated in sign and magnitude because in this case the Cepheid samples defining the means are identical, thereby giving

$$\varepsilon_{\mu_o}^C = R_{VI} \, (\varepsilon_V - \varepsilon_I)$$

As can readily be seen, uncertainties in the photometric zero points dominate the error budget for the calculated distance to M100; with additional ground-based observing this error can be significantly reduced.

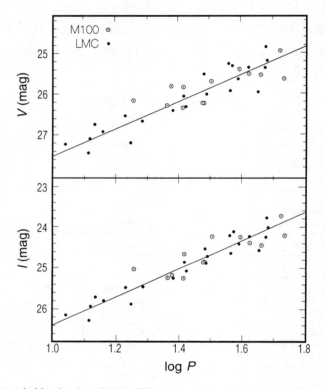

Fig. 2. Composite period-luminosity relations (*V*-band upper panel; *I*-band lower panel) for Cepheids in M100 (white circles) and Cepheids in the LMC (black circles, shifted to the distance of M100). Apparent *V* and *I* distance moduli for M100 are obtained by minimizing the residuals in the combined *P–L* relations for the two galaxies, and determining the relative offset with respect to the calibrating LMC sample. Consistent with previous studies[3,20], only high signal-to-noise variables (those having an average of their absolute deviations from the mean exceeding 1.5 times the mean error) are plotted, whereas only stars with log*P* < 1.8 are included in the fit. The difference in the *V* and *I* apparent moduli for M100 is assumed to be due to interstellar dust present both in M100 and our own galaxy. Correcting for this effect yields a reddening-corrected (true) distance to M100 of 17.1 ± 1.8 Mpc.

This first Cepheid distance to M100 falls toward the low end of the published range of distance values to the Virgo cluster. How does this distance compare with previous distance estimates to M100 itself? We discuss four recent measurements of the distance to M100. The first

关的，则可以得到：

$$\varepsilon_{\mu_0}^U = R_{VI}(\varepsilon_V^2 + \varepsilon_I^2)^{1/2}$$

其中 $R_{VI} = A_V/E(V-I) = 2.6$ 是整体吸收和选择性吸收的比。就目前的情况来说，确立这一方式的造父变星的样本是相同的，所以对于单独的波长依赖的模数而言，不确定性在符号和数量上都是相关的，因此有

$$\varepsilon_{\mu_0}^C = R_{VI}(\varepsilon_V - \varepsilon_I)$$

容易看出，测光零点的不确定性主导了计算得到的到 M100 的距离结果的误差区间，使用附加的地基观测，这一误差可以显著减小。

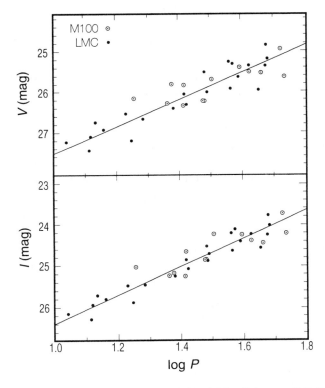

图 2. 合成的造父变星周光关系图（上图为 V 波段，下图为 I 波段），其中 M100 的造父变星标为白圆圈，大麦哲伦云内的造父变星标为黑圆圈并且移动到 M100 的距离处。M100 在 V 波段和 I 波段的视距离模数可以通过将这两个星系合并的周光关系的残差最小化而得到，并且得到相对于定标的大麦哲伦云造父变星样本的相对偏差。同已有的研究相一致的是 [3,20]，图中只画出了具有高信噪比的变星样本（它们相对于平均星等的绝对偏差大于 1.5 倍的平均误差），只有周期 $\log P < 1.8$ 的恒星用到拟合中。假设 M100 在 V 波段和 I 波段视距离模数结果的不同是由 M100 内以及我们所在星系内都存在的星际尘埃造成的。对这一影响的改正可以得到 M100 红化改正了的（真实的）距离 17.1 ± 1.8 Mpc。

这第一个到 M100 的造父距离处在已经发表的到室女星系团距离范围的低值端。如何将这个距离与之前估计的到 M100 的距离进行比较呢？我们讨论四个最近

measurement is based on a comparison of the observed diameters of the ScI galaxies. Assuming that M100 has the same diameter as M101, Sandage[21] concluded that M100 is located at a distance of 27.7 Mpc. Ten years earlier, de Vaucouleurs[22] discussed the relative positions of 37 spirals in the Virgo cluster based on a variety of secondary distance indicators available at that time. He found a distance to M100 of 11.8 Mpc, which places M100 on the near side of the Virgo cluster which he estimated to be at a distance of 15.0 Mpc. A third estimate of the distance to M100 is obtained from the expanding photosphere method[15,16] applied to the type II supernova SN1979c. The most recent application of this method yields a distance of 15 ± 4 Mpc. As discussed further (J.R.M. *et al.*, manuscript in preparation), the distances to the four galaxies now available using both Cepheids and type II supernovae all show good agreement. Fourth, M100 is contained, in the Virgo galaxy sample studied by Pierce and Tully[23]. On the basis of the Tully–Fisher (TF) relationship, these authors conclude that M100 lies at a distance of 18.4 ± 2.2 Mpc, which they claim is within 1σ of their mean distance to the Virgo cluster (15.6 ± 1.5 Mpc). A somewhat closer distance of 14.5 ± 2.7 Mpc is given in Table 3 by Pierce[24]. The M100 Tully–Fisher and type II supernova estimates are in good agreement with the distance derived by Cepheids.

Where does M100 lie with respect to the centre of the Virgo cluster? An answer to this question is needed to determine H_0 from the present data. M100 is projected on the sky 3.9° from the centre of the Virgo cluster as defined by the giant elliptical galaxy M87. The angular extent of the core is about 6° radius, corresponding to 1.8 Mpc at a distance of 17.1 Mpc. The full front-to-back depth of the elliptical galaxy component of the cluster has been estimated to be 8 Mpc (ref. 25). This range would imply an r.m.s. variation in depth of ± 2 Mpc for the elliptical galaxies, if the radial distribution is gaussian. However, the distribution in depth of the spiral galaxies in the cluster appears to be larger, with a full range of ~13 Mpc (ref. 23), and this distribution is more complex than a simple gaussian model. With these uncertainties in mind we conservatively assign an error of $\pm 20\%$ in the mean distance of the Virgo cluster. The confidence limits that can be placed on this Virgo distance will be discussed in more details (J.R.M. *et al.*, manuscript in preparation).

By contrast, is there any reason to believe that M100 lies in the foreground? Sandage and Bedke[26] present a list of 75 galaxies in the direction of the Virgo cluster that resolve most easily into individual stars. On the basis of their resolution, 45 of these galaxies are classified as "excellent", "good" or "good-to-fair", whereas M100 itself is classified as "fair". It then seems unlikely that M100 is significantly closer than most of the Virgo spiral galaxies discussed by Sandage because resolution is distance dependent. Nevertheless, the line-of-sight position of M100 with respect to the core of the Virgo cluster is the major source of uncertainty in what follows.

There is a second source of uncertainty in estimating H_0 from the Virgo cluster even if the distance were accurately known. The cluster is sufficiently far that its Hubble recession velocity is larger than its peculiar velocity. However, there are many difficulties in determining the Hubble velocity: our own Local Group is infalling toward the Virgo cluster, and the presence of foreground plus background galaxies complicates the determination of the

的关于 M100 距离的测量。第一个测量是基于比较观测到的 ScI 型星系的直径。假设 M100 与 M101 有相同的直径，桑德奇[21] 得出结论，M100 位于 27.7 Mpc 距离处。十年前，德·沃库勒尔[22] 基于当时已知的各种次级示距天体，讨论了室女星系团内 37 个旋涡星系的相对位置。他发现到 M100 的距离为 11.8 Mpc，这一距离表明 M100 位于室女星系团的近端，他估计室女星系团的距离为 15.0 Mpc。到 M100 距离的第三种估计是通过将膨胀光球方法应用到 II 型超新星 SN1979c 得到的[15,16]。使用这一方法得到的最新的结果为 15±4 Mpc。进一步讨论表明（杰里米·莫尔德等，稿件准备中），由造父变星方法和 II 型超新星方法测定的到这四个星系的距离非常一致。第四，M100 包含在皮尔斯与塔利所研究的室女星系团的星系样本中[23]。基于塔利 – 费希尔关系，这些作者得出，M100 位于 18.4±2.2 Mpc 距离处，并认为这一结果在 1σ 的误差范围内与室女星系团的平均距离 15.6±1.5 Mpc 是一致的。在皮尔斯的表格 3 中也列出了更接近的距离 14.5±2.7 Mpc[24]。由塔利 – 费希尔关系以及 II 型超新星得到的 M100 的距离与使用造父变星得到的结果是非常一致的。

相对于室女星系团的中心，M100 位于什么位置呢？回答这一问题对于由目前的数据确定 H_0 的值是必需的。M100 到由巨椭圆星系 M87 确定的室女星系团中心的角距离为 3.9°。核心区域的角半径大约为 6°，在 17.1 Mpc 的距离上相当于 1.8 Mpc。星系团内的椭圆星系的纵深范围大约为 8 Mpc[25]。这个范围表明，对于椭圆星系而言，如果其径向分布是高斯形式的，那么纵深的均方根误差（rms）应该是 ±2 Mpc。然而，星系团内旋涡星系的纵深分布显示出更大的范围，大致为 13 Mpc[23]，这种分布比简单的高斯模型更为复杂。基于以上不确定性的考虑，我们保守地估计室女星系团平均距离的误差为 ±20%。关于室女星系团距离的置信度限制将在其他地方进行详细讨论（杰里米·莫尔德等，稿件准备中）。

相比之下，有什么理由相信 M100 位于室女星系团的前方呢？桑德奇与贝德克[26] 列出了在室女星系团方向最容易分辨出单颗恒星的 75 个星系。根据分辨率，其中 45 个星系被分类成"极清楚"、"很清楚"或"大致清楚"，而 M100 本身被分类成"清楚"。由于分辨率是依赖于距离的，M100 不太可能明显比室女星系团内其他桑德奇讨论过的大部分旋涡星系更靠近我们。然而，M100 相对于室女星系团核心的视线方向的位置是下面将讨论的不确定性的主要来源。

即使准确地知道距离，在用室女星系团估计 H_0 时，仍然存在着第二个不确定因素。这个星系团已经足够远，使得它的哈勃退行速度大于它的本动速度。然而，在确定哈勃速度的过程中仍然存在很多困难：我们自身所在的本星系群正朝向室女星系团沉降，前景与背景星系的存在使测定室女星系团速度本身复杂化了。本星系群

Virgo cluster velocity itself. The range of corrections for the Local Group centroid, the adopted infall velocity and the random velocity can lead to Virgo recession velocities[27] from 1,200 to 1,600 km s^{-1}. Adopting the recession velocity of $1,404 \pm 80$ km s^{-1} preferred by Huchra[27] and a Virgo cluster distance of 17.1 Mpc yields a value of $H_0 = 82 \pm 17$ km s^{-1} Mpc^{-1}. The cumulative errors entering this estimate are listed in Table 1. (However, we note that adopting the velocity[6,31] of $1,179 \pm 17$ km s^{-1} results in $H_0 = 69 \pm 14$ km s^{-1} Mpc^{-1} for the same distance.)

A means of avoiding the uncertainty in the Virgo cluster recession velocity in determining H_0 is to make use of the well measured distance ratio between the Virgo and Coma clusters[28]. The Coma cluster is located about 6 times more distant than the Virgo cluster. Its peculiar velocity is $\lesssim 80$ km s^{-1} (ref. 29) and it has a recession velocity[9,30,31] of $7,200 \pm 100$ km s^{-1}. Hence its peculiar velocity contributes a very small fractional uncertainty to the cosmological velocity. The Virgo–Coma cluster distance ratio has been measured using a variety of techniques (for example, the Tully–Fisher relationship, the D_n–Σ relation, and type Ia supernovae). There is excellent agreement among a number of different authors[4,32] resulting in a mean relative Coma–Virgo distance modulus of $3.71 \pm \lesssim 0.10$ mag. Adopting a distance of 17.1 Mpc for the Virgo cluster yields a distance to the Coma cluster of 94 Mpc. The corresponding value of the Hubble constant is $H_0 = 7,200/94 = 77 \pm 16$ km s^{-1} Mpc^{-1}. This value agrees well with values determined for the Virgo cluster velocities given above. Thus a value of the Hubble constant $\sim 80 \pm 17$ km s^{-1} Mpc^{-1} is indicated extending out to a distance of ~ 100 Mpc.

Systematic Errors

Could there by a systematic error in the local calibrators, possibly associated with the zero point of the Cepheid distance scale? This possibility seems very unlikely given that the distances to nearby galaxies have been measured using several different methods completely independent of the Cepheids; for example, using RR Lyrae variables[33,34], using the photoionized disk around SN1987A[35], the expanding photosphere method applied to SN1987A[15], and using the luminosity of the tip of the red giant branch[36]. Although as recently as a decade ago the distances to the local calibrators were in disagreement at a level of a factor of two, newer data obtained from CCDs and near-infrared arrays have led to a convergence of the distances to local galaxies with differences amounting to less than 0.3 mag, or 15% in distance[37].

Are we measuring the true global value of H_0? Given the observational evidence for large-scale velocity flows[9,38], and theoretical models for structure formation (such as cold dark matter), it is possible that measurement of H_0 locally does not yield a value representative of that on a larger global scale[39,40]. However, there are several direct lines of evidence that do not support this hypothesis. At the distance of the Coma cluster such fluctuations are predicted to be less than 5–10%, based both on models and considerations of the observed local bulk motion with respect to the microwave background[39]. At least three distance indicators presently extend well beyond the distance of the Coma cluster and yield internally consistent values of H_0 both locally and out to redshifts > 14,000 km s^{-1}. These are the type

中心位置的修正幅度，所采用的降落速度和随机速度可能导致室女座星系团的退行速度 [27] 为 1,200 km·s^{-1} 到 1,600 km·s^{-1}。采用修兹劳 [27] 提出的室女星系团的退行速度 1,404±80 km·s^{-1} 以及 17.1 Mpc 的距离，得出哈勃常数 H_0 = 82±17 km·s^{-1}·Mpc^{-1}。估算中的累计误差列在表 1 当中。（然而，我们注意到，如果采用 1,179±17 km·s^{-1} 的速度 [6,31]，对于同样的距离将得出 H_0 = 69±14 km·s^{-1}·Mpc^{-1}。）

避免测定 H_0 过程中室女星系团退行速度不确定性的一种方法是：利用已经准确测定的室女星系团与后发星系团的距离比 [28]。后发星系团位于大约 6 倍于室女星系团的距离上。它的本动速度 ≤80 km·s^{-1} [29]，退行速度 [9,30,31] 为 7,200±100 km·s^{-1}。因此，其本动速度对宇宙学速度只贡献了非常小的不确定性。室女 – 后发星系团的距离比已经使用各种技术（例如，塔利 – 费希尔关系、D_n–$\sum$ 关系以及 Ia 型超新星）测量过。由许多作者得到的结果是很一致的 [4,32]，后发 – 室女星系团之间的相对距离模数的平均值为 3.71 ± ≤0.10 mag。如果采用 17.1 Mpc 作为室女星系团的距离，那么到后发星系团的距离为 94 Mpc。相应的哈勃常数的值 H_0 = 7,200/94 = 77±16 km·s^{-1}·Mpc^{-1}。这一结果与前面采用室女星系团的速度测定的结果是很一致的。因此，延伸到约 100 Mpc 的距离之外，哈勃常数大约为 80±17 km·s^{-1}·Mpc^{-1}。

系 统 误 差

局域定标天体里的系统误差会不会与造父距离标尺的零点有关联呢？这种可能性是非常低的，因为测量邻近星系所使用的各种方法完全不依赖于造父变星；例如使用天琴 RR 型变星 [33,34]，使用超新星 SN1987A 周围的光电离盘 [35]，将膨胀光球方法用于 SN1987A [15]，以及使用红巨星支上端的光度 [36]。尽管近十年以来，到局域定标天体的距离相差了一倍。然而，由 CCD 和近红外探测阵列得到的较新的数据表明到近邻星系的距离的误差量已经减小到小于 0.3 mag，或者按距离小于 15% [37]。

我们测量的是 H_0 真实的全局值吗？尽管给出了大尺度速度流的观测证据 [9,38] 以及结构形成的理论模型（例如冷暗物质），局部区域里测量的 H_0 不一定能代表更大的宇宙学尺度上的值 [39,40]。然而，存在几条直接的证据链不支持这样的假设。基于理论模型以及考虑观测到的相对于微波背景的局部团块运动 [39]，在后发星系团的距离处预测这样的扰动小于 5%~10%。目前，至少有三种示距天体很好地扩展到了后发星系团的距离之外，并且对于近邻的以及红移大于 14,000 km·s^{-1} 的地方都得到了自洽的 H_0 值。这些示距天体是 II 型超新星 [15,16]、Ia 型超新星 [6] 以及最亮的星系团成

II supernovae[15,16], type Ia supernovae[6], and brightest cluster members[41,42]. Moreover, the Hubble diagram for the brightest cluster members of Sandage and Hardy[42] is well-defined to velocities $> 40,000\,\mathrm{km\ s^{-1}}$ and appears to remain linear out to $\sim 100,000\,\mathrm{km\ s^{-1}}$. The zero-point calibration of these various methods is still a subject of debate (and the goal of the Key Project) but, for example, it is concluded[41] that the variation of H_0 over the redshift range $0.01 < z < 0.05$ is constrained to be within $\pm 7\%$ r.m.s.

Implications

The HST measurement of the Cepheid distance to M100 enables us to place constraints on the range of plausible values of H_0 and the expansion age. The current limits on H_0 are illustrated in Fig. 3. Also shown in Fig. 3 are the expansion ages for various values of (H_0, Ω_0) corresponding to 14 ± 2 Gyr. These limits are broadly consistent with estimates of the ages of globular clusters from stellar evolution theory[43-45], estimates of the age of the Galactic disk based on white dwarf cooling times[46,47], and radioactive dating of elements[48,49]. All of these age estimates generally span a full range between 10 to 18 Gyr, consistent with the 1σ error limits quoted above. A value of $H_0 = 80 \pm 17\,\mathrm{km\ s^{-1}\ Mpc^{-1}}$ is consistent with a low-density $(0.1 < \Omega < 0.3)$ Universe and $T_0 = 12$ Gyr.

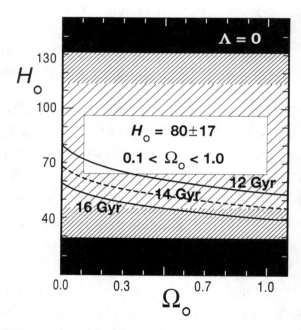

Fig. 3. Current limits on H_0 (in km s^{-1} Mpc^{-1}) and the age and density of the Universe. Expansion ages of 14 ± 2 Gyr, corresponding to globular cluster ages, are illustrated as a function of H_0 and the density parameter Ω for models with the cosmological constant $\Lambda = 0$. The 2σ, 3σ and 4σ confidence intervals on the Hubble constant presented here are shown by the lightly hatched, densely hatched and black horizontal areas, respectively. Broad limits on Ω are illustrated at 0.1 and 1.0.

员 [41,42]。而且，对于桑德奇与哈迪的最亮的星系团成员星系 [42]，其哈勃图可以很好地延伸到速度大于 40,000 km·s⁻¹，一直到 ~100,000 km·s⁻¹ 仍能保持线性关系。以上各种方法的零点定标仍然是有争议的（包括关键项目的目标）。然而，举例来说，我们可以得出的结论是 [41]，将红移限定在 $0.01 < z < 0.05$ 的范围内，H_0 的变化范围限定在了均方根 ±7% 的范围内。

启　示

使用哈勃空间望远镜测定的到 M100 的造父距离使得我们可以对哈勃常数 H_0 以及膨胀年龄的合理值的范围进行限制。图 3 中给出了当前对 H_0 的限制。图 3 中也显示了对应于膨胀年龄为 140 亿 ±20 亿年的各种值（H_0，Ω_0）。这些年龄限制与基于恒星演化理论的球状星团的年龄 [43-45]，基于白矮星冷却时间的银盘的年龄 [46,47]，以及元素的放射性计年 [48,49] 都是一致的。所有这些年龄估计大体上覆盖了 100 亿年到 180 亿年间的范围，在上述的 1σ 误差范围内是一致的。$H_0 = 80 \pm 17$ km·s⁻¹·Mpc⁻¹ 的结果同一个低密度（$0.1 < \Omega < 0.3$）以及年龄 $T_0 = 120$ 亿年的宇宙一致。

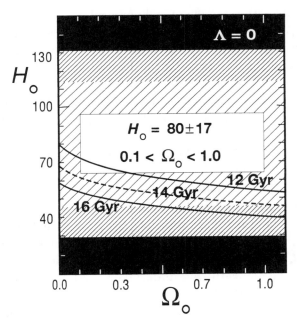

图 3. 当前对 H_0（单位为 km·s⁻¹·Mpc⁻¹）以及宇宙年龄和密度的限制。对具有宇宙学常数 Λ = 0 的模型，图中画出了对应于球状星团的年龄，140 亿 ±20 亿年的膨胀年龄作为 H_0 以及密度参数 Ω 的函数的变化趋势。哈勃常数 2 倍、3 倍、4 倍标准误差的置信区间在图中分别显示为稀疏的阴影线、致密的阴影线以及黑色的水平区域。图中标明了位于 0.1 到 1.0 之间的对于 Ω 宽松的限制。

The Einstein–de Sitter cosmological model (often referred to as the standard model) has a mean mass density equal to the critical density ($\Omega = 1$) and a cosmological constant, $\Lambda = 0$. In the standard model the expansion age is given by $T_0 = 2/3\ H_0^{-1}$. (For models with $\Lambda > 0$ the Universe undergoes an accelerating expansion resulting in ages that are older than $\Lambda = 0$ models[50].) For $H_0 = 80$ km s^{-1} Mpc^{-1} the standard model gives an expansion age of 8 Gyr, well below the other age estimates cited above. This "age conflict" suggests that either the standard cosmological model needs to be revised, or present theories (or observations) bearing on stellar and galactic evolution may need to be re-examined.

Concerns and Future Plans

The weakest point in the present analysis is of course that we have measured a distance to only one galaxy. However, there has recently been reported[51] the discovery of three Cepheid candidates in the Virgo cluster spiral galaxy NGC4571 based on observations taken at the Canada–France–Hawaii Telescope. It is concluded from these data that NGC4571 lies at a distance of 14.9 ± 1.2 Mpc, yielding a Hubble constant $H_0 = 87 \pm 7$ km s^{-1} Mpc^{-1}. Clearly, however, the distances to more galaxies are required to define the mean Virgo cluster distance. We do not wish to mislead the reader into believing that the problem of determining H_0 has been solved. It has not. Our analysis has shown that the remaining uncertainty in the value of the Hubble constant is dominated by systematic errors, which are difficult to quantify with a sample of only one galaxy. An accuracy of 10% or better in the value of H_0 will only be reached when we have measured Cepheid distances to a larger sample of galaxies so that the magnitude of these systematic errors can be assessed directly. However, the independent estimate of the distance to NGC4571, the consistency of the type II supernovae and Tully–Fisher distance scales with the direct Cepheid measurement to M100, and the agreement of the distance to the Virgo cluster based on elliptical galaxies[14,25], lead us to conclude that the evidence at this time favours a value of $H_0 \approx 80 \pm 17$ km s^{-1} Mpc^{-1}.

The two remaining years of the Key Project will be critical. We have been awarded time and are currently obtaining data to measure Cepheid distances to a total of ~20 calibrating spirals both in the field and in small groups (for example, Leo I and Coma I), and including two additional galaxies in each of the Virgo and Fornax clusters. A direct comparison of the Tully–Fisher, surface brightness fluctuation, planetary nebula luminosity function, and type I and II supernovae (and other) distance scales can then be made. In parallel, independent horizontal-branch distances to M33 and M31 will be measured, and main-sequence fitting undertaken for LMC clusters, allowing further checks on the zero point of the Cepheid P–L relation. These data will provide a direct means of assessing the systematic errors in the current extragalactic distance scale at each stage of its application, and allow a determination of the Hubble constant to unprecedented accuracy. The results of this paper suggest that a Hubble constant, accurate to 10%, and measured through secondary techniques out to scales of hundreds of Mpc, is now a realizable goal.

(**371**, 757-762; 1994)

爱因斯坦－德西特宇宙模型（通常称作标准模型）的平均物质密度等于临界密度（$\Omega = 1$），宇宙学常数 $\Lambda = 0$。在标准模型中膨胀年龄由 $T_0 = 2/3\ H_0^{-1}$ 决定。（对于 $\Lambda > 0$ 的模型，宇宙在加速膨胀从而导致了比 $\Lambda = 0$ 的模型更老的年龄[50]。）对于 $H_0 = 80\ \text{km} \cdot \text{s}^{-1} \cdot \text{Mpc}^{-1}$，标准模型给出的膨胀年龄为 80 亿年，远远小于上述其他年龄的估计值。这一"年龄矛盾"表明要么标准宇宙模型需要修正，要么目前关于恒星和星系演化的理论（或者观测）需要重新检验。

各种考虑及未来的计划

在目前分析当中最为薄弱的一点是我们只测量了到一个星系的距离。然而，最近已经有报告指出基于加拿大－法国－夏威夷望远镜对室女星系团内的旋涡星系 NGC4571 的观测发现了三个造父变星的候选体[51]。从这些数据得出的结论是 NGC4571 位于距离 14.9 ± 1.2 Mpc 处，得出的哈勃常数 $H_0 = 87 \pm 7\ \text{km} \cdot \text{s}^{-1} \cdot \text{Mpc}^{-1}$。然而，很明显，确定室女星系团的平均距离需要确定到更多星系的距离。我们并不想误导读者相信 H_0 测定的问题已经解决了。这一问题还没有解决。我们的分析表明哈勃常数的值仍然存在的不确定性主要由系统误差主导，而这些系统误差对于只有一个星系的样本而言很难给出定量结果。只有当测出更大的星系样本的造父距离时，H_0 值的精度会达到 10%，甚至更好，而系统误差的大小也可以直接估计。然而，对于 NGC4571 距离的独立测量，使用 II 型超新星以及塔利－费希尔关系得到的距离尺度与直接使用造父变星测定的到 M100 的距离的一致。以及与基于椭圆星系测得的到室女星系团距离一致[14,25]，使得我们得出以下结论：目前的证据表明哈勃常数最为可取的结果是 $H_0 \approx 80 \pm 17\ \text{km} \cdot \text{s}^{-1} \cdot \text{Mpc}^{-1}$。

剩下的两年对关键项目将是至关重要的。我们已经获得了观测时间，并且目前正在获取数据，以便测量总数大约为 20 个定标的旋涡星系的造父距离。这些星系有的位于星场中，有的处在小的星系群（举例来说如狮子座 I 星系和后发星系团 I），还有另外两个星系分别在室女星系团和天炉星系团。这样一来，塔利－费希尔关系、面亮度起伏、行星状星云光度函数以及 I 型和 II 型超新星（以及其他方法）得出的距离就可以进行直接的比较。与此同时，也将测量到 M33 和 M31 独立的水平支星距离，以及对大麦哲伦云内星团做主序星拟合，使得可以对造父变星的周光关系零点进行进一步检测。这些数据将为当前河外星系距离尺度在每一应用阶段系统误差的估计提供一个直接的方法，并且能够使哈勃常数的测定达到空前的精度。本文的结果表明，目前，哈勃常数的值精度达到 10%，并且通过各种次级技术测量到几百兆秒差距的距离是可实现的目标。

（武振宇 翻译；何香涛 审稿）

Wendy L. Freedman[*], **Barry F. Madore**[†], **Jeremy R. Mould**[‡], **Robert Hill**[*], **Laura Ferrarese**[§¶], **Robert C. Kennicutt Jr**[‖], **Abhijit Saha**[¶], **Peter B. Stetson**[#], **John A. Graham**[**], **Holland Ford**[§¶], **John G. Hoessel**[††] , **John Huchra**[‡‡], **Shaun M. Hughes**[§§] **& Garth D. Illingworth**[‖‖]

[*] Carnegie Observatories, 813 Santa Barbara Street, Pasadena, California 91101, USA

[†] NASA/IPAC Extragalactic Database, Infrared Processing and Analysis Center, Jet Propulsion Laboratory, California Institute of Technology, Pasadena, California 91125, USA

[‡] Mount Stromlo and Siding Spring Observatories, Private Bag, Weston Creek Post Office ACT 2611, Sydney, Australia

[§] Department of Physics and Astronomy, Bloomberg 501, Johns Hopkins University, 3400 North Charles Street, Baltimore, Maryland 21218, USA

[‖] Steward Observatory, University of Arizona, Tucson, Arizona 85721, USA

[¶] Space Telescope Science Institute, Homewood Campus, Baltimore, Maryland 21218, USA

[#] Dominion Astrophysical Observatory, 5071 West Saanich Road, Victoria, British Columbia, V8X 4M6, Canada

[**] Department of Terrestrial Magnetism, Carnegie Institution of Washington, 5241 Broad Branch Road North West, Washington DC 20015, USA

[††] Department of Astronomy, University of Wisconsin, 475 North Charter Street, Madison, Wisconsin 53706, USA

[‡‡] Harvard-Smithsonian, Center for Astrophysics, 60 Garden Street, Cambridge, Massachusetts 02138, USA

[§§] Royal Greenwich Observatory, Madingley Road, Cambridge CB3 0HA, UK

[‖‖] Lick Observatory, University of California, Santa Cruz, California 95064, USA

Received 20 September; accepted 26 September 1994.

References:

1. Fukugita, M., Hogan, C. & Peebles, P. J. E. *Nature* **366**, 309-312 (1993).

2. Kolb, E. W. & Turner, M. S. *The Early Universe* (Addison-Wesley, Redwood City, 1990).

3. Madore, B. F. & Freedman, W. L. *Publ. Astron. Soc. Pac.* **103**, 933-957 (1991).

4. van den Bergh, S. *Publ. Astron. Soc. Pac.* **104**, 861-883 (1992).

5. Jacoby, G. H. *et al. Publ. Astron. Soc. Pac.* **104**, 599-662 (1992).

6. Sandage, A. R. & Tammann, G. A. *Astrophys. J.* **415**, 1-9 (1993).

7. Hubble, E. P. *Astrophys. J.* **62**, 409-443 (1925).

8. Hubble, E. P. *Astrophys. J.* **63**, 236-274 (1926).

9. Aaronson, M. *et al. Astrophys. J.* **302**, 536-563 (1986).

10. Dressler, A. *et al. Astrophys. J.* **313**, L37-L42 (1987).

11. Tully, R. B. & Fisher, J. R. *Astr. Astrophys.* **54**, 661-673 (1977).

12. Pierce, M. J. & Tully, R. B. *Astrophys. J.* **387**, 47-55 (1992).

13. Tonry, J. & Schneider, D. P. *Astr. J.* **96**, 807-815 (1988).

14. Jacoby, J., Ciardullo, R. & Ford, H. C. *Astrophys. J.* **356**, 332-349 (1990).

15. Schmidt, B. P., Kirshner, R. P. & Eastman, R. G. *Astrophys. J.* **395**, 366-386 (1992).

16. Schmidt, B. P., Kirshner, R. P. & Eastman, R. G. *Astrophys. J.* **432**, 42-48 (1994).

17. Branch, D. &. Miller, D. L. *Astrophys. J.* **405**, L5-L8 (1993).

18. Phillips, M. M. *Astrophys. J.* **413**, L105-L108 (1993).

19. Saha, A. *et al. Astrophys. J.* **425**, 14-34 (1994).

20. Freedman, W. L. *et al. Astrophys. J.* **427**, 628-655 (1994).

21. Sandage, A. R. *Astrophys. J.* **402**, 3-14 (1993).

22. de Vaucouleurs, G. *Astrophys. J.* **253**, 520-525 (1982).

23. Pierce, M. J. & Tully, R. B. *Astrophys. J.* **330**, 579-595 (1988).

24. Pierce, M. J. *Astrophys. J.* **430**, 53-62 (1994).

25. Tonry, J. L., Ajhar, E. A. & Luppino, G. A. *Astr. J.* **100**, 1416-1423 (1990).

26. Sandage, A. R. & Bedke, J. *Atlas of Galaxies Useful For Measuring the Cosmological Distance Scale,* SP-496 (NASA, 1988).

27. Huchra, J. in *Extragalactic Distance Scale* (eds van den Bergh, S. & Pritchet, C. J.) *Publ. Astron. Soc. Pac. Conf. Series* **4**, 257-280 (1988).

28. Tammann, G. A. & Sandage, A. R. *Astrophys. J.* **294**, 81-95 (1985).

29. Han, M. & Mould, J. R. *Astrophys. J.* **396**, 453-459 (1992).

30. Fukugita, M. *et al. Astrophys. J.* **376**, 8-22 (1991).

31. Jergen, H. & Tammann, G. A. *Astr. Astrophys.* **276**, 1-8 (1993).

32. de Vaucouleurs, G. *Astrophys. J.* **415**, 10-32 (1993).

33. Pritchet, C. J. & van den Bergh, S. *Astrophys. J.* **316**, 517-529 (1987).

34. Saha, A., Freedman, W. L., Hoessel, J. G. & Mossman, A. E. *Astr. J.* **104**, 1072-1085 (1992).

35. Panagia, N. *et al. Astrophys. J.* **380**, L23-L26 (1991).

36. Lee, M. G., Freedman, W. L. & Madore, B. F. *Astrophys. J.* **417**, 553-559 (1993).

37. Freedman, W. L. & Madore, B. F. in *New Perspectives on Stellar Pulsation and Pulsating Stars* (eds Nemec, J. & Matthews, J.) (Cambridge Univ. Press, 1993).

38. Lynden-Bell, D., Lahav, O. & Burstein, D. *Mon. Not. R. astr. Soc.* **241**, 325-345 (1989).

39. Turner, E., Cen, R. & Ostriker, J. P. *Astr. J.* **103**, 1427-1437 (1992).

40. Bartlett, J. G. *et al. Science* (submitted).

41. Lauer, T. & Postman, M. *Astrophys. J.* **400**, L47-L50 (1992).

42. Sandage, A. R. & Hardy, E. *Astrophys. J.* **183**, 743-757 (1973).

43. Renzini, A. in *Observational Tests of Inflation* (eds Shanks, T. *et al.*), (Kluwer, Boston, 1991).

44. Sandage, A. R. *Astr. J.* **106**, 719-725 (1993).

45. Shi, X., Schramm, D. N., Dearborn, D. S. P. & Truran, J. W. *Science* (submitted).

46. Winget, D. E. *et al. Astrophys. J.* **315**, L77-L81 (1987).

47. Pitts, E. & Taylor, R. J. *Mon. Not. R. astr. Soc.* **255**, 557-560 (1992).

48. Fowler, W. in *14th Texas Symp. on Relativistic Astrophysics* (ed Fenyores, E. J.) 68-78 (N.Y. Acad. Sci., New York, 1989).

49. Clayton, D. D. in *14th Texas Symp. on Relativistic Astrophysics* (ed. Fenyores, E. J.). 79- 89 (N.Y. Acad. Sci., New York, 1989).

50. Carroll, S. M., Press, W. J. & Turner, E. L. *A. Rev. Astr. Astrophys.* **30**, 499-542 (1992).

51. Pierce, M. J. *et al. Nature* **371**, 385-389 (1994).

Acknowledgements. We sincerely thank the many scientists, engineers and astronauts who contributed to HST, making these observations possible. This research was supported by NASA, through a grant from the Space Telescope Science Institute (which is operated by the Association of Universities for Research in Astronomy), and by the NSF. This work has benefitted from the use of the NASA/IPAC Extragalactic Database (NED).

Massive Iceberg Discharges as Triggers for Global Climate Change

W. S. Broecker

Editor's Note

In this paper Wallace Broecker reviews the evidence that had accumulated over the previous several years that rapid climate-change events during the last ice age, recorded in ice cores from Greenland, were triggered by the discharge of icebergs into the North Atlantic from the Laurentide ice sheet covering Canada. These episodes, called Heinrich events, were first identified from the detritus deposited in ocean sediments when the icebergs melted. The ice-core records showed that they were accompanied by abrupt cooling. Broecker suggested that this cooling was triggered by changes in ocean circulation as the fresh water from melted ice altered seawater density. The cause of the iceberg discharges remained open, specifically whether this was a result or a driver of climate change.

Observations of large and abrupt climate changes recorded in Greenland ice cores have spurred a search for clues to their cause. This search has revealed that at six times during the last glaciation, huge armadas of icebergs launched from Canada spread across the northern Atlantic Ocean, each triggering a climate response of global extent.

IN 1988 Hartmut Heinrich published an article summarizing his study of a curious set of sedimentary layers in cores from the Dreizack seamounts in the eastern North Atlantic[1]. His conclusion was that these layers record the melting of six great armadas of icebergs which flooded the northern Atlantic during the last glaciation. Each of these bursts produced a prominent sediment layer rich in Canadian-derived ice-rafted debris and poor in foraminifera shells. When Heinrich's paper was published, the attention of the palaeoclimate community was directed towards the climate response to the Earth's orbital cycles, so his discovery went largely unnoticed. Only when a nearly identical record was published[2] from a core located several hundred kilometres away, with a claim that the fresh water generated by the melting of these ice armadas might have disrupted deep-water formation in the northern Atlantic, did the palaeoclimate community recognize the possibility that Heinrich's layers were more than a curiosity. Suddenly attention was refocused on the coupling between surging ice sheets and northward heat transport by the Atlantic's thermohaline circulation.

It was already known from the Greenland ice cores[44,45] that during the last glacial period the northern Atlantic region experienced repeated large and abrupt climate changes. So far only one mechanism—changes in ocean circulation—has been put forward to explain

大规模冰筏涌出是全球气候变化的触发器

布勒克

编者按

华莱士·布勒克在本文中回顾了近些年来积累的一些证据，这些证据表明格陵兰冰芯记录的末次冰期快速气候变化事件是由覆盖加拿大的劳伦太德冰盖产生的冰筏涌进北大西洋所致。这些被称为海因里希事件的系列气候变化事件最先是由大洋沉积物中出现的冰筏融化所产生的碎屑沉积所识别出来。冰芯记录显示这些事件发生时伴随有急剧变冷。布勒克认为冰川融化产生的淡水改变了海水密度，使得海洋环流发生变化，从而引发气候变冷。冰筏涌出的原因，尤其是关于它是气候变化的驱动器还是结果这个问题目前尚无定论。

格陵兰冰芯中记录到的大尺度快速气候变化的观测结果促使人们探究导致该现象的线索。本研究显示，末次冰期时曾发生过六次大规模的冰筏群从加拿大开始扩散到整个北大西洋，而每一次都导致了全球范围的气候响应。

1988年哈特穆特·海因里希发表了一篇论文总结了他对北大西洋东部德雷扎克海山岩芯中一组特殊的沉积层的研究结果[1]。他的结论是，这些沉积层记录了末次冰期时存在六次大型冰筏群涌入北大西洋的冰筏消融事件。每一次消融都形成一个富含来自加拿大的冰筏碎屑且贫有孔虫壳体的明显的沉积层。海因里希的文章发表时，古气候学领域的注意力主要集中在气候对地球轨道周期的响应上，因此他的发现基本上未得到注意。直到位于几百千米以外的一个岩芯中近乎相同的记录被发表[2]，并认为这些冰山融化形成的淡水可能扰乱了北大西洋深层水的形成，此时古气候学领域才意识到海因里希沉积层很可能并不仅仅是一个特殊现象。很快，人们的注意力重新集中到涌出的冰盖和大西洋热盐环流向北输送的热量之间的耦合机制上。

从格陵兰冰芯中我们已经知道[44,45]，末次冰期时，北大西洋地区曾经历了多次大尺度快速气候变化事件。目前为止，人们只提出了一种解释这些变化的机制——

these jumps. The idea behind this mechanism is that high-latitude climate is strongly influenced by heat released from the sea. The amounts and routings of this heat are closely tied to the global pattern of thermohaline circulation. One such route, a conveyor-like circulation operating in the Atlantic, is particularly important. The heat it carries maintains the anomalously warm climate enjoyed by western Europe. The abrupt climate changes revealed in the Greenland record seem to be telling us that the conveyor has turned on and off. Modelling efforts reveal that such changes can be triggered by inputs of fresh water. One potential source of fresh water is that released by the melting of icebergs, such as the discharges recorded in Heinrich's layers (now known as Heinrich events).

Here I review the evidence that Heinrich events are indeed connected with rapid climate variations in the North Atlantic region. The timing of the events is in striking coincidence with the pattern of climate fluctuations documented from ice cores. But the mechanism that drives the events remains a matter of debate. One possibility is that the iceberg discharges reflect an internal oscillatory feature of the dynamics of the Laurentide ice sheet, from which the icebergs come. Alternatively, Heinrich events might represent a response to, rather than a cause of, climate change—external factors may induce global cooling, causing the ice sheets to surge. Although the true picture is likely to emerge only when our understanding of ocean circulation, ice-sheet dynamics and detailed regional palaeoclimate has improved substantially, there can be no doubt that Heinrich events provide a vivid illustration of the way in which the coupled influence of the atmosphere, geosphere and cryosphere may be a dominant control on the Earth's climate.

Anatomy of Heinrich Layers

Although glacial sediments of the northern Atlantic are uniformly rich in ice-rafted debris, that contained in Heinrich layers differs in three distinct ways. First, 20% of the sand-sized fragments are detrital limestone (a constituent nearly absent in ambient glacial sediment)[3]. Second, the clay-sized minerals in Heinrich layers have twofold higher K–Ar ages (~1,000 million years) than those for their ambient glacial equivalents[4-6]. Third, Heinrich layers are devoid of the basal-derived clay minerals so abundant in ambient glacial sediment[4-6]. Coupled with the observation that the detrital layers thin by more than an order of magnitude from the Labrador Sea to the European end of the 46° N iceberg route[3], these composition differences point strongly to a Canadian origin for the Heinrich ice armadas.

Surprisingly, the dominant feature of Heinrich layers is not a greatly enhanced abundance of ice-rafted debris, but rather a dearth of foraminiferal shells[2,3]. The abundance of these shells drops from its usual glacial value of thousands per gram to hundreds or less per gram in the Heinrich layers. Dilution with ice-rafted debris cannot be the sole cause of this reduction because the geographical extent of sediment sparse in foraminifera exceeds that of the Canada-derived detritus[2,3]. Rather, the low abundance of foraminifera must reflect, in part, a dramatic decrease in marine productivity. Heinrich events occurred when the northern Atlantic was at its coldest, as signalled by the geographical extent of the polar

大洋环流的变化。支撑该机制的思想是高纬地区的气候受到海洋释放热量的强烈影响。这些热量的多少及其输送路径与全球热盐环流模式紧密相关。其中，活跃在大西洋中的传输带式的环流尤其重要。它所携带的热量维持了西欧地区享有的异常温暖的气候。格陵兰记录中揭示出的快速气候变化似乎告诉我们"传输带"曾多次打开和关闭。模拟研究显示，此类变化可能是由淡水的输入所致。而淡水的一个潜在来源就是冰筏融水，例如在海因里希层记录的大量淡水的释放（现在被称为海因里希事件）。

本文将回顾关于海因里希事件确实与北大西洋地区快速气候变化有关的证据。对海因里希事件的定年结果与冰芯记录所证明的气候波动模式惊人地一致。不过关于这些事件发生的驱动机制尚存争议。一种可能是，冰筏的涌出反映了冰山来源地——劳伦太德冰盖内部振荡的动力学特征。或者，海因里希事件可能代表了对气候变化的响应，而不是导致气候变化的原因，即也许是一些外部因素引发了全球变冷，从而导致冰川涌出。虽然只有当我们对大洋环流、冰盖动力学以及详细的区域古气候的理解有实质性进步时，才有可能知道真实情况，但毫无疑问，海因里希事件为我们提供了一个实例，生动地描述了大气圈、地圈与冰圈之间的相互影响可能是控制地球气候的主控因素。

海因里希层剖析

虽然北大西洋冰期沉积物都一致富含冰筏碎屑，但海因里希层与其他的相比却存在三方面的差异。首先，砂粒级碎屑中有 20% 为灰岩碎屑（该组分在周围的冰期沉积物中几乎没有）[3]。其次，海因里希层中黏土粒级矿物的 K–Ar 测年年龄（约10 亿年）是周围冰期沉积物中的黏土级矿物年龄的两倍[4-6]。第三，在海因里希层中没有见到周围冰期沉积物中所富含的基底来源的黏土矿物[4-6]。结合所观测到的情况，即碎屑层厚度从拉布拉多海到 46°N 冰筏路径上的欧洲末端减少了不止一个数量级[3]，这些组成上的差异充分说明海因里希冰筏群来自于加拿大。

令人意外的是，海因里希层的主要特征并非冰筏碎屑的大量存在，而是有孔虫壳体的缺乏[2,3]。此类壳体的丰度在普通的冰期沉积物中平均为每克几千个，而在海因里希层中则降低到每克几百个甚至更少。冰筏碎屑的稀释作用并非是导致这种丰度降低的唯一原因，因为缺少有孔虫的沉积物的地理范围已经超出了来自加拿大的碎屑的地理范围[2,3]。更准确地说，有孔虫的低丰度值应该部分地反映了海洋生产力的急骤下降。海因里希事件发生于北大西洋地区最冷的时期，其典型特征就是极地

foraminifera, *Neogloboquadrina pachyderma* (left coiling) which extended all the way to 40° N. The depleted ^{18}O content in the few foraminifera present in Heinrich layers suggests the presence of a low-salinity lid[3]. These observations suggest episodes of extensive sea-ice cover similar to that of today's Arctic.

Timing of Heinrich Events

Perhaps the most startling aspect of the timing of these events is their occurrence at major climate boundaries[7]. As shown in Fig. 1, Heinrich event number 6 marks the transition from the relatively warm northern Atlantic of the last interglacial (that is, marine stage 5) to the cold conditions prevailing during the last glacial (marine stages 4, 3 and 2). Heinrich event 1 marks the onset of the termination which brought the last glacial to a close. There is unpublished evidence (J. McManus, personal communication) of a seventh Heinrich event right at termination of the penultimate glaciation (that is, marine stage 6). The coincidence between Heinrich events and the major changes in the temperature regime of the northern Atlantic leads to the speculation that fresh water released as the result of the melting of Heinrich's icebergs disrupted deep-water formation, thereby permitting switches between glacial and interglacial modes of thermohaline circulation.

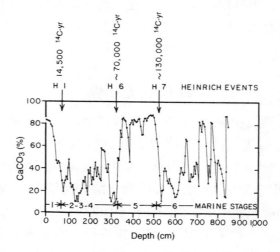

Fig. 1. Depth dependence of CaCO$_3$ content in core V28-82 from the northern Atlantic (50° N, 24° W) showing an alternation between coccolith-rich interglacial sediment (stages 1 and 5) and ice-rafted debris-rich glacial sediment (stages 2–4 and 6). Heinrich layers mark both the transitions from glacial to interglacial conditions and from interglacial to glacial conditions[7].

Another intriguing feature of the timing of the Heinrich events is their spacing at intervals of roughly 10,000 years (ref. 8). This spacing suggests forcing associated with the alternation of the relative strength of the seasonality in the two polar hemispheres brought about by the Earth's precession. Perhaps this alternation influences the dynamics of the tropical atmosphere in such a way that the water-vapour burden of the temperate latitudes is changed. But the significance of this observation is not clear, given that the spacing

有孔虫——厚壁新方球虫（*Neogloboquadrina pachyderma*）（左旋）的地理范围一直扩展到了 40°N 的位置。海因里希层中出现的少数有孔虫中 ^{18}O 含量的亏损说明当时冰盖盐度较低[3]。上述观测结果表明，类似今天北冰洋的大范围的海冰覆盖在末次冰期时的北大西洋曾发生过多次。

海因里希事件的定年

也许关于海因里希事件的发生年代，最令人惊讶的是它们总是出现在重大气候变化的界限上[7]。如图 1 所示，6 号海因里希事件标志着从末次间冰期时相对温暖的北大西洋气候（即氧同位素 5 期）向末次冰期时盛行的寒冷环境（氧同位素 4、3 和 2 期）的过渡。1 号海因里希事件标志着代表末次冰期结束的冰期终止期的开始。未发表的证据（麦克马纳斯，个人交流）显示，7 号海因里希事件则恰处于倒数第二次冰期（即氧同位素 6 期）的终止期。海因里希事件与北大西洋区域温度状况的重大变化之间的吻合导致了一种推测，即海因里希冰山融化释放的淡水扰乱了北大西洋深层水的形成，进而使得热盐环流在冰期与间冰期之间来回进行模式转换。

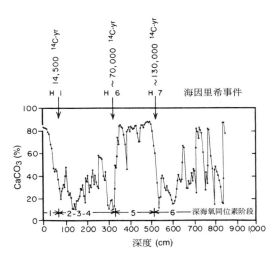

图 1. 在北大西洋 V28-82 站（50°N，24°W）岩芯中 $CaCO_3$ 含量随深度的变化。其中，富含颗石藻的间冰期沉积物（氧同位素 1 期和 5 期）与富含冰筏碎屑的冰期沉积物（氧同位素 2~4 期和 6 期）交替出现。海因里希层标志着由冰期向间冰期环境以及由间冰期向冰期环境的转换[7]。

海因里希事件的发生年代另一个有趣的特征是，它们之间的间隔大体在 1 万年左右（参考文献 8）。该间隔长度提示存在与由地球岁差引起的南北两极半球季节性相对强度交替变化有关的强迫因子。也许这种交替变化以这样的途径影响着热带地区大气层的动力学特征，以致中纬度地区的水汽承载发生了变化。已确认的末次冰

between Heinrich events decreases through the course of the last glacial period from about 13,000 years to about 7,000 years.

Relationship to Dansgaard–Oeschger Cycles

The glacial portion of the Greenland ice-core record is dominated by rectangular climate cycles averaging a few thousand years in duration[9-11]. These so-called Dansgaard–Oeschger (D–O) cycles are characterized by abrupt jumps in temperature, dust content, ice accumulation rate, and concentration of methane and perhaps carbon dioxide. It is puzzling that Heinrich events are not prominent in this record. But as shown by Bond *et al.*[12], there is a tie between Heinrich events and D–O cycles. Bond *et al.* have shown that the ice armadas were launched during the most intense cold phase of a package of several D–O cycles, and that each Heinrich event was followed by a prominent warming which initiated a new package of D–O cycles (see Fig. 2). This bundling of progressing colder D–O cycles into subsets gives rise to what has come to be called Bond cycles.

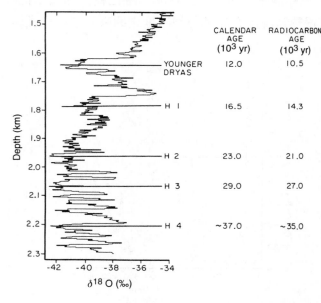

Fig. 2. Bond's placement of Heinrich events[11] in the Summit Greenland GRIP ice-core oxygen-isotope record[9]. Heinrich events occur in the last cold phase of a series of Dansgaard–Oeschger cycles and precede a major interstitial warm pulse[11]. ($\delta^{18}O$ is the relative deviation of the $^{18}O/^{16}O$ ratio in a sample from that in standard mean ocean water.)

The last of the D–O cold events is the Younger Dryas (YD). Its abrupt end ushered in the Holocene, a period of stable warm climate which has now lasted for about 11,500 calendar years (10,000 ^{14}C-years). The climate signal of the YD can be seen clearly in records from throughout the northern Atlantic basin. Bond's discovery[3] of detrital carbonate in marine sediments of YD age from the northern Atlantic suggests that it may also have an affinity to the Heinrich events.

期期间海因里希事件之间的间隔从约 13,000 年逐渐减小到约 7,000 年，但这一事实的意义尚不是很清楚。

与丹斯果－厄施格尔旋回的关系

格陵兰冰芯记录中的冰期部分主要为平均持续时间为几千年的呈矩形的气候旋回[9-11]。这些所谓的丹斯果－厄施格尔（D–O）旋回（也称丹斯果－厄施格尔循环）均以气温、粉尘含量、冰川加积速率、甲烷浓度甚至二氧化碳浓度的突然变化为特征。令人不解的是，在该记录中海因里希事件并不显著。但正如邦德等所示[12]，海因里希事件与 D–O 旋回之间存在特定的关系。邦德等曾指出，大量冰筏群是在一系列D–O 旋回的最冷期开始出现的，而每一次海因里希事件之后紧接着是一段显著变暖时期，变暖期开启了新一轮的 D–O 旋回（见图 2）。较冷的几个连续的 D–O 旋回，被称作邦德旋回。

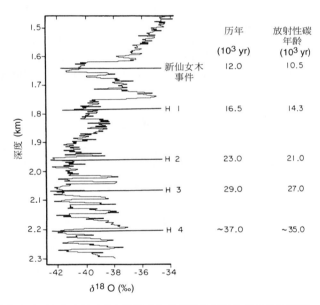

图 2. 邦德给出的格陵兰顶部萨米特冰芯氧同位素记录[9]的海因里希事件的位置[11]。海因里希事件发生在一系列丹斯果－厄施格尔旋回的最后一个冷期中，处于一次较大的间冰阶温暖期之前[11]。（$\delta^{18}O$ 是指样品中 $^{18}O/^{16}O$ 比值与标准平均海水中该比值的相对标准偏差。）

最后一次 D–O 变冷事件为新仙女木事件（YD）。该事件的突然结束宣告了全新世的开始，全新世是一段非常稳定的温暖时期，到目前为止已持续了 11,500 历年（^{14}C 年龄约为 10,000 年）。在整个北大西洋海盆的岩芯记录中都能清晰地看到新仙女木期的气候信号。邦德在北大西洋新仙女木期的海洋沉积物中发现了碎屑碳酸盐[3]，这说明它可能与海因里希事件之间也有密切关系。

The Global Imprint

Evidence is rapidly accumulating that D–O cycles, Bond cycles and the YD all have global signatures (Fig. 3). Analyses of the air trapped in Greenland ice have revealed minima in methane concentrations associated with the cold phases of D–O cycles (including the YD event)[13]. As the major source for this gas during glacial time is thought to have been tropical wetlands, climate effects not directly attributable to changes in the north-ward transport of heat by the Atlantic's conveyor must have been operative. Wet events in the pollen record from Lake Tulane in Florida appear to correlate with Heinrich events[14]. At least four maxima of the extent of Andean mountain glaciers in the lowlands of Chile have been identified by Denton and colleagues (personal communication). Radiocarbon ages for the last three of these maxima correspond within a few hundred years to the times of Heinrich events 3, 2 and 1. Denton and Hendy have also convincingly documented that mountain glaciers in the Alps of New Zealand reached an intermediate maximum precisely at the time of the onset of the YD[15]. Evidence of the YD has also been reported in foraminiferal records from the Sulu Sea[16], pollen records from British Columbia[17], lake levels in Africa[18] and oxygen and hydrogen isotope ratios in Antarctic ice[19]. These data are summarized in ref. 20. So no longer can it be assumed that the influence of these events was restricted to the northern Atlantic basin, weakening the case that they are tied exclusively to the heat release to the atmosphere in association with the formation of deep water in the northern Atlantic[21].

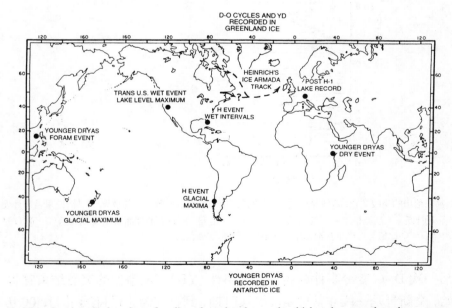

Fig. 3. Map showing the location of radiocarbon-dated records which, taken together, demonstrate the global signature of Heinrich events (H event) and the related Dansgaard–Oeschger (D–O), Bond cycles and the Younger Dryas.

对全球的影响

综合所有证据证明，D–O旋回、邦德旋回以及新仙女木事件均具有全球性特征（图3）。对保存在格陵兰冰芯中的气体的分析显示，甲烷浓度最低值与D–O旋回中的冷事件（包括新仙女木事件）有关[13]。由于热带湿地被认为是冰期时该气体的主要来源，气候效应在其中起到了一定的作用，该气候效应并未直接由大西洋"传输带"将热量向北输送的变化所引起。取自佛罗里达图兰湖的孢粉记录揭示的湿润事件似乎也与海因里希事件有关[14]。登顿和他的同事在智利低地中识别出了至少四次安第斯山冰川扩展到最大范围（个人交流）。这些冰川扩展到最大范围的事件中，最后三次的放射性碳测年结果与海因里希事件3、2和1的测年结果相差都在几百年以内。登顿和亨迪也有力地证明，位于新西兰的阿尔卑斯山地冰川在新仙女木事件开始时刚好达到极大值期[15]。来自苏禄海的有孔虫记录[16]、不列颠哥伦比亚省的孢粉记录[17]、非洲的湖水水位[18]以及南极冰川的氧、氢同位素比值[19]中均有关于新仙女木事件证据的报道。参考文献20对上述资料作了总结。因此，我们不能再继续假设这些事件的影响仅局限于北大西洋海盆，这样削弱了这些事件与因北大西洋深层水的形成而受到影响的向大气释放的热量之间具有独有关系的情况[21]。

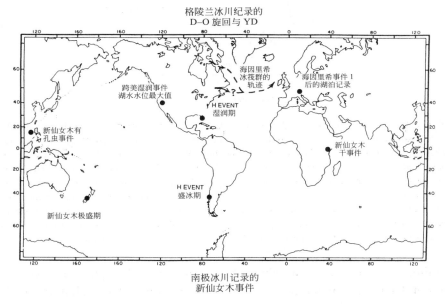

图3. 具有放射性碳测年数据的站位位置图，从中可证明海因里希事件（H event）和相关的丹斯果–厄施格尔（D–O）旋回、邦德旋回以及新仙女木事件都具有全球性特征。

The Trans-US Wet Event

A possibly important clue regarding the role of Heinrich armadas in perturbing ocean circulation comes from the sequence of events following the last of the six Heinrich outbursts. It seems that close to the time of this event, ice caps throughout the world reached prominent maxima[22]. Then shortly after Heinrich event 1, these glaciers went into rapid retreat (Fig. 4). This retreat is heralded by the basal sediments of the numerous small lakes in Switzerland's major Alpine valleys which document that by about 14,000 ^{14}C-years ago the valleys had become ice-free[23]. However, pollen in the sediments of these lakes reveals that conditions remained sufficiently cold to suppress the reappearance of trees[24]. Then at about 12,700 ^{14}C-years ago, a sudden warming occurred, not only in Switzerland, but throughout the northern Atlantic basin. Climate proxies from oxygen isotope[25,26], beetle[27] and pollen[26] records show that within a period of a few decades, warm climates prevailed. This warming has been widely attributed to a turn-on of the Atlantic's thermohaline circulation[21].

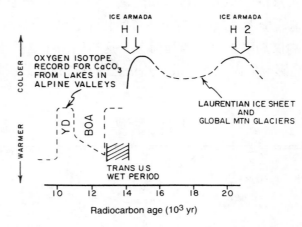

Fig. 4. Events of the last deglaciation: glaciers throughout the world achieved maxima close to 20,000 and to 14,500 radiocarbon-years (^{14}C-yr) ago. Based on the radiocarbon dates in hand, Heinrich armadas of icebergs were launched into the Atlantic close to the times of these glacial maxima. Following the second glacial maximum, the world's glaciers began a rapid retreat. In Europe this retreat opened the major Alpine valleys by 14,000 ^{14}C-yr ago allowing lakes to form. However, ~1,400 years passed before a second phase of warming occurred which allowed trees to colonize these valleys. This warming, which marked the onset of the northern Atlantic basin's Bølling-Allerød (BOA) warm period, occurred abruptly. The interval between the first Heinrich event (H 1) and the onset of the BOA corresponds to the time of an extreme wet interval across the southern tier of the United States (trans-US wet period).

But this raises a difficult question. What transpired during the 1,400 or so years between the launch of Heinrich armada no. 1 and the resumption of thermohaline circulation? A major clue comes from the global pattern of precipitation. Closed basin Lake Lahontan in the Great Basin of the western United States achieved its maximum size (Fig. 5) during this time interval and then underwent an abrupt major dessication just after 13,000 ^{14}C-years ago[28,29]. As suggested by the pollen records from Lake Tulane, Florida[14], and from

跨越整个美国的湿润事件

关于海因里希事件期间冰筏群在扰动大洋环流中所扮演角色的一个潜在重要线索来自最近一次海因里希事件后出现的系列气候事件。全世界的冰盖范围大概就是在该事件发生前后达到最大[22]。随后，在海因里希事件 1 结束后不久，冰川开始迅速消退（图 4）。这种消退在瑞士各大阿尔卑斯峡谷中不计其数的小湖泊的湖底沉积物中都有记录，这些记录显示，到距今 14,000 [14]C 年左右这些峡谷已完全处于无冰状态[23]。不过这些湖泊沉积物中的孢粉记录显示，当时的环境仍非常寒冷以至阻碍了树木的重新出现[24]。之后在距今大约 12,700 [14]C 年前，出现了一次突然变暖，其范围不仅仅限于瑞士，而且遍及整个北大西洋海盆。来自氧同位素[25,26]、甲虫[27]和孢粉记录[26]等气候替代指标显示，温暖气候持续了仅仅几十年的时间。该次变暖事件普遍被认为是由大西洋热盐环流的一次开启所致[21]。

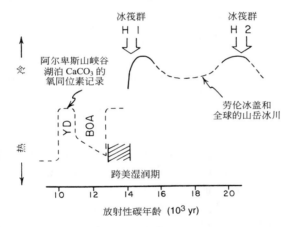

图 4. 末次冰消期的事件：放射性碳年龄（[14]C 年）为距今 20,000 年和 14,500 年左右时，全世界冰川范围达到最大值。根据获得的放射性碳测年结果，海因里希事件期间的冰筏群正是在冰川范围达最大时到达大西洋的。第二次冰川极盛期以后，世界冰川开始快速消退。在欧洲，这次冰川消退到距今 14,000 [14]C 年时开辟了阿尔卑斯峡谷，从而使湖泊得以形成。而在又过了 1,400 年后出现的第二次变暖期，使峡谷中长满了树木。该变暖事件的突然发生，标志着北大西洋海盆波令 – 阿勒罗德（BOA）暖期的开始。海因里希事件 1（H1）到 BOA 开始之间的间隔对应着贯穿美国南部地区的一段极其湿润的时期（跨美湿润期）

但由此却引出一个难题。即在海因里希事件 1 发生到热盐环流重新开始的这 1,400 年左右的时间里到底发生了什么？其中一条重要线索就是全球的降水模式。该时期内，美国西部大盆地中如今已干涸的盆地拉洪坦湖在当时达到最大值（图 5），随后在距今约 13,000 [14]C 年前突然变干涸[28,29]。来自佛罗里达图兰湖[14]以及弗吉尼

Brown's Pond, Virginia[30], the southeastern United States was also unusually wet between 14,000 and 13,000 ^{14}C-years ago. This pattern of excess precipitation is similar to that experienced during El Niño periods[31].

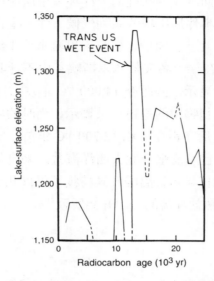

Fig. 5. The level of Lake Lahontan in the Great Basin of the western United States reached a brief late-Quaternary maximum, which dates between 12,700 and 14,500 ^{14}C-years ago (that is, 14,900–16,700 calendar years ago)[28]. This age range is based on ^{14}C-ages for the organic material beneath desert varnish on shoreline cobbles[28], ^{14}C-ages for algal carbonate shoreline deposits[28,29] and [230]Th–[234]U isochron ages on the same algal carbonates[29].

Ocean models offer a possible explanation for this curious interval. They show that sudden freshwater releases into polar regions can easily disrupt the existing pattern of thermohaline circulation. Whereas in some situations, the ocean immediately switches to an alternate thermohaline mode[32-34], in others, the model ocean lapses into what Manabe calls a "drop dead" mode with no deep-water formation[35,36]. In either case, after a thousand or so years, the model's conveyor circulation can suddenly resume. Thus it is tempting to speculate that the interval between ~14,000 and ~12,600 ^{14}C-years ago was a "drop dead" ocean circulation phase which ended with a sudden rejuvenation of the Atlantic's conveyor. Of course, this line of speculation carries with it the implication that a lapse in deep-water formation somehow gives rise to wet events in North America akin to those characterizing El Niño intervals[31]. The nature of this connection remains a mystery.

Surges or Fast-flowing Ice Streams?

The most obvious explanation for Heinrich events is that they result from surges of the ice stream that drained the Hudson Bay portion of the Laurentian ice sheet. Debris-laden basal ice issued forth from the Hudson Straits and gradually melted as it was carried by the prevailing currents across the Atlantic (along a track 10° wide in latitude centred at

604

亚布朗池中[30]的孢粉记录显示,在距今 14,000~13,000 [14]C 年前美国南部也异常湿润。所表现的过量降雨情形与厄尔尼诺期间的极为相似[31]。

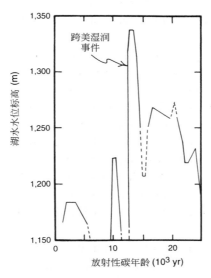

图 5. 美国西部大盆地中拉洪坦湖的水位在晚第四纪达到一次短暂的极大值,其测年结果为距今 12,700~14,500 [14]C 年前(即距今 14,900~16,700 历年前)[28]。该年龄范围是根据沿海卵石的荒漠漆皮下的有机质的 [14]C 年龄[28]、沿海沉积物中藻类碳酸盐的 [14]C 年龄[28,29] 和 [230]Th−[234]U 等时线年龄[29] 得出的。

海洋模型为该段异常时期提供了一种可能的解释。模拟结果显示,淡水突然释放进入极地地区可能极易扰乱热盐环流的存在模式。在某些情况下,大洋环流会即刻转变为另一种热盐模式[32-34],另一些情况下,模式海洋则陷入被真锅称为"落毙"的状态,此时不再有深层水形成[35,36]。无论在哪种情况下,大约 1,000 年以后,模式的传输带环流都会突然重新启动。因此,这似乎说明在距今约 14,000~12,600 [14]C 年间是大洋环流的"落毙"期,这一时期以大西洋"传输带"的再次启动而结束。当然,这一系列的推测可能意味着,深层水形成的中止从一定程度上导致了北美地区类似于厄尔尼诺期的湿润事件的发生[31]。该相互关联的本质仍是个谜。

是激增的涌流还是快速流动的冰流?

对海因里希事件的一个最直观的解释就是它们源自冰流的激增,这使得劳伦冰盖位于哈得孙湾的部分逐渐流走。携带碎屑的基底冰体由哈得孙海峡流出并在被盛行洋流携带下穿过大西洋的过程中逐渐融化(其轨迹为以 46°N 为中心的 10 个纬度范围以内地带)。目前我们所知道的关于海因里希层的所有问题都可由此得到充分解

46° N). Such an origin can adequately account for all we currently know about Heinrich layers. MacAyeal[37,38] has proposed a binge-and-purge model for the Hudson Bay lobe of the Laurentian ice sheet to account for these surges. He and Alley have shown that this model has the added attraction of explaining how the large amount $(0.1-1.0\,km^3)$ of debris making up the Heinrich layers became frozen into the cap's basal ice[39,40].

But the binge-and-purge hypothesis suffers from one major drawback—the timing of the surges would be controlled by internal properties of the ice sheet and not by external climatic forcing. If so, it is not so easy to understand what ties the advances of the Chilean mountain glaciers to the surges of the Laurentian ice sheet. As already stated, the two records are as near to synchronous as can be documented by existing radiocarbon measurements (within ± 300 years). Thus if the binge-and-purge theory is correct, each surge must somehow have sent out a signal to all the world's glaciers telling them to advance. The most likely carrier for this message would be the ocean's thermohaline circulation. Somehow its change would have to have led to a corresponding change in the Earth's temperature (perhaps via a change in the inventory of atmospheric water vapour).

Denton prefers to turn the situation around and invokes global temperature changes to drive both the glacial advances and generation of Heinrich icebergs. He calls on a global cooling to propel the rapid advances which pushed large quantities of Canadian ice into the sea, and allowed the icebergs to be carried far across the sea before melting. A problem with this interpretation is that because the response time of ice sheets to surface forcing is measured in tens of thousands of years[41,42], a close synchronism with rapidly responding mountain glaciers is not to be expected.

One important testable distinction exists between MacAyeal's and Denton's hypotheses. The former would restrict the release of Heinrich icebergs to the Hudson Straits whereas the latter would have them coming as well from the St Lawrence valley and even New England. There is a possibility that lead isotope measurements on individual feldspar grains, together with K–Ar measurements on individual amphibole grains would allow a determination of the source of Heinrich's icebergs. Their source would be defined unambiguously if they contained exclusively material from the older Precambrian Churchill Province (which underlies Hudson Bay) of if they also contained material from later Precambrian and Palaeozoic igneous bodies located to the south of the Canadian Archaean shield and also in eastern Greenland. Indeed, Gwiazda and Hemming have very recently obtained lead isotope measurements that clearly demonstrate that ice-rafted feldspars from Heinrich layer 2 are exclusively from older Precambrian rocks, whereas their equivalents in ambient glacial age sediment are derived from a wide range of terrains. This finding is consistent with MacAyeal's scenario.

Summary

So where does this leave us? First, the relationship between Bond cycles and D–O cycles

释。麦克阿耶尔[37,38]曾针对劳伦冰盖的哈得孙湾舌状体提出了一种增长和消融（binge and purge）模型来解释冰山的这种激增现象。他和阿利指出，该模型可以很好地解释构成海因里希层的大量（0.1~1.0 km³）碎屑是如何冰冻于冰盖中的基底冰中[39,40]。

但是增长与消融假说存在一个重大不足——冰量激增发生的时间受冰盖内部性质而非外部气候强迫的影响。倘使如此，那么要想理解智利山地冰川的前进与劳伦冰盖的激增之间的关系并不容易。如上所述，已有的放射性碳测年结果证明这两个记录几乎是同时发生的（相差在 300 年以内）。因此，倘若增长与消融假说是正确的，则每次激增发生时必定会向全世界冰川发出某种信号告知其前进，而最有可能携带该信息的就是大洋热盐环流。大洋热盐环流的变化会以某种方式导致全球温度发生相应变化（有可能是通过改变大气中的水汽总量来实现）。

登顿则倾向于相反的情况，即认为全球温度的变化造成了冰川的前进以及海因里希冰筏的形成。他认为全球变冷推进了冰川的快速前进，从而推动大量加拿大冰川进入大洋，并使冰山在融化之前可在海中穿越很长的距离。该解释中存在的一个问题是，由于测得的冰盖对表面应力的响应时间通常为成千上万年[41,42]，所以不太可能与同一时期快速响应的山地冰川同时发生。

麦克阿耶尔和登顿的假说之间存在的一个重要的、可验证的区别。前者认为海因里希冰筏的释放仅限于哈得孙海峡，而后者则认为它们也来自圣劳伦斯河谷，甚至新英格兰地区。单个斜长石晶粒的铅同位素测定结果以及单个角闪石晶粒的 K-Ar 测年结果也许可以确定海因里希冰筏的来源。如果确定了这些冰筏中只包含来自早前寒武纪丘吉尔省（位于哈得孙湾下部）的物质，或者其中还包含来自加拿大太古代地盾南部和格陵兰东部的晚前寒武纪和古生代的火成岩体物质，这都可以明确确定其来源。实际上，格威亚兹达和亨明刚刚测得的铅同位素结果已清楚地证明，海因里希层 2 中的冰漂斜长石均只来自早前寒武纪岩石，而其周围的冰期沉积物中相应的斜长石则来自广大不同地域。该发现与麦克阿耶尔的理论一致。

小　结

那么本文所留给我们的是什么呢？首先，邦德旋回与 D-O 旋回之间的关系仍

remains a mystery. Bond cycles show up in the glaciation of mountains in the Southern Hemisphere, pollen records from Florida, and iceberg records from the North Atlantic. Dansgaard–Oeschger cycles are found in global methane levels and in the Greenland ice-core records of temperature and dust. The YD displays characteristics of D–O and Bond cycles. As both phenomena seem to have their roots in the northern Atlantic, it is tempting to suggest the involvement of changes in the mode of thermohaline circulation, driven by the effect of fresh water on the formation of deep water in the northern Atlantic. Perhaps the D–O cycles are caused by a "salt oscillator" operating in the Atlantic, with Heinrich icebergs disrupting the regular progression of these oscillations. Perhaps the changes in ocean circulation perturb the strength of upwelling in the equatorial zone, affecting the operation of the great tropical convective systems that load the atmosphere with much of its moisture. In this way, the climatic effects of ocean-circulation changes could be carried beyond the northern Atlantic into other parts of the Earth. If so, then one would expect that Denton's mountain glaciation record will eventually reveal lesser advances associated with individual D–O cold phases.

Although this all sounds feasible, I am not convinced. Lurking on the horizon is an as yet untapped source of information—the record of atmospheric $^{14}C/^{12}C$ ratios. As deep-water formation in the northern Atlantic is presently the dominant conduit for the transfer of ^{14}C from the upper ocean to the deep sea, any major changes in thermohaline circulation should measurably perturb the distribution of ^{14}C within the sea and hence $^{14}C/^{12}C$ ratio in atmospheric CO_2. So far, we have suitable radiocarbon information (from independently dated tree rings, varved sediments and corals) only for the YD interval. These results clearly eliminate the possibility that thermohaline circulation was shut down during the Younger Dryas. Perhaps instead a shallower conveyor with a source region shifted to lower latitudes operated in its place[43]. In any case the ^{14}C results loom as dark clouds on the horizon of an ocean-based model. Unfortunately, no atmosphere-based hypothesis has been proposed. Neither models nor theory provide a mechanism whereby the atmosphere on its own could jump from one quasi-stable mode of operation to another.

It must be pointed out that this subject is of more than academic interest. We are currently provoking the Earth's climate with a steady build-up of greenhouse gases. It would be prudent to find out what it might take to kick the system into one of its alternate modes of operation. Could this happen in the absence of greatly extended ice cover?

(**372**, 421-424; 1994)

Wallace S. Broecker
Lamont-Doherty Earth Observatory, Columbia University, Route 9W, Palisades, New York 10964, USA.

References:
1. Heinrich, H. *Quat. Res.* **29**, 143-152 (1988).
2. Broecker, W. *et al. Clim. Dyn.* **6**, 265-273 (1992).
3. Bond, G. *et al. Nature* **360**, 245-249 (1992).

是一个谜。邦德旋回出现在南半球的山地冰川作用、佛罗里达的孢粉记录以及北大西洋的冰筏记录中。D-O 旋回见于全球甲烷浓度记录以及格陵兰冰芯的温度和粉尘记录中。新仙女木期表现出了 D-O 旋回和邦德旋回的特征。由于两种现象都起源于北大西洋，因此可能意味着这是由热盐环流的模式发生变化所致，其驱动机制是淡水对北大西洋深层水形成的影响。也许 D-O 旋回是由大西洋中的"盐度振荡"引起的，而海因里希冰筏扰乱了这种振荡的常规进展。同时大洋环流的变化很有可能扰乱了赤道地区上升流的强度，从而影响巨大的热带对流系统，导致大气湿度增加。在这样的方式下，大洋环流变化对气候的影响应该能够从北大西洋扩展到地球上其他地区。倘使如此，那么我们可以预期，登顿提出的山地冰川作用记录最终对单个 D-O 冷期的推动作用将很小。

虽然上述情况似乎都有可能，但我还不确定。大气中 CO_2 的 $^{14}C/^{12}C$ 比值记录正是潜在的信息来源。由于北大西洋深层水的形成是目前 ^{14}C 由海洋上层向深海转移的主要途径，热盐环流的任何明显变化都可能通过海洋中 ^{14}C 的分布得以测定，进而由此测出大气中 CO_2 的 $^{14}C/^{12}C$ 比值。目前为止，我们仅有新仙女木事件期间的放射性碳测年信息（来自经独立测年的树木年轮、纹层沉积物和珊瑚）。上述结果显然可以排除热盐环流在新仙女木期关闭的可能性。或许，在该位置上很有可能存在一个较浅的"传输带"在起作用，而其源区则向低纬度转移[43]。不管怎样，^{14}C 测年结果像乌云一样笼罩在基于海洋模型得出的认识之上。不幸的是，还没有基于大气的假说提出。没有任何模型或理论能够提出大气本身可以由一种准稳定模态向另一模态转换的机制。

必须要指出的是，这一问题远不仅是个学术兴趣问题。我们现在正使温室气体逐渐增加，从而破坏地球气候。我们需要谨慎地找出使该系统变为另一种作用模态的办法。在大范围展布的冰盖已不复存在的情况下这可能么？

（齐红艳 翻译；李铁刚 审稿）

4. Huon, S. *et al. Schweiz. Miner. Petrogr. Mitt.* **71**, 275-280 (1991).

5. Huon, S. & Ruch, P. *Mar. Geol.* **107**, 275-282 (1992).

6. Jantschik, R. & Huon, S. *Eclog. geol. Helv.* **85/1**, 195-212 (1992).

7. Broecker, W. S., Bond, G. & McManus, J. in *Ice in the Climate System* (ed. Peltier, W. R.) 161-166 (NATO ASI Ser. 12, Springer, Berlin, 1993).

8. Hagelberg, T. K., Bond, G. & deMenocal, P. *Paleoceanography* **9**, 545-558 (1994).

9. Dansgaard, W. *et al. Science* **218**, 1273-1277 (1982).

10. Johnsen, S. J. *et al. Nature* **359**, 311-313 (1992).

11. Dansgaard, W. *et al. Nature* **364**, 218-220 (1993).

12. Bond, G. *et al. Nature* **365**, 143-147 (1993).

13. Chappellaz, J. *et al. Nature* **366**, 443-445 (1993).

14. Grimm, E. C. *et al. Science* **261**, 198-200 (1993).

15. Denton, G. & Hendy, C. N. *Science* **264**, 1434-1437 (1994).

16. Linsley, B. K. & Thunell, R. C. *Paleoceanography* **5**, 1025-1039 (1990).

17. Mathewes, R. W., Heusser, L. E. & Patterson, R. T. *Geology* **21**, 101-104 (1993).

18. Roberts, N. *et al. Nature* **366**, 146-148 (1993).

19. Jouzel, J. *et al. The Last Deglaciation: Absolute and Radiocarbon Chronologies* (eds Bard, E. & Broecker, W. S.) 229-266 (Springer, New York, 1992).

20. Peteet, D. *et al. EOS* **74**, 587-589 (1993).

21. Broecker, W. S. *Oceanography* **4**, 79-89 (1991).

22. Broecker, W. S. & Denton, G. H. *Quat. Sci. Rev.* **9**, 305-341 (1990).

23. Schlüchter, C. *Bull. Ass. fr. Étude Quaternaire* **2/3**, 141-145 (1988).

24. Lotter, A. F. & Zbinden, H. *Eclog. geol. Helv.* **82/1**, 191-202 (1989).

25. Siegenthaler, U., Eicher, U. & Oeschger, H. *Ann. Glaciol.* **5**, 149-152 (1984).

26. Lotter, A. F. *Quat. Res.* **35**, 321-330 (1991).

27. Atkinson, T. C., Briffa, K. R. & Coope, G. R. *Nature* **325**, 587-592 (1987).

28. Benson, L. V. *J. Paleolimnol.* **5**, 115-126 (1991).

29. Lin, J. C. *et al. Geochim. Cosmochim. Acta* (in the press).

30. Kneller, M. & Peteet, D. *Quat. Sci. Rev.* **12**, 613-628 (1993).

31. Ropelewski, C. F. & Halpert, M. S. *Mon. Weath. Rev.* **115**, 1606-1626 (1987).

32. Stommel, H. *Tellus* **13**, 224-230 (1961).

33. Welander, P. in *Large-Scale Transport Processes in the Oceans and Atmosphere* (eds Anderson, D. L. T. & Willebrand, J.) 379 (NATO ASI ser. C, Dordrecht, Reidel, 1986).

34. Marotzke, J. in *Oceanic Circulation Models: Combining Data and Dynamics* (eds Anderson, D. L. T. & Willebrand, J.) 501-511 (NATO ASI ser., Kluwer, Dordrecht, 1989).

35. Manabe, S. & Stouffer, R. J. *J. Clim.* **1**, 841-866 (1988).

36. Manabe, S. & Stouffer, R. J. *Nature* **364**, 215-218 (1993).

37. MacAyeal, D. R. *Paleoceanography* **8**, 767-773 (1993).

38. MacAyeal, D. R. *Paleoceanography* **8**, 775-784 (1993).

39. Alley, R. B. & MacAyeal, D. R. (abstr.) *EOS* **74**, 359 (1993).

40. Alley, R. B. & MacAyeal, D. R. *Paleoceanography* **9**, 503-511 (1994).

41. Whillans, I. M. *J. Geophys. Res.* **86**, 4274-4282 (1981).

42. Alley, R. B. & Whillans, I. M. *J. Geophys. Res.* **89**, 6487-6493 (1984).

43. Rahmstorff, S. *Nature* **372**, 82-85 (1994).

44. Dansgaard, W., Johnsen, S. J., Clausen, H. B. & Langway, C. C. Jr in *Late Cenozoic Ice Ages* (ed. Turekian, K. K.) 37-56 (Yale Univ. Press, 1970).

45. Oeschger, H. *et al.* in *Climate Processes and Climate Sensitivity* (eds Hansen, J. E. & Takahachi, T.) 299-306 (Geophys. Monogr. 29, Am. Geophys. Un., Washington DC, 1984).

Acknowledgements. I am indebted to many people for helping to shape my thinking on this subject, including G. Bond, R. Alley, D. MacAyeal, S. Lehman, J. Andrews and H. Heinrich, I particularly thank G. Denton for regular correspondence about a whole range of aspects of this problem. Many of the ideas presented here have their origin in our dialogue, so in a sense, he is a shadow coauthor.

Positional Cloning of the Mouse *obese* Gene and Its Human Homologue

Yiying Zhang *et al.*

Editor's Note

The *obese* mouse carries a mutation that causes profound obesity and type II diabetes, but in the early 1990s the mechanism underlying this syndrome was far from clear. Here American biologist Jeffrey M. Friedman and colleagues describe the cloning and sequencing of the mouse *obese* gene and its human homologue, and speculate that the encoded fat-produced protein acts on the brain to inhibit food intake and/or regulate energy expenditure. The protein turned out to be the hormone leptin, which is released into the blood and transported to the hypothalamus, where it suppresses food intake. A mutation in the leptin gene has since been linked to obesity, and animal models of obesity continue to boost our understanding of weight control.

The mechanisms that balance food intake and energy expenditure determine who will be obese and who will be lean. One of the molecules that regulates energy balance in the mouse is the *obese* (*ob*) gene. Mutation of *ob* results in profound obesity and type II diabetes as part of a syndrome that resembles morbid obesity in humans. The *ob* gene product may function as part of a signalling pathway from adipose tissue that acts to regulate the size of the body fat depot.

OBESITY is the commonest nutritional disorder in Western societies. More than three in ten adult Americans weigh at least 20% in excess of their ideal body weight[1]. Increased body weight is an important public health problem because it is associated with type II diabetes, hypertension, hyperlipidaemia and certain cancers[2]. Although obesity is often considered to be a psychological problem, there is evidence that body weight is physiologically regulated[3].

The molecular pathogenesis of obesity is unknown. To identify components of the physiological system controlling body weight, we have applied positional cloning technologies in an attempt to isolate mouse obesity genes. Five single-gene mutations in mice that result in an obese phenotype have been described[3]. The first of the recessive obesity mutations, the *obese* mutation (*ob*), was identified in 1950[4]. *ob* is a single gene mutation that results in profound obesity and type II diabetes as part of a syndrome that resembles morbid obesity in humans[5]. Neither the primary defect nor the site of synthesis of the *ob* gene product is known. Cross-circulation experiments between mutant and wild-type mice suggest that *ob* mice are deficient for a blood-borne factor that regulates nutrient intake and metabolism[6], but the nature of this putative factor has not been determined.

612

小鼠肥胖基因及其人类同源基因的定位克隆

张一影（音译）等

编者按

肥胖小鼠携带一种基因突变体，该突变能引起严重的肥胖症和 II 型糖尿病，但是在 20 世纪 90 年代早期，人们并不清楚这种综合征的机制。在本文中，美国生物学家杰弗里·弗里德曼和同事描述了小鼠 obese（肥胖）基因及其人类同源基因的克隆和测序，推测该基因所编码的脂生成蛋白作用于大脑来抑制食物摄入和（或）调控能量代谢。结果显示，该蛋白是种激素——瘦蛋白，它可以释放到血液中并运送到下丘脑，而下丘脑正是抑制进食的功能部位。瘦蛋白基因的突变与肥胖有关，肥胖动物模型有助于加深我们对于体重控制的理解。

平衡进食和能量消耗的机制决定了谁会肥胖而谁会纤瘦。在小鼠体内，调节能量平衡的其中一个分子就是肥胖（ob）基因。ob 基因突变会导致人类出现类似病态肥胖的综合征，其中包括严重的肥胖和 II 型糖尿病。ob 基因产物可能是脂肪组织中调节体脂存储量的信号通路中的一员。

在西方社会，肥胖是最普遍的营养失调疾病。超过三成的美国成年人体重至少超过理想体重的 20%[1]。体重的增加是一个严重的公共健康问题，因为它总会伴随着 II 型糖尿病、高血压、高血脂和某些癌症[2]。虽然肥胖通常被认为是一种心理疾病，但是现在有证据表明体重是受生理调节的[3]。

肥胖的分子发病机理还不清楚。为了确定控制体重的生理系统的组成，我们尝试利用定位克隆技术来分离出小鼠的肥胖基因。现在已有报道显示，小鼠体内 5 种单基因突变可导致其肥胖表型[3]。第一个发现的隐性肥胖突变就是 1950 年报道的肥胖（ob）基因突变[4]。ob 是一个单基因突变，会导致人类出现类似于病态肥胖的综合征，其中包括严重的肥胖和 II 型糖尿病[5]。ob 基因产物的主要缺陷和合成位点均是未知的。突变型和野生型小鼠的交叉循环实验表明，ob 小鼠缺少一种调节营养摄入和代谢的血源性因子[6]，但是这种假定因子的性质仍不明确。

We report the cloning and sequencing of the mouse *ob* gene and its human homologue. *ob* encodes a 4.5-kilobase (kb) adipose tissue messenger RNA with a highly conserved 167-amino-acid open reading frame. The predicted amino-acid sequence is 84% identical between human and mouse and has features of a secreted protein. A nonsense mutation in codon 105 has been found in the original congenic C57BL/6J *ob/ob* mouse strain, which expresses a twentyfold increase in *ob* mRNA. A second *ob* mutant, the co-isogenic SM/Ckc-$+^{Dac}ob^{2J}/ob^{2J}$ strain, does not synthesize *ob* RNA. These data suggest that the *ob* gene product may function as part of a signalling pathway from adipose tissue that acts to regulate the size of the body fat depot.

For the positional cloning of mutant genes from mammals, it is necessary first to obtain genetic and physical maps, then to isolate the gene and detect the mutation. Here we describe the successful use of this approach to identify the *ob* gene.

Genetic and Physical Mapping of ob

The first *ob* mutation (carried on the congenic C57BL/6J *ob/ob* strain) was found proximal to the *Microphthalmia* (*Mi*) and *waved-1* (*wav-1*) loci on proximal mouse chromosome 6 (ref. 7); a second co-isogenic allele of *ob* has been identified in the SM/Ckc-Dac mouse strain (S. Lane, personal communication). We previously positioned *ob* relative to a series of molecular markers on mouse chromosome 6 and mapped the *ob* gene close to a restriction-fragment length polymorphism (RFLP) marker, D6Rck13, derived from chromosome microdissection[5,8]; we also found that *Pax4* in the proximal region of mouse chromosome 6 is tightly linked to *ob* (ref. 9). Both loci were initially used to type a total of 835 informative meioses derived from both interspecific and intersubspecific mouse crosses that were segregating *ob*. *Pax4* was mapped proximal to *ob* and was recombinant in two animals (111 and 420 in Fig. 1); no recombination between D6Rck13 and *ob* was detected among the first 835 meioses scored[8].

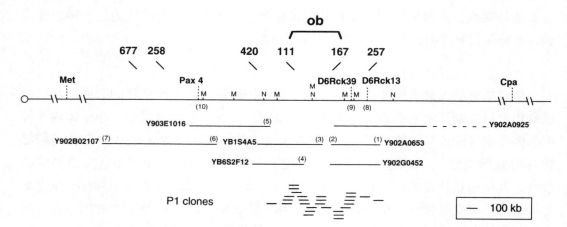

Fig. 1. Physical map of the mouse *ob* locus. A chromosome walk across the *ob* locus was completed in YACs and P1 clones using the flanking markers D6Rck13 and *Pax4* as starting points. The position of

在这篇文章里我们报道了小鼠 *ob* 基因及其人类同源基因的克隆与测序。*ob* 基因编码了一个 4.5 kb 的脂肪组织信使 RNA(mRNA),该 mRNA 有一个高度保守的、由 167 个氨基酸组成的开放阅读框。预测的氨基酸序列在人与小鼠之间有 84% 的一致性,并且具有一些分泌蛋白的特性。在原始同类的 C57BL/6J *ob/ob* 小鼠品系里,我们发现了第 105 个密码子处的无义突变。这些突变小鼠中,*ob* 基因的 mRNA 表达量增加至原来的 20 倍。第二个 *ob* 突变体发现于同类的 SM/Ckc-+$^{Dac}ob^{2J}$/ob^{2J} 品系的小鼠中,该小鼠不能合成 *ob* 基因的 RNA。这些数据提示了 *ob* 基因产物可能是脂肪组织中调节体脂存储量的信号通路中的一员。

为了从哺乳动物中定位克隆突变基因,我们必须先要得到遗传图谱和物理图谱,然后分离基因和检测突变。在这篇文章里面,我们成功应用这种方法确定了 *ob* 基因。

绘制 *ob* 基因突变的遗传图谱和物理图谱

在同类的 C57BL/6J *ob/ob* 的小鼠品系里,发现了第一个 *ob* 突变,它位于 6 号染色体的 *Microphthalmia*(*Mi*)和 *waved-1*(*wav-1*)两个基因座附近(参考文献 7);随后,在 SM/Ckc-Dac 小鼠品系里发现了另外一个 *ob* 同源等位突变(莱恩,个人交流)。我们首先将 *ob* 基因的位置用一系列小鼠 6 号染色体的分子标记进行定位,并且确定 *ob* 基因位于一个限制性片段长度多态性(RFLP)标记——D6Rck13 附近,这个分子标记是通过染色体显微切割得到的 [5,8]。我们还发现在小鼠 6 号染色体近端区域的 *Pax4* 与 *ob* 基因紧密连锁(参考文献 9)。D6Rck13、*Pax4* 这两个基因座最初是用来鉴定 835 个种间和亚种间小鼠因杂交 *ob* 基因被隔离的减数分裂配子的。*Pax4* 邻近 *ob* 基因,杂交时在两个动物间可以发生重组(图 1 的 111 和 420);而在第一轮得到的 835 个减数分裂里面没有检测到 D6Rck13 与 *ob* 基因之间发生重组 [8]。

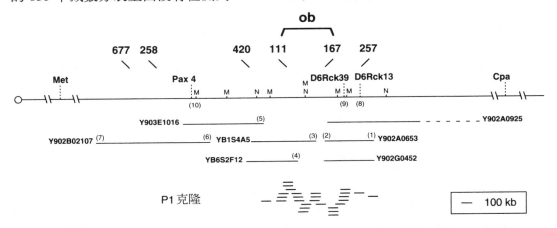

图 1. 小鼠 *ob* 基因座的物理图谱。以侧翼标记 D6Rck13 和 *Pax4* 作为起始位点通过一系列 YAC 和 P1 克隆完成了 *ob* 基因座的染色体步移。一些罕见的限制性酶切位点 *Mlu*1 (M) 和 *Not*1 (N) 的位置也被标记

the rare-cut restriction enzymes *Mlu*1 (**M**) and *Not*1 (**N**) are indicated. Numbers in bold type indicate designation of recombinant animals in the region of *ob* among the 1,606 meioses scored. Each of the ends of the YAC clones isolated with D6Rck13 and *Pax4* were recovered using vectorette PCR and/or plasmid end rescue and used to type the recombinant animals. These ends were sequenced and used in turn to isolate new YACs. The resulting YAC contig is shown on the middle panel. One of the YACs in this contig, y902A0925, was chimaeric. Each of the probes used to genotype the recombinant animals is indicated in parentheses. On this basis, *ob* was localized to the interval between the recombination events in animals 111 and 167, (between end (5) and D6Rck39). Selected probes were also used to isolate bacteriophage P1 clones across the non-recombinant region. The resulting P1 contig is shown in the bottom panel. These P1 bacteriophage spanned a ~70-kb interval between probes (2) and (3) which could not be recovered in a YAC clone. The *ob* gene was identified in a P1 clone isolated using the distal end of YAC yB6S2F12 (end 4).

Methods. YAC clones were isolated by PCR screening or hybridization to high-density filters of available mouse YAC libraries[38,40]. The YACs from ICRF begin with a 902 prefix. YAC clones were sized on a CHEF MAPPER (Bio-Rad). Restriction enzyme digestions were done according to the manufacturers recommendations. YAC ends were recovered using vectorette PCR and plasmid end rescue[10,11]. P1 clones were isolated by sending specific pairs of PCR primers to Genome Systems Inc (St Louis, MO) who provided single picks of individual mouse P1 clones[12]. P1 ends were recovered using vectorette PCR[13]. Cosmid subclones from YAC y902A0653 were isolated as described[41]. Primer selection and PCR amplification of simple sequence repeats were performed as described: initial denaturation at 94 °C for 3 min, 25 cycles of 94 °C for 1 min, 55 °C for 2 min and 72 °C for 3 min. Primer sequences for *Pax4*: *Pax4F*, 5'-GGAGGTAGAGATGGCAGCAG-3'; *Pax4R*, 5'-ACAGA-AAGCAAGGAGGATTTC-3', with a product size of 126 bp. Primer sequences for D6Rck39 were: 39GTF, 5'-GCACACTGACAGTGCCCTTA-3'; 39GTR, 5'-TGTAACCTGGAATTGGGAGC-3' with a product size of 128 bp. The breeding and maintenance of the various mouse crosses have been described[8,42].

To isolate the *ob* gene we cloned the DNA in the region of *Pax4* and D6Rck13 (Fig. 1), using both probes to start the construction of a physical map in the region of *ob*. Yeast artificial chromosomes (YACs) corresponding to *Pax4* and D6Rck13 were isolated and characterized. Centromeric and telomeric ends of each YAC were recovered, and ends mapping closer to *ob* used to screen for new YACs. YAC ends were recovered using either vectorette polymerase chain reaction (PCR) or the plasmid end-rescue technique[10,11]. One of the ends (labelled (1) in Fig. 1) of a D6Rck13 YAC, 902A0653, was recombinant in animal 257, positioning *ob* between this YAC end and *Pax4*. We were unable to recover any YACs linking the ends of YACs yBlS4A5 and 902A0653 (labelled (2) and (3) in Fig. 1). Pulsed-field gel electrophoresis (PFGE) indicated that there was a ~70-kb gap separating the two YAC ends. To bridge this gap, we used both YAC ends to isolate a set of mouse P1 clones[12,13]. Analysis of the ends of these Pl clones showed that they overlapped and that the gap in the YAC contig was ~70 kb. The size of the contig spanning the *ob* locus was 2.2 megabases (Mb) and *ob* was localized to the 900 kb between the distal end of YAC 903E1016 (labelled (5) in Fig. 1) and the distal end of YAC 902A0653 (labelled (1) in Fig. 1).

To position *ob* more precisely, we genotyped an additional 771 meioses derived from both a C57BL/6J *ob/ob* × DBA/2J intercross and backcross[5]. The typing of the intraspecific crosses required the development of informative single-strand length polymorphisms (SSLPs) for both D6Rck13 and *Pax4*. Sequencing of the *Pax4* gene itself revealed a microsatellite sequence, and an SSLP near D6Rck13, D6Rck39, was identified by sequencing cosmid subclones from YAC y902A0653 (a YAC isolated with D6Rck13).

616

出来了。粗体数字表示在记录的 1,606 次减数分裂中 *ob* 的位置上重组动物的名称。每个通过 D6Rck13 和 *Pax4* 分离得到的 YAC 克隆的末端都会用载体小件 PCR 和（或）质粒末端修复技术进行修复并且用于鉴定重组动物。这些末端序列先被测序然后被用于分离新的 YAC。最终找到的 YAC 重叠群在图中间区域。这个重叠群中有一个标号为 y902A0925 的 YAC，是嵌合的。每一个用于鉴定重组动物的探针都用圆括号在图中表示出来了。根据这个结果，*ob* 基因位于 111 和 167 号动物发生重组处的中间（在（5）号末端和 D6Rck39 之间）。一些挑选的探针也被用来寻找位于非重组区的噬菌体 P1 克隆。得到的 P1 重叠群在图的底部展示。得到的 P1 克隆横跨了探针（2）和（3）之间约 70 kb 的区域，该区域不能通过 YAC 克隆进行修复。*ob* 基因是通过标号 yB6S2F12 的 YAC 远末端探针（（4）号末端）在一个 P1 克隆上找到的。

方法。YAC 克隆是通过 PCR 筛选或者含有小鼠 YAC 文库的高密度滤纸杂交分离得到[38,40]。英国皇家癌症研究基金会（ICRF）来源的 YAC 都有一个 902 前缀。这些 YAC 克隆用 CHEF MAPPER（伯乐公司）分出大小，根据制造商的推荐进行限制性酶切，然后用载体小件 PCR 和质粒末端修复对相应的 YAC 末端进行修复[10,11]。P1 克隆则是将特定的 PCR 引物送到基因组系统公司（圣路易斯，密苏里），它们会提供单个小鼠 P1 克隆的分离[12]。P1 克隆末端用载体小件 PCR 修复[13]。来自 y902A0653 的 YAC 亚克隆黏粒根据文献描述的方法分离[41]。引物筛选和简单重复序列的 PCR 扩增根据以下描述进行：预变性用 94 ℃ 持续 3 分钟，接下来 25 个循环是 94 ℃ 持续 1 分钟，55 ℃ 持续 2 分钟，72 ℃ 持续 3 分钟。*Pax4* 的引物序列：*Pax4F*，5′–GGAGGTAGAGATGGCAGCAG–3′；*Pax4R*，5′–ACAGAAAGCAAGGAGGATTTC–3′，产物大小是 126 bp。D6Rck39 的引物序列：39GTF，5′–GCACACTGACAGTGCCCTTA–3′；39GTR，5′–TGTAACCTGGAATTGGGAGC–3′，产物大小 128 bp。小鼠品系的杂交和传代按照相关文献操作[8,42]。

为了分离 *ob* 基因，我们克隆了 *Pax4* 和 D6Rck13 之间的 DNA（图 1），并用这两个探针来构建 *ob* 基因区域的物理图谱。对应于 *Pax4* 和 D6Rck13 序列的酵母人工染色体（YACs）被分离出来并得到鉴定。对每一个 YAC 的着丝粒和端粒末端进行恢复，而靠近 *ob* 基因的末端则被用来筛选新的 YAC。这些 YAC 末端序列的恢复是靠载体小件聚合酶链式反应（PCR）或质粒末端拯救技术[10,11] 实现的。含有 D6Rck13 的 YAC（编号 902A0653）的一个末端（图 1 的标记（1））在 257 号小鼠里发生重组，使得 *ob* 基因处于这个 YAC 末端和 *Pax4* 之间。我们得不到任何可以将编号为 yB1S4A5 和 902A0653 的两个 YAC 末端（图 1 的标记（2）和（3））连接起来的 YAC。脉冲场凝胶电泳（PFGE）结果显示有一个 70 kb 的间隙将这两个 YAC 末端隔开。为了桥连这个间隙，我们用这两个 YAC 末端的序列分离一系列小鼠 P1 克隆[12,13]。通过分析这些 P1 克隆末端，我们发现这些克隆之间有重叠，而且 YAC 重叠群中这个间隙的大小是 70 kb 左右。这个跨越 *ob* 基因基因座的 YAC 重叠群大小为 2.2 Mb，并且 *ob* 基因就在 YAC 903E1016 的远末端（图 1 的标记（5））和 YAC 902A0653 的远末端（图 1 的标记（1））之间的 900 kb 区域内。

为了进一步精确定位 *ob* 基因，我们分析了 C57BL/6J *ob/ob* 品系和 DBA/2J 品系互交和回交得到的额外 771 个减数分裂后的基因型[5]。种内杂交的分型分析需要利用 D6Rck13 和 *Pax4* 的单链长度多态性（SSLPs）技术的发展。通过单独对 *Pax4* 基因测序我们得到了一个微卫星 DNA 序列，而在 D6Rck13 标记附近，通过对来自 YAC y902A0653（由 D6Rck13 分隔）的黏粒进行测序我们发现了另外一个 SSLP，标

PCR amplification of genomic DNA with primers flanking these microsatellites revealed polymorphisms among the various progenitor strains of the genetic crosses. No additional recombinants between *ob* and *Pax4* were identified after genotyping the obese backcross and intercross progeny from the crosses to DBA mice. The genetic results indicated that D6Rck39 was distal to *ob* and recombined with *ob* in a single obese animal derived from the C57BL/6J *ob*/*ob* × DBA/2J backcross, animal 167. This recombination occurred between D6Rck39 and the distal end of YAC yB6S2F12 (end (4) in Fig. 1) because a B × D polymorphism defined by this end indicated that it was non-recombinant in animal 167 as well as animals 111 and 420. Thus the distal end of YAC yB6S2F12 (end (4) in Fig. 1) failed to recombine with *ob* among the 1,606 meioses scored. As recombination in animal 111 was localized between this end and the distal end of YAC y903E1016 (end (5), which was non-recombinant in animal 420), the combined data from animals 111 and 167 placed *ob* in, at most, a 650-kb interval between D6Rck39 and YAC end (5). The exact size of the critical region could not be determined until the points of recombination in these animals were precisely localized. For reasons discussed later, fine mapping of these recombination events was not necessary. There was a total of 6 recombination events in this 2.2-Mb contig among 1,606 meioses. Therefore in the region of *ob*, 1 cM of genetic distance corresponded to ~5.8 Mb, a rate of recombination nearly threefold lower than average for the entire mouse genome[14].

To facilitate the identification of genes in the region of *ob*, we isolated P1 clones using the ends of the YACs in this region as well as the ends derived from the initial set of P1 clones. Twenty-four P1 clones were used to construct a contig across most of the 650-kb critical region of *ob*.

Gene Identification

Genes from this 650-kb interval were isolated using the method of exon trapping[15]. DNA from individual or pools of P1 clones was subcloned as *Bam*H1/*Bgl*II digests into the pSPL3 exon trapping vector. Briefly, each exon trapping product was sequenced and compared to all sequences in Genbank using the BLAST computer programme[16]. Putative exons were screened for the presence of corresponding RNA from a variety of tissues using northern blots and reverse-transcription PCR. Six genes were identified: four mapped within the 650-kb critical region of *ob* and two to outside this region.

One of the trapped exons, 2G7, was hybridized to a northern blot of mouse tissues and detected a ~4.5-kb RNA only in white adipose tissue (Fig. 2*a*). This exon was derived from a P1 isolated with the distal end of YB6S2F12 YAC (labelled (4) in Fig. 1). Even when autoradiographs were exposed for up to a week, no signal was detected in any other tissue, but we cannot exclude the possibility that this gene may be expressed elsewhere or below

号 D6Rck39。通过这些微卫星两侧的引物对基因组 DNA 进行 PCR 扩增，我们发现在用来基因杂交的不同原始小鼠品系里面，这些微卫星 DNA 序列具有多态性。在分析与 DBA 品系的互交和回交后代中的肥胖小鼠的基因型后，我们没有发现 ob 基因和 Pax4 之间有其他的重组发生。这些遗传结果显示 D6Rck39 在 ob 基因的远端，并且与 C57BL/6J ob/ob×DBA/2J 回交得到的 167 号小鼠的 ob 基因发生重组。这个重组发生在 D6Rck39 与 YAC yB6S2F12 的末端之间（图 1 的（4）号末端）。因为我们分析了这个 YAC 末端的一个约 B×D 多态标记，并且发现它在 167 号小鼠以及 111 号和 420 号小鼠里面全都没有重组。因此在记录的 1,606 次减数分裂中，YAC yB6S2F12 的远末端（图 1 的（4）号末端）都没有与 ob 基因发生重组。由于 111 号小鼠的重组发生在 yB6S2F12 的末端与 YAC y903E1016 远末端之间（末端（5）在 420 号小鼠中未发生重组），所以从 111 号和 167 号小鼠重组的数据分析可知，ob 基因最有可能在 D6Rck39 标记和 YAC（5）号末端之间这 650 kb 间隙之内。更为精确的区域大小只有在准确定位这些小鼠体内的重组位点之后才能确定。后面会说到，这样精确的重组位置分析对我们这里来说是不必要的。我们分析的 1,606 次减数分裂中有 6 次重组发生在这个 2.2 Mb 的重叠群里。因此，在 ob 基因这个区域中 1 cM 遗传距离大致相当于 5.8 Mb，这大约是小鼠整个基因组的重组频率的 1/3[14]。

为了促进 ob 区域的基因鉴定，我们用该区域的 YAC 末端序列和先前得到的一些 P1 克隆末端序列分离 P1 克隆。我们总共用 24 个 P1 克隆来构建了一个涵盖了这 650 kb ob 基因临界区域的绝大部分的重叠群。

基 因 鉴 定

利用外显子捕获技术[15]，我们找到了这 650 kb 间隙里面的基因。单个 P1 克隆或者 P1 克隆库中提取的 DNA，用 BamH1/BglII 消化并亚克隆进 pSPL3 外显子捕获载体。简而言之，就是将外显子捕获的产物测序，然后在 Genbank 数据库里用 BLAST 软件[16] 和已知基因序列比对。假定的外显子再用 RNA 印迹或者逆转录 PCR（RT-PCR）技术检测是否在不同组织里有相应的 RNA。用这个方法找到 6 个基因：4 个在这 650 kb ob 基因临界区域内，另外 2 个在该区域外。

其中一个名为 2G7 的外显子与小鼠组织进行 RNA 印迹实验，只在白色脂肪组织中检测到一个约 4.5 kb 的 RNA（图 2a）。这个外显子是来自 YB6S2F12 这个 YAC 远末端的一个 P1 克隆（图 1 的（4）号标记）。即使放射自显影的胶片曝光一周时间，也没有检测到来自其他组织的信号，但是我们不能排除这个基因在别处表达或

the level of detection in some tissues. Actin mRNA was detected in all samples (data not shown). Apparent adipose-tissue-specific expression was also seen after RT-PCR of RNA from a variety of tissues using specific primers from the 2G7 exon, with a strong signal being seen only in white fat and actin being detectable in all tissues tested (Fig. 2*b*). The high level of expression of 2G7 in adipose tissue suggested that this exon might be derived from the *ob* gene.

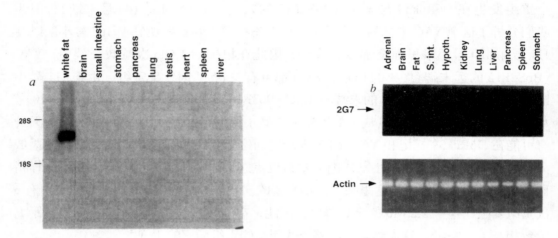

Fig. 2. Tissue distribution of the 2G7 transcript. *a*, Northern blot of total RNA (10 µg) from various tissues probed with labelled 2G7 exon. The 2G7 exon was identified using exon trapping with DNA from a pool of P1 clones in the region of *ob*. This probe hybridized specifically to RNA from white adipose tissue. Autoradiograph signals appeared after 1-h exposure (24-h exposure shown here). The transcript migrated between 28S and 18S ribosomal RNA markers and is estimated to be ~4.5 kb. *b*, Reverse transcription-PCR (RT-PCR) was performed with RNA from each of the tissue samples shown using primers specific for the 2G7 exon or actin. A positive signal was detectable only in white adipose tissue, even when PCR amplification was continued for 30 cycles.

Methods. *a*, Exon trapping was done by ligating *Bgl*II / *Bam*H1 digestion products of a pool of P1 clones into the pSPLIII vector as described[15]. Total RNA was prepared and electrophoresed in formaldehyde gels as in ref. 43. Northern blots were transferred to Immobilon and hybridized to radiolabelled probes as described[44]. *b*, Reverse-transcription PCR reactions were performed using 100 ng total RNA[45]. First-strand cDNA, prepared using random hexamers as primers, was PCR-amplified using primers derived from the 2G7 exon as well as mouse actin. The primers used to detect 2G7 were selected using the Primer program and were: 2G7F(5′CCAGGGCAGGAAAATGTG3′): 2G7R(5′CATCCTGGACTTTCTGGATAGG3′). The mouse actin primers were purchased from Clonetech. PCR amplification was performed for 30 cycles with 94 °C denaturation for 1 min 55 °C hybridization for 1 min, and 72 °C extensions for 2 min with a 1-s autoextension per cycle. RT-PCR products were resolved in a 1.5% low-melting-point agarose (Gibco/ BRL) gel run in 0.5 × TBE buffer.

The level of expression of the 2G7 exon was then assayed in the two available *ob* strains by hybridization to northern blots as well as by RT-PCR. Northern blots showed that 2G7 RNA was absent in SM/Ckc-+$^{Dac}ob^{2J}/ob^{2J}$ adipose tissue (Fig. 3*a*). This lack of 2G7 RNA in these animals was demonstrated by RT-PCR of the fat cell RNA, as shown by the absence of a signal after thirty cycles of amplification (Fig. 3*b*). As the ob^{2J} mutation is relatively recent and is maintained as a co-isogenic strain, these data indicate that 2G7

者以极低的水平在其他组织表达的可能性。肌动蛋白的 mRNA 可以在所有组织中被检测到(结果没有展示)。用 2G7 外显子的特异引物对来自不同组织的 RNA 进行 RT-PCR,我们同样可以明显检测到 2G7 在脂肪组织中特异性表达,只在白色脂肪组织中有强信号,并且肌动蛋白在所有组织中均被检测到(图 2b)。2G7 外显子在脂肪组织中的高表达提示它可能来自 ob 基因。

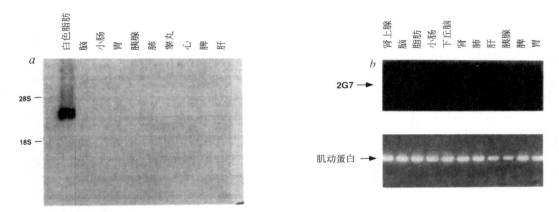

图 2. 2G7 转录产物的组织分布。a,不同组织来源的总 RNA(10 μg)用带标签的 2G7 外显子探针的 RNA 印迹结果。2G7 外显子是用外显子捕获技术从含有 ob 基因区域的 P1 克隆库的 DNA 序列中找到的。这个探针特异性地与白色脂肪组织的 RNA 杂交。放射自显影信号在曝光 1 小时后出现(这里显示的是 24 小时曝光的信号)。这个转录产物在 28S 和 18S 核糖体 RNA 之间,大小大概是 4.5 kb。b,利用特异的引物从各个组织的 RNA 里扩增 2G7 外显子或肌动蛋白基因的逆转录 PCR(RT-PCR)结果。即使是用 30 个循环的 PCR 扩增也只在白色脂肪组织检测到阳性信号。

方法。a,外显子捕获是按照文献描述操作,即将 P1 克隆库中 BglⅡ/BamH1 消化产物连接到 pSPLⅢ 载体里面 [15]。按照参考文献 43 提取总 RNA,并用甲醛胶进行电泳。按照文献描述的方法将 RNA 印迹转到 Immobilon 膜上,用同位素标记的探针进行 RNA 杂交 [44]。b,100 ng 总 RNA 用来进行逆转录 PCR [45]。单链 cDNA 使用随机六聚体引物进行合成,然后用 2G7 外显子和小鼠肌动蛋白的引物进行 PCR 扩增。用来扩增 2G7 外显子的引物是用 Primer 软件设计的,如下所示:2G7F(5'CCAGGGCAGGAAAATGTG3'),2G7R(5'CATCCTGGACTTTCTGGATAGG3')。小鼠肌动蛋白引物购自 Clonetech 公司。PCR 扩增 30 个循环,94 ℃变性 1 分钟,55 ℃退火 1 分钟,72 ℃延伸 2 分钟加上每个循环有 1 秒的自动延伸。RT-PCR 产物用 1.5% 低熔点琼脂糖凝胶(Gibco/BRL 公司)在 0.5 倍 TBE 缓冲液中进行电泳分离。

接下来,用 RNA 杂交和 RT-PCR 检测 2G7 外显子在含有 ob 基因的两个小鼠品系中的表达水平。RNA 印迹显示 2G7 RNA 没有在 SM/Ckc-+^Dacob^{2J}/ob^{2J} 小鼠的脂肪组织中表达(图 3a)。这些小鼠缺少 2G7 RNA 表达的结论同时也被脂肪细胞 RNA 的 RT-PCR 结果证实,RT-PCR 显示 30 个扩增循环之后都没有任何信号(图 3b)。由于 ob^{2J} 突变是新近发现的并且一直作为同类品系保存,这些结果提示 2G7 确实是 ob 基

encodes an exon from the *ob* gene. This was confirmed by characterization of the mutation in C57BL/6J *ob/ob* mice. Northern blots of adipose tissue RNA from C57BL/6J *ob/ob* mice showed a ~20-fold increase in the level of *ob* RNA (Fig. 3*a*), suggesting that the original *ob* allele (C57BL/6J *ob/ob*) was associated with a non-functional gene product and that the mRNA was increased as part of a possible feedback loop. This turned out to be the case (Fig. 4*b*) as the C57BL/6J *ob/ob* phenotype is the result of a nonsense mutation.

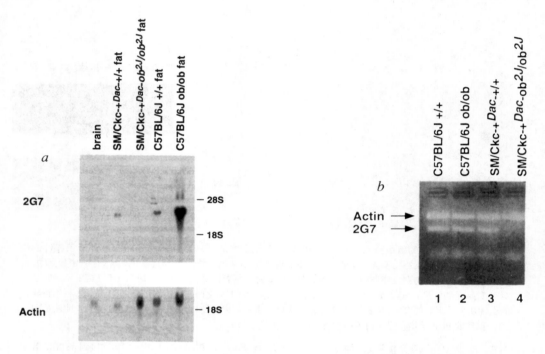

Fig. 3. 2G7 expression in mutant mice. *a*, Northern blot of fat cell RNA isolated from *obese* and lean mice. The 2G7 exon was hybridized to northern blots with 10 μg total RNA from white adipose tissue from each of the strains indicated. An approximately 20-fold increase in the level of 2G7 RNA was apparent in white fat RNA from the C57BL/6J *ob/ob* strain relative to lean littermates. There was no detectable signal in RNA from the SM/Ckc-+Dac*ob2J/ob2J* mice even after a 2-week exposure. A 24-h autoradiographic exposure is shown. The same filter was hybridized to an actin probe (bottom panel). SM/Ckc-+Dac and SM/Ckc-+Dac*ob2J/ob2J* mice were provided by S. Lane and B. Paigen of the Jackson Laboratory. C57BL/6J *ob/ob* mice were purchased from the Jackson Laboratory. *b*, RT-PCR of mutant RNA. Reverse-transcription PCR was performed for 30 cycles of amplification using 100 ng total fat RNA from each of the samples shown. In this experiment both the actin and 2G7 primer pairs were included in the same PCR reaction. The complete absence of 2G7 RNA was demonstrated in the SM/Ckc-+Dac*ob2J/ob2J* adipose tissue. For RT-PCR reactions, 100 ng total RNA was used[45].

因的一个外显子。这个猜想被 C57BL/6J *ob/ob* 小鼠的突变特征所证实。C57BL/6J *ob/ob* 小鼠脂肪组织的 RNA 印迹结果显示，*ob* 基因的 RNA 水平增加至原来的约 20 倍（图 3*a*）。这可能是由于原始 *ob* 基因的等位基因（C57BL/6J *ob/ob*）与一个非功能的基因产物有关，而 mRNA 作为可能的反馈环的一部分其表达量增加。图 4*b* 的结果正说明 C57BL/6J *ob/ob* 小鼠的表型是由一个无义突变导致的。

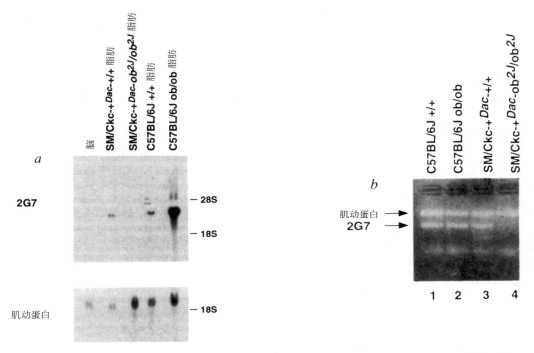

图 3. 2G7 在突变小鼠体内的表达。*a*，从肥胖和纤瘦小鼠脂肪细胞中提取的 RNA 的 RNA 印迹结果。如图所示，不同品系白色脂肪组织提取 10 μg 总 RNA 与 2G7 外显子杂交进行 RNA 印迹。从 C57BL/6J *ob/ob* 品系白色脂肪组织提取的 RNA，相对于同一窝较瘦小鼠的 RNA，2G7 外显子的表达水平大约增加至原来的 20 倍。即使是曝光两个星期，从 SM/Ckc-+$^{Dac}ob^{2J}/ob^{2J}$ 品系小鼠提取的 RNA 也检测不到信号。这里展示的是一个 24 小时放射自显影的图片。肌动蛋白的探针也是在同一张膜上杂交（底下一个图片）。SM/Ckc-+^{Dac} 和 SM/Ckc-+$^{Dac}ob^{2J}/ob^{2J}$ 小鼠是杰克逊实验室的莱恩和帕伊根提供的。而 C57BL/6J *ob/ob* 小鼠则是从杰克逊实验室购买。*b*，突变 RNA 的 RT-PCR 结果。如图所示，不同小鼠的 100 ng 总脂肪 RNA 用来进行 30 个循环的逆转录 PCR。在这个实验中肌动蛋白和 2G7 外显子的引物是加到同一个 PCR 反应里面。这个结果证明了 2G7 RNA 在 SM/Ckc-+$^{Dac}ob^{2J}/ob^{2J}$ 品系小鼠的脂肪组织中完全没有表达。100 ng 总 RNA 用做 RT-PCR 反应[45]。

a

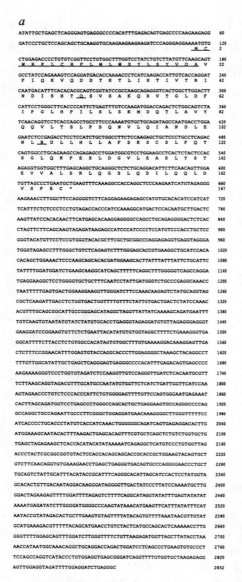

b

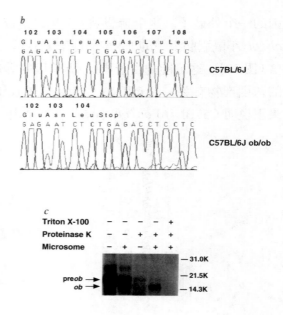

c

Fig. 4. *a*, Sequence of *ob* cDNA. 22 cDNA clones were isolated from a mouse white fat cDNA library and sequenced. A 97-bp 5′ leader was followed by a predicted 167-amino-acid ORF and a ~3,700-kb 3′-untranslated sequence. A total of ~2,500 base pairs of the 3′-untranslated sequence is shown. Analysis of the predicted protein sequence using the *sigseq* computer program suggests the presence of a signal sequence (underlined)[21]. Microheterogeneity of the cDNA was noted in that ~70% of the cDNAs had a glutamine codon at codon 49 and 30% did not. This amino acid is underlined as is the arginine codon that is mutated in C57BL/6J *ob/ob* mice (see *b*). After cleavage of the signal sequence, two cysteines remain at the C terminus of the molecule, possibly with formation of a disulphide bond. cDNA clones were isolated from a mouse adipose tissue library (Clonetech)[46]. Inserts were prepared directly from phage DNA or by PCR amplification of the insert using primers from the λgt10 cloning site (Clonetech). PCR products were prepared for sequencing after electrophoresis in low-melting-point agarose gels (Gibco/BRL) using agarase[47]. DNA was sequenced manually or using an ABI 373A automated sequencer[48,49]. 5′ RACE was done after dG tailing of first-strand cDNA using terminal transferase followed by PCR amplification with the reverse complement of the 2G7F primer and oligo (dC)[18]. *b*, The C57BL/6J *ob/ob* mutation. RT-PCR

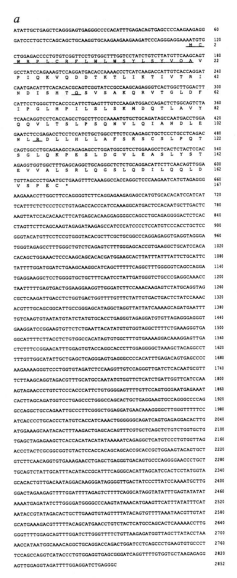

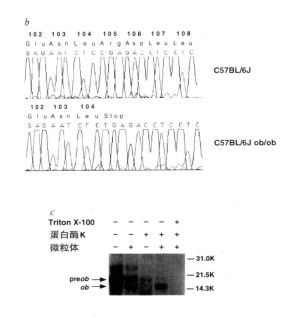

图 4. *a*, *ob* 基因 cDNA 序列。从小鼠白色脂肪组织 cDNA 文库中分离的 22 个 cDNA 克隆被用来测序。整个 cDNA 包括一个 97 bp 的 5′ 前导序列，然后是一个预测有 167 个氨基酸的开放阅读框和一个约 3,700 kb 的 3′ 非翻译序列。3′ 非翻译区的约 2,500 bp 在图中表示出来了。用 *sigseq* 软件分析预测的蛋白序列提示存在一个信号肽序列（图中下划线标注）[21]。cDNA 的微不均一性表现为，大约 70% cDNA 在 49 位密码子处有谷氨酰胺但是另外 30% 没有。该氨基酸用下划线标注，因为在 C57BL/6J *ob/ob* 小鼠体内突变为精氨酸密码子（见图 *b*）。信号肽被剪切以后，在蛋白的 C 端仍然有两个半胱氨酸可能会形成二硫键。cDNA 的克隆是从小鼠白色脂肪组织文库中筛选出来的（Clonetech 公司）[46]。插入片段直接是噬菌体 DNA 中得到或者用 λgt10 克隆位点的引物从插入片段中 PCR 扩增出来（Clonetech 公司）。PCR 产物在低熔点琼脂糖凝胶（Gibco/BRL 公司）中电泳，再用琼脂酶处理后进行测序[47]。DNA 测序是用手工或者 ABI 373A 测序仪进行[48,49]。5′ RACE 是用末端转移酶在单链 cDNA 上加脱氧鸟苷序列之后用 2G7F 引物和寡脱氧胞苷进行 PCR 扩增[18]。*b*，C57BL/6J *ob/ob* 突变。用 C57BL/6J+/+ 和 C57BL/6J *ob/ob* 小鼠的白色脂肪组织 RNA 和 5′ 端以及 3′ 端非翻译区的引物进行 RT-PCR，扩增的产物经胶纯化后，用引物编码区的双链进行测序。C57BL/6J *ob/ob* 的小鼠有一个 C 到 T 的突变，导致第 105 位精

625

was carried out using white fat RNA from C57BL/6J+/+ and C57BL/6J *ob/ob* mice and primers from the 5′ and 3′ untranslated regions. PCR reaction products were gel-purified and sequenced using primers along both strands of the coding sequence. The C57BL/6J *ob/ob* mice had a C → T mutation which changed Arg 105 to a stop codon. This base change is shown as the output from the automated sequencer. The cDNA sequences of mutant and wild-type mice were otherwise identical. The wild-type cDNA sequence was also seen in genomic DNA from v/Le and C57BL/10 mice, the progenitor strains of the stock on which the C57BL/6J *ob/ob* mutation originally arose (data not shown). *c, In vitro* translation of *ob* RNA. A human *ob* cDNA was subcloned into the pGEM cloning vector (see Fig. 5*b*). Plus-strand RNA was synthesized using SP6 polymerase. The *in vitro* synthesized RNA was translated in the presence or absence of canine pancreatic microsomal membranes. An ~18K primary translation product was seen after *in vitro* translation. The addition of microsomal membranes (mb) to the reaction led to the appearance of a second translation product ~2K smaller than the primary translation product. The 16K product was resistant to proteinase K but was rendered protease-sensitive when the microsomal membranes were permeabilized by Triton X-100, indicating that a functional signal sequence was present. A human *ob* cDNA was cloned into the pGEM-3zf(+) plasmid. *In vitro* transcription was carried out using a Ribo MAX large-scale RNA production system with SP6 polymerase (Promega). The transcription mixture was used without further purification in a wheat-germ translation system (Promega) with or without 5 μg of a canine pancreas microsomal membrane preparation[50] at 27 °C for 2 h. Proteinase K (100 μg ml⁻¹) digests were performed on ice for 1 h with and without 0.1% Triton X-100. Translation products were analysed by SDS–PAGE.

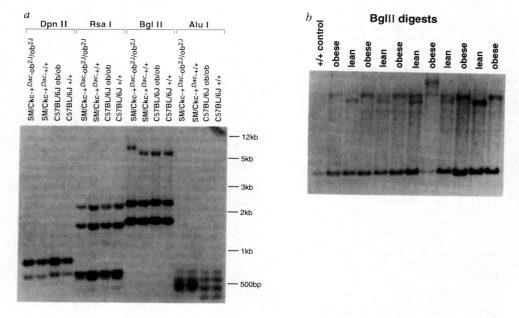

Fig. 5. The *ob²ᴶ* mutation. *a*, Southern blots of genomic DNA from mutant animals. The 2G7 probe was hybridized to 5 μg of restriction-enzyme-digested genomic DNA from each strain. Restriction digestion with *Bgl*II revealed an increase in the size of a ~9 kb (the largest) *Bgl*II fragment in SM/Ckc-+^{Dac}*ob²ᴶ*/*ob²ᴶ* DNA. RFLPs were not detectable with any other restriction enzymes. Preliminary restriction mapping of genomic DNA indicated that the polymorphic *Bgl*II site is ~7 kb upstream of the transcription start site (data not shown). None of the other enzymes tested extend past the mRNA start site. Genomic DNA preparation and Southern blotting have been described[8]. *b*, Segregation of a *Bgl*II polymorphism in the SM/Ckc-+^{Dac}*ob²ᴶ*/*ob²ᴶ*. Six obese and five lean progeny from the same generation of the coisogenic SM/Ckc-+^{Dac}*ob²ᴶ*/*ob²ᴶ* colony were genotyped by scoring the *Bgl*II polymorphism in *a*. All of the phenotypically obese animals were homozygous for the larger allele of the polymorphic *Bgl*II fragment. The DNA in the control lane was prepared from an unrelated SM/Ckc-Dac$^{+/+}$ mouse, bred separately from the SM/Ckc-+^{Dac}*ob²ᴶ*/*ob²ᴶ* colony.

氨酸密码子变成终止密码子。这个碱基突变在自动测序仪的测序结果中显示出来了。突变型和野生型小鼠的其他测序结果是一致的。野生型小鼠的 cDNA 序列也存在于 v/Le 和 C57BL/10 两个小鼠的基因组 DNA 中(结果没有展示)。这两个品系是最初出现 C57BL/6J *ob/ob* 突变的小鼠的原品系。*c, ob* 基因 RNA 的体外翻译。人 *ob* 基因 cDNA 被亚克隆到 pGEM 克隆载体里(见图 5*b*)。利用 SP6 聚合酶来合成正链 RNA。这个体外合成的 RNA 在犬胰腺微粒体膜系统存在或缺失的情况下被翻译。体外翻译得到一个约 18K 大小的初始翻译产物。反应中存在微粒体膜系统时会得到一个次生的、比原始产物小约 2K 的翻译产物。这个 16K 的蛋白对蛋白酶 K 不敏感,但是如果微粒体膜系被 Triton X-100 透化以后这个蛋白对蛋白酶又再次敏感了。这个结果提示存在一个功能性的信号肽。人类的 *ob* 基因 cDNA 被克隆到 pGEM-3zf(+)质粒里面。使用 Ribo MAX 大规模 RNA 转录系统和 SP6 聚合酶(普洛麦格公司)进行体外转录。没有经过进一步纯化的转录混合物接下来被直接用在加或者不加 5 μg 犬胰腺微粒体膜系统的小麦胚芽翻译系统(普洛麦格公司)[50]中,然后 27 ℃温浴 2 小时。在加或者不加 0.1% Triton X-100 的情况下,冰上进行蛋白酶 K(100 μg·ml⁻¹)消化 1 小时。用十二烷基硫酸钠-聚丙烯酰胺凝胶电泳(SDS-PAGE)分析翻译产物。

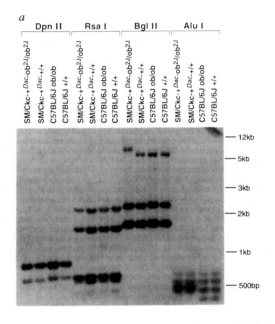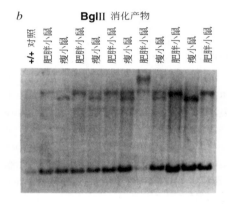

图 5. *ob²ᴶ* 突变。*a*,突变小鼠基因组的 DNA 印迹结果。2G7 的探针与来自各个小鼠品系的经内切酶酶切后的 5 μg 基因组 DNA 进行杂交。*Bgl*II 酶切 SM/Ckc-+ᴰᵃᶜ*ob²ᴶ/ob²ᴶ* DNA 出现一个更大的约 9 kb(最大的)的产物。用其他的内切酶没有发现任何限制性片段长度多态性。基因组 DNA 的初步内切酶位点图谱显示这个 *Bgl*II 酶切位点的多态性位于转录起始位点上游大概 7 kb 的位置(结果没有展示)。在 mRNA 起始位点以后没有任何其他的酶切位点。基因组 DNA 的提取和 DNA 杂交的方法按照文献描述进行[8]。*b*,*Bgl*II 位点多态性在 SM/Ckc-+ᴰᵃᶜ*ob²ᴶ/ob²ᴶ* 小鼠中得到分离。在图 *a* 中,SM/Ckc-+ᴰᵃᶜ*ob²ᴶ/ob²ᴶ* 品系同窝的六只肥胖小鼠和五只瘦小鼠的后代通过 *Bgl*II 多态性来进行基因型确定。所有肥胖表型的小鼠都是比较大的多态性 *Bgl*II 片段等位基因纯合子。图中对照组的 DNA 是从一个与 SM/Ckc-+ᴰᵃᶜ*ob²ᴶ/ob²ᴶ* 小鼠分开饲养的、无关的 SM/Ckc-Dac⁺/⁺ 小鼠品系中提取的。

Sequence of the *ob* Gene

The 2G7 exon was used to isolate a total of 22 complementary DNA clones from a mouse adipose tissue cDNA library. None of the cDNA clones extended more than 97 base pairs upstream of 2G7, whereas each extended a variable distance downstream. Sequencing of the cDNA clones revealed a methionine initiation codon in the 2G7 exon, with a 167-amino-acid open reading frame followed by a long 3'-untranslated sequence (Fig. 4). A potential Kozak translation initiation consensus sequence was present with an adenosine residue three bases upstream of the ATG[17]. One of the cDNA clones extended to the 5' end of the mRNA because its sequence was identical to that of the 5' RACE (rapid amplification of cloned ends) products of adipose tissue RNA (data not shown)[18]. A total of 2.9 kb of cDNA sequence is shown, most of which is 3'-untranslated sequence. A search for internal homology within the cDNA revealed a 50-base-pair (bp) direct repeat in both the 5' and 3' untranslated sequence; this sequence was not found in Genbank and there were no additional segments of internal homology.

Two classes of cDNA were found which differed by inclusion or exclusion of a single glutamine codon (underlined in Fig. 4). This residue is found in a position immediately 3' to the splice acceptor of the 2G7 exon. As the CAG codon of glutamine includes a possible AG splice-acceptor sequence, there appears to be slippage at the splice-acceptor site, with an apparent 3-bp deletion in a subset of the cDNAs[19]. This glutamine residue is located in a highly conserved region of the molecule but its significance is unknown.

To identify the mutation in C57B6/J *ob/ob* mice, RT–PCR products from the entire open reading frame (ORF) were prepared from adipose tissue RNA from this mutant and both strands sequenced. The coding sequences were identical apart from a C→T mutation in C57BL/6J *ob/ob* mice that results in a change of an arginine at position 105 to a stop condon (Fig. 4*b*). This amino acid is also underlined in Fig. 4*a*. This base change did not occur in genomic DNA from v/Le or C57BL/10 mice, the strains in which this mutation was carried before it was transferred to C57BL/6J (S. Lane, personal communication). DNA sequence changes from CGA to TGA are not uncommon as a result of the high mutation rate of methyl cytosine to thymidine[20]. This *ob* mutation is presumed to inactivate the protein as the phenotype in both C57BL/6J and SM/Ckc-+[Dac]*ob*[2J]/*ob*[2J] mice is identical (S. Lane, personal communication; data not shown).

A database search of the *ob* protein using the BLAST program[16] identified no significant homology to any sequences in Genbank. The predicted polypeptide was largely hydrophilic and had a putative N-terminal signal sequence[22]. Amino-acid sequence analysis using the *sigseq* computer program indicated a 98% likelihood that a signal sequence was present at the N terminus[21] (underlined in Fig. 4*a*). The predicted signal sequence cleavage site is C terminal to an alanine at position 21. Computer analysis of the human protein (Fig. 6*b*) also suggests that it has an N-terminal signal sequence, so human and mouse *ob* may both encode secreted proteins. There is some divergence in the mouse

ob 基因的序列

用 2G7 外显子从小鼠脂肪组织的 cDNA 文库里找到 22 个互补 DNA（cDNA）克隆。但是没有任何一个 cDNA 克隆超过 2G7 上游 97 个碱基对，而且每一个克隆的下游序列长度都不一样。通过对 cDNA 克隆测序，我们在 2G7 外显子上找到一个甲硫氨酸的起始密码子和一个有很长的 3′ 非翻译序列的 167 个氨基酸的开放阅读框（图 4）。在起始位点 ATG 上游的 3 个碱基处是一个腺苷酸残基以及类似 Kozak 翻译起始的共有序列[17]。其中一个 cDNA 克隆其实是延伸到了 mRNA 的 5′ 末端，因为它的序列和脂肪组织 RNA 的 cDNA 5′ RACE（末端快速扩增法）得到的产物一致（结果没有展示）[18]。这个全长 2.9 kb 的 cDNA 序列，绝大部分是 3′ 非翻译序列。对基因内部的同源性进行分析，我们在 5′ 和 3′ 非翻译序列各发现一个 50 碱基对（bp）的重复；这个重复序列在 Genebank 数据库没有找到，并且也没有其他的内部同源性片段。

研究发现两类 cDNA，它们的不同之处在于是否包括单个谷氨酰胺密码子（图 4 下划线）。这个残基位于 2G7 外显子 3′ 末端剪接受体处。由于谷氨酰胺的密码子 CAG 中包含一个可能的 AG 剪接受体序列，这就可能导致剪接位点有一个偏移进而导致后面的 cDNA 序列缺失 3 个碱基对[19]。这个谷氨酰胺残基位于整个分子的一个非常保守的区域，但是它的重要性还未知。

为了鉴定 C57B6/J *ob/ob* 小鼠基因的突变，我们从突变小鼠的脂肪组织 RNA 里面扩增出基因的整个开放阅读框（ORF）cDNA 并且对双链进行测序。所有编码序列都进行了鉴定，在 C57BL/6J *ob/ob* 小鼠体内发现了一个会导致 105 位精氨酸变成终止密码子的一个 C 到 T 的突变（图 4*b*）。这个氨基酸在图 4*a* 用下划线标记。这个碱基的改变并不存在于 v/Le 或 C57BL/10 两种小鼠的基因组 DNA 中，在这两种小鼠中，这种突变被转移到 C57BL/6J 品系之前已携带（莱恩，个人交流）。CGA 到 TGA 的突变在 DNA 里面也很常见，因为甲基化的胞嘧啶变成胸腺嘧啶的突变率很高[20]。由于 C57BL/6J 和 SM/Ckc-+^Dac*ob^2J*/*ob^2J* 的表型一样，所以这个 *ob* 突变也被认为可以导致蛋白完全失活（莱恩，个人交流；结果没有展示）。

在 Genebank 数据库里面用 BLAST 软件[16]搜索不到任何高度同源的 OB 蛋白序列。预测的蛋白序列基本是亲水性的，而且 N 端可能有信号序列[22]。用 *sigseq* 软件分析氨基酸序列表明有 98% 的可能性蛋白 N 端有信号序列[21]（图 4*a* 下划线标记）。C 端的第 21 位的丙氨酸是预测的信号肽酶切位点。计算机分析人类的 OB 蛋白（图 6*b*）也有一个 N 端信号序列，所以人和小鼠的 *ob* 基因可能都编码分泌蛋白。小鼠和人类的信号序列虽然有些差异，但是 *sigseq* 软件给出了同样高的分数。为了确认

and human signal sequences, but both give identical scores when analysed using *segseq*. To confirm the presence of a functional signal sequence, a human cDNA that included the entire ORF was subcloned into a pGEM vector (suitable mouse subclones were not recovered). Positive-strand human *ob* RNA was transcribed using SP6 polymerase and translated *in vitro* with and without canine pancreatic microsomal membranes[50]. The primary translation product migrated with an apparent relative molecular mass of ~18K, consistent with that predicted from the cDNA sequence. Inclusion of microsomal membranes in the reaction inhibited translation ~5-fold, but about half of the *ob* primary translation product was truncated by ~2K in the presence of microsomal membranes, which suggests that the signal sequence is functional (Fig. 4c). To confirm that the *ob* protein had been translocated, we treated *in vitro* translation products with proteinase K, which caused complete proteolysis of the 18K primary translation product whereas the 16K processed form was unaffected, indicating that the translation product had been translocated into the microsomal lumen. Permeabilization of the membranes with Triton X-100 rendered the processed form protease-sensitive and is compatible with the hypothesis that *ob* is a secreted molecule. After signal-sequence cleavage, two cysteine residues would remain within the predicted protein, suggesting that the molecule may contain the disulphide bond characteristic of other secreted polypeptides. Amino-acid sequence and secondary structure prediction support a globular structure for the protein (data not shown). The largely hydrophilic amino-acid sequence had no notable structural motifs or membrane-spanning domains other than the N-terminal signal sequence. We find no consensus for *N*-linked glycosylation or dibasic amino-acid sequences indicative of protein cleavage in the predicted processed protein[22].

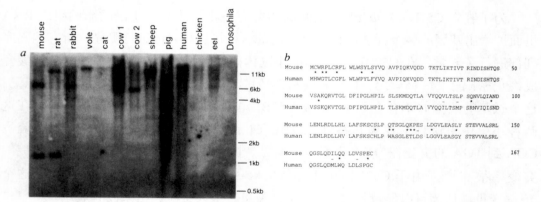

Fig. 6. Evolutionary conservation of *ob*. *a*, Cross-species hybridization of *ob*. Genomic DNA from each of the species shown was Southern blotted after *Eco*RI digestion and probed with *ob* cDNA. Hybridization signals were detectable in every vertebrate sample even after moderate-stringency hybridization. The cat DNA used in this experiment was slightly degraded. DNA was prepared from tissues or cell lines from the organisms shown. Southern blot hybridization was at 65 °C, with two washes in 2 × SSC/0.2% SDS at 65 °C for 20 min, and autoradiograph exposure was for 3 d using Kodak X-OMAT film. *b*, Sequence of human *ob* protein. The mouse *ob* gene was used as a probe to isolate human adipose tissue cDNA clones from a λgtII library. The sequence of human *ob* cDNA was highly homologous to that of the mouse cDNA in the predicted 167-amino-acid coding sequence. There was 30% homology in the 5′ and 3′ untranslated sequences in this tissue. Predicted amino-acid sequences of the human and mouse proteins have been

这个功能信号序列的存在，我们将一个含有整个开放阅读框的人类 cDNA 亚克隆到 pGEM 载体里（没有能够得到合适的小鼠亚克隆）。SP6 聚合酶用来反转录人 *ob* RNA 的正链，然后在有和没有犬胰腺微粒体膜系统[50]的两种情况下进行体外翻译。最初的翻译产物跑胶测量的相对分子质量大约 18K，这与 cDNA 序列预测的大小一致。如果翻译在微粒体膜系统进行，翻译效率大概下降为 1/5 左右，但是一半的翻译产物在这种情况下约被剪切了 2K。这个结果提示信号序列确实具有功能（图 4*c*）。为了确认 OB 蛋白确实可以易位，我们用蛋白酶 K 处理了体外翻译产物。结果 18K 的最初产物被全部酶解，但是剪切后的 16K 产物基本不受影响。这个结果提示我们翻译产物被转运进了微粒体腔内。用 Triton X-100 透化的微粒体膜可以让剪切后的产物对蛋白酶敏感，这个结果符合 OB 是分泌蛋白的假设。信号肽被剪切掉以后，OB 蛋白仍然有两个半胱氨酸残基，说明该分子可能像其他分泌蛋白一样具有二硫键。氨基酸序列和二级结构预测则支持这是一个球状蛋白（结果没有展示）。除了 N 端的信号序列，主要的亲水性氨基酸序列没有明显的结构模体或者跨膜结构域。在预测的剪切蛋白中，我们没有发现提示蛋白裂解的 *N* 连接糖基化或者预示蛋白酶位点的双碱基氨基酸序列[22]。

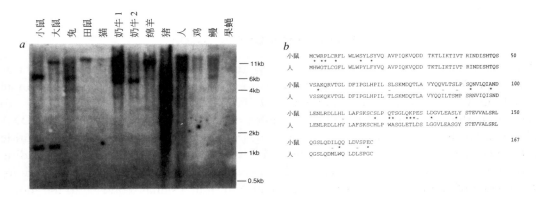

图 6. *ob* 基因的进化保守性。*a*，物种间 *ob* 基因的杂交。各个物种的基因组 DNA 都先用 *Eco*RI 酶切，然后与 *ob* 基因 cDNA 探针进行 DNA 印迹杂交。所有脊椎动物的基因组 DNA 即使在中等严格的杂交条件下都有信号显示。猫的 DNA 在这个实验中有少许降解。这些 DNA 是从图中所示的动物组织或者细胞系中提取。DNA 印迹杂交温度为 65 ℃，用 2×SSC/0.2% SDS 缓冲液在 65 ℃下洗脱 20 分钟，洗脱两次后用柯达 X-OMAT 显影膜放射自显影 3 天。*b*，人类 OB 蛋白的序列。小鼠的 *ob* 基因序列被用作探针从人类 λgtⅡ 脂肪组织 cDNA 文库中分离人类 *ob* 基因。人类 *ob* 基因的 cDNA 序列在预测的 167 个氨基酸的编码区内与小鼠的同源性非常高。在该组织内 5′ 和 3′ 非翻译区域有 30% 的同源性。图示为预测的小鼠和人类蛋白序列比对，保守的氨基酸改变用虚线表示而不保守的改变为星号。那个可变的谷氨酰胺密码子用下划线标出，该位点同时是 C57BL/6J *ob/ob* 小鼠的无义突变位点。虽然从 22 位缬氨酸（紧

aligned. Conservative changes are noted by a dash and non-conservative changes by an asterisk. The variable glutamine codon is underlined, as is the position of the nonsense mutation in C57BL/6J *ob/ob* mice. Overall there is 84% identity at the amino-acid level, although only seven substitutions were found between the valine at codon 22 (immediately downstream of the signal sequence overage) and the cysteine at position 117. cDNA clones were isolated from a human adipose tissue cDNA library (Clonetech) as described for Fig. 4, except that PCR amplification of the phage insert was carried out using primers adjacent to the cloning site of λgtlI. PCR products were sequenced directly.

The *ob²ᴶ* Mutation

We next explored the molecular basis for the mutation in SM/Ckc-+^{Dac}*ob²ᴶ*/*ob²ᴶ* mice. In these animals, the absence of 2G7 RNA was associated with an increase in the size of an ~9 kb *Bgl*II fragment of genomic DNA in affected animals (Fig. 5*a*). Although the precise nature of this polymorphism is not established, the altered *Bgl*II site maps ~7 kb upstream of the mRNA start site for the 4.5 kb *ob* RNA (data not shown), suggesting that this mutation may be the result of a structural alteration or sequence variation in the promoter. None of the other restriction fragments reach the promoter region. Nevertheless, this polymorphism is significant because it is always associated with the obese phenotype in a colony that segregates the *ob* 2J mutation (Fig. 5*b*). In this experiment, DNA from a total of six obese and five lean animals was Southern-blotted after *Bgl*II digestion and probed with 2G7. In each case homozygosity for the larger of the polymorphic *Bgl*II fragments was associated with an obese phenotype. Each of the lean animals was either homozygous for the smaller *Bgl*II allele (+/+) or heterozygous (*ob*/+). As reported, no overt phenotypic differences were apparent between +/+ and *ob*/+ mice[23].

ob Sequence Conservation

The coding sequence of the *ob* gene was hybridized to genomic Southern blots of vertebrate DNAs (Fig. 6*a*). Even at moderate stringency, there were detectable signals in all vertebrate DNAs tested, demonstrating that *ob* is highly conserved among vertebrates. To determine the extent of this *ob* sequence conservation, we isolated and sequenced cDNA clones hybridizing to *ob* from a human adipose tissue cDNA library. The nucleotide sequences from human and mouse were highly homologous in the predicted coding sequence, but had only 30% homology in the available 5' and 3' untranslated regions. Homology of the human polypeptide apparent N-terminal signal sequence to the mouse equivalent region was slightly lower than in the rest of the molecule. The signal sequence is seen to be functional from the truncation of the primary translation product in the presence of canine pancreas microsomal membranes (Fig. 4*c*). Alignment of the predicted human and mouse amino-acid sequences (Fig. 6*b*) shows that there is 84% overall identity and more extensive identity in the N terminus of the mature protein, with only four conservative and three non-conservative substitutions among the residues between the signal sequence cleavage site and the conserved cysteine at position 117. As in mouse, 30% of the clones were missing a glutamine at codon 49.

接着信号肽的下游）到 117 位半胱氨酸之间只有 7 个替换，但是氨基酸水平共有 84% 的一致性。如图 4 所示，除使用 λgtⅡ 克隆位点附近的引物 PCR 扩增噬菌体插入片段以外，cDNA 克隆是从人类脂肪组织 cDNA 文库（Clonetech 公司）中分离的。PCR 产物直接用于测序。

*ob*²ʲ 的 突 变

我们接下来研究了 SM/Ckc-+^Dac*ob*²ʲ/*ob*²ʲ 小鼠突变的分子机制。在这些突变体中，2G7 RNA 的缺少与患病小鼠基因组 DNA 中一个大约 9 kb 的 *Bgl*Ⅱ 酶切片段的增加是相关的（图 5*a*）。虽然关于这个多态性的确切机制未知，但是改变的 *Bgl*Ⅱ 内切酶位点在 4.5 kb *ob* RNA 的 mRNA 起始位点上游大约 7 kb 处（结果没有展示），由此提示这个突变可能是由启动子结构或者序列的改变导致的。在此启动子区域内没有任何其他酶切片段。然而这个多态位点还是非常重要，因为从群体中分离 *ob* 2J 突变的时候，它总是和肥胖表型联系在一起（图 5*b*）。在这个实验中，总共 6 只肥胖小鼠和 5 只瘦小鼠的 DNA 用 *Bgl*Ⅱ 消化，然后用 2G7 探针进行 DNA 印迹杂交。在每个实验里面，多态性 *Bgl*Ⅱ 大片段的纯合性总是和肥胖表型联系在一起；而瘦小鼠则可能是纯合小片段（+/+）或者是杂合子（*ob*/+）。与先前报道的结果一样，+/+ 和 *ob*/+ 小鼠并没有明显的表型不同 [23]。

ob 序列的保守性

ob 基因的编码区序列与其他脊椎动物的 DNA 进行 DNA 印迹杂交（图 6*a*）。即使是在中等严格的条件下，我们也能够在所有的脊椎动物 DNA 中检测到信号，这表明 *ob* 基因在所有脊椎动物里都非常保守。为了进一步确定 *ob* 基因序列保守性的程度，我们分离并且测定了从人类脂肪组织 cDNA 文库分离的与 *ob* 基因杂交的 cDNA 克隆。在编码区，人与小鼠的核酸序列是非常保守的，但是在得到的 5′ 和 3′ 非翻译区则只有 30% 的同源性。两个多肽的 N 端信号序列的同源性也稍微比其他区域低一些。而这些信号序列的功能性已经被含有犬胰腺微粒体膜系统的体外翻译实验证明（图 4*c*）。预测的人与小鼠氨基酸序列比对结果（图 6*b*）显示有 84% 的相同序列，并且成熟蛋白的 N 端相似性更高。在 N 端信号序列切割位点和第 117 位的保守半胱氨酸之间就只有 4 个保守和 3 个不保守的氨基酸残基替换。与小鼠体内一样，30% 的克隆缺少第 49 位密码子编码的谷氨酰胺。

Discussion

Obesity has been a focus of discussion[24], with a line of research dating back to Lavoisier and Laplace (1783) implying that energy balance—food intake versus energy output—is physiologically regulated[25-27]. The site of this regulation has been the subject of nearly one hundred years of debate[28-30]. Of the brain regions implicated in the regulation of feeding behaviour, the ventromedial nucleus of the hypothalamus (VMH) is considered to be the most important satiety centre in the central nervous system (CNS). The increase in body weight associated with VMH lesions is a result of both increased food intake and decreased energy expenditure[29].

The energy balance in mammals was therefore postulated to be controlled by a feedback loop in which the amount of stored energy is sensed by the hypothalamus, which adjusts food intake and energy expenditure to maintain a constant body weight[31,32]. The nature of the inputs to the hypothalamus was unclear[27]. According to the lipostasis theory[32], the size of the body fat depot is regulated by the CNS, with a product of fat metabolism circulating in plasma and affecting energy balance by interacting with the hypothalamus. The glucostasis theory[33] suggested that the plasma glucose level is a key signal regulating energy stores. A third possibility is that body temperature is an important input to the CNS centres controlling food intake[31]. The inability to identify the putative signal from fat has hindered the validation of the lipostasis theory. Moreover, neither the glucostasis theory nor theories on the thermal regulation of food intake fully account for the precision with which energy balance is regulated *in vivo*. The possibility that at least one component of the signalling system circulates in the bloodstream was first suggested by Hervey[34], who showed that the transfer of blood from an animal with a VMH lesion across a vascular graft to an untreated animal (a parabiosis experiment) resulted in a reduction of food intake in the intact animal. The biochemical nature of the putative signal has remained elusive, although it has been suggested that *ob* is responsible for the generation of this blood-borne factor[6].

Our results, particularly the evidence that the *ob* protein product is secreted, suggest that *ob* may encode this circulating factor. Evidence that the gene described here is *ob* includes the identification of a nonsense mutation in the C57BL/6J *ob/ob* strain and a genomic alteration in the SM/Ckc-+$^{Dac}ob^{2J}/ob^{2J}$ strain that is associated with an absence of RNA. The data showing that one strain overproduces *ob* RNA while the other fails to express this gene, make it unlikely that these changes are secondary. This conclusion can be confirmed using transgenic mice to complement the obese mutation. The nature of the mutation in the co-isogenic SM/Ckc-+$^{Dac}ob^{2J}/ob^{2J}$ mice is as yet unknown. Preliminary analysis of the gene structure has indicated that the polymorphic *Bgl*II site maps ~7 kb upstream of the promoter. As this mutation is co-isogenic, the data strongly suggest that this polymorphism is associated with the mutation, although it is not yet clear whether there is a structural alteration (insertion or deletion) or base change. Further studies will be required to identify the molecular basis for the absence of *ob* RNA expression in SM/Ckc-+$^{Dac}ob^{2J}/ob^{2J}$ mice, as well as the molecular mechanisms that result in the increased expression of *ob* RNA in C57BL/6J *ob/ob* mice.

讨　论

　　肥胖症已经是一个讨论的焦点[24]，追溯到拉瓦锡和拉普拉斯（1783 年）时代的一系列研究已经暗示能量的平衡——食物的摄取与能量的消耗——是受生理因素调节的[25-27]。这种调节位点已经争论了上百年[28-30]。大脑的某个区域与调节进食行为有关，下丘脑腹内侧核（VMH）就是这样的一个区域，它被认为是中枢神经系统（CNS）最重要的饱中枢。与 VMH 的损伤相关的身体重量增加是由进食增加和能量代谢下降所致[29]。

　　因此，哺乳动物的能量平衡假定是由一个反馈环控制的，下丘脑能感受在反馈环中能量存储的数量，并以此调节进食和能量代谢来保持体重恒定[31,32]。输入到下丘脑的信息的本质并不清楚[27]。根据脂肪稳态学说[32]，体脂存量的体积是受中枢神经系统调节的。存在于血浆中的某种脂肪代谢产物会在下丘脑发生作用从而调节能量平衡。血糖稳态学说[33]则认为血糖水平是调节能量存储的重要信号分子。第三种可能性则是体温会作为中枢神经系统调节进食的重要信息[31]。不能从脂肪中找到假定的信号分子，这阻碍了脂肪稳态学说的证实。此外，血糖稳态学说和体温调节进食的学说都不能完全解释体内能量平衡的精确调节。赫维[34]通过血管嫁接手术将下丘脑腹内侧核受损动物的血液输入正常动物体内（连体共生的实验）导致正常动物进食减少，从而首次提出血液中至少存在一种信号分子调节进食。虽然 OB 被认为可能是这样一种血源性因子[6]，但是假定信号分子的生化性质仍然未知。

　　我们的结果，特别是 OB 作为一种分泌蛋白的证据，提示 ob 基因可能编码这样一种循环因子。文章中所说的基因就是 ob 基因的证据包括在 C57BL/6J ob/ob 小鼠中发现无义突变和 ob RNA 缺失的 SM/Ckc-+^{Dac}ob^{2J}/ob^{2J} 小鼠品系的基因组改变。数据显示，一个品系 ob RNA 表达增加而另外一个品系 ob 表达缺失的结果也不太可能是继发性效应。这个结论可以由转基因小鼠修复肥胖突变体来证实。在同类系的 SM/Ckc-+^{Dac}ob^{2J}/ob^{2J} 小鼠体内，基因突变的机制还是未知的。基因结构的初步分析结果显示，启动子上游约 7 kb 处有一个多态性 BglII 位点。由于这个突变是同类系的，虽然不知道是否有结构变化（插入或者缺失）或碱基改变，但是这个数据还是强烈暗示这个多态性与基因突变有关。进一步研究需要明确 SM/Ckc-+^{Dac}ob^{2J}/ob^{2J} 突变体中 ob RNA 表达缺失的分子基础，以及 C57BL/6J ob/ob 突变体中 ob RNA 表达增加的分子机制。

The increased level of *ob* RNA in the C57BL/6J mutant, which has greatly increased fat cell mass, raises the possibility that the level of expression of this gene signals the size of the adipose depot. This hypothesis is consistent with the lipostasis theory, implying that an increase in the level of the *ob* signal (as might occur after a prolonged binge of eating) may act directly or indirectly on the CNS to inhibit food intake and/or regulate energy expenditure as part of a homeostatic mechanism to maintain constancy of the adipose mass. Such effects could be explained if the *ob* protein activated the sympathetic nervous system via interactions with the VMH. Direct effects of *ob* on the CNS would require that mechanisms exist to allow its passage across the blood-brain barrier. The means by which the CNS effects changes in body weight remain to be elucidated and may include mechanisms independent of effects on food intake and energy expenditure. In addition, *ob* may have endocrine, paracrine and autocrine effects on different tissues. These and other possibilities will be testable if the active form of the *ob* protein can be shown to circulate in plasma.

The *ob* mutation is associated with a myriad of hormonal and metabolic alterations[35]. These include effects on thermo-regulation, fertility, adrenal and thyroid function as well as a wide range of biochemical abnormalities. Although we cannot exclude the possibility that many of these pleiotypic effects are the result of the expression of *ob* in sites not included in our initial survey of mouse tissues, the apparent expression of *ob* in only adipose tissue suggests that many of these changes are secondary. It has been suggested that the complex *ob* phenotype reflects an imbalance in the activity of the autonomic nervous system with low sympathetic and high parasympathetic tone[35]. If *ob* is a signal molecule that regulates body weight, it may act by interacting with CNS (and other) receptors to modulate food intake and the activity of the autonomic nervous system. Parabiosis experiments suggest that the *ob* receptor is encoded by the mouse *db* (diabetes) gene[6], a possibility that can be tested by positional cloning of *db* or by expression cloning and mapping of the *ob* receptor[36].

The extensive homology of the *ob* gene product among vertebrates suggests that its function is highly conserved. Now that the human homologue of *ob* is cloned, it will be possible to test for mutations in the human *ob* gene. As *ob* heterozygotes have an enhanced ability to survive a prolonged fast[23], heterozygous mutations at *ob* may provide a selective advantage in human populations subjected to caloric deprivation[37]. Identification of *ob* now offers an entry point into the pathways that regulate adiposity and body weight and should provide a fuller understanding of the pathogenesis of obesity.

(**372**, 425-432; 1994)

Yiying Zhang[*†], Ricardo Proenca[*†], Margherita Maffei[†], Marisa Barone[*†], Lori Leopold[*†] & Jeffrey M. Friedman[*†‡]
* Howard Hughes Medical Institute, †The Rockefeller University, 1230 York Avenue, New York, New York 10021, USA
‡ To whom correspondence should be addressed.

Received 17 October; accepted 4 November 1994.

C57BL/6J 突变小鼠的 *ob* RNA 表达增加同时脂肪细胞的质量也增加许多，这增加了这个基因表达水平是脂肪组织积累的一个信号的可能性。这个假设与脂肪稳态学说吻合，暗示增加 *ob* 信号分子的表达（可能发生在长期暴饮暴食之后）可能直接或者间接地影响中枢神经系统来抑制进食和（或）调节能量消耗，作为维持脂肪质量恒定的一个稳态机制。如果 OB 蛋白可以通过下丘脑腹内侧核激活交感神经系统，那么就能解释这个效果了。当然，OB 如果直接作用于中枢神经系统，它必须能够通过血脑屏障。中枢神经系统调节体重的方式仍然不清楚，可能包括不受进食和能量消耗影响的机制。另外，OB 在不同组织内可能起内分泌、旁分泌和自分泌作用。如果有活性的 OB 蛋白能在血液内循环，这些所有的可能性都要被考虑到。

ob 突变伴随着大量的激素和代谢水平的改变[35]，这些改变包括体温调节，生育能力，肾上腺和甲状腺功能，以及大量的生化异常问题。虽然我们不能完全排除这些多效性是由 *ob* 在我们最初研究的小鼠组织之外的组织中表达造成的，但 *ob* 只在脂肪组织明显表达这一点提示所有这些变化都是继发效应。*ob* 突变体复杂的性状已经反映了自主神经系统活动的紊乱，即交感神经兴奋性低且副交感神经兴奋性高[35]。如果 OB 真的可以作为一个信号分子调节体重，那么它可能与中枢神经系统（或者其他系统）的受体相互作用来调节进食和自主神经系统的活动。异种共生的实验提示 OB 的受体可能是由小鼠糖尿病（*db*）基因编码的[6]。通过定点克隆 *db* 基因，或者表达性克隆 OB 受体和绘制 OB 受体的遗传图，我们可以验证这个假说[36]。

脊椎动物 *ob* 基因产物的高度同源性提示它的功能是高度保守的。现在人类 *ob* 同源基因已经被克隆了，我们就可以检测人类 *ob* 基因里面的突变。由于 *ob* 杂合子能够活得更长[23]，*ob* 基因的杂合突变可能在热量不足的人群中具有选择优势[37]。*ob* 基因的鉴定会给脂肪和体重调节通路的研究提供一个突破口并让我们对肥胖的致病机制有更完善的了解。

（莫维克 翻译；焦炳华 审稿）

References:

1. Burros, M. *Despite awareness of risks, more in US are getting fat* in *The New York Times* 17 July 1994.

2. Grundy, S. M. & Barnett, J. P. *Disease-a-Month* **36**, 645-696 (1990).

3. Friedman, J. M. & Leibel, R. L. *Cell* **69**, 217-220 (1990).

4. Ingalls, A. M., Dickie, M. M. & Snell, G. D. *J. Hered.* **41**, 317-318 (1950).

5. Friedman, J. M. *et al. Genomics* **11**, 1054-1062 (1991).

6. Coleman, D. L. *Diabetologia* **14**, 141-148 (1978).

7. Dickie, M. M. & Lane, P. W. *Mouse News Lett.* **17**, 52 (1957).

8. Bahary, N. *et al. Mamm. Genome* **4**, 511-515 (1993).

9. Walther, C. *et al. Genomics* **11**, 424-434 (1991).

10. Riley, J. *et al. Nucleic Acids Res.* **18**, 2887-2890 (1990).

11. Hermanson, G. G. *et al. Nucleic Acids Res.* **19**, 4943-4948 (1991).

12. Sternberg, N. *Trends Genet.* **8**, 11-16 (1992).

13. Hartl, D. L. & Nurminsky, D. I. *BioTechniques.* **15**, 201-208 (1993).

14. Dietrich, W. *et al. Genetics* **131**, 423-447 (1992).

15. Church, D. M. *et al. Nature Genet.* **6**, 98-105 (1994).

16. Gish, W. & States, D. J. *Nature Genet.* **3**, 266-272 (1993).

17. Kozak, M. *Cell* **44**, 283 -292 (1986).

18. Frohman, M. A., Dush, M. K. & Martin, G. R. *Proc. Natl. Acad. Sci. U.S.A.* **85**, 8998-9002 (1988).

19. Padgett, R. A. *et al. A. Rev. Biochem.* **55**, 1119-1150 (1986).

20. Cooper, D. N. & Youssoufian, H. *Hum. Genet.* **78**, 151-155 (1988).

21. Heijne, G. v. *Nucleic Acids Res.* **14**, 4683-4690 (1986).

22. Sabatini, D. D. & Adesnick, M. B. *The Metabolic Basis of Inherited Disease* (eds Scriver, C. R. *et al.*) 177-223 (McGraw-Hill, New York, 1989).

23. Coleman, D. L. *Science* **203**, 663-665 (1979).

24. Bray, G. A. *Int. J. Obesity* **14**, 909-926 (1990).

25. Rubner, M. *Ztschr. Biol.* **30**, 73-142 (1894).

26. Adolph, E. F. *Am. J. Physiol.* **151**, 110-125 (1947).

27. Hervey, G. R. *Nature* **222**, 629-631 (1969).

28. Cannon, W. B. & Washburn, A. L. *Am. J. Physiol.* **29**, 441-454 (1912).

29. Brobeck, J. R. *Physiol. Rev.* **25**, 541-559 (1946).

30. Hetherington, A. W. & Ranson, S. W. *Am. J. Physiol.* **136**, 609-617 (1942).

31. Brobeck, J. R. *Yale J. Biol. Med.* **20**, 545-552 (1948).

32. Kennedy, G. C. *Proc. R. Soc.* B**140**, 578-592 (1953).

33. Mayer, J. *Ann. N.Y. Acad. Sci.* **63**, 15-43 (1955).

34. Hervey, G. R. *J. Physiol.* **145**, 336-352 (1959).

35. Bray, G. A. *J. Nutrition* **121**, 1146-1162 (1991).

36. Bahary, N. *et al. Proc. Natl. Acad. Sci. U.S.A.* **87**, 8642-8646 (1990).

37. Neel, J. V. *Am. J. Hum. Genet.* **14**, 353-362 (1962).

38. Larin, Z., Monaco, A. P. & Lehrach, H. *Proc. Natl. Acad. Sci. U.S.A.* **88**, 4123-4127 (1991).

39. Green, E. D. & Olson, M. V. *Proc. Natl. Acad. Sci. U.S.A.* **87**, 1213-1217 (1990).

40. Kusuml, K. *et al. Mamm. Genome* **4**, 391-392 (1993).

41. Vidal, S. M. *et al. Cell* **73**, 469-485 (1993).

42. Friedman, J. M. *et al. Genomics* **11**, 1054-1062 (1991).

43. Chirgwin, J. M. *et al. Biochemistry* **18**, 5294-5299 (1979).

44. Friedman, J. M., Cheng, E. & Darnell, J. E. *J. Molec Biol.* **179**, 37-53 (1984).

45. Wang, A. M., Doyle, M. V. & Mark, D. F. *Proc. Natl. Acad. Sci. U.S.A.* **86**, 9717-9721 (1989).

46. Benton, W. D. & Davis, R. W. *Science* **195**, 180-182 (1977).

47. Burmeister, M. & Lehrach, H. *Trends. Genet.* **5**, 41 (1989).

48. Sanger, F., Nicklen, S. & Coulson, A. R. *Proc. Natl. Acad. Sci. U.S.A.* **74**, 5463-5467 (1977).

49. Venter, C. J. *Automated DNA Sequencing and Analysis* (Academic, New York, 1993).

50. Yu, Y. *et al. Proc. Natl. Acad. Sci. U.S.A.* **86**, 9931-9935 (1989).

Acknowledgements. We thank D. Coleman for prior genetic and physiological analysis; R. Leibel and N. Bahary for their important contributions to the early phases of this work; D. Koos and R. Cox for help in isolating the first set of YAC clones; A. Buckler, J. Rutter and C. Stotler for instruction in exon trapping; Y. Yu and B. Lauring for advice on *in vitro* translation and for canine pancreatic microsomal membranes; P. Gruss for providing the *Pax4* probe before publication and communicating its map position; J. E. Darnell, N. Heintz, R. Kucherlapati, S. Burley, J. Froude, D. Luck, C. Winestock and L. Safani for comments; S. Korres for preparing the manuscript; J. Sholtis for photography; F. Ilchert for help in preparing the figures; A. Popowicz, P. Dash and the staff of computing services for assistance; D. Sabatini for expert advice on the characterization of the *ob* polypeptide; and J. E. Darnell Jr, who provided the environment to initiate this work. J.M.F. is an investigator of the Howard Hughes Medical Institute. This work was supported by a grant from NIH/NIDDK.

Viral Dynamics in Human Immunodeficiency Virus Type 1 Infection

Xiping Wei *et al.*

Editor's Note

By 1995, experimental drugs that block the replication of the AIDS virus HIV-1 were being tested in patients. These studies provided an opportunity to study the dynamics of viral replication and of the CD4 immune-response cells (lymphocytes) that HIV attacks. In this paper, HIV researcher George M. Shaw and colleagues show that the composite lifespan of plasma virus and CD4 lymphocytes is remarkably short. The results suggested that the steady, persistent viral levels seen in patients actually represent a balance between the rapid destruction of infected cells and the ongoing infection of new cells. The findings surprised those involved in developing AIDS treatments, offering new understanding of how HIV works.

The dynamics of HIV-1 replication *in vivo* are largely unknown yet they are critical to our understanding of disease pathogenesis. Experimental drugs that are potent inhibitors of viral replication can be used to show that the composite lifespan of plasma virus and virus-producing cells is remarkably short (half-life ~2 days). Almost complete replacement of wild-type virus in plasma by drug-resistant variants occurs after fourteen days, indicating that HIV-1 viraemia is sustained primarily by a dynamic process involving continuous rounds of *de novo* virus infection and replication and rapid cell turnover.

THE natural history and pathogenesis of human immunodeficiency virus type-1 (HIV-1) infection are linked closely to the replication of virus *in vivo*[1-17]. Clinical stage is significantly associated with all measures of virus load, including infectious virus titres in blood, viral antigen levels in serum, and viral nucleic acid content of lymphoreticular tissues, peripheral blood mononuclear cells (PBMCs) and plasma (reviewed in ref. 18). Moreover, HIV-1 replication occurs preferentially and continuously in lymphoreticular tissues (lymph node, spleen, gut-associated lymphoid cells, and macrophages)[11,19,20]; virus is detectable in the plasma of virtually all patients regardless of clinical stage[6,10,13,21]; and changes in plasma viral RNA levels predict the clinical benefit of antiretroviral therapy (R. Coombs, unpublished results). These findings emphasize the central role of viral replication in disease pathogenesis.

Despite the obvious importance of viral replication in HIV-1 disease, relatively little quantitative information is available regarding the kinetics of virus production and clearance *in vivo*, the rapidity of virus and $CD4^+$ cell population turnover, and the

640

人免疫缺陷病毒 1 型感染的病毒动力学研究

魏西平（音译）等

编者按

截至 1995 年，多个用于阻断艾滋病病毒 HIV-1 复制的实验性药物用于临床测试。这些研究为研究病毒复制以及 HIV 攻击的 CD4 免疫应答细胞（淋巴细胞）的动力学提供了机会。在这篇文章中，HIV 研究者乔治·肖及其同事指出血浆病毒和 CD4 淋巴细胞的复合生存期非常短。研究结果表明，HIV 患者稳定且持续的病毒水平实际上是感染细胞迅速消亡与大量新感染细胞生成的平衡结果。这些发现使开发抗艾滋病疗法的研究者感到意外，为理解 HIV 发病机制提供新见解。

尽管 HIV-1 体内复制动力学对我们了解疾病的发病机制至关重要，但目前研究相对匮乏。有效抑制病毒复制的实验性药物结果显示，血浆病毒和产病毒细胞的复合生存周期非常短暂（半衰期大约是 2 天）。14 天治疗以后，血浆内野生型病毒几乎被耐药的变异体完全替代。这表明，HIV-1 病毒血症主要通过包括持续的新病毒感染、复制以及快速的细胞更替在内的动态过程维持。

人免疫缺陷病毒 1 型（HIV-1）感染的自然病史和发病机制都与病毒体内复制密切相关 [1-17]。临床分期与各种测量方式测定的病毒载量显著相关。这些测量方式包括血液感染性病毒滴度，血清病毒抗原水平，淋巴网状组织、外周血单个核细胞（PBMCs）和血浆内的病毒核酸含量（参考文献 18 中综述）。此外，HIV-1 病毒优先并持续在淋巴网状组织（淋巴结、脾、肠相关淋巴样细胞和巨噬细胞）内复制 [11,19,20]；临床各期患者血浆中均能检测到病毒 [6,10,13,21]；而且血浆病毒 RNA 水平的改变可预测抗逆转录病毒治疗的临床疗效（库姆斯，未发表的结果）。这些结果强调了病毒复制在疾病发病中的关键作用。

尽管病毒复制在 HIV-1 型艾滋病中具有明显重要性，但是有关病毒在体内产生和清除、病毒及 CD4+ 细胞群快速更替、生物学相关病毒突变固定速率的动力学定量信息相对较少 [22,23]。造成这种情况的原因，一方面是已有的抗逆转录病毒药物缺乏足够

fixation rates of biologically relevant viral mutations[22,23]. This circumstance is largely due to the fact that previously available antiretroviral agents lacked sufficient potency to abrogate HIV-1 replication, and methods to quantify virus and determine its genetic complexity were not sufficiently sensitive or accurate. We overcame these obstacles by treating subjects with new investigational agents which potently inhibit the HIV-1 reverse transcriptase (nevirapine, NVP)[24] and protease (ABT-538; L-735,524)[25,26]; by measuring viral load changes using sensitive new quantitative assays for plasma virus RNA[6,18,27]; and by quantifying changes in viral genotype and phenotype in uncultured plasma and PBMCs using automated DNA sequencing[28] and an *in situ* assay of RT function[29,30].

Virus Production and Clearance

Twenty-two HIV-1-infected subjects with CD4$^+$ lymphocyte counts between 18 and 251 per mm^3 (mean ± s.d., 102 ± 75 cells per mm^3) were treated with ABT-538 ($n = 10$), L-735,524 ($n = 8$) or NVP ($n = 4$) as part of phase I/IIA clinical studies. The design and clinical findings of those trials will be reported elsewhere (K. Squires *et al.*, and V.A.J. *et al.*, manuscripts in preparation). Plasma viral RNA levels in the 22 subjects at baseline ranged from $10^{4.6}$ to $10^{7.2}$ molecules per ml (geometric mean of $10^{5.5}$) and exhibited maximum declines generally within 2 to 4 weeks of initiating drug therapy (Figs 1 and 2a). For ABT-538- and L-735,524-treated patients, virus titres fell by as much as $10^{3.9}$-fold (mean decrease of $10^{1.9}$-fold) whereas for NVP-treated patients virus fell by as much as $10^{2.0}$-fold (mean decrease of $10^{1.6}$-fold). The overall kinetics of virus decline during the initial weeks of therapy with all three agents corresponded to an exponential decay process (Figs 1 and 2a).

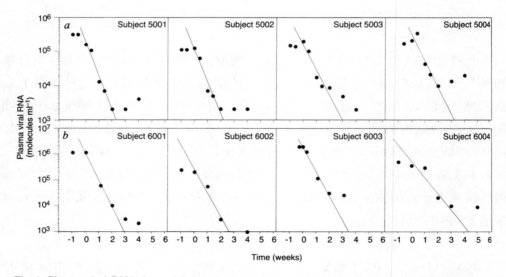

Fig. 1. Plasma viral RNA determinations in representative subjects treated with the HIV-1 protease inhibitors ABT-538 (*a*) and L-735,524 (*b*). Subjects had not received other anti-retroviral agents for at least 4 weeks before therapy. Treatment was initiated at week 0 with 400–1,200 mg d^{-1} of ABT-538 or

的效力抑制病毒 HIV-1 的复制，另一方面是量化病毒和测定病毒基因复杂性的方法不足够敏感或准确。我们通过多种手段克服这些障碍：使用新研发的高效 HIV-1 逆转录酶抑制剂（奈韦拉平，NVP）[24] 和蛋白酶抑制剂（ABT-538；L-735,524）[25,26] 治疗患者；使用新的敏感定量方法监测血浆中的病毒 RNA，进而评估病毒载量的改变 [6,18,27]；使用自动化的 DNA 测序 [28] 和原位 RT 功能检测方法来量化未培养的血浆和 PBMC 中病毒基因型和表型的变化 [29,30]。

病毒产生和清除

作为 I/IIA 期临床研究的一部分，22 名 HIV-1 感染受试者接受 ABT-538（$n = 10$）、L-735,524（$n = 8$）或者 NVP（$n = 4$）治疗。这些患者的 CD4+ 淋巴细胞计数范围为每立方毫米 18~251 个（均值 ± 标准差：每立方毫米 102 ± 75 个）。相关临床研究的设计和结果将另有报道（斯夸尔斯等和约翰逊等，稿件准备中）。22 名受试者血浆病毒 RNA 的基线水平为每毫升 $10^{4.6}$~$10^{7.2}$ 分子（几何平均数是 $10^{5.5}$）。血浆病毒 RNA 水平通常在药物治疗后的 2~4 周内出现最大下降（图 1 和图 2a）。经 ABT-538 和 L-735,524 治疗的 HIV 感染患者，血内病毒滴度下降为 $1/10^{3.9}$（平均下降为 $1/10^{1.9}$），而经 NVP 治疗的患者病毒滴定最低降为 $1/10^{2.0}$（平均下降为 $1/10^{1.6}$）。在所有三种药物治疗的前几周，病毒减少的整体动力学呈现指数式衰减（图 1 和图 2a）。

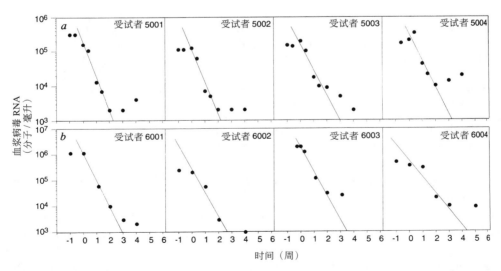

图 1. HIV-1 蛋白酶抑制剂 ABT-538（a）和 L-735,524（b）治疗后，代表性受试者血浆病毒 RNA 水平的测定。受试者开始此项研究前至少 4 周未接受其他抗逆转录病毒药物治疗。治疗开始后，患者全程接受

1,600–2,400 mg d⁻¹ of L-735,524 and was continued throughout the study. Viral RNA was determined by modified branched DNA (bDNA)[18] (*a*) or RT-PCR[27] (*b*) assay and confirmed by QC-PCR[6]. Shown are the least-squares fit linear-regression curves for data points between days 0 and 14 indicating exponential (first-order) viral elimination.

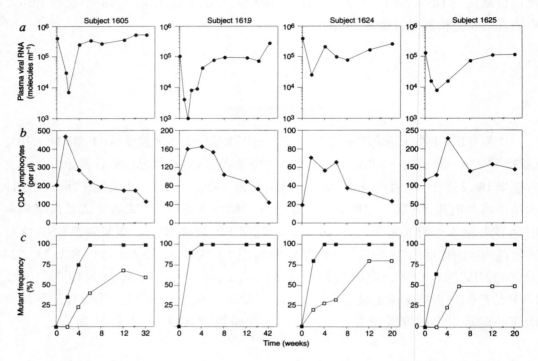

Fig. 2. Plasma viral RNA determinations (*a*), CD4⁺ lymphocyte counts (*b*), and percentages of mutant viral genomes in plasma and PBMCs (*c*) of subjects initiating treatment with NVP. Subjects were participants in a clinical protocol assessing the effects of NVP when added to existing treatment with ddI (subject 1605) or ddI plus zidovudine (subjects 1619, 1624, 1625). Treatment with NVP was initiated at week 0 using 200 mg per day and was increased to 400 mg per day after 2 weeks. ddI and zidovudine dosages were 400 mg per day and 300–600 mg per day, respectively. Viral RNA (●) was determined by QC-PCR assay[6]. CD4⁺ lymphocytes (◆) were quantified by flow cytometry. Frequencies of viral genomes containing NVP-resistance-associated mutations in plasma (■) and PBMCs (□) were determined by automated DNA sequence analysis (Fig.3, legend), with each data point representing the average of 3–6 independent PCR amplifications and sequence determinations.

The antiretroviral agents used in this study, despite their differing mechanisms of action, have a similar overall biological effect in that they block *de novo* infection of cells. Thus the rate of elimination of plasma virus that we measured following the initiation of therapy is actually determined by two factors: the clearance rate of plasma virus *per se* and the elimination (or suppression) rate of pre-existing, virus-producing cells. To a good approximation, we can assume that virus-producing cells decline exponentially according to $y(t) = y(0)e^{-\alpha t}$, where $y(t)$ denotes the concentration of virus-producing cells at time t after the initiation of treatment and α is the rate constant for the exponential decline. Similarly, we

644

400~1,200 mg·d⁻¹ ABT-538 或 1,600~2,400 mg·d⁻¹ L-735,524 治疗。病毒 RNA 通过改良的分支 DNA 测定法 (bDNA)[18](a) 或者 RT-PCR 法 [27](b) 测定，并经 QC-PCR 确证 [6]。图中显示了第 0 天和第 14 天之间数据点的最小二乘法拟合的线性回归曲线，结果表明病毒呈指数式减少（一级动力学）。

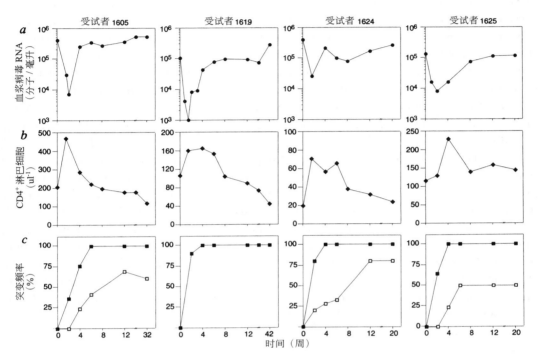

图 2. NVP 治疗组受试者的血浆病毒 RNA 水平 (a)，CD4⁺ 淋巴细胞计数 (b)，血浆和 PBMC 中突变病毒基因组的比例 (c)。NVP 治疗组受试者在接受 NVP 临床试验方案前已接受 ddl 治疗（受试者 1605）或者 ddl 复合齐多夫定治疗（受试者 1619、1624、1625）。初始 2 周内，NVP 剂量为 200 mg·d⁻¹，2 周后增加到 400 mg·d⁻¹。ddl 和齐多夫定的剂量分别是 400 mg·d⁻¹ 及 300~600 mg·d⁻¹。病毒 RNA(●) 经 QC-PCR 法测定 [6]。CD4⁺ 淋巴细胞(◆) 由流式细胞仪定量。血浆(■) 和 PBMC(□) 中 NVP 耐药相关病毒基因组突变频率由自动化 DNA 测序分析确定（图 3，图注），每一个数据点代表 3~6 个独立的 PCR 扩增和序列测量的均值。

尽管本研究使用的抗逆转录病毒药物作用机制不同，但是它们具有类似的生物学效果，主要表现在阻滞细胞重新感染。因此，药物治疗后我们测得的血浆病毒消除率实际上由两个因素共同决定：血浆病毒自身清除速率和早已存在的产病毒细胞的清除（或者抑制）速率。近似地，我们可以假设产病毒细胞按照 $y(t) = y(0)e^{-\alpha t}$ 呈指数式减少，其中 $y(t)$ 表示开始治疗后 t 时间的产病毒细胞数量，α 是指数式下降的速率常数。类似地，我们假设游离病毒 $v(t)$ 由产病毒细胞以速度 $ky(t)$ 产生，并

assume that free virus $v(t)$ is generated by virus-producing cells at the rate $ky(t)$ and declines exponentially with rate constant u. Thus, for the overall decline of free virus, we obtain $v(t) = v(0)[ue^{-\alpha t} - \alpha e^{-ut}]/(u-\alpha)$. The kinetics are largely determined by the slower of the two decay processes. As we have data only for the decline of free virus, and not for virus-producing cells, we cannot determine which of the two decay processes is rate-limiting. However, the half-life ($t_{1/2}$) of neither process can exceed that of the two combined. With these considerations in mind, we estimated the elimination rate of plasma virus and of virus-producing cells by three different methods: (1) first-order kinetic analysis of that segment of the viral elimination curve corresponding to the most rapid decline in plasma virus, generally somewhere between days 3 and 14; (2) fitting of a simple exponential decay curve to all viral RNA determinations between day 0 and the nadir or inflection point (Fig. 1); and (3) fitting of a compound decay curve that takes into account the two separate processes of elimination of free virus and virus-producing cells, as described. Method (1) gives a $t_{1/2}$ of 1.8 ± 0.9 days; method (2) gives a $t_{1/2}$ of 3.0 ± 1.7 days; and method (3) gives a $t_{1/2}$ of 2.0 ± 0.9 days for the slower of the two decay processes and a very similar value, 1.5 ± 0.5 days, for the faster one. These are averages (± 1 s.d.) for all 22 patients. Method (3) arguably provides the most complete assessment of the data, whereas method (2) provides a simpler interpretation (but slightly slower estimate) for virus decline because it fails to distinguish the initial delay in onset of antiviral activity due to the drug accumulation phase, and the time required for very recently infected cells to initiate virus expression, from the subsequent phase of exponential virus decline. There were no significant differences in the viral clearance rates in subjects treated with ABT-538, L-735,524 or NVP, and there was also no correlation between the rate of virus clearance from plasma and either baseline CD4$^+$ lymphocyte count or baseline viral RNA level.

Virus Turnover

Direct population sequencing. As an independent approach for determining virus turnover and clearance of infected cells, we quantified serial changes in viral genotype and phenotype with respect to drug resistance in the plasma and PBMCs of four subjects treated with NVP (Fig. 2). NVP potently inhibits HIV-1 replication but selects for one or more codon substitutions in the reverse transcriptase (RT) gene[24,31,32]. These mutations result in dramatic decreases (up to 1,000-fold) in drug susceptibility and are associated with a corresponding loss of viral suppression *in vivo*[32]. Genetic changes resulting in NVP resistance can thus serve as a quantifiable molecular marker of virus turnover. A rapid decline in plasma viral RNA was observed following the institution of NVP therapy and this was associated with a reciprocal increase in CD4$^+$ lymphocyte counts (Fig. 2a and b). Both responses were of limited duration, returning to baseline within 6–20 weeks in these four patients. The proportion of virus in uncultured plasma and PBMCs that contain NVP-resistance-conferring mutations (Fig. 2c) was determined by direct automated nucleotide sequencing of viral nucleic acid (Fig. 3), as previously described[28]. We first validated this method by reconstitution experiments, confirming its sensitivity for detecting RT mutants that comprise as little as 10% of the overall virus population. Defined mixtures of wild-type

646

且以速率常数 u 呈指数式下降。因此，我们获得游离病毒总体下降速率 $v(t) = v(0)$ $[ue^{-\alpha t} - \alpha e^{-ut}]/(u-\alpha)$。整体病毒动力学较大程度上由前述两项衰减中较慢的过程决定。由于我们仅有游离病毒减少的数据，而没有产病毒细胞的数据，所以我们不能决定哪一个是限速因素。但是，任何一个过程的半衰期 $(t_{1/2})$ 都不超过两者联合的半衰期。在此设想下，我们通过三种方法估算血浆病毒和产病毒细胞的清除速率：（1）血浆病毒清除速率曲线下降最快区段进行一级动力学分析，此区段多发生在用药后第 3 天到第 14 天；（2）从第 0 天至最低点或拐点，拟合总病毒 RNA 测定水平的单一指数衰减曲线（图 1）；（3）综合考虑游离病毒清除和产病毒细胞清除这两个独立过程，拟合复合衰减曲线。方法（1）得出 $t_{1/2}$ 是 1.8 ± 0.9 天；方法（2）得出 $t_{1/2}$ 是 3.0 ± 1.7 天；方法（3）得出两种衰变 $t_{1/2}$ 慢速率 $t_{1/2}$ 是 2.0 ± 0.9 天，快速率 $t_{1/2}$ 是 1.5 ± 0.5 天。以上数据为 22 名患者的平均值（ ± 1 标准差）。方法（3）可以说提供了最全面的数据分析，而方法（2）为病毒减少提供了一种相对简单直接的估算。方法（2）估算显得有些缓慢，这是由于没有把治疗早期由于药物蓄积而导致抗病毒起效滞后，以及最新感染的细胞产生病毒所需时间跟病毒指数减少后期时间区分开来。使用 ABT-538 或 L-735,524 或者 NVP 治疗的受试者病毒清除速率没有显著差异，而且血浆中病毒清除速率与基础 CD4$^+$ 淋巴细胞数或基础病毒 RNA 水平无相关性。

病 毒 更 替

直接群体测序。 作为一种独立确定病毒更替和感染细胞清除的方法，我们连续定量检测 4 名 NVP 治疗的受试者血浆和 PBMC 中与药物耐受相关的病毒基因型和表型的系列改变（图 2）。NVP 能高效抑制 HIV-1 复制，但是从逆转录酶（RT）基因中选择出一个或者多个密码子的替换 [24,31,32]。这些突变导致药物敏感性急剧下降（低至 1/1,000），同时也与药物丧失体内病毒抑制效果相关 [32]。因此，导致 NVP 耐药的基因型改变可以作为定量病毒更替的分子标记。NVP 介入治疗能快速降低血浆病毒 RNA 水平，这与 CD4$^+$ 淋巴细胞数目增加相对应（图 2a 和图 2b）。两种反应均呈现时效性，4 名患者在 6~20 周治疗后均恢复到基础基线水平。正如之前文献报道 [28]，在未培养的血浆和 PBMC 中 NVP 耐药突变体的病毒比例（图 2c）通过自动化核酸测序对病毒核酸进行直接测定（图 3）。我们首先通过重建实验证实这种方法的有效性，结果发现此法灵敏度高，当病毒群体存在仅 10% RT 突变体时即可确认。我们对具有明确比例的野生型和突变型 HIV-1 RT cDNA 克隆（仅密码子 190 的第二位

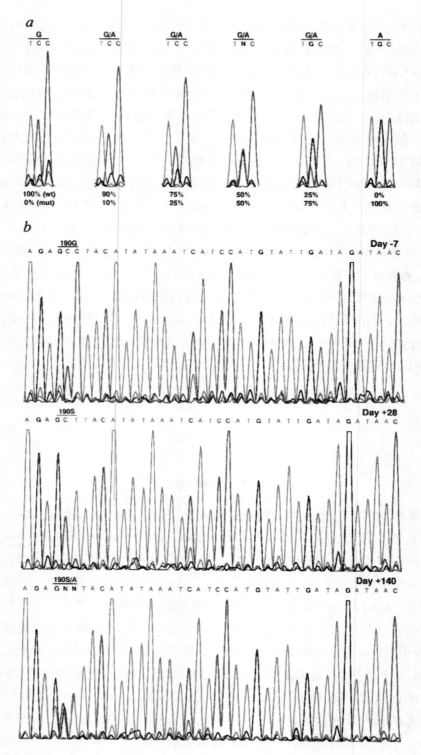

Fig. 3. Quantitative detection of HIV-1 drug-resistance mutations by automated DNA sequencing. *a*, DNA sequence chromatograms of RT codon 190 from a defined mixture of wild-type (wt) and mutant (mut)

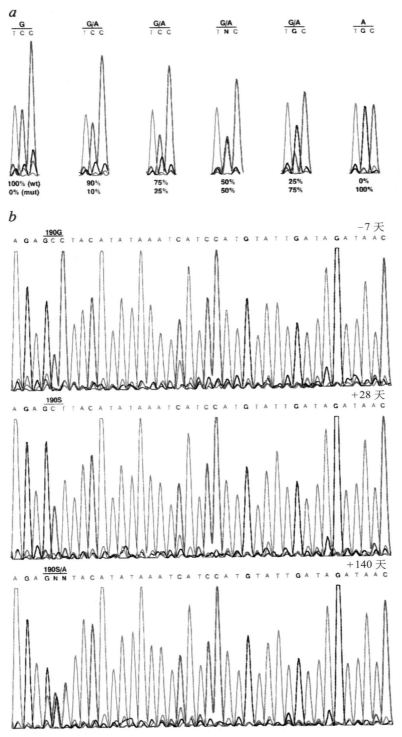

图 3. 自动化 DNA 测序定量检测 HIV-1 耐药突变体。a，特定比例的野生型（wt）和突变型（mut）HIV-1 cDNA 克隆混合物在 RT 密码子 190 区域的 DNA 序列层析谱，两者差别仅在于密码子第二位碱基。图

HIV-1 cDNA clones differing only at the second base position of the codon. Sequences shown were obtained from, and therefore are presented as, the minus (non-coding) DNA strand. For example, the minus-strand TCC sequence shown corresponds to the plus-strand codon GGA (glycine, G). Similarly, the minus-strand TGC sequence corresponds to the plus-strand codon GCA (alanine, A). The single-letter amino-acid code corresponds to the plus-strand DNA sequence. Mixed bases approximating a 50/50 ratio are denoted as N. *b*, DNA sequence chromatograms of RT codons 179–191 (again displayed as the minus-strand sequence) derived from plasma-virion-associated RNA of subject 1625 before (day −7) and after (days +28 and +140) starting NVP therapy. Codon changes resulting in amino-acid substitutions at position 190 are indicated for the plus strand. For example, the GCC minus-strand sequence at position 190 (day −7) corresponds to GGC (glycine, G), and the GCT minus-strand sequence at position 190 (day +28) corresponds to AGC (serine, S) in the respective plus strands.

Methods. Mixtures of wild-type and mutant cDNA clones (*a*) were prepared and diluted such that first-round PCR amplifications were done with 1,000 viral cDNA target molecules per reaction. HIV-1 RNA was isolated from virions pelleted from uncultured plasma specimens (*b*), as described[18]. cDNA was prepared using Moloney murine leukaemia virus reverse transcriptase (GIBCO BRL)[6] and an oligonucleotide primer corresponding to nucleotides 4,283 to 4,302 of the HXB2 sequence[43]. The full-length viral reverse transcriptase gene (1,680 bp) was amplified by means of a nested PCR using conditions and oligonucleotide primers (outer primers: nt 2,483–2,502 and 4,283–4,302; inner primers: nt 2,549–2,565 and 4,211–4,229), previously reported[30]. Subgenomic fragments of the RT gene were also amplified using combinations of the following oligonucleotide primers: (5′) 2,585–2,610; (5′) 2,712–2,733; (3′) 2,822–2,844; (3′) 3,005–3,028; (3′) 3,206–3,228; (3′) 3,299–3,324; (3′) 3,331–3,350; (3′) 3,552–3,572; and (3′) 3,904–3,921. All 3′ primers incorporated the universal primer sequence for subsequent dye-primer sequence analysis. The HIV-1 copy number in every PCR reaction was determined (100–10,000 copies). A total of three to six separate PCR amplifications of primary patient material was done on each sample using different combinations of primers, and representative chromatograms are shown. Rarely, codon interpretation was ambiguous. In the day +140 plasma sample from subject 1625 (bottom of panel *b*), the complementary (plus) strand could read: AGC (serine), GCN (alanine), ACN (threonine), AGA/AGG (arginine) or GGN (glycine). In this case, we sequenced 7 full-length RT molecular clones and found that they encoded only serine or alanine. For sequencing, an automated ABI 373A sequenator and the Taq Dye Primer Cycle Sequencing Kit (ABI) were used. Sequences were analysed using Sequencher (Gene Codes Corp.) and Microgenie (Beckman) software packages, and base-pair mixtures were quantified by measuring relative peak-on-peak heights[28].

and mutant HIV-1 RT cDNA clones (differing only at the second base position of codon 190) were amplified and sequenced (Fig. 3*a*). Varying proportions of wild-type and mutant viral sequences present in the original DNA mixtures (mutant composition: 0, 10, 25, 50, 75 and 100%) were faithfully represented in the relative peak-on-peak heights (and in the relative peak-on-peak areas) of cytosine (C) and guanine (G) residues at the second base position within this codon. Ratios of (mutant)/(mutant+wild type) nucleotide peak heights expressed in arbitrary fluorescence units were as follows (predicted/observed): 0/ < 10%; 10/18%; 25/29%; 50/49%; 75/71% and 100/94%.

We next determined the ability of direct population sequencing to quantify wild-type and mutant viral RNA genomes in clinical specimens. Figure 3*b* shows the sequence chromatograms of RT codons 179–191 from virions pelleted directly from uncultured plasma specimens of subject 1625 before (day −7) and after (days +28 and +140) the initiation of NVP therapy. At day −7, all codons within the amino-terminal half of the RT gene (codons 1–250), including those shown, were wild-type at positions associated with NVP resistance[31,32]. However, after only 28 days of NVP therapy, the wild-type plasma

中所显示的序列来自于 DNA 负链（非编码链）。例如，显示的负链 TCC 序列对应于正链密码子 GGA（甘氨酸，G）。类似地，负链 TGC 序列对应于正链密码子 GCA（丙氨酸，A）。这些单字母氨基酸编码对应于正链 DNA 序列。当混合碱基比例大约为 50/50 时以 N 表示。b，受试者 1625 在 NVP 治疗前（治疗前的第 7 天）以及治疗后（第 28 天及第 140 天）血浆病毒粒子相关 RNA 在 RT 密码子 179~191 区域的 DNA 序列层析谱（仍以负链序列显示）。密码子的改变导致 190 位氨基酸替换（以正链显示）。例如，190 位的 GCC 负链序列（治疗前的第 7 天）对应于正链的 GGC（甘氨酸，G）；而 190 位的 GCT 负链序列（治疗后的第 28 天）对应于正链的 AGC（丝氨酸，S）。

方法。野生型和突变型 cDNA 克隆的混合物（a）通过第一轮 PCR 扩增及稀释后制备，每次反应以 1,000 个病毒 cDNA 为目标分子。如参考文献所述[18]，从未培养血浆标本的病毒粒子中分离出 HIV-1 RNA（b）。cDNA 通过莫洛尼氏鼠白血病病毒逆转录酶（GIBCO BRL）[6] 和对应于 HXB2 序列的 4,283 到 4,302 位核苷酸的寡核苷酸引物制备[43]。病毒逆转录酶全长基因（1,680 bp）使用参考文献[30] 所述的条件和寡核苷酸引物（外部引物：nt 2,483~2,502 和 4,283~4,302；内部引物：nt 2,549~2,565 和 4,211~4,229）经巢式 PCR 扩增得到。RT 基因的亚基因组片段联合以下寡核苷酸引物进行扩增：(5′)2,585~2,610；(5′)2,712~2,733；(3′)2,822~2,844；(3′)3,005~3,028；(3′)3,206~3,228；(3′)3,299~3,324；(3′)3,331~3,350；(3′)3,552~3,572；(3′)3,904~3,921。所有的 3′ 端引物均整合用于随后染色引物序列分析的通用引物序列。每个 PCR 反应的 HIV-1 拷贝数是确定的（100~10,000 拷贝）。每份样本数据均使用原始样本通过不同引物组经 3~6 次独立 PCR 扩增获得，图中显示典型 DNA 序列层析谱。极少情况下出现模糊解码，例如受试者 1625 第 140 天血浆样本（b 栏底部）互补链（正链）序列可解码为 AGC（丝氨酸），GCN（丙氨酸），ACN（苏氨酸），AGA（AGG）（精氨酸）或者 GGN（甘氨酸）。在此特例中，我们对 7 个全长 RT 分子克隆进行测序。结果发现，这些克隆仅编码丝氨酸或丙氨酸。使用自动化 ABI 373A 测序仪和 Taq Dye 引物循环测序试剂盒（ABI）进行测序。使用 Sequencher 软件（Gene Codes 公司）以及 Microgenie 软件包（贝克曼公司）进行序列分析，通过测量相对峰高对碱基对混合物进行定量[28]。

碱基不同）混合物进行扩增并测序（图 3a）。原始 DNA 混合物中存在的不同比例野生型和突变型病毒序列（突变成分：0，10%，25%，50%，75% 和 100%）真实地被该密码子内第二位碱基的胞嘧啶（C）和鸟嘌呤（G）残基的相对峰高（以及相对峰面积）所展示。（突变型）/（突变型 + 野生型）核苷酸峰高度的比例通过荧光单位相对表达量（预测值 / 观察值）表示：0/ < 10%；10%/18%；25%/29%；50%/49%；75%/71% 和 100%/94%。

我们下一步确定是否可用直接群体测序来量化临床标本中的野生型和突变型病毒 RNA 基因组。图 3b 序列层析谱显示了受试者 1625 开始 NVP 治疗前（治疗前的第 7 天）以及治疗后（第 28 天和第 140 天）未培养血浆标本病毒粒子 RT 密码子 179~191 的测序结果。治疗前的第 7 天，RT 基因（密码子 1~250）的氨基末端所有 NVP 耐药相关密码子均为野生型[31,32]。但是，仅经过 28 天 NVP 治疗，野生型血浆

virus population was completely replaced by a NVP-resistant mutant population differing from the wild-type at codon 190 (glycine-to-serine substitution). After 140 days of drug therapy, this codon had evolved further such that the plasma virus population consisted of an equal mixture of two drug-resistant strains, one containing G190S and the other containing G190A. There were no other NVP-resistance-conferring mutations detectable within the viral RT gene.

In all four subjects evaluated by direct viral population sequencing (Fig. 4), specific NVP-resistance-conferring mutations within the RT gene could be unambiguously identified and subsequently confirmed by molecular cloning, expression and drug susceptibility testing. In all cases, mutant virus increased rapidly in the plasma and virtually replaced wild-type virus after only 2–4 weeks of NVP therapy (Fig. 2c). By analysing the rate of accumulation of resistant mutants in the plasma population, we could obtain an independent estimate of the turnover rate of free virus. The rise of drug-resistant mutant virus is influenced substantially by the preceding increase in the CD4$^+$ cell population (which provides additional resources for virus production[33]) and therefore follows complex dynamics. However, we could obtain an estimate of these dynamics by making simplifying assumptions. We assume that wild-type virus declines exponentially with a decay rate α, and that the drug-resistant mutant increases exponentially with the rate β. Thus, the ratio of mutant to wild-type virus increases exponentially at the combined rate $\alpha + \beta$. Our genetic RNA (cDNA) data allow us to estimate this sum. Knowing α from our data on virus decline, we get $\beta \approx 0.27$, or a 32% daily virus production (average over 4 patients). Assuming that mutant virus rises exponentially, this corresponds to a doubling time of ~2 days, which is in excellent agreement with the measured elimination half-life of 2.0 ± 0.9 days for plasma virus (Figs 1 and 2a). Turnover of viral DNA from wild-type to drug-resistant mutant in PBMCs was delayed and less complete compared to plasma virus, reaching levels of only 50–80% of the total PBMC-associated viral DNA population by week 20 (Fig. 2c). Measurement of the time required for resistant virus to spread in the PBMC population allowed us also to estimate the half-life of infected PBMCs. After complete turnover of mutant virus in the plasma pool, we may assume that PBMCs infected with wild-type virus decline exponentially at a rate d, whereas cells infected by mutant virus are generated at a constant rate, but also decline exponentially at rate d. With these simplifying assumptions, the rate at which the frequency of resistant virus in the PBMC population increases provides an estimate for the parameter d and hence for the half-life of infected PBMCs. We obtained a half-life of ~50–100 days. This means that the average half-life of infected PBMCs is very long and of the same order of magnitude as the half-life of uninfected PBMCs[34,35]. Based on the long half-life of PBMCs, and the fact that these cells harbour predominantly wild-type virus at a time (days 14–28) when most virus in plasma is mutant, we conclude that most PBMCs contribute comparatively little to plasma virus load. Instead, other cell populations, most probably in the lymphoreticular system[11,19,20], must be the major source of virus production.

652

病毒群体完全被耐药突变型所替代。突变型仅在密码子 190 与野生型存在不同（甘氨酸替换为丝氨酸）。140 天的药物治疗后，此密码子发生进一步改变。血浆病毒群体由两种分别包括 G190S 和 G190A 的耐药病毒突变型等比例共存。在病毒 RT 基因内没有检测到其他 NVP 耐药相关的基因突变。

在经过直接病毒群体测序的四名受试者中（图 4），通过分子克隆、表达和药物易感性测试可以清楚地鉴定并随后确认 RT 基因中的特异性 NVP 耐药性基因。在所有病例中，血浆中 NVP 耐药突变体可在治疗后 2~4 周迅速增加并取代野生型病毒（图 2c）。通过分析耐药突变体在血浆群体中的聚集速度，我们能够估算游离病毒更替速率。耐药突变型病毒的增加很大程度上受 CD4+ 细胞增加的影响（这些细胞提供病毒生成的额外来源[33]），因此形成复杂的动力学变化。然而，我们可以通过简化的假设估算此动力学过程。我们假设野生型病毒以速率 α 呈指数式减少，而耐药突变型以速率 β 呈指数式增加。这样，突变型和野生型病毒的比例以速率 $\alpha+\beta$ 指数式增加。我们的遗传 RNA（cDNA）数据帮助我们估计出总量。从病毒减少的数据中获得 α，同时我们得出 $\beta \approx 0.27$，或者病毒以每天 32% 的速率增加（4 名患者的平均值）。假设突变型病毒以指数式增长，我们估算出病毒倍增时间约为 2 天。这与测得的血浆病毒的清除半衰期 2.0 ± 0.9 非常相符（图 1 和图 2a）。与血浆病毒相比，PBMC 中病毒 DNA 从野生型更替成突变型呈不完全、相对延迟等特性。在 20 周时，突变型仅占到总 PBMC 相关病毒 DNA 数量的 50%~80%（图 2c）。测定耐药病毒突变体在 PBMC 群体中扩散时间使得我们能够估计感染 PBMC 的半衰期。血浆中发生完全突变型病毒更替后，我们可以假设感染野生型病毒的 PBMC 以速率 d 呈指数式减少，而感染突变型病毒的细胞在以恒定速度增长的同时也以速率 d 呈指数式减少。经过这些简化假设，我们通过 PBMC 群体中耐药病毒增长频率估计参数 d，然后估算感染 PBMC 的半衰期。结果发现，感染 PBMC 的半衰期约 50~100 天。这意味着感染 PBMC 的平均半衰期非常长，与未感染 PBMC 的半衰期量级一致[34,35]。基于 PBMC 的长半衰期，以及这些细胞在一段时间内（第 14~28 天）主要产生野生型病毒，而此时血浆中的大部分病毒都是突变型，我们得出结论：大部分 PBMC 对血浆病毒载量的贡献相对很小，病毒主要来源于其他细胞群体。这些细胞群最有可能位于淋巴网状系统[11,19,20]。

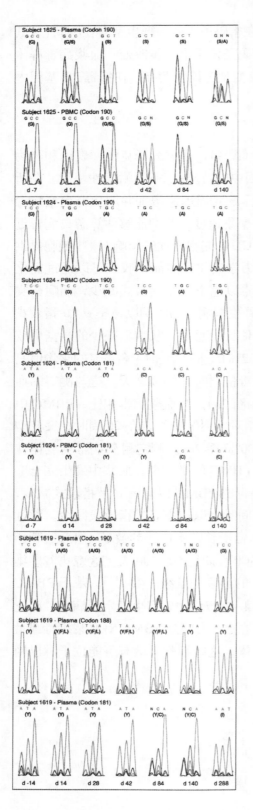

Fig. 4. Quantitative detection of HIV-1 drug resistance mutations by automated DNA sequencing in plasma viral RNA (cDNA) and PBMC-associated viral DNA populations before and after the initiation of NVP on day 0. As in Fig. 3, minus-strand sequences are shown together with single-letter amino-acid codes of the corresponding plus-strand sequence. Mixed bases approximating a 50/50 ratio are denoted as N.

Methods. HIV-1 cDNA was prepared from virions pelleted from uncultured plasma as described for Fig. 3. Viral DNA was isolated from uncultured PBMCs, as described[44]. The full-length viral reverse transcriptase genes as well as subgenomic fragments were amplified and sequenced as described for Fig. 3. The HIV-1 copy number in every PCR reaction was determined (100–10,000 copies). Some sequences were determined from both coding and non-coding DNA strands to ensure the accuracy of quantitative measurements.

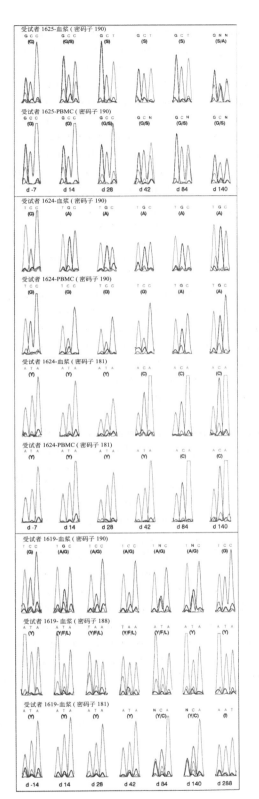

图 4. NVP 治疗前后经自动化 DNA 测序法定量检测血浆病毒 RNA（cDNA）和 PBMC 相关病毒 DNA 群体中的 HIV-1 耐药突变。如图 3 所示，负链序列与对应的正链序列的单字母氨基酸编码同时显示。当碱基大约以 50/50 比例混合时以 N 表示。

方法。如图 3 中所述，HIV-1 cDNA 从未培养血浆中分离的病毒粒子中制备。如参考文献所述[44]，病毒 DNA 从未培养的 PBMC 中分离。按照图 3 所述方法扩增全长病毒逆转录酶基因和亚基因组片段并测序。每个 PCR 反应中的 HIV-1 拷贝数是确定的（100~10,000 拷贝）。为确保定量检测的准确性，一些序列同时通过编码和非编码 DNA 链确定。

Direct sequence analysis of viral nucleic acid revealed not only rapid initial turnover in viral populations but also continuing viral evolution with respect to drug resistance mutations. In subject 1625 (Fig. 4, top panel), wild-type virus in plasma was completely replaced after 28 days of NVP therapy by mutant virus (G190S), which in turn evolved by day 140 into a mixture of G190S and G190A. In subject 1624 (Fig. 4, middle panel), two codon changes conferring NVP resistance occurred. A G190A substitution appeared in plasma virus at day 14 and a Y181C appeared at day 42. Similarly, in subject 1605 (not shown), a Y181C mutation appeared in plasma at day 14 and a Y188L mutation at day 28. The sequential changes in plasma virus were mirrored by similar changes in PBMCs at later timepoints. In subject 1619, the pattern of resistance changes was even more complex (Fig. 4, bottom panel). By day 14, approximately 70% of plasma virus contained a G190A mutation. By day +28, this mutant population was largely replaced by virus containing a Y188F/L substitution. By day 84, still another major shift in the viral quasispecies occurred, this time resulting in a population of viruses containing mutations at both Y181C and G190A. Finally, by day 288 the viral population in plasma consisted exclusively of a mutant exhibiting a single tyrosine-to-isoleucine substitution at position 181 (Y181I); mutations at codons 188 and 190 were not present in this virus population. All of these amino-acid substitutions at RT codons 181, 188 and 190 were shown in our *in situ* expression studies and by others[31,32,36] to confer high-level NVP resistance. The direct sequence analyses thus demonstrate that major changes in the HIV-1 quasispecies occur quickly and continuously in response to selection pressures and that these changes are reflected first and most prominently in the plasma virus compartment.

***In situ* RT gene expression and drug susceptibility testing**. Because direct sequence analysis of viral mixtures provides only semiquantitative information and does not distinguish between viruses with functional rather than defective RT genes, we employed another method for quantifying virus turnover in uncultured plasma and PBMC compartments. Full-length RT genes were amplified by polymerase chain reaction (PCR), cloned into pLG18-l, expressed in *Escherichia coli*, and tested individually for enzymatic function and NVP susceptibility by *in situ* assay[29,30] (Table 1). For subject 1625 at day −7, 100% (80/80) of RT clones from plasma and 100% (163/163) of RT clones from PBMCs expressed enzyme that was sensitive to NVP inhibition. By day 14, however, 62% of plasma-derived clones expressed enzyme that was resistant to NVP, and by days 28, 84 and 140, 100% were resistant. Conversely, at day 14, 0% of PBMC-derived clones expressed NVP-resistant enzyme, and even after 28, 84 and 140 days, only 48–75% of clones were resistant. Similar results were obtained for the other study subjects (Table 1). Thus, the kinetics of virus population turnover determined by a quantitative RT *in situ* expression assay corresponded closely with those determined by direct population sequencing (Fig. 2c).

病毒核酸的直接序列分析不但显示了病毒群体的快速早期更替，同时也反映出病毒持续产生耐药突变。受试者 1625（图 4，上图）血浆中的野生型病毒在 NVP 治疗 28 天后完全被突变型（G190S）取代，进而在第 140 天进化成 G190S 和 G190A 突变体的混合物。受试者 1624（图 4，中图）发生了两个与 NVP 耐药相关的密码子改变。治疗后第 14 天血浆病毒出现 G190A 突变体，第 42 天出现 Y181C 突变体。与此类似，受试者 1605（未显示）第 14 天出现血浆病毒 Y181C 突变体，第 28 天出现 Y188L 突变体。血浆病毒的改变由后期 PBMC 内病毒类似的改变反映出来。受试者 1619 耐药突变的形式更加复杂（图 4，下图）。治疗后第 14 天，几乎 70% 的血浆病毒含有 G190A 突变体。治疗后第 28 天，这些突变体大部分被 Y188F 或 Y188L 突变体取代。治疗后第 84 天，病毒准种再次发生重大转变，导致含有 Y181C 和 G190A 两种突变体的群体占主导。最后，到第 288 天，血浆中的病毒完全由 Y181I(181 位的酪氨酸被异亮氨酸替换）突变体组成。密码子 188 和 190 的突变在此病毒群体中不存在。所有这些 RT 密码子 181、188 和 190 的氨基酸替换都在我们的原位表达研究和其他研究[31,32,36]中显示出高水平的 NVP 耐药性。直接序列分析显示 HIV-1 病毒准种应对选择压力时发生快速和持续的改变。这些变化最先且最明显地反映在血浆病毒成分中。

原位 RT 基因表达和药物敏感性测试。因为病毒混合物的直接测序分析仅仅提供半定量的信息，不能鉴别含功能性 RT 基因和缺陷 RT 基因的病毒。我们使用另一种方法来定量测定未培养血浆和 PBMC 中的病毒更替。用聚合酶链式反应（PCR）扩增全长的 RT 基因，克隆到 pLG18-1 载体并在大肠杆菌中表达。各种突变体分别用原位检测测定酶功能和 NVP 敏感性[29,30]（表 1）。受试者 1625 治疗前的第 7 天，血浆中 100%(80/80) 的 RT 克隆和 PBMC 中 100%(163/163) 的 RT 克隆表达 NVP 敏感酶。但是治疗后第 14 天，62% 的血浆病毒来源的克隆表达 NVP 耐药酶。治疗后的第 28 天、84 天和 140 天，100% 克隆表达 NVP 耐药酶。与此相反，治疗后第 14 天，PBMC 来源的克隆没有表达耐药酶，即便是 28 天、84 天和 140 天后，仅有 48%~75% 的克隆表达耐药酶。其他研究对象得到类似的研究结果（表 1）。因此，通过定量 RT 原位表达与直接群体测序法（图 2c）得到的病毒群体更替动力学结果非常接近。

Table 1. *In situ* functional analysis of HIV-1 RT clones

Subject	Specimen		Functional clones	NVP-sensitive clones		NVP-resistant clones	
1625	Plasma	day −7	80	80	(100%)	0	(0%)
		+14	72	27	(38%)	45	(62%)
		+28	57	0	(0%)	57	(100%)
		+84	67	0	(0%)	67	(100%)
		+140	86	0	(0%)	86	(100%)
1625	PBMC	−7	163	163	(100%)	0	(0%)
		+14	121	121	(100%)	0	(0%)
		+28	258	134	(52%)	124	(48%)
		+84	133	43	(32%)	90	(68%)
		+140	261	65	(25%)	196	(75%)
1624	Plasma	−7	19	19	(100%)	0	(0%)
		+14	34	4	(12%)	30	(88%)
		+28	79	6	(8%)	73	(92%)
		+140	27	0	(0%)	27	(100%)
1624	PBMC	−7	24	24	(100%)	0	(0%)
		+14	34	29	(85%)	5	(15%)
		+28	52	42	(81%)	10	(19%)
		+140	87	26	(30%)	61	(70%)
1605	PBMC	−7	31	31	(100%)	0	(0%)
		+140	31	11	(35%)	20	(65%)
1619	Plasma	−14	79	79	(100%)	0	(0%)
		+28	41	0	(0%)	41	(100%)
		+140	38	0	(0%)	38	(100%)

Full-length RT genes were amplified by PCR from uncultured plasma and uncultured PBMCs as described in Fig. 3 legend. DNA products were cloned into the *Eco*RI and *Hin*dIII sites of the bacterial expression plasmid pLG18-1(refs 29, 30). The expression plasmids were screened for the presence of functional RT and tested *in situ* for susceptibility to NVP inhibition at 3,000 nM (~50–75 fold greater than the IC_{50})[24,31,32]. To ensure accuracy in distinguishing RT genes encoding NVP-resistant versus sensitive enzymes, and to confirm the identification of specific NVP-resistance-conferring RT mutations obtained by direct sequencing (Figs 3 and 4), we determined the complete nucleotide sequences of 21 cloned RT genes which had been phenotyped in the *in situ* assay (V.A.J. and G.M.S., submitted). There was complete concordance between the phenotypes and genotypes of these 21 clones with respect to NVP-resistance-conferring mutations, as well as complete concordance between direct viral population sequences and clone-derived sequences at NVP-resistance-conferring codons.

Infectious virus drug susceptibility testing. Plasma and PBMCs are known to harbour substantial proportions of defective or otherwise non-infectious virus[6,37]. To determine whether the viral genomes represented in total viral nucleic acid (Fig. 4 and Table 1) corresponded to infectious virus with respect to NVP-resistance-conferring mutations, we co-cultivated PBMCs from three of the study subjects (1605, 1624, 1625) with normal

表 1. HIV-1 RT 克隆的原位功能分析

受试者	标本		功能性克隆	NVP 敏感克隆		NVP 耐药克隆	
1625	血浆	天 −7	80	80	(100%)	0	(0%)
		+14	72	27	(38%)	45	(62%)
		+28	57	0	(0%)	57	(100%)
		+84	67	0	(0%)	67	(100%)
		+140	86	0	(0%)	86	(100%)
1625	PBMC	−7	163	163	(100%)	0	(0%)
		+14	121	121	(100%)	0	(0%)
		+28	258	134	(52%)	124	(48%)
		+84	133	43	(32%)	90	(68%)
		+140	261	65	(25%)	196	(75%)
1624	血浆	−7	19	19	(100%)	0	(0%)
		+14	34	4	(12%)	30	(88%)
		+28	79	6	(8%)	73	(92%)
		+140	27	0	(0%)	27	(100%)
1624	PBMC	−7	24	24	(100%)	0	(0%)
		+14	34	29	(85%)	5	(15%)
		+28	52	42	(81%)	10	(19%)
		+140	87	26	(30%)	61	(70%)
1605	PBMC	−7	31	31	(100%)	0	(0%)
		+140	31	11	(35%)	20	(65%)
1619	血浆	−14	79	79	(100%)	0	(0%)
		+28	41	0	(0%)	41	(100%)
		+140	38	0	(0%)	38	(100%)

如图 3 图注所述，通过 PCR 扩增来自未培养血浆和未培养 PBMC 标本的全长 RT 基因。DNA 产物克隆到细菌表达质粒 pLG18-1 的 *Eco*RI 和 *Hind*III 位点之间 (参考文献 29，参考文献 30)。筛查表达质粒是否存在功能 RT，并原位检测对 3,000 nM (约 50~75 倍的 IC_{50} 浓度)NVP 的易感性 [24,31,32]。为了确保准确鉴别特异性 NVP 耐药酶和敏感酶，并通过直接测序确认找到的特异性 NVP 耐药相关 RT 突变 (图 3 和图 4)，我们确定了原位实验中表达的所有 21 个克隆的 RT 基因完整核苷酸序列 (约翰逊和肖，已投稿)。结果发现，这 21 个突变克隆在 NVP 耐药突变上的基因型和表型完全一致，而且直接病毒群体测序的结果和 NVP 耐药相关密码上克隆来源序列也完全一致。

感染性病毒药物敏感性检测。血浆和 PBMC 能够大比例容纳缺陷或非感染性病毒 [6,37]。为了确定用整个病毒核苷酸 (图 4 和表 1) 表示的病毒基因组是否与 NVP 耐药突变相关的感染病毒的基因组一致，我们将三名研究对象 (1605、1624、1625) 的 PBMC 与正常供体淋巴母细胞共同培养，建立初始的病毒分离株。将治疗前和治疗

donor lymphoblasts in order to establish primary virus isolates. The RT genes of these cultured viruses, obtained before and after therapy, were cloned (Fig. 3 and Table 1 legends) and sequenced in their entirety (V.A.J. and G.M.S., submitted). RT codons associated with NVP susceptibility were completely concordant in cultured and uncultured virus strains. Furthermore, the virus isolates exhibited NVP susceptibility profiles[38] consistent with their genotypes.

CD4+ Lymphocyte Dynamics

Changes in CD4+ lymphocyte counts during the first 28 days of therapy could be assessed in 17 of our patients (Fig. 2b and data not shown). CD4+ cell numbers increased in every patient by between 41 and 830 cells per mm^3. For the entire group, the average increase was 186 ± 199 cells per mm^3 (mean $\pm$ s.d.), or $268 \pm 319\%$ from baseline. As CD4+ lymphocytes increase in numbers because of (1) exponential proliferation of CD4+ cells in peripheral tissue compartments, and/or (2) constant (linear) production of CD4+ cells from a pool of precursors, we analysed our data based on each of these assumptions. The average percentage increase in cell number per day (assumption (1)) was $5.0 \pm 3.1\%$ (mean $\pm$ 1 s.d.). The average absolute increase in cell number per day (assumption (2)) was 8.0 ± 7.8 cells mm^{-3} d^{-1}. Given that peripheral blood contains only 2% of the total body lymphocytes[35] and that the average total blood volume is ~5 litres, an increase of 8 cells mm^{-3} d^{-1} implies an overall steady-state CD4+ cell turnover rate (where increases equal losses) of $(50) \times (5 \times 10^6 \text{mm}^3) \times (8$ cells mm^{-3} d^{-1}), or 2×10^9 CD4+ cells produced and destroyed each day.

Discussion

Previously, it was shown that lymphoreticular tissues serve as the primary reservoir and site of replication for HIV-1 (refs 11, 19, 20) and that virtually all HIV-1-infected individuals, regardless of clinical stage, exhibit persistent plasma viraemia in the range of 10^2 to 10^7 virions per ml[6]. However, the dynamic contributions of virus production and clearance, and of CD4+ cell infection and turnover, to the clinical "steady-state" were obscure, although not unanticipated[22,23,39]. We show by virus quantitation and mutation fixation rates that the composite lifespan of plasma virus and of virus-producing cells is remarkably short ($t_{1/2} = 2.0 \pm 0.9$ days). This holds true for patients with CD4+ lymphocyte counts as low as 18 cells per mm^3 and as high as 355 cells per mm^3 (Figs 1 and 2; G.M.S., unpublished). These findings were made in patients treated with three different antiretroviral agents having two entirely different mechanisms of action and using three different experimental approaches for assessing virus turnover. The viral kinetics thus cannot be explained by a unique or unforeseen drug effect or a peculiarity of any particular virological assay method. Moreover, when new cycles of infection are interrupted by potent antiretroviral therapy, plasma virus levels fall abruptly by an average of 99%, and in some cases by as much as 99.99% (10,000-fold). This result indicates that the vast majority of circulating plasma virus derives from continuous rounds of *de*

后获得的这些培养病毒的 RT 基因进行克隆（图 3 图注和表 1 表注）并全部测序（约翰逊和肖，已投稿）。与 NVP 敏感性相关的 RT 密码子在培养的和未培养的病毒株中完全一致。此外，这些病毒分离株呈现的 NVP 敏感性 [38] 与其基因型也完全一致。

CD4[+] 淋巴细胞动力学

我们有 17 位患者可以评价治疗初始 28 天内 CD4[+] 淋巴细胞数目的变化（图 2b，数据未显示）。患者每立方毫米血液中 CD4[+] 淋巴细胞增加 41 到 830 个。在整个实验组中，患者每立方毫米血液平均增加 186 ± 199 个 CD4[+] 淋巴细胞（平均值 ± 标准差），或者比基线水平增加 $268\% \pm 319\%$。CD4[+] 淋巴细胞数量增加存在多种原因，(1) 外周组织中 CD4[+] 淋巴细胞呈指数式增殖，和（或）(2) 从前体细胞恒定（线性）地生成 CD4[+] 淋巴细胞。我们基于以上假设分析数据。结果发现，每天细胞数量增加的平均百分比（假设 (1)）是 $5.0\% \pm 3.1\%$（平均值 ±1 标准差）。每天细胞数目的绝对增加值（假设 (2)）为每立方毫米 8.0 ± 7.8 个。考虑到外周血仅含有 2% 的全身淋巴细胞 [35]，平均全血容量约 5 升，每天每立方毫米 8 个细胞意味着总体稳定的 CD4[+] 淋巴细胞更替速度（增加与减少相互平衡）为 $(50) \times (5 \times 10^6$ 立方毫米$) \times$（每天每立方毫米 8 个细胞），相当于每天有 2×10^9 个 CD4[+] 淋巴细胞生成和消亡。

讨　论

过去的研究发现，淋巴网状组织是 HIV-1 的主要储存地和复制区域（参考文献 11，参考文献 19，参考文献 20）。同时，各期 HIV-1 感染者均存在持续的血浆病毒血症，血浆病毒粒子浓度为每毫升 $10^2 \sim 10^7$ 个 [6]。尽管有过预期 [22,23,39]，但由于病毒产生和清除动态变化以及 CD4[+] 淋巴细胞的感染和更替动力学过于复杂，目前对 HIV-1 患者出现的临床"稳态"机制尚不明确。我们通过病毒定量和固定突变速率发现血浆病毒以及产病毒细胞的复合生存周期非常短（$t_{1/2} = 2.0 \pm 0.9$ 天）。此项发现在低 CD4[+] 淋巴细胞数目（每立方毫米 18 个）患者和高 CD4[+] 淋巴细胞数目（每立方毫米 355 个）患者中均成立（图 1 和图 2；肖，未发表）。这些发现是通过三种具有两类完全不同作用机制的抗逆转录病毒药物，同时使用三种不同实验方法来评测 HIV 患者病毒的更替获得的。因此，特殊的或未知的药效以及特殊病毒学检测方法的特性均不能解释病毒动力学。此外，新的病毒感染周期被强效抗逆转录病毒治疗打断后，平均血浆病毒水平迅速下降了 99%，某些特例甚至下降 99.99%（$1/10,000$）。这个结果提示大部分的循环血浆病毒来自于持续的新病毒感染、复制和细胞更替，而不是感染细胞缓慢产生病毒或者感染细胞休眠再激活。与之前报告一致，这个活

novo virus infection, replication and cell turnover, and not from cells that produce virus chronically or are latently infected and become activated. The identity and location of this actively replicating cell population is not known, but appears not to reside in the PBMC pool, consistent with prior reports[11,19,20]. Nevertheless, PBMCs traffic through secondary lymphoid organs and to some extent are in equilibrium with these cells[35]. It is thus possible that a small fraction of PBMCs[8,9,14-17], like a small fraction of activated lymphoreticular cells[20], could make an important contribution to viraemia.

The magnitude of ongoing virus infection and production required to sustain steady-state levels of viraemia is extraordinary: based on a virus $t_{1/2}$ of 2.0 days and first-order clearance kinetics ($v(t) = v(0)e^{-at}$, where $\alpha = 0.693/t_{1/2}$), 30% or more of the total virus population in plasma must be replenished daily. For a typical HIV-1-infected individual with a plasma virus titre equalling the pretreatment geometric mean in this study ($10^{5.5}$ RNA molecules per ml/2 RNA molecules per virion = $10^{5.2}$ virions per ml) and a plasma volume of 3 litres, this amounts to $(0.30) \times (10^{5.2}) \times (3 \times 10^3) = 1.1 \times 10^8$ virions per day (range for all 22 subjects, 2×10^7 to 7×10^9). Even this may be a substantial underestimate of virus expression because virions may be inefficiently transported from the interstitial extravascular spaces into the plasma compartment and viral protein expression alone (short of mature particle formation) may result in cytopathy or immune-mediated destruction. Because the half-life of cells producing the majority of plasma virus cannot exceed 2.0 days, at least 30% of these cells must also be replaced daily. In our patients, we estimated the rate of CD4$^+$ lymphocyte turnover to be, on average, 2×10^9 cells per day, or about 5% of the total CD4$^+$ lymphocyte population, depending on clinical stage. This rapid and ongoing recruitment of CD4$^+$ cells into a short-lived virus-expressing pool probably explains the abrupt increase in CD4$^+$ lymphocyte numbers that is observed immediately following the initiation of potent antiretroviral therapy, and suggests the possibility of successful immunological reconstitution even in late-stage disease if effective control of viral replication can be sustained.

The kinetics of virus and CD4$^+$ lymphocyte production and clearance reported here have a number of biological and clinical implications. First, they are indicative of a dynamic process involving continuous rounds of *de novo* virus infection, replication and rapid cell turnover that probably represents a primary driving force underlying HIV-1 pathogenesis. Second, the demonstration of rapid and virtually complete replacement of wild-type virus by drug-resistant virus in plasma after only 14–28 days of drug therapy is a striking example of the capacity of the virus for biologically relevant change. In particular, this implies that HIV-1 must have enormous potential to evolve in response to selection pressures as exerted by the immune system[39]. Although other studies[40-42] have provided some evidence that virus turnover occurs sooner in plasma than in PBMCs, our data show this phenomenon most clearly. A similar experimental approach involving the genotypic and phenotypic analysis of plasma virus could be helpful in identifying viral mutations and selection pressures involved in resistance to other drugs, immune surveillance and viral pathogenicity. Third, the difference in lifespan between virus-producing cells and latently infected cells (PBMCs) suggests that virus expression *per se* is directly involved in CD4$^+$ cell destruction. The data do not suggest an "innocent bystander" mechanism of cell

跃复制细胞群体的本质和位置尚不明确，但活跃复制中心可能不在 PBMC[11,19,20]。无论怎样，PBMC 经过次级淋巴器官在某种程度上与这些细胞达到动态平衡 [35]。这提示 PBMC 的小亚群 [8,9,14-17] 可能与这些活化的淋巴网状细胞 [20] 一样，对病毒血症起关键作用。

维持病毒血症稳态水平所需的持续性病毒感染量和产生量非常可观。根据病毒 2.0 天的半衰期及其一级清除动力学 ($v(t) = v(0)e^{-\alpha t}$，其中 $\alpha = 0.693/t_{1/2}$)，每天血浆中总病毒群体的 30% 甚至更多都需要被重新补足。一个典型 HIV-1 患者血浆病毒滴度约为本研究治疗前的几何平均数（每毫升 $10^{5.5}$ 个 RNA 分子 / 每个病毒粒子 2 个 RNA 分子 = 每毫升 $10^{5.2}$ 个病毒粒子）。患者血浆体积约 3 升，每天需要的病毒粒子数为 $(0.30) \times (10^{5.2}) \times (3 \times 10^3) = 1.1 \times 10^8$ 个（所有 22 名患者每日所需病毒粒子数范围为 $2 \times 10^7 \sim 7 \times 10^9$）。尽管此数值可能低估了病毒的表达量，这是由于病毒粒子可能不能有效地从血管外间隙转运到血浆中，同时病毒蛋白表达本身（缺乏成熟颗粒）可能会导致细胞病变或者免疫介导损伤。由于产生大部分血浆病毒的产病毒细胞半衰期不会超过 2.0 天，所以每天至少 30% 的产病毒细胞要被替换。在目前研究的 HIV 感染患者群中，我们估算 CD4+ 淋巴细胞更替速率平均是每天 2×10^9 个，或大约总 CD4+ 淋巴细胞群体的 5%。这些估算会随着临床病期不同而有所差异。这种快速而持续的 CD4+ 淋巴细胞补充至寿命短暂的病毒生成细胞群，可能是有效的抗逆转录病毒治疗后立即出现 CD4+ 淋巴细胞数目增多的原因。同时提示只要有效地控制病毒复制，即便在 HIV 感染晚期也存在进行免疫重建的可能。

本文报道的病毒动力学和 CD4+ 淋巴细胞产生及清除动力学具有多种生物学和临床应用前景。首先，这些结果提示持续的重复病毒感染、复制和快速细胞更替等动力学过程可能是 HIV-1 发病机制中的主要驱动力。其次，在药物治疗仅 14~28 天后就出现野生型血浆病毒几乎完全被耐药突变体替代，这是一个令人惊奇的病毒生物学相关变化。尤其是，这提示 HIV-1 病毒具有强大的潜力应对免疫系统的选择压力 [39]。尽管其他的研究 [40-42] 已经发现病毒更替在血浆中的发生比在 PBMC 中的发生更快，我们的数据更加清楚地阐释这种现象。类似的分析血浆病毒基因型和表型的实验方法可能对于发现病毒突变体或发现包括耐药性、免疫监视和病毒致病性等选择压力下病毒的改变是非常有帮助的。第三，产病毒细胞和潜伏感染细胞（PBMC）寿命不同表明病毒表达本身就直接导致 CD4+ 淋巴细胞的损伤。这些研究结果并没有暗示在细胞杀伤机制中存在"旁观者效应"，也没有暗示未感染或处于潜伏期感染

killing whereby uninfected or latently infected cells are indirectly targeted for destruction by adsorption of viral proteins or by autoimmune reactivities.

Although we have emphasized that most virus in plasma derives from an actively replicating short-lived population of cells, latently infected cells that become activated or chronically producing cells that generate proportionately less virus (and thus do not contribute substantially to the plasma virus pool) may nonetheless be important in HIV-1 pathogenesis. Based on *in situ* analysis[20], these cells far outnumber the actively replicating pool and the diversity of their constituent viral genomes represents a potentially important source of clinically relevant variants, including those conferring drug resistance. In future studies, it will be important not only to discern the specific elimination rates of free virus and of the most actively producing cells, but also the dynamics of virus replication and cell turnover in other cell populations and in patients at earlier stages of infection. Such information will be essential to developing a better understanding of HIV-1 pathogenesis and a more rational approach to therapeutic intervention.

(**373**, 117-122; 1995)

Xiping Wei[*], **Sajal K. Ghosh**[*], **Maria E. Taylor**[*], **Victoria A. Johnson**[†], **Emilio A. Emini**[‡], **Paul Deutsch**[§], **Jeffrey D. Lifson**[||], **Sebastian Bonhoeffer**[¶], **Martin A. Nowak**[¶], **Beatrice H. Hahn**[*], **Michael S. Saag**[†] **& George M. Shaw**[*#]

Divisions of [*] Hematology/Oncology and [†] Infectious Diseases, University of Alabama at Birmingham, 613 Lyons-Harrison Research Building, 701 South 19th Street, Birmingham, Alabama 35294, USA

Departments of [‡]Antiviral Research and [§]Clinical Pharmacology, Merck Research Laboratories, West Point, Pennsylvania 19486, USA

[||] Division of HIV and Exploratory Research, Genelabs Technologies Inc., Redwood City, California 94063, USA

[¶] Department of Zoology, University of Oxford, Oxford OX1 3PS, UK

[#] To whom correspondence should be addressed.

Received 22 November; accepted 16 December 1994.

References:

1. Ho, D. D., Moudgil, T. & Alam. M. *New Engl. J. Med.* **321**, 1621-1625 (1989).

2. Coombs, R. W. *et al. New Engl. J. Med.* **321**, 1626-1631 (1989).

3. Saag, M. S. *et al. J. Infect. Dis* **164**, 72-80 (1991).

4. Clark, S. J, *et al. New Engl. J. Med.* **324**, 954-960 (1991).

5. Daar, E. S., Mougdil, T., Meyer, R. D. & Ho, D.D. *New Engl. J. Med.* **324**, 961-964 (1991).

6. Piatak, M. Jr *et al. Science* **259**, 1749-1754 (1993).

7. Piatak, M. *et al. Lancet* **341**,1099 (1993).

8. Schnittman, S. M., Greenhouse, J. J., Lane, H. C., Pierce, P. F. & Fauci, A. S. *AIDS Res. Hum. Retrovir.* **7**, 361-367 (1991).

9. Michael, N. L., Vahey, M., Burke, D. S. & Redfield, R. R. *J. Virol.* **66**, 310-316 (1992).

10. Winters, M. A., Tan, L. B., Katzenstein, D. A. & Merigan, T. C. *J. Clin. Microbiol.* **31**, 2960- 2966 (1993).

11. Pantaleo, G. *et al. Proc. Natl. Acad.* Sci. *U.S.A.* **88**, 9838-9842 (1991).

12. Connor, R. I., Mohri, H., Cao, Y. & Ho, D. D. *J. Virol.* **67**, 1772-1777 (1993).

13. Bagnarelli, P. *et al. J. Virol.* **66**, 7328-335 (1992).

14. Bagnarelli, P. *et al. J. Virol.* **68**, 2495-2502 (1994).

15. Graziosi, C. *et al. Proc. Natl. Acad. Sci. U.S.A.* **90**, 6405-6409 (1993).

16. Patterson, B. K. *et al. Science* **260**, 976-979 (1993).

17. Saksela, K., Stevens, C., Rubinstein, P. & Baltimore, D. *Proc. Natl. Acad. Sci. U.S.A.* **91**, 1104-1108 (1994).

细胞间接通过吸附病毒蛋白或者自身免疫反应造成损伤。

尽管我们强调血浆病毒大部分源于复制活跃且寿命短暂的细胞群体，但那些激活的潜伏感染细胞或者产生相对较少病毒的慢速产病毒细胞（因此不能对血浆病毒群产生较大的作用）仍然在 HIV-1 发病机制中发挥重要作用。根据原位分析[20]，这些细胞的数量远远超过复制活跃的细胞，而且这些病毒基因组构成的多样性是临床治疗过程中产生耐药性变异体的潜在重要来源。在今后的研究中，不仅要关注特异性游离病毒以及复制活跃的细胞的清除速率，而且要重视其他细胞群体以及早期感染阶段的患者的病毒复制和细胞更替动力学。这些信息对于更好地了解 HIV-1 发病机制以及开发更合理的治疗性干预艾滋病的方法至关重要。

（毛晨晖 翻译；胡卓伟 审稿）

18. Cao, Y. *et al. AIDS Res. Hum. Retrovir.* (in the press).

19. Pantaleo, G. *et al. Nature* **362**, 355-358 (1993).

20. Embretson, J. *et al. Nature* **362**, 359-362 (1993).

21. Aoki-Sei, S. *et al. AIDS Res. Hum. Retrovir.* **8**, 1263-1270 (1992).

22. Coffin, J. M. *Curr. Top. Microbiol. Immun.* **176**, 143-164 (1992).

23. Wain-Hobson, S. *Curr. Opin. Genet. Dev.* **3**, 878-883 (1993).

24. Meriuzzi, V. J. *et al. Science* **250**, 1411-1413 (1990).

25. Kempf, D. *et al. Proc. Natl. Acad. Sci. U.S.A.* (in the press).

26. Vacca, J. P. *et al. Proc. Natl. Acad. Sci. U.S.A* **91**, 4096-4100 (1994).

27. Mulder, J. *et al. J. Clin. Microbiol.* **32**, 292-300 (1994).

28. Larder, B. A. *et al. Nature* **365**, 671-675 (1993).

29. Prasad, V. R. & Goff, S. P. *J. Biol. Chem.* **264**, 16689-16693 (1989).

30. Saag, M. S. *et al. New Engl. J. Med.* **329**, 1065-1072 (1993).

31. Richman, D. D. *et al. Proc. Natl. Acad. Sci. U.S.A.* **88**, 11241-11245 (1991).

32. Richman, D. D. *et al. J. Virol.* **68**, 1660-1666 (1994).

33. McLean, A. R. & Nowak, M. A. *AIDS* **6**, 71-79 (1992).

34. Michie, C., McLean, A., Alcock, C. & Beverley, P. C. L. *Nature* **360**, 264-265 (1992).

35. Sprent, J. & Tough, D. F. *Science* **265**, 1395-1400 (1994).

36. Balzarini, J. *et al. Proc. Natl. Acad. Sci. U.S.A.* **91**, 6599-6603 (1994).

37. Meyerhans, A. *et al. Cell* **58**, 901-910 (1989).

38. Japour, A. J. *et al. Antimicrob. Agents Chemother.* **37**, 1095-1101 (1993).

39. Nowak, M. A. *et al. Science* **254**, 963-969 (1991).

40. Simmonds, P. *et al. J. Virol.* **65**, 6266-6276 (1991).

41. Smith, M. S., Koerber, K. L. & Pagano, J. S. *J. Infect. Dis.* **167**, 445-448 (1993).

42. Zhang, Y.-M., Dawson, S. C., Landsman, D., Lane, H. C. & Salzman, N. P. J. *Virol.* **68**, 425- 432 (1994).

43. Myers, G. K., Korber, B., Berzofsky, J. A. & Smith, R.F. *Human Retroviruses and AIDS 1993* (Los Alamos National Laboratory, New Mexico, 1993).

44. Shaw, G. M. *et al. Science* **226**, 1165-1171 (1984).

Acknowledgements. We thank the study participants; K. Squires, J. M. Kilby, M. Trechsel, L. DeLoach and the UAB 1917 Clinic staff; Abbott Laboratories, Merck & Co. and Boehringer Ingelheim Pharmaceuticals Inc. (BIPI); J. Coffin, R. May and F. Gao for discussion; J. Decker, S. Campbell-Hill, Y. Niu and S. Yin Jiang for technical assistance; and J. Wilson for artwork. This study was supported by the NIH, the US Army Medical Research Acquisition Activity, BIPI, the Wellcome Trust, Keble College and Boehringer Ingelheim Stiftung. Core research facilities were provided by the UAB Center for AIDS Research, the UAB AIDS Clinical Trials Unit and the Birmingham Veterans Administration Medical Center.

Rapid Turnover of Plasma Virions and CD4 Lymphocytes in HIV-1 Infection

D. D. Ho *et al.*

Editor's Note

This paper by David Ho of the New York University School of Medicine and coworkers, along with an accompanying paper by a British and American team reporting the same result, provided a fundamental insight into the behaviour of the AIDS virus HIV-1, which altered the thinking behind strategies to combat the virus. It had been widely thought that, after infection, HIV has an inactive period of "latency". Ho *et al.* show here that, on the contrary, the virus has a very rapid and active cycle of replication, which both exhausts the CD4 immune-response cells trying to combat it and enables the virus to rapidly evolve drug-resistance. This finding recommended an approach of hitting HIV with drugs "early and hard".

Treatment of infected patients with ABT-538, an inhibitor of the protease of human immunodeficiency virus type 1 (HIV-1), causes plasma HIV-1 levels to decrease exponentially (mean half-life, 2.1 ± 0.4 days) and CD4 lymphocyte counts to rise substantially. Minimum estimates of HIV-1 production and clearance and of CD4 lymphocyte turnover indicate that replication of HIV-1 *in vivo* is continuous and highly productive, driving the rapid turnover of CD4 lymphocytes.

IN HIV-1 pathogenesis, an increased viral load correlates with CD4 lymphocyte depletion and disease progression[1-9], but relatively little information is available on the kinetics of virus and CD4 lymphocyte turnover *in vivo*. Here we administer an inhibitor of HIV-1 protease, ABT-538 (refs 10, 11), to twenty infected patients in order to perturb the balance between virus production and clearance. From serial measurements of the subsequent changes in plasma viraemia and CD4 lymphocyte counts, we have been able to infer kinetic information about the pretreatment steady state.

ABT-538 has potent antiviral activity *in vitro* and favourable pharmacokinetic and safety profiles *in vivo*[10]. It was administered orally (600–1,200 mg per day) on day 1 and daily thereafter to twenty HIV-1-infected patients, whose pretreatment CD4 lymphocyte counts and plasma viral levels ranged from 36 to 490 per mm^3 and from 15×10^3 to 554×10^3 virions per ml, respectively (Table 1). Post-treatment CD4 lymphocyte counts were monitored sequentially, as were copy numbers of particle-associated HIV-1 RNA in plasma, using an ultrasensitive assay (Fig. 1 legend) based on a modification of the branched DNA signal-amplification technique[12,13]. The trial design and clinical findings of this study will be reported elsewhere (M.M. *et al.*, manuscript in preparation).

668

HIV-1 感染患者血浆内病毒粒子和 CD4 淋巴细胞的快速更新

何大一等

编者按

这篇由纽约大学医学院的何大一及其同事发表的文章提供了对艾滋病病毒 HIV-1 行为的基本认知。另一篇由英美团队发表的文章报道了相同的结果。这一结果改变了抗病毒的策略。人们广泛认为，HIV 病毒感染后有一个不活跃的"潜伏期"。何大一他们在这篇文章中指出，与这一认知相反，病毒有一个快速且活跃的复制期，这一时期不仅会耗尽试图对抗病毒的 CD4 免疫应答细胞而且会使病毒迅速出现耐药性。这一发现建议尽早用药物猛烈对抗 HIV。

使用 ABT-538（一种人免疫缺陷病毒 I 型（HIV-1）蛋白酶抑制剂）治疗 HIV-1 感染患者后，引起血浆内 HIV-1 水平指数式下降（平均半衰期为 2.1 ± 0.4 天）而 CD4 淋巴细胞数目显著升高。HIV-1 的产生和清除以及 CD4 淋巴细胞更新的最小估测值表明，HIV-1 在体内的复制是持续的、高产的，并可促使 CD4 淋巴细胞快速更新。

在 HIV-1 的发病机制中，体内病毒载量的增加与 CD4 淋巴细胞减少以及疾病进展密切相关 [1-9]，但是目前关于体内病毒和 CD4 淋巴细胞更新的动力学信息相对较少。本文中我们在 20 名感染患者身上使用一种 HIV-1 蛋白酶抑制剂——ABT-538（参考文献 10，参考文献 11）以干预病毒产生和清除之间的平衡。通过检测血浆病毒血症和 CD4 淋巴细胞数目的后续改变，我们已经能够推断治疗前稳态的动力学信息。

ABT-538 在体外具有强大的抗病毒活性，而且在体内有良好的药动学特性和安全性 [10]。20 名 HIV-1 感染患者每天口服药物（600~1,200 毫克／天），他们的 CD4 淋巴细胞数目和血浆内病毒水平在治疗前分别是每立方毫米 36~490 个细胞和每毫升 15×10^3~554×10^3 个病毒粒子（表 1）。随后使用基于改良的分支 DNA 信号扩增技术 [12,13] 的超敏感检测方法（图 1 图注）监测治疗后的 CD4 淋巴细胞数目以及血浆中 HIV-1 颗粒相关 RNA 的拷贝数。本研究的实验设计和临床结果将另有报道（马科维茨等，稿件准备中）。

669

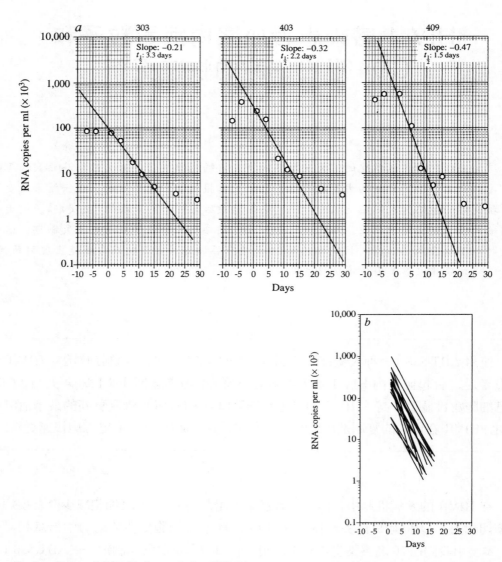

Fig. 1. *a*, Plasma viral load before and after ABT-538 treatment was begun on day 1 for three representative cases. Plasma samples were tested with the branched DNA signal-amplification assay as previously described[12,13]. Those samples with RNA levels below the detection sensitivity of 10,000 copies per ml were then tested using a modified assay differing from the original in two ways: hybridization of the bDNA amplification system is mediated by binding to overhangs on contiguous target probes; and the enzymatic amplification system has been enhanced by modification of wash buffers and the solution in which the alkaline phosphatase probe is diluted. The results of these changes are a diminution of background signals, an enhancement of alkaline phosphatase activity, and thus a greater detection sensitivity (500 copies per ml). Linear regression was used to obtain the best-fitting straight line for 3–5 data points between day 1 and the inflection point before the plateau of the new steady-state level. The slope, S, of each line represents the rate of exponential decrease; that is, the straight-line fit indicates that the viral load decreases according to $V(t) = V(0)\exp(-St)$. Given the exponential decay, $V(t_{1/2}) = V(0)/2 = V(0)\exp(-St_{1/2})$, and hence the viral half-life, $t_{1/2} = \ln(2)/S$. Before drug administration, the change in viral load with time can be expressed by the differential equation, $\mathrm{d}V/\mathrm{d}t = P - cV$, where P is the viral production rate, c is the viral clearance rate constant, and V is the number of plasma virions. During the pretreatment steady state, $\mathrm{d}V/\mathrm{d}t = 0$, and hence $P = cV$. We have also tested more intricate models, in

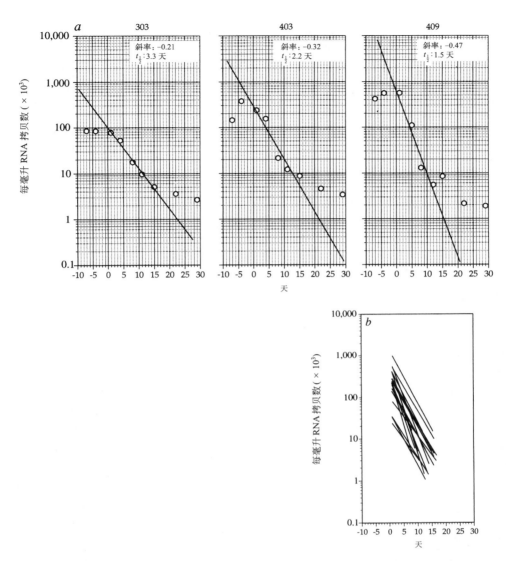

图 1. *a*，三个代表性病例开始 ABT-538 治疗前后的血浆内病毒载量。如参考文献所述 [12,13] 血浆样本用分支 DNA 信号扩增法检测。那些 RNA 水平处于检测敏感度（10,000 拷贝／毫升）以下的样本随后用改良的方法检测，该方法与前者有两方面的不同：bDNA 扩增系统的杂交是通过结合到邻近目标探针的突出部分上，而且酶扩增系统通过改良冲洗缓冲液和稀释碱性磷酸酶探针的溶液加以强化。这些改变可以减少背景信号，增强碱性磷酸酶活性从而提高检测敏感性（500 拷贝／毫升）。使用线性回归来获得第 1 天和新稳态水平平台期之前的拐点之间 3~5 个数据点的最合适直线。每一条直线的斜率 *S* 代表了指数式减少的速率。也就是说，直线拟合表示病毒载量的减少符合 $V(t) = V(0)\exp(-St)$。鉴于存在指数式衰减，$V(t_{1/2}) = V(0)/2 = V(0)\exp(-St_{1/2})$，因此病毒的半衰期 $t_{1/2} = \ln(2)/S$。药物使用前，病毒载量随时间的改变可以表达成微分方程 $\mathrm{d}V/\mathrm{d}t = P - cV$，其中 *P* 表示病毒产生速率，*c* 表示病毒清除速率常数，*V* 是血浆内病毒粒子的数量。在治疗前的稳态期，$\mathrm{d}V/\mathrm{d}t = 0$，因此 $P = cV$。我们也检测了更多复杂的模型，其病毒减少由 2 到 3 种指数式速率决定，分别是病毒清除速率、产病毒细胞的减少速率和潜伏感染细胞的减少速率。但是这次没有足够的数据分别估计多个参数。然而，使用参考文献 14 中的模型，我们发现如果潜伏感染细胞的死亡速率相对于其他两个速率非常小的话，那么病毒的减少呈一种简单的指

which the viral decay is governed by two or three exponential rates, namely the viral clearance rate, the decay rate of virus-producing cells, and the decay rate of latently infected cells. But there are insufficient data at this time to estimate the multiple parameters separately. Nonetheless, using the model in ref. 14, we find that if the death rate of latently infected cells is very small compared with the other two rates, then viral decay follows a simple exponential decline, with $S = c$, because the slow activation of a large number of latently infected cells offsets the loss of actively infected cells. Irrespective of the model, on a log plot, $S = -d(\ln V)/dt = c - P/V$. If drug inhibition is complete and virus-producing cells are rapidly lost (so $P = 0$), then $S = c$. If viral production continues, S is still $\leq c$, so the slope is a minimum estimate of the viral clearance efficiency, b, Decline of plasma viral load after ABT-538 treatment in all 20 patients. The slope for each case was obtained as already discussed, and the length of each line was determined by the initial viral load and the new steady-state level.

Table 1. Summary data of HIV-1 and CD4 lymphocyte turnover during the pretreatment steady state

| Patient | Baseline values | | Kinetics of HIV-1 turnover | | | Kinetics of CD4 lymphocyte turnover* | | |
| | CD4 cell count (mm⁻³) | Plasma viraemia (virions per ml × 10³)† | Slope | $t_{1/2}$ (days) | Minimum production and clearance‡ (virions per day × 10⁹) | Slope | Minimum production and destruction | |
							Blood§ (cells per day × 10⁶)	Total‖ (cells per day × 10⁹)
301	76	193	−0.30	2.3	0.56	0.070 (6.9)	21.7 (28.1)	1.1 (1.4)
302	209	80	−0.27	2.6	0.26	0.004 (0.5)	4.3 (2.7)	0.2 (0.1)
303	293	41	−0.21	3.3	0.11	0.005 (1.4)	9.9 (9.5)	0.5 (0.5)
304	174	121	−0.28	2.5	0.54	0.019 (1.9)	22.2 (13.0)	1.1 (0.6)
305	269	88	−0.33	2.1	0.50	0.055 (21.5)	108.0 (157.0)	5.4 (7.8)
306	312	175	−0.52	1.3	1.27	0.058 (25.7)	105.0 (150.0)	5.3 (7.5)
308	386	185	−0.46	1.5	1.48	0.020 (9.1)	55.9 (65.8)	2.8 (3.3)
309	49	554	−0.29	2.4	1.85	0.088 (11.8)	20.7 (56.6)	1.0 (2.8)
310	357	15	−0.26	2.7	0.05	0.038 (15.6)	71.0 (81.9)	3.6 (4.1)
311	107	130	−0.29	2.4	0.51	0.064 (11.0)	38.9 (62.8)	2.0 (3.1)
312	59	70	−0.30	2.3	0.30	0.048 (4.5)	17.0 (26.9)	0.8 (1.4)
313	47	100	−0.54	1.3	0.88	0.077 (5.9)	24.7 (40.5)	1.2 (2.0)
401	228	101	−0.40	1.7	0.47	NA	NA	NA
402	169	55	−0.28	2.5	0.21	0.014 (3.1)	13.4 (17.4)	0.7 (0.9)
403	120	126	−0.32	2.2	0.74	0.015 (2.4)	13.8 (18.7)	0.7 (0.9)
404	46	244	−0.27	2.6	1.06	0.080 (8.5)	24.6 (57.5)	1.2 (2.9)
406	490	18	−0.31	2.2	0.08	NA	NA	NA
408	36	23	−0.25	2.8	0.08	0.059 (3.4)	12.5 (19.7)	0.6 (1.0)
409	67	256	−0.47	1.5	2.07	0.073 (15.9)	35.3 (115.0)	1.8 (5.7)
410	103	99	−0.36	1.9	0.53	0.051 (5.6)	32.4 (34.5)	1.6 (1.7)
Range	36–490	15–554	−0.21 to −0.54	1.3–3.3	0.05–2.07	0.004–0.088 (0.5–25.7)	4.3–108.0 (2.7–157.0)	0.2–5.4 (0.1–7.8)
Mean	180±46	134±40	−0.34±0.06	2.1±0.4	0.68±0.13	0.047 (8.6)	35.1 (53.2)	1.8 (2.6)

* The results for the kinetics of CD4 lymphocyte turnover generated by an exponential growth model are shown without parentheses; results generated by a linear production model are shown in parentheses.

数式减少，其 $S = c$，因为大量潜伏感染细胞的缓慢激活抵消了活跃感染细胞的减少。不考虑这个模型，在对数图上，$S = -d(\ln V)/dt = c - P/V$。如果药物的抑制作用是完全的，而且产病毒细胞很快减少（那么 $P = 0$），那么 $S = c$。如果病毒持续产生，$S \leqslant c$，因此斜率是病毒清除效率的最小估测值。b，20 名患者 ABT-538 治疗后血浆内病毒载量的减少。每个病例的斜率是通过之前讨论的方法得到的，每条线的长度由初始病毒载量和新的稳态水平决定。

表 1. 在治疗前稳态期 HIV-1 和 CD4 淋巴细胞更新的数据总结

| 患者 | 基线值 | | HIV-1 更新动力学 | | | CD4 淋巴细胞更新动力学 * | | |
| | CD4 细胞数目（每立方毫米） | 血浆病毒血症（每毫升病毒粒子 × 10^3）† | 斜率 | $t_{1/2}$（天） | 最小生成和清除速率‡（每日病毒粒子 × 10^9） | 斜率 | 最小生成和破坏速率 | |
							血液§（每日细胞 × 10^6）	总计‖（每日细胞 × 10^9）
301	76	193	−0.30	2.3	0.56	0.070 (6.9)	21.7 (28.1)	1.1 (1.4)
302	209	80	−0.27	2.6	0.26	0.004 (0.5)	4.3 (2.7)	0.2 (0.1)
303	293	41	−0.21	3.3	0.11	0.005 (1.4)	9.9 (9.5)	0.5 (0.5)
304	174	121	−0.28	2.5	0.54	0.019 (1.9)	22.2 (13.0)	1.1 (0.6)
305	269	88	−0.33	2.1	0.50	0.055 (21.5)	108.0 (157.0)	5.4 (7.8)
306	312	175	−0.52	1.3	1.27	0.058 (25.7)	105.0 (150.0)	5.3 (7.5)
308	286	185	−0.46	1.5	1.48	0.020 (9.1)	55.9 (65.8)	2.8 (3.3)
309	49	554	−0.29	2.4	1.85	0.088 (11.8)	20.7 (56.6)	1.0 (2.8)
310	357	15	−0.26	2.7	0.05	0.038 (15.6)	71.0 (81.9)	3.6 (4.1)
311	107	130	−0.29	2.4	0.51	0.064 (11.0)	38.9 (62.8)	2.0 (3.1)
312	59	70	−0.30	2.3	0.30	0.048 (4.5)	17.0 (26.9)	0.8 (1.4)
313	47	100	−0.54	1.3	0.88	0.077 (5.9)	24.7 (40.5)	1.2 (2.0)
401	228	101	−0.40	1.7	0.47	NA	NA	NA
402	169	55	−0.28	2.5	0.21	0.014 (3.1)	13.4 (17.4)	0.7 (0.9)
403	120	126	−0.32	2.2	0.74	0.015 (2.4)	13.8 (18.7)	0.7 (0.9)
404	46	244	−0.27	2.6	1.06	0.080 (8.5)	24.6 (57.5)	1.2 (2.9)
406	490	18	−0.31	2.2	0.08	NA	NA	NA
408	36	23	−0.25	2.8	0.08	0.059 (3.4)	12.5 (19.7)	0.6 (1.0)
409	67	256	−0.47	1.5	2.07	0.073 (15.9)	35.3 (115.0)	1.8 (5.7)
410	103	99	−0.36	1.9	0.53	0.051 (5.6)	32.4 (34.5)	1.6 (1.7)
范围	36~490	15~554	−0.21 至 −0.54	1.3~3.3	0.05~2.07	0.004~0.088 (0.5~25.7)	4.3~108.0 (2.7~157.0)	0.2~5.4 (0.1~7.8)
均值	180±46	134±40	−0.34±0.06	2.1±0.4	0.68±0.13	0.047 (8.6)	35.1 (53.2)	1.8 (2.6)

* 通过指数式增长模型得出的 CD4 淋巴细胞更新动力学的结果显示为不带括号的；通过线性模型得到的结果在括号内显示。

† Each virion contains two RNA copies.

‡ Calculated using plasma and extracellular fluid volumes estimated from body weights, and assuming that plasma and extracellular fluid compartments are in equilibrium.

§ Calculated using blood volumes estimated from body weights.

‖ Calculated on the assumption that the lymphocyte pool in blood represents 2% of the total population[16]. NA, not analysed owing to large fluctuations in CD4 cell counts.

Kinetics of HIV-1 Turnover

Following ABT-538 treatment, every patient had a rapid and dramatic decline in plasma viraemia over the first two weeks. As shown using three examples in Fig. 1a, the initial decline in plasma viraemia was always exponential, demonstrated by a straight-line fit to the data on a log plot. The slope of this line, as defined by linear regression, permitted the half-life ($t_{1/2}$) of viral decay in plasma to be determined (Fig. 1 legend): for example, patient 409 was found to have a viral decay slope of −0.47 per day, yielding a $t_{1/2}$ of 1.5 days (Fig. 1a). Hence the rate and extent of decay of plasma viraemia was determined for each patient. As summarized in Fig. 1b, in every case there was a rapid decline, the magnitude of which ranged from 11- to 275-fold, with a mean of 66-fold (equivalent to 98.5% inhibition). The residual viraemia may be attributable to inadequate drug concentration in certain tissues, drug resistance, persistence of a small long-lived virus-producing cell population (such as macrophages), and gradual activation of a latently infected pool of cells. As summarized in Table 1, the viral decay slopes varied from −0.21 to −0.54 per day, with a mean of −0.34 ± 0.06 per day; correspondingly, $t_{1/2}$ varied from 1.3 to 3.3 days, with a mean of 2.1 ± 0.4 days. The latter value indicates that, on average, half of the plasma virions turn over every two days, showing that HIV-1 replication *in vivo* must be highly productive.

The exponential decline in plasma viraemia following ABT-538 treatment reflects both the clearance of free virions and the loss of HIV-1-producing cells as the drug substantially blocks new rounds of infection. But although drug inhibition is probably incomplete and virus-producing cells are not lost immediately, a minimum value for viral clearance can still be determined (Fig. 1 legend) by multiplying the absolute value of the viral decay slope by the initial viral load. Assuming that ABT-538 administration does not affect viral clearance, this estimate is also valid before treatment. As the viral load varies little during the pretreatment phase (Fig. 1a, and data not shown), we assume there exists a steady state and hence the calculated clearance rate is equal to the minimum virion production rate before drug therapy. Factoring in the patient's estimated plasma and extracellular fluid volumes based on body weight, we determined the minimum daily production and clearance rate of HIV-1 particles for each case (Table 1). These values ranged from 0.05 to 2.07×10^9 virions per day with a mean of $0.68 \pm 0.13 \times 10^9$ virions per day. Although these viral turnover rates are already high, true values may be up to a few-fold higher, depending on the $t_{1/2}$ of virus-producing lymphocytes. The precise kinetics of this additional parameter remains undefined. However, the mean $t_{1/2}$ of virus-producing cells is probably less, or in any case cannot be much larger, than the mean $t_{1/2}$ of 2.1 days observed for plasma virion elimination, demonstrating that turnover of actively infected cells is both

† 每个病毒粒子含有 2 个 RNA 拷贝。

‡ 用从体重估计的血浆和细胞外液计算得出，并假设血浆和细胞外液成分相同。

§ 用从体重估计的血容量计算得出。

∥ 假设血液中的淋巴细胞占总细胞数的 2% 得出的结果 [16]。NA，由于 CD4 细胞数目波动太大而未分析。

HIV-1 更新的动力学

随着 ABT-538 治疗，每名患者在起始 2 周内血浆病毒血症出现快速且明显的降低。正如图 1a 中三个例子所示，血浆病毒血症的初始降低是指数式的，在以数据的对数值作出的图上显示为一条直线。其斜率可通过线性回归得出，并可用于确定血浆中病毒减少的半衰期（$t_{1/2}$）（图 1 图注）。例如，患者 409 的病毒减少斜率是每天 −0.47，得出其半衰期是 1.5 天（图 1a）。这样就可以得到每名患者血浆病毒血症减少的速率和程度。如图 1b 总结的，每个病例中血浆内病毒载量都有快速的减少，其降低程度从 1/11 到 1/275 不等，平均 1/66（相当于抑制了 98.5% 的病毒）。剩余的病毒血症可能是由某些组织中的药物浓度不够、耐药、存在一小群长寿命的产病毒细胞（比如巨噬细胞）以及潜伏的感染细胞池的逐步激活引起的。如表 1 所总结的，病毒减少的斜率从每天 −0.21 到 −0.54 不等，平均每天 −0.34±0.06；相应地，$t_{1/2}$ 从 1.3 天到 3.3 天不等，平均 2.1±0.4 天。后一个数值表明平均起来每两日就有一半的血浆病毒粒子发生更新，说明 HIV-1 在体内的复制肯定是高产量的。

ABT-538 治疗后血浆病毒血症的指数式减少说明同时发生了游离病毒粒子的清除和产 HIV-1 细胞的清除，因为该药物能有效地阻断进一步的感染。尽管药物的抑制可能是不完全的而且产病毒细胞并不是立即就被清除，但是仍能通过病毒减少斜率的绝对值与初始病毒载量相乘来确定病毒清除的最小数值（图 1 图注）。假设 ABT-538 的使用没有影响病毒的清除，这种治疗前的估计也仍然是有效的。因为在治疗前，病毒载量变化很小（图 1a，数据未显示），我们假设存在一个稳定状态，因此在药物治疗前计算出来的清除速率与最小病毒粒子产生速率是相等的。将基于体重估计的患者血浆和细胞外液容积计算在内，我们得出每一例患者 HIV-1 颗粒的每日最小生产速率和清除速率（表 1）。这些数值从每天 0.05×10^9 到 2.07×10^9 个病毒粒子不等，平均每天 $(0.68 \pm 0.13) \times 10^9$ 个。尽管这些病毒更新速率已经非常快，根据产病毒淋巴细胞的半衰期，其真实数值可能会高出几倍。这些指标的准确动力学参数仍然未知。但是，产病毒细胞的平均半衰期很可能少于而不是大于血浆内病毒粒子清除的平均半衰期 2.1 天。这表明活跃感染细胞的更新是非常快速和持续的。从我们的

rapid and continuous. It could also be inferred from our data that nearly all (98.5%) of the plasma virus must come from recently infected cells.

Examination of Fig. 1*b* shows that the viral decay slopes (clearance rate constants) are independent of the initial viral loads. The slopes do not correlate with the initial CD4 lymphocyte counts (Fig. 2*a*), another indicator of the disease status of patients. Therefore these observations strongly suggest that the viral clearance rate constant is not dependent on the stage of HIV-1 infection. Instead, they indicate that viral load is largely a function of viral production, because clearance rate constants vary by about 2.5-fold whereas the initial loads vary by almost 40-fold (Table 1).

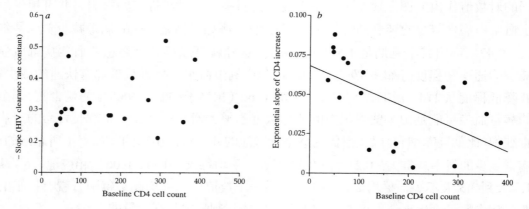

Fig. 2. *a*, Lack of correlation between viral decay slopes and disease status as indicated by baseline CD4 cell counts. Correlation coefficient = 0.05 (*P* value > 0.1). *b*, Inverse correlation between the exponential CD4 increase slopes and baseline CD4 cell counts. Correlation coefficient = −0.57 (*P* value < 0.01). Such an inverse correlation would be expected if T-cell proliferation were governed by a density-dependent growth function (logistic, for example), in which the growth rate decreases with increasing population level, if T cells were produced from precursors at a constant rate or from a combination of these two effects.

Kinetics of CD4 Lymphocyte Turnover

After ABT-538 treatment, CD4 lymphocyte counts rose in each of the 18 patients that could be evaluated. As shown in three examples in Fig. 3, some increases were dramatic (patient 409, for example) whereas others (such as patient 303) were modest. Based on the available data, it was not possible to determine with confidence whether the rise was strictly exponential (Fig. 3, top) or linear (Fig. 3, bottom). An exponential increase would be consistent with proliferation of CD4 lymphocytes in the periphery, particularly in secondary lymphoid organs, whereas a linear increase would indicate cellular production from a precursor source such as the thymus[14]. Given that the thymus involutes with age and becomes further depleted with HIV-1 infection[15], it is more likely that the rise in CD4 lymphocytes is largely due to proliferation. Nevertheless, as both components may contribute, we analysed the observed CD4 lymphocyte data by modelling both exponential and linear increases.

数据也能推断出几乎所有(98.5%)的血浆内病毒都来自于新近感染的细胞。

图 1b 显示病毒减少的斜率(清除速率常数)与初始病毒载量无关，也与初始的 CD4 淋巴细胞数目(患者疾病状态的另一个指标)无关(图 2a)，提示患者处于疾病的稳态。因此这些结果显示病毒清除速率常数并不依赖于 HIV-1 感染的时期，并且说明病毒载量很大程度上是病毒产生引起的。因为清除速率常数变化了大约 2.5 倍，而初始载量则变化了几乎 40 倍(表 1)。

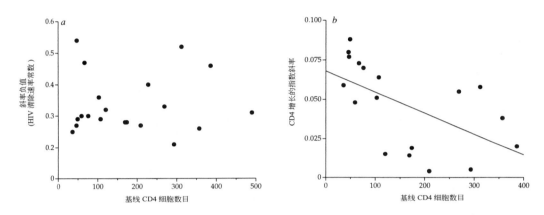

图 2. a，由基线 CD4 细胞数目所示，病毒减少斜率与疾病状态之间不存在相关性。相关系数 = 0.05 (P 值 > 0.1)。b，CD4 增长的指数斜率与基线 CD4 细胞数目之间存在负相关性。相关系数 = -0.57 (P 值 < 0.01)。出现这种负相关的情况如下：T 细胞的增殖是密度依赖的(比如对数式)，即增长速率随着群体量的增加而降低，或 T 细胞的增殖是以恒定的速率来源于前体，或两者的混合效果。

CD4 淋巴细胞更新动力学

经过 ABT-538 治疗后，所有可以评价的 18 名患者的 CD4 淋巴细胞数目都增加了。如图 3 中的三个例子所示，一些增加是非常显著的(比如患者 409)，而其他则相对适度(比如患者 303)。根据这些获得的数据，还不足以明确地确定这种增长是严格指数式的(图 3，上部)还是线性的(图 3，下部)。外周 CD4 淋巴细胞的增殖，尤其是次级淋巴器官中的增殖是指数式的增加，而线性增加则表明细胞来源于前体，比如胸腺[14]。考虑到胸腺随年龄增长而退化并因 HIV-1 感染而进一步耗竭[15]，很可能 CD4 淋巴细胞的增加大部分都来源于增殖。不管怎样，两种来源都可能发挥作用，我们分别用指数式和线性增长建模，分析观察到的 CD4 淋巴细胞数据。

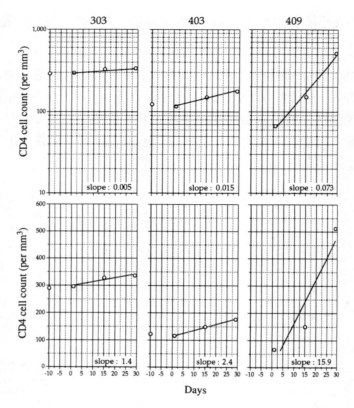

Fig. 3. Increase in CD4 cell counts after ABT-538 treatment plotted on a logarithmic (top) or linear (bottom) scale. Each slope was obtained from the best-fit line derived from linear regression on 2–4 data points. In the model for exponential increase, the doubling time was determined by dividing ln(2) by the slope. From the slope, we obtained minimum estimates of the CD4 lymphocyte production rate. The change in CD4 cell number over time can be described by the equation, $dT/dt = P - \mu T$, where T is the cell count, P is the cell production rate, and μ is the cell decay rate. The slope, S, on a log plot is thus $= d(\ln T)/dt = P/T - \mu$. Hence, $S \times T$ must be less than P, showing that our estimates indeed represent minimum CD4 lymphocyte production rates. Using a similar argument, slopes derived from a model of linear increases are also minimum estimates of CD4 lymphocyte production.

The slope of the line depicting the rise in CD4 lymphocyte counts on a log plot was determined for each case (Fig. 3, top). Individual slopes varied considerably, ranging from 0.004 to 0.088 per day, with a mean of 0.047 per day (Table 1), corresponding to a mean doubling time of ~15 days (Fig. 3 legend). On average, the entire population of peripheral CD4 lymphocytes was turning over every 15 days in our patients during the pretreatment steady state when CD4 lymphocyte production and destruction were balanced. Moreover, the slopes were inversely correlated with baseline CD4 lymphocyte counts (Fig. 2b) in that patients with lower initial CD4 cell counts had more prominent rises. This demonstrates convincingly that the CD4 lymphocyte depletion seen in AIDS is primarily a consequence of the destruction of these cells induced by HIV-1 not a lack of their production.

As ABT-538 treatment reduces virus-mediated destruction of CD4 lymphocytes, the observed increase in CD4 cells provides a minimum estimate (Fig. 3 legend) of the

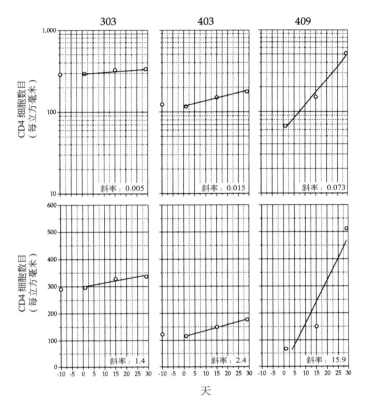

图 3. 在对数（上部）和线性（下部）坐标上绘出的 ABT-538 治疗后 CD4 淋巴细胞数目的增长。每一个斜率是通过 2~4 个数据点的线性回归得出的最适合直线获得的。在指数式增长模型上，倍增时间用 ln(2) 除以斜率得到。从斜率我们可以得到 CD4 淋巴细胞产生的速率的最小估测值。CD4 细胞数目随时间变化可以用以下公式描述 $dT/dt = P - \mu T$，其中 T 是细胞数目，P 是细胞生成速率，μ 是细胞减少速率。在对数图上斜率 $S = d(\ln T)/dt = P/T - \mu$。因此，$S \times T$ 必定小于 P，表明我们的估算确实代表了 CD4 淋巴细胞生成的最小速率。利用类似的论据，线性模型上得到的斜率也是 CD4 淋巴细胞生成的最小估测值。

我们确定了每个病例在对数图上描述 CD4 淋巴细胞数目增加的直线的斜率（图 3，上部）。各斜率差别很大，从每日 0.004 到 0.088 不等，平均每日 0.047（表 1），与平均倍增时间约是 15 天相对应（图 3 图注）。平均来说，在 CD4 淋巴细胞生成和破坏处于平衡状态的治疗前稳态阶段，患者整个外周 CD4 淋巴细胞群每 15 日更新一次。此外，CD4 增长的指数式斜率与基线 CD4 淋巴细胞数目（图 2b）呈负相关，即初始 CD4 淋巴细胞数目低的患者增加更明显。这就有力地证明了艾滋病患者体内 CD4 淋巴细胞的减少是 HIV-1 诱导的细胞破坏的结果，而不是产生不足的结果。

由于 ABT-538 的治疗减少了病毒介导的 CD4 淋巴细胞的破坏，观察到的 CD4 细胞增长值可以作为治疗前 CD4 淋巴细胞产生速率的最小估测值（图 3 图注），反

pretreatment CD4 lymphocyte production rate, which in turn equals the destruction rate during the steady state. Minimum production (destruction) rates were calculated for each case by multiplying the slope, the initial CD4 cell count, and the estimated blood volume. The minimum numbers of CD4 cells in blood produced or destroyed each day ranged from 4.3×10^6 to 108×10^6, with a mean of 35.1×10^6 (Table 1). Given that the blood lymphocyte pool is about 2% of the total population[16], the overall CD4 lymphocyte turnover in our patients was calculated to vary from 0.2×10^9 to 5.4×10^9 cells per day, with a mean of 1.8×10^9 cells per day.

The increase in CD4 lymphocyte counts following ABT-538 administration was also modelled linearly (Fig. 3, bottom). The slope of the line depicting the increase for each case was determined, and the values varied from 0.5 to 25.7 cells per mm³ per day, with a mean of 8.6 cells per mm³ per day (Table 1). Using the same argument as for the exponential case, minimum estimates of total CD4 production (or destruction) rates at baseline were determined to vary from 0.1×10^9 to 7.8×10^9 cells per day, with a mean of 2.6×10^9 cells per day.

Although our two sets of CD4 lymphocyte analyses do not yield identical numerical results, they are in close agreement and emphasize the same qualitative points about HIV-1 pathogenesis. The number of CD4 lymphocyte destroyed and replenished each day is of the order of 10^9, which is strikingly close to estimates of the total number of HIV-1 RNA-expressing lymphocytes in the body determined using *in situ* polymerase chain reaction and hybridization methods[8,17]. In addition, CD4 replenishment appears to be highly stressed in many patients in that the faster production rates are ~25–78-fold higher than the slowest rate (Table 1), which is presumably still higher than the as-yet-undefined normal CD4 turnover rate. The precise mechanisms of CD4 lymphocyte repopulation, however, will have to be addressed in the future by studies on phenotypic markers and functional status of the regenerating cells. Nonetheless, the rapid CD4 lymphocyte turnover has several implications. First, the apoptosis commonly observed in the setting of HIV-1 infection[18] may simply be an expected consequence of an active lymphocyte regenerative process. Second, the CD4 lymphocyte depletion seen in advanced HIV-1 infection may be likened to a sink containing a low water level, with the tap and drain both equally wide open. As the regenerative capacity of the immune system is not infinite, it is not difficult to see why the sink eventually empties. It is also evident from this analogy that our primary strategy to reverse the immunodeficiency ought to be to target virally mediated destruction (plug the drain) rather than to emphasize lymphocyte reconstitution (put in a second tap).

Discussion

We believe our new kinetic data have important implications for HIV-1 therapy and pathogenesis. It is self-evident that, with rapid turnover of HIV-1, generation of viral diversity and the attendant increased opportunities for viral escape from therapeutic agents are unavoidable sequelae[19,20]. Treatment strategies, if they are to have a dramatic clinical impact, must therefore be initiated as early in the infection course as possible, perhaps even

过来，这个值等于稳态期细胞的破坏速率。通过将斜率、初始 CD4 细胞数目和估计的血容量相乘计算出每个病例的最小产生（破坏）速率。每日血液中产生或者破坏的 CD4 细胞的最小数量是 4.3×10^6 到 108×10^6 不等，平均 35.1×10^6（表 1）。考虑到血液淋巴细胞只占全体细胞的大约 2%[16]，计算出我们的患者中整体 CD4 淋巴细胞更新速率是每日 0.2×10^9 到 5.4×10^9 个细胞不等，平均每日 1.8×10^9 个细胞。

ABT-538 治疗后 CD4 淋巴细胞的增加也可以线性建模（图 3，下部）。直线的斜率描述了每个病例细胞的增加，其数值是确定的，从每日每立方毫米 0.5 到 25.7 个细胞不等，平均每日每立方毫米 8.6 个细胞（表 1）。使用相同的数据用于指数式模型，确定基线总 CD4 细胞产生速率（或者破坏速率）的最小估测值为每日 0.1×10^9 到 7.8×10^9 个细胞不等，平均每日 2.6×10^9 个细胞。

尽管我们的两种 CD4 淋巴细胞分析方法没有得出完全一致的结果，但它们是非常接近的，并进一步明确了 HIV-1 发病机制中病毒粒子与 CD4 淋巴细胞之间存在明确的反转关系。每日清除和补充的 CD4 淋巴细胞数量级是 10^9，这与使用原位聚合酶链式反应和杂交方法得到的体内表达 HIV-1 RNA 的淋巴细胞总数的估计值惊人地相近 [8,17]。此外，CD4 细胞补充在许多患者中存在较大差异，其产生速率快者是最慢者的 25~78 倍（表 1），而且很有可能比目前未明确的正常 CD4 细胞更新速率更快。但是，CD4 淋巴细胞补充的精确机制需要通过进一步对再生细胞的表型标记和功能状态进行深入研究来确定。然而，这种快速的 CD4 淋巴细胞更新仍然具有研究价值。首先，在 HIV-1 感染中经常观察到的细胞凋亡现象 [18] 可能就是活跃的淋巴细胞再生引起的。其次，可以将 HIV-1 感染晚期出现的 CD4 淋巴细胞耗竭比喻成一个含有少量水的盆，其注入和排放水的速率相等。由于免疫系统的再生能力不是无限的，不难想象为什么最终水盆变空了。从这个类比中，我们也可以发现我们想要逆转免疫缺陷状态的主要措施应该是针对病毒介导的淋巴细胞破坏（堵住出水口）而不是强调淋巴细胞的再生（增加一个进水口）。

讨 论

我们相信我们新的动力学数据对 HIV-1 的治疗和发病机制探索具有重要的应用价值。显而易见，随着 HIV-1 的快速更新，必将引起病毒多样化、增加病毒逃逸治疗药物的机会等后遗症 [19,20]。因此治疗策略想要取得显著的临床效果，就必须尽可能在感染早期进行干预，甚至可能在血清转化时就开始。血浆中 HIV-1 的快速更新

during seroconversion. The rapid turnover of HIV-1 in plasma also suggests that current protocols for monitoring the acute antiviral activity of novel compounds must be modified to focus on the first few days following drug initiation. Our interventional approach to AIDS pathogenesis has shown that HIV-1 production and clearance are delicately balanced but highly dynamic processes. Taken together, our findings strongly support the view that AIDS is primarily a consequence of continuous, high-level replication of HIV-1, leading to virus- and immune-mediated killing of CD4 lymphocytes.

(**373**, 123-126; 1995)

David D. Ho, Avidan U. Neumann[*†]**, Alan S. Perelson**[†]**, Wen Chen, John M. Leonard**[‡] **& Martin Markowitz**
Aaron Diamond AIDS Research Center, NYU School of Medicine, 455 First Avenue, New York, New York 10016, USA
[*] Santa Fe Institute, Santa Fe, New Mexico 87501, USA
[†] Theoretical Division, Los Alamos National Laboratory, Los Alamos, New Mexico 87545, USA
[‡] Pharmaceutical Products Division, Abbott Laboratories, Abbott Park, Illinois 60064, USA

Received 16 November; accepted 15 December 1994.

References:

1. Weiss, R. A. *Science* **260**, 1273-1279 (1993).
2. Ho, D. D., Moudgil, T. & Alam, M. *New Engl. J. Med.* **321**, 1621-1625 (1989).
3. Simmonds, P. *et al. J. Virol.* **64**, 864-872 (1990).
4. Connor, R. l., Mohri, H., Cao, Y. & Ho, D. D. *J. Virol.* **67**, 1772-1777 (1993).
5. Patterson, B. K. *et al. Science* **260**, 976-979 (1993).
6. Piatak, M. *et al. Science* **259**, 1749-1754 (1993).
7. Pantaieo, G. *et al. Nature* **362**, 355-359 (1993).
8. Embretson, J. *et al. Nature* **362**, 359-362 (1993).
9. Wain-Hobson, S. *Nature* **366**, 22 (1993).
10. Kempf, D. *et al. Proc. Natl. Acad. Sci. U.S.A.* (in the press).
11. Markowitz, M. *et al. J. Virol.* (in the press).
12. Pachl, C. *et al. J. AIDS* (in the press).
13. Cao, Y. *et al. AIDS Res. Human Retroviruses* (in the press).
14. Perelson, A. S., Kirschner, D. E. & De Boer, R. *J. Math. Biosci.* **114**, 81-125 (1993).
15. Grody, W. W., Fligiel, S. & Naeim, F. *Am. J. Clin. Path.* **84**, 85-95 (1985).
16. Paul, W. E. *Fundamental Immunology* (Raven, New York, 1985).
17. Haase, A. T. *Ann. N. Y. Acad. Sci.* **724**, 75-86 (1994).
18. Ameisen, J. C. & Capron, A. *Immun. Today* **12**, 102-105 (1991).
19. Wain-Hobson, S. *Curr. Opin. Genet. Dev.* **3**, 878-883 (1993).
20. Coffin, J. M. *Curr. Top. Microbiol. Immun.* **176**, 143-164 (1992).

Acknowledgements. We thank the patients for their participation, Y. Cao and J. Wilbur for assistance with branched DNA assays, A. Hsu and J. Valdes for input on trial design, and J. Moore and R. Koup for helpful discussions. This work was supported by grants from Abbott Laboratories, the NIH and NYU Center for AIDS Research, the Joseph P. and Jeanne M. Sullivan Foundation, Los Alamos National Laboratory LRDR Program and The Aaron Diamond Foundation.

也提示目前监测新药的急性抗病毒活性的方法需要进行修改，特别是要着眼于开始治疗后前几日的检测。我们对艾滋病发病机制的研究显示 HIV-1 产生和清除存在微妙的平衡并且是高度动态的过程。综上所述，我们的发现强烈地支持这一观点，即艾滋病主要是持续的、高水平的 HIV-1 病毒复制以及病毒和免疫介导的 CD4 淋巴细胞死亡共同引起的。

（毛晨晖 翻译；胡卓伟 审稿）

A Plio-Pleistocene Hominid from Dmanisi, East Georgia, Caucasus

L. Gabunia and A. Vekua

Editor's Note

The conventional model of human evolution has it that the first hominid to leave the African homeland, around 1.8 million years ago, was *Homo erectus*, which migrated throughout Eurasia. Hence the interest of an excavation beneath a medieval monastery at Dmanisi in the Caucasus mountains, which has yielded primitive hominids and stone tools since the early 1990s. This paper—the description of a jawbone and its attribution to *Homo erectus*—was merely a harbinger. Dmanisi has since yielded several skulls and some skeletal material of a 1.8–1.6-million-year-old *erectus*-like creature, more like the primitive African form (known as *Homo ergaster*) than the more sophisticated East Asian forms. The migration from Africa was clearly a more complicated affair than had been thought.

Archaeological excavations at the mediaeval site of Dmanisi (East Georgia) revealed that the town was built on a series of deposits yielding Late Villafranchian mammalian fossils and led to the discovery in late 1991 of a well preserved early human mandible. Dmanisi, where excavations are being carried out by a joint expedition of the Archaeological Research Centre of the Georgian Academy of Sciences and the Römisch-Germanisches Zentralmuseum (Mainz, Germany), is located southwest of Tbilisi, at about 44° 20′ N, 41° 20′ E (Fig. 1). The fossils date to the latest Pliocene (or perhaps to the earliest Pleistocene), probably between 1.8 and 1.6 million years ago (Myr). Here we identify the mandible as belonging to the species *Homo erectus*, of which it is the earliest known representative in western Eurasia. It shows a number of similarities to the African and Chinese representatives of this species.

THE geology of the Dmanisi region and the stratigraphy of the continental deposits yielding the human jaw and the associated vertebrate fauna have been described in preliminary reports[1,2]. A basalt layer 80 m thick is overlain by about 4 m of alluvial (subaerial) deposits containing mammalian fossils and marked in places by soil horizons (Fig. 1b). The presence of *Kowalskia* sp., *Mimomys* sp. (*M. reidi-pitymyoides* group)[3], *Hypolagus brachygnathus* Kormos, *Pachycrocuta* cf *perrieri* (Croizet et Jobert), *Archidiskodon meridionalis* Nesti, *Equus* cf *stenonis* Cocchi, *Dicerorhinus etruscus etruscus* (Falconer), and *Cervus perrieri* Croizet et Jobert aligns the fauna with the Late Villafranchian of Europe, perhaps especially its earlier part[4]. A potassium-argon date of 1.8 ± 0.1 Myr was obtained on the basalt[1], which is in broad agreement with this age. Moreover, both the basalt and the

在高加索格鲁吉亚东部的德马尼西发现的上新世 – 更新世时期的原始人类

加布尼亚，韦夸

编者按

人类演化的传统模式认为，大约180万年前离开非洲家园的第一支人类是直立人，他们迁徙到整个欧亚大陆。因此大家关心在高加索山脉德马尼西的一个中世纪修道院地下的考古发掘，这里自20世纪90年代初以来就出土了原始人类化石和石器。本文描述了一个下颌骨并论及其归属于直立人，这只是一篇先期的报告。之后，德马尼西又出土了几个头骨和生活于180万～160万年前的一个类似直立人的生物的一些骨骼材料，相比进化得更为复杂的东亚化石类型，这种生物与被认为是匠人的非洲原始化石类型较为相似。从非洲迁徙出来显然是一个比早先认为的更复杂的事情。

在德马尼西（格鲁吉亚东部）中世纪遗址的考古发掘揭示出这个小镇是建立在一系列埋藏有维拉弗朗晚期哺乳类化石的堆积物之上的，并且1991年年末在这里发现了一块保存完好的早期人类下颌骨。由格鲁吉亚科学院考古研究中心和罗马 – 日耳曼中央博物馆（德国美因茨）联合组成的探险队正在德马尼西进行考古挖掘工作。德马尼西位于第比利斯西南，地理坐标大约为44°20′N，41°20′E（图1）。这些化石可以追溯到上新世最晚的一段时期（或者也可能是更新世最早的一段时期），大约是180万年前到160万年前。我们在本文中将该下颌骨鉴定为属于直立人这一物种，这是目前已知的欧亚大陆西部最早的直立人代表。该标本显示出很多与该物种的非洲代表和中国代表的相似性。

德马尼西地区的地质学和产出人类颌骨及相关的脊椎动物群的陆相堆积物的地层学特征在初步报告中已有所描述[1,2]。一层80米厚的玄武岩被约4米厚的包含哺乳动物化石的（接近地面的）冲积层所覆盖，玄武岩层中有些地方间杂有土壤层（图1b）。科氏仓鼠未定种、模鼠未定种（里德 – 小拟模鼠组）[3]、低颌次兔（科尔莫什）、佩里埃硕鬣狗（克鲁瓦泽和若贝尔）、南方原齿象（内斯蒂）、似古马（科基）、埃楚斯堪双角犀（福尔克纳）和佩里埃鹿（克鲁瓦泽和若贝尔）与欧洲的维拉弗朗晚期的动物群相匹配，尤其可能是该阶段的早一部分[4]。根据钾 – 氩法对玄武岩测得的年代为180万 ±10万年[1]，该年龄值与上述估计的年代大体一致。此外，玄武岩层和含骨

685

bone-bearing layer show normal geomagnetic polarity[1,5], which may indicate that they belong to the end of the Olduvai Subchron (1.95–1.77 Myr), although more detailed studies would clarify this point. Numerous stone tools of "Oldowan" appearance (Fig. 1c) also occur in the bone-bearing layers, at and above the level with the human mandible.

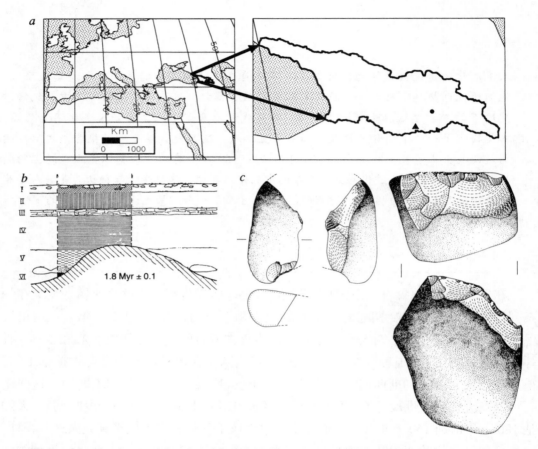

Fig. 1. *a*, Map showing rough location of Dmanisi (left, position of Georgia within Europe; right, Georgia, with Tbilisi (circle) and Dmanisi (triangle); *b*, simplified stratigraphic column of hominid locality; and *c*, two artefacts found in the fossiliferous horizons (*b* and *c* after refs 2 and 15 respectively). In *b*, the sequence includes, from top downward: (I) grey clays with limestone blocks, of which the top formed the habitation surface for the mediaeval town (0.4 m); (II) yellow-brown loam with many artefacts but few bones (0.5 m); (III) thin limestone crust (0.2 m); (IV) brown loam with many fossil vertebrates and artefacts (1.5 m); (V) blackish-brown loam with thin sandy layers, many fossil vertebrates including the hominid mandible and numerous artefacts (1.0 m); (VI) compact blackish sand and volcanic ash with rare mammalian fossils; basalt with unaltered surface. In *c*, distance between vertical lines is 9.5 cm.

The Dmanisi hominid mandible consists of an almost entirely preserved corpus with complete and little-worn dentition (Fig. 2). The base is damaged and both rami are broken away. The general appearance is of a jaw with small teeth but a thick corpus, especially below the first and second molars (see Table 1). It is not possible to determine its sex unambiguously.

层都显示出了地磁正极性[1,5]，这可能指示它们都属于奥杜威亚期末期（195万至177万年前），但是要确定这一点，还需要更详细的研究。大量属于"奥杜威文化"（图1c）的石器也出现在含骨层中，与人类下颌骨位于同一层位或在其上位。

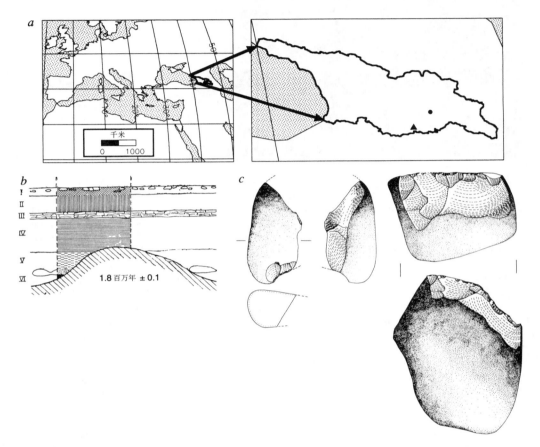

图1. a，显示德马尼西大体位置的地图（左图：格鲁吉亚在欧洲的位置；右图，第比利斯（圆圈）和德马尼西（三角形）在格鲁吉亚的位置）；b，原始人类化石所在地点的地层剖面简图；c，在含有化石的地层发现的两件人工制品（在参考文献2和15中对b和c分别有介绍）。b图中，地层顺序从上到下依次为：(I) 含有石灰石块的灰色黏土，其顶层为这个中世纪小镇的居住地表面（0.4米）；(II) 含有许多人工制品但是骨骼少的黄棕色壤土（0.5米）；(III) 薄的石灰岩壳（0.2米）；(IV) 含有许多脊椎动物化石和人工制品的棕色壤土（1.5米）；(V) 含有薄砂层、许多脊椎动物化石（包括原始人类下颌骨）和许多人工制品的黑褐色壤土（1.0米）；(VI) 含有稀少的哺乳动物化石的密实的黑砂和火山灰；未改变表面的玄武岩。c图中，垂线之间的距离是9.5厘米。

德马尼西原始人类下颌骨包括一块保存几乎完整的下颌体，其上带有完全的、磨损轻微的齿系（图2）。下颌体基底损坏，两侧下颌支都脱落了。其整体外观就是一个带有小型牙齿和较厚下颌体的颌骨，尤其是第一、第二臼齿下的下颌体特别厚（见表1）。不能明确地判断出它的性别。

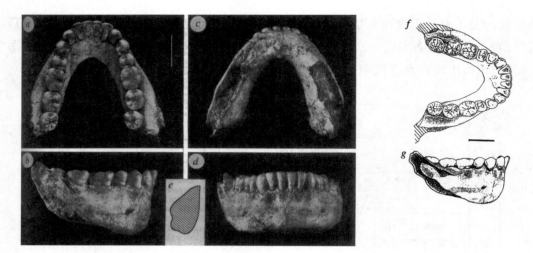

Fig. 2. Occlusal (*a*), right lateral (*b*), basal (*c*) and anterior (*d*) views of Dmanisi mandible, and symphyseal cross-section (*e*). Partially reconstructed drawing of Dmanisi mandible, in occlusal (*f*) and right lateral (*g*) views. Scale bars in *a* and *f*, 2 cm. The symphysis is nearly vertical in profile, with no sign of a mental protuberance, and it curves smoothly into the inferior border of the corpus. In anterior view, the shape appears subsquare. On each side a central swelling merges upward into the medioincisive and canine jugum, but does not extend anteriorly onto the symphysis; moreover, there is no incurvation below the incisors and thus no mental trigone. Internally, the laterally extensive alveolar planum slopes gently down to the superior transverse torus, but it does not extend posteriorly in a shelf. The genial fossa is distinct; the symphyseal base is flattened and thick anteroposteriorly, with weak digastric markings. The corpus is thick, and its superior and inferior borders may have been nearly parallel, although the base is broken below the molars (increasingly lacking posteriorly); anteriorly, the base is thick and slightly everted. A single large mental foramen is placed 14 mm below the mesial edge of P_4 on the right, whereas two smaller foramina occur on the left. A lateral prominence is developed below the anterior border of M_2, extending antero-inferiorly to merge with the well-defined superior lateral torus. The alveolar arcade is broadly U-shaped, each set of cheek teeth curving inward at both ends (the M_1s are most lateral). The retromolar space is small, whereas the extramolar sulcus is broad and hollowed. The anterior end of the buccinator groove lies at the level of mesial M_2, and the base of the triangular torus points superiorly, suggesting that the anterior border of the ramus might have been placed anteriorly and vertically. The slightly anteriorly inclined incisors show a small amount of flattened incisal edge wear. The canines are somewhat pointed, with a distinct external cingulum, but they do not project above the incisors. Both premolars bear distinct traces of cingulum and have a relatively large talonid. The P_3 is markedly asymmetric and rather triangular in outline, its buccal face being convex near the cervix. The anterior fovea is short and oriented nearly mesiodistally, whereas the posterior fovea is somewhat deeper and extends mesially to the very small lingual cusp. The crown of P_4 is almost quadrilateral in outline, wider than long and distinctly smaller (shorter) than that of P_3. The first and somewhat smaller second molars are quadrilateral in outline. The third molar is distinctly smaller, with a rather rounded outline. All three molars present a Y-6 cusp pattern, with the hypoconid surrounded by distinct grooves. The talonid of M_3 is somewhat longer than the trigonid and narrows distally; the occlusal surface of this tooth is tilted lingually by comparison to those of the other molars.

On the basis of the features detailed in Fig. 2, especially the overall size and robustness of the corpus and the teeth, shape of the symphysis, and dental proportions, the Dmanisi jaw represents an early form of *Homo*. Comparisons can be made with: east Asian populations of *H. erectus*, from Sangiran (Java) and Zhoukoudian (China); early African fossils assigned to that species or to *Homo ergaster* (mainly ER 730 and 992, WT 15000); later African

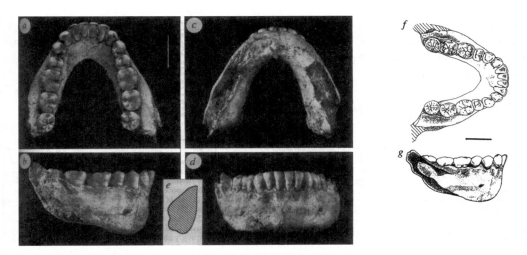

图 2. 德马尼西下颌骨。咬合面(*a*)、右侧面(*b*)、基底(*c*)和前面(*d*)视图,以及下颌联合部位的断面图(*e*)。德马尼西下颌骨部分复原的效果图,以咬合面(*f*)和右侧面(*g*)视图示出。*a* 和 *f* 中的比例尺是 2 厘米。下颌联合的侧面观轮廓接近垂直,没有颏隆凸的迹象,其平缓地弯曲过渡到下颌体的下边缘。从前面观察,其形状接近正方形。每侧都有一中央膨胀部,向上合并入内侧门齿和犬齿轭,但是并不向前延伸到下颌联合;此外,在门齿下没有内曲,所以没有颏三角。在下颌骨内侧面,向外侧延伸的牙槽平面平缓地向下倾斜至上横圆枕处,但是并没有向后延伸成类似猿板的构造。颏窝很明显;联合部位基底扁平,前后方向上很厚,具有微弱的二腹肌附着的痕迹。下颌体厚,虽然在臼齿以下的基底部分断裂了(越往后缺少的越多),其上边缘和下缘可能近乎平行;在前面,基底厚且有些外翻。一个单一的大颏孔位于右侧 P₄ 的近中侧边缘之下 14 毫米处,而两个较小的颏孔出现在左侧。在 M₂ 前边缘的下方发育出了一个侧面隆起,其向前向下延伸与明显的上外侧圆枕融合在一起。齿槽弓呈现宽阔的 U 字形,每套颊齿都在两端向内弯曲(两侧的 M₁ 位置在最外侧,最靠边)。臼齿后空间小,而臼齿外沟宽阔且中空。颊肌沟的前端位于 M₂ 近中侧水平,三角形圆枕的基底指向上方,提示着下颌支的前端可能靠前并且是垂直的。稍微向前倾斜的门齿表现出轻微的扁平的切缘磨损迹象。犬齿有点尖,具有明显的外侧齿带,但是它们并不突出于门齿之上。两颗前臼齿都具有明确的齿带痕迹,并且具有相对较大的跟座。P₃ 明显不对称,外廓有点儿呈三角形,其颊面在接近齿颈处呈凸形。前凹短,位置接近近 − 远中方向,而后凹稍微深些,向近中侧延伸至很小的舌尖。P₄ 的牙冠外形上几乎是四边形的,宽度比长度要大,比 P₃ 明显要小(短)。第一和稍微有点小的第二臼齿外形上也是四边形的。第三臼齿明显较小,外廓有点儿接近圆形。三颗臼齿都具有 Y-6 牙尖的模式,具有被明显的沟槽围绕的下次尖。M₃ 的跟座比三角座稍长,远侧端狭窄;与其他臼齿的相比,这颗牙的咬合面向舌侧倾斜。

    根据图 2 中详细描述的特征,尤其是下颌体和牙齿的总体尺寸和粗壮性、下颌联合的形状、牙齿的比例等方面,可知德马尼西颌骨代表的是人属的一种早期类型。可以与如下几种原始人类进行比较:来自桑吉兰(爪哇岛)和周口店(中国)的东亚直立人群体;被归属于直立人或匠人的早期非洲化石(主要有 ER 730 和 ER 992、WT

H. erectus (OH 22, Tighenif (ex-Ternifine), Thomas Quarry 1); members of *Homo habilis* or *Homo rudolfensis* (such as OH 7 and 13, ER 1802); and early European fossils of archaic *Homo sapiens* (such as Mauer, Arago, Atapuerca). Selected comparative data on these fossils are included in Tables 1 and 2.

Table 1. Measurements (in mm) of the mandibular corpus in selected late Pliocene to late Middle Pleistocene *Homo* fossils

	Symphysis depth	Symphysis thickness	Symphysis ratio	$P_{(3-)4}$ depth	$P_{(3-)4}$ thickness	$P_{(3-)4}$ ratio	$M_{(1-)2}$ depth	$M_{(1-)2}$ thickness	$M_{(1-)2}$ ratio
Dmanisi 211 R	30.8	16.8	55%	26.8	18.5	69%	*24.7	18.4	74%
KNM ER 1802 R[10]	36.0	24.5	68%	40.0	20.0	50%	38.0	27.0	71%
OH 13 R[10]	25.0	18.0	72%	26.0	16.5	63%	28.5	22.5	79%
KNM ER 730[10]	32.5	17.5	54%	32.5	19.0	58%	31.5	19.0	60%
KNM ER 992 L[10]	37.0	21.0	57%	31.0	20.0	65%	33.0	22.0	67%
KNM WT 15000 L[11]				27.2	18.1	67%	24.8	21.0	85%
OH 22[10]	33.5	20.0	60%	29.0	20.5	71%	28.5	21.0	74%
Sangiran 1b[10]	32.0	17.0	53%	33.0	16.0	48%	33.0	17.0	52%
Sangiran 9 R[10]	41.0	19.0	46%	39.0	21.5	55%	32.0	23.0	72%
Zhoukoudian G 1-6[12]	40.0	13.7	34%				34.0	17.3	51%
Zhoukoudian H 1[12]	32.3	14.0	43%				26.0	14.9	57%
Zhoukoudian Mean[12]	34.5			28.5					
Tighenif 1[13]	37.5	18.5	49%	33.0	19.0	58%	35.0	22.0	63%
Tighenif 2[13]	31.0	17.0	55%	32.0	15.0	47%	31.5	17.5	56%
Tighenif 3[13]	35.0	19.0	54%	35.0	19.0	54%	38.0	21.0	55%
Thomas Quarry 1[13]				28.5	16.0	56%	26.5	*18.0	68%
Mauer	32.0	18.5	58%	32.5	18.5	57%	33.0	19.0	58%
Arago 2[10]	31.0	16.0	52%	30.5	17.0	56%	30.0	17.0	57%
Arago 13[10]	36.0	20.0	56%	31.0	22.5	73%	31.0	23.5	76%

Symphysis depth, minimum superoinferior distance between infradentale and base of symphysis (termed height in ref. 10, measurement no. 141); symphysis thickness, maximum mesiodistal (anteroposterior) distance perpendicular to preceding (termed depth, measurement no. 142); Symphysis ratio, percentage thickness/depth (rounded up); $P_{(3-)4}$ depth, minimum depth of corpus below septum between P_3 and P_4 or below middle of P_4 , depending on authority (ref. 10, measurement no. 147, at P_4, lingual side; termed minimum height in ref. 13); $P_{(3-)4}$ thickness, maximum thickness of corpus perpendicular to preceding (ref. 10, measurement no. 148; minimum corpus breadth[13]). Ratio as for symphysis. $M_{(1-)2}$, as $P_{(3-)4}$ (ref. 10, measurement nos 154–155, at M_2; at M_2 in ref. 13). L or R following specimen identification refers to side of mandible when both are present; superscript number gives source of data.

* Value estimated on Dmanisi mandible (see Fig. 2g) or roughly estimated by authors from data in cited source.

15000）；较晚的非洲直立人（OH 22、提盖尼夫（以前的特尼芬）、托马斯采石场 1）；能人或鲁道夫人的成员（例如 OH 7、OH 13、ER 1802）；以及早期的欧洲古老型智人化石（例如摩尔、阿拉戈、阿塔普埃尔卡）。对这些化石有选择地进行了比较，相关数据列于表 1 和表 2 中。

表 1. 选择的晚上新世到中更新世晚期的人属化石的下颌体的测量尺寸（单位：毫米）

	下颌联合深度	下颌联合厚度	下颌联合比例	P(3-)4 深度	P(3-)4 厚度	P(3-)4 比例	M(1-)2 深度	M(1-)2 厚度	M(1-)2 比例
德马尼西样本 211 R	30.8	16.8	55%	26.8	18.5	69%	*24.7	18.4	74%
KNM ER 1802 R[10]	36.0	24.5	68%	40.0	20.0	50%	38.0	27.0	71%
OH 13 R[10]	25.0	18.0	72%	26.0	16.5	63%	28.5	22.5	79%
KNM ER 730[10]	32.5	17.5	54%	32.5	19.0	58%	31.5	19.0	60%
KNM ER 992 L[10]	37.0	21.0	57%	31.0	20.0	65%	33.0	22.0	67%
KNM WT 15000 L[11]				27.2	18.1	67%	24.8	21.0	85%
OH 22[10]	33.5	20.0	60%	29.0	20.5	71%	28.5	21.0	74%
桑吉兰样本 1b[10]	32.0	17.0	53%	33.0	16.0	48%	33.0	17.0	52%
桑吉兰样本 9 R[10]	41.0	19.0	46%	39.0	21.5	55%	32.0	23.0	72%
周口店样本 G 1-6[12]	40.0	13.7	34%				34.0	17.3	51%
周口店样本 H 1[12]	32.3	14.0	43%				26.0	14.9	57%
周口店样本平均值[12]	34.5			28.5					
提盖尼夫样本 1[13]	37.5	18.5	49%	33.0	19.0	58%	35.0	22.0	63%
提盖尼夫样本 2[13]	31.0	17.0	55%	32.0	15.0	47%	31.5	17.5	56%
提盖尼夫样本 3[13]	35.0	19.0	54%	35.0	19.0	54%	38.0	21.0	55%
托马斯采石场样本 1[13]				28.5	16.0	56%	26.5	*18.0	68%
摩尔样本	32.0	18.5	58%	32.5	18.5	57%	33.0	19.0	58%
阿拉戈样本 2[10]	31.0	16.0	52%	30.5	17.0	56%	30.0	17.0	57%
阿拉戈样本 13[10]	36.0	20.0	56%	31.0	22.5	73%	31.0	23.5	76%

下颌联合部的深度，即下颌左右内侧门齿间隔顶点和下颌联合基底之间的最短上下距离（参考文献 10 中称为高度，测量数值编号为 141）；下颌联合的厚度，即与前一侧径垂直的最大近中远中侧（前后）距离（称为深度，测量数值编号为 142）；下颌联合的比例，即厚度 / 深度百分比（取整）；P(3-)4 深度，即 P3 和 P4 之间的中隔之下或 P4 中部之下的下颌体的最小深度，依研究者而定（参考文献 10，测量数值编号为 147，在 P4 处测量，舌侧；参考文献 13 中称为最小高度）；P(3-)4 厚度，即与前一侧径垂直的下颌体的最大厚度（参考文献 10，测量数值编号为 148；下颌体最小宽度[13]）。比例同下颌联合。M(1-)2 的情况同 P(3-)4（参考文献 10 中的 M2 处测量，测量数值编号为 154~155；参考文献 13 在 M2 处测量）一样。当下颌左右侧都存在时，附在标本名称之后的 L 或 R 指的是左侧或右侧；上标的数字给出了数据出处。

* 数值是根据德马尼西下颌骨（见图 2g）估计出来的，或是作者根据引用来源中的数据粗略估算出来的。

Table 2. Measurements (in mm) of the mandibular dentition in selected late Pliocene to late Middle Pleistocene *Homo* fossils

	I_1 m-d	I_1 b-l	I_2 m-d	I_2 b-l	C_1 m-d	C_1 b-l	P_3 m-d	P_3 b-l	P_4 m-d	P_4 b-l	M_1 m-d	M_1 b-l	M_2 m-d	M_2 b-l	M_3 m-d	M_3 b-l	M_1/M_2	M_3/M_2	Molar Sizes
Dmanisi 211 R	5.9	5.8	6.6	6.4	8.7	8.2	9.0	9.2	8.1	9.2	13.2	12.3	12.3	11.5	11.2	10.6	115%	84%	1 > 2 > 3
Dmanisi 211 L	6.2	5.9	6.4	6.3	8.6	7.9	8.9	9.6	8.0	9.6	13.0	12.5	11.5	11.6	10.7	10.6	122%	85%	1 > 2 > 3
KNM ER 1802 R[10]							10.7	11.5	11.4	12.0	14.8	13.0	16.6	14.2			82%		2 > 1
OH 7 L[10]	6.5	6.7	7.3	7.6	8.9	10.1	9.5	9.7	10.4	10.7	14.1	12.5	15.7	13.7			82%		2 > 1
OH 13 R[10]					7.6	7.9	9.0	8.7	9.0	9.9	13.0	11.6	14.2	12.0	14.8	12.4	88%	108%	3 > 2 > 1
KNM ER 820 L[10]	6.1	6.3	6.3	6.9							12.5	10.6							
KNM ER 992 L[10]		6.8	7.2	7.0	8.9	9.5	9.7	10.3	8.8	10.9	12.7	10.9	13.0	12.2	13.4	12.3	87%	104%	3 > 2 > 1
KNM WT 15000 L[14]	6.6	6.8	7.5	8.3	8.9	9.6	8.9	10.1	9.0	10.1	12.4	11.0	12.5	12.0			91%		2 > 1
OH 22[10]							10.1	9.2	9.0	10.0	13.4	12.0	13.0	11.7			106%		1 > 2
Sangiran 1b[13]									8.9	10.8	12.9	12.9	13.2	13.4	14.4	12.5	94%	102%	3 > 2 > 1
Sangiran 9 R[10]		6.8		7.3	7.0	8.8	9.1	11.3	9.3	11.6			14.1	12.7	13.8	12.7		98%	2 > 3
Zhoukoudian G1-6 L[12]	6.2	6.8			8.1	8.2	9.1	10.7	8.5	11.0	13.2	12.5	12.5	12.7	12.0	12.3	104%	93%	1 > 2 > 3
Zhoukoudian G1-7[12]													12.6	12.9	12.9	12.4		98%	2 > 3
Zhoukoudian Mean[12]	6.4	6.4	6.8	7.0	8.7	9.4	8.7	9.9	9.0	9.8	12.5	11.8	12.5	12.1	11.7	11.3	98%	87%	2 > 1 > 3
Tighenif 1[13]			6.0	8.0			8.5	10.2	8.3	10.1	13.0	12.5	13.0	13.0	12.0	12.2	96%	87%	2 > 1 > 3
Tighenif 2[13]					8.6		8.6	11.1	8.8	11.0	13.9	12.8	14.1	13.3	13.4	12.5	95%	89%	2 > 1 > 3
Tighenif 3[13]			5.0	9.0	7.7		8.0	10.2	8.2	10.0	12.4	12.0	12.0	12.2	12.0	11.5	102%	94%	1 > 2 > 3
Thomas Quarry 1[13]						10.7			9.0	10.5	14.0	12.8	14.8	13.0	12.8	11.7	93%	78%	2 > 1 > 3
Mauer	5.5	7.5	6.9	7.7	7.4	8.9	8.1	9.0	7.5	9.2	11.3	11.2	12.7	12.0	10.9	11.9	83%	85%	2 > 3 > 1
Arago 13							10.1	11.0	9.5	12.9	13.6	13.6	14.6	14.0	13.4	13.0	90%	85%	2 > 1 > 3

Maximum mesiodistal (m-d) and buccolingual (b-l) dimensions of lower teeth. L or R following specimen identification refers to side of mandible when both are present; superscript number gives source of data. Module ratios represent products of m-d and b-l diameters of first and third molars, respectively, divided by those of second molars. ER 1802 is identified as *Homo rudolfensis*, OH 7 and OH 13 as *H. habilis*, Thomas Quarry, Mauer and Arago as early *H. sapiens*, other specimens as *H. erectus*, although ER 820–OH 22 are sometimes considered *H. ergaster*.

表 2. 选择的晚上新世到中更新世晚期的人属化石的下颌骨齿系的测量尺寸（单位：毫米）

	I_1		I_2		C_1		P_3		P_4		M_1		M_2		M_3		模数比		白齿
	m-d	b-l	m-d	b-l	m-d	b-l	m-d	b-l	m-d	b-l	m-d	b-l	m-d	b-l	m-d	b-l	M_1/M_2	M_3/M_2	尺寸
德马尼西样本 211 R	5.9	5.8	6.6	6.4	8.7	8.2	9.0	9.2	8.1	9.2	13.2	12.3	12.3	11.5	11.2	10.6	115%	84%	1 > 2 > 3
德马尼西样本 211 L	6.2	5.9	6.4	6.3	8.6	7.9	8.9	9.6	8.0	9.6	13.0	12.5	11.5	11.6	10.7	10.6	122%	85%	1 > 2 > 3
KNM ER 1802 R[10]							10.7	11.5	11.4	12.0	14.8	13.0	16.6	14.2			82%		2 > 1
OH 7 L[10]	6.5	6.7	7.3	7.6	8.9	10.1	9.5	9.7	10.4	10.7	14.1	12.5	15.7	13.7			82%		2 > 1
OH 13 R[10]					7.6	7.9	9.0	8.7	9.0	9.9	13.0	11.6	14.2	12.0	14.8	12.4	88%	108%	3 > 2 > 1
KNM ER 820 L[10]	6.1	6.3	6.3	6.9							12.5	10.6							
KNM ER 992 R[10]			7.2	7.0	8.9	9.5	9.7	10.3	8.8	10.9	12.7	10.9	13.0	12.2	13.4	12.3	87%	104%	3 > 2 > 1
KNM WT 15000 L[14]	6.6	6.8	7.5	8.3	8.9	9.6	8.9	10.1	9.0	10.1	12.4	11.0	12.5	12.0			91%		2 > 1
OH 22[10]							10.1	9.2	9.0	10.0	13.4	12.0	13.0	11.7			106%		1 > 2
桑吉兰样本 1b[13]					7.0	8.8	9.1	11.3	8.9	10.8	12.9	12.9	13.2	13.4	14.4	12.5	94%	102%	3 > 2 > 1
桑吉兰样本 9 R[10]					8.1	8.2	9.1	10.7	9.3	11.6			14.1	12.7	13.8	12.7		98%	2 > 3
周口店样本 G1-6 L[12]	6.2	6.8		7.3					8.5	11.0	13.2	12.5	12.5	12.7	12.0	12.3	104%	93%	1 > 2 > 3
周口店样本 G1-7[12]													12.6	12.9	12.9	12.4		98%	2 > 3
周口店样本平均值[12]	6.4	6.4	6.8	7.0	8.7	9.4	8.7	9.9	9.0	9.8	12.5	11.8	12.5	12.1	11.7	11.3	98%	87%	2 > 1 > 3
提盖尼夫样本 1[13]			6.0	8.0			8.5	10.2	8.3	10.1	13.0	12.5	13.0	13.0	12.0	12.2	96%	87%	2 > 1 > 3
提盖尼夫样本 2[13]							8.6	11.1	8.8	11.0	13.9	12.8	14.1	13.3	13.4	12.5	95%	89%	2 > 1 > 3
提盖尼夫样本 3[13]			5.0	9.0	7.7	10.7	8.0	10.2	8.2	10.0	12.4	12.0	12.0	12.2	12.0	11.5	102%	94%	1 > 2 > 3
托马斯采石场样本 1[13]									9.0	10.5	14.0	12.8	14.8	13.0	12.8	11.7	93%	78%	2 > 1 > 3
摩尔样本	5.5	7.5	6.9	7.7	7.4	8.9	8.1	9.0	7.5	9.2	11.3	11.2	12.7	12.0	10.9	11.9	83%	85%	2 > 3 > 1
阿拉戈样本 13							10.1	11.0	9.5	12.9	13.6	13.6	14.6	14.0	13.4	13.0	90%	85%	2 > 1 > 3

下牙的最大近中远中径 (m-d) 和颊舌径 (b-l)。附于标本名称后面的 L 或 R 是指当下颌的左侧或右侧都保存时，进行测量的是下颌的左侧或右侧部分。ER 1802 被鉴定为能人，OH 7 和 OH 13 被鉴定为能人，托马斯采石场标本、摩尔和阿拉戈标本被鉴定为早期智人，其他标本被鉴定为直立人，而 ER 820~OH 22 有时被认为属于匠人。

模数比代表第一和第二白齿的近中远中径和第三白齿的近中远中径和颊舌径分别除以第二白齿的相应测量值的结果。

The Dmanisi mandible appears to be most similar to African *H. erectus* fossils, with fewer similarities to those from Zhoukoudian. It is clearly smaller than mandibles of earliest *Homo*, especially in the P_4 and $M_{2,3}$ and in the corpus under the cheek teeth. The most striking feature of the tooth row is perhaps the great proportional decrease in tooth module ("area"), about 15–20% from M_1 to M_2 and from M_2 to M_3. No other specimen included in Table 2 presents such a strong distal reduction pattern, the closest approximations being OH 22 (from Bed IV, ~0.6 Myr, but lacking M_3 and all teeth mesial to P_3), Zhoukoudian Gl-6 (~0.4 Myr) and Tighenif 3 (~0.7 Myr). If the total Zhoukoudian and Tighenif samples are considered, however, the first two molars are nearly equal in module, with M_3 smaller. Other *H. erectus* jaws, such as ER 992, Sangiran 1 and 9, and Zhoukoudian Gl-7, have similar sized M_2 and M_3, usually with a smaller M_1, whereas the small M_1 of Mauer and Arago sets them apart from Dmanisi. The Thomas Quarry 1 mandible (~0.4 Myr) has very large mesial molars with a greatly reduced M_3. The Dmanisi M_3 (and to a lesser degree M_2) tilt lingually in their sockets, as seen also in ER 992 and WT 15000. The anterior teeth appear morphologically similar to those of African and Asian *H. erectus* (*sensu lato*).

In terms of tooth size, the Dmanisi M_2 is most comparable to those in the ER 992, WT 15000, OH 22, Zhoukoudian, Tighenif 3 and Mauer jaws. The Dmanisi premolars are small within the comparative sample, and especially narrow; they conform most closely to those of OH 13, the Zhoukoudian mean, Tighenif 3 and Mauer. The P_3 lingual cusp is strongly reduced, as seen also in the Zhoukoudian unworn specimen Uppsala M3549 described by Zdansky. The Dmanisi canine is small, with the buccolingual diameter only slightly smaller than the mesiodistal; its closest match is with those from Zhoukoudian and, surprisingly, OH 13. The incisors are close in size to those of the young juvenile ER 820 and the Zhoukoudian mean, lacking the buccolingual dominance of the North African and European specimens.

The Dmanisi corpus (Table 1) increases in relative thickness from the symphysis distally, although it must be emphasized that submolar depth is estimated. This pattern is also seen in ER 730 and 992, OH 22, Sangiran 9 (but not 1), possibly at Zhoukoudian, and in some but not all of the Tighenif and Arago jaws. The remaining Tighenif, Arago, Mauer and Sangiran specimens have a rather consistent relative thickness along the tooth row. The Dmanisi jaw is small; its symphysis is comparable in size, and also in overall morphology, to that of ER 730, as well as to Sangiran 1, Tighenif 2, Thomas Quarry, Arago 2 and perhaps Zhoukoudian H1. By contrast, the symphysis neither slopes backward as much as in the early African fossils, nor is there a well-developed trigone as in early European specimens. The corpus under the premolars is most similar in size to those of OH 13, OH 22 and Arago 2, as well as to the subadult WT 15000. Under the molars, size similarity is greatest to Zhoukoudian H1, Thomas Quarry and WT 15000, which probably would have presented a deeper (and thus far larger) corpus as an adult.

德马尼西下颌骨似乎与非洲直立人化石最相似，与周口店化石的相似性较少。该下颌骨比最早人属的下颌骨要小很多，尤其是 P_4 和 $M_{2,3}$ 以及颊齿以下的下颌体部分。齿列最明显的特征可能就是齿模数（"面积"）大比例减少，从 M_1 到 M_2 以及从 M_2 到 M_3 约减少了 15%~20%。表 2 列出的标本中没有其他标本表现出如此强烈的远端缩减模式，与该下颌骨具有最接近近似值的是 OH 22（来自奥杜威峡谷第 IV 层，约 60 万年前，但缺少 M_3 和 P_3 近中侧的所有牙齿）、周口店 G1-6（约 40 万年前）和提盖尼夫 3（约 70 万年前）。然而，如果我们将周口店和提盖尼夫的所有样本都纳入考虑范围内的话，那么前两颗臼齿在模数上几乎是相等的，而 M_3 稍小。其他的直立人颌骨，例如 ER 992、桑吉兰 1 和桑吉兰 9 以及周口店 G1-7 的 M_2 和 M_3 大小都相似，通常 M_1 较小，不过摩尔和阿拉戈的小型 M_1 与德马尼西不同。托马斯采石场 1 的下颌骨（约 40 万年前）具有非常大的近中侧臼齿和大大减小的 M_3。德马尼西样本的 M_3（以及程度稍小的 M_2）在其牙槽内朝向舌侧倾斜，就像在 ER 992 和 WT 15000 中看到的一样。前牙在形态上与非洲和亚洲的直立人（广义上）都很像。

从牙齿大小来看，德马尼西标本的 M_2 与 ER 992、WT 15000、OH 22、周口店、提盖尼夫 3 和摩尔颌骨的 M_2 非常相近。德马尼西标本的前臼齿在所有这些进行比较的样本中算是比较小的，并且格外狭窄；它们与 OH 13、周口店样本的平均值、提盖尼夫 3 和摩尔样本的最为接近。P_3 的舌侧尖减小明显，这种情况在师丹斯基描述的未磨损的周口店标本乌普萨拉 M3549 中也看到过。德马尼西标本的犬齿小，颊舌径只比近中远中径略小；与其最匹配的是周口店的标本以及 OH 13，后者与其惊人地相似。门齿大小与年轻的青少年标本 ER 820 的门齿和周口店标本的平均值很接近，缺少北非和欧洲标本所具有的颊舌径优势。

德马尼西标本的下颌体（表 1）在相对厚度上从联合部向远侧有所增加，但是这里必须强调的是，其臼齿以下的高度是估计出来的。这种模式在 ER 730 和 ER 992、OH 22、桑吉兰 9（而不是桑吉兰 1）中都有发现，可能在周口店标本中以及某些（但非全部）提盖尼夫和阿拉戈颌骨中也可见这种模式。其余的提盖尼夫、阿拉戈、摩尔和桑吉兰标本与整个齿列对应的相对厚度颇为一致。德马尼西的颌骨小；其下颌联合在尺寸以及总体形态学上与 ER 730 和桑吉兰 1、提盖尼夫 2、托马斯采石场标本、阿拉戈 2 相当，可能与周口店 H1 也是相当的。相比之下，下颌联合既不像早期非洲化石那么向后倾斜，也没有像早期欧洲标本具有非常发达的三角座。前臼齿下方的下颌体与 OH 13、OH 22 和阿拉戈 2 在大小上非常相似，也与亚成年的 WT 15000 的尺寸相仿。在臼齿下方的部分，其尺寸与周口店 H1、托马斯采石场标本和 WT 15000 的最为相似，这可能代表了一种成人所具有的较高（因此也更大）的下颌体。

There are thus both morphological and metrical similarities to fossils spanning a wide range of time and space. The Dmanisi jaw is distinctive in the great dental reduction distally, as well as in relatively small tooth and corpus size combined with apparently great corpus robusticity under the cheek teeth; in addition, the alveolar arcade is narrow and the beginning of the ramus is placed far anteriorly. Among the most similar specimens overall are certain Turkana Basin fossils (ER 730 and 992, WT 15000), OH 22 (lacking M_3) and Zhoukoudian Gl-6 (with a much larger corpus). Selected members of the Tighenif/ Thomas, Arago/Mauer and Sangiran samples show specific similarities as well. The most reasonable interpretation of this jaw is that it belonged to a population of *H. erectus*, possibly foreshadowing (European) early *H. sapiens*.

The date provided by the faunal and geophysical evidence indicates that the Dmanisi population was one of the oldest human groups outside Africa, certainly the most ancient in western Eurasia. Dates for Chinese and Indonesian *H. erectus* have long been in doubt, but recent studies have suggested ages of ~1.1 Myr for the Lantian Gongwangling cranium[6] and ~1.7 Myr for the oldest Sangiran and Mojokerto fossils[7]. Although there are potential problems with these dates, the Indonesian evidence especially suggests hominid presence at least between 1.5–1.0 Myr. A similar age is estimated for the 'Ubei-diya archaeological site in Israel[8]. Ages between 2 and 1 Myr have also been suggested for a variety of localities in Europe, but the most recent review of this work[9] indicates that there is little support for demonstrated human occupation before ~0.5 Myr. The Dmanisi human mandible, attributed to *H. erectus* and dated around 1.8 Myr or slightly younger, might be the oldest evidence of humans outside Africa. Its presence in Georgia further suggests that humans either waited outside the "gates to Europe" for more than 1 Myr or inhabited the subcontinent at very low density during that interval.

(**373**, 509-512; 1995)

L. Gabunia & A. Vekua

Institute of Paleobiology, Georgian Academy of Sciences, 9 Sulkhan-Saba, Tbilisi 380007, Georgia

Received 11 August; accepted 1 December 1994.

References:

1. Majsuradze, G., Pavlenshvili, E., Schmincke, H. & Sologashvili, D. *Jahrb. Römisch-German. Zentralmus.* **36**, 74-76 (1991).
2. Bosinski, G., Lordkipanidze, D., Majsuradze, G. & Tvaicrelidze, M. *Jahrb. Römisch-German. Zentralmus.* **36**, 76-83 (1991).
3. Muskhelishvili, A. *Jahrb. Römisch-German. Zentralmus.* (in the press).
4. Gabunia, L. & Vekua, A. *Dmanisi Man and the Accompanying Vertebrate Fauna* 1-60 (Metsniereba, Tbilisi, 1993).
5. Sologashvili, D., Majsuradze, G., Pavlenshvili, E. & Klopotovskaja, N. *Jahrb. Römisch-German. Zentralmus.* (in the press).
6. An, Z. & Ho, C. K. *Quat. Res.* **32**, 213-221 (1989).
7. Swisher, C. C. *et al. Science* **263**, 1118-1121 (1994).
8. Verosub, K. L. & Tchernov, E. in *Les Premiers Européens* (eds Bonifay, E. & Vandermeersch, B.) 237-242 (Comité Travaux Historiques Scientifiques, Paris, 1991).
9. Roebroeks, W. *Curr. Anthropol.* **35**, 301-305 (1994).
10. Wood, B. A. *Koobi Fora Research Project, Vol. 4: Hominid Cranial Remains* (Clarendon, Oxford, 1991).
11. Walker, A. & Leakey, R. in *The Nariokotome* Homo erectus *Skeleton* (eds Walker, A. & Leakey, R.) 63-94 (Harvard Univ. Press, 1993).

因此该化石与横跨了大范围时间和空间的化石在形态学和测量方面都有相似性。德马尼西标本的颌骨的独特性表现在它的牙齿越向远端越表现出巨大缩减，它的牙齿和下颌体相对较小，却与粗壮度明显很大的颊齿下的下颌体相结合；另外，其齿弓狭，下颌支开始的部位很靠前。在所有标本中，最相似的当属图尔卡纳盆地的某些化石（ER 730、ER 992、WT 15000）、OH 22（缺少 M_3）和周口店 G1-6（具有大得多的下颌体）了。选择的提盖尼夫 / 托马斯、阿拉戈 / 摩尔和桑吉兰样本的成员也显示出了特定的相似性。对于该颌骨的最合理的解释就是它属于直立人群体，可能是（欧洲）早期智人的先驱。

动物群和地球物理学证据所提供的年代表明德马尼西群体是非洲之外的最古老的人类群体之一，他们肯定是欧亚大陆西部最古老的人群。长期以来一直有人对中国和印度尼西亚的直立人所处的年代表示怀疑，但是最近的研究显示公王岭蓝田人头盖骨 [6] 的年代为约 110 万年前，最古老的桑吉兰化石和莫佐克托化石的年代为约 170 万年前 [7]。尽管这些年代存在着潜在的问题，但是印度尼西亚的证据显示了至少在 150 万 ~ 100 万年前就已经存在原始人类了。以色列的乌贝迪亚考古学遗址 [8] 估计出的年代也与此相似。欧洲的许多遗址也显示了原始人类早在 200 万 ~ 100 万年前就存在了，但是该项工作的最新综述 [9] 指出还没有多少证据支持在约 50 万年以前人类就在此居住了。德马尼西人类下颌骨被归属于直立人，年代为距今约 180 万年，也可能稍晚一些，它可能是非洲之外存在人类的最古老的证据。其在格鲁吉亚的出现进一步提示人类或者是在"通向欧洲的大门"之外等待了 100 多万年，或者在那段时间以非常低的密度居住在次大陆上。

（刘皓芳 翻译；吴新智 审稿）

12. Weidenreich, F. *Palaeontol. Sinica n.s.* **D1**, 1-180 (1937).

13. Rightmire, G. P. *The Evolution of* Homo erectus (Cambridge Univ. Press, 1990).

14. Brown, B. & Walker, A. in *The Nariokotome* Homo erectus *Skeleton* (eds Walker, A. & Leakey, R.) 161-192 (Harvard Univ. Press, 1993).

15. Bosinski, G., Bugianisvili, T., Mgeladze, N., Nioradze, M. & Tusabramisvili, D. *Jahrb. Römisch-German. Zentralmus.* **36**, 93-107 (1991).

Acknowledgements. We thank H. and M.-A. de Lumley for access to the rich comparative collections in the Laboratoire d'Anthropologie in Marseilles, G. Bosinski (Römisch-Germanisches Zentralmuseum, Neuwied), E. Delson (Anthropology, Lehman College of the City University of New York), J. L. Franzen (Forschungsinstitut Senckenberg, Frankfurt), F. C. Howell (Anthropology, University of California, Berkeley), G. P. Rightmire (Anthropology, State University of New York at Binghamton), A. Walker (Cell Biology and Anatomy, The Johns Hopkins University School of Medicine, Baltimore), T. White (Anthropology, University of California, Berkeley), D. Dean (Anatomy, Case Western Reserve University School of Medicine, Cleveland), H. Roth (Département d'Anthropologie et d'Ecologie, Université de Genève), B. Senut (Laboratoire d'Anthropologie du Muséum National d'Histoire Naturelle, Paris) for their help. E. Delson prepared the final versions of the manuscript and L. Meeker prepared Fig. 2, for which we are most grateful.

Gravitationally Redshifted Emission Implying an Accretion Disk and Massive Black Hole in the Active Galaxy MCG–6–30–15

Y. Tanaka *et al.*

Editor's Note

Although today the presence of supermassive black holes at the centres of most galaxies is accepted almost universally by astronomers, in 1995 the situation was not yet resolved. One of the key predictions from the combination of general relativity and black-hole physics was that spectral emission lines from gas near the event horizon should show a characteristic width, and a shape redshifted by the strong gravity there. Here Yasuo Tanaka and colleagues report the first such gravitationally redshifted line (from highly ionized iron) in the galaxy MCG–6–30–15. Several other examples have since been found. Combined with the orbits of stars near the centre of the Milky Way, they make the case for supermassive black holes at galactic centres essentially airtight.

Active galactic nuclei and quasars are probably powered by the accretion of gas onto a supermassive black hole at the centre of the host galaxy[1], but direct confirmation of the presence of a black hole is hard to obtain. As the gas nears the event horizon, its velocity should approach the speed of light; the resulting relativistic effects, and a gravitational redshift arising from the proximity to the black hole, should be observable, allowing us to test specific predictions of the models with the observations. Here we report the detection of these relativistic effects in an X-ray emission line (the $K\alpha$ line) from ionized iron in the galaxy MCG–6–30–15. The line is extremely broad, corresponding to a velocity of $\sim 100,000 \, \text{km s}^{-1}$ and asymmetric, with most of the line flux being redshifted. These features indicate that the line most probably arises in a region between three and ten Schwarzschild radii from the centre, so that we are observing the innermost region of the accretion disk.

RECENT optical and radio observations[2-4] of gas motions show a large, central concentration of mass (probably a black hole) in a number of galaxies. But this gas lies beyond $\sim 30,000$ Schwarzschild radii so the characteristic signatures of the black hole itself—relativistic effects due to its strong gravitational field—were not observed. X-rays are produced much closer to the black hole and provide better access to these effects, particularly if a spectral line is emitted for which energy shifts can be clearly measured.

An iron $K\alpha$ emission line close to 6.4 keV and an additional, hard-continuum component are imprinted on the primary, power-law, X-ray continuum of most Seyfert 1 active galactic nuclei (AGN)[5,6]. They arise via fluorescence and back-scattering ("reflection") from optically

活动星系 MCG-6-30-15 的引力红移辐射暗示吸积盘和大质量黑洞的存在

虽然现在天文学家们普遍接受了"在绝大部分星系的中心都存在超大质量黑洞"这一观点，但是在 1995 年的时候，这个问题还没有得到解决。在结合了广义相对论和黑洞物理的理论中，一个关键的预言是：来自黑洞视界附近的气体的光谱发射线，应该有一个特征展宽，以及经过强引力红移后的形状。在这篇文章中，田中靖郎和他的合作者们报道了在 MCG-6-30-15 星系中探测到的第一条引力红移谱线（来自高电离铁的）。至今为止，已经有几个其他这样的例子存在。结合银河系中心附近的恒星运动轨道，这些观测基本证实了星系中心存在超大质量黑洞的观点。

活动星系核与类星体很可能由位于寄主星系中心的超大质量黑洞的气体吸积提供能量 [1]，但是直接确认黑洞的存在却非常困难。随着气体靠近视界，其速度也会接近光速；这时就会观察到由于靠近黑洞而产生的相对论效应和引力红移，为我们观测检验模型的具体预言创造了条件。这里我们将报道对星系 MCG-6-30-15 中铁离子 X 射线的发射线（Kα 线）的相对论效应的探测。该发射线非常宽，对应速度约为 $100,000 \ km \cdot s^{-1}$，并且具有非对称结构，其中的大部分谱线流量发生红移。这些特征表明，这些谱线很可能来自距离黑洞中心 3~10 倍施瓦西半径的区域；因此，事实上我们观察的是吸积盘最内区。

最近对气体运动的光学和射电观测 [2-4] 表明，在许多星系中存在大质量的中心聚集（可能是黑洞）。但是这些气体位于大约 30,000 倍施瓦西半径之外，因此并没有观测到黑洞自身独有的特征（由于强引力场产生的相对论效应）。X 射线产生于更靠近黑洞的地方，因此也提供了更好的途径研究这些效应，尤其是当有一条谱线发射出来，并且可以清楚地测出能量改变的情况下。

大多数赛弗特 1 型（Seyfert 1）活动星系核（AGN）的主要 X 射线幂律连续谱上 [5,6]，会叠加一条约 6.4 keV 的铁 Kα 发射线，以及一个额外的硬连续谱成分。这些谱线产

thick material which covers about half the sky seen by the primary continuum source[7,8]. The data do not allow the geometry of the material to be determined unambiguously, but are consistent with an irradiated accretion disk[9-12]. The emission lines from such a system are expected to be very broad, as most fluorescence occurs in a regime where Doppler and gravitational shifts are large[9,12,13]. Clear evidence for significant broadening—at a level compatible with accretion-disk models—has now come from new data (from the ASCA satellite) on several AGN, including MCG-6-30-15[14,15]. The emission lines should also have a characteristic profile. The strongest lines are produced in a face-on geometry[10], where gravitational and transverse Doppler effects dominate, producing a profile skewed to the red. For edge-on disks the line is weaker, and the blue side of the profile (the blue "wing") more prominent[9,16].

MCG-6-30-15 was observed by ASCA[17] on 23 July 1994 for approximately four days, with both the CCD (charge-coupled device) detectors (SIS) and gas-scintillation proportional counters (GIS) in operation. Here we present only the SIS data, which have the better energy resolution; the GIS and SIS data are entirely consistent. A complicating factor in the analysis of the integrated SIS spectra is the presence of features from highly ionized gas in the line of sight, the so-called warm absorber[18], which is now well established in this source[14,19,20]. Initially, then, we fitted the spectra in the range 0.4–10 keV with a model consisting of a power law emitter and photoionized absorber. This shows that the absorption only affects the spectrum below 2 keV, and therefore in analysing the line data we have restricted the energy range to 2.5–10 keV. Previous data from the Ginga satellite also showed[6] strong evidence for a reflection continuum component accompanying the iron-emission line. We have assumed a face-on slab subtending 2π sr at the X-ray source and calculated the reflection spectrum using the model of Lightman and White[8]. As expected from previous observations[6], the spectrum and residuals for the 3–10 keV continuum fit show a well defined excess in the residuals at ~6 keV (Fig. 1), most probably an iron Kα line, but much broader than the instrument resolution for a single narrow line. We emphasize that the statistical quality of the data is sufficient to allow the precise determination of the continuum above and below the line; the derived line profile depends little on the uncertainty in the continuum shape, or the normalization of the reflection continuum.

It is clear from the residuals (Fig. 1) that the line profile is not gaussian. It consists of a relatively narrow core around 6.4 keV with a very broad wing extending to the red. We have modelled the line with two gaussians, one each for the core and wing (see Fig. 1 legend for details). This fit allows us to determine the best-fit model for the continuum. The deviations of the data from this continuum model represent the line profile, which is shown in Fig. 2. The data have been rebinned to approximately the instrumental resolution and are shown in incident (photon) flux. The profile is clearly extremely broad and asymmetric. Most of the flux is strongly redshifted from the rest energy of even the lowest-energy Kα lines (6.4 keV), by as much as $\Delta E/E \approx 0.3$. The full width at zero intensity corresponds to a velocity of the order of $100,000 \text{ km s}^{-1}$.

生于光学厚物质中的荧光辐射和反向散射（"反射"），这些光学厚物质大约覆盖了主要连续谱源的半个天区[7,8]。虽然从这些谱线数据中尚不能清楚地断定这些物质的几何形态，但是它们和一个被辐射的吸积盘相符合[9-12]。由于大多数荧光辐射发生在多普勒效应和引力偏移较强的物理条件下，因此这类系统的发射线将会很宽[9,12,13]。包括 MCG-6-30-15 在内的若干活动星系核的最新数据（数据源自宇宙学和天体物理学高新卫星，ASCA）也提供了显著展宽的明确证据（在与吸积盘模型相符合的水平上)[14,15]。这些发射线也应该具有特征轮廓。强发射线产生自正向（朝向我们观测者）几何[10]，在正向几何中，由引力效应和横向多普勒效应主导，使得谱线轮廓偏向红端。而侧向吸积盘的发射线较弱，谱线轮廓的蓝端（蓝翼）更加突出[9,16]。

从 1994 年 7 月 23 日起，ASCA 卫星对 MCG-6-30-15 进行了大约四天的观测[17]，观测中采用了电荷耦合器件（CCD）探测器（SIS）与气体闪烁正比计数器（GIS）。在这里我们只给出 SIS 数据，该数据具有较好的能量分辨率；GIS 和 SIS 数据是完全一致的。在积分 SIS 光谱的分析过程中，一个使问题复杂化的因素是存在位于视线方向的高度电离气体的特征，即温吸收体[18]，如今这种温吸收体在这个源中已经得到了清楚的认识[14,19,20]。最初，我们用包含幂律发射体和光电离吸收体的模型对 0.4~10 keV 范围内的光谱进行拟合。这种拟合表明这种吸收只影响能量小于 2 keV 的光谱，因此在分析谱线数据的时候，我们将能量限制在 2.5~10 keV 范围内。银河号卫星以前提供的数据也给出很强的证据[6]，显示铁的发射线总伴有一个反射连续谱成分。我们假设在 X 射线源处正向平面所对应着的立体角为 2π sr，然后采用莱特曼和怀特的模型[8]计算反射光谱。正如以前观测所预期的那样[6]，对 3~10 keV 连续谱拟合给出的光谱和残差都表明，在 6 keV 附近的拟合残差明显过大（如图 1），这说明发射线很可能是铁 Kα 线，但是它比仪器对单条窄线能分辨的宽度要宽。这里我们强调一下，这些数据的统计质量足以精确地确定该谱线能量附近的连续谱。推导出来的谱线轮廓几乎不依赖于连续谱形状的不确定度或反射连续谱的归一化。

从残差（图 1）中可以清楚地看出该谱线的轮廓并不是高斯形的；该轮廓包括一个位于 6.4 keV 附近的相对窄的核和一个延伸到红端的非常宽的翼。我们采用两个高斯函数来拟合该谱线，分别代表核成分和翼成分（详见图 1 的图例）。这种拟合让我们得以确定连续谱的最佳拟合模型。观测数据与连续谱模型的差异代表了该谱线的轮廓，如图 2 所示，其中的数据已经调整到接近仪器的分辨率，并表示为入射（光子）流量的形式。从图中可知谱线轮廓非常宽且不对称；大部分流量即使相对于静止能量最低的 Kα 线（6.4 keV）也发生了很大的红移，偏移量高达 $\Delta E/E \approx 0.3$；零强度全宽对应的速度量级为 100,000 km · s^{-1}。

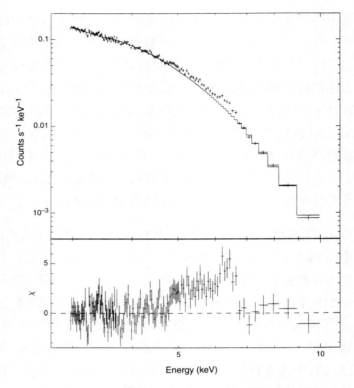

Fig. 1. X-ray spectrum of MCG–6–30–15, as observed by the ASCA satellite using the SIS detectors. Top panel, observed spectrum (crosses) and fitted "power-law plus continuum reflection" model (stepped line; the model has the same energy bins as the data). This fit excludes data between 5 and 7 keV. Bottom panel, data-minus-model residuals. The emission line is clearly visible with an asymmetry to the red. Parametrizing the observed emission line with a single gaussian improved the fit by $\Delta\chi^2 = 82$ with a centroid energy of $E_{\mathrm{K}} = 5.92^{+0.16}_{-0.15}$ keV, width $\sigma = 0.74^{+0.24}_{-0.18}$ keV and equivalent width EW $= 330^{+180}_{-120}$ eV. The power-law continuum has photon index $\Gamma = 2.05 \pm 0.07$. Adding an additional gaussian improved the fit further, with $\Delta\chi^2 = 39$, to $\chi^2 = 656.0$ (675 degrees of freedom). The double-gaussian parametrization consists of a relatively narrow ($\sigma = 0.18$ keV) component at 6.4 keV and a broader ($\sigma = 0.64$ keV) wing at ~5.5 keV. The red wing carries more flux than the core, with equivalent widths of 200 eV and 120 eV respectively.

From the large redshift, we can immediately reject the hypothesis that Compton scattering produces the observed line profile[21]. Such scattering requires that energy is transferred from the photons to the electrons and thus that $kT < 1.6$ keV in any scattering plasma ($4kT <$ photon energy). The energy shift per scattering is small (~80 eV) and a high Thomson optical depth (~5) is required for the scattering plasma to produce the total shift in the line centroid. Such a plasma would also Compton scatter the continuum photons to lower energies, creating a break at around 20 keV. No such break is observed[22].

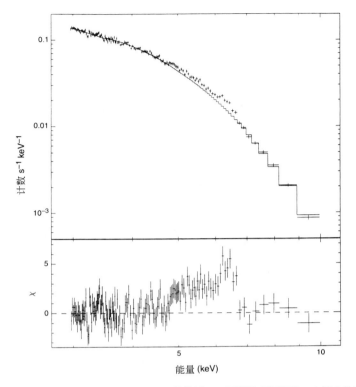

图 1. MCG-6-30-15 的 X 射线光谱，由 ASCA 卫星使用 SIS 探测器观测得到。上部分的图给出了实际观测能量谱（十字标记）和"幂律加反射连续谱"的模型拟合曲线（阶梯线；模型和数据有着相同的能量间隔）。该拟合不包括 5~7 keV 之间的数据。下部分的图是将上部分中的观测数据与相应拟合值相减后得到的残差，显然发射线不对称且向红端发生偏移。观测到的发射线可以通过用单个高斯函数对观测到的发射线进行参数化来改进谱线的拟合，所使用的拟合参数为：$\Delta\chi^2 = 82$，平均能量 $E_K = 5.92^{+0.16}_{-0.15}$ keV，宽度 $\sigma = 0.74^{+0.24}_{-0.18}$ keV，等值宽度 EW $= 330^{+180}_{-120}$ eV。幂律连续谱的光子谱指数 $\Gamma = 2.05 \pm 0.07$。引入另一高斯函数可以进一步改进以上拟合，相应参数为：$\Delta\chi^2 = 39$，$\chi^2 = 656.0$（675 个自由度）。双高斯参量拟合包括位于 6.4 keV 的较窄成分（$\sigma = 0.18$ keV）和位于约 5.5 keV 附近较宽的翼成分（$\sigma = 0.64$ keV）。其中红翼部分比中心部分的流量更大，二者等值宽度分别为 200 eV 和 120 eV。

从这个较高的红移，我们可以立刻排除以下假说：观测到的谱线轮廓是由康普顿散射产生的 [21]。这种散射需要能量从光子传递给电子，因此对于任何发生散射的等离子体（$4kT <$ 光子能量），其 $kT < 1.6$ keV。每次散射的能量偏移是非常小的（~80 eV），且为了实现谱线中心的整体偏移需要较高的汤姆孙光深（~5）。这种等离子体同时也会通过康普顿散射使连续谱的光子能量变低，从而在 20 keV 附近的位置发生截断。然而我们并没有观察到这种截断 [22]。

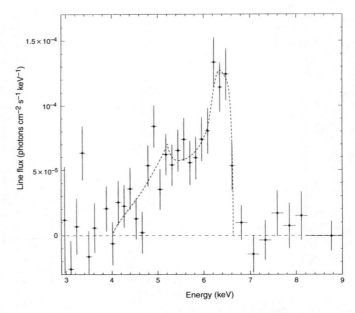

Fig. 2. The line profile of iron Kα in the X-ray emission from MCG−6−30−15. The data have been rebinned to approximately the instrumental resolution. The emission line is very broad, with full width at zero intensity of ~100,000 km s⁻¹. There is a marked asymmetry at energies lower than the rest-energy of the emission line (6.35 keV at the source redshift of 0.008). The most plausible mechanisms which can produce this extensive red wing are transverse Doppler and gravitational shifts close to a central black hole. The dotted line shows the best-fit line profile from the model of Fabian *et al.*[9], an externally-illuminated accretion disk orbiting a Schwarzschild black hole.

The Doppler width of the line implies velocities of the order of $0.3c$ (where c is the velocity of light), indicating highly relativistic motions. The line flux drops sharply above the rest energy of 6.4 keV, which excludes any velocity distribution where substantial amounts of the material is moving towards us. This would cause enhancement of the blue wing, which is not observed. Symmetrical outflows and spherical or quasi-spherical distributions of orbiting clouds therefore cannot account for the observed profile. The observation of broad redshifted lines in several objects[15], but no strong blue-shifted lines, argues against any asymmetrical-outflow hypothesis in which the flow is directed away from us (some objects should then have the flow directed towards us). It is therefore most probable that the material is moving primarily transversely at a large fraction of the speed of light with the width of the line being produced by transverse Doppler and gravitational redshifts close to a central black hole. The profile seems to be remarkably similar to that predicted for a face-on accretion disk[9,12].

To determine whether our line profile can be accounted for by a black hole and accretion disk, we initially employed a model which assumes a disk orbiting a Schwarzschild black hole[9]. The free parameters in this model are the inclination of the disk, i, its inner and outer radii, R_i and R_o and the index of the emissivity function, α; the line emissivity is assumed to vary as $R^{-\alpha}$. Initially, we assumed a rest energy of 6.4 keV appropriate to species less ionized than Fe XVI (more highly ionized species are discussed later). The model gives $\chi^2 = 655.7$ (676 degrees of freedom), very similar to the double-gaussian model, but with

706

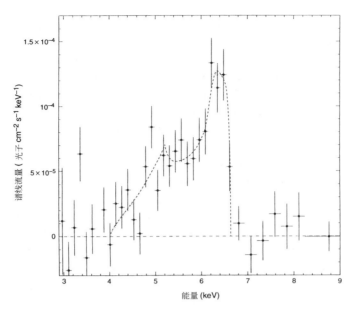

图 2. MCG−6−30−15 星系 X 射线发射中铁 Kα 发射线的谱线轮廓。图中的数据已经重新调整到接近仪器分辨率。图中发射线非常的宽，零强度全宽大约为 100,000 km·s⁻¹。在低于发射线静止能量（6.35 keV，对应源红移量为 0.008）的范围内，谱线轮廓具有明显的非对称性。产生这个高强度红翼轮廓的最合理机制是横向多普勒效应和中心黑洞附近的引力偏移。图中的点线给出了谱线轮廓的最佳拟合，该拟合结果由法比安等人 [9] 的模型（一个围着施瓦西黑洞运行且外部被照亮的吸积盘）得到。

由谱线的多普勒宽度可推出对应速度大约在 0.3c 的量级（其中 c 为光速），这意味为高度相对论性运动。当能量超过 6.4 keV 的静止能量时，谱线流量迅速下降，从而排除了大量物质朝向我们运动引起的任何速度分布。因为朝向我们的运动将引起谱线的蓝翼加强，然而迄今尚未观察到这一现象。因此，对称外向流以及做轨道运动的气体云的球状或准球状分布不可能解释观察到的轮廓。在一些天体中都观测到了宽的红移谱线而没有强的蓝移谱线 [15]，这与任何非对称外向流假说相矛盾，这些假说认为流向是远离我们的（那么一些天体就应该有朝向我们的喷流）。因此，最可能的情况是，这些物质主要以接近光速的速度横向运动，谱线宽度由多普勒效应和中心黑洞附近的引力红移造成。该轮廓看起来和正向吸积盘的预言非常相似 [9,12]。

为了确定我们的谱线轮廓是否可以用黑洞和吸积盘来解释，我们最初采用以下模型：假设存在一个环绕施瓦西黑洞的吸积盘 [9]。该模型中的自由参量是：吸积盘的倾角，用 i 表示；其内外半径，分别用 R_i 和 R_o 表示；发射率函数的指数，用 α 表示；假定谱线发射率按 R^α 规律变化。最初，我们将静止能量设定为 6.4 keV，该值适合电离程度比 Fe XVI 弱的核素（电离程度更高的核素在后面进行讨论）。模型给出 $\chi^2 = 655.7$（676 个自由度），与双高斯模型非常相似，但是少了一个自由参数。最

one fewer free parameter. The best-fitting value is $\alpha = 0.7$, but is not well determined. For a centrally illuminated disk, we expect a rather flat emissivity profile in the central regions, $\alpha \approx 1$ increasing to $\alpha \approx 3$ in the outer disk[10]. We have fixed α at these two values, which both fall within the 68% confidence region in the fit, to determine the other parameters. For $\alpha = 1$, we find $i = 30.2°^{+1.5}_{-2.7}$, $R_i = 3.4^{+3.0}_{-0.4}\,R_s$ and $R_o = 7.4^{+2.5}_{-0.8}\,R_s$, with equivalent width EW $= 390^{+90}_{-130}$ eV. For $\alpha = 3$, the parameters are $i = 29.7°^{+2.9}_{-3.9}$, $R_i = 3.7^{+1.8}_{-0.7}\,R_s$, $R_o = 10.0^{+12.5}_{-3.2}\,R_s$ and EW $= 380^{+100}_{-110}$ eV, very similar to those for $\alpha = 1$. Note that the minimum value for R_i in the Schwarzschild geometry is $3R_s$, so the lower error bar on this value is not statistical. In the Kerr metric of a spinning black hole the last stable orbit is closer to the central hole. We have also tested this condition[19], for which the parameters, $i = 26.8°^{+2.1}_{-1.0}$, $R_i = 4.7^{+0.83}_{-0.9}\,R_s$, $R_o = 16.7^{+\infty}_{-7.6}\,R_s$, $\alpha = 4.5^{+3.9}_{-3.7}$ and EW $= 300^{+70}_{-50}$ eV, and χ^2 are very similar to those of the Schwarzschild black hole. The uncertainties in the parameter values depend on the assumptions inherent in the models. For example, the value of R_o does not necessarily represent the true outer radius of the accretion disk, but is simply that radius beyond which no significant iron $K\alpha$ line emission occurs. The rather low value derived in our fits implies that the emission line is produced very near to the central black hole and that the primary X-rays originate close to the surface of the inner disk.

An iron-line equivalent width of 250–400 eV is a factor of ~2–3 higher than the predictions of simple disk reflection models[10,11]. There are several possible explanations for this. First, a modest increase of a factor ~1.5–3 in the iron abundance relative to the lighter elements would produce a line flux compatible with that reported here[10,23], the primary uncertainty being the assumed cosmic abundances. Another possibility is that there is another source of line emission. For example, there may be a contribution to the emission line from a molecular torus[24-26] surrounding the nucleus at a distance of ~1 pc. Because of this large distance we expect the $K\alpha$ line to be narrow compared to the instrumental resolution and centred at 6.4 keV in the rest frame. The addition of a narrow (dispersion $\sigma = 10$ eV) gaussian at 6.4 keV to our "power-law plus reflection continuum" model gives an equivalent width of only ~45 eV. This is a conservative upper limit to the torus contribution, because it allows no emission at 6.4 keV from the disk line. A large contribution from a torus is therefore unlikely, and in any case does not change our conclusions regarding the remainder of the line. A final possibility is that the material is highly ionized[27,28]. An increase in the effective fluorescence yield and reduced photoelectric opacity between 6 and 7 keV would then result in a higher line flux, provided that a large proportion of the iron is in the helium-like and hydrogen-like states. Such a scheme is compatible with our data; the increase in rest energy to 6.7–6.9 keV can be compensated for by a smaller inclination angle and/or concentrating the emission closer to the black hole, thereby increasing the gravitational shift.

Given the strong evidence for the black-hole/accretion-disk model in MCG–6–30–15, we infer that the broad lines observed in other AGN (even though less well-resolved) are produced by the same process. Modelling these profiles can reveal extraordinary detail about the central regions of the AGN, as illustrated by the disk line fit above. We already have indications that the X-rays are produced very close to the surface of the disk, and close to the black hole. Observations of variability of the emission line, and its time-lag

佳拟合值是 $\alpha = 0.7$，但是还没有很好地确定。对于一个中心受照的吸积盘，在中心区域将存在相当平坦的发射轮廓，并从内部的 $\alpha \approx 1$ 逐渐增加到外部的 $\alpha \approx 3$ [10]。下面我们采用 $\alpha \approx 1$ 与 $\alpha \approx 3$ 两个取值，这两个值的拟合都落在 68% 的置信区域内。对于 $\alpha = 1$ 的情况，我们发现 $i = 30.2°^{+1.5}_{-2.7}$、$R_i = 3.4^{+3.0}_{-0.4} R_s$ 以及 $R_o = 7.4^{+2.5}_{-0.8} R_s$，等值宽度为 EW $= 390^{+90}_{-130}$ eV。对于 $\alpha = 3$ 的情况，相应参数分别为 $i = 29.7°^{+2.9}_{-3.9}$、$R_i = 3.7^{+1.8}_{-0.7} R_s$ 以及 $R_o = 10.0^{+12.5}_{-3.2} R_s$，等值宽度为 EW $= 380^{+100}_{-110}$ eV，与 $\alpha = 1$ 情况的取值相近。注意到在施瓦西几何中，R_i 的最小值为 $3R_s$，因此该值的下误差棒不具有统计性。在一个自旋转黑洞的克尔度规中，最内的稳定轨道更为靠近黑洞中心。我们也检验了这一情况 [19]，其参数为 $i = 26.8°^{+2.1}_{-1.0}$、$R_i = 4.7^{+0.83}_{-0.9} R_s$、$R_o = 16.7^{+3.9}_{-7.6} R_s$、$\alpha = 4.5^{+3.9}_{-3.7}$、EW $= 300^{+70}_{-50}$ eV 以及 χ^2，与施瓦西黑洞的相应参数非常相近。这些参数的不确定度依赖于模型的内在假设。比如，R_o 的值不一定代表实际的吸积盘外半径，而只是简单地表示该半径以外就没有明显的铁 Kα 谱线发射。我们通过拟合得到的半径参数值非常的小，这意味着发射线产生于非常靠近黑洞中心的地方，主要的 X 射线来自吸积盘内区的表面附近。

250~400 eV 的铁线等值宽度是简单吸积盘反射模型预言的 2~3 倍 [10,11]。对于这一现象存在以下几种可能的解释。一种可能是，如果铁元素的丰度是更轻元素丰度的 1.5~3 倍，其谱线流量就会与文中的值相符 [10,23]；其主要的不确定度来自假定的宇宙丰度。另一种可能是，存在另一个线发射源，比如约 1 pc 的距离处围绕核心运动的分子环 [24-26] 可能也会贡献部分发射线。由于该距离较大，Kα 线相对仪器分辨率应该较窄，且在静止参考架中的中心能量位于 6.4 keV。在"幂律加反射连续谱"模型中添加一个位于 6.4 keV 的窄高斯分布（弥散度 $\sigma = 10$ eV），则可以给出仅约 45 eV 的等值宽度。这是分子环贡献的保守上限，因为该模型允许吸积盘可以不发射 6.4 keV 的谱线。因此，环面不可能有非常大的贡献，并且任何情况都不可能改变我们关于剩余谱线的结论。最后一种可能性是，物质高度电离 [27,28]。如果一大部分铁处于类氦和类氢状态，在 6~7 keV 之间有效荧光产额的增加和光电不透明度的减小将造成更高的谱线流量。这种机制与我们的数据也是一致的；其中静止能量增加到 6.7~6.9 keV 可以通过以下方式得到补偿，即减小倾角和（或）将辐射集中到更靠近黑洞的位置，从而增加了引力偏移。

鉴于 MCG−6−30−15 中存在黑洞／吸积盘模型的有力证据，我们推断在其他活动星系核（即使分辨率稍差）所观察到的宽线也是由于相同的过程产生的。对这些轮廓的模型拟合可以进一步揭示活动星系核中心区域的更多细节，如上面提到的盘谱线拟合。通过模型拟合，我们已经获得以下迹象，即 X 射线在非常靠近吸积盘表面

with respect to variations in the intensity of the continuum emission may allow us to measure the black hole mass and spin[9,29].

(**375**, 659-661; 1995)

Y. Tanaka[*†], K. Nandra[‡], A. C. Fabian[‡], H. Inoue[*], C. Otani[*], T. Dotanl[*], K. Hayashida[§], K. Iwasawa[‖], T. Kll[*], H. Kunieda[‖], F. Maklno[*] & M. Matsuoka[¶]

[*] Institute of Space and Astronautical Science, 3-1-1 Yoshinodai, Sagamihara, Kanagawa 229, Japan
[†] Max-Planck-Institut fur Extraterrestrische Physik, D-85740 Garching, Germany
[‡] Institute of Astronomy, Madingley Road, Cambridge CB3 OHA, UK
[§] Osaka University, Machikaneyama-cho 1-1, Osaka, Japan
[‖] Department of Astrophysics, Nagoya University, Chikusa-ku, Nagoya 464-01, Japan
[¶] RIKEN, Institute of Physical and Chemical Research, Hirosawa, Wako, Saitama 351-01, Japan

Received 2 March; accepted 23 May 1995.

References:

1. Rees, M. J. A. *Rev. Astr. Astrophys.* **22**, 471-506 (1984).
2. Ford, H. C. *et al. Astrophys. J.* L27-L30 (1994).
3. Harmes, R. J. *et al. Astrophys. J.* L35-L38 (1994).
4. Miyoshi, M. *et al. Nature* **373**, 127-129 (1995).
5. Pounds, K. A., Nandra, K., Stewart, G. C., George, I. M. & Fabian, A. C. *Nature* **344**, 132- 133 (1990).
6. Nandra, K. & Pounds, K. A. *Mon. Not. R. astr. Soc.* **268**, 405-429 (1994).
7. Guilbert, P. W. & Rees, M. J. *Mon. Not. R. astr. Soc.* **233**, 475-484 (1994).
8. Lightman, A. P. & White, T. R. *Astrophys. J.* **335**, 57-66 (1988).
9. Fabian, A. C., Rees, M. J., Stella, L. & White, N. E. *Mon. Not. R. astr. Soc.* **238**, 729-736 (1989).
10. George, I. M. & Fabian, A. C. *Mon. Not. R. astr. Soc.* **249**, 352-367 (1991).
11. Matt, G., Perola, G. C. & Piro, L. *Astr. Astrophys.* **245**, 75 (1991).
12. Matt, G., Perola, G. C., Piro, L. & Stella, L. *Astr. Astrophys.* **257**, 63 (1992).
13. Laor, A. *Astrophys. J.* **376**, 90-94 (1991).
14. Fabian, A. C. *et al. Publ. Astron. Soc. Jpn* **46**, L59-L64 (1994).
15. Mushotzky, R. F. *et al. Mon. Not. R. astr. Soc.* **272**, L9-L12 (1995).
16. Chen, K., Halpern, J. P. & Filippenko, A. V. *Astrophys. J.* **339**, 742-751 (1989).
17. Tanaka, Y., Inoue, H. & Holt, S. S. *Publ. Astron. Soc. Jpn* **46**, L37-L41 (1994).
18. Halpern, J. P. *Astrophys. J.* **281**, 90-94 (1984).
19. Nandra, K., Pounds, K. A. & Stewart, G. C. *Mon. Not. R. astr. Soc.* **242**, 660-668 (1990).
20. Nandra, K. & Pounds, K. A. *Nature* **359**, 215-216 (1992).
21. Czerny, B., Zbyszewska, M. & Raine, D. J. in *Iron Line Diagnostics in X-ray Sources* (ed. Treves, A.) 226-229 (Springer, Berlin, 1991).
22. Zdziarski, A. A., Johnson, W. N., Done, C., Smith, D. & McNaron-Brown, K. *Astrophys. J.* **438**, L63-L66 (1995).
23. Reynolds, C. S., Fabian, A. C. & Inoue, H. *Mon. Not. R. astr. Soc.* (submitted).
24. Krolik, J. H. & Kallman, T. R. *Astrophys. J.* **320**, L5-L8 (1987).
25. Ghisellini, G., Haardt, F. & Matt, G. *Mon. Not. R. astr. Soc.* **267**, 743-754 (1994).
26. Krolik, J. H., Madau, P. & Zycki, P. *Astrophys. J.* **420**, L57-L61 (1994).
27. Ross, R. R. & Fabian, A. C. *Mon. Not. R. astr. Soc.* **261**, 74-82 (1993).
28. Matt, G., Fabian, A. C. & Ross, R. *Mon. Not. R. astr. Soc.* **262**, 179-186 (1993).
29. Stella, L. *Nature* **344**, 747-749 (1990).

Acknowledgements. We thank A. Laor for use of his disk fine model. Y.T., K.N. and A.C.F. were supported by an Alexander von Humboldt Research Award, PPARC, and the Royal Society and British Council, respectively.

并且非常接近黑洞的地方产生。对发射线的变化，以及对其相对连续谱发射强度变化的时滞的观测，让我们有可能测量黑洞的质量和自转[9,29]。

（金世超 翻译；吴学兵 审稿）

A Three-dimensional Self-consistent Computer Simulation of a Geomagnetic Field Reversal

G. A. Glatzmaier and P. H. Roberts

Editor's Note

Evidence from magnetic rocks that cooled and acquired their magnetic polarization long ago indicates that the Earth's magnetic field has reversed its polarity many times. These reversals are typically preceded by wandering motion of the poles. Geomagnetic reversals are deemed to be caused by changes in the turbulent convective flow of the Earth's molten iron core—the "geodynamo" from which the field arises. But it isn't clear how this happens. Here geophysicists Gary Glatzmaier and Paul Roberts report the first three-dimensional computer simulation of a reversal in the geodynamo. It shows how the shape and strength of the geomagnetic field changes during the reversal, which happens over about 1,000 years after a stable period of nearly 40,000 years.

A three-dimensional, self-consistent numerical model of the geodynamo is described, that maintains a magnetic field for over 40,000 years. The model, which incorporates a finitely conducting inner core, undergoes several polarity excursions and then, near the end of the simulation, a successful reversal of the dipole moment. This simulated magnetic field reversal shares some features with real reversals of the geomagnetic field, and may provide insight into the geomagnetic reversal mechanism.

A fundamental goal of geophysics is a coherent understanding of the structure and dynamics of the Earth's interior. An integral part of this understanding must be a model of the Earth's magnetic field that reproduces its salient features: a field that is maintained for many magnetic diffusion times, is dominantly dipolar at the surface with a dipole axis that on the average lies close to the geographic axis of rotation, and exhibits secular variation with occasional excursions and reversals. The only plausible candidate for such a model is the dynamo model, in which new magnetic field is continually being generated by the shearing and twisting fluid motions within the Earth's liquid, electrically conducting, outer core[1,2]. According to ref. 3, Albert Einstein considered understanding the origin of the Earth's magnetic field as being one of the five most important unsolved problems in physics. Today we know that a nonlinear three-dimensional model of the magnetohydrodynamics (MHD) of the Earth's core is needed to explain the structure and the long-term evolution of the geomagnetic field.

There are two principal reasons for this. First, it is widely perceived that linear mathematical analysis, which has provided great insights into basic dynamo processes, is unlikely to contribute as fundamentally to the understanding of the geodynamo because the Earth

地磁场倒转的三维自洽计算机模拟

格拉茨梅尔，罗伯茨

编者按

磁性岩石在地史上冷却并获取磁性极化的这一证据表明地球磁场的磁极已经历了多次倒转。倒转发生前一般伴随着磁极的无规则运动。地磁极倒转被认为是由熔融的含铁地核内（"地球发电机"磁场产生的地方）具湍流性质的对流流体的变化引起的。但地磁倒转的具体过程仍不清楚。在本文中，地球物理学家加里·格拉茨梅尔和保罗·罗伯茨首次报道了地球发电机的三维计算机模拟中出现的地磁场倒转现象。研究显示了地磁场倒转期间，磁场形态和强度的变化；倒转发生在大约四万年磁场稳定周期后，并且持续了约 1,000 年。

本文描述了维持地磁场超过四万年的地球发电机三维自洽数值模型。该模型包含一个有限导电内核，其在经历了数次极性漂移后，在接近模拟的末期出现了偶极矩的成功倒转。本次模拟的磁场倒转与真实的地磁场倒转具有一些共同特征，为更深刻地理解磁场的倒转机理提供了基础。

地球物理学的一个基本目标是对地球内部结构和动力学有一个清楚的理解。这一理解的一个主要部分必须是能够重现地磁场显著特征的地磁场模型：一个持续多次磁扩散的地磁场，在地球表面主要表现为偶极场，其平均偶极子轴靠近地理旋转轴，并表现出长期变化以及偶尔的漂移和倒转。这种地磁场模型的唯一合理候选模型就是发电机模型：在地球液态导电外核之内，剪切、扭曲的流体运动产生了持续的新磁场 [1,2]。根据参考文献 3 可知，爱因斯坦认为理解地磁场起源是物理学中五个最重要的未解决的问题之一。现在我们已知，对于地磁场结构和长期演化的解释，我们需要一个地核的非线性三维磁流体动力学（MHD）模型。

这样做有两个主要原因。一是，虽然普遍认为通过线性数学分析可以深入了解发电机基本过程，但在理解地球发电机的基本原理上很可能不可行，因为地球运行

operates in the so-called "strong-field" regime. Analytical methods are successful in studying "weak-field" regimes, in which the magnetic forces can be treated as a perturbation in the dynamics. However, in the strong-field regime the nonlinear magnetic Lorentz force is as large as the Coriolis force and therefore cannot be treated as a perturbation. A nonlinear numerical computation is therefore required to simulate the MHD.

The second reason arises from Cowling's theorem[4], which shows that a self-sustained magnetic field produced by a dynamo cannot be axisymmetric. But most numerical models of dynamos have been "mean-field" kinematic models, which require a prescription of the axisymmetric effects of some hypothetical three-dimensional convection and solve for the evolution of only the two-dimensional axisymmetric parts of the magnetic fields[5]. Intermediate mean-field models[6-11] go somewhat further by also solving for the axisymmetric zonal flow and meridional circulation, but still require a prescribed two-dimensional structure of some hypothetical averaged helical flow (the alpha effect[2]) and usually a prescribed structure for the buoyancy force or for the zonal thermal wind shear it produces (the omega effect[1]). They are therefore not self-consistent because the solutions strongly depend on how one chooses to prescribe the alpha and omega structures. The simplest way to generate a three-dimensional magnetic field is to drive it with a prescribed three-dimensional velocity profile[12-14]; but in this approach the (kinematic) velocity is not a self-consistent convective solution with nonlinear feedback from the Lorentz force. Travelling-wave solutions can also be generated[15] but lack mode-dependent temporal behaviour. Magneto-convection simulations in three dimensions are closer to self-consistency because the time-dependent thermodynamic, velocity, and magnetic fields are all solved in three dimensions with nonlinear feedback[16-19]; but the main part of the magnetic field is maintained via boundary conditions. These approaches have been used because of their simplicity and relatively small computing resource requirements; but they are limited because either they do not produce self-consistent solutions of the full three-dimensional MHD equations or, in magneto-convection, they do not produce self-sustaining magnetic fields and are therefore not suitable for studying field reversals. They have been and continue to be extremely useful for providing a relatively cheap way of testing the influence of new physics[9] or studying secular variation of the field on short timescales[19].

Self-consistent numerical simulations of three-dimensional convective dynamos have been computed in planar (cartesian) geometry to study local dynamo action[20-23] and in global (spherical) geometry[24-29] to study the solar dynamo. Of these, however, the only models that generate magnetic energy an order of magnitude greater than kinetic energy and therefore begin to approach the strong-field regime appropriate for studying the geodynamo are the recent models by St Pierre[23] and Kageyama et al.[29]. In the other models, the generated magnetic energy is several orders of magnitude less than the kinetic energy.

Here we present a fully self-consistent three-dimensional numerical simulation of a convective strong-field dynamo in a spherical shell with a finitely conducting inner core[30]. A magnetic field is maintained for more than three magnetic diffusion times and has energy

在所谓的强场区。在弱场区，磁力被视为动力学的扰动，分析方法在研究弱场区是成功的。但是，在强场区，非线性磁洛伦兹力与科里奥利力大小相同，所以不能被视为扰动。因此需要用非线性数值计算来模拟磁流体动力学。

第二个原因来源于整流罩定理[4]，该定理显示了由发电机产生的自给的磁场不可能是轴对称的。但是大多数发电机数值模型是"平均场"运动模型，需要一些理论上的三维对流的轴对称效果，并且只能解决磁场二维轴对称部分的演化[5]。中间的平均场模型[6-11]则更加深入，解决了轴对称纬向流和经向环流，但是仍然需要一些理论上的平均螺线流（alpha 效应[2]）的二维结构，还有通常的浮力或者由此产生的纬向热成风切变（omega 效应[11]）结构。因此它们都是不自洽的，因为结果严重依赖于预设的 alpha 和 omega 结构。产生三维磁场的最简单方法是用既定的三维速度场结构驱动它[12-14]；但是在这种方法中，（动力学的）速度不是一个有洛伦兹力非线性反馈的、自洽的对流解。行波解也可以产生[15]，但是缺少模式依赖的时间行为。三维磁发电机对流模拟更加接近于自洽，因为依赖时间的热动力学、速度和磁场都在有非线性反馈的三维空间中有解[16-19]；但是磁场的主要部分是通过边界条件维持的。由于它们的简单和相对小的计算资源需求，这些方法已经被使用；但是它们有限制，因为它们既不能产生全三维磁流体动力学方程的自洽解，也不能在磁发电机对流中产生自给的磁场，因此不适合研究磁场倒转。它们已经并且将持续成为在测试新物理的影响[9]或者在研究短时间尺度上的长期变化[19]等方面相对廉价的一种方法。

三维自洽对流发电机的数值模拟已经在平面几何（笛卡儿坐标）上计算过，用来研究局部的发电机行为[20-23]，也在整体几何（球坐标）上计算过[24-29]，用来研究太阳发电机。但是，在这些模型中，只有由圣皮埃尔[23]和阴山聪等[29]最近建立的模型能产生比动能大一个数量级的磁能量，因而开始接近适合研究地球发电机的强场区域。在其他模型中，产生的磁能比动能少几个数量级。

本文展示了一个在拥有有限导电内核的球壳中，对流强磁场发电机的完全自洽三维数值模拟[30]。磁场维持时间超过了三个磁扩散时间，磁场能量至少比维持其对

at least three orders of magnitude greater than the kinetic energy of the convection that maintains it. The exciting feature that we focus on in this paper is a reversal of the dipole polarity that occurs near the end of our simulation. The simulation required over 2,000,000 computational time steps that, over a period of more than a year, took more than 2,000 CPU hours on a Cray C-90, which is why we have decided to report on our results now instead of waiting for our simulation to span a much longer period of time. With only one reversal simulated we cannot yet say anything about the statistical behaviour of reversals in our model. Some minor changes in our model would also bring it closer to geophysical reality. But because our simulation is self-consistent and maintains a field that resembles the Earth's in many respects, we believe that it provides a plausible description of the geomagnetic field and the way it reverses.

Model Description

The numerical model (G.A.G., manuscript in preparation) solves the nonlinear MHD equations that govern the three-dimensional structure and evolution of an electrically conducting fluid undergoing thermal convection in a rapidly rotating spherical shell, our model of the Earth's outer fluid core. A specified heat flux at the inner core boundary (ICB) drives thermal convection in the fluid core. This convection, influenced by the rotation of the core, twists and shears magnetic field, generating new magnetic field to replace that which diffuses away. The field diffuses into a solid, electrically conducting, inner core providing magnetic torque between the inner and outer cores. Magnetic torque also exists between the outer fluid core and a solid mantle above through a thin conducting layer at the core–mantle boundary (CMB). The rest of the mantle is assumed to be an insulator, so the field above this layer is a source-free potential field. Time-dependent rotation rates of the solid inner core and solid mantle are determined by the net torques at the ICB and CMB, respectively.

The model prescriptions[30] (mass, dimensions, rotation rate and material properties) are Earth-like, except the applied heat flux at the ICB, which is somewhat higher to compensate for the lack of compositional buoyancy sources in this version of our model, and the viscosity of the fluid core, which owing to computational limitations was chosen to be larger than the Earth's. But because the viscous forces in our model (outside the thin viscous boundary layers) are already about six orders of magnitude smaller than the Coriolis and Lorentz forces, our solution is probably in the correct asymptotic regime for the Earth. In comparison with two other strong-field dynamos, Kageyama et al.[29] assume that the convecting fluid is a compressible gas with a viscosity more than two orders of magnitude greater than our viscosity (when scaled appropriately, using the Earth's rotation rate and core radius), and St Pierre[23] uses a viscosity slightly larger than in our model.

The electrical conductivity of the solid inner core is probably much the same as that of the fluid outer core but, in our initial test calculations (those done before the simulation we are reporting on here), we assumed for simplicity an insulating inner core. The result

流的运动能大三个数量级。在本文中我们关注的最激动人心的特征是发生在接近模拟末尾的偶极子极性倒转。这次模拟需要超过 200 万的计算时间步,历时要超过一年,在 Cary C-90 机上要花费 2,000 个 CPU 小时,这就是为什么我们决定现在来报道我们的结果,而不是等着花费更长时间去模拟之后再报道。因为模拟只出现了一次倒转,所以在我们的模型中,我们不能讨论任何关于地磁倒转的统计行为。在我们模型中的一些微小变化可能会使其更接近于地球物理的真实情况。但是因为我们的模拟是自洽的,并且维持了一个在许多方面与地球磁场相像的场,我们相信这个模型为地磁场以及其倒转方式提供了一个合理描述。

模 型 描 述

数值模型(格拉茨梅尔,稿件准备中)解出了非线性 MHD 方程,这些方程控制了存在于快速旋转球壳(我们的地球液态外核模型)中的正经历热对流的导电流体的三维结构及演化。在内核边界(ICB)的特定热流驱动了液态核的热对流。受地核旋转的影响,这种对流产生扭曲并剪切磁场,产生的新磁场又代替扩散的磁场。磁场扩散到固态导电内核,提供了内核与外核之间的磁力矩。磁力矩也存在于液态外核和之上的固态地幔之间的核幔边界(CMB)薄导电层之中。剩余的地幔被认为是绝缘体,所以这层之上的磁场是无源势场。固体内核与固体地幔随时间变化的旋转速率分别由在 ICB 和 CMB 的净力矩所决定。

除了在 ICB 的热流值和液态核的黏滞力,模型参数[30](质量、尺寸、旋转率、材料性质)与地球类似,ICB 热流值有点高是用于补偿我们这个版本的模型中成分浮力源的缺失,模型中的黏滞力被设为比地球相应值要高是出于计算的限制。但是因为在我们的模型中(在黏性薄边界层之外)黏滞力已经比科里奥利力和洛伦兹力小六个数量级,所以我们的解很可能落在对于地球而言正确的渐进区里。与另外两个强场发电机进行对比,阴山聪等[29]假设对流场是一个黏度比我们黏度(使用地球旋转速率和地核半径来合理刻度)大两个数量级的压缩气体,而圣皮埃尔[23]使用了比我们模型中的黏度大一点点的黏度。

固态内核的电导率很可能与液态外核相同,但在我们的初始测试计算(在本文所做的模拟之前)中,为了简便,我们假设这个固态内核为一个绝缘的内核。测试计

was a chaotic magnetic field that, unlike the Earth's, reversed its dipole polarity roughly every thousand years. Hollerbach and Jones[9] then demonstrated, in their two-dimensional mean-field dynamo model, that a finitely conducting solid inner core provides a degree of stability to the magnetic field. Their alpha–omega dynamo generates a field that never reverses, although the magnetic energy undergoes periodic changes. The lack of field reversals in their solution is probably because of the particular prescription of their alpha and omega driving terms that are held constant in time. But the reversal inhibition they demonstrated and the reversal mechanism they suggested motivated us to include a finitely conducting inner core in our three-dimensional convective model. Again, in comparison, Kageyama et al.[29] do not have a finitely conducting inner core and therefore have no magnetic coupling between their outer and inner cores, and the model by St Pierre[23] is planar.

Our present solution, with a finitely conducting inner core, spans $> 40,000$ years, more than three magnetic diffusion times, with no indication that it will decay away, which is suggestive evidence that our solution is a self-sustaining convective dynamo. The solution begins with random small-scale temperature perturbations and a seed magnetic field. After an initial period of adjustment ($\sim 10,000$ years) during which the dipole part of the field gradually becomes dominant, our time-dependent solution maintains its dipole polarity until near the end of the simulation, when it reverses in little more than 1,000 years and then maintains the new dipole polarity for roughly the remaining 4,000 years of the simulation.

Field Structure during the Reversal

To illustrate the magnetic field reversal mechanism, we display the change in the structure of the field during the last 9,000 years of our simulation with three snapshots in each of Figs 1–4. The three-dimensional field structure is portrayed in Fig. 1 via lines of force at 9,000 years before the end of our simulation (Fig. 1a), at roughly the middle of the polarity transition as seen at the surface ($\sim 4,000$ years before the end; Fig. 1b), and at the end of our simulation (Fig. 1c). We begin plotting the lines of force at the surface of our modelled Earth. They penetrate inward through the insulating mantle and then into the outer fluid core where the field is generated. The transition from the relatively smooth structure of the potential field outside the core to the much more complicated and intense field structure inside the core is quite striking. The maximum field intensity usually occurs near the ICB and is typically between 30 and 50 mT. The field at the surface has a dominantly dipolar structure before (Fig. 1a) and after (Fig. 1c) the reversal, with the dipole axis nearly aligned with the rotation axis, which is vertical in Fig. 1. During the polarity transition (Fig. 1b) the field structure at the surface is much more complicated and the dipole axis passes through the equatorial plane.

算结果是一个与地球磁场不一样的混乱的磁场，大约每隔几千年偶极子极性会倒转。霍勒巴赫和琼斯[9]论证了在他们的二维平均场发电机模型中，一个有限传导固态内核给磁场提供了一些稳定性。在他们的alpha–omega发电机模型中，虽然磁场能量经历了周期性变化，但产生的磁场从不倒转。他们结果中缺少磁场倒转的很可能的原因是他们的alpha–omega驱动项在时间上是不变的这一特殊设定。但是他们论证的倒转抑制和他们提出的倒转机理，激励我们在我们的三维对流模型中包含有限的传导内核。再次，作为对比，阴山聪等[29]没有包含有限的传导内核，因此他们在内外核之间没有磁耦合，而圣皮埃尔[23]的模型是平面的。

在一个有限传导内核的假设下，我们当前的模型解经历了超过四万年的时间（长达三个磁扩散时间），且并没有迹象表明它将会衰变，这说明了我们的解是一个自给的对流发电机。这个解的开始是随机的小规模的温度扰动和一个种子磁场。经过初始调整周期（大约一万年）之后，磁场的偶极子部分逐渐占据主导地位，我们随时间变化的解一直维持着偶极子极性，直到接近模拟的末尾，这时磁场在1,000年多点的时间内发生了倒转，然后在模拟的剩余4,000年中一直维持新的偶极子极性。

倒转期间的磁场结构

为了说明磁场倒转机理，我们在图1~4中分别以三张快照的形式展示了数值模拟的最后9,000年的磁场结构的变化。图1中通过磁力线刻画了模拟结束前的9,000年的三维磁场结构（图1a）、模拟结束前的4,000年大约位于极性转换中期的三维磁场结构（图1b）以及模拟末期的三维磁场结构（图1c）。我们从描绘地球模型表面上的磁力线开始。这些磁力线向内穿过绝缘地幔，然后进入产生磁场的液态外核。从地核外相对平滑的势场结构，到地核内更加复杂和更强的场结构，这之间的转换是非常明显的。最大磁场强度通常出现在ICB界面附近，典型值为30~50 mT。在倒转之前（图1a）和倒转之后（图1c），表面磁场主要是偶极子结构，其偶极子轴与旋转轴（在图1中是竖直的）几乎是平行的。在极性倒转期间（图1b），表面的磁场结构更加复杂，并且偶极子轴穿过赤道面。

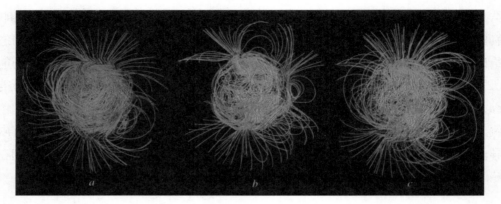

Fig. 1. The three-dimensional (3D) magnetic field structure portrayed through lines of force plotted out to the surface of our modelled Earth. Snapshots are displayed: *a*, before the reversal (9,000 years before the end of our simulation); *b*, midway through the transition as seen at the surface (that is, when the axial dipole part of the field at the surface goes through zero, about 4,000 years before the end); *c*, after the reversal (at the end of our simulation). Lines are yellow (blue) where the radial component of the field is directed outward (inward). The rotation axis is vertical. One hundred lines of force are plotted in each snapshot, so the relative field intensity is not represented in this figure.

To illustrate the field structure within the inner and outer cores more easily, we plot in Fig. 2 the longitudinal average of the three-dimensional field at 9,000 years before the end (Fig. 2*a*), at roughly the middle of the polarity transition as seen at the ICB (~5,000 years before the end; Fig. 2*b*), and at the end of our simulation (Fig. 2*c*). The right side of each plot shows contours of the east–west (toroidal) part of the field; the left side shows lines of force of the meridional (poloidal) part of the field. There are typically two main toroidal field concentrations, one in each hemisphere, in opposite directions and usually inside the imaginary cylinder tangent to the inner core where large zonal flows shear poloidal field, so generating toroidal field. Toroidal field also diffuses into the inner core from the ICB, where it is generated when poloidal field is sheared by the inner core as it moves differentially with respect to the fluid just outside the ICB.

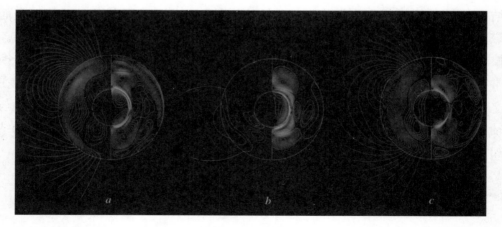

Fig. 2. The longitudinal average of the 3D magnetic field displayed with contours of the toroidal (east–west) part of the field plotted in the right hemispheres and lines of force of the meridional (poloidal) part

720

图 1. 我们地球模型表面所画出的磁力线显示了三维地磁场结构。快照：a，倒转之前（模拟结束前的 9,000年）；b，地球表面可见的倒转中期（也就是当地球表面场的轴向偶极子部分趋于零时，大约是结束前的4,000 年）；c，倒转后（模拟结束时）。黄（蓝）线表明磁场的径向部分是向外（内）的。地球旋转轴是竖直的。每个快照都画了 100 条磁力线，因此相对磁场强度没有体现在图中。

为了更加容易说清楚在内外核中的场结构，我们分别在图 2 中画出了以下三种情况的三维场的经向平均值：模拟结束前的 9,000 年（图 2a），在 ICB 界面可见的极性转换中期（模拟结束之前的 5,000 年，图 2b），以及在模拟结束时（图 2c）。每个子图右边都显示了场的东－西（环向）部分的等值线图；左边显示了场的南－北（极向）部分的磁力线。这里主要存在两种环形场聚集，每个半球一种，方向相反，且通常在与内核相切的虚拟圆柱体内（圆柱体内有大量纬向流剪切极向场，因此会产生环形场）。环形场也会从 ICB 界面扩散到内核，在 ICB 处，当极向场相对于 ICB 界面外的流体运动速度不同时，极向场被内核剪切而产生环形场。

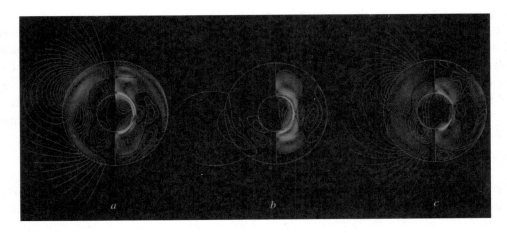

图 2. 三维磁场经向平均值，右半球磁场环向（东－西）部分以等值线表示，左半球磁场的经向（极向）部

of the field plotted in the left hemispheres. Snapshots are displayed: *a*, before the reversal (9,000 years before the end of our simulation); *b*, midway through the transition as seen at the ICB (that is, when the axial dipole part of the field at the ICB goes through zero, about 5,000 years before the end); *c*, after the reversal (at the end of our simulation). The north (south) geographic pole is at the top (bottom) of each plot. The outer circular boundary is the core–mantle boundary and the inner circular boundary is the inner core boundary. Red (blue) contours are eastward (westward)-directed toroidal field. Green (yellow) lines of force are clockwise (anticlockwise)-directed poloidal field that are plotted out to the surface. Note that for the series of plots in this figure the relative field intensity is represented in terms of the number of toroidal field contours and the density of poloidal field lines.

The longitudinally averaged poloidal field (left sides of Fig. 2) typically has two dipolar polarities: one in the outer part of the fluid core, which is also the dipole polarity observed at the surface, and the opposite polarity in the inner part of the fluid core and the inner solid core. Poloidal field is generated by helical flow that twists toroidal field; in the Northern Hemisphere, for example, the time-dependent helicity of the flow (that is, the correlation between velocity and vorticity) is usually right-handed and much larger inside the "tangent cylinder" and left-handed outside[30]. This illustrates one of the limitations of models that require, unlike ours, a prescription of the fluid flow instead of solving for it self-consistently. For example, the helical flow structure prescribed by Hollerbach and Jones[9] has no radial or time dependence and the field has only a single dipole polarity that never reverses. By contrast, it is the interaction of the two dipolar polarities present in our solution that plays an essential role in our reversal mechanism in a way that brings to mind the simple interaction between the two disks of the Rikitake dynamo model[31].

A movie of our simulation shows how the field in the fluid outer core is continually attempting to reverse its axial dipole polarity on a short timescale ($\sim$100 years) corresponding to convective overturning but usually fails because the field in the solid inner core, which can only change on a longer diffusive timescale ($\sim$1,600 years), usually does not have enough time to diffuse away before it is regenerated at the ICB. It also shows how the axial quadrupole part of the outer field tends to reverse its polarity on a roughly thousand-year timescale, causing a hemispheric (non-reversing dipole) oscillation in the structure and intensity of the outer poloidal field[10] because the sum of an axial dipole and an axial quadrupole results in an enhanced axial poloidal field in one hemisphere and a diminished poloidal field in the other. Once in many attempts the three-dimensional configurations of the buoyancy, flow and magnetic fields in the outer core are right for a long enough period of time for the inner core axial dipole field to diffuse away (Fig. 2*b*), thus allowing the reversed axial dipole polarity in the outer core to diffuse into the inner core. If this one model is representative of the Earth, it suggests that the strong nonlinear feedbacks in three dimensions and the different timescales of the fluid and solid cores are responsible for the Earth's stochastic reversal record.

When the reversal occurs in our simulation, the energy of the total field in the core is about one-quarter of its typical value. Once the new field polarity has become established, the magnetic energy in the fluid core quickly recovers. During the transition, eastward and westward toroidal field are alternately generated several times in both hemispheres at the

分以磁力线来表示。快照：a，倒转之前（模拟结束前的 9,000 年）；b，内外核边界（ICB）可见的倒转中期（也就是当磁场的轴向偶极子部分在 ICB 趋于零时，大约是结束前的 5,000 年）；c，倒转后（模拟结束时）。地理北（南）极位于图中上（下）。外部圆形边界是核幔边界，内部圆形边界是内外核边界。红（蓝）色等值线是东（西）向环向场。画到地球表面的绿（黄）磁力线是顺时针（逆时针）极向场。请注意图中相对磁场强度以环向场等值线的数量和极向场磁场线的密度来表示。

经向平均极向场（图 2 左侧）一般具有两个偶极子极性：一个在液态核的外层，即在核表面观察到的偶极子极性；另一个相反的极性存在于液态核的内层和固态内核之内。极向场由扭曲了环向场的螺旋流所产生；例如，在北半球，螺旋流随时间变化的螺旋度（就是速度与涡度的相关性）通常在切圆柱外是左旋的，而在切圆柱内是右旋的，并且螺旋度大得多[30]。这说明了模型存在的一个限制：不像我们的模型，这个模型需要一个液流的设定，而不是自洽解。例如，由霍勒巴赫和琼斯[9]规定的螺旋流结构与径向、时间无关，并且磁场只有一个永不倒转的偶极子极性。相反，在我们的解中，两个偶极子极性的相互作用在倒转机理中扮演了重要角色，使人想起力武常茨发电机模型中双盘之间的简单相互作用[31]。

模拟的短片中显示了在短时间尺度（~100 年）内（对应对流倒转的时间），液态外核中的场是怎样持续地尝试去倒转轴向偶极子极性的，但是倒转通常失败，因为在固态内核中的场只能在更长的扩散时间尺度（~1,600 年）上变化，所以当其在 ICB 界面重新产生前，通常没有足够的时间扩散开。这也显示了外部场的轴向四极子部分是如何在大约千年的时间尺度上倒转极性的，并且由于轴向偶极子和轴向四极子共同作用导致一个半球的轴向极向场增强，另一个半球中的极向场减弱，从而在外部极向场的结构和强度上引起半球（非倒转偶极子）振荡[10]。一旦外核中浮力、螺旋流、磁场的三维配置的多次尝试正好在足够长的扩散时间内使得内核轴向偶极子场可以扩散（图 2b），外核中的倒转偶极子极性就因此可以扩散到内核中。如果这一个模型代表地球，那么这暗示了液态外核和固态内核在三维尺度和不同时间尺度上的强烈的非线性反馈引起了地球随机倒转的记录。

当我们的模拟中出现倒转时，地核的总磁场能量大约在通常值的四分之一。一旦新的磁极建立，液态外核的磁场能量便迅速恢复。转换过程中，在倒转的极性最终建立之前，在 ICB 界面的两个半球内，东西向环向场几次轮流生成。请注意在转

ICB before the reversed polarity finally becomes established. Notice how the toroidal field is asymmetric with respect to the Equator before (Fig. 2a) and after (Fig. 2c) the transition but is symmetric midway through the transition (Fig. 2b). In our simulation, the toroidal field reverses first, then the inner poloidal field that penetrates the solid core, and finally, somewhat later, the outer poloidal field that appears at the Earth's surface reverses. This entire process takes (depending on how one defines the beginning and end of the reversal) a little more than 1,000 years, roughly the characteristic magnetic diffusion timescale for the inner core.

Figure 3 shows snapshots of just the radial component of the field plotted at the CMB (lower plots) and at the surface (upper plots) at the same three times as those depicted in Fig. 1. Because the dipolar part of the pattern decays the most slowly with radius, its contribution is greater at the surface than at the CMB. The dipole parts of these fields are nearly axial before (Fig. 3a) and after (Fig. 3c) the transition and equatorial midway through the transition (Fig. 3b). But the dipole part of the field decreases more during the transition than the other modes do; therefore the equatorial dipole part of our transitional field is less dominant than the axial dipole part typically is before and after the transition. For example, the large radial fields at the poles in Fig. 3b are the result of a relatively strong quadrupole mode.

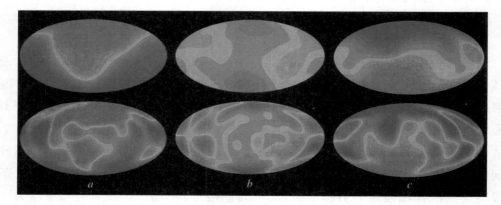

Fig. 3. The radial component of the magnetic field plotted in a Hammer projection of the core–mantle boundary (lower plots) and of the surface (upper plots). Snapshots a, b and c are displayed at the same times as those in Fig. 1. Red (blue) contours represent outward (inward)-directed field. The relative intensities at the different times are also reflected in the colour contours. But the field intensity at the surface has been multiplied by a factor of ten to obtain colours in the surface plots that are comparable to those in the CMB plots.

The CMB plots of Fig. 3a, c are qualitatively similar to the Earth's present field projected onto the CMB[32] with multimode contributions and several flux concentrations. The maximum intensity of the radial component of the field at the CMB in Fig. 3a, c is ~3.0 mT; the maximum intensity in Fig. 3b is 0.8 mT. These values can be compared with the maximum intensity of the Earth's present radial field at the CMB (ref. 32), which is ~1.0 mT.

换之前（图 2*a*）和转换之后（图 2*c*），环形场是怎样关于赤道不对称的，以及在转换途中（图 2*b*）又是怎样关于赤道对称的。在我们的模拟中，环向场首先倒转，然后是穿过固态内核的内部极向场倒转，最后，即稍晚些，出现在地球表面的外部极向场出现倒转。整个过程花了稍大于一千年的时间（具体取决于怎样定义倒转的开始和结束），这大约就是内核的特征磁场扩散时间尺度。

　　图 3 显示了在核幔边界（图下排）和地球表面（图上排）上，与图 1 相同的三个时刻的磁场径向部分的快照。由于模式的偶极子部分沿着半径衰减得最慢，它的贡献在地球表面比在核幔边界更大。在转换之前（图 3*a*）、转换之后（图 3*c*），这些场的偶极子部分几乎是轴向的，而转换途中（图 3*b*），这些场的偶极子部分是赤道向的。但是场的偶极子部分在转换期间比其他模衰减地更多；因此，在转换前后，转换场的赤道偶极子部分与轴向偶极子部分相比，不太明显。例如，在图 3*b* 中的位于两极的巨大径向场是相对强的四极子模引起的。

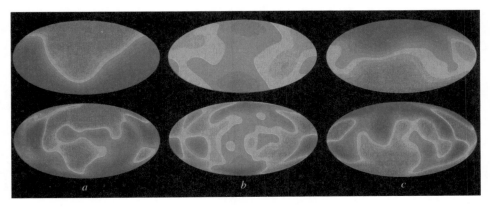

图 3. 核幔边界（下排）和地球表面（上排）的径向磁场分量（哈默投影）。快照 *a*、*b*、*c* 的时间与图 1 中的相同。红（蓝）等值线代表向外（内）磁场。不同时间的相对磁场强度也反映在彩色的等值线中。为了可与核幔边界的磁场强度相比较，图中的地球表面的磁场强度已经扩大为原来的十倍。

　　图 3*a* 和 *c* 的 CMB 图像，与当今地球的磁场以多模贡献和通量集中的形式投影到 CMB 的图像 [32] 是定性相似的。图 3*a* 和 *c* 中，在 CMB 界面，径向磁场部分的最大强度是 3.0 mT；图 3*b* 中，最大强度是 0.8 mT。这些值能够与当今地球的径向磁场在 CMB 的最大值（参考文献 32），即约 1.0 mT 的值相比较。

Our simulated field structure at the surface can be compared with the Earth's present surface field structure by plotting the mean-square field intensity over the surface as a function of the spherical harmonic degree, with the traditional Gauss coefficients[33,34]. The spectra (displayed only out to spherical harmonic degree 12) at the same three times as those used in Figs. 1 and 3 are plotted in Fig. 4. The spectra corresponding to the snapshots long before (squares) and long after (diamonds) the transition show the dipolar ($l = 1$) contribution dominant over the quadrupolar ($l = 2$) and octupolar ($l = 3$) contributions. These two spectra indicate that we could be driving the convection a little too hard because our magnetic energies for the low degrees are higher than those of the present-day Earth[33,34], which are plotted as filled circles in Fig. 4. Also, because we have no crustal magnetic fields in our model, the slopes of our spectra do not become shallower with increasing degree above $l = 12$ (not shown), in contrast with the Earth's[33,34]. Our spectrum taken midway through the transition (open circles) shows that the dipole contribution has decreased more than the other modes during the reversal, as is also apparent in Fig. 1. During our entire simulation, magnetic energy is continually being exchanged in a chaotic manner between the modes, especially back and forth between the dipole ($l = 1$) and quadrupole ($l = 2$) modes on a few-thousand-year timescale. Could the decrease in the Earth's dipole moment over the past 150 years[34] be a similar adjustment?

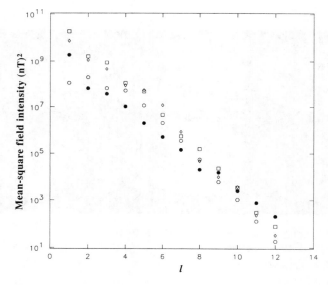

Fig. 4. The mean-square field intensity over the surface plotted as $(l+1) \sum_m [(g_l^m)^2 + (h_l^m)^2]$, where g_l^m and h_l^m are the traditional Gauss coefficients for the potential field outside the core, and l and m are the degree and order, respectively, in the spherical harmonic expansion. Spectra are displayed at the same three times as those in Figs 1 and 3: squares before, open circles during, and diamonds after the reversal. The spectrum for the present-day Earth, based on MAGSAT data[34], is plotted as filled circles.

The Reversal Sampled at Different Sites

To compare our simulated reversal with the palaeomagnetic reversal record we now

通过计算地球表面以地磁场球谐阶数，即传统高斯系数 [33,34] 为函数的场方磁场强度（即磁场功率谱），可以对比分析我们模拟的地表磁场结构与当今地磁场的地表结构。与图 1 和图 3 相同的三个时刻得到的谱（仅仅显示了球谐阶数大到 12 的情况）画在图 4 中。谱与快照对应：转换很久之前（方形）和很久之后（菱形）的谱显示了偶极子的贡献（$l = 1$）远大于四极子（$l = 2$）、八极子（$l = 3$）的贡献。这两个功率谱的对比表明，可能我们模型中对流分量稍高导致了其低阶磁场能量略高于当今地磁场的相应值 [33,34]（图 4 中实心圆所示）。并且，因为在我们的模型中，没有地壳地磁场，所以与地球的情况 [33,34] 相比，谱的斜率没有随着球谐阶数（大于 $l = 12$）的增加而变缓（图中没有展示）。在转换途中的谱（图中空心圆）显示了偶极子的贡献比转换期间的其他模衰减得快，这在图 1 中也是非常明显的。在整个模拟期间，磁场能量在模之间混乱地持续交换，特别是在几千年尺度上偶极子（$l = 1$）和四极子（$l = 2$）模之间的反复。那么地球偶极矩在过去 150 年间的减少 [34] 也是类似的调整吗？

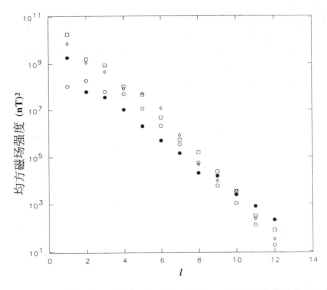

图 4. 地球表面均方磁场强度：$(l+1) \sum_m [(g_l^m)^2 + (h_l^m)^2]$，这里 g_l^m 和 h_l^m 是地核外势场的传统高斯系数。l 和 m 是球谐项的阶和次。谱对应的三个时刻和图 1、3 中的一样：方形表示倒转前，空心圆表示倒转期间，菱形表示倒转后。基于磁场卫星（MAGSAT）数据 [34] 的当今地球谱以实心圆表示。

不同采样地点的倒转

为了将模拟的倒转与古地磁倒转记录相对比，现在描述我们模拟的倒转在地球

describe how our reversal appears as observed locally at different sampling sites at the surface. We have analysed directional plots (declination and inclination) of our surface field at 50 sites distributed over the surface spanning the last 9,000 years of the simulation. These plots (not shown) indicate that the evolution of the local field direction depends greatly on the sampling location; but they all show that a reversal has occurred. By monitoring the rate of change of our surface field direction at these 50 sites we find the largest rate (at one site, at one time) to be 0.1° per day. But most sites have a maximum rate of ~0.01° per day during the reversal, which is larger than the rate observed in the secular variation of the present-day geomagnetic field[34] but much less than the impulse of 6° per day inferred from the Steens Mountain record[35], the largest rate seen in the palaeomagnetic reversal record.

By knowing the local direction of the surface field at a sampling site (that is, declination and inclination) and assuming the field to be purely dipolar, one can determine the geographical location of the virtual geomagnetic pole (VGP)[3]. In our model we can isolate just the dipolar part of the field (that is, spherical harmonics of degree $l = 1$) and compute the geographical location of the true geomagnetic pole (TGP), a luxury that palaeomagnetists do not enjoy owing to the relatively sparse set of sampling sites and the uncertainty in correlating the ages of samples from the different sites. The TGP path (Fig. 5a) during the last 9,000 years of our simulation shows several excursions (or aborted reversals)[36] occurring at different longitudes before and after the successful dipole reversal occurs. The transition itself, seen in our TGP path, takes only ~1,200 years (depending on how one defines the beginning and end of the transition) compared with estimates that range from 1,200 years to the more likely ~5,500 years, seen in the palaeomagnetic reversal record[35,37,38].

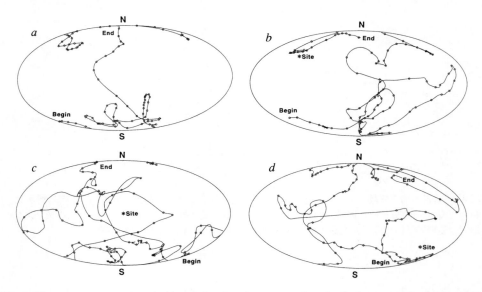

Fig. 5. The true geomagnetic pole (*a*) and the virtual geomagnetic poles (*b–d*) computed using the field directions at three surface sites: *b*, +40° latitude and 60° longitude, *c*, 0° latitude and 180° longitude, and *d*, −40° latitude and 300° longitude. The pole, with the inward-directed field, is plotted in a Hammer projection of the surface with markers at 100-year intervals during the last 9,000 years of our simulation.

728

表面不同采样地点的观测结果。我们已经分析了模拟最后 9,000 年期间 50 处位于地球表面的磁场方位图（磁倾角和磁偏角）。这些图（这里未展示）表明了局部场方向的演化很依赖于采样地点；但是它们都显示已发生了一次倒转。通过监测这 50 处磁场方向的变化速率，我们找到了最大变化速率（某一个时刻，某一个地点）是每天 0.1 度。但是在倒转期间，大多数采样地点的最大变化速率是每天 0.01 度，比当今地磁场的长期变化速率 [34] 要大一些，但比从哥伦比亚斯廷山记录推测的每天 6 度的快速变化 [35]（这是古地磁倒转记录中看到的最大的速率）还是要小得多。

　　通过了解采样点的表面磁场的局部方向（也就是磁倾角和磁偏角），并假设磁场为完全偶极子场，可以计算出虚地磁极（VGP）[3] 的地理位置。在我们的模型中，我们可以单独分离出磁场的偶极子部分（就是球谐阶数 $l = 1$），并计算出真实地磁极（TGP）的地理位置，这对古地磁学家来说是不能奢求的事情，因为他们的采样地点相对稀疏，并且不同地点样品年龄之间的关联具有不确定性。模拟末期 9,000 年内的 TGP 路径（图 5a）显示了在偶极子场倒转成功发生之前和之后，不同经度发生的数次漂移（或者说是不成功的倒转）[36]。与古地磁倒转记录中得到的从 1,200 年到更可能的 5,500 年的估计值范围相比，在我们的 TGP 路径上看到的转换本身只花了约 1,200 年的时间（取决于怎样定义转换的开始和结束）[35,37,38]。

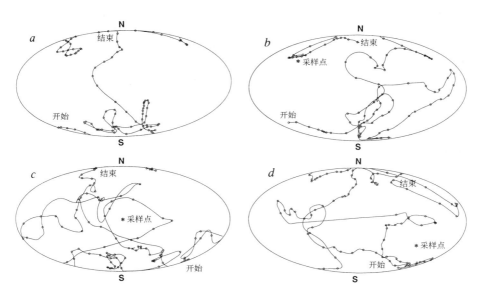

图 5. 真实地磁极（a）和利用三处表面采样点的场方向计算得到的虚地磁极（b~d）：b，北纬 40°、东经 60°；c，纬度 0°、东经 180°；d，南纬 40°、西经 60°。模拟末期 9,000 年内磁极（磁场向内）每隔 100 年用哈默投影的方式画在地球表面上。

We have plotted in Fig. 5*b*–*d* the VGP paths over the surface during the last 9,000 years of our simulation at three arbitrary sampling sites. Although these VGP paths show that a reversal has occurred, the details are strongly dependent on the sampling site (marked by an asterisk) and do not resemble the TGP path. For example, the long, nearly horizontal, 100-year segment of the VGP path in Fig. 5*d* corresponds to an "impulse" that is also seen in the directional plot at the same site but is not seen in the other VGP paths or in the TGP path. In addition, our estimate of the transition time would be significantly longer than 1,200 years if we based it only on these VGP paths.

These plots can be compared with VGP transition paths or patches from the palaeomagnetic record, which some argue occur at preferred longitudes[36,39-42] and others interpret in other ways[43-47]. But because the boundary conditions at the ICB and CMB in our present simulation are spherically symmetric, we do not and would not expect to see our excursions and transition occur along preferred longitudes[41,48,49], although we do intend to investigate this intriguing issue with modified versions of our model.

If, in addition to measuring the inclination and declination, one measures the field intensity at a given sampling site, the virtual dipole moment (VDM) of the assumed dipolar field can be computed[3]. In Fig. 6 we plot the VDM computed with the field at our same three sampling sites during the last 9,000 years of our simulation. Also plotted in Fig. 6 is our true dipole moment (TDM). The VDMs provide crude approximations to the TDMs; they correctly reflect the general decrease of the TDM before and during the transition and the recovery after the transition, which is similar to what is seen in palaeointensity records[3]. An asymmetric "saw-tooth" pattern is also seen in filtered palaeointensity records[50] but the typical time constant of the cycles is ~500,000 years, much longer than the time of our simulation spans. It is interesting that our TDM decreases to nearly its minimum value almost 2,000 years before the mid-point in the transition as seen at the ICB (the left arrow in Fig. 6). It remains low until the mid-point in the transition as seen at the surface (the right arrow in Fig. 6), when it begins its recovery. It is typically between 10×10^{22} and 20×10^{22} A m^2 during most of the simulation, compared with the Earth's present value of $\sim 8 \times 10^{22}$ A m^2. It reaches a minimum of 1.6×10^{22} A m^2 midway through the transition, which is $\sim 10\%$ of its usual value compared with the average drop to 25% seen in plots of the VDM for the Earth[3].

我们在图 5b~d 中画出了模拟最后 9,000 年，位于地球表面的三个随机采样地点的 VGP 路径。虽然这些 VGP 路径显示了倒转已经发生，但是具体细节强烈依赖于采样地点（星号标注），并且与 TGP 路径不一致。例如，图 5d 中 VGP 路径中几乎水平的、长达 100 年的那部分对应于一个"脉冲"，也可以在相同地点的方位图中看到，但是在其他 VGP 路径或者 TGP 路径上看不到。另外，如果我们只根据这些 VGP 路径，那么估计得到的转换时间会远长于 1,200 年。

这些图可以与古地磁中记录的 VGP 转换路径或者部分区域进行比较，一些人主张古地磁记录出现在特定经度[36,39-42]，另一些人则以其他方式进行解释[43-47]。但是因为在我们目前的模拟中，ICB 和 CMB 的边界条件是球对称的，所以我们不能也不将期待我们的漂移和倒转沿着特定的经度[41,48,49]发生，虽然我们确实也打算通过修改我们的模型来研究这个有趣的问题。

如果我们在给定采样点，除了能测量磁倾角和磁偏角，还能测量磁场强度的话，那么我们能够计算出假设的偶极子场产生的虚偶极矩（VDM）[3]。在图 6 中，我们用与刚才模拟中相同的三个采样点处的磁场计算画出最后 9,000 年 VDM 的变化。真实偶极矩（TDM）也画在图 6 中。VDM 提供了 TDM 的粗略的近似；VDM 正确反映了在转换前、转换中以及转换后的恢复中三种情况下 TDM 值的普遍减少，这与在地球磁场古强度记录[3]中看到的类似。一种非对称锯齿形模式也在筛选过的古强度记录[50]上出现过，但是它的典型周期是 50 万年左右，比我们的模拟时间长得多。有趣的是，大约在 ICB 可见的转换中点（图 6 左边箭头）的 2,000 年前，我们的 TDM 值就几乎减小到最小值。直到在地球表面可见的转换中点（图 6 右边箭头，TDM 值开始恢复）时，TDM 值仍然很低。与当今地球的 TDM 的典型值在 8×10^{22} A·m² 左右相比，在模拟的大部分时间，我们得到的 TDM 的典型值在 10×10^{22} A·m² 和 20×10^{22} A·m² 之间。它在转换途中达到最小值 1.6×10^{22} A·m²，与在地球 VDM 图中看到的平均降至 25% 的情况[3]相比，这个最小值是 TDM 通常值的 10%。

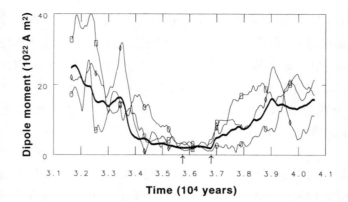

Fig. 6. The true dipole moment (heavy curve) and virtual dipole moments (marked by squares, circles and diamonds) computed using the field at the three sampling sites used in Fig. 5 during the last 9,000 years of our simulation. The times indicated are from the beginning of our simulation. The left arrow marks the mid-point in the transition as seen at the ICB, and the right arrow marks the mid-point as seen at the surface.

The relatively poor correlations in Figs 5 and 6 between the three sampling sites are due to the fact that the dipole contribution in our simulated magnetic field is not always strongly dominant (Fig. 4). This illustrates how uncertain the details of the VGPs and VDMs could be if the Earth's field were not strongly dipolar during its reversals as some palaeomagnetic reversal records suggest[44,51].

Model Limitations and Needed Improvements

With these initial results from our self-consistent global three-dimensional simulation of the geodynamo we have attempted to bridge the palaeomagnetic and dynamo modelling communities. But with so far only one reversal simulated, our explanations and conclusions about geomagnetic reversals are speculative. Certainly, more analysis is required to improve our understanding of the geodynamo and its reversal mechanism. In addition, several model improvements, which could alter our results and conclusions, will be required for more realistic simulations in the future. For example, more detailed thermodynamics, including compositional convection, is needed. The viscous, thermal and compositional eddy diffusivities should be variable and anisotropic. The effects of topography at the CMB, heterogeneous heat flux and electrical conductivity at the CMB, and luni-solar precession of the mantle could also provide interesting new insights.

(**377**, 203-209; 1995)

Gary A. Glatzmaier[*] **& Paul H. Roberts**[†]
[*] Institute of Geophysics and Planetary Physics, Los Alamos National Laboratory, Los Alamos, New Mexico 87454, USA
[†] Institute of Geophysics and Planetary Physics, University of California, Los Angeles, California 90024, USA

Received 16 June; accepted 23 August 1995.

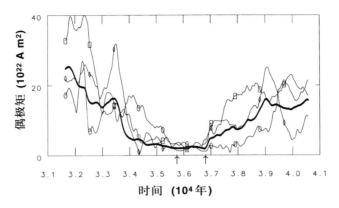

图 6. 真偶极矩（粗实线）和虚偶极矩（以方形、圆形、菱形标记），用与图 5 中相同的三处采样点的场计算得到的模拟末期 9,000 年内的虚偶极矩。标记的时间是我们模拟开始之后的时间。左边箭头标记了 ICB 处观测到的转换中点，右边箭头标记了地球表面观测到的转换中点。

在图 5 与图 6 中，三个采样点之间的相对较差的相关关系是因为在我们模拟的地磁场中，偶极场贡献率不总是非常占优势（图 4）。这说明了就像一些古地磁极性倒转记录所表明的那样，如果在倒转期间，地磁场不是以偶极子场为主的话，那么 VGPs 和 VDMs 的具体细节将会多么不确定[44,51]。

模型限制和所需改进

通过地球发电机的自洽三维模拟的初步结果，我们已经尝试了构建古地磁和发电机模拟研究团体之间联系的桥梁。但是到目前为止只有唯一一次模拟倒转，所以我们关于地磁场倒转的解释和结论都是推测的。当然，需要更多的分析来增进我们对地球发电机和其倒转机理的理解。除此之外，为了将来进行更接近实际的模拟，我们需要对我们的模型进行一些改进，这可能会改变我们的结果和结论。例如，需要考虑更详细的热力学过程（包括成分对流）。涡流的黏性扩散率、热扩散率及组分扩散率应该是变化的且各向异性的。CMB 处地形、非均质热流和电导率的影响，以及地幔的日月岁差的影响也都能提供新的、有趣的视角。

（王振华 翻译；常燎 黄宝春 审稿）

References:

1. Elsasser, W. M. *Phys. Rev.* **72**, 821-833 (1947).

2. Parker, E. N. *Astrophys. J.* **122**, 293-314 (1955).

3. Merrill, R. T. & McElhinny, M. W. *The Earth's Magnetic Field* (Academic, London, 1983).

4. Cowling, T. G. *Mon. Not. R. astr. Soc.* **94**, 34-48 (1934).

5. Roberts, P. H. & Soward, A. M. *A. Rev. Fluid Mech.* **24**, 459-512 (1992).

6. Braginsky, S. I. & Roberts, P. H. *Geophys. Astrophys. Fluid Dyn.* **38**, 327-349 (1987).

7. Olson, P. *Geophys. Res. Lett.* **16**, 613-616 (1989).

8. Barenghi, C. F. & Jones, C. A. *Geophys. Astrophys. Fluid Dyn.* **60**, 211-243 (1991).

9. Hollerbach, R. & Jones, C. A. *Nature* **365**, 541-543 (1993).

10. Glatzmaier, G. A. & Roberts, P. H. *J. Geomag. Geoelectr.* **45**, 1605-1616 (1993).

11. Nakajima, T. & Roberts, P. H. *Proc. R. Soc. Lond.* A **448**, 1-28 (1995).

12. Pekeris, C. L., Accad., Y. & Shkoller, B. *Phil. Trans. R. Soc. Lond.* A **275**, 425-461 (1973).

13. Kumar, S. & Roberts, P. H. *Proc. R. Soc. Lond.* A **314**, 235-258 (1975).

14. Gubbins, D. & Sarson, G. *Nature* **368**, 51-55 (1994).

15. Zhang, K. K. & Busse, F. H. *Phys. Earth Planet. Inter.* **59**, 208-222 (1990).

16. Arter, W. *Geophys. Astrophys. Fluid Dyn.* **31**, 311-344 (1985).

17. Matthews, P. C. in *Solar and Planetary Dynamos* (eds Proctor, M. R. E., Matthews, P. C. & Rucklidge, A. M.) 211-218 (Cambridge Univ. Press, 1993).

18. Fearn, D. R., Proctor, M. R. E. & Sellar, C. C. *Geophys. astrophys. Fluid Dyn.* **77**, 111-132 (1994).

19. Olson, P. & Glatzmaier, G. A. *Phys. Earth Planet. Inter.* (in the press).

20. Meneguzzi, M. & Pouquet, A. *J. Fluid Mech.* **205**, 297-318 (1989).

21. Brandenburg, A., Nordlund, A., Pulkkinen, P., Stein, R. F. & Tuominen, I. *Astr. Astrophys.* **232**, 277-291 (1990).

22. Nordlund, A. *et al. Astrophys. J.* **392**, 647-652 (1992).

23. St Pierre, M. G. in *Solar and Planetary Dynamos* (eds Proctor, M. R. E., Matthews, P. C. & Rucklidge, A. M.) 295-302 (Cambridge Univ. Press, 1993).

24. Gilman, P. A. & Miller, J. *Astrophys. J. Suppl.* **46**, 211-238 (1981).

25. Gilman, P. A. *Astrophys. J. Suppl.* **53**, 243-268 (1983).

26. Glatzmaier, G. A. *J. Comput. Phys.* **55**, 461-484 (1984).

27. Glatzmaier, G. A. *Astrophys. J.* **291**, 300-307 (1985).

28. Glatzmaier, G. A. *Geophys. Astrophys. Fluid Dyn.* **31**, 137-150 (1985).

29. Kageyama, A. *et al. Phys. Plasmas* **2**, 1421-1431 (1995).

30. Glatzmaier, G. A. & Roberts, P. H. *Phys. Earth Planet. Inter.* **91**, 63-76 (1995).

31. Rikitake, T. *Proc. Camb. Phil. Soc.* **54**, 89-105 (1966).

32. Bloxham, J. & Gubbins, D. *Nature* **317**, 777-781 (1985).

33. Cain, J. C., Wang, Z., Schmitz, D. R. & Meyer, J. *Geophys. J.* **97**, 443-447 (1989).

34. Langel, R. in *Geomagnetism* (ed. Jacobs, J. A.) Vol. 1, 249-512 (Academic, San Diego, 1987).

35. Coe, R. S., Prevot, M. & Camps, P. *Nature* **374**, 687-692 (1995).

36. Hoffman, K. A. *Nature* **359**, 789-794 (1992).

37. Opdyke, N. D., Kent, D. V. & Lowrie, W. *Earth Planet. Sci. Lett.* **20**, 315-324 (1973).

38. Kristjansson, L. *Geophys. J. R. astr. Soc.* **80**, 57-71 (1985).

39. Tric, E. *et al. Phys. Earth Planet. Inter.* **65**, 319-336 (1991).

40. Clement, B. M. *Earth Planet. Sci. Lett.* **104**, 48-58 (1991).

41. Laj, C., Mazaud, A., Weeks, R., Fuller, M. & Herrero-Bervera, E. *Nature* **351**, 447 (1991).

42. Ratcliff, C. D., Geissman, J. W., Perry, F. V., Crowe, B. M. & Zeitler, P. K. *Science* **266**, 412-416 (1994).

43. Langeres, C. G., van Hoof, A. A. M. & Rochette, P. *Nature* **358**, 226-230 (1992).

44. Valet, J.-P., Tuchloka, P., Courtillot, V. & Meynadier, L. *Nature* **356**, 400-407 (1992).

45. McFadden, P. L., Barton, C. E. & Merrill, R. T. *Nature* **361**, 342-344 (1993).

46. Prevot, M. & Camps, P. *Nature* **366**, 53-57 (1993).

47. McFadden, P. L. & Merrill, R. T. *J. Geophys. Res.* **100**, 307-316 (1995).

48. Runcorn, S. K. *Nature* **356**, 654-656 (1992).

49. Clement, B. M. & Stixrude, L. *Earth Planet. Sci. Lett.* **130**, 75-85 (1995).

50. Valet, J.-P. & Meynadier, L. *Nature* **366**, 234-238 (1993).

51. Clement, B. M. & Kent, D. V. *Geophys. Res. Lett.* **18**, 81-84 (1991).

Acknowledgements. The computing resources for this simulation were provided by the NSF Pittsburgh Supercomputing Center. Support for this research was provided by the Institute of Geophysics and Planetary Physics and the LDRD program at Los Alamos.

734

Bifurcations of the Atlantic Thermohaline Circulation in Response to Changes in the Hydrological Cycle

S. Rahmstorf

Editor's Note

Recent studies of ancient climate had suggested that the circulation pattern of the North Atlantic could be altered by inputs of fresh water. If the conveyor-like circulation were shut down, heat transport to high latitudes would decline, altering climate at least in the Northern Hemisphere. The possibility that melting of polar ice or sea temperature changes due to global warming could induce such a shut-down led to speculations that abrupt climate change might lie ahead. Here oceanographer Stefan Rahmstorf reports theoretical results showing that North Atlantic circulation might indeed have two distinct states, and that warming-induced changes in the hydrological cycle might be sufficient to prompt a switch between them, producing large temperatures changes in some regions within decades.

The sensitivity of the North Atlantic thermohaline circulation to the input of fresh water is studied using a global ocean circulation model coupled to a simplified model atmosphere. Owing to the nonlinearity of the system, moderate changes in freshwater input can induce transitions between different equilibrium states, leading to substantial changes in regional climate. As even local changes in freshwater flux are capable of triggering convective instability, quite small perturbations to the present hydrological cycle may lead to temperature changes of several degrees on timescales of only a few years.

THE North Atlantic Ocean today carries $(1.2 \pm 0.2) \times 10^{15}$ W of heat northwards[1,2]. Most of this heat transport is due to the vertical overturning cell associated with North Atlantic Deep Water (NADW) formation[3]; warm surface water flows northwards, sinks, and flows southwards as cold deep water. The volume transport of this "conveyor belt" is about 17 ± 4 Sv (ref. 3; 1 sverdrup $= 10^6$ m^3 s^{-1}). This heating system makes the northern North Atlantic about 4 °C warmer than corresponding latitudes in the Pacific[4] and is responsible for the mild climate of Western Europe. Variations in NADW circulation therefore have the potential to cause significant climate change in the North Atlantic region.

Previous modelling studies have suggested that the NADW circulation is a nonlinear system which is highly sensitive to changes in freshwater forcing; it may collapse if a certain threshold is exceeded[5-9] and can show hysteresis behaviour[10,11]. There is mounting palaeoclimate evidence, particularly from sediment cores, showing that past climate shifts were associated with changes in NADW flow[12-15]. Recent coupled ocean–atmosphere model experiments investigating the effect of anthropogenic greenhouse gases on climate find that

736

大西洋热盐环流的分岔对水文循环的响应

拉姆斯托夫

编者按

最近对古气候的研究表明，淡水的注入可能会改变北大西洋的环流模式。如果这种类似"传输带"的环流模式被关闭，那么传送至高纬地区的热量将会下降，这至少会改变北半球的气候。全球变暖可能导致极地冰川融化或海洋温度发生变化，继而诱发这种环流模式被关闭，由此可以推测，急剧的气候变化可能即将发生。本文中，海洋学家斯特凡·拉姆斯托夫报道了其理论结果，指出北大西洋环流可能确实存在两种不同的状态，由变暖引起的水文循环方面的一系列变化可能足以促使这两种不同状态之间相互转换，导致部分地区的温度在数十年内出现很大的变化。

利用全球大洋环流模式结合简化的大气模式对北大西洋热盐环流对淡水输入的敏感性作了研究。由于系统的非线性特征，适度的淡水输入变化会使环流模式在不同的平衡状态之间转换，进而导致区域性气候发生显著变化。由于即使淡水通量的局部变化也能够触发对流的不稳定，所以现今水文循环即使受到非常小的扰动，也可能导致在短短数年时间里温度发生几度的变化。

现今北大西洋携带着 $(1.2\pm0.2)\times10^{15}$ W 的热量向北输送[1,2]。大部分热量的输送是通过与形成北大西洋深层水（NADW）有关的垂直翻转循环完成的[3]：温暖的表层水向北流动，然后下沉，再以寒冷的深层水向南流。该"传输带"的输送量约为 17 ± 4 Sv（参考文献 3；1 sverdrup $=10^{6}$ m$^{3}\cdot$s^{-1}）。该加热体系使得北大西洋北部比相同纬度的太平洋地区高出 4 ℃左右[4]，而西欧宜人的气候正源于此。因此 NADW 环流的变化可能引起北大西洋地区气候的明显变化。

前人的模拟研究结果表明，NADW 环流是一个非线性系统，它对淡水强迫的变化高度敏感。当超过某一阈值时可能会崩溃[5-9]，并且还表现出滞后性[10,11]。越来越多的古气候证据，特别是来自沉积物岩芯的证据显示，过去气候的转换均与 NADW 环流的变化有关[12-15]。最近的海气耦合模式实验研究了人类排放的温室气体对气候

global warming would probably lead to reduced NADW formation[16,17].

Given the possibility of an anthropogenically triggered transition in NADW circulation, a systematic study of its sensitivity is urgently needed. Excessive computation costs make this not yet feasible using fully coupled ocean–atmosphere models. Here, a study of circulation transitions made with a global ocean circulation model coupled to a greatly simplified atmospheric model is presented. It is found that NADW circulation winds down when a bifurcation (first suggested by Stommel[5]) is passed, which the model predicts to occur when an additional freshwater input of less than 0.06 Sv is introduced into the catchment area of the North Atlantic. Convective instability can trigger a local shutdown of deep convection for even smaller regional changes in freshwater forcing, leading to rapid regional sea surface temperature (SST) changes within a few years. A transition to oscillatory behaviour[38] (a Hopf bifurcation) was also discovered, leading to a parameter range with self-sustained interdecadal oscillations.

Model and Experiment Design

The ocean model used in this study is the general circulation model (GCM) developed at the Geophysical Fluid Dynamics Laboratory (GFDL) in Princeton[18], in a coarse-resolution global configuration (Fig. 1a) with twelve vertical levels, similar to the models used in refs 17, 19 and 39. The model was driven by observed annual mean wind stress[20]. The surface flux of fresh water was derived from a spin-up experiment and prescribed as a fixed flux thereafter; this flux field is illustrated in ref. 21, where details of the model spin-up are also described. Regional integrals of the flux are shown in Fig. 1b; perturbations added to the freshwater flux for the sensitivity experiments are described below.

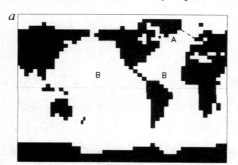
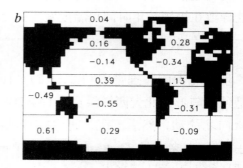

Fig. 1. a, Location map for the model experiments. The shaded areas A and B mark regions where freshwater forcing was varied; for region B the change was of opposite sign in the Atlantic and the Pacific. The Labrador Sea is marked with an asterisk, and the Greenland–Iceland–Scotland ridge separating the Atlantic from the Arctic is indicated as a dashed line. b, Regional integrals of net freshwater forcing in sverdrup (1 Sv = 10^6 m^3 s^-1). Positive values indicate net precipitation and occur in the intertropical convergence zone and in high latitudes; the subtropical gyre regions are characterized by net evaporation. The fluxes were obtained by forcing the ocean model towards observed surface salinity[4], and thus include the effect of river runoff. Note that there is no net volume transport and negligible net freshwater transport through Bering Strait in this model, so that oceanic transport across a given latitude in the Atlantic can be obtained by summing the surface fluxes from the Arctic; at the latitude of South Africa, the ocean circulation exports salt equivalent to a freshwater inflow of 0.2 Sv.

的影响，结果发现全球气候变暖很可能会导致 NADW 形成的减少[16,17]。

由于人类活动的影响可能会引起 NADW 环流的转变，因此亟需对其敏感性进行系统研究。由于完全耦合的海气模式需要的计算量太大，所以不易实现。本文将利用全球大洋环流模式结合一个极度简化的大气模式来研究环流的转变。研究结果表明，一旦通过分岔点（由施托梅尔[5]首先提出），NADW 环流将逐渐停止，而根据模式的预测，当有仅仅不到 0.06 Sv 的额外的淡水进入北大西洋补充区域时，此种情况就会发生。在淡水仅有很小的区域性变化时，它所带来的对流的不稳定都可能会引起局部深水对流关闭，进而导致区域海表温度（SST）在几年之内发生快速变化。研究中还发现了向振荡特征的过渡[38]（一种霍普夫分岔），使得各项参数以几十年为周期呈自持式振荡变化。

模式及实验设计

本研究采用的海洋模式是由位于普林斯顿的地球物理流体动力学实验所（GFDL）设计的普通环流模式（GCM）[18]。模型获得了一个分辨率不是很高的全球环流概貌图（图 1a），垂直网格分为 12 层，与参考文献 17、19 和 39 中的模式类似。该模式的驱动力为实测年均风应力[20]。表层淡水通量是根据旋转加速实验得到的，此后预设为固定通量。关于该通量场的描述见文献 21，其中还对模式旋转加速作了详细介绍。该通量在区域上的积分见图 1b。下文将介绍对淡水通量施加扰动后进行的敏感性实验情况。

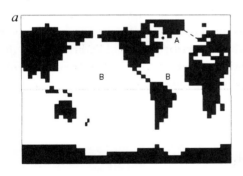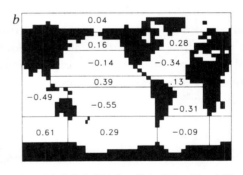

图 1. a，模式实验位置图。阴影区域 A 和 B 表示淡水强迫因子发生变化的地方。其中对于 B 区，大西洋和太平洋中的变化是相反的。拉布拉多海以星号标记，格陵兰岛－冰岛－苏格兰洋脊将大西洋与北冰洋分隔开来，在图中以虚线表示。b，净淡水强迫的区域积分，以 Sv 为单位（1 Sv = 10^6 m^3 · s^{-1}）。正值表示存在净降雨输入，通常发生在热带辐合区和高纬度地区。而亚热带环流区则以净蒸发为特征。上述通量值是通过驱动海洋模式使之达到观测的表层水盐度[4]获得的，因此也包括了径流的影响。注意，由于在该模式中没有净体积输运通过白令海峡，白令海峡的淡水净通量可以忽略不计，因此穿过大西洋上某一纬度的海洋输运量可由表面通量从北冰洋开始的加和得到。在南非所在纬度上，海洋环流输出的盐分相当于有 0.2 Sv 的淡水流入。

For thermal forcing, neither prescribing a fixed heat flux nor restoring the SST to prescribed values provides a realistic feed-back response to large-scale ocean circulation changes[22]. Therefore, a simple atmospheric energy balance was used, which damps SST anomalies by horizontal diffusion of heat in the atmosphere and by longwave radiation. This approach is discussed in detail in refs 21 and 22. It reproduces the correct SST contrast between North Pacific and North Atlantic oceans in the model equilibrium as a result of oceanic heat transport, without prescribing it in the forcing. The damping of SST anomalies depends on their spatial scale; small anomalies are removed rapidly by atmospheric transport, and the largest scales damped only by longwave radiation to space. Scale selectivity is crucial for successfully modelling local heat loss in small convection regions at the same time as the large-scale response to oceanic heat transport.

With this surface forcing, the model reaches a steady equilibrium state after an integration time of ~5,000 years. This is used as a starting point for the experiments described below. In this state, the Atlantic thermohaline circulation has the familiar two-storey structure with a NADW overturning cell of 20 Sv stacked above an opposite turning cell of Antarctic Bottom Water of 7 Sv; the Pacific and Indian oceans derive their entire deep water from an inflow of 11 Sv from the south.

In the experiments reported here, slowly varying freshwater flux perturbations were added in different ocean regions (Fig. 1a). The perturbations were increased or decreased linearly in time, in order to trace the hysteresis response of the ocean circulation. The method was inspired by a study by Mikolajewicz and Maier-Reimer[11], who investigated the effect of thermal restoring boundary conditions on freshwater discharge events of 1,000–2,000 years duration. The aim of our study is different: we attempt to trace the equilibrium response of the NADW circulation to freshwater forcing changes, that is, to construct a bifurcation map and to identify critical transitions. Consequently, the forcing was varied at a much slower rate (up to 230 times slower than described in ref. 11). Freshwater flux is used as control variable for the experiments and is therefore specified. In reality there is a feedback of sea surface temperature on the freshwater flux[23], but recent work suggests this is only weak[24].

Conveyor Hysteresis

Figure 2 shows the NADW circulation (defined as the maximum of the meridional mass transport in the Atlantic, excluding the near-surface wind-driven layers) as a function of the freshwater perturbation for a number of experiments. In Fig. 2, top panel, fresh water was added to a region south of Greenland (labelled A on Fig. 1a), with the inflow increasing or decreasing by 0.05 Sv per 1,000 years; Fig. 2, bottom panel, shows experiments where fresh water was taken from the tropical Pacific and added to the tropical Atlantic (in the regions labelled B on Fig. 1a). Figure 2 bottom also includes two additional experiments where the forcing was changed at the slower rates of 0.006 and 0.02 Sv per 1,000 years. The initial state is labelled a.

对于热强迫，不管是假定一个热通量的固定值还是将 SST 恢复至指定值都不能提供对大尺度海洋环流变化的实际反馈响应[22]。因此，我们采用了一个简单的大气能量平衡，即通过大气中热量的水平扩散和长波辐射来抵消 SST 异常。关于该方法的详细讨论见参考文献 21 和 22。在模拟平衡关系中，通过海洋热量传输，可以再现北太平洋与北大西洋之间正确的 SST 差异，而无需在强迫因子中指定。SST 异常的衰减依赖于其空间尺度，小的异常通过大气输送即可快速消除，而最大的异常则只能通过向宇宙空间的长波辐射进行消除。在小对流海域，且当海洋热量传输的大规模响应发生时，选择合适的尺度对于成功模拟局域的热量损失非常关键。

在该表层强迫因子的作用下，大约积分 5,000 年模型可达稳定平衡状态。下文所述实验即以这种平衡态作为起点。在这种状态下，大西洋热盐环流具有我们熟悉的双层结构，即 20 Sv 的 NADW 翻转流层覆盖于翻转方向与之相反的 7 Sv 南极底层水体之上。太平洋和印度洋的全部深层水则由来自南部的 11 Sv 的水流输入形成。

在本文介绍的实验中，对不同海域都加入了缓慢变化的淡水扰动流（图 1a）。扰动流流速随时间呈线性增加或降低，以便追踪大洋环流的滞后响应。该方法是受米科瓦耶维奇和迈尔–赖默尔[11]的研究所启发得到的，他们研究了热恢复边界条件对周期在 1,000~2,000 年间的淡水释放事件的影响。本研究的目的与之不同：我们试图追踪 NADW 环流对淡水强迫因子变化的平衡响应，即为了构建分岔图并确定临界点。因此，强迫因子的变化速率要低得多（为文献 11 所述值的 1/230）。淡水通量在实验中作为可控变量是人为指定的。实际上，海表温度对淡水通量有反馈作用[23]，不过新近研究表明，这种作用非常微弱[24]。

"传输带"的滞后效应

图 2 所示为多次实验中 NADW 环流（被定义为大西洋南北向水体输运最大值，不包括近海表的风驱动层）相对于淡水扰动流的变化。在图 2 中上图为淡水加到格陵兰南部海域的情况（在图 1a 中以标签 A 表示），水流输入以每 1,000 年 0.05 Sv 的速度增大或减小。图 2 中下图所示为热带太平洋中的淡水加入热带大西洋后的情况（该区域在图 1a 中以 B 表示）。图 2 中的下图还包含了另外两次实验，其中淡水强迫的变化速率较慢，约每 1,000 年 0.006 Sv 和 0.02 Sv。初始状态以 a 表示。

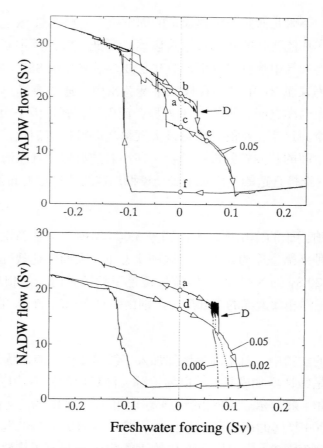

Fig. 2. Hysteresis response of the North Atlantic overturning circulation to a slowly changing freshwater forcing in the high latitudes (top panel) and the tropics (bottom panel; see Fig. 1 for exact locations). (NADW, North Atlantic Deep Water). Open circles mark true model equilibria obtained with constant freshwater forcing; the equilibrium marked a is the initial state at the start of the experiment. Arrows mark the direction in which the curve is traced. After one hysteresis loop, starting from a towards the right, the model arrives at equilibrium b. From there the right half of the hysteresis curve was traced a second time. Point c was reached by reversing at point e. Point f is an equilibrium with no NADW formation, under present-day forcing. The discontinuity D is the point where Labrador Sea convection ceases. In the lower panel, the right half of the hysteresis curve was traced at three different rates; the rate of freshwater forcing change is labelled in units of 10^{-3} Sv yr^{-1}.

The hysteresis curves show a decline in NADW overturning with increasing freshwater input into the North Atlantic. Beyond a certain value, overturning is essentially zero (the small remaining background transport is due to the fact that the meridional stream function never becomes negative everywhere, even in the absence of NADW formation). For an intermediate forcing range which includes present-day climate, NADW overturning can be either "on" or "off" (as in equilibrium f), depending only on initial conditions.

The inflow of Antarctic Bottom Water into the Atlantic decreases slightly as NADW flow weakens in the model. In the Pacific, the bottom water circulation also weakens, and after the breakdown of NADW flow an overturning cell of 10 Sv starts between 30° N and 60° N. This

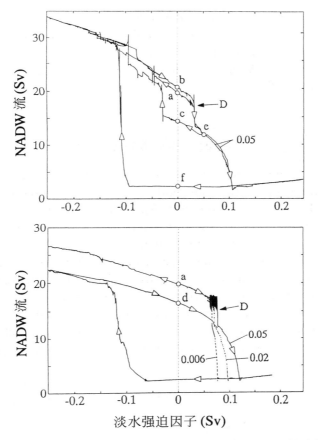

图 2. 在高纬（上图）和热带地区（下图，确切位置见图 1），北大西洋翻转流对缓慢变化的淡水强迫因子的滞后响应。(NADW 代表北大西洋深层水)。空心圆圈表示当淡水强迫因子保持不变时得到的真实模拟平衡态，平衡态 a 表示实验开始时的初始状态。箭头表示追踪曲线的方向。一次滞后循环以后，由 a 向右开始，模型再次达到平衡状态 b。从这开始对滞后循环的右半部分作了二次追踪。点 c 是从 e 点反转后到达的。点 f 是当今淡水通量条件下无 NADW 形成时的一种平衡状态。不连续点 D 表示拉布拉多海对流停止的位置。在下图中，以三种不同速率研究了滞后循环的右半部分的变化情况，淡水强迫变化速率的单位为 10^{-3} Sv · yr^{-1}。

　　滞后曲线显示 NADW 翻转流随向北大西洋输入的淡水的增加呈降低趋势。超过一定值以后翻转流的量实质上已变为零（剩余的很少量的背景输送值是因为无论在什么地方经向流函数都不会是负值，即使没有 NADW 形成时也一样）。当包括现代气候的强迫变化适中时，NADW 翻转流可能是"开"亦可能是"关"（如同点 f 所处的平衡状态），具体情况仅取决于初始条件。

　　在模式中，随着 NADW 流的减弱，流入大西洋的南极底层水体亦缓慢减少。在太平洋，底层环流亦有所减弱，而当 NADW 流瓦解以后，在 30°N 和 60°N 之间开始

North Pacific cell (not shown) reaches 1,500 m depth and recirculates within the Northern Hemisphere with no outflow to the south, resembling the hemispheric circulation envisaged in Stommel's[5] original box model. It shows a clear hysteresis response even if the forcing changes only in the North Atlantic, constituting an interesting oceanic teleconnection between Atlantic and Pacific oceans.

Saddle-node Bifurcation

The general shape of the hysteresis curves and their bimodal structure can be understood with the help of Stommel's[5] classical box model of the thermohaline circulation (which can be generalized to allow cross-hemispheric flow). Figure 3 shows the equilibrium solutions of this simple model as a function of freshwater flux. The positive branch corresponds to the overturning of NADW, while the negative flow branch corresponds to a reverse flow. The branch shown dashed is unconditionally unstable, and separates the basins of attraction of the two stable branches. Point S is a turning point, or saddle-node bifurcation, beyond which no stable positive solution exists. The thin lines were obtained by time integration with slowly increasing fresh-water flux, as in the GCM experiments shown in Fig. 2. They show that the equilibrium branch can be tracked closely by a slow forcing increase—except near the bifurcation point, where the model response becomes infinitely sluggish.

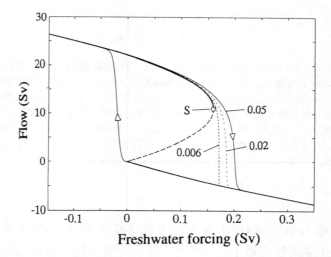

Fig. 3. Equilibrium flow and hysteresis response of Stommel's box model. Heavy curves show the analytical equilibrium solution; the dashed branch is unstable. S is the location of the saddle-node bifurcation. Thin lines are the result of a time integration with a freshwater forcing cycle identical to that used in the GCM experiments shown in Fig. 2. Note that freshwater forcing is given in absolute values for the box model, whereas for the GCM it is relative to the present-day climate.

A crucial question is where Stommel's bifurcation is located in the real world, and, as an approximation to this, in the GCM. In other words, what is the critical change in hydrological

形成一个 10 Sv 大小的翻转流循环。该北太平洋环流（图中未标出）深度可达 1,500 m，且在北半球范围内往复循环，并不向南流动，这与施托梅尔[5]提出的原始箱式模型中的半球环流相似。这表明，即使仅北大西洋的淡水通量发生变化，也会存在明显的滞后响应，由此形成一个在大西洋与太平洋之间有趣的海洋遥相关关系。

鞍 结 分 岔

根据施托梅尔[5]提出的热盐环流的经典箱式模型（该模型可推广应用至跨半球的环流模式中），有助于理解滞后曲线的一般形态及其双峰结构。图 3 所示为根据该简易模型得到的随淡水通量变化的平衡解。正向分支对应 NADW 翻转流，而负向分支则对应一股反向水流。虚线所示分支是无条件不稳定解，它将两个稳定分支的吸引盆分隔开来。S 点是一个转向点，或称为鞍结分岔点，该点以外不存在稳定正解。图中细线是缓慢增大的淡水通量随时间的积分得到的，与图 2 所示 GCM 实验中相同。这些细线表明，我们可以通过缓慢提高强迫因子来密切跟踪平衡分支的变化，但结点附近除外，因为在结点附近模型的响应变得无限滞后。

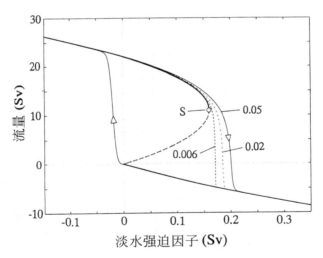

图 3. 平衡流及施托梅尔箱式模型的滞后响应。粗线表示解析平衡解，虚线分支为不稳定解。S 为鞍结分岔点的位置。细线为一个时间积分曲线，其中淡水强迫循环与图 2 中所示 GCM 实验中的相同。需要注意的是，在箱式模型中淡水强迫是一个给定的绝对值，而在 GCM 中则是一个与现今气候对应的相对值。

其中一个关键问题是：现实世界中施托梅尔模型的分岔点位于何处，以及它的近似值——GCM 中的分岔点位置。换句话说，引起现今 NADW 传输带环流关闭的

forcing which would trigger the shutdown of the present NADW conveyor belt circulation? From the box-model analogy, we conclude that the hysteresis experiments with the GCM can only provide an upper limit of this value. Figure 2, bottom panel, shows three GCM runs with different rates of forcing change (as in Fig. 3) and gives an upper limit of 0.075 Sv for the critical flux. To test for equilibrium, in a number of further experiments freshwater forcing was held constant after certain values had been reached. For the high-latitude perturbation (Fig. 2, top), the model was still stable and the hysteresis curve close to equilibrium at a flux of 0.05 Sv, but at 0.06 Sv it was beyond the bifurcation and wound down. Similarly, for the low-latitude perturbation the bifurcation was found to be between 0.056 and 0.062 Sv. The corresponding critical rate of NADW overturning is close to 12 Sv; smaller rates of NADW formation cannot apparently be sustained by the model.

It is remarkable that the critical amount of freshwater input is essentially the same, whether added in the high-latitude convection region or in the low latitudes. This is because the mechanism underlying Stommel's bifurcation is a large-scale advective mechanism. It does not much matter where the fresh water is added, as long as it passes through the NADW loop before leaving the Atlantic, that is, it is added to the "NADW catchment area". This catchment area will not have a sharp boundary in a turbulent ocean; for example, fresh water added to the South Atlantic can be expected partly to flow north in the conveyor and partly to exit to the Southern Ocean through wind-driven circulation. The catchment area also depends on the circulation itself.

It is difficult to assess which changes in atmospheric circulation would be required to increase the freshwater transport into the NADW catchment area by 0.06 Sv, but Fig. 1*b* indicates that the change would only be a fraction of the climatological flux. In the coupled experiment of Manabe and Stouffer[17,25] for a quadrupling of the atmospheric level of CO_2, NADW formation is completely extinguished by a net precipitation increase in the North Atlantic, while sea-ice melting makes a negligible contribution. If a freshwater flux of 0.06 Sv were to be obtained only by melting sea ice, the entire Arctic sea-ice volume ($2-3 \times 10^{13}\,\mathrm{m}^3$) would need to melt during a period of 10–15 years, a time span too short to cause an advective spin-down of the circulation. The timescale of the shutdown is determined by the advection of salt in the overturning circulation and is typically several hundred years; the more the critical flux is exceeded, the faster the spin-down. Sea-ice melting is, therefore, not a viable mechanism for causing an advective spin-down, but could lead to convective transitions as discussed in the next section. For comparison, meltwater inflow from the disintegration of continental ice sheets at the end of the last glacial peaked at 0.44 Sv and lasted many centuries[26].

Convective Instability

Although the overall shape of the hysteresis curves can be explained by Stommel's box model, there are also interesting discontinuities, most notably the one marked D in Fig. 2. When we start from point e on the equilibrium curve and move to the left, a new

水文强迫因子所发生的关键变化是什么？根据箱式模型的类比，我们可以得出结论，GCM 滞后实验只能获得该值的上限。图 2 中下图所示为三种不同强迫因子变化速率下的 GCM 实验结果（如图 3），从中得到的临界通量的上限为 0.075 Sv。为了对平衡状态作进一步测试，在后续的诸多实验中，当达到一定值后淡水通量保持恒定。对于高纬扰动流（图 2 上图），当通量为 0.05 Sv 时，该模型仍保持稳定，且其滞后曲线与平衡时非常接近，但在 0.06 Sv 时，就超出了鞍结分岔点，并逐渐停止。类似地，对于低纬扰动流，分岔点见于 0.056 Sv 和 0.062 Sv 之间。与此对应的 NADW 翻转流的临界速率接近 12 Sv。该模型无法维持更小的 NADW 形成的速率。

值得注意的是，不管是在高纬对流海域还是低纬海域，淡水输入的临界通量均基本相同。这是因为在隐藏于施托梅尔的鞍结分岔理论下的机制，是一个大尺度平流机制。因此，淡水输入在哪增加并不是非常重要，只要它在离开大西洋之前会穿过 NADW 环流圈即可，也就是说，只要它进入"NADW 补充区域"内即可。在动荡的海洋中，该补充区域并无明显边界。例如，进入到南大西洋的淡水可能一部分在"传输带"的作用下向北流动，而另一部分通过风生环流离开并进入南大洋。此外，补充区域还取决于环流本身。

我们很难评估大气环流中哪些变化能够使进入 NADW 补充区域的淡水输送量提高 0.06 Sv，但图 1b 显示，该变化量应该只有一部分属于气候学通量。在真锅和斯托弗 [17,25] 的耦合实验中，他们将大气 CO_2 含量提高至四倍，北大西洋地区净降水量的增加即可导致 NADW 的形成完全消失，而海冰融化的贡献则可忽略不计。倘若 0.06 Sv 的淡水通量仅靠海冰融化，则北极地区全部海冰（$2 \times 10^{13} \sim 3 \times 10^{13}$ m³）需要在 10~15 年期间全部融化，而这样一个时间跨度太短，不足以促使环流关闭。环流关闭的时间尺度取决于翻转环流的盐度平流，通常为数百年。临界通量被超出得越多，环流关闭越快。因此，海冰融化并非导致平流关闭的可行机制，但它可能会引起对流形式的转变，关于这一点我们将在下节讨论。为了比较，我们应该知道，在末次冰期的末期，大陆冰川碎裂形成的融水输入通量的最大值为 0.44 Sv 并且持续了数百年 [26]。

对流的不稳定性

虽然滞后曲线的总体形状可用施托梅尔的箱式模型来解释，但其中还存在一些有趣的不连续现象，最显著的一个就是图 2 中的 D 点。当我们在平衡曲线上由点 e

equilibrium branch is found with a lesser NADW overturning rate. And when a full hysteresis cycle is completed, we arrive at not the initial state a, but a different equilibrium state (b or d respectively). We are thus finding multiple equilibrium states with different NADW formation rates under the same forcing.

Similar multiple equilibria have previously been found and analysed in idealized models[27-29]; they are linked to different stable convection patterns and are caused by a positive feedback mechanism which can make convection self-sustaining once it has been established at a certain point. The convection patterns for several equilibria marked in Fig. 2 are shown in Fig. 4. The crucial difference between model states with ~20 Sv overturning and those with only ~16 Sv overturning is the absence of Labrador Sea convection in the latter. Time series of convection depth at single points (not shown) confirm that at the discontinuity D Labrador convection shuts down. Other small jumps in the circulation time series can generally be attributed to a change in convection somewhere in the model. Associated circulation changes appear almost instantaneous, as adjustment to convection changes occurs through a mechanism of wave propagation[30,31] which takes only a few years to complete. Convective instability is therefore a mechanism that could lead to rapid climate shifts such as the Younger Dryas event[29].

Convective instability does not depend on the large-scale freshwater budget but on local flux. This is why the shutdown of Labrador convection occurs for a much smaller freshwater input for the high-latitude perturbation than for the low-latitude perturbation (compare Fig 2 top and bottom). Further experiments showed that a perturbation of 0.015 Sv is enough to cause the shutdown if targeted directly at the Labrador Sea. This demonstrates that rather small changes in freshwater forcing may lead to regional shutdown of convection. In the real world and in fully coupled models, the distinction between similar equilibria (such as a and b) may be blurred by atmospheric variability, but qualitatively different convection patterns (such as a and c) should represent distinct climate states (see the discussion in Rahmstorf[21]). Sediment-core results[15] have linked past climate change to a regional shift in NADW convection, from the Norwegian Sea to a location south of Iceland.

开始向左移动时，就可以发现个一新的平衡分支，而其 NADW 翻转速率相对较小。当一个完整的滞后循环完成时，并不是回到起始状态 a，而是到达另一种不同的平衡状态（分别为 b 或 d）。由此我们就找到了在同等外界强迫因素作用下，与不同 NADW 形成速率对应的多个平衡态。

类似的多平衡在理想化模型中[27-29]已有发现，并且作过分析，它们与不同的稳定对流模式有关，并且均由正反馈机制所导致，一旦在某点建立起平衡，它可以形成对流的自维持机制。图 2 中标出的多个平衡态的对流模式见图 4。当翻转流分别为 20 Sv 和 16 Sv 时，两种模拟状态的主要差异是，后者不存在拉布拉多海对流。在单个点上（未在图中标出）对流深度的时间序列证明，在 D 不连续处拉布拉多对流关闭。环流时间序列中其他小的跳跃通常可认为是模型中某处对流变化的结果。与此相关的环流变化几乎是瞬时的，对流变化的调节机制是通过波动传播的[30,31]，而完成这种波动传播所需的时间仅为数年。因此，对流不稳定性是一种能够导致快速气候变化，如新仙女木事件[29]的机制。

对流不稳定性并不依赖于大尺度的淡水收支平衡，而是取决于局部的淡水通量大小。这正是在高纬扰动下拉布拉多对流关闭时淡水输入远小于低纬扰动下相应情况的原因所在（比较图 2 中上下两幅图）。进一步的实验结果显示，倘若扰动流直接流向拉布拉多海，那么当通量为 0.015 Sv 时即足以导致该环流关闭。由此证明，即使淡水强迫发生很小的变化都有可能导致区域性的对流关闭。在现实世界以及完全耦合模式中，相似平衡态（如 a 和 b）之间的区别可能会因大气的变化而难以区分，不过性质不同的对流模式（如 a 和 c）代表着不同的气候状态（见拉姆斯托夫[21]中的讨论）。沉积物岩芯研究结果[15]已将过去的气候变化与 NADW 对流从挪威海到冰岛南部站位的区域性转换联系在了一起。

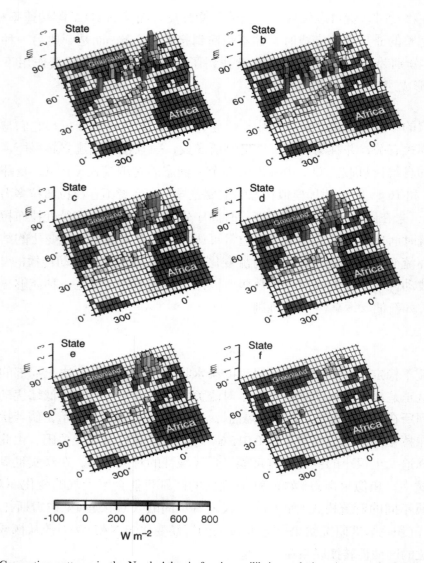

Fig. 4. Convection patterns in the North Atlantic for six equilibrium solutions (states a–f) of the ocean model as labelled in Fig. 2. The height of the columns shows convection depth from the surface, and colour indicates the amount of heat (W m^{-2}) brought to the surface by convection. Convection is the main process by which the heat brought to the north in the conveyor circulation is released from the water column. Note that states a and b have convection in the Labrador Sea, whereas in c–e NADW is formed only east of Greenland. State f is a "southern sinking" state without NADW formation.

Interdecadal Oscillations

A further interesting feature of the hysteresis curves is the occurrence of interdecadal oscillations in certain parameter ranges. The most spectacular oscillation arises in Fig. 2, bottom panel, just before the Labrador discontinuity D. Figure 5 shows a close-up view of

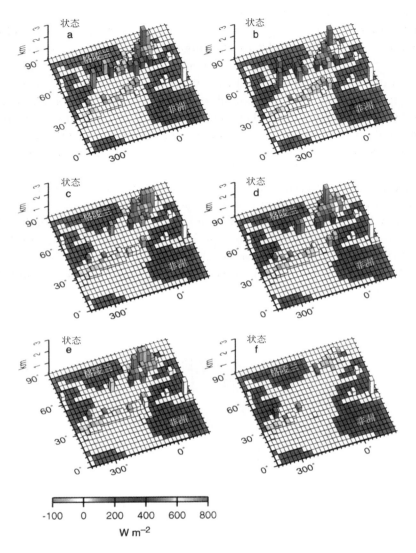

W m⁻²

图 4. 图 2 中标出的海洋模型的六个平衡状态下北大西洋中的对流模式（状态 a~f）。柱体的高度代表从表层算起的对流深度，其颜色则表示由对流带到表层的热量的多少（$W \cdot m^{-2}$）。传输带环流将热量向北输送，这些热量通过对流过程从水柱中释放出来。注意，状态 a 和 b 下拉布拉多海中存在对流，而在 c~e 中，NADW 则仅形成于格陵兰岛东部。f 状态是一种"南部下沉"状态，无 NADW 形成。

年代际振荡

滞后曲线的另一个有趣特征是一定参数范围内年代际振荡的出现。最壮观的一次振荡（见图 2 的下图）就出现在拉布拉多不连续点 D 之前。图 5 所示为曲线上相关部分的近景图，图中揭示，一个霍普夫分岔（H）导致一个稳定模式转变为一次为期 22

the relevant section of the curve; it reveals that a Hopf bifurcation (H) leads to a transition from a stable model solution to a limit cycle with a period of 22 years. This period is independent of the rate at which freshwater input is increased. The overturning rate varies by as much as 3 Sv, and the average temperature of the high-latitude North Atlantic by 0.2 °C. The temperature maximum lags behind the overturning maximum by about 3 years. As one would expect from the short period, this oscillation is local to the North Atlantic; it is also deep—the flow oscillates in a region between 20° N and 60° N over the whole depth range. Surprisingly, Labrador Sea convection is not affected; convection depths remain completely stationary throughout the oscillation. The sea surface temperature pattern associated with the oscillation is shown in Fig. 6a. With its maximum near Newfoundland, it resembles the observed interdecadal variability pattern shown by Kushnir[32], except that it lacks the second maximum found in the data near the sea-ice margin north of Iceland. This second maximum may be linked to sea-ice variations; no ice model is included in the present study. A much weaker oscillation with a period of 16 years arises in the high-latitude experiment (Fig. 2, top), again just before the Labrador convection shuts down. Similar interdecadal SST oscillations centred on the Labrador region have been found in a number of studies with different models[33-35].

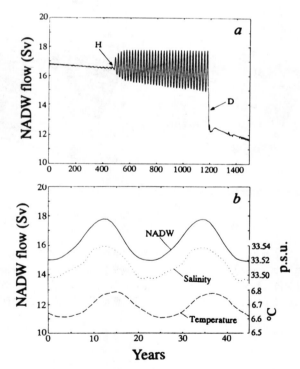

Fig. 5. *a*, Close-up view of the oscillations visible in Fig. 2, bottom panel, just before the shut-down point D of Labrador convection. The time axis is labelled in years with an arbitrary origin. At point H, the model passes a Hopf bifurcation, where the stable equilibrium state gives way to a limit cycle with a period of 22 years. Note that the amplitude initially increases as the square root of the control parameter (freshwater flux, which in this case is proportional to time); a characteristic feature of Hopf bifurcations[38]. *b*, Two periods of the oscillation at higher time resolution. Also shown are surface salinity and temperature, averaged over the Atlantic north of 50° N.

年的有限循环。该周期与淡水输入的增加速率无关。翻转速率的变化可达 3 Sv，北大西洋的高纬地区平均温度变化则为 0.2 ℃。温度极大值比翻转极大值滞后约达 3 年。正如短期变化一样，该振荡也仅限于北大西洋。而且该振荡也很深，在 20°N 和 60°N 之间振荡可达到全水深。令人意外的是，拉布拉多海对流并未受影响，在整个振荡过程中其对流深度仍完全保持不变。与该振荡有关的海表温度模式见图 6a。其最大值出现在纽芬兰岛附近，与库什尼尔[32] 给出的年代际变化类型相似，只是缺少在冰岛北部的海冰边缘附近数据中发现的第二个最高值。第二个最高值可能与海冰的变化有关，但是在本研究中并未包含任何冰川模型。在高纬海域实验中，在拉布拉多对流关闭之前见到一个为期 16 年振荡，但其强度要弱得多（图 2 的上图）。利用不同模型得到的多项研究均发现，类似的年代际 SST 振荡集中在拉布拉多海域中[33-35]。

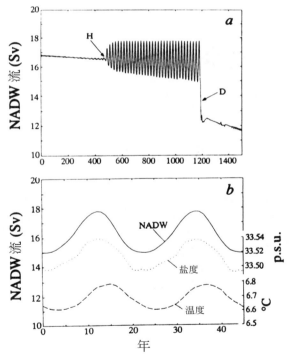

图 5. *a*，图 2 的下图中可以看到的拉布拉多对流关闭点 D 之前的振荡变化的近视图。时间轴的单位为年，原点任意指定。在 H 点模型穿过了一个霍普夫分岔点，由稳定平衡态转变为周期为 22 年的有限循环。注意，曲线的振幅以控制参数（淡水通量，在这里它与时间呈正比）的平方根递增，这正是霍普夫分岔的典型特征[38]。*b*，高时间分辨率下的两个振荡周期。图中还给出 50°N 以北的大西洋中表层盐度和温度的平均值。

Consequences for Climate

Given the large heat transport of the NADW conveyor belt, it is natural to ask what the bifurcations described above mean for Atlantic surface temperatures. Because of the simple atmospheric heat budget employed, the model has a limited capacity to predict SST changes resulting from circulation changes. The equilibrium with the strongest overturning (state b), also has the warmest high-latitude SST. Figure 6 shows SST differences of other model states compared to initial state a, as well as the SST change over one of the oscillation cycles discussed above (Fig. 6a). The interdecadal oscillation has a range of 0.7 °C near Newfoundland and decreases to under 0.2 °C near the European coast. The difference between normal and weak NADW circulation equilibria (Fig. 6b) is larger; it reaches a maximum of 2.5 °C near Newfoundland. The cooling predicted for a total shutdown of NADW circulation (Fig. 6c) reaches a maximum of 6 °C near Greenland, with widespread cooling of over 4 °C across the Atlantic. Note that a fully coupled experiment would probably show an amplified temperature response near ice margins due to the ice–albedo feedback (not included in this model). The cooling effect would also extend further north in a model that produces more NADW north of the Greenland–Scotland ridge.

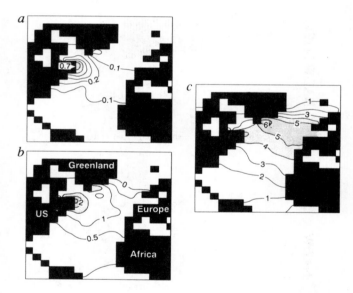

Fig. 6. Sea surface temperature change (in °C) for three types of NADW circulation changes. a, Difference between warm and cold phase of the inter-decadal oscillation; b, difference between "normal" and "weak" NADW equilibria (states a minus c of Fig. 2); c, difference between "normal" and absent NADW circulation (states a minus f of Fig. 2). Shading highlights regions of strongest sea surface temperature change; states with stronger NADW overturning are warmer in each case.

对气候的影响

鉴于 NADW"传输带"输送的大量热能，我们很自然地要问，上述分岔点对大西洋表层温度有何意义？由于我们所采用的大气热收支平衡非常简单，所以该模型在预测环流变化导致的 SST 变化方面具局限性。最强翻转流的平衡状态（状态 b）下的高纬 SST 也最高。图 6 给出了其他模型状态与初始态 a 的差异以及上述某个振荡循环中 SST 的变化（图 6a）。在纽芬兰岛附近，年代际振荡的范围为 0.7 ℃，而到欧洲海岸附近则降为 0.2 ℃ 以内。正常的 NADW 环流平衡与减弱的环流平衡之间的差异（图 6b）则更大，在纽芬兰岛附近可达 2.5 ℃ 的最大值。据预测，在格陵兰岛附近，当 NADW 环流完全关闭时（图 6c），温度最大可降低 6 ℃，同时大西洋中广泛区域降温超过 4 ℃。需要注意的是，由于冰的反射反馈（并未包括在本模型内），完全耦合实验很可能会放大冰缘附近的温度响应。在格陵兰－苏格兰洋脊北部有更多 NADW 生成的模型中这种降温效应也会扩至更北部。

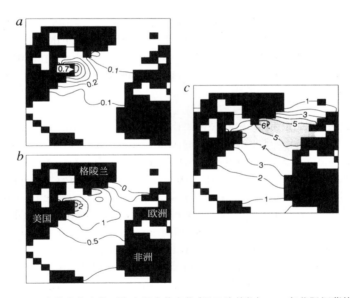

图 6. 三种类型 NADW 环流变化条件下海表温度的变化（以 ℃ 为单位）。a，年代际振荡的冷相位和暖相位的差异；b，"正常"和"减弱"状态下 NADW 平衡态的差异（图 2 中状态 a 减状态 c）；c，"正常"与缺乏 NADW 环流下的差异（图 2 中状态 a 减状态 f）。阴影部分表示海表温度变化最强的区域，各种情形下都是 NADW 翻转流越强温度越高。

Overall Features of the Bifurcation Map

The experiments discussed in this Article provide a map of the equilibrium states and bifurcation points of the Atlantic thermohaline circulation in a global ocean GCM, as a function of the surface freshwater flux. The central feature is a saddle-node bifurcation first described by Stommel[5] in 1961; it is the point beyond which the NADW circulation cannot be sustained, winding down on an advective timescale of centuries. The spin-down is characterized by gradually weakening heat transport and convection, and must be distinguished from the dramatic instability which occurs when convection is suddenly interrupted in the entire North Atlantic—a much faster process known as "polar halocline catastrophe". Due to the slow forcing change this kind of collapse, which may be temporary or permanent, was not observed in the experiments reported here, but it has been found in models subjected to rapid and massive meltwater discharge[9,22,39].

Stommel's bifurcation is a very robust feature, found in models of different complexity—from simple box models to GCMs. In our GCM, the critical point is reached for an additional freshwater input of only 0.06 Sv into the NADW catchment area. This is much less than a previous estimate of 0.3 Sv, which was obtained with an idealized two-dimensional model without wind forcing[10]. The new estimate is an uncomfortably small perturbation to the present hydrological cycle (compare Fig. 1b). It is impossible to give an error margin on this estimate, but it depends not on regional details, only on the basin-scale circulation, which the model reproduces quite well. A slow spin-down, which seems to be of the type discussed here, was found in a coupled model scenario[17] for a quadrupling of atmospheric CO_2.

A second feature of the bifurcation map is the existence of multiple states with different rates of NADW formation. Transitions between these states can be triggered for even smaller, regional changes in the freshwater budget, and they can lead to substantial SST changes within a few years. In this model, the major transition is between states with and without convection in the Labrador Sea. This result, however, depends on regional details of convection, which are not properly resolved in a coarse model; the physical principle is likely to be robust, although the specific details may not be. In the real world, a substantial part of NADW is formed north of Iceland, but present climate models have trouble representing the physics of the overflow over the Greenland–Scotland ridge. There is good evidence that convection north of Iceland shut down in glacial times[15]. It is possible that this convection region is more vulnerable to climate change than the one in the Labrador Sea; this cannot be determined using the present model. The freshwater balance of this convection region can be upset by precipitation changes, by melting ice (melting Arctic sea ice at a rate of 5 cm yr^{-1} would provide a freshwater flux of ~0.01 Sv), but also by changes in regional currents. For example, the East Greenland current presently removes some of the net precipitation falling over the Arctic seas, transporting it southwards over the sill[36]. It is therefore difficult to establish how vulnerable the present convection pattern is to climate changes, or indeed whether deep convection north of Iceland has ceased already[37].

分岔图的总体特征

本文所讨论的实验为我们提供以表层淡水通量的函数表示的全球海洋环流模式中北大西洋热盐环流的平衡状态和分岔结点图。其中心特征是由施托梅尔[5]于1961年首先提出的一个鞍结点分岔，该点以外NADW环流无法继续维持，并以数百年的对流时间尺度减小。环流的关闭以热量输送和对流的逐渐减弱为特征，而这种关闭应该与当整个北大西洋中的对流突然被打断时发生的显著不稳定区别开来，后者是一种快得多的过程，通常被称为"极地盐跃层灾难"。由于强迫因子的变化非常缓慢，本文所介绍的实验中并未见到此类崩溃（有些是暂时，有些是永久性的），但在有大量融水快速释放时的模型中发现过[9,22,39]。

施托梅尔提出的分岔是一种非常强的特征，见于不同复杂程度的模型中——从简单的箱式模型到GCM模型都有。在我们的GCM模型中，当额外淡水向NADW补充区域的输入通量仅为0.06 Sv时即达临界点。这远低于之前估计的0.3 Sv，当时是根据理想化二维模型得到的，未考虑风强迫的影响[10]。对于现今的水文循环来说新估计值只是很小的一个扰动（对比图1b）。要想给出该值的一个误差界限是不可能的，不过该误差并不取决于区域细节，而只取决于海盆尺度上的环流，该模型在这个尺度上模拟得很好。当大气CO_2浓度提高至原来的四倍时，在耦合模型中[17]见到了一种缓慢的关闭形式，似乎正是本文所讨论的类型。

分岔图的另一个特征是不同NADW形成速率下多种平衡状态的存在。淡水通量中即使存在很小的、区域性的变化也会引发这些状态之间的转换，从而导致数年内SST发生实质性变化。在该模型中，最主要的是拉布拉多海中有无对流状态的转换。然而，该结果取决于对流的区域性详细特征，这一点在粗略的模型中无法得到很好的解决。不过，虽然其中具体细节有些变化，但其物理原理是不变的。现实世界中，有相当一部分的NADW形成于冰岛北部，但现今的气候模型在描述越过格陵兰–苏格兰洋脊的溢流的物理学方面存在一些问题。有足够的证据显示，冰岛北部的对流在冰期时是关闭的[15]。可能相比于拉布拉多海，该区域的对流对气候变化更加敏感，关于这一点，利用现今的模型还无法确定。该对流区域的淡水收支平衡可能会受到降水变化、融冰（北极海冰融化速率为5 cm·yr^{-1}时，它所能提供的淡水通量将达0.01 Sv左右）等的影响，但同时也受区域性海流变化的影响。例如，东格陵兰海流现今正将北极海域的部分净降水量跨过海槛向南输送[36]。因此，很难确定现今的对流模式对于气候变化到底有多敏感，或者冰岛北部的深层水对流现在是否已经停止[37]。

The third feature is the existence of the Hopf bifurcation, leading to an oscillation of the meridional overturning rate centred on the Labrador region. This bifurcation suggests that there are parameter ranges where the ocean circulation is intrinsically steady and would vary only in response to variable atmospheric forcing, and other parameter regions where the ocean generates self-sustained interdecadal oscillations. This opens the possibility that a change in hydrological forcing can shift the North Atlantic from a stable climate to an oscillatory regime, or vice versa. It will be an important topic of future research to establish the exact forcing conditions under which oscillations occur.

(378, 145-149; 1995)

Stefan Rahmstorf

Institut für Meereskunde, Düsternbrooker Weg 20, 24105 Kiel, Germany

Received 7 July; accepted 13 October 1995.

References:

1. Hall, M. M. & Bryden, H. L. *Deep-Sea Res.* **29**, 339-359 (1982).
2. Rintoul, S. R. & Wunsch, C. *Deep-Sea Res.* **38**, S355-S377 (1991).
3. Roemmich, D. H. & Wunsch, C. *Deep-Sea Res.* **32**, 619-664 (1985).
4. Levitus, S. *Climatological Atlas of the World Ocean* (US Dept of Commerce, NOAA, Washington DC, 1982).
5. Stommel, H. *Tellus* **13**, 224-230 (1961).
6. Bryan, F. *Nature* **323**, 301-304 (1986).
7. Manabe, S. & Stouffer, R. J. *J. Clim.* **1**, 841-866 (1988).
8. Marotzke, J. & Willebrand, J. *J. Phys. Oceanogr.* **21**, 1372-1385 (1991).
9. Maier-Reimer, E. & Mikolajewicz, U. in *Oceanography* (eds Ayala-Castañares. A., Wooster, W. & Yáñez-Arancibia, A.) 87-100 (UNAM, Mexico, 1989).
10. Stocker, T. F. & Wright, D. G. *Nature* **351**, 729-732 (1991).
11. Mikolajewicz, U. & Maier-Reimer, E. *J. Geophys. Res.* **99**, 22633-22644 (1994).
12. Broecker, W. S., Peteet, D. M. & Rind, D. *Nature* **315**, 21-26 (1985).
13. Boyle, E. A. & Keigwin, L. *Nature* **330**, 35-40 (1987).
14. Keigwin, L. D., Curry, W. B., Lehman, S. J. & Johnson, S. *Nature* **371**, 323-326 (1994).
15. Sarnthein, M. *et al. Paleoceanography* **9**, 209-267 (1994).
16. Cubasch, U. *et al. Clim. Dyn.* **8**, 55-69 (1992).
17. Manabe, S. & Stouffer, R. J. *Nature* **364**, 215-218 (1993).
18. Pacanowski, R., Dixon, K. & Rosati, A. *The GFDL Modular Ocean Model Users Guide* (Tech. Rep. Vol. 2, Geophysical Fluid Dynamics Laboratory Ocean Group, Princeton, 1991).
19. England, M. H. *J. Phys. Oceanogr.* **23**, 1523-1552 (1993).
20. Hellerman, S. & Rosenstein, M. *J. Phys. Oceanogr.* **13**, 1093-1104 (1983).
21. Rahmstorf, S. *Clim. Dyn.* **11**, 447-458 (1995).
22. Rahmstorf, S. & Willebrand, J. *J. Phys. Oceanogr.* **25**, 787-805 (1995).
23. Marotzke, J. in *Ocean Processes in Climate Dynamics: Global and Mediterranean Examples* (eds Malanotte-Rizzoli, P. & Robinson, A. R.) 79-109 (Kluwer, Dordrecht, 1994).
24. Hughes, T. M. C. & Weaver, A. J. *J. Phys. Oceanogr.* (in the press).
25. Manabe, S. & Stouffer, R. J. *J. Clim.* **7**, 5-23 (1994).
26. Fairbanks, R. G. *Nature* **342**, 637-642 (1989).
27. Lenderink, G. & Haarsma, R. J. *J. Phys. Oceanogr.* **24**, 1480-1493 (1994).
28. Rahmstorf, S. *J. Clim.* (in the press).
29. Rahmstorf, S. *Nature* **372**, 82-85 (1994).
30. Kawase, M. *J. Phys. Oceanogr.* **17**, 2294-2316 (1987).
31. Döscher, R., Böning, C. W. & Herrmann, P. *J. Phys. Oceanogr.* **24**, 2306-2320 (1994).

第三个特征就是霍普夫分岔的存在，它导致以拉布拉多海域为中心的经向翻转流振荡变化。该分岔说明存在一定的参数范围，在该范围内海洋环流本质上是稳定的，只有当它对大气强迫的变化作出响应时才会改变；而在其他参数范围内，海洋则形成可自维持的年代际振荡。由此使得水文强迫的改变导致北大西洋由稳定气候转变为振荡状态成为可能，反之亦然。建立振荡发生情况下的精准驱动条件是未来研究的重要论题。

（齐红艳 翻译；李铁刚 审稿）

32. Kushnir, Y. *J. Clim.* **7**, 142-157 (1994).

33. Delworth, T., Manabe, S. & Stouffer, R. J. *J. Clim.* **6**, 1993-2011 (1993).

34. Weaver, A. J., Aura, S. M. & Myers, P. G. *J. Geophys. Res.* **99**, 12423-12442 (1994).

35. Weisse, R., Mikolajewicz, U. & Maier-Reimer, E. *J. Geophys. Res.* **99**, 12411-12421 (1994).

36. Stigebrandt, A. *Palaeogeogr. Palaeoclimatol. Palaeoecol.* **50**, 303-321 (1985).

37. Schlosser, P. *et al. Science* **251**, 1054-1056 (1991).

38. Drazin, P. G. *Nonlinear Systems* (Cambridge Univ. Press, 1992).

39. Manabe, S. & Stouffer, R. J. *Nature* **378**, 165-167 (1995).

Acknowledgements. I thank J. Willebrand for supporting my work, M. England for sharing his model code, and D. Smart for editing the manuscript. This work was funded by the German Research Ministry; computations were performed at the German Climate Computer Centre in Hamburg.

A Jupiter-mass Companion to a Solar-type Star

M. Mayor and D. Queloz

Editor's Note

Although "extrasolar" planets had several years earlier been discovered around pulsars, the exotic environment precluded any possibility of these worlds hosting "life as we know it". Michel Mayor and Didier Queloz, along with four other groups, had been searching for the signature of planets orbiting solar-like stars for over a decade. Numerous claims had been reported, all subsequently shown to be wrong. But here Mayor and Queloz report the reliable signature of a Jupiter-mass planet in the spectra of the star 51 Pegasi. The planet was orbiting very close to its parent star—0.05 astronomical units (AU—the Sun-Earth distance). Many such planets have now been discovered, and they are generically called "hot Jupiters".

The presence of a Jupiter-mass companion to the star 51 Pegasi is inferred from observations of periodic variations in the star's radial velocity. The companion lies only about eight million kilometres from the star, which would be well inside the orbit of Mercury in our Solar System. This object might be a gas-giant planet that has migrated to this location through orbital evolution, or from the radiative stripping of a brown dwarf.

FOR more than ten years, several groups have been examining the radial velocities of dozens of stars, in an attempt to identify orbital motions induced by the presence of heavy planetary companions[1-5]. The precision of spectrographs optimized for Doppler studies and currently in use is limited to about $15 \, \mathrm{m \, s^{-1}}$. As the reflex motion of the Sun due to Jupiter is $13 \, \mathrm{m \, s^{-1}}$, all current searches are limited to the detection of objects with at least the mass of Jupiter (M_J). So far, all precise Doppler surveys have failed to detect any jovian planets or brown dwarfs.

Since April 1994 we have monitored the radial velocity of 142 G and K dwarf stars with a precision of $13 \, \mathrm{m \, s^{-1}}$. The stars in our survey are selected for their apparent constant radial velocity (at lower precision) from a larger sample of stars monitored for 15 years[6,7]. After 18 months of measurements, a small number of stars show significant velocity variations. Although most candidates require additional measurements, we report here the discovery of a companion with a minimum mass of 0.5 M_J, orbiting at 0.05 AU around the solar-type star 51 Peg. Constraints originating from the observed rotational velocity of 51 Peg and from its low chromospheric emission give an upper limit of 2 M_J for the mass of the companion. Alternative explanations to the observed radial velocity variation (pulsation or spot rotation) are unlikely.

类太阳恒星的一个类木伴星

马约尔，奎洛兹

编者按

尽管系外行星在很多年前就被发现围绕着脉冲星公转，其特殊的环境却排除了这些地方存在任何已知生命形式的可能性。米歇尔·马约尔和迪迪埃·奎洛兹以及其他四个团队，在超过十年的时间里一直在搜寻绕类太阳恒星运转的行星的特征。很多的断言都被报道过了，但随后都被证实是不对的。本文中，马约尔和奎洛兹报道了在飞马座 51 恒星光谱中发现的近似木星质量的行星存在的可靠特征。行星以非常近的距离——0.05 个天文单位（天文单位 AU：地球到太阳的距离）——绕它的母星公转。许多类似的行星现在已经被发现，它们一般都被称为"热木星"。

从飞马座 51 恒星观测到的视向速度周期性变化可以推断出其存在一个木星质量量级的伴星。该伴星和主星的距离只有 8,000,000 km，等于完全在太阳系中的水星轨道内。这个可能为气态巨行星的天体大概是在轨道演化过程中移居到此位置的，或者来自于褐矮星的辐射剥离。

早在十多年前，就有一些小组致力于观测许多恒星的视向速度，试图确认由于存在巨型行星伴星 [1-5] 而产生的轨道运动。光谱仪的精度因为多普勒运动的研究而提高，现在可用的精度已提高至大约 15 m·s⁻¹。太阳相对于木星的反应运动的精度是 13 m·s⁻¹，现阶段的所有研究都局限于被探测的天体至少要有木星的质量（M_J）。迄今为止，所有精确的多普勒巡天观测都还未探测到任何类木行星及褐矮星。

自从 1994 年 4 月，我们已经监测了 142 个 G 型矮星和 K 型矮星精度为 13 m·s⁻¹ 的视向速度。我们观测的恒星都是从 15 年来监测得到的大的恒星样本 [6,7] 中，根据其不变的可见视向速度（较低精度下）挑选出的。在 18 个月的测量后，少数恒星表现出了显著的速度变化。虽然许多候选天体还需要进行更多的观测，但是我们先在此公布质量下限是 0.5 M_J，距飞马座 51 恒星的轨道距离为 0.05 AU 的伴星的相关发现。源于观测到的飞马座 51 恒星的自转速度和低层色球辐射的限制，可以得到这个伴星的质量上限是 2 M_J。关于观测到的视向速度变化的其他解释（脉动或黑子自转）是不太可能的。

The very small distance between the companion and 51 Peg is certainly not predicted by current models of giant planet formation[8]. As the temperature of the companion is above 1,300 K, this object seems to be dangerously close to the Jeans thermal evaporation limit. Moreover, non-thermal evaporation effects are known to be dominant[9] over thermal ones. This jovian-mass companion may therefore be the result of the stripping of a very-low-mass brown dwarf.

The short-period orbital motion of 51 Peg also displays a long-period perturbation, which may be the signature of a second low-mass companion orbiting at larger distance.

Discovery of Jupiter-mass Companion(s)

Our measurements are made with the new fibre-fed echelle spectrograph ELODIE of the Haute-Provence Observatory, France[10]. This instrument permits measurements of radial velocity with an accuracy of about $13 \ \mathrm{m \, s^{-1}}$ of stars up to 9 mag in an exposure time of $< 30 \ \mathrm{min}$. The radial velocity is computed with a cross-correlation technique that concentrates the Doppler information of about 5,000 stellar absorption lines. The position of the cross-correlation function (Fig. 1) is used to compute the radial velocity. The width of the cross-correlation function is related to the star's rotational velocity. The very high radial-velocity accuracy achieved is a result of the scrambling effect of the fibres, as well as monitoring by a calibration lamp of instrumental variations during exposure.

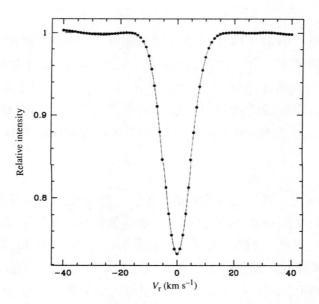

Fig. 1. Typical cross-correlation function used to measure the radial velocity. This function represents a mean of the spectral lines of the star. The location of the gaussian function fitted (solid line) is a precise measurement of the Doppler shift.

现在的巨型行星形成模型 [8] 显然不能预测该伴星和飞马座 51 恒星之间有这么近的距离。由于这个伴星的温度在 1,300 K 以上，它可能非常接近金斯热蒸发极限。而且，还有已知的非热蒸发作用主要影响 [9] 着这些热天体。因此这个木星质量量级的伴星可能是一个小质量褐矮星剥离后的结果。

飞马座 51 恒星存在着短周期的轨道运动，还伴随着长周期的扰动。这也许表示在更远的距离处，还有第二个小质量的伴星在做轨道运动。

木星质量量级伴星的发现

在法国的上普罗旺斯天文台 [10]，我们利用新型的光纤反馈中阶梯光栅摄谱仪 ELODIE 进行测量。这个设备在小于 30 分钟的曝光时间内，对亮度达 9 mag 的恒星，可以测出精度达 13 m·s⁻¹ 的视向速度。这些视向速度是基于一种互相关法，利用约 5,000 条恒星吸收线的多普勒信息计算得到的。互相关函数（图 1）的位置被用来计算视向速度。互相关函数的宽度和恒星的自转速度有关。高精度的视向速度是来源于光纤的加扰效应，以及在曝光过程中定标灯对仪器变化的监测。

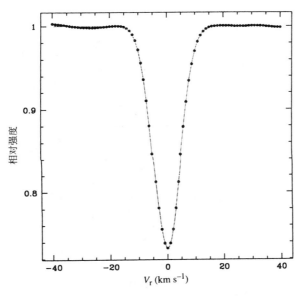

图 1. 被用来计算视向速度的典型的互相关函数。这个函数表示恒星谱线的平均值。拟合出的高斯函数（实线）的位置精确地表征出了多普勒频移。

The first observations of 51 Peg started in September 1994. In January 1995 a first 4.23-days orbit was computed and confirmed by intensive observations during eight consecutive nights in July 1995 and eight in September 1995. Nevertheless, a $24\,\mathrm{m\,s^{-1}}$ scatter of the orbital solution was measured. As this is incompatible with the accuracy of **ELODIE** measurements, we adjusted an orbit to four sets of measurements carried out at four different epochs with only the γ-velocity as a free parameter (see Fig. 2). The γ-velocity in Fig. 3 shows a significant variation that cannot be the result of instrumental drift in the spectrograph. This slow perturbation of the short-period orbit is probably the signature of a second low-mass companion.

Table 1. Orbital parameters of 51 Peg

P	4.2293 ± 0.0011 d
T	$2{,}449{,}797.773 \pm 0.036$
e	0 (fixed)
K_1	$0.059 \pm 0.003\,\mathrm{km\,s^{-1}}$
$a_1 \sin i$	$(34 \pm 2)\,10^5\,\mathrm{m}$
$f_1\,(m)$	$(0.91 \pm 0.15)\,10^{-10}\,M_\odot$
N	35 measurements
$(O-C)$	$13\,\mathrm{m\,s^{-1}}$

P, period; T, epoch of the maximum velocity; e, eccentricity; K_1 half-amplitude of the velocity variation; $a_1 \sin i$, where a_1 is the orbital radius; $f_1\,(m)$, mass function; N, number of observations; $(O-C)$, r.m.s. residual.

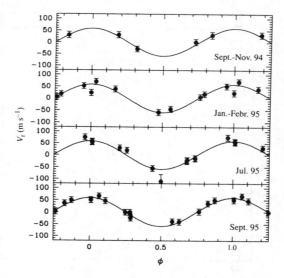

Fig. 2. Orbital motion of 51 Peg at four different epochs corrected from the γ-velocity. The solid line represents the orbital motion fitted on each time span with only the γ-velocity as a free parameter and with the other fixed parameters taken from Table 1.

1994 年 9 月，对飞马座 51 恒星进行了第一次观测。在 1995 年 1 月首次计算出了周期为 4.23 天的轨道，该计算值分别于 1995 年 7 月和 1995 年 9 月通过连续 8 天的密集观测结果所证实。但是，精度为 24 m·s⁻¹ 的轨道离散值还是被测量到了。这是和 ELODIE 仪器的精度不相合的，所以我们分别在四个不同时间，对同一个轨道采用了四套测量方法以进行调整，其中只有 γ 速度被定为自由参量（见图 2）。在图 3 中，γ 速度表现出的明显变化不可能来自于摄谱仪仪器本身的零点漂移。这些短周期轨道运动中的小扰动可能是第二个小质量伴星存在的特征。

表 1. 飞马座 51 恒星的轨道参数

P	4.2293 ± 0.0011 d
T	$2{,}449{,}797.773 \pm 0.036$
e	0（固定的）
K_1	0.059 ± 0.003 km · s⁻¹
$a_1 \sin i$	$(34 \pm 2)10^5$ m
$f_1(m)$	$(0.91 \pm 0.15)10^{-10}\ M_\odot$
N	35 次测量
$(O-C)$	13 m · s⁻¹

P，周期；T，最大速度出现时间；e，偏心率；K_1，速度变化的半振幅；$a_1 \sin i$，其中 a_1 是轨道半径；$f_1(m)$，质量函数；N，观测次数；$(O-C)$，均方根残差。

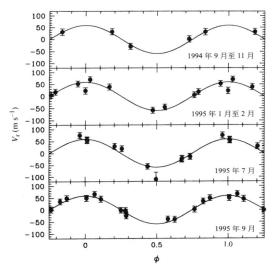

图 2. 在四个不同时期，修正了 γ 速度的飞马座 51 恒星的轨道运动。实线表示了分别在每个时间跨度内，仅取 γ 速度为自由参量，其他参量取自表 1 时的轨道运动拟合图。

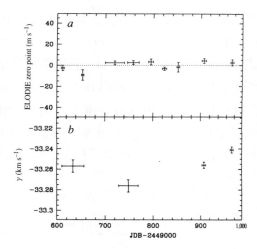

Fig. 3. *a*, ELODIE zero point computed from 87 stars of the sample having more than two measurements and showing no velocity variation. No instrumental zero point drift is detected. *b*, Variation of the γ-velocity of 51 Peg computed from the orbital fits displayed in Fig. 2. Considering the long-term stability of ELODIE this perturbation is probably due to a low-mass companion.

The long-period orbit cannot have a large amplitude. The 26 radial velocity measurements made during > 12 years with the CORAVEL spectrometer do not reveal any significant variation at a $200\,\mathrm{m\,s^{-1}}$ level. Intensive monitoring of 51 Peg is in progress to confirm this long-period orbit.

In Fig. 4 a short-period circular orbit is fitted to the data after correction of the variation in γ-velocity. Leaving the eccentricity as a free parameter would have given $e = 0.09 \pm 0.06$ with almost the same standard deviation for the r.m.s. residual ($13\,\mathrm{m\,s^{-1}}$). Therefore we consider that a circular orbit cannot be ruled out. At present the eccentricity range is between 0 and about 0.15. Table 1 lists the orbital parameters of the circular-orbit solution.

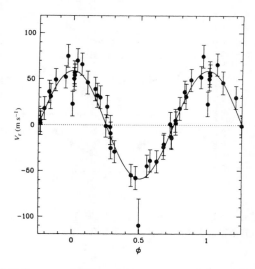

Fig. 4. Orbital motion of 51 Peg corrected from the long-term variation of the γ-velocity. The solid line represents the orbital motion computed from the parameters of Table 1.

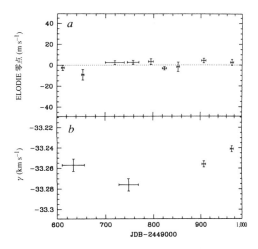

图 3. *a*, ELODIE 零点由样本中的 87 颗恒星计算所得，这些恒星都至少经过了两次测量，并且未显示出速度的变化。并没有发现存在仪器本身的零点漂移。*b*, 由图 2 中拟合出的飞马座 51 恒星轨道中的 γ 速度变化。考虑到 ELODIE 的长期稳定性，这个扰动很可能来自于一个小质量的伴星。

长周期轨道运动不可能有大振幅。在长于 12 年的 26 个视向速度测量中，相关式视向速度仪（CORAVEL）并未显示出存在 $200\ \mathrm{m \cdot s^{-1}}$ 量级上显著的变化。对飞马座 51 恒星已经开始了更高密集程度的监测用来确定该长周期轨道。

在图 4 中，对修正了 γ 速度变化的数据使用一个短周期的圆轨道进行拟合。保留轨道偏心率作为自由参数，可以得到 $e = 0.09 \pm 0.06$，拟合的标准均方根残差几乎不变（$13\ \mathrm{m \cdot s^{-1}}$），因此我们认为圆形轨道不可能被排除。现在偏心率的范围在 0 到 0.15 之间。表 1 列出了在解圆轨道时所用的轨道参量。

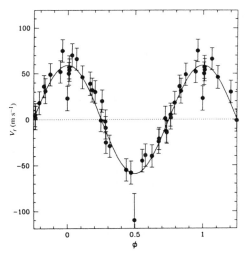

图 4. 飞马座 51 恒星经过 γ 速度长期变化项修正后的轨道运动。实线表示了由表 1 参量计算得到的轨道运动结果。

An orbital period of 4.23 days is rather short, but short-period binaries are not exceptional among solar-type stars. (Five spectroscopic binaries have been found with a period < 4 days in a volume-limited sample of 164 G-type dwarfs in the solar vicinity[6].) Although this orbital period is not surprising in binary stars, it is puzzling when we consider the mass obtained for the companion:

$$M_2 \sin i = 0.47 \pm 0.02 \ M_J$$

where i is the (unknown) inclination angle of the orbit.

51 Peg (HR8729, HD217014 or Gliese 882) is a 5.5 mag star, quite similar to the Sun (see Table 2), located 13.7 pc (45 light yr) away. Photometric and spectroscopic analyses indicate a star slightly older than the Sun, with a similar temperature and slight overabundance of heavy elements. The estimated age[11] derived from its luminosity and effective temperature is typical of an old galactic-disk star. The slight overabundance of heavy elements in such an old disk star is noteworthy. But this is certainly not a remarkable peculiarity in view of the observed scatter of stellar metallicities at a given age.

Table 2. Physical parameters of 51 Peg compared with those of the Sun

	Sun	51 Peg		
		Geneva photometry*	Spectroscopy†	Strömgren photometry and spectroscopy[11]
T_{eff} (K)	5,780	5,773	5,724	5,775
$\log g$	4.45	4.32	4.30	4.18
Fe/H	0		0.19	0.06‡
M/H	0	0.20		
M_v	4.79	4.60		
$R/R_\odot$	1	1.29		

M/H is the logarithmic ratio of the heavy element abundance compared to the Sun (in dex).

* M. Grenon (personal communication).

† J. Valenti (personal communication).

‡ But other elements such as Na I, Mg I, Al I are overabundant, in excess of 0.20.

Upper Limit for the Companion Mass

A priori, we could imagine that we are confronted with a normal spectroscopic binary with an orbital plane almost perpendicular to the line of sight. Assuming a random distribution of binary orbital planes, the probability is less than 1% that the companion mass is larger than 4 M_J, and 1/40,000 that it is above the hydrogen-burning limit of 0.08 $M_\odot$. Although these probability estimates already imply a low-mass companion for 51 Peg, an even stronger case can be made from considerations of rotational velocity. If we assume that the

一个轨道的周期只有 4.23 天实在有点短，但是在类太阳恒星中短周期双星也不是特殊的情况。(在太阳附近 [6]164 颗 G 型矮星的限定体积样本中，已经发现了 5 组分光双星，其周期都小于 4 天。)尽管在双星系统中这种轨道周期一点都不特殊，但是当我们考虑这些伴星的质量时还是会令人困惑：

$$M_2 \sin i = 0.47 \pm 0.02 \ M_{\mathrm{J}}$$

其中 i 是轨道倾角(未知)。

飞马座 51 恒星(HR8729、HD217014 或者 Gliese 882)是一颗光度为 5.5 mag 的恒星，和太阳很相似(见表 2)，距离为 13.7 pc(45 光年)。测光分析和光谱分析显示该星比太阳要稍微年老一些，温度相近，重元素有点过丰。从光度和有效温度上得到的估计年龄 [11] 表明该星为典型的年老银盘恒星。对于这样一个老年盘族星，其重元素丰度轻微高于太阳丰度是值得注意的。但是对于这种给定年龄的恒星，被观测到金属元素丰度存在偏离也并不是很特别。

表 2. 飞马座 51 恒星和太阳各项物理参数的比较

	太阳	飞马座 51 恒星		
		日内瓦测光 *	光谱 †	斯特龙根测光和光谱 [11]
T_{eff} (K)	5,780	5,773	5,724	5,775
log g	4.45	4.32	4.30	4.18
Fe/H	0		0.19	0.06‡
M/H	0	0.20		
M_{v}	4.79	4.60		
$R/R_{\odot}$	1	1.29		

M/H 是飞马座 51 恒星和太阳的重元素丰度对数比比值(指数)。
* 格勒农(个人交流)。
† 瓦伦蒂(个人交流)。
‡ 但是其他元素，例如 Na I、Mg I、Al I 等元素都过丰，超过 0.20。

伴星的质量上限

先验地，假设我们面对着一个普通的分光双星系统，其轨道平面是和我们的视线方向垂直的。假设双星的轨道面随机分布，则伴星质量大于 4 M_{J} 的概率小于 1%，伴星质量超过氢燃烧极限，即 0.08 $M_{\odot}$($M_{\odot}$ 太阳质量)的概率是 1/40,000。尽管这些概率估计暗示了飞马座 51 恒星存在一个小质量的伴星，但是从自转速度考虑可以更有力地支持这个情况。如果我们假设飞马座 51 恒星的自转轴和轨道平面方向是平行的，

rotational axis of 51 Peg is aligned with the orbital plane, we can derive sin i by combining the observed projected rotational velocity (v sin i) with the equatorial velocity $V_{equ} = 2\pi R / P$ (v sin $i = V_{equ} \cdot$ sin i).

Three independent precise v sin i determinations of 51 Peg have been made: by line-profile analysis[12], v sin $i = 1.7 \pm 0.8$ km s^{-1}; by using the cross-correlation function obtained with the CORAVEL spectrometer[13], v sin $i = 2.1 \pm 0.6$ km s^{-1}; and by using the cross-correlation function obtained with ELODIE, v sin $i = 2.8 \pm 0.5$ km s^{-1}. The unweighted mean v sin i is 2.2 ± 0.3 km s^{-1}. The standard error is probably not significant as the determination of very small v sin i is critically dependent on the supposed macroturbulence in the atmosphere. We accordingly prefer to admit a larger uncertainty: v sin $i = 2.2 \pm 1$ km s^{-1}.

51 Peg has been actively monitored for variability in its chromospheric activity[14]. Such activity, measured by the re-emission in the core of the Ca II lines, is directly related to stellar rotation via its dynamo-generated magnetic field. A very low level of chromospheric activity is measured for this object. Incidentally, this provides an independent estimate of an age of 10 Gyr (ref. 14), consistent with the other estimates. No rotational modulation has been detected so far from chromospheric emission, but a 30-day period is deduced from the mean chromospheric activity level S-index. A V_{equ} value of 2.2 ± 0.8 km s^{-1} is then computed if a 25% uncertainty in the period determination is assumed

Using the mean v sin i and the rotational velocity computed from chromospheric activity, we finally deduce a lower limit of 0.4 for sin i. This corresponds to an upper limit for the mass of the planet of 1.2 M_J. Even if we consider a misalignment as large as 10°, the mass of the companion must still be less than 2 M_J, well below the mass of brown dwarfs.

The 30-day rotation period of 51 Peg is clearly not synchronized with the 4.23-day orbital period of its low-mass companion, despite its very short period. (Spectroscopic binaries with similar periods are all synchronized.) The lack of synchronism on a timescale of 10^{10}yr is a consequence of the q^{-2} ($q = M_2/M_1$) dependence of the synchronization timescale[15]. In principle this can be used to derive an upper limit to the mass of the companion. It does at least rule out the possibility of the presence of a low-mass stellar companion.

Alternative Interpretations?

With such a small amplitude of velocity variation and such a short period, pulsation or spot rotation might explain the observations equally well[16,17]. We review these alternative interpretations below and show that they can probably be excluded.

Spot rotation can be dismissed on the basis of the lack of chromospheric activity and the large period derived from the S chromospheric index, which is clearly incompatible with the observed radial-velocity short period. A solar-type star rotating with a period of 4.2 days would have a much stronger chromospheric activity than the currently observed

根据可观测的自转速度投影（$v \sin i$）和赤道速度 $V_{equ} = 2\pi R/P$（$v \sin i = V_{equ} \times \sin i$）我们可以得到 $\sin i$。

三种独立的方法都分别给出了飞马座 51 恒星 $v \sin i$ 的精确值：根据谱线轮廓[12]分析，得到 $v \sin i = 1.7 \pm 0.8\ \mathrm{km \cdot s^{-1}}$；用互相关函数对相关式视向速度仪[13]得到的结果进行处理，得到 $v \sin i = 2.1 \pm 0.6\ \mathrm{km \cdot s^{-1}}$；用互相关函数对 ELODIE 得到的结果进行处理，得到 $v \sin i = 2.8 \pm 0.5\ \mathrm{km \cdot s^{-1}}$。$v \sin i$ 的非加权平均值为 $v \sin i = 2.2 \pm 0.3\ \mathrm{km \cdot s^{-1}}$。我们认为因为 $v \sin i$ 这么小的数值会和大气中假想的宏观湍流有着精确的依赖关系，所以标准差并没有那么明显。因此我们宁愿承认一个更大的不确定度：$v \sin i = 2.2 \pm 1\ \mathrm{km \cdot s^{-1}}$。

飞马座 51 恒星的色球活动[14]变化一直在被密切地监测着。这些活动是通过测量恒星核心中 CaII 线的再发射确定的，这直接和恒星发电机机制下磁场对其自转的影响相关。根据这种方式，在其色球观测到了较微弱的活动迹象。另外，这也独立地提供了 10 Gyr(参考文献 14) 的年龄估计，这和其他估计值是一致的。从色球辐射上并未观测到自转的调制作用，但从色球平均活动水平中的 S 指数却推导出了 30 天的周期。如果假设该时间段内的不确定度为 25%，则可得到 $V_{equ} = 2.2 \pm 0.8\ \mathrm{km \cdot s^{-1}}$。

根据观测色球活动计算得到的平均 $v \sin i$ 和自转速度，我们推导出了 $\sin i$ 的下限为 0.4。这和质量上限为 $1.2\ M_J$ 的行星是相对应的。就算我们考虑角度偏差达到 $10°$，相对应的伴星的质量仍然要小于 $2\ M_J$，这也远低于褐矮星的质量。

尽管飞马座 51 恒星 30 天的自转周期很短，但也很显然和 4.23 天的低质量伴星的轨道运动周期是不同步的。(有着相似周期的分光双星都是同步的。) 在 10^{10} 年尺度上的不同步来源于与同步化时标[15]有关的 q^{-2}（$q = M_2/M_1$）。原则上是可以根据这来推导伴星的质量上限的。它起码可以排除低质量恒星伴星存在的可能性。

另一种解释？

基于很小的速度变化波动和很短的周期，脉动或黑子自转理论似乎也可以将观测解释得同样好[16,17]。接下来我们就回顾一下这些解释，并证明它们可能被排除在外。

黑子自转理论被排除是基于其缺乏色球活动和由色球 S 指数推得的长周期，这长周期明显与观测到的短周期视向速度不符合。一个自转周期为 4.2 天的类太阳恒

value[14]. Moreover, a period of rotation of 4.2 days for a solar-type star is typical of a very young object (younger than the Pleiades) and certainly not of an old disk star.

Pulsation could easily yield low-amplitude velocity variations similar to the one observed, but would be accompanied by luminosity and colour variations as well as phase-related absorption line asymmetries. The homogeneous photometric survey made by the Hipparcos satellite provides a comprehensive view of the intrinsic variability of stars of different temperatures and luminosities. The spectral type of 51 Peg corresponds to a region of the Hertzsprung–Russell diagram where the stars are the most stable[18].

Among solar-type stars no mechanisms have been identified for the excitation of pulsation modes with periods as long as 4 days. Only modes with very low amplitude ($\ll 1$ m s^{-1}) and periods from minutes to 1 h are detected for the Sun.

Radial velocity variations of a few days and < 100 m s^{-1} amplitude have been reported for a few giant stars[19]. Stars with a similar spectral type and luminosity class are known to be photometric variables[18]. Their observed periods are in agreement with predicted pulsation periods for giant stars with radii > 20 $R_\odot$. 51 Peg, with its small radius, can definitely not be compared to these stars. These giant stars also pulsate simultaneously in many short-period modes, a feature certainly not present in the one-year span of 51 Peg observations. It is worth noticing that 51 Peg is too cold to be in the δ Scuti instability strip.

G. Burki *et al.* (personal communication) made 116 photometric measurements of 51 Peg and two comparison stars in the summer of 1995 at ESO (la Silla) during 17 almost-consecutive nights. The observed magnitude dispersions for the three stars are virtually identical, respectively $V = 0.0038$ for 51 Peg, and $V = 0.0036$ and 0.0039 for the comparison stars. The fit of a sine curve with a period of 4.2293 days to the photometric data limits the possible amplitude to 0.0019 for V magnitude and 0.0012 for the $[B_2-V_1]$ Geneva colour index. Despite the high precision of these photometric measurements we cannot completely rule out, with these photometric data alone, the possibility of a very low-amplitude pulsation. In the coming months, stronger constraints can be expected from the numerous Hipparcos photometric data of this star.

Pulsations are known to affect the symmetry of stellar absorption lines. To search for such features we use the cross-correlation technique, as this technique is a powerful tool for measuring mean spectral line characteristics[20]. The difference in radial velocity of the lower and upper parts of the cross-correlation function is an indicator of the line asymmetry. The amplitude of a 4.2-day sine curve adjusted to this index is less than 2 m s^{-1}. The bisector of the cross-correlation function does not show any significant phase variation.

From all the above arguments, we believe that the only convincing interpretation of the observed velocity variations is that they are due to the orbital motion of a very-low-mass companion.

星会产生比现在观测值[14]更强的色球活动。而且，一个自转周期为 4.2 天的类太阳恒星是典型的年轻天体（比昴星团还要年轻），肯定不是一个老年盘族星。

脉动理论很容易与观测到的小幅速度变化符合，但是同时也伴随有光度和色指数变化以及出现相位相关不对称的吸收线。依巴谷卫星曾经进行过光度一致性的研究，对恒星不同温度和不同光度的本质性变化进行了广泛的采样调查。飞马座 51 恒星所属的光谱型对应赫罗图中最稳定[18]的恒星区域。

在类太阳恒星中没有什么机制被证明可以激发出周期为 4 天的脉动模式。在太阳上仅仅发现了具有很小振幅（$\ll 1\,\mathrm{m\cdot s^{-1}}$），周期为几分钟到 1 小时范围的模式。

周期为几天、振幅小于 $100\,\mathrm{m\cdot s^{-1}}$ 的视向速度变化已经在一些巨星[19]中被发现。这样光谱类型相似且光度同等级别的恒星都已知为测光变星[18]。它们被观测到的周期和对半径大于 $20\,R_\odot$ 的巨星预估出的脉动周期是一致的。由于飞马座 51 恒星的半径较小，所以完全无法与这类恒星相比。这类巨星同时还会有伴随许多短周期的脉动模式，这在飞马座 51 恒星为期一年时间跨度的观测中是没有明显出现的。值得注意的是，飞马座 51 恒星的温度相对于盾牌 δ 型星不稳定带也是过低的。

在 1995 年夏季几乎连续的 17 个夜晚，伯基等人（个人交流）在欧南台（智利拉西亚）对飞马座 51 恒星及两颗比较星进行了 116 次测光观测。这三颗星观测到的星等弥散看起来是一样的，飞马座 51 恒星及另两颗比较星的星等弥散分别是 $V=0.0038$，$V=0.0036$ 和 $V=0.0039$。用周期为 4.2293 天的正弦函数拟合测光数据，将 V 星等的可能振幅限制在 0.0019，以及日内瓦色指数 $[B_2-V_1]$ 振幅限制在 0.0012。尽管这些测光观测精度很高，但是我们不能只靠这些测光数据完全将这种小振幅脉动存在的可能性完全排除。在以后几个月，我们会通过依巴谷卫星得到更多关于该星的测光数据，以此进一步对其限制。

现已知脉动会对恒星吸收线的对称性产生影响。互相关法是一种测量平均光谱线特征[20]很有力的工具，所以我们用它来寻找脉动的特征。视向速度的互相关函数中上限和下限的差值就表征了光谱线的不对称性。周期为 4.2 天的正弦函数的振幅转化为这种指数会小于 $2\,\mathrm{m\cdot s^{-1}}$。互相关函数的等分线并没有表现出任何明显的相位变化。

根据以上的讨论，我们可以相信对于观测到的速度变化，唯一使人信服的解释就是：速度变化是由一个非常小质量伴星的轨道运动引起的。

Jupiter or Stripped Brown Dwarf?

At the moment we certainly do not have an understanding of the formation mechanism of this very-low-mass companion. But we can make some preliminary comments about the importance of evaporation as well as the dynamic evolution of the orbit.

If we compare 51 Peg b with other planets or G-dwarf stellar companions (Fig. 5) it is clear that the mass and the low orbital eccentricity of this object are in the range of heavy planets, but this certainly does not imply that the formation mechanism of this planet was the same as for Jupiter.

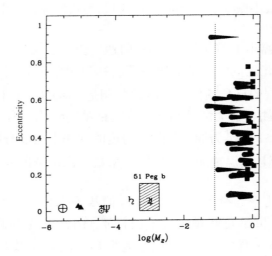

Fig. 5. Orbital eccentricities of planets as well as companion of G-dwarf binaries[8] in the solar vicinity as a function of their mass M_2. The planets of the Solar System are indicated with their usual symbols. The planets orbiting around the pulsar[24,25] PSR B 1257+12 are indicated by filled triangles. The uncertainties on the mass of SB1 (single-spectrum spectroscopic binaries), owing to their unknown orbital inclination, are indicated by an elongated line that thins to a sin i probability of 99%. SB2s are indicated by filled squares. (Only the stellar orbits not tidally circularized with periods larger than 11 days are indicated.) Note the discontinuity in the orbital eccentricities when planets are binary stars are compared, and the gap in masses between the giant planets and the lighter secondaries of solar-type stars. The dotted line at 0.08 $M_\odot$ indicates the location of the minimum mass for hydrogen burning. The position of 51 Peg b with its uncertainties is indicated by the hatched rectangle.

Present models for the formation of Jupiter-like planets do not allow the formation of objects with separations as small as 0.05 AU. If ice grains are involved in the formation of giant planets, the minimum semi-major axis for the orbits is about 5 AU (ref. 8), with a minimum period of the order of 10 yr. A Jupiter-type planet probably suffers some orbital decay during its formation by dynamic friction. But it is not clear that this could produce an orbital shrinking from 5 AU to 0.05 AU.

All of the planets in the Solar System heavier than 10^{-6} $M_\odot$ have almost circular orbits

木星或褐矮星剥离？

目前我们对这小质量伴星的形成机制还没有充分地理解。但是就蒸发机制的重要性和轨道的动力学演化而言，我们可以做出一些初步的解释。

如果我们将飞马座 51 的行星 b 和其他行星，其至 G 型矮星的伴星进行比较（图 5），很显然这个天体的质量和较小的轨道偏心率属于重行星的范围，但是这并不表示它的形成机制和木星的一样。

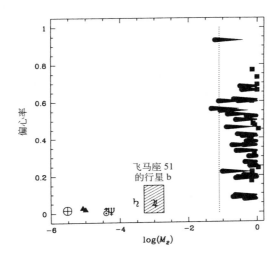

图 5. 行星及太阳附近 G 型矮星双星系统 [8] 中伴星的轨道偏心率与它们的质量 M_2 的函数关系。太阳系中的行星均用常用的符号进行了标注。围绕脉冲星 [24,25]PSR B 1257+12 做轨道运动的行星都用实心三角形进行了标注。由于不知道 SB1（单谱分光双星）的轨道倾角，所以 SB1 质量的不确定度用 sin i 置信度减小到 99% 的延长线进行了标注。SB2 用实心正方形标注出来了。（只有轨道未受潮汐圆化影响，且周期大于 11 天的恒星才被标注了。）值得注意的是，图中比较了双星系统中伴星轨道偏心率的不连续性和巨行星与类太阳恒星的较轻伴星之间的质量差距。在 0.08 $M_\odot$ 处的点线表示了满足氢燃烧的最小质量所在位置。飞马座 51 恒星及其不确定度在图中用阴影线的长方形标注出来了。

现有关于类木行星的各种形成模式中，并不允许天体在 0.05 AU 距离内形成。如果在巨行星形成中包括冰颗粒，则轨道的最小半长轴约为 5 AU（参考文献 8），最小周期的量级为 10 年。一个类木行星在形成的过程中，可能会由于动力学摩擦而经历轨道衰减的过程。但是我们还不清楚这是否会使轨道从 5 AU 缩小到 0.05 AU。

太阳系内所有质量超过 $10^{-6}M_\odot$ 的行星，因为都形成于原行星气体盘而有一个接

as a result of their origin from a protoplanetary gaseous disk. Because of its close separation, however, the low eccentricity of 51 Peg b is not a proof of similar origin. Tidal dissipation acting on the convective envelope is known[15] to circularize the orbit and produce a secular shrinking of the semi-major axis of binary systems. The characteristic time is essentially proportional to $q^{-1}P^{16/3}$. For stars of the old open cluster M67, orbital circularization is observed for periods lower than 12.5 days (ref. 21). We derive for 51 Peg a circularization time of a few billion years, shorter than the age of the system. The low orbital eccentricity of 51 Peg b could result from the dynamic evolution of the system and not necessarily from its formation conditions.

A Jupiter-sized planet as close as 0.05 AU to 51 Peg should have a rather high temperature of about 1,300 K. To avoid a significant evaporation of a gaseous atmosphere, the escape velocity V_e has to be larger than the thermal velocity V_{th}: $V_e > \alpha V_{th}$. This imposes a minimum mass for a gaseous planet at a given separation:

$$\frac{M_P}{M_J} > \alpha^2 \left(\frac{kT_*}{m}\right)\left(\frac{GM_J}{R_P}\right)^{-1} (1-\gamma)^{1/4}\left(\frac{R_*}{2a}\right)^{1/2}$$

where γ denotes the albedo of the planet, R_p and M_p are its radius and mass, m is the mass of atoms in the planet atmosphere, and R_* and T_* are the radius and effective temperature of the star.

Our lack of knowledge of the detailed structure of the atmosphere of the planet prevents us from making an accurate estimate of α. A first-order estimate of $\alpha \approx 5$–6 is nevertheless made by analogy with planets of the Solar System[22]. We find that with a planetary radius probably increased by a factor of 2–3 owing to the high surface temperature (A. Burrows, personal communication), gaseous planets more massive than 0.6–1.0 M_J are at the borderline for suffering thermal evaporation. Moreover, for the Solar-System planets, non-thermal evaporative processes are known to be more efficient than thermal ones[9]. The atmosphere of 51 Peg b has thus probably been affected by evaporation.

Recent work[23] on the fragmentation of molecular clouds shows that binary stars can be formed essentially as close to each other as desired, especially if the effects of orbital decay are considered. We can thus speculate that 51 Peg b results from a strong evaporation of a very close and low-mass brown dwarf. In such a case 51 Peg b should mostly consist of heavy elements. This model is also not free of difficulties, as we expect that a brown dwarf suffers less evaporation owing to its larger escape velocity.

We are eager to confirm the presence of the long-period companion and to find its orbital elements. If its mass is in the range of a few times that of Jupiter and its orbit is also quasi-circular, 51 Peg could be the first example of an extrasolar planetary system associated with a solar-type star.

The search for extrasolar planets can be amazingly rich in surprises. From a complete planetary

近圆形的轨道。然而因为其过近的间距，飞马座 51 恒星的较小偏心率不足以成为类似形成过程的证据。已知作用于对流包层的潮汐摩擦作用[15]，造成了轨道趋于圆形并使双星系统的半长轴在长期地缩小。实际上特征时间是和 $q^{-1}P^{16/3}$ 成比例的。年老的疏散星团 M67 中的恒星观测到的轨道圆化，其周期小于 12.5 天（参考文献 21）。我们推算飞马座 51 恒星的圆化时间为几十亿年，这要比整个系统的年龄短。飞马座 51 的行星 b 的较小轨道偏心率可能产生于系统的动力学演化，并不一定和形成条件有关。

和飞马座 51 恒星相距仅 0.05 AU 的一个木星大小的行星，其温度应该要高于 1,300 K。要避免明显的气态大气蒸发，逃逸速度 V_e 要比热力学速度 V_{th} 大：$V_e > \alpha V_{th}$。这就给出了一个气态行星在给定距离内的最小质量：

$$\frac{M_P}{M_J} > \alpha^2 \left(\frac{kT_*}{m}\right)\left(\frac{GM_J}{R_P}\right)^{-1}(1-\gamma)^{1/4}\left(\frac{R_*}{2a}\right)^{1/2}$$

其中 γ 表示行星的反照率，R_P 和 M_P 表示行星的半径和质量，m 是行星大气中的原子质量，R_* 和 T_* 是恒星的半径和有效温度。

我们对行星大气的细节结构了解还不够，这阻碍了我们对 α 做出精确的估计。最初级的估计是 $\alpha = 5 \sim 6$，这不过是我们根据太阳系内的行星进行的类推结果[22]。我们发现由于表面温度较高，行星的半径可能增至 2~3 倍（伯罗斯，个人交流），质量超过 0.6~1.0 M_J 的气态行星处于发生热蒸发效应的边缘。而且，在太阳系行星中，已知的非热蒸发过程产生的作用远比热蒸发产生的大[9]。因此，飞马座 51 的行星 b 的大气很可能会受到蒸发作用的影响。

最近关于分子云分裂的研究[23]表明，实际上双星系统中的双星在形成时是很接近的，这点当轨道衰减的作用被考虑后变得尤为明显。因此我们可以猜测飞马座 51 的行星 b 产生于一颗相距很近、小质量的褐矮星的强劲蒸发作用。在这种情况下，飞马座 51 的行星 b 应该由重元素组成。但是这个模型也不是没有问题，正如我们考虑到的褐矮星具有较大的逃逸速度，相应就只会有较微弱的蒸发效应。

我们迫切想确认是否存在长周期运动的伴星，并且得到其轨道组成。如果它的质量在木星质量的几倍范围之内，且其轨道是准圆形的，则飞马座 51 恒星将是第一个太阳系以外类太阳恒星的行星系统实例。

对于太阳系外行星的研究是充满惊喜的。从在脉冲星附近发现的完整的行星系

system detected around a pulsar[24,25], to the rather unexpected orbital parameters of 51 Peg b, searches begin to reveal the extraordinary diversity of possible planetary formation sites.

Note added in revision: After the announcement of this discovery at a meeting held in Florence, independent confirmations of the 4.2-day period radial-velocity variation were obtained in mid-October by a team at Lick Observatory, as well as by a joint team from the High Altitude Observatory and the Harvard–Smithsonian Center for Astrophysics. We are deeply grateful to G. Marcy, P. Butler, R. Noyes, T. Kennelly and T. Brown for having immediately communicated their results to us.

(**378**, 356-359; 1995)

Michel Mayor & Didier Queloz
Geneva Observatory, 51 Chemin des Maillettes, CH-1290 Sauverny, Switzerland

Received 29 August; accepted 31 October 1995.

References:

1. Walker, G. A. H., Walker, A. R. & Irwin, A. W., *Icarus* **116**, 359-375 (1995).

2. Cochran, W. D. & Hatzes, A. P. *Astrophys. Space Sci.* **212**, 281-291 (1994).

3. Marcy, G. W. & Butler, R. P. *Publ. Astron. Soc. Pacif.* **104**, 270-277 (1992).

4. McMillan, R. S., Moore, T. L., Perry, M. L. & Smith, P. H. *Astrophys. Space Sci.* **212**, 271- 280 (1994).

5. Marcy, G. W. & Butler, R. P. in *The Bottom of the Main Sequence and Beyond* (ESO Astrophys. Symp.) (ed. Tinney, C. G.) 98-108 (Springer, Berlin, 1995).

6. Duquennoy, A. & Mayor, M. *Astr. Astrophys.* **248**, 485-524 (1991).

7. Mayor, M., Duquennoy, A., Halbwachs, J. L. & Mermilliod, J. C. in *Complementary Approaches to Double and Multiple Star Research* (eds McAlister, A. A. & Hartkopf, W. I.) (ASP Conf. Ser. **32**, 73-81 (Astr. Soc. Pacific, California, 1992).

8. Boss, A. P. *Science* **267**, 360-362 (1995).

9. Hunten, D. H., Donahue, T. M., Walker, J. C. G. & Kasting, J. F. in *Origin and Evolution of Planetary and Satellite Atmospheres* (eds Atreya, S. K., Pollack, J. B. & Matthews, M. S.) 386-422 (Univ. of Arizona Press, Tucson, 1989).

10. Baranne, A. *Astrophys. J. Suppl.* (submitted).

11. Edvardsson, B. *et al. Astr. Astrophys.* **275**, 101-152 (1993).

12. Soderblom, D. R. *Astrophys. J. Suppl. Ser.* **53**, 1-15 (1983).

13. Baranne, A., Mayor, M. & Poncet, J. L. *Vistas Astr.* **23**, 279-316 (1979).

14. Noyes, R. W., Hartmann, L. W., Baliunas, S. L., Duncan, D. K. & Vaughan, A. H. *Astrophys. J.* **279**, 763-777 (1984).

15. Zhan, J. P. *Astr. Astrophys.* **220**, 112-116 (1989).

16. Walker, G. A. H. *et al. Astrophys. J.* **396**, L91-L94 (1992).

17. Larson, A. M. *et al. Publ. Astron. Soc. Pac.* **105**, 825-831 (1993).

18. Eyer, L., Grenon, M., Falin, J. L., Froeschlé, M. & Mignard, F. *Sol. Phys.* **152**, 91-96 (1994).

19. Hatzes, A. P. & Cochran, W. D. *Proc. 9th Cambridge Workshop* (ed. Pallavicini, R.) (Astronomical Soc. of the Pacific) (in the press).

20. Queloz, D. in *New Developments in Array Technology and Applications* (eds Davis Philip, A. G. *et al.*) 221-229 (Int. Astr. Union, 1995).

21. Latham, D. W., Mathieu, R. D., Milone, A. A. E. & Davis, R. J. in *Binaries as Tracers of Stellar Formation* (eds Duquennoy, A. and Mayor, M.) 132-138 (Cambridge Univ. Press, 1992).

22. Lewis, J. S. & Prinn, R. G. *Planets and their Atmospheres—Origin and Evolution* (Academic, Orlando, 1984).

23. Bonnell, I. A. & Bate, M. R. *Mon. Not. R. astr. Soc.* **271**, 999-1004 (1994).

24. Wolszczan, A. & Frail, D. A. *Nature* **355**, 145-147 (1992).

25. Wolszczan, A. *Science* **264**, 538-542 (1994).

Acknowledgements. We thank G. Burki for analysis of photometric data, W. Benz for stimulating discussions, A. Burrows for communicating preliminary estimates of the radius of Jupiter at different distances from the Sun, and F. Pont for his careful reading of the manuscript. We also thank all our colleagues of Marseille and Haute-Provence Observatories involved in the building and operation of the ELODIE spectrograph, namely G. Adrianzyk, A. Baranne, R. Cautain, G. Knispel, D. Kohler, D. Lacroix, J.-P. Meunier, G. Rimbaud and A. Vin.

统 [24,25]，到意外发现的飞马座 51 的行星 b 的轨道参数，研究正在揭开行星形成可能位置的非凡多样性。

修订中的说明： 在我们于佛罗伦萨的会议上公布这一发现后，在 10 月中利克天文台的一个小组以及来自高山天文台及哈佛–史密森天体物理中心组成的联合团队分别对周期为 4.2 天的视向速度变化进行独立的确认。我们对马西、巴特勒、诺伊斯、肯内利和布朗及时与我们交流结果表示深深的谢意。

（冯翀 翻译；周济林 审稿）

Sequence Variation of the Human Y Chromosome

L. S. Whitfield *et al.*

Editor's Note

The non-recombining region of the Y chromosome makes it an excellent tool for studying male human evolution. In this paper, clever comparisons and statistical analyses of Y chromosome DNA from five men of different geographical origin and one chimpanzee suggest that the men's most recent common ancestor lived somewhere between 37,000 and 49,000 years ago. Maternally derived mitochondrial DNA analyses, however, yielded a time of origin of modern humans between 120,000 and 474,000 years ago. The findings, presented by geneticists Simon Whitfield, John Sulston and Peter Goodfellow, fit with the idea of male migration. But an accompanying paper by evolutionary geneticist Michael Hammer places the common ancestral human Y chromosome at 188,000 years.

We have generated over 100 kilobases of sequence from the non-recombining portion of the Y chromosomes from five humans and one common chimpanzee. The human subjects were chosen to match the earliest branches of the human mitochondrial tree. The survey of 18.3 kilobases from each human detected only three sites at which substitutions were present, whereas the human and chimpanzee sequences showed 1.3% divergence. The coalescence time estimated from our Y chromosome sample is more recent than that of the mitochondrial genome. A recent coalescence time for the Y chromosome could have been caused by the selected sweep of an advantageous Y chromosome or extensive migration of human males.

IT has been suspected for some time that the non-recombining portion of the human Y chromosome might harbour a low level of variation compared with the autosomes and the X chromosome. However, studies of restriction-enzyme site polymorphism have not included determinations of the interspecies divergence needed to correct for the mutation rate of the region examined[1,2]. The amount of divergence between two sequences depends on the time since their last common ancestor and the rate of mutation. More recent comparisons of Y chromosome and autosomal or X chromosome DNA sequence have incorporated an estimate of mutation rate but have not allowed for the different modes of inheritance and levels of recombination[3,4].

The Y chromosome region that we have surveyed lies immediately proximal to the Yp pseudoautosomal boundary. It ends at the boundary and includes *SRY*, the mammalian testis-determining gene. This sequence has been extensively investigated to confirm

人类 Y 染色体的序列变异

惠特菲尔德等

编者按

Y 染色体的非重组区使其成为研究人类男性进化的绝佳工具。在这篇文章中，通过对五个不同地区起源的人类和一只黑猩猩的 Y 染色体 DNA 进行比较和统计分析，表明人类的最近共同祖先生活在 37,000 到 49,000 年前。然而，母系线粒体 DNA 分析得出现代人类起源于 120,000 到 474,000 年前。遗传学家西蒙·惠特菲尔德、约翰·萨尔斯顿和彼得·古德费洛的这些发现支持男性迁移的观点。但是进化遗传学家迈克尔·哈默在相应的一篇文章中将人类共同祖先的 Y 染色体定在 188,000 年前。

对来自于五个人类个体和一只黑猩猩的 Y 染色体的非重组区，我们完成了大于 100 kb 序列的测定。人类样本的选择标准是他们的序列要与人类线粒体系统树最早期的分支相匹配。通过对每个人类样本 18.3 kb 序列进行分析，发现仅 3 个位点检测到碱基替换，而人类和黑猩猩碱基序列的差异为 1.3%。我们根据 Y 染色体样本估计的溯祖时间比由线粒体基因组估计得到的溯祖时间更为晚近。Y 染色体估计出了更近的溯祖时间可能是由两方面的原因引起的：一是优势 Y 染色体的选择性清除，二是人类男性的广泛迁移。

很长一段时间以来，人们就怀疑人类的 Y 染色体非重组区的变异水平与常染色体和 X 染色体相比较低。然而，目前在限制性酶切位点的多态性研究中，尚不包括可以用来确定种间差异的位点信息，而这些确定种间差异的信息对于校正我们所考察区域的突变速率来说是必需的 [1,2]。两条序列的差异程度依赖于他们的最近共祖时间以及突变速率。近来更多的研究在比较 Y 染色体与常染色体的 DNA 序列或 Y 染色体与 X 染色体的 DNA 序列时，都会将突变速率的估计纳入考虑范围之内，但尚未考虑到不同的遗传模式和重组水平的影响 [3,4]。

我们研究的 Y 染色体区域位于最接近 Y 染色体短臂假常染色体区的边界处。其终止于该边界处，且包含哺乳动物的睾丸决定基因——*SRY*。这一序列已被广泛地

that it contains no coding sequences other than *SRY*[5]. The sequences at the three sites that show substitutions in humans are presented in Table 1 and the genealogy that this suggests is depicted in Fig. 1.

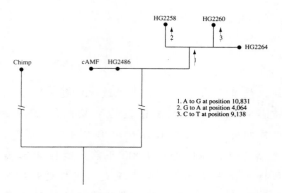

Fig. 1. Genealogy of Y chromosome sequences estimated using the principle of maximum parsimony.

Table 1. Nucleotides in human and chimpanzee subjects at three sites on the Y chromosome

Subjects	Origin	Language	Nucleotide position		
			4,064	9,138	10,831
cAMF	European	Italian	G	C	A
HG2260	Melanesian	Nasioi	G	T	G
HG2264	Rondonian surui	Tupi	G	C	G
HG2486	Tsumkwe san	!Kung	G	C	A
HG2258	Mbuti pygmy	Niger/Kordofanian	A	C	G
Chimpanzee			G	C	A

The names, origins and languages of the human subjects are given, together with the nucleotide that each human and the chimpanzee show at the three positions that are variable in the human sequences. Numbering refers to the sequence of cosmid cAMF3.1 (ref. 5). Sequences with names prefixed HG were obtained from direct sequencing of PCR products; HG numbers are accession numbers of lymphoblastoid cell lines (in the Y Chromosome Consortium repository) from which PCR-template DNA was prepared. cAMF is from the cosmid clone cAMF3.1, the sequencing of which is described in ref. 5. The sequence of cAMF3.1 was used to design PCR primers to produce amplification products covering the whole 18.3-kb region. All PCR primers were tailed at the 5' end with M13 forward or reverse primer sequence. Products from PCR amplifications were purified on agarose gels, then electroeluted, precipitated and washed. Sequencing was by a linear amplification dideoxy termination method using fluorescent dye-labelled primers matching one of the tail sequences[5]. Candidate nucleotide variants were checked by hybridization of radiolabelled allele-specific oligonucleotides to PCR products fixed to nylon membranes (Hybond N+, Amersham). The same PCR primers and methods were used to obtain sequence from the chimpanzee. The lymphoblastoid cell line Colin (S. Marsh and P. Parham) was the source of genomic DNA. The numerous sites at which the chimpanzee sequence differed from the human sequence were not checked with allele-specific oligonucleotides. Some PCR primers did not readily produce template; although a complete sequence contig of the region was produced, only the 15.7 kb of sequence for which both DNA strands were sequenced at least once were used for analysis. This value represents the amount of sequence left after removal of insertions and deletions.

Interspecific comparison was made using 15,680 base pairs (bp) of sequence (after the removal of insertions and deletions) from the same region of the chimpanzee Y chromosome.

研究并证实该区域除了 *SRY* 外不再包含其他编码序列 [5]。表 1 列出了在人类 Y 染色体中存在碱基替换的三个位点的序列，图 1 则描绘了不同序列间的谱系关系。

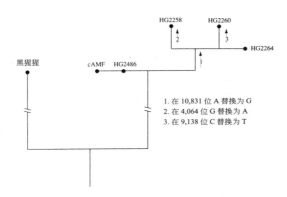

1. 在 10,831 位 A 替换为 G
2. 在 4,064 位 G 替换为 A
3. 在 9,138 位 C 替换为 T

图 1. 使用最大简约性原则估计的 Y 染色体序列谱系关系

表 1. 人类和黑猩猩样本 Y 染色体三个位点的核苷酸

样本	来源	语言	核苷酸位置		
			4,064	9,138	10,831
cAMF	欧洲人	意大利语	G	C	A
HG2260	美拉尼西亚人	Nasioi	G	T	G
HG2264	朗多尼亚苏瑞族	图皮语	G	C	G
HG2486	楚姆奎桑人	!Kung	G	C	A
HG2258	姆布蒂俾格米人	尼日尔 / 科尔多凡语系	A	C	G
黑猩猩			G	C	A

该表给出了人类样本的名字、来源和语言，以及每个人和黑猩猩在人类序列中三个可变位置处对应的核苷酸。编号指的是黏粒 cAMF3.1（参考文献 5）的序列。名字前缀为"HG"的序列是由 PCR 产物直接测序得到的；HG 后的数字是类淋巴母细胞系在 Y 染色体联合资源库中的注册号，PCR 模板 DNA 是从该细胞系制备的。cAMF 来自黏粒克隆 cAMF3.1，其序列在参考文献 5 中有介绍。我们用 cAMF3.1 的序列设计了多对 PCR 引物，以产生涵盖整个 18.3 kb 区域的扩增产物。所有 PCR 引物都在 5′ 端加上了 M13 正向或反向引物序列的尾巴。PCR 扩增产物用琼脂糖凝胶进行纯化，然后电洗脱、沉淀和洗涤。使用荧光染料标记的引物与尾部序列之一配对，通过线性扩增双脱氧终止法进行测序 [5]。候选核苷酸变异通过放射标记的等位基因特异性寡核苷酸与固定在尼龙膜上（尼龙膜 N+ 购自安马西亚公司）的 PCR 产物杂交的方法来检测。黑猩猩的序列使用同样的 PCR 引物和方法获得。基因组 DNA 来源于类淋巴母细胞系 Colin（马什和帕勒姆）。对于黑猩猩与人类序列中的众多碱基不同的位点，没有用等位基因特异性寡核苷酸进行检测。有些 PCR 引物并没有轻易地产生出模板；尽管该区域的全部序列重叠群都已经产生出来了，但只有 15.7 kb 的序列用于分析，这 15.7 kb 序列的 DNA 双链至少进行了一次测序。这一数值代表了去除了插入和缺失之后剩下的序列数量。

　　我们在去除了序列中的碱基插入和缺失情况后，选取了黑猩猩 Y 染色体上同一区域的长度为 15,680 bp 的序列进行种间比较。黑猩猩与人的 cAMF 序列在这

207 (1.32%) of these 15,680 bp differ by substitution between the chimpanzee and human sequence cAMF. The *SRY* coding sequence was removed before the calculation of the number of substitutions per site. This does not eliminate any of the three sites found to be variable in humans.

The non-recombining region of the Y chromosome has properties similar to those of the mitochondrial genome (mtDNA). Neither the mtDNA nor the Y-specific portion of the Y chromosome undergoes conventional meiotic recombination and both the Y chromosome and the mitochondrion are inherited from one sex only: the mtDNA is inherited matrilinearly and the Y chromosome patrilinearly. We have compared the variation of the human Y chromosome population with that of the mtDNA in a manner that corrects for the different respective mutation rates; a coalescence time for the Y chromosome sample has been calculated using the method of Tamura and Nei[6], and this has been compared to an estimate of a mtDNA coalescence time made using the same methodology (Table 2)[6]. The method of Tamura and Nei for estimating the numbers of substitutions between pairs of sequences allows for variation of the substitution rate over sites: ignoring such variation, where it exists, can drastically affect estimates of distance. Assuming that the Homo and Pan clades diverged 6 million years before present, the coalescence time of the mtDNA sample is estimated to be between 120,000 and 474,000 years, and the coalescence time of the Y chromosome sample is estimated to be 37,000 and 49,000 years. If the population samples are equivalent, this suggests a significant difference in the population genetics and demography of the Y chromosome and mtDNA.

Table 2. Estimates of numbers of nucleotide substitutions per site, rate of nucleotide substitution and time taken for human sequences to coalesce

	Y	mtDNA
d_{hh} (s.e.) Mean human-human distance via deepest fork (substitutions per site)	0.0000942 (0.0000732)	0.024 (0.006)
d_{ch} (s.e.) Mean chimp-human distance (substitutions per site)	0.0135 (0.000962)	0.752 (0.224)
λ_{max} Maximum substitution rate (substitutions per site per year)	1.284×10^{-9}	1.00×10^{-7}
λ_{min} Minimum substitution rate (substitutions per site per year)	9.631×10^{-10}	2.53×10^{-8}
Minimum age of coalescence $(d_{hh} / 2\lambda_{max})$	37,000 yr	120,000 yr
Maximum age of coalescence $(d_{hh} / 2\lambda_{min})$	49,000 yr	474,000 yr

The approach was as follows: (1) construction of a tree from human and chimpanzee sequences (Fig. 1), which indicates the location of the deepest human fork; (2) estimation of the average number of substitutions per site (using the method

15,680 bp 中有 207 个 (1.32%) 位点由于发生碱基替换而存在差异。我们在计算每个位点的替换数之前，会先将 *SRY* 的编码序列去掉，这样做并没有去除在人类中发现的那三个碱基可变的位点。

Y 染色体的非重组区与线粒体基因组 (mtDNA) 有着相似的特点。线粒体 DNA 和 Y 染色体的 Y 特异区段都不进行常规的减数分裂重组过程，并且 Y 染色体和线粒体都只能由一种性别遗传而来：线粒体是母系遗传，而 Y 染色体是父系遗传。我们将人类 Y 染色体和 mtDNA 各自的突变率进行修正后，再对二者的群体变异情况进行比较；此外，我们采用 Tamura-Nei 法[6] 计算 Y 染色体样本的溯祖时间，并与用同样方法估算出的 mtDNA 溯祖时间进行比较 (表 2)[6]。在估算成对序列间的碱基替换数时，使用 Tamura-Nei 法能够考虑到各位点替换率的变化；当该类变化存在时，如果将其忽略就会明显影响对遗传距离的估计。假设人属和黑猩猩属的进化枝在距今 600 万年前发生分歧，根据 mtDNA 样本估计出的溯祖时间在 120,000 年到 474,000 年之间，而根据 Y 染色体样本估计的溯祖时间为 37,000 年到 49,000 年之间。如果群体样本没有差异，那么这就提示：Y 染色体和 mtDNA 在群体遗传学和人口学方面存在显著差异。

表 2. 对每个位点的核苷酸替换数、核苷酸替换率及人类序列溯祖时间的估计

	Y	mtDNA
$\hat{d}_{hh}$(se) 通过最远的分叉测得的人与人之间的平均距离 （每个位点发生的替换）	0.0000942 (0.0000732)	0.024 (0.006)
$\hat{d}_{ch}$(se) 黑猩猩与人之间的平均距离 （每个位点发生的替换）	0.0135 (0.000962)	0.752 (0.224)
$\hat{\lambda}_{max}$ 最大替换率 （每年每个位点发生的替换）	1.284×10^{-9}	1.00×10^{-7}
$\hat{\lambda}_{min}$ 最小替换率 （每年每个位点发生的替换）	9.631×10^{-10}	2.53×10^{-8}
最小溯祖时间 $(\hat{d}_{hh}/2\hat{\lambda}_{max})$	37,000 年	120,000 年
最大溯祖时间 $(\hat{d}_{hh}/2\hat{\lambda}_{min})$	49,000 年	474,000 年

方法如下：（1）基于人类和黑猩猩序列构建系统树（图 1），该树表明人类分叉最远能到达的位置；（2）对人类系统树最深处的分叉上，处于相反分支上的个体进行两两比较后，估计每个位点的替换平均数（采用参考文献 6 描述

described in ref. 6) for all pairwise human comparisons involving individuals from opposite branches of the deepest fork of the human tree (d_{hh}); (3) estimation of the average number of substitutions per site between chimpanzees and human (d_{ch}) using the same method, and from this estimate the rate of substitution (λ, substitutions per site per year) as a fraction of the time (T) of the separation of the Homo and Pan clades ($\lambda = d_{ch}/2T$); (4) use of the estimate of the rate of substitution, λ, to calculate the age of the coalescence time of the human sequences (Age = $d_{hh}/2\lambda$). mtDNA values are taken from ref. 6 (but with λ recalculated using a single value of T). The method models variation of the substitution rate over sites on a γ distribution. Parameter α determines the shape of the γ distribution and hence the degree of variation. Estimation of α is difficult for the Y chromosome data. Yang[16] suggests that $\alpha = 0.2$ may represent extreme variation whereas $\alpha = 0.8$ may represent little variation. Tamura and Nei estimated and used $\alpha = 0.11$ for the mtDNA control region. $\alpha = 0.11$, $\alpha = 2$ and $\alpha = 100$ give very similar coalescence times for our Y data. All values given in the table and in the text are derived with $\alpha = 2$. The ranges of values given for coalescence times arise from the error for the substitution rate λ. The mean of d_{hh} is used in this calculation rather than the minimum and maximum; the error for d_{hh} is not independent of the error for the substitution rate λ which has been considered[6].

We have tested three key aspects of the analysis. First, the positioning of the chimpanzee branchpoint during the construction of the human mtDNA tree determines where the human coalescence occurs. Rather than attempt to recover the true phylogeny of the mtDNA dataset, a range of tree reconstruction models were applied and the coalesence times of the trees that they suggested were assessed. The methods employed were maximum parsimony[7], neighbourhood joining and UPGMA[8], with several distance estimates, and maximum likelihood[7] with a variety of transition/transversion ratios. A total of 57 different candidate trees were obtained (after elimination of duplicates). Among these trees were three roots that were different from that used by Tamura and Nei[6]. None made a significant alteration to the date of the mtDNA coalescence.

Second, our Y chromosome sample is small and might be prone to sampling error. It is, however, not a random sample and it is difficult to say, therefore, what is the posterior probability of observing this level of Y chromosome variation. To estimate the number of new variable sites that would have to be observed in a human sample for the estimated Y chromosome coalescence time to overlap that of the mtDNA, we created a hypothetical sequence that has the ancestral sequence at the three known variable sites and then created "new" substitutions. Whereas we found only three variable sites in five sequences, six new substitutions are required before the resultant coalescence time approached that of the mtDNA (that is, the dataset of the five original human sequences plus the hypothetical sequence gave the Y coalescence time as 90,000–120,000 years).

Third, the method used assumes that the substitution rate is constant in all parts of the tree. This "molecular clock" assumption was tested for the mtDNA data set (we have insufficient data to test the Y clock) using the program BASEML from the PAML package[9]. A maximum-likelihood fit of the data to the range of reasonable trees was made under a general reversible "discrete gamma" model[10], with and without the assumption of a molecular clock. The likelihood ratio statistic ($2\Delta l$) from estimates with and without the clock assumption from each of several best trees could then be compared to a χ^2 distribution with 23 degrees of freedom[11,12]. This analysis indicated that the molecular clock was a reasonable assumption.

的方法）(d_{hh})；（3）采用相同方法对黑猩猩与人类之间各个位点发生的替换平均数的估计(d_{ch})，以及基于此对人属和黑猩猩属进化枝发生分离的时间段(T)的分数——替换率（λ，每年每个位点发生的替换）（$\lambda = d_{ch}/2T$）进行估计；（4）使用替换率估计量 λ 计算人类序列溯祖时间发生的年代（年代 = $d_{hh}/2\lambda$）。mtDNA 值引自参考文献 6（但使用 T 的单一值重新计算了 λ）。该方法模拟了 γ 分布中各位点的替换率变异情况。参数 α 决定了 γ 分布的形状以及变异程度。根据 Y 染色体数据很难估计出 α 值。杨子恒[16] 建议用 $\alpha = 0.2$ 代表极端变异情况，而 $\alpha = 0.8$ 代表几乎没有变异发生的情况。田村和根井估计出 mtDNA 控制区中 $\alpha = 0.11$，并且使用了这一数值。对于我们的 Y 染色体数据，$\alpha = 0.11$，$\alpha = 2$ 和 $\alpha = 100$ 给出的溯祖时间非常相似。表中及文中给出的所有数值都是从 $\alpha = 2$ 推导出来的。给出的溯祖时间的取值范围是由替换率 λ 的误差产生的。该计算中使用了 d_{hh} 的平均值而没有使用最小和最大值；d_{hh} 的误差并不独立于曾经认为的替换率 λ 的误差[6]。

我们从三个主要方面对这一分析进行了检验。首先，在构建人类 mtDNA 系统树的过程中将黑猩猩分支点定位在何处决定了人类溯祖发生的位置。我们并没有尝试从 mtDNA 数据库去复原真正的系统发生，而是采用了一系列系统树重建模型，并且对根据这些模型构建的进化树的溯祖时间进行评估。使用的方法包括基于数个距离估计值的最大简约法[7]、近邻结合法和非加权分组平均法（UPGMA）[8] 以及基于各种转换 / 颠换比值的最大似然法[7]。在去除了重复的系统树之后，我们共得到了 57 个不同的候选树。这些系统树中，有三个根与田村和根井使用的根[6] 不同。它们与 mtDNA 溯祖时间相比都没有显著变化。

其次，我们的 Y 染色体样本较少，因此易存在抽样误差。但是它并不是一个随机样本，所以很难说清楚观察到 Y 染色体这一变异水平的后验概率是多少。要使估计出的 Y 染色体溯祖时间和 mtDNA 的重叠，就必须观察人类样本中存在的新的可变位点，而为了对这些新可变位点的数目进行估计，我们创建了一条假定的序列，该序列上已知的三处可变位点具有祖先序列，然后又创建了"新"的替换位点。然而我们发现在五条序列中仅存在三个可变位点，而要使 Y 染色体的合成溯祖时间接近于 mtDNA 的溯祖时间，必须要有六个新的替换位点（即由原有的五条人类序列加上假定序列构成的数据集，共同给出的 Y 染色体的溯祖时间是 90,000 年到 120,000 年之间）。

再次，我们使用的方法假定整棵系统树的所有部分的替换率都是恒定的。我们使用 PAML 软件包[9] 里的 BASEML 程序来检验 mtDNA 数据集是否符合"分子钟"假设（我们没有足够的数据来检测 Y 染色体的分子钟）。无论是否符合分子钟假设，合理的进化树范围内的数据最大似然度是根据一个一般可逆的"离散 γ"模型[10] 确定的。因此，考虑或不考虑分子钟假设，我们得到的几棵最好的进化树的似然比统计量（$2\Delta l$）的估计值都可以与自由度为 23 的 χ^2 分布相比较[11,12]。这一分析暗示分子钟是一个合理的假设。

The "globalization" of the human population might be expected to have created isolated subpopulations. True isolation would prevent the homogenization of the whole population by hindering the complete fixation of individual variants. A post-globalization coalescence time for the Y chromosome sample would suggest that there has been recent replacement of Y chromosomes. The conclusion that our sample has a very recent coalescence may be a consequence of our sampling strategy, and the accuracy of the precise coalescence time for the Y chromosome also depends upon the accuracy of our date for the Homo-Pan divergence and upon undetected fluctuations in the molecular clock.

Y chromosome lineages are not shuffled by recombination. When selection acts upon a single Y-linked locus, the whole non-recombining region "hitchhikes" towards fixation as well[13-15]. The spread of an individual Y chromosome can occur purely by chance, but it is likely to be greatly influenced by selective advantage, male migration and even reproductive behaviour. For example the practice of polygyny may enable a small number of males to father a disproportionately large number of offspring, and their Y chromosomes could increase in frequency very rapidly. Nonetheless, widespread replacement of Y chromosomes is most readily explained by male migration and the occurrence of a selectively favoured Y chromosome.

(**378**, 379-380; 1995)

L. Simon Whitfield[*], **John E. Sulston**[†] **& Peter N. Goodfellow**[*]
[*] Department of Genetics, University of Cambridge, Cambridge CB2 3EH, UK
[†] Sanger Centre, Hinxton Hall, Hinxton, Cambridgeshire CB10 1RQ, UK

Received 18 September; accepted 14 October 1995.

References:

1. Jakubiczka, S., Arnemann, J., Cooke, H. J., Krawczak, M. & Schmidtke, J. *Hum. Genet.* **84**, 86-88 (1989).

2. Malaspina, P. *et al. Ann. Hum. Genet.* **54**, 297-305 (1990).

3. Dorit, R. L., Akashi, H. & Gilbert, W. *Science* **268**, 1183-1185 (1995).

4. Ellis, N. *et al. Nature* **344**, 663-665 (1990).

5. Whitfield, L. S., Hawkins, T. L., Goodfellow, P. N. & Sulston, J. *Genomics* **27**, 306-311 (1995).

6. Tamura, K. & Nei, M. *Molec. Biol. Evol.* **10**, 512-526 (1993).

7. Felsenstein, J. *PHYLIP (Phylogeny Inference Package)* (University of Washington, Seattle, USA, 1993).

8. Kumar, S., Tamura, K. & Nei, M. *MEGA (Molecular Evolutionary Genetics Analysis)* (Pennsylvania State University, University Park, PA, 1993).

9. Yang, Z. *PAML (Phylogenetic Analysis by Maximum Likelihood)* (Inst. Molec. Evol. Genet., Pennsylvania State University, University Park, PA, 1995).

10. Yang, Z. B. *J. Molec. Evol.* **39**, 105-111 (1994).

11. Yang, Z., Goldman, N. & Friday, A. *Syst. Biol.* **44**, 385-400 (1995).

12. Felsenstein, J. *J. Molec. Evol.* **17**, 368-376 (1981).

13. Maynard-Smith, J. & Haigh, J. *Genet. Res.* **23**, 23-35 (1974).

14. Begun, D. J. & Aquadro, C. F. *Nature* **356**, 519-520 (1992).

15. Clark, A. G. *Genetics* **115**, 569-577 (1987).

16. Yang, Z. H. *J. Molec. Evol.* **40**, 689-697 (1995).

Acknowledgements. We thank N. Barton and J. Barrett for their comments on the manuscript, A. Friday for discussion, N. Ellis and M. Hammer for cells and DNA from the Y Chromosome Consortium repository, and T. Hawkins for his input to the design of the sequencing strategy. This work was supported by grants from the Wellcome Trust (to P.N.G. and J.E.S.). L.S.W. is supported by an Imperial Cancer Research Fund graduate bursary.

  人们可能期望人类群体的"全球化"创造出了隔离的亚种群。真正的隔离会通过阻止个体变异的完全固定来阻止整个群体的均一化。Y 染色体样本后全球化的溯祖时间提示 Y 染色体在最近发生过替换。我们使用的样本得到了非常近的溯祖时间，这可能是因为我们的抽样策略，Y 染色体的准确溯祖时间的精确度也依赖于我们所选用的人属–黑猩猩属分歧时间的精确性以及未检测到分子钟的波动情况。

  Y 染色体世系不会因为重组而发生重排。当选择作用于一个单独的 Y 连锁基因座时，整个非重组区也会通过"搭便车"而趋于固定[13-15]。个体 Y 染色体的传播有可能只是偶然发生的，但也可能是选择优势、雄性迁移甚至繁殖行为对其产生了重大影响。例如一夫多妻制有可能使一小部分男性不成比例地生育了大量的后代，使得他们的 Y 染色体频率急速增加。然而，对 Y 染色体广泛替代最好的解释还是雄性迁移和选择上有利的 Y 染色体的出现。

（刘皓芳 翻译；文波 审稿）

Asymmetric Autocatalysis and Amplification of Enantiomeric Excess of a Chiral Molecule

K. Soai *et al.*

Editor's Note

The molecular components of biological molecules, such as amino acids, can exist in two chemically identical but mirror-image forms, called enantiomers and related like left and right hands. But only one "handedness" appears in nature. In 1953 Charles Frank argued that the preference may have been sheer chance: a spontaneous "breaking" of the left-right symmetry by random fluctuations can be amplified into dominance of one enantiomer if the respective molecules are generated in an autocatalytic reaction, where each enantiomer facilitates its own formation. Here Kenso Soai and his coworkers report the first experimental demonstration of Frank's hypothetical mechanism. Later studies showed the reaction to be a subtle variant of Frank's, albeit governed by the same general principle.

The homochirality of natural amino acids and sugars remains a puzzle for theories of the chemical origin of life[1-18]. In 1953 Frank[7] proposed a reaction scheme by which a combination of autocatalysis and inhibition in a system of replicating chiral molecules can allow small random fluctuations in an initially racemic mixture to tip the balance to yield almost exclusively one enantiomer. Here we show experimentally that autocatalysis in a chemical reaction can indeed enhance a small initial enantiomeric excess of a chiral molecule. When a 5-pyrimidyl alkanol with a small (2%) enantiomeric excess is treated with diisopropylzinc and pyrimidine-5-carboxaldehyde, it undergoes an autocatalytic reaction to generate more of the alkanol. Because the reaction involves a chiral catalyst generated from the initial alkanol, and because the catalytic step is enantioselective, the enantiomeric excess of the product is enhanced. This process provides a mechanism by which a small initial imbalance in chirality can become overwhelming.

IN earlier studies of asymmetric autocatalytic reactions[19-21], the enantiomeric excess (e.e.) of chiral products has always been lower than that of the chiral catalysts. In our studies[22] of the enantioselective addition of dialkylzincs to aldehydes using chiral β-aminoalcohols[23,24] and piperazines[25], we have discovered that the pyrimidine-containing secondary alcohol, 2-methyl-l-(5-pyrimidyl) propan-1-ol (**1**), is an efficient asymmetric autocatalyst. We find that with only a small e.e., (*S*)-**1** catalyses the enantioselective addition of diisopropylzinc to pyrimidine-5-carboxaldehyde (**3**) (ref. 26) to yield (*S*)-**1** with significantly higher enantiomeric enrichment.

不对称自催化与手性分子对映体过量值的放大

硖合宪三等

编者按

生物分子（例如氨基酸）的分子组成存在两种化学上完全相同但互为镜像的形式，称为对映异构体，它们就像左手同右手的关系一样。但是自然界中仅存在其中一种手性形式。1953 年查尔斯·弗兰克提出自然界的偏好可能完全是偶然的：如果分子是在自催化反应中产生的，即每种对映异构体都更有助于自身的形成，那么由随机波动引起的左右对称的自发"破缺"就可能被放大到使得一种对映异构体占据优势。这里硖合宪三和他的同事们首次以实验论证了弗兰克的假定机制。后续的研究表明虽然控制反应的基本原理与弗兰克的假说相同，但存在细微差别。

天然氨基酸和糖类的同手性对于生命的化学起源理论 [1-18] 来说仍然是一个谜。1953 年，弗兰克提出一种反应理论 [7]，手性分子复制系统中的自催化与抑制作用相结合，能够允许初始外消旋混合物中的微小随机波动破坏平衡，从而几乎是专一地产生出一种对映异构体。这里，我们通过实验来说明，化学反应中的自催化确实能够提高手性分子在初始状态下较低的对映体过量值。较低对映体过量值（2%）的 5–嘧啶烷醇，在用二异丙基锌和嘧啶–5–甲醛处理后，在自催化反应下生成更多的该烷醇。因为反应涉及由最初烷醇产生的手性催化剂，而且由于催化的步骤具有对映选择性，因此产物的对映体过量值升高了。这个过程为初始状态较小的手性失衡演变为压倒性失衡的现象提供了一种机制。

在对不对称自催化反应的早期研究 [19-21] 中，手性产物的对映体过量值（ee）一直低于手性催化剂的对映体过量值。我们在利用手性 β–氨基醇 [23,24] 和哌嗪 [25] 进行二烷基锌对醛的不对称加成反应研究中 [22]，发现含嘧啶的仲醇，2–甲基–1–（5–嘧啶基）–1–丙醇（1），是一种有效的不对称自催化剂。我们发现只需较低对映体过量值的 (S)–1，就能催化二异丙基锌对嘧啶–5–甲醛（3）（参考文献 26）的对映选择性加成，产生的 (S)–1 对映体含量得到显著提高。

When a mixture with 5% e.e. of (S)-1 (S-isomer : R-isomer = 52.5 : 47.5) was treated as an asymmetric autocatalyst (20 mol%) with aldehyde 3 and diisopropylzinc, pyrimidyl alcohol (S)-1 was obtained with a 62% yield as a mixture of the newly formed product 1 and the catalyst (S)-1 (run A1; Table 1). The amount of (S)-1 in the catalyst increased by a factor of 4.1. It is surprising that the enantiomeric excess of the mixture of the newly formed product 1 and the catalyst 1 has increased to 39% (S-isomer : R-isomer = 69.5 : 30.5) (Fig. 1). This shows that (S)-1 with 55% e.e. (note; > 5% e.e.) was newly formed in 42% yield as a result of the asymmetric autocatalytic reaction of catalyst (S)-1 (Table 1, run A1; Fig. 1). The reaction was performed successively, with the products of one round serving as the reactants for the next, resulting in an overwhelming imbalance between the two stereo isomers (Table 1).

Table 1. Asymmetric autocatalysis of chiral pyrimidyl alcohol 1

Run*	Catalyst 1 (% e.e.)	Time (h)	Mixture of catalyst (1) and product 1		Factor by which the amount of (S)-1 has increased	Newly formed product 1†	
			Yield (%)	e.e. (%)		Yield (%)	e.e. (%)
Series A‡							
A1	5 (S)	74	62	39 (S)	4.1	42	55 (S)
A2	39 (S)	60	86	76 (S)	22	66	87 (S)
A3	76 (S)	68	80	85 (S)	94	60	88 (S)
A4	85 (S)	66	86	89 (S)	413	66	90 (S)
A5	89 (S)	60	81	89 (S)	1,674	61	90 (S)
Series B‡							
B1	2 (S)	74	46	10 (S)	2.5	26	16 (S)
B2	10 (S)	91	75	57 (S)	13	55	74 (S)
B3§	57 (S)	96	80	81 (S)	61	60	89 (S)
B4	81 (S)	70	75	88 (S)	239	55	90 (S)
B5	88 (S)	77	79	88 (S)	942	59	88 (S)
Series C							
C1	10 (R)	70	81	53 (R)		61	67 (R)
C2	30 (R)	65	79	72 (R)		59	86 (R)
Run D	Racemate	55	68	BDL ‖		48	BDL ‖

* Molar ratio. Pyrimidine-5-carboxaldehyde (3) : diisopropylzinc : catalyst 1 = 1 : 1.2 : 0.2. All reactions were reproducible.
† The amount of pyrimidyl alcohol 1 after subtracting that of 1 used as a catalyst from that of total pyrimidyl alcohol.
‡ In each series, the mixture of catalyst and the newly formed product are used as a catalyst of the next run.
§ As an example, details of the experimental procedure, and of the calculation of yield and e.e. are given for run B3. Pyrimidyl alcohol 1 (31.7 mg, 0.208 mmol), 57% e.e., containing (S)-1 (24.9 mg) and (R)-1 (6.8 mg) in toluene (49 ml) and diisopropylzinc (1.2 ml of 1 M toluene solution, 1.2 mmol) was stirred for 20 min at 0 °C, and then a toluene solution (1.8 ml) of pyrimidine-5-carboxaldehyde (3) (112.7 mg, 1.04 mmol) (ref. 26, purified by sublimation) was added at 0 °C. This reaction mixture was stirred for 96 h at 0 °C, and was then quenched by the addition of 1.0 M hydrochloric acid (5 ml) and saturated aqueous sodium hydrogen carbonate (15 ml) at 0 °C. The mixture was filtered using celite and the filtrate was extracted with ethyl acetate. The extract was dried over anhydrous sodium sulphate and allowed to evaporate until dry. Purification of the crude product using thin-layer chromatography yielded pyrimidyl alcohol 1 (127.3 mg)—a mixture of the newly formed alcohol and the catalyst alcohol (31.7 mg). Analysis of the product by high-performance liquid chromatography using a chiral column (Daicel Chiralcel OD) showed it has 81% e.e. (see run B3); it therefore must consist of (S)-1 (115.4 mg) and (R)-1 (11.9 mg). The amount of newly formed alcohol 1 is 127.3 − 31.7 = 95.6 mg (0.628 mmol, 60% yield), which consists of (S)-1 (115.4 − 24.9 = 90.5 mg) and (R)-1 (11.9 − 6.8 = 5.1 mg). The newly formed alcohol thus has an enantiomeric purity of 89% e.e.
‖ Below the detection level.

794

　　以对映体过量值为5%($S-$异构体:$R-$异构体 = 52.5:47.5)的(S)–1混合物作为一种不对称自催化剂(20 mol%)，与醛类物质3和二异丙基锌一起反应时，得到产率为62%的嘧啶基醇(S)–1，它是新生成的产物1和催化剂(S)–1的混合物(实验轮次A1，表1)。催化剂中(S)–1的量增加了3.1倍。令人惊讶的是，新生成的产物1与催化剂1的混合物的对映体过量值增加到了39%($S-$异构体:$R-$异构体 = 69.5:30.5)(图1)。这表明(S)–1具有55%的对映体过量值(注释，> 5%的对映体过量值)是由催化剂(S)–1的不对称自催化反应新生成的，产率为42%(表1，实验轮次A1；图1)。连续进行这样的反应，一轮下来的产物充当下一轮的反应物，最终导致了两种立体异构体之间压倒性的不均衡(表1)。

表1. 手性嘧啶基醇1的不对称自催化

实验轮次*	催化剂1 (% ee)	时间 (h)	催化剂(1)和产物1的混合物		(S)–1的量增加前后的倍数关系	新生成产物1†	
			产率(%)	ee(%)		产率(%)	ee(%)
系列A‡							
A1	5 (S)	74	62	39 (S)	4.1	42	55 (S)
A2	39 (S)	60	86	76 (S)	22	66	87 (S)
A3	76 (S)	68	80	85 (S)	94	60	88 (S)
A4	85 (S)	66	86	89 (S)	413	66	90 (S)
A5	89 (S)	60	81	90 (S)	1,674	61	90 (S)
系列B‡							
B1	2 (S)	74	46	10 (S)	2.5	26	16 (S)
B2	10 (S)	91	75	57 (S)	13	55	74 (S)
B3§	57 (S)	96	80	81 (S)	61	60	89 (S)
B4	81 (S)	70	75	88 (S)	239	55	90 (S)
B5	88 (S)	77	79	88 (S)	942	59	88 (S)
系列C							
C1	10 (R)	70	81	53 (R)		61	67 (R)
C2	30 (R)	65	79	72 (R)		59	86 (R)
轮次D	外消旋体	55	68	BDL‖		48	BDL‖

* 摩尔比。嘧啶–5–甲醛(3)：二异丙基锌：催化剂1 = 1:1.2:0.2。所有反应都具有重现性。

† 从嘧啶基醇总量中减去作为催化剂的嘧啶基醇1后剩余的1的量。

‡ 在每个反应系列中，催化剂与新生成产物的混合物用作下一轮反应的催化剂。

§ 作为一个实例，给出了实验轮次B3反应的实验过程以及产率和对映体过量值计算的细节。嘧啶基醇1 (31.7 mg, 0.208 mmol)的对映体过量值为57%，含(S)–1 (24.9 mg)和(R)–1 (6.8 mg)，将其与甲苯(49 ml)和二异丙基锌(1.2 ml 1 M的甲苯溶液，1.2 mmol)混合，于0 ℃下搅拌20分钟，接着在0 ℃下加入嘧啶–5–甲醛(3) (112.7 mg, 1.04 mmol) (参考文献26，升华提纯)的甲苯溶液(1.8 ml)。在0 ℃下将此反应混合物搅拌96小时，接着通过加入0 ℃的1.0 M盐酸(5 ml)和饱和碳酸氢钠水溶液(15 ml)来终止反应。用硅藻土过滤混合物，滤液用乙酸乙酯萃取。将萃取液用无水硫酸钠干燥，蒸发至干。利用薄层色谱进行粗产品的提纯，得到嘧啶基醇1 (127.3 mg)——新生成的醇与作为催化剂的醇(31.7 mg)的混合物。利用带有手性色谱柱(型号：大赛璐手性OD)的高效液相色谱对产物进行分析，结果显示它有81%的对映体过量值(参见实验轮次B3)；因此它必定是由(S)–1 (115.4 mg)和(R)–1 (11.9 mg)组成的。新生成的醇1的量为127.3 – 31.7 = 95.6 mg (0.628 mmol，产率60%)，其中含(S)–1 (115.4 – 24.9 = 90.5 mg)和(R)–1 (11.9 – 6.8 = 5.1 mg)。因此新生成的醇具有对映体过量值为89%的对映体纯度。

‖ 低于检测水平。

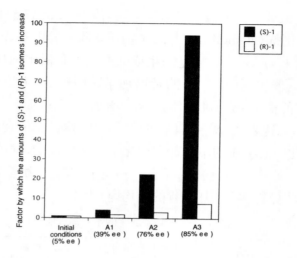

Fig. 1. Asymmetric autocatalysis of chiral pyrimidyl alkanol (**1**). Runs A1–3 correspond to Table 1. The enantiomeric excess of (*S*)-**1** increases from 5 to 89% e. e. without the use of additional chiral auxiliaries. During the reactions (runs A1–3), the (*S*)-**1** increases by a factor of 94 times, while (*R*)-**1** increases by a factor of only eight times.

In a similar manner, starting from the chiral catalyst (*S*)-**1** with even lower enantiomeric excess (2% e.e., *S*-isomer : *R*-isomer = 51 : 49) (20 mol%), asymmetric autocatalytic reaction of **1** and the amplification of the e.e. of **1** are also observed (series B in Table 1, runs 1–5). The e.e. of (*S*)-**1** has increased successively from 2% to 10%, 57%, 81% and 88% (runs 1–5). The amount of (*S*)-**1** of the initial catalyst (2% e.e., run B1) has increased by the factor of 942 times (run B5). When (*S*)-**1** with 88% e.e. was employed as asymmetric autocatalyst, the e.e. of the mixture of catalyst and the product was also 88% (run B5). Thus in series A and B, the low e.e. of (*S*)-**1** was autocatalytically amplified to 88–89%, and the amount of (*S*)-**1** was increased by a factor of 942 and 1,674.

On the other hand, when the opposite enantiomer, (*R*)-**1**, with 10% e.e. was employed as an asymmetric autocatalyst, the *R*-enantiomer of the mixture of the catalyst and the newly formed **1** was obtained in comparable enantiomeric excess (53% e.e.) (run C1; Table 1). When the asymmetric autocatalyst was (*R*)-**1** with 30% e.e., (*R*)-**1** increased to yield a mixture of the catalyst and the product with 72% e.e. (run C2). In addition, the enantioselectivity of a racemic **1** as autocatalyst was below the detection level (run D; Table 1). These results show that the configurations of the asymmetric autocatalyst, (*S*)- or (*R*)-**1**, determine the configuration of the product, (*S*)- or (*R*)-**1**. In other words, (*S*)- or (*R*)-**1** do work as asymmetric autocatalysts.

We propose the following reaction scheme for asymmetric autocatalysis of (*S*)-**1** (Fig. 2). Pyrimidyl alcohol (*S*)-**1** reacts with an equimolar amount of diisopropylzinc to form *in situ* the chiral isopropylzinc alkoxide **2** (characterized by proton NMR). Compound **2** catalyses the enantioselective addition of diisopropylzinc to aldehyde **3** to yield **2** with increased e.e.

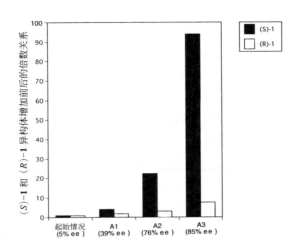

图 1. 手性嘧啶基醇(1)的不对称自催化。实验轮次 A1~A3 与表 1 相对应。在不使用外加手性助剂的条件下(S)-1 的对映体过量值从 5% 增加到 89%。在反应过程中(实验轮次 A1~A3)，(S)-1 增加了 93 倍，而(R)-1 只增加了 7 倍。

通过类似的方式，甚至从具有更低的对映体过量值(对映体过量值为 2%，$S-$ 异构体:$R-$ 异构体 = 51:49)(20 mol%)的手性催化剂开始，也可以观测到 1 的不对称自催化反应和 1 中对映体过量值的放大(表 1 中的系列 B，实验轮次 1~5)。(S)-1 的对映体过量值从 2% 依次增加到 10%，57%，81% 和 88%(实验轮次 1~5)。初始催化剂中的 (S)-1 的量(2% 对映体过量值，实验轮次 B1)增加了 941 倍(实验轮次 B5)。在使用对映体过量值为 88% 的 (S)-1 作为不对称自催化剂时，催化剂与产物的混合物的对映体过量值还是 88%(实验轮次 B5)。因此在系列 A 和 B 中，(S)-1 的低对映体过量值以自催化方式增大到 88%~89%，(S)-1 的量增加了 941 倍和 1,673 倍。

另一方面，在使用相反的对映异构体，即对映体过量值为 10% 的 (R)-1 作为不对称自催化剂时，所获得的催化剂与新生成 1 的混合物中的 R 型对映异构体也达到了可观的对映体过量值(对映体过量值为 53%)(实验轮次 C1，表 1)。当不对称自催化剂为对映体过量值 30% 的 (R)-1 时，(R)-1 增加后产生了对映体过量值为 72% 的催化剂与产物的混合物(实验轮次 C2)。此外，以外消旋体 1 作为自催化剂时对映选择性低于检测水平(实验轮次 D，表 1)。这些结果表明，不对称自催化剂 (S)-1 或 (R)-1 的构型决定了产物 (S)-1 或 (R)-1 的构型。换言之，(S)-1 或 (R)-1 确实是作为不对称自催化剂而起作用的。

我们对于 (S)-1 的不对称自催化提出如下反应规律(图 2)。嘧啶基醇 (S)-1 与等摩尔的二异丙基锌反应，在原位生成手性异丙基锌醇盐 2 (用质子 NMR 表征)。化合物 2 催化二异丙基锌对醛 3 的对映选择性加成反应，产生了对映体过量值增大

Subsequent hydrolysis of **2** gives (*S*)-**1** with amplified e.e. (Fig. 3). Even when the catalyst has an e.e. of just 5%, the newly formed product (that is, **1**) had enantiomeric excess of 55%.

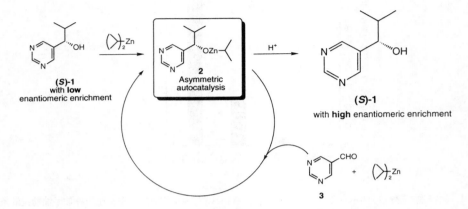

Fig. 2. Proposed reaction scheme of asymmetric autocatalysis of (*S*)-**1**.

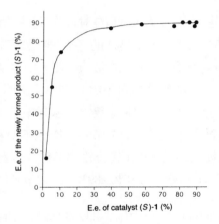

Fig. 3. Relation between the enantiomeric excess (e.e.) of catalyst (*S*)-**1** and that of the newly formed product (*S*)-**1** in asymmetric autocatalytic reaction of (*S*)-**1**.

It seems conceivable that the reaction reported here may be an example of the scheme proposed by Frank[7]. The symmetry breaking by spontaneous crystallization reported by Kondepudi[27], which involves indirect inhibition, is the only other possible experimental realization of this scheme so far, and that involved physical rather than chemical processes. But the detailed mechanism of the autocatalytic steps in our reaction, and in particular, whether an inhibitory mechanism is present, remains to be clarified.

(**378**, 767-768; 1995)

Kenso Soai, Takanori Shibata, Hiroshi Morioka & Kaori Choji

Department of Applied Chemistry, Faculty of Science, Science University of Tokyo, Kagurazaka, Shinjuku-ku, Tokyo 162, Japan

的 **2**。随后 **2** 水解生成对映体过量值增大的 (S)–**1**（图 3）。即使催化剂的对映体过量值仅有 5%，新生成的产物（即 **1**）也有 55% 的对映体过量值。

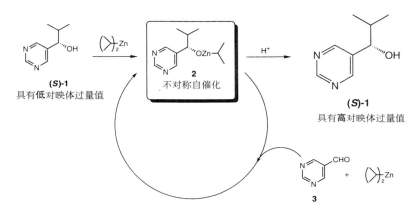

图 2. 我们提出的 (S)–**1** 不对称自催化的反应规律。

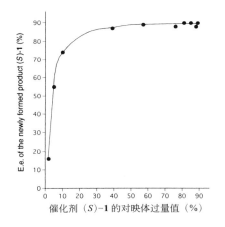

图 3. 催化剂 (S)–**1** 的对映体过量值与 (S)–**1** 的不对称自催化反应中新生成产物 (S)–**1** 的对映体过量值之间的关系。

看来可以接受的是，这里报道的反应可能是弗兰克所提出理论[7]的一个实例。孔德普迪[27] 所报道的自发结晶造成的对称性破缺——涉及间接抑制——是该理论到目前为止仅有的另外一个可能的实验例子，并且其涉及的是物理过程而不是化学过程。但是我们的反应中自催化步骤的详细机制，尤其是是否存在抑制机制的问题，仍然有待于阐明。

（王耀杨 翻译；许家喜 审稿）

Received 27 June; accepted 16 November 1995.

References:

1. Bada, J. L. *Nature* **374**, 594-595 (1995).

2. Mason, S. F. *Nature* **314**, 400-401 (1985).

3. Bonner, W. A. *Topics Stereochem.* **18**, 1-96 (1988).

4. Mason, S. F. & Tranter, G. E. *Proc. R. Soc. Lond.* A **397**, 45-65 (1985).

5. Kagan, H. B. *et al. Tetrahedron Lett.* **27**, 2479-2482 (1971).

6. Meiring, W. J. *Nature* **329**, 712-714 (1987).

7. Frank, F. C. *Biochim. Biophys. Acta* **11**, 459-463 (1953).

8. Calvin, M. *Chemical Evolution* Ch. 7 (Clarendon, London, 1969).

9. Wynberg, H. *J. Macromolec. Sci.–Chem.* A**26**, 1033-1041 (1989).

10. Kondepudi, D. K. & Nelson, G. W. *Nature* **314**, 438-441 (1985).

11. Tranter, G. E. *Nature* **318**, 172-173 (1985).

12. Havinga, E. *Biochim. Biophys. Acta* **13**, 171-174 (1954).

13. Baker, W., Gilbert, B. & Ollis, W. D. *J. Chem. Soc.* 1443-1446 (1952).

14. Berkovitch-Yellin, Z. *et al. J. Am. Chem. Soc.* **107**, 3111-3122 (1985).

15. Pincock, R. E., Perkins, R. R., Ma, A. S. & Wilson, K. R. *Science* **174**, 1018-1020 (1971).

16. Puchot, C. *et al. J. Am. Chem. Soc.* **108**, 2353-2357 (1986).

17. Oguni, N. & Kaneko, T. *J. Am. chem. Soc.* **110**, 7877-7878 (1988).

18. Noyori, R. & Kitamura, M. *Angew. Chem. int. Ed. Engl.* **30**, 49-69 (1991).

19. Soai, K., Niwa, S. & Hori, H. *J. Chem. Soc., Chem. Commun.* 982-983 (1990).

20. Soai, K., Hayase, T., Shimada, C. & Isobe, K. *Tetrahedron: Asymmetry* **5**, 789-792 (1994).

21. Soai, K., Hayase, T. & Takai, K. *Tetrahedron: Asymmetry* **6**, 637-638 (1995).

22. Soai, K. & Niwa, S. *Chem. Rev.* **92**, 833-856 (1992).

23. Soai, K., Hayase, T., Takai, K. & Sugiyama, T. *J. Org. Chem.* **59**, 7908-7909 (1994).

24. Sato, T., Soai, K., Suzuki, K. & Mukaiyama, T. *Chem. Lett.* 601-604 (1978).

25. Niwa, S. & Soai, K. *J. Chem. Soc., Perkin Trans. 1* 2717-2720 (1991).

26. Rho, T. & Abuh, Y. F. *Synth. Commun.* **24**, 253-256 (1994).

27. Kondepudi, D. K., Kaufman, R. J. & Singh, N. *Science* **250**, 975-976 (1990).

Acknowledgements. We thank Y. Aizu, S. Sakaguchi, H. Tabira and S. Tanji for experimental assistance. This work was supported by the Ministry of Education, Science and Culture and by The SUT Special Grant for Research Promotion 1994-95.

Sheep Cloned by Nuclear Transfer from a Cultured Cell Line

K. H. S. Campbell *et al.*

Editor's Note

Here British biologist Ian Wilmut and colleagues announce the arrival of Morag and Megan, the first mammals cloned from an established cell line. The team injected DNA from cultured, differentiated sheep embryo cells into unfertilized sheep eggs lacking nuclei, then used an electrical prompt to trigger development. Several hundred attempted nuclear transfers yielded five live births and just two healthy, fertile adult sheep. The experiment confirmed that nuclear reprogramming was possible in mammals, but sceptics demanded the production of clones derived from adult donor DNA as final proof. One year later, that proof came with the birth of Dolly the sheep, and the prospect of therapeutic cloning, which aims to produce therapeutically useful, donor-matched stem cells, moved a step closer.

Nuclear transfer has been used in mammals as both a valuable tool in embryological studies[1] and as a method for the multiplication of "elite" embryos[2-4]. Offspring have only been reported when early embryos, or embryo-derived cells during primary culture, were used as nuclear donors[5,6]. Here we provide the first report, to our knowledge, of live mammalian offspring following nuclear transfer from an established cell line. Lambs were born after cells derived from sheep embryos, which had been cultured for 6 to 13 passages, were induced to quiesce by serum starvation before transfer of their nuclei into enucleated oocytes. Induction of quiescence in the donor cells may modify the donor chromatin structure to help nuclear reprogramming and allow development. This approach will provide the same powerful opportunities for analysis and modification of gene function in livestock species that are available in the mouse through the use of embryonic stem cells[7].

THE cells used in these experiments were isolated by microdissection and explantation of the embryonic disc (ED) of day 9 *in vivo* produced "Welsh mountain" sheep embryos. The line was established from early passage colonies with a morphology like that of embryonic stem (ES) cells. By the second and third passages, the cells had assumed a more epithelial, flattened morphology (Fig. 1*a*) which was maintained on further culture (to at least passage 25). At passage 6, unlike murine ES cells they expressed cytokeratin, and nuclear lamin A/C which are markers associated with differentiation[8]. This embryo-derived epithelial cell line has been designated TNT4 (for totipotent for nuclear transfer).

从体外培养的细胞系中通过
核移植获得克隆羊的方法

坎贝尔等

编者按

在本文中英国生物学家伊恩·威尔穆特及其同事宣布了莫拉格和梅甘的诞生。它们是由已建立的细胞系克隆得到的首批哺乳动物。该团队将培养的已分化的绵羊胚胎细胞 DNA 注入未受精的去核绵羊卵母细胞中，然后用电脉冲诱导发育。在数百次核移植试验中得到五只羊羔，但仅得到两只健康的、有生殖能力的成年绵羊。这个实验证实了哺乳动物细胞核重编程的可行性，但持怀疑态度的人要求提供成年供体 DNA 的克隆产物作为最终的证据。一年后，作为证据的多莉羊诞生，而旨在产生有益于治疗的、与供体匹配的干细胞的治疗性克隆又向前迈进了一大步。

核移植是哺乳动物胚胎研究中一种很有价值的工具 [1]，同时也是扩增优良胚胎的一种方法 [2-4]。以往研究中，只以早期胚胎或原代培养的胚胎来源细胞为细胞核供体得到后代的报道 [5,6]。本研究首次报道了（据我们所知）对已建立的细胞系进行核移植并成功获得成活的哺乳类后代的方法。从绵羊胚胎分离细胞经传代培养 6~13 代后，采用血清饥饿法诱导其进入静止期，再将该细胞核移植到去核卵母细胞中，获得成活羔羊。诱导供体细胞进入静止期，这可能会修饰供体细胞的染色质结构以利于细胞核重编程并允许细胞发育。本方法可为分析和修饰家畜的基因功能提供强大的机遇，目前已经在小鼠上采用胚胎干细胞实现了这一点 [7]。

这些实验中所使用的细胞，是利用显微切割术从体内生长到第 9 天的"威尔士山"绵羊的胚盘（ED）上分离出来并进行后续移植的。该细胞系来自传代早期的细胞克隆，其形态类似胚胎干（ES）细胞。到第 2 代和第 3 代，细胞呈现出上皮扁平的形态（图 1a），并在此后的培养中持续保持这一形态（至少到第 25 代）。在第 6 代，与鼠类 ES 细胞不同的是，这些细胞开始表达细胞角蛋白和核纤层蛋白 A/C（这是与分化有关的标记物）[8]。这一来源于胚胎的上皮细胞系被命名为 TNT4（即对核移植是全能的）。

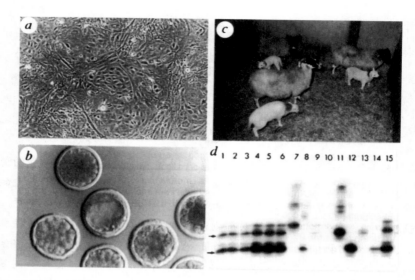

Fig. 1 . Production and characterization of the TNT4 cell line and the offspring produced by nuclear transfer from TNT4 cells. *a*, Morphology of the TNT4 cell line at passage 6. *b*, Group of embryos including a single blastocyst on day 7 after reconstruction. *c*, Group of three Welsh mountain lambs produced by nuclear transfer with surrogate Scottish blackface ewes. *d*, Autoradiogram showing the alleles generated following amplification of the microsatellite FCB266 (ref. 18). Lanes 1–6 are from, respectively, TNT4 cells and the five lambs generated by nuclear transfer. Both lambs and cells display an identical pattern, revealing 2 alleles (arrowed) at 114 and 125 bp. Lanes 7–15, nine randomly chosen Welsh mountain sheep, none of whom show an identical pattern to the nuclear transfer group. Lambs and TNT4 cells were also identical at six further microsatellite loci: MAF33, MAF48, MAF65, MAF209, OarFCB11, OarFCB128, OarRCB304 (data not shown). The nine unrelated random control animals showed extensive variation at all of these loci.

Methods. Groups of 4–6 microdissected embryonic discs were cultured on feeder layers of mitotically inactivated primary murine fibroblasts in Dulbeccos Modified Eagles medium (GIBCO) containing 10% fetal calf serum, 10% newborn serum and supplemented with recombinant human leukaemia inhibition factor (LIF). After 5–7 days of culture, expanding discs were treated with trypsin and passaged onto fresh feeders yielding 4 similar lines. At passage 12 of the $2n$ chromosome complement of 54 was observed in 31 of 50 spreads, the remaining aneuploid spreads are thought to be artefacts of preparation. For microsatellite analysis genomic DNA was extracted from whole blood, tissue culture cells or fetal tissues using a Puregene DNA isolation kit (Gentra Systems Inc., Minneapolis, USA). The PCR analysis of microsatellites was carried out using an end-labelled primer ([γ-^{32}P]ATP). All other aspects of labelling and thermal cycling conditions were as described elsewhere[17].

The development of embryos reconstructed by nuclear transfer is dependent upon interactions between the donor nucleus and the recipient cytoplasm. We have previously reported the effects of the cytoplasmic kinase activity, maturation/mitosis/meiosis promoting factor (MPF), on the incidence of chromosomal damage and aneuploidy in reconstructed embryos and established two means of preventing such damage[9]. First, the effects of the donor cell-cycle stage can be overcome by transferring nuclei after the disappearance of MPF activity by prior activation of the recipient enucleated M II oocyte[9,10]. Using this approach we obtained the birth of lambs by nuclear transfer during establishment of the cell line (up to and including passage 3). On subsequent culture (passages 6 and 11) no development to term was obtained (see Table 1). From these numbers we cannot

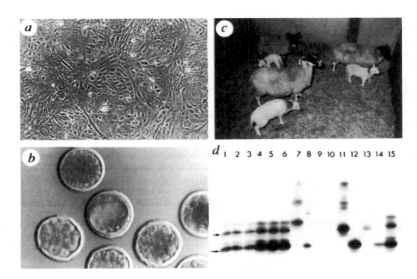

图 1. TNT4 细胞系的制备和鉴定，以及 TNT4 细胞核移植产生的羔羊后代。*a*，TNT4 细胞系传代培养至第 6 代的细胞形态。*b*，重组 7 天后含有单独胚泡的胚胎形态。*c*，以苏格兰黑脸母羊为受体代孕羊，通过核移植产生的三只威尔士山羊羔。*d*，通过扩增微卫星 FCB266 得到的等位基因的放射自显影图（参考文献 18）。泳道 1~6 分别代表来自 TNT4 细胞系以及通过核移植产生的五只羊羔的自显影结果。羊羔与 TNT4 细胞呈现一致的分布模式，显示了大小分别为 114 bp 和 125 bp 的两个等位基因（箭头所指的）的存在。泳道 7~15 代表九只随机挑选的威尔士山绵羊的自显影结果，没有一个与核移植出现相同的模式。出生的羊羔与 TNT4 细胞在其他 6 个微卫星基因座上也显示出一致性：MAF33、MAF48、MAF65、MAF209、OarFCB11、OarFCB128、OarRCB304（数据未显示）。九只随机选择的对照组动物在这些基因座上显示了极高的变异性。

方法。将 4~6 个显微切割的胚盘在有丝分裂失活的原代鼠成纤维细胞饲养层上培养。培养体系为含有 10% 胎牛血清、10% 新生小牛血清，并添加重组人类白血病抑制因子（LIF）的 GIBCO 公司的 DMEM 培养基。培养 5~7 天之后，用胰蛋白酶处理膨大的胚盘并传代到新鲜的饲养层，产生 4 个相似的细胞系。当传代到第 12 代时，获得的 50 个细胞克隆中有 31 个含有 54 条染色体组成的 2 倍染色体组，其他非整倍的克隆则被认为是制备过程中的伪迹。为进行基因组 DNA 的微卫星分析，我们用 Puregene DNA 分离试剂盒（Gentra Systems 公司，明尼阿波利斯，美国）从全血、组织培养细胞或胎儿组织中提取基因组 DNA。微卫星 PCR 实验使用了 [γ-^{32}P]ATP 的末端标记引物。标记和热循环条件参考了其他研究中的方法 [17]。

通过核移植重新构建的胚胎，其发育过程依赖于供体细胞核与受体细胞质间的相互作用。我们以前报道过在重组的胚胎中细胞质激酶以及细胞成熟／有丝分裂／减数分裂促进因子（MPF）对染色体损伤以及染色体非整倍体发生率的影响，并建立了两种方法以防止这种损伤的发生 [9]。在第一种方法中，可以预先激活处于减数第二次分裂中期（MII）的去核卵母细胞（受体）以使 MPF 活性消失，再移植细胞核，以消除供体细胞周期的影响 [9,10]。利用该手段，我们在细胞系建立阶段（第 3 代及以内）进行核移植并获得了新生羔羊。在随后的培养中（第 6 代和第 11 代），没有获得完成体内发育的胚胎（见表 1）。从这些数字中我们并不能得出这一方法不能获得完成体

conclude that development to term will not be obtained using this method. The lack of development of some control embryos is thought to relate to an infection in the oviduct of the temporary recipient ewe from which 6 were recovered.

Table 1. Development using unsynchronized TNT4 cells

Donor cell type	Number of morula and blastocysts/total embryos (%)	Number of lambs/ embryos transferred
October 1993–February 1994		
16 cell	6/11 (27.3)	2/6
ED cell	1/15 (6.7)	0/1
ED P1	4/19 (21.0)	1/4
ED P2	1/11 (9.1)	1/1
ED P3	2/36 (5.5)	2/2
October–December 1994		
16 cell	14/28 (50.0)	0/14
TNT4 P6	9/98 (9.2)	0*/9
TNT4 P11	10/92 (10.9)	0/10

Development of ovine embryos reconstructed by nuclear transfer of unsynchronized cells during isolation and after establishment of the TNT4 line to enucleated preactivated ovine oocytes. P, Passage number; ED, embryonic disc. For embryo reconstruction, donor oocytes were placed into calcium-free M2 containing 10% FCS, 7.5 μg ml^{-1} Cytochalasin B (Sigma) and 5.0 μg ml^{-1} Hoechst 33342 (Sigma) at 37 °C for 20 min to aspirate. A small amount of cytoplasm enclosed in plasma membrane was removed from directly beneath the 1st polar body using a glass pipette (~20 μm tip external diameter). Enucleation was confirmed by exposing this karyoplast to ultraviolet light and checking for the presence of a metaphase plate. At 34–36 h after GnRH injection enucleated oocytes were activated. Following further culture for 4–6 h in TC199, 10% FCS a single cell was fused. All activations and fusions were accomplished as previously described[10,17] in 0.3 M mannitol, 0.1 mM MgSO$_4$, 0.0005 mM CaCl$_2$[17]. For activation a single DC pulse of 1.25 kV cm^{-1} for 80 μs and for fusion an AC pulse of 3 V for 5 s followed by 3 d.c. pulses of 1.25 kV cm^{-1} for 80 μs were applied. All oocyte/cell couplets were cultured in TC199, 10% FCS 7.5 μg ml^{-1} Cytochalasin B (SIGMA) for 1 h following application of the fusion pulse and then in the same medium without Cytochalasin until transferred to temporary recipient ewes. Reconstructed embryos were cultured in the ligated oviduct of a recipient "blackface" ewe until day 7 after reconstruction. All morula and blastocyst stage embryos were transferred to synchronized recipient blackface ewes for development to term.

* A single pregnancy was established but subsequently lost at about 70–80 days.

An alternative means of avoiding damage due to the activity of MPF is to transfer diploid nuclei into metaphase II oocytes that have a high level of MPF activity[9]. The availability of TNT4 cells allows this approach to be used. In this study a synchronous population of diploid donor nuclei was produced by inducing the cells to exit the growth cycle and arrest in G0 in a state of quiescence. In the presence of a high level of MPF activity the transferred nucleus undergoes nuclear membrane breakdown and chromosome condensation. It has been argued[11] that the developmental potential of reconstructed embryos depends upon the "reprogramming of gene expression" by the action of cytoplasmic factors and that this might be enhanced by the prolongation of this period of exposure. To assess these effects donor cells were fused to oocytes either (1) 4–8 h before activation "post-activated" or (2) at the time of activation "fusion and activation" or (3) to preactivated oocytes "preactivated".

内发育的胚胎的结论。某些对照胚胎没有发育被认为是与临时受体绵羊的输卵管炎症有关，因为这些受体绵羊中有六只后来恢复了体内胚胎发育。

表 1. 采用未同步 TNT4 细胞的发育情况

供体细胞类型	桑椹胚和胚泡数 / 总胚胎数 (%)	羊羔数 / 移植的胚胎数
1993 年 10 月至 1994 年 2 月		
16 细胞	6/11 (27.3)	2/6
ED 细胞	1/15 (6.7)	0/1
ED P1	4/19 (21.0)	1/4
ED P2	1/11 (9.1)	1/1
ED P3	2/36 (5.5)	2/2
1994 年 10 月至 12 月		
16 细胞	14/28 (50.0)	0/14
TNT4 P6	9/98 (9.2)	0*/9
TNT4 P11	10/92 (10.9)	0/10

处于分离或已建立 TNT4 细胞系阶段的非同步细胞，与去核并事先激活的绵羊卵母细胞进行核移植后得到的重组绵羊胚胎的发育情况。P：传代数；ED：胚盘。为进行胚胎重组，将供体卵母细胞放入含 10% FCS、7.5 μg·ml⁻¹ 细胞松弛素 B（西格玛公司）和 5.0 μg·ml⁻¹ Hoechst 33342（西格玛公司）的无钙离子 M2 培养基中，37 ℃ 放置 20 分钟以便吸入细胞。用一支玻璃移液管（尖端外径约 20 μm），将少量贴附在细胞质膜上的细胞质直接从第一极体下方移走。将该细胞核暴露在紫外线下，并检查赤道板是否存在，以确认去核成功。在注射 GnRH 34~36 小时之后，去核卵母细胞即被激活，在含有 10% FCS 的 TC199 培养基中继续培养 4~6 小时，单细胞即可用于融合。按照参考文献所述 [10,17]，所有激活与融合过程是在含 0.3 M 甘露醇、0.1 mM MgSO₄、0.0005 mM CaCl₂[17] 的培养基中完成的。激活时，使用 1.25 kV·cm⁻¹ 单次直流脉冲，持续 80 微秒。融合时先采用单次 3 V 交流脉冲，持续 5 秒，随后采用 3 次 1.25 kV·cm⁻¹，持续 80 微秒的直流脉冲。融合脉冲之后，需要在 10% FCS、7.5 μg·ml⁻¹ 细胞松弛素 B（西格玛公司）的 TC199 培养基中培养所有卵母细胞 / 细胞组 1 小时，随后采用融合脉冲，然后在没有细胞松弛素的相同培养基中培养，直至移植到临时受体绵羊体内。重组的胚胎于 7 天后移植到受体"黑脸"母绵羊结扎的输卵管内。所有桑椹胚和胚泡阶段的胚胎被移植到同步了的受体黑脸母绵羊体内完成体内发育。

* 一次成功妊娠，但在 70~80 天时流产。

另一种避免因 MPF 活性导致损伤发生的方法，是将二倍体细胞核移植到 MPF 活性很高的减数第二次分裂中期的卵母细胞中 [9]。TNT4 细胞的可用性使得这一方法很奏效。本研究中，通过诱导细胞退出生长周期，并锁定在静止期 G0 阶段，从而获得一群同步的二倍体供体细胞核。由于 MPF 活性处于高水平，移植后的细胞核会经历核膜破裂和染色体浓缩。有人争论说 [11] 重组胚胎的发育潜能依赖于细胞质因子活动所致的"基因表达重编程"，并可能通过延长这一暴露期而得以加强。为评估这些影响，我们将供体细胞与卵母细胞分别在以下时期融合进行研究：(1) 在"后激活"4~8 小时之前，或 (2) 在"融合与激活"期间，或 (3)"预先激活"卵母细胞。

During these studies *in vivo* ovulated metaphase arrested (M II) oocytes were flushed from the oviduct of "Scottish blackface" ewes. The methodology used was as previously described[10] with the following exceptions; oocytes were recovered 28–33 h after injection of gonadotropin-releasing hormone (GnRH), calcium/magnesium-free PBS containing 1.0% FCS was used for all flushing, and recovered oocytes were transferred to calcium-free M2 medium[12] containing 10% FCS and were maintained at 37 °C in 5% CO_2 in air until use. As soon as possible after recovery oocytes were enucleated and embryos reconstructed. At 50–54 h after GnRH injection, reconstructed embryos were embedded in agar and transferred to the ligated oviduct of dioestrus ewes. After 6 days the embryos were retrieved and development assessed microscopically (see Fig. 1*b*).

The development of embryos reconstructed using quiescent TNT4 cells and 3 different cytoplast recipients is summarized in Table 2. No significant difference was observed in the frequency of development with high and low passage number donor cells or with cytoplast recipient type used (results were analysed by the marginal model in ref. 13). All embryos that had developed to the morula/blastocyst stage were transferred as soon as possible to the uterine horn of synchronized final recipient ewes for development to term. Recipient ewes were monitored for pregnancy by ultrasonography. Ewes that were positive at day 35 were classified as pregnant (Table 3). A total of eight fetuses were detected in seven recipient ewes including a single twin pregnancy. A total of five phenotypically female Welsh mountain lambs were born from the Scottish blackface recipient ewes (Fig. 1*c*). Two of these lambs died within minutes of birth and a third at 10 days; the remaining two lambs are apparently normal and healthy (8–9 months old). Of the remaining 3 fetuses, one was lost at about 80 days of gestation, and a second was lost at 144 days of gestation. The third fetus was thought to be a twin pregnancy and was either misdiagnosed or lost at an unknown time. Microsatellite analysis of the cell line, fetuses and lambs showed that all of the female lambs were derived from a single cell population (Fig. 1*d*).

Table 2. Development to morula and blastocyst stage of ovine embryos reconstructed using quiescent TNT4 cells and 3 different cytoplast recipients (January–March 1995)

Cytoplast type		Number of morulae and blastocysts/total number of embryos recovered (%)		
Experiment number	TNT passage number	Post-activated	Activation and fusion	Preactivated
1	6	4/28	6/32*	–
2	7	1/10	1/26*	–
3	13	0/2	–	2/14
4	13	0/14	0/11	–
5	11	1/9	–	0/9
6	11	1/2	9/29***	–
7	12	–		6/45*
8	13	3/13*		–
Total		10/78(12.8%)	16/98 (16.3%)	8/68 (11.7%)

Development to the morula and blastocyst stage of ovine embryos recovered on day 7 after reconstruction by nuclear transfer of quiescent TNT4 cells at different passages into 3 cytoplast recipients. To induce quiescence, TNT4 cells

在这些研究中，体内处于 MII 的卵母细胞从"苏格兰黑脸"母羊的输卵管中被冲洗出来。实验方法如参考文献所述[10]，但有以下不同：卵母细胞被注射促性腺激素释放激素（GnRH）28~33 小时后恢复，整个实验过程中用含 1.0% FCS 的 PBS（不含钙离子和镁离子）进行漂洗，恢复后的卵母细胞被转移到含 10% FCS 但不含钙离子的 M2 培养基[12] 中，并在含 5% CO_2 的气体中 37 ℃保存待用。在卵母细胞恢复后尽快去核，并重组胚胎。在注射 GnRH 50~54 小时后，重组胚胎被埋植在琼脂中，并移植到间情期母羊被结扎的输卵管上。6 天后取回胚胎，并用显微镜评估其发育情况（见图 1b）。

使用静止期 TNT4 细胞和三种不同胞质体受体重组得到的胚胎的发育情况归纳为表 2。对于采用不同传代次数的供体细胞，或是不同类型的胞质体受体，其发育频率并未观察到显著差异（采用参考文献 13 的边际模型分析结果）。所有已经发育到桑椹胚 / 胚泡阶段的胚胎，都被迅速地移植到同步的受体母绵羊的子宫角内进行体内发育。研究中采用超声检查法来监控受体母绵羊的怀孕过程。第 35 天时呈现阳性的母绵羊即被归为怀孕组（表 3）。一共在七只受体母羊身上检测到 8 个胎儿，其中包括一例双胎妊娠。苏格兰黑脸受体母绵羊共生下了五只表型为雌性的威尔士山羔羊（图 1c）。其中两只在出生后几分钟即死亡，一只在第 10 天死亡，其他两只羔羊显然是正常且健康的（8 至 9 个月大）。其余 3 个胎儿，一只在妊娠 80 天时流产，另一只在妊娠 144 天时流产。而被认为是双胞胎的那例，也许是误诊，也许在某个未知的时间其中一只流产了。对细胞系、胎儿和羔羊的微卫星分析表明，所有雌性羔羊均来自一个单独的细胞群（图 1d）。

表 2. 静止期 TNT4 细胞和三种不同的胞质体受体重组得到的绵羊胚胎发育
到桑椹胚和胚泡阶段的情况（1995 年 1 月至 3 月）

胞质体类型		桑椹胚和胚泡数 / 恢复胚胎的总数（%）		
试验编号	TNT 传代数	后激活	激活与融合	预先激活
1	6	4/28	6/32*	–
2	7	1/10	1/26*	–
3	13	0/2	–	2/14
4	13	0/14	0/11	–
5	11	1/9	–	0/9
6	11	1/2	9/29***	–
7	12	–	–	6/45*
8	13	3/13*		
总计		10/78（12.8%）	16/98（16.3%）	8/68（11.7%）

处于不同传代阶段的静止期 TNT4 细胞核移植到三种胞质体受体中进行重组，恢复 7 日后绵羊胚胎发育到桑椹胚和胚泡阶段的情况。为诱导细胞进入静止期，将 TNT4 细胞放置于预先铺好饲养层的 29 cm^2 培养瓶（GIBCO 公司）中

were plated into feeder layers in 29-cm^2 flasks (GIBCO) and cultured for 2 days, the semiconfluent exponentially growing cultures were then washed three times in medium containing 0.5% FCS and cultured in this low-serum medium for 5 days. Embryos were reconstructed using preactivated cytoplasts as previously described (Table 1) and by two other protocols. (1) post-activation, as soon as possible after enucleation a single cell was fused to the cytoplast in 0.3 M mannitol without calcium and magnesium, to prevent activation. Couplets were washed and cultured in calcium-free M2, 10% FCS at 37 °C, 5% CO$_2$ for 4–8 h. Thirty minutes before activation the couplets were transferred to M2 medium, 10% FCS containing 5 μM Nocodazole (SIGMA). Following activation the reconstructed zygotes were incubated in medium TC199, 10% FCS, 5.0 μM Nocodazole for a further 3 h. (2) Preactivation, at 34–36 h after GnRH injection a single cell was fused to an enucleated oocyte. The same pulse also induced activation of the recipient cytoplast. All activations and fusions were accomplished as described in Table 1 unless otherwise stated.

* Denotes number of pregnancies following transfer of morula and blastocyst stage embryos to synchronized final recipient ewes.

Table 3. Induction of pregnancy and further development following transfer of morula and blastocyst stage embryos reconstructed from quiescent TNT4 cells

Cytoplast type	Post-activated	Activation and fusion	Preactivated
Total number of morula and blastocyst stage embryos transferred	10	16	8
Total number of ewes	6	9	4
Number of pregnant ewes (%)	1 (16.7)	5 (55.5)	1 (25.0)
Number of fetuses/total embryos transferred (%)	2/10 (20.0)	5/16 (31.25)	1/8 (12.5)
Number of live births	1	3	1
Passage number of cells resulting in offspring	1 × P11	1 × P6, 2 × P11	1 × P13

Induction of pregnancy following transfer of all morula/blastocyst stage reconstructed embryos to the uterine horn of synchronized final recipient blackface ewes. The table shows the total number of embryos from each group transferred, the frequency of pregnancy in terms of ewes and embryos (in the majority of cases 2 embryos were transferred to each ewe and a single twin pregnancy was established (using the "post-activated" cytoplast)) and the number of live lambs obtained.

Because of the seasonality of sheep a direct comparison of all of these methods of embryo reconstruction has not yet been made. The success of the later studies may be due to a number of factors. First, quiescent nuclei are diploid and therefore the cell-cycle stages of the karyoplast and cytoplast in both the "post-activation" and "fusion and activation" methods of reconstruction are coordinated. The preactivated cytoplast will accept donor nuclei from G0, G1, S and G2 cell-cycle phases. Second, the G0 phase of the cell cycle has been implicated in the differentiation process and the chromatin of quiescent nuclei has been reported to undergo modification[14]. As a result the chromatin of quiescent donor nuclei may be more readily modified by oocyte cytoplasm. The TNT4 cells resemble several cell lines derived previously in sheep[15] and also pigs[16]. It remains to be determined whether comparable development is obtained with other such lines or other cell types. At the present time we are unable to differentiate the mechanisms involved and report that the combination of nuclear transfer and cell type described here support development to term of cloned ovine embryos from cells that had been in culture through up to 13 passages. As cell-cycle duration was about 24 h, this period of culture before nuclear transfer would be sufficient to allow genetic modification and selection if procedures comparable to those used in murine ES cells can be established.

培养 2 天，将半融合的呈指数型增长的培养物在含 0.5% FCS 的培养基中漂洗三次，然后在该低血清培养基中培养 5 天。采用以下两种方法，用此前描述的预先激活的胞质体 (表 1) 对胚胎进行重组。(1) 后激活方法：对单个细胞去核后，尽快在 0.3 M 的无钙镁甘露醇中将其融入胞质体，以防止激活。将细胞组在无钙离子但含有 10% FCS 的 M2 培养基中进行漂洗，并于 5% CO_2 环境中 37 ℃培养 4~8 小时。在激活之前 30 分钟，将细胞组转移到含 5 μM 诺考达唑 (西格玛公司) 以及 10% FCS 的 M2 培养基中。在激活之后，将重组的合子置于含有 10% FCS 和 5.0 μM 诺考达唑的 TC199 培养基中继续孵育 3 小时。(2) 预先激活方法：在注射 GnRH 34~36 小时之后，单个细胞融合到去核卵母细胞中。同样的脉冲也诱导激活了受体胞质体。除特别声明外，所有激活与融合操作均如表 1 所述。

* 指的是把桑椹胚和胚泡期的胚胎移植到同步化的最终受体母羊之后的受孕数量。

表 3. 处于静止期的 TNT4 细胞经重组获得的桑椹胚和胚泡移植后诱导妊娠和发育的情况

胞质体类型	后激活	激活与融合	预先激活
所移植的桑椹胚和胚泡期胚胎的总数	10	16	8
母绵羊总数	6	9	4
受孕绵羊数量 (%)	1 (16.7)	5 (55.5)	1 (25.0)
胎儿数量 / 移植的胚胎总数 (%)	2/10 (20.0)	5/16 (31.25)	1/8 (12.5)
生育数量	1	3	1
成功产生后代的细胞传代数	1 × P11	1 × P6, 2 × P11	1 × P13

把所有桑椹胚 / 胚泡期的重组胚胎移植到同步化的最终受体——黑脸母绵羊的子宫角后，诱导妊娠的情况。该表格给出了每个移植组得到的胚胎总数，与母绵羊以及胚胎有关的妊娠频率 (大多数情况下，每只母羊移植两个胚胎，获得了一次双胎妊娠 (采用 "后激活" 的胞质体))，以及得到的成活羊羔的数量。

　　由于绵羊的季节周期性，本研究尚无法对所有胚胎重组的方法进行直接比较。随后研究的成功可能与多种因素有关。首先，静止的细胞核为二倍体，"后激活" 和 "融合与激活" 两种重组方法中的核体与胞质体的细胞周期阶段可以有效兼容。而 "预先激活" 的胞质体能接受来自细胞周期 G0、G1、S 和 G2 阶段的供体细胞核。其次，细胞周期的 G0 阶段与分化过程有关。另外，有报道指出处于休眠期的细胞核中的染色质会进行修饰 [14]。因此休眠期供体核中的染色质可能更容易被卵母细胞的细胞质所改变。TNT4 细胞与先前来源于绵羊 [15] 和猪 [16] 的几个细胞系类似。因此，类似的发育过程是否可利用其他细胞系或其他细胞类型得到，仍有待进一步证实。目前，我们尚不能区分相关分子机制，也无法表明本研究中所展示的核移植及其所涉及的细胞类型可以支持体外培养传代至 13 代以内的细胞系完成体内发育，并最终发育为成活个体。由于细胞周期大约为 24 小时，如果能够建立与鼠科 ES 细胞类似的程序，那么在核移植之前的培养阶段就可以充分地进行遗传修饰和选择。

The production of cloned offspring in farm animal species could provide enormous benefits in research, agriculture and biotechnology. The modification by gene targeting and selection of cell populations before embryo reconstruction coupled to the clonal origin of the whole animal provides a method for the dissemination of rapid genetic improvement and/or modification into the population.

(**380**, 64-66; 1996)

K. H. S. Campbell, J. McWhir, W. A. Ritchie & I. Wilmut
Roslin Institute (Edinburgh), Roslin, Midlothian EH25 9PS, UK

Received 27 November 1995; accepted 5 January 1996.

References:

1. McGrath, J. & Solter, D. *Science* **220**, 1300-1302 (1983).

2. Bondioli, K. R., Westhusin, M. E. & Looney, C. R. *Therio* **33**, 165-174 (1990).

3. Prather, R. S. & First, N. L. *Int. Rev. Cytol.* **120**, 169-190 (1990).

4. Chesne, P., Heyman, Y., Peynot, N. & Renard, J.-P. *C.R. Acad. Sci. Paris Life Sci.* **316**, 487-491 (1993).

5. Sims, M. & First, N. L. *Proc. Natl. Acad. Sci. U.S.A.* **91**, 6243-6147 (1994).

6. Collas, P. & Barnes, F. L. *Molec. Repr. Dev.* **38**, 264-267 (1994).

7. Hooper, M. L. *Embryonal Stem Cells: Introducing Planned Changes into the Germline* (ed. Evans, H. J.) (Harwood Academic, Switzerland, 1992).

8. Galli, C., Lazzari, G., Flechon, J. & Moor, R. M. *Zygote* **2**, 385-389 (1994).

9. Campbell, K. H. S., Ritchie, W. A. & Wilmut, I. *Biol. Reprod.* **49**, 933-942 (1993).

10. Campbell, K. H. S., Loi, P., Capai, P. & Wilmut, I. *Biol. Reprod.* **50**, 1385-1393 (1994).

11. Szollosi, D., Czolowska, R., Szollosi, M. S. & Tarkowski, A. K. *J. Cell Sci.* **91**, 603-613 (1988).

12. Whitten, W. K. & Biggers, J. D. *J. Reprod. Fertil.* **17**, 399-401 (1968).

13. Breslaw, N. E. & Clayton, D. G. *J. Am. Stat. Assoc.* **88**, 9-25 (1993).

14. Whitfield, J. F., Boynton, A. L., Rixon, R. H. & Youdale, T. *Control of Animal Cell Proliferation* Vol. 1 (eds Boynton, A. L. & Leffert, H. L.) 331-365 (Academic, London, 1985).

15. Piedrahita, J. A., Anderson, G. B. & Bon Durrant, R. H. *Therio* **34**, 879-901 (1990).

16. Gerfen, R. W. & Wheeler, M. B. *Anim. Biotechnol.* **6**, 1-14 (1995).

17. Willadsen, S. M. *Nature* **320**, 63-65 (1986).

18. Buchanan, F. C., Galloway, S. M. & Crawford, A. M. *Anim. Genet.* **25**, 60 (1994).

Acknowledgements. We thank M. Ritchie, J. Bracken, M. Malcolm-Smith and R. Ansell for technical assistance; D. Waddington for statistical analysis; and H. Bowran and his colleagues for their care of the animals. This research was supported by Ministry of Agriculture Fisheries and Food and the Roslin Institute.

　　农畜克隆后代的产生，将为科研、农业和生物技术领域带来巨大的研究与应用价值。在胚胎重组之前通过基因靶向修饰或在细胞群中选择优良细胞并克隆整只动物，将提供一种迅速将改良和(或)修饰基因分散到该种群中的有效方法。

（周志华 翻译；方向东 审稿）

A Comprehensive Genetic Map
of the Mouse Genome

W. F. Dietrich *et al.*

Editor's Note

Linkage maps reveal the relative positions of genes and/or genetic markers in terms of recombination frequency, rather than distance along a chromosome. Here geneticist Eric S. Lander and colleagues report a complete genetic linkage map of the mouse genome, with over 7,000 genetic markers. The markers are sufficiently abundant, polymorphic and stable to enable mapping of simple and complex traits in different mouse crosses. The map also helped researchers positionally clone and pinpoint mouse mutations and provided a common framework for the mapping of mutations and cloned genes. The paper was published alongside a human genetic linkage map, marking the close of the first phase of the Human Genome Project: the construction of dense genetic maps of mouse and man.

The availability of dense genetic linkage maps of mammalian genomes makes feasible a wide range of studies, including positional cloning of monogenic traits, genetic dissection of polygenic traits, construction of genome-wide physical maps, rapid marker-assisted construction of congenic strains, and evolutionary comparisons[1,2]. We have been engaged for the past five years in a concerted effort to produce a dense genetic map of the laboratory mouse[3-6]. Here we present the final report of this project. The map contains 7,377 genetic markers, consisting of 6,580 highly informative simple sequence length polymorphisms integrated with 797 restriction fragment length polymorphisms in mouse genes. The average spacing between markers is about 0.2 centimorgans or 400 kilobases.

To construct a simple sequence length polymorphism (SSLP) map, we identified more than 9,000 sequences from random genomic clones and public databases containing simple sequence repeats (mostly, $(CA)_n$-repeats), designed polymerase chain reaction (PCR) primers flanking the repeat, and tested each for polymorphism by measuring the allele sizes in 12 inbred mouse strains. Of the successful PCR assays, we genotyped the 90% of loci that revealed different alleles between the OB and CAST strains in an (OB × CAST) F_2 intercross with 46 progeny. These data were assembled into a map by performing genetic linkage analysis with the MAPMAKER computer package[7,8].

A total of 6,336 SSLP loci were scored in the F_2 intercross, with 6,111 derived from anonymous sequence and 225 from known genes (Table 1). Of these, 5,905 were scored as codominant markers and 431 as dominant markers (because the pattern of one allele

一张高精度的小鼠基因组遗传图谱

迪特里希等

编者按

连锁图显示的是根据重组率得到的基因和（或）遗传标记的相对位置，而不是在染色体上的距离。本文中，遗传学家埃里克·兰德及其同事报告了一个完整的小鼠基因组遗传连锁图，该图谱包含 7,000 多个遗传标记。这些标记具有较高的丰度、多态性和稳定性，能够用于不同小鼠杂交品系的单基因和多基因性状作图。此图还提供了一个突变和克隆基因作图的共同框架，能帮助研究人员进行定位克隆和小鼠突变位点定位。这篇文章与人类遗传连锁图谱同时发表，标志着人类基因组计划第一期工作——构建小鼠和人类的高密度遗传图谱的结束。

哺乳动物基因组的高密度遗传连锁图谱可用于广泛的研究领域，包括单基因性状的定位克隆、多基因性状的遗传解析、全基因组物理图谱的构建、快速标记辅助的同品系构建及进化比较 [1,2]。过去五年里，我们共同致力于构建实验小鼠的高密度遗传图谱 [3-6]。这里我们公布这一项目的最终结果。这张图谱包含 7,377 个遗传标记，由 6,580 个高信息量的简单序列长度多态性（SSLPs）标记与 797 个小鼠基因内的限制性片段长度多态性（RFLPs）标记组成。标记之间的平均间距约为 0.2 厘摩或 400,000 碱基。

为构建一个 SSLP 图谱，我们从随机基因组克隆和公共数据库中含有简单重复序列（多数是 $(CA)_n$ 重复）的数据中鉴定出 9,000 多个序列，在重复序列两侧设计聚合酶链式反应（PCR）引物，通过在 12 个小鼠近交品系中鉴定每一个等位基因的大小来检验它们的多态性。对（OB×CAST）F_2 代互交的 46 个后代的成功 PCR 结果统计表明，我们可检出 90% 在 OB 品系和 CAST 品系间不同的等位基因的基因座。利用 MAPMAKER 程序包进行遗传连锁分析，将这些数据组装成遗传图谱 [7,8]。

在 F2 代互交实验中共评价了 6,336 个 SSLP 基因座，其中 6,111 个来自未知序列，225 个来自已知基因（表 1）。它们中有 5,905 个是共显性标记，431 个是显性标记

obscured the other). The map provides dense coverage of all 20 mouse chromosomes, with a total genetic length of 1,361 centimorgans (cM). Because the cross involves 92 meioses, the mean spacing between crossovers is 1.1 cM and thus loci can be mapped to "bins" of this average size. The map has 1,001 occupied bins (Table 3(*a*)), with an average of 6.3 markers per bin and an average spacing of 1.36 cM between consecutive bins.

Table 1. Genetic markers, genetic length and polymorphism* by chromosome

Chromosome	No. of markers	No. of random markers	No. from GENBANK	"Consensus" genetic length†	Observed genetic length‡	Polymorphism among lab strains (%)§‖	Lab strains versus SPR or CAST (%)‖
1	511	494	17	98	109.9	57	92
2	507	491	16	107	95.7	49	94
3	343	332	11	100	67.5	51	95
4	350	342	8	81	74.2	51	93
5	402	391	11	93	82.9	48	95
6	368	349	19	74	59.1	46	94
7	357	341	16	89	59.8	48	94
8	350	345	5	81	72.0	44	94
9	336	318	18	70	62.9	52	95
10	293	286	7	78	73.0	35	96
11	350	326	24	78	82.0	53	94
12	278	268	10	68	61.5	50	94
13	303	296	7	72	60.2	48	95
14	259	246	13	53	65.6	49	94
15	264	257	7	62	62.2	51	94
16	215	214	1	59	51.0	43	94
17	255	239	16	53	51.0	56	93
18	231	226	5	57	39.7	53	95
19	134	131	3	42	57.2	52	93
X	230	219	11	88	73.5	33	95
Total	6,336	6,111	225	1,503	1,360.9¶	48	94

* Polymorphism survey was based on visual comparisons of fragments across large acrylamide gels and was thus subject to mobility differences among lanes. To assess the accuracy of data in our database, 3,000 individual pairwise comparisons were repeated. Some 6% of reported polymorphic pairs turn out to be monomorphic upon careful comparison, while 4% of reported monomorphic pairs turn out to be polymorphic. The data are thus accurate enough to allow selection of markers for crosses, but geneticists wishing to know every polymorphic marker in a narrow region (for fine-structure genetic mapping and positional cloning, for example) are advised to recheck each locus.

† Based on "consensus" genetic map in Encyclopedia of the Mouse Genome, http://www.informatics.jax.org/encyclo. html (1993).

‡ Distance between most proximal and most distal markers in the map reported here.

（因为一个等位基因的模式会掩盖另一个等位基因）。这张高密度图谱覆盖了小鼠的 20 条染色体，总遗传长度达 1,361 厘摩。因为杂交涉及 92 次减数分裂，交换位点间的平均距离为 1.1 厘摩，因此可将这些基因座定位到以此平均值为单位的"箱子"中。这张图谱共覆盖 1,001 个"箱子"（表 3 (a)），平均每个"箱子"含有 6.3 个标记，连续"箱子"之间的平均距离为 1.36 厘摩。

表 1. 染色体上的遗传标记、遗传长度和多态性统计 *

染色体	标记数目	随机标记数目	来自 GENBANK 的数目	"共有"遗传长度†	观察的遗传长度‡	实验室品系间的多态性(%)§‖	实验室品系比 SPR 或 CAST(%)‖
1	511	494	17	98	109.9	57	92
2	507	491	16	107	95.7	49	94
3	343	332	11	100	67.5	51	95
4	350	342	8	81	74.2	51	93
5	402	391	11	93	82.9	48	95
6	368	349	19	74	59.1	46	95
7	357	341	16	89	59.8	48	94
8	350	345	5	81	72	44	94
9	336	318	18	70	62.9	52	95
10	293	286	7	78	73	35	96
11	350	326	24	78	82	53	94
12	278	268	10	68	61.5	50	94
13	303	296	7	72	60.2	48	95
14	259	246	13	53	65.6	49	94
15	264	257	7	62	62.2	51	94
16	215	214	1	59	51	43	94
17	255	239	16	53	51	56	93
18	231	226	5	57	39.7	53	95
19	134	131	3	42	57.2	52	93
X	230	219	11	88	73.5	33	95
总计	6,336	6,111	225	1,503	1,360.9¶	48	94

* 多态性检测是通过比较 PCR 片段在长的聚丙烯酰胺凝胶泳道间迁移率的差异来实现。为评估我们数据库中数据的准确性，对 3,000 个标记对进行了重复比较。仔细比较后发现，已报道的多态性标记对中大约 6% 实际上是单态性的，而报道的单态性标记对中 4% 实际上是多态性的。因此这些数据足够准确，可用于筛选杂交标记。但是对于希望知道在一个很小的区域内每一个多态性标记（如用于精细结构遗传作图和定位克隆）的遗传学家，建议重新检查每个基因座。

† 基于小鼠基因组百科全书中的"共有"遗传图谱，http://www.informatics.jax.org/encyclo.html（1993）。

‡ 本图谱中最近端和最远端标记之间的距离。

817

§ Pairwise comparisons of OB, B6, DBA, A, C3H, BALB, AKR, NON, NOD and LP.

‖ Standard error of the mean for each chromosome depends on number of markers studied, but is < 1% in all cases.

¶ Distance is shorter than in previously published versions of this map (ref. 6) because final error checking reduced the number of apparent crossovers.

We next sought to integrate the map of largely anonymous SSLPs with the locations of known genes, because this information can suggest candidates for the genes underlying mouse mutations. We analysed a (B6 × SPRET) backcross that has been extensively used for restriction fragment length polymorphism (RFLP) mapping[9-11]. The backcross has been genotyped for 797 RFLPs. To integrate the maps, we genotyped 1,245 SSLPs from our map in 46 progeny from the SPRET backcross, providing a common reference point approximately every 1.1 cM. We also genotyped 244 additional SSLPs that were not polymorphic—and thus could not be mapped—in the (OB × CAST) intercross, but were polymorphic in the (B6 × SPRET) backcross. The SPRET cross was thus scored for a total of 1,543 SSLPs and 797 RFLPs.

The final map with 7,377 loci is shown in Fig. 1, with the SSLP map on the right and the integration with the RFLP map on the left. A full description of the markers— including primer sequences, locus sequence, genotypes in each cross, and allele sizes in the characterized strains—would require over 500 pages of this journal. The complete information is available electronically on the World Wide Web (see Fig. 1 legend).

The maps constructed in the CAST intercross and SPRET backcross maps have similar lengths (1,361 and 1,385 cM respectively), despite the fact that the intercross reflects sex-averaged recombination rates and the backcross reflects female recombination rates (because heterozygous mothers were used). Because there is typically about 80% more recombination in females than males, the SPRET backcross map might be expected to be about 40% longer. That it is not probably reflects recombinational suppression owing to structural heterogeneity (inasmuch as the laboratory mouse is evolutionarily twice as distant from SPRET as from CAST).

The SSLP map constructed in the cross was subjected to rigorous quality control and quality assessment[3,8]. All obligate double crossovers were identified and rechecked. The final data set contained no obligate double crossovers involving markers separated by less than 21 cM, indicating strong crossover interference in the mouse. (In the absence of interference, about 100 such events would be expected.) We also filled in any missing genotypes that could alter the position of a locus (by virtue of being adjacent to the site of a crossover). Despite our best efforts, some errors surely remain: in particular, an incorrect genotype adjacent to the site of a crossover would not necessarily produce a double crossover, and could shift a locus by 1.1 cM. Each chromosome is thus likely to contain a handful of loci that are slightly misplaced. The SSLPs used for integration with the SPRET backcross provided a different assessment of accuracy. We checked whether these 1,245 loci mapped to the same location in both crosses. There were ten apparent discrepancies. In five cases (*D5Mit198*, *D7Mit173*, *D9Mit132*, *D9Mit150* and *D19Mit61*), the loci were found to reproducibly amplify polymorphic fragments at

§ OB、B6、DBA、A、C3H、BALB、AKR、NON、NOD 和 LP 小鼠品系之间成对比较。

‖ 每条染色体的平均数标准误差依赖于所研究的标记数目，但在所有情况下都小于 1%。

¶ 因为在最终的错误检查时减少了明显交换的数目，距离较此图谱以前的版本（参考文献 6）短。

下一步，我们想将大量未命名的 SSLP 基因座与已知基因的位置整合在一起，因为这个信息可以提示携带潜在突变的小鼠候选基因。我们分析了一个被广泛用于 RFLP 作图的 (B6 × SPRET) 回交系 [9-11]。从这个回交系中已经鉴定出 797 个 RFLP。为了整合图谱，我们从 SPRET 的 46 个回交后代中鉴定了 1,245 个 SSLP，约每 1.1 厘摩可提供一个共同参考点。我们还鉴定了另外 244 个在 (OB × CAST) 互交系中不具多态性的 SSLP，因此这些基因座不能体现在 (OB × CAST) 互交系图谱中，但在 (B6 × SPRET) 回交系中有多态性。因此，在 SPRET 杂交系中共获得了 1,543 个 SSLP 和 797 个 RFLP。

包含 7,377 个基因座的最终图谱如图 1 所示，右侧为 SSLP 图谱，左侧为整合的 RFLP 图谱。全面描述这些标记——包括引物序列、基因座序列、每个杂交中的基因型和某些品系中的等位基因长度——将需要本杂志 500 多页的篇幅。完整的电子版信息可在万维网上获得（见图 1 图注）。

尽管互交反映的是性别的平均重组率，而回交反映的是雌性重组率（因为采用的是杂合子母本），但 CAST 互交系和 SPRET 回交系所构建的图谱具有相似的长度（分别为 1,361 厘摩和 1,385 厘摩）。因为典型的雌性重组比雄性多 80%，所以预期的 SPRET 回交图谱应大约比 CAST 互交图谱长 40%。因此它不太能反映出因为结构异质性所造成的重组抑制（因为实验室小鼠与 SPRET 的进化距离是它与 CAST 进化距离的两倍）。

杂交的 SSLP 图谱构建受到严格的质量控制和质量评价 [3,8]。所有必需双交换事件都被鉴定出来并重新检查。最终的数据集不包含任何涉及标记间距离小于 21 厘摩的必需双交换事件，这表明在小鼠中存在强交换干扰。（在无干扰条件下，预计将有 100 个这种事件发生。）我们还填补了任何可能改变一个基因座位置的缺失基因型（借助于与一个交换事件的位点毗邻）。虽然我们尽了最大努力，但肯定仍存在一些错误：特别是，一个与交换位点毗邻的错误基因型不一定会产生双交换，但是会造成基因座偏移 1.1 厘摩。每条染色体因此都可能包含少量稍有错位的基因座。用于与 SPRET 回交系整合的 SSLP 提供了一种不同的精度评估。我们检查了这 1,245 个基因座在两个杂交系中是否定位在相同的位置上，发现有 10 处明显的差异。我们发现有 5 处基因座（*D5Mit198*、*D7Mit173*、*D9Mit132*、*D9Mit150* 和 *D19Mit61*）在这两个

different chromosomal locations in the two crosses. This probably occurs because strain variation creates an alternative target for amplification, although the possibility that CAST and SPRET differ by small insertional translocations cannot be excluded. In remaining five cases, the results from the CAST cross were found not to be reproducible. These probably arose from laboratory errors that unfortunately cannot be identified in retrospect. These five loci were removed from the map. Based on the frequency (5 of 1,245), we would expect that 20 further erroneous loci remain, which corresponds to about one per chromosome.

We used several criteria to analyse the genomic distribution of loci. The spacing between SSLPs agrees reasonably well with expectation under a random distribution, although some deviation from randomness can be detected. The relative positions of markers and crossovers can be inferred completely in an experimental cross, and the entire data set can be reduced to a string of the form "mmcccmmmcccmcmcm...", with each m and c denoting the occurrence of a marker or a crossover, respectively. The hypothesis that markers are randomly distributed with respect to crossovers can be tested by comparing the observed clustering of consecutive markers and crossovers to that expected for tossing a biased coin with the probability of a marker being $p_m = M/(M+C)$, where M is the number of markers and C the number of crossovers[6]. There is some statistically significant evidence of clustering by this test (Table 3). The map contains an interval with eight consecutive crossovers (on chromosome 19) and a block of 54 recombinationally inseparable markers (on chromosome 2); the probability of such clusters of crossovers and markers occurring at random somewhere in the map is 0.5% and 3.4%, respectively. More generally, the frequency of both large and small clusters slightly exceeds expectation. Nonetheless, the distribution is not far from random expectation, at least at the level of resolution provided by the meioses studied here.

The chromosomal distribution of SSLPs among the autosomes agrees well with expectation under the assumption that loci are uniformly distributed with respect to cytogenetic length. (Chromosome 19 shows a slight deficit, which is not statistically significant after correction for multiple testing; it may reflect the unusually large proportion of heterochromatin on this chromosome.) In contrast, chromosome X shows a clear deficit, with only about 57% as many as expected (Table 2). This phenomenon appears to be general in mammalian genomes, as we have also found a similar deficit in an SSLP map of the rat[12] (62% of expectation), and Weissenbach and colleagues report a slightly less pronounced deficit in the human genome[13] (75% of expectation). In principle, the deficit of SSLPs on chromosome X could occur if $(CA)_n$-repeats were either less frequent on chromosome X, or were equally frequent but less polymorphic. The latter hypothesis would predict that the deficit of polymorphic loci on chromosome X would be offset by a great excess of non-polymorphic repeats. Of the SSLPs monomorphic between OB and CAST, 37% would have to lie to chromosome X to explain the observed data. We determined the chromosomal location of > 100 monomorphic loci (by genetic mapping for those that were polymorphic between B6 and SPRET and by somatic cell hybrid mapping for those that were not), but we found no significant excess on chromosome X.

杂交系中再扩增出位于染色体不同位置上的多态性片段。这可能是由品系间变异产生另外的扩增靶造成的，但不能排除小插入易位引起 CAST 和 SPRET 产生差别的可能性。而在剩余的 5 个基因座中，CAST 杂交系的结果不可重复。这可能是由实验错误引起的，遗憾的是无法追溯出原因，因此将这 5 个基因座从图谱中去除。基于这个频率 (5/1,245)，我们预计仍存在 20 个错误基因座，大约是每条染色体上一个。

我们用了几个标准来分析基因座在基因组上的分布。虽然可以检测到一些随机性偏差，但 SSLP 之间的距离与随机分布模式下的预测非常一致。标记与交换的相对位置完全可以通过一个实验性杂交推断出来，并且所有数据可以简化为一串 "mmcccmmmcccmcmcm…"，每个 m 和 c 分别代表一个标记或交换的出现。标记相对于交换是随机分布的这一假设可以通过观察的连续标记簇和交换簇与期望值的比较来检验，犹如投掷硬币，一个标记的概率是 $p_m = M/(M+C)$，M 是标记数目，C 是交换数目 [6]。通过这个检验我们发现了一些具有显著统计学意义的簇 (表 3)。图谱中含有一个由 8 个连续交换组成的区间 (19 号染色体上) 和一个由 54 个重组不分离标记组成的区间 (2 号染色体上)；图谱上随机出现这种交换簇和标记簇的可能性分别为 0.5% 和 3.4%。更普遍的是，大、小簇的频率都略超预期。尽管如此，至少在本研究所提供的减数分裂这种分辨率水平上其分布仍接近随机分布预期。

SSLP 在常染色体上的分布与基因座相对于染色体细胞遗传学长度均匀分布的假设预期高度吻合。(经多重校验后，19 号染色体表现出略微差别，但不具有显著统计学意义；这可能反映了这条染色体上存在超高比例的异染色质区间。) 相反，X 染色体表现出明显的差别，其仅为预期的 57% (表 2)。这一现象在哺乳动物基因组中似乎很普遍，我们在大鼠的 SSLP 图谱中也发现了相似的差别 [12] (预期的 62%)，而韦森巴赫及其同事报道了在人类基因组中一处略小的差别 [13] (预期的 75%)。原则上，X 染色体上 SSLP 较少的原因可归结为 X 染色体上 (CA)$_n$ 重复频率低或频率相等但多态性低。后一种假设预期 X 染色体上多态性基因座的不足会被大量过剩的非多态性重复抵消。在 OB 和 CAST 间的单态 SSLP 中，必须有 37% 定位在 X 染色体上才可以解释所观察到的数据。我们鉴定出含有超过 100 个单态标记的基因座所在的染色体位置 (通过遗传作图确定的在 B6 和 SPRET 之间存在多态性的基因座，通过体细胞杂交作图确定的不存在多态性的基因座)，但并未在 X 染色体上观察到显著富

Accordingly, the deficit appears to be primarily due to an actual shortage of $(CA)_n$-repeats on chromosome X.

Table 2. Distribution of random markers based on cytogenetic length of chromosomes

Chromosome	No. of random markers[†]	Based on cytogenetic length[*]		
		Percentage of total length	Expected number of markers[‡]	Z-score[§]
Autosomes only				
1	494	7.68 ± .15	452.7 ± 22.4	1.84
2	491	7.42 ± .15	437.0 ± 21.9	2.47
3	332	6.39 ± .13	376.7 ± 20.2	−2.20
4	342	6.29 ± .13	360.4 ± 20.0	−1.41
5	391	6.06 ± .12	356.2 ± 19.7	1.73
6	349	5.90 ± .12	347.7 ± 19.4	0.07
7	341	5.54 ± .11	326.4 ± 18.7	0.79
8	345	5.30 ± .11	312.5 ± 18.3	1.78
9	318	5.11 ± .10	301.2 ± 17.9	0.94
10	286	5.06 ± .10	298.1 ± 17.8	−0.67
11	326	5.04 ± .10	296.8 ± 17.8	1.65
12	268	5.21 ± .10	306.9 ± 18.1	−2.14
13	293	4.67 ± .09	275.4 ± 17.1	1.21
14	246	4.76 ± .10	280.5 ± 17.3	−1.99
15	257	4.32 ± .09	254.7 ± 16.4	0.15
16	214	4.07 ± .08	239.6 ± 15.9	−1.60
17	239	4.12 ± .08	242.7 ± 16.0	−0.22
18	226	4.14 ± .08	244.0 ± 16.0	−1.11
19	131	2.91 ± .06	171.7 ± 13.4	−3.04
Total	5,892	100	5,892.0	
Autosomes versus X chromosome				
Autosomes	5,892	93.76 ± .12	5,729.7 ± 20.4	7.96
X	219	6.24 ± .12	381.3 ± 20.4	−7.96
Total	6,111	100.0	6,111.0	

* Cytogenetic length taken from previous measurements[19]. Standard error of the mean was calculated directly from the raw data on chromosome measurements, generously provided by E. Evans.

† Only random markers are considered to avoid biases in chromosomal distribution of known genes.

‡ Mean ± standard deviation. Standard deviation in number of markers expected combines both standard error in the measurement of chromosome length and sampling error given to the total number of loci examined. Uncertainty in the precise length of chromosomes was not included in previous analyses[6], owing to its small magnitude, but it becomes relevant as the number of loci increases and sampling error correspondingly decreases. For comparison of autosomes to X chromosome, the expectation reflects the fact that 5% of the random markers were derived from male DNA (thus underrepresenting the X chromosome by a factor of two) and 95% from female DNA.

集。因此，造成这种差别的主要原因是 X 染色体上实际的 $(CA)_n$ 重复过少。

表 2. 基于染色体细胞遗传学长度的随机标记分布

染色体	随机标记数目†	基于细胞遗传学长度 *		
		总长度的百分比	期望的标记数目‡	Z 值§
仅常染色体				
1	494	7.68±.15	452.7±22.4	1.84
2	491	7.42±.15	437.0±21.9	2.47
3	332	6.39±.13	376.7±20.2	−2.20
4	342	6.29±.13	360.4±20.0	−1.41
5	391	6.06±.12	356.2±19.7	1.73
6	349	5.90±.12	347.7±19.4	0.07
7	341	5.54±.11	326.4±18.7	0.79
8	345	5.30±.11	312.5±18.3	1.78
9	318	5.11±.10	301.2±17.9	0.94
10	286	5.06±.10	298.1±17.8	−0.67
11	326	5.04±.10	296.8±17.8	1.65
12	268	5.21±.10	306.9±18.1	−2.14
13	293	4.67±.09	275.4±17.1	1.21
14	246	4.76±.10	280.5±17.3	−1.99
15	257	4.32±.09	254.7±16.4	0.15
16	214	4.07±.08	239.6±15.9	−1.60
17	239	4.12±.08	242.7±16.0	−0.22
18	226	4.14±.08	244.0±16.0	−1.11
19	131	2.91±.06	171.7±13.4	−3.04
总计	5,892	100	5,892.0	
常染色体对 X 染色体				
常染色体	5,892	93.76±.12	5729.7±20.4	7.96
X 染色体	219	6.24±.12	381.3±20.4	−7.96
总计	6,111	100.0	6,111.0	

* 染色体细胞遗传学长度来自以前测量的结果 [19]。平均数标准误差直接根据染色体上测量的原始数据计算，由埃文斯慷慨提供。

† 只考虑随机标记，以避免已知基因在染色体上分布所造成的偏差。

‡ 平均值 ± 标准差。期望标记数目的标准差包括染色体长度测量的标准误差和检测基因座总数产生的取样误差。由于规模小，以前的分析不包括染色体精确长度所造成的不确定性 [6]，但其随着基因座数目的增加和取样偏差的相应减少而变得相关。对于常染色体和 X 染色体的比较，期望值反映的是 5% 的随机标记来自父本 DNA（因此代表 1/2 的 X 染色体）而 95% 来自母本 DNA 的事实。

§ Z-score = (observed−expected)/standard deviation. For the autosomes, none of the Z-scores are significant at the $P = 0.05$ level after Bonferroni correction for multiple testing. For the comparison of autosomes to X chromosome, the Z-score is significant at $P < 10^{-14}$.

The SSLPs show a polymorphism rate of about 50% among inbred laboratory strains surveyed and about 95% between laboratory strains and CAST or SPR (Table 1). The pairwise polymorphism rates among the 12 strains surveyed have not changed significantly from our previous report[6] and are not presented here. Interestingly, the distribution of polymorphism across the genome is not uniform[11]. The average polymorphism rate among the *Mus musculus* strains surveyed was just under 50%, but two chromosomes showed substantially lower polymorphism rates: chromosome X at 33%, and chromosome 10 at 35% (Table 1). Decreased polymorphism could reflect recent selection for specific ancestral chromosomes. For the X chromosome, it could also reflect a different mutation rate (inasmuch as each chromosome X resides in males only two-thirds as often each autosome, and most mutations are thought to occur in male germline) or different population genetic forces (with hemizygosity affecting selection and effective population size).

Table 3. Clusters of consecutive crossovers and markers

(a) Number of crossovers between consecutive random markers*					
No. of crossover per interval	Observed		Expected†		P (longest run $\geqslant n$) (%)†
	No.	(percentage)	No.	(percentage)	
0	5,095	(83.85)	5,035.5 ± 29.6	(82.59)	
1	784	(12.90)	876.7 ± 27.4	(14.38)	100.0
2	151	(2.49)	152.6 ± 12.2	(2.50)	100.0
3	27	(0.44)	26.6 ± 5.1	(0.44)	100.0
4	14	(0.23)	4.6 ± 2.2	(0.08)	99.6
5	4	(0.07)	0.8 ± 0.9	(0.01)	62.2
6	0	(0.00)	0.1 ± 0.4	(<0.01)	15.6
7	0	(0.00)	0.0 ± 0.2	(<0.01)	2.9
8	1	(0.02)	0.0 ± 0.1	(<0.01)	0.5
Total	6,076				
(b) Random markers occurring between consecutive crossovers‡					
No. of markers per block	Observed		Expected§		P (longest run $\geqslant n$) (%)§
	No.	(percentage)	Number	(percentage)	
0	288	(22.3)	227.9 ± 13.7	(17.4)	100.0
1	208	(16.1)	188.2 ± 12.7	(14.4)	100.0
2	126	(9.8)	155.5 ± 11.7	(11.9)	100.0
3	111	(8.6)	128.4 ± 10.8	(9.8)	100.0
4	84	(6.5)	106.0 ± 9.9	(8.1)	100.0
5	73	(5.7)	87.6 ± 9.0	(6.7)	100.0

§ Z 值 =（观察的 − 期望的）/ 标准差。对于常染色体而言，在邦费罗尼校正多重检验后，所有 Z 值在 $P = 0.05$ 水平都不显著。常染色体和 X 染色体比较时，Z 值在 $P < 10^{-14}$ 时具有显著性。

SSLP 在所检测的近交实验室品系间的多态率约为 50%，在实验室品系和 CAST 或 SPR 间约为 95%（表 1）。在检测的 12 个品系间，成对多态率与我们先前的报道[6] 没有明显的差别，这里未显示。有趣的是，多态性在基因组中的分布并不均一[11]。在所检测的 *Mus musculus* 品系间，平均多态率刚好低于 50%，但是有两条染色体的多态率更低：X 染色体为 33%，10 号染色体为 35%（表 1）。多态性的降低可能反映了近期对特定祖先染色体的选择。对于 X 染色体而言，还可能反映了不同的突变率（因为每个雄性的 X 染色体只有常染色体的三分之二，而大多数突变被认为发生在雄性种系中）或不同的群体遗传压力（半合子状态会影响选择和有效群体大小）。

表 3. 连续交换簇和标记簇

(a) 连续随机标记之间的交换数目 *					
每个区间的交换数	观察		预期 †		P(最大游程 ≥ n)
	数量	（百分比）	数量	（百分比）	(%)†
0	5,095	(83.85)	5,035.5 ± 29.6	(82.59)	
1	784	(12.90)	876.7 ± 27.4	(14.38)	100.0
2	151	(2.49)	152.6 ± 12.2	(2.50)	100.0
3	27	(0.44)	26.6 ± 5.1	(0.44)	100.0
4	14	(0.23)	4.6 ± 2.2	(0.08)	99.6
5	4	(0.07)	0.8 ± 0.9	(0.01)	62.2
6	0	(0.00)	0.1 ± 0.4	(<0.1)	15.6
7	0	(0.00)	0.0 ± 0.2	(<0.1)	2.9
8	1	(0.02)	0.0 ± 0.1	(<0.1)	0.5
总计	6,076				
(b) 连续交换之间的随机标记 ‡					
每个区间的标记数	观察		预期 §		P(最大游程 ≥ n)
	数量	（百分比）	数量	（百分比）	(%)§
0	288	(22.3)	227.9 ± 13.7	(17.4)	100.0
1	208	(16.1)	188.2 ± 12.7	(14.4)	100.0
2	126	(9.8)	155.5 ± 11.7	(11.9)	100.0
3	111	(8.6)	128.4 ± 10.8	(9.8)	100.0
4	84	(6.5)	106.0 ± 9.9	(8.1)	100.0
5	73	(5.7)	87.6 ± 9.0	(6.7)	100.0

Continued

No. of markers per block	Observed		Expected§		P (longest run $\geqslant n$) (%)§
	No.	(percentage)	Number	(percentage)	
(b) Random markers occurring between consecutive crossovers‡					
6	62	(4.8)	72.3 ± 8.3	(5.5)	100.0
7	51	(4.0)	59.7 ± 7.6	(4.6)	100.0
8	36	(2.8)	49.3 ± 6.9	(3.8)	100.0
9	38	(2.9)	40.7 ± 6.3	(3.1)	100.0
10	32	(2.5)	33.7 ± 5.7	(2.6)	100.0
11	37	(2.9)	27.8 ± 5.2	(2.1)	100.0
12	19	(1.5)	23.0 ± 4.7	(1.8)	100.0
13	28	(2.2)	19.0 ± 4.3	(1.4)	100.0
14	18	(1.4)	15.7 ± 3.9	(1.2)	100.0
15	7	(0.5)	12.9 ± 3.6	(1.0)	100.0
16	12	(0.9)	10.7 ± 3.3	(0.8)	100.0
17	5	(0.4)	8.8 ± 3.0	(0.7)	100.0
18	5	(0.4)	7.3 ± 2.7	(0.6)	100.0
19	6	(0.5)	6.0 ± 2.4	(0.5)	100.0
20	10	(0.8)	5.0 ± 2.2	(0.4)	100.0
21	3	(0.2)	4.1 ± 2.0	(0.3)	100.0
22	5	(0.4)	3.4 ± 1.8	(0.3)	100.0
23	7	(0.5)	2.8 ± 1.7	(0.2)	100.0
24	4	(0.3)	2.3 ± 1.5	(0.2)	100.0
25	0	(0.0)	1.9 ± 1.4	(0.1)	100.0
26	5	(0.4)	1.6 ± 1.3	(0.1)	99.9
27	1	(0.1)	1.3 ± 1.1	(0.1)	99.8
28	1	(0.1)	1.1 ± 1.0	(0.1)	99.3
29	0	(0.0)	0.9 ± 0.9	(0.1)	98.4
30	1	(0.1)	0.7 ± 0.9	(0.1)	96.7
31	1	(0.1)	0.6 ± 0.8	(< 0.1)	94.0
32	0	(0.0)	0.5 ± 0.7	(< 0.1)	90.3
33	0	(0.0)	0.4 ± 0.6	(< 0.1)	85.4
34	1	(0.1)	0.3 ± 0.6	(< 0.1)	79.6
35	1	(0.1)	0.3 ± 0.5	(< 0.1)	73.1
38	1	(0.1)	0.2 ± 0.4	(< 0.1)	52.2
40	1	(0.1)	0.1 ± 0.3	(< 0.1)	39.6
54	1	(0.1)	$< 0.1 \pm 0.1$	(< 0.1)	3.4
Total	1,289				

* The intervals with $\geqslant 1$ crossover represent the 981 gaps between consecutive bins of recombinationally inseparable markers. Only random markers are considered to avoid biases in distribution of known genes.

续表

	(b)连续交换之间的随机标记‡				
每个区间的标记数	观察		预期§		P(最大游程≥n)(%)§
	数量	(百分比)	数量	(百分比)	
6	62	(4.8)	72.3±8.3	(5.5)	100.0
7	51	(4.0)	59.7±7.6	(4.6)	100.0
8	36	(2.8)	49.3±6.9	(3.8)	100.0
9	38	(2.9)	40.7±6.3	(3.1)	100.0
10	32	(2.5)	33.7±5.7	(2.6)	100.0
11	37	(2.9)	27.8±5.2	(2.1)	100.0
12	19	(1.5)	23.0±4.7	(1.8)	100.0
13	28	(2.2)	19.0±4.3	(1.4)	100.0
14	18	(1.4)	15.7±3.9	(1.2)	100.0
15	7	(0.5)	12.9±3.6	(1.0)	100.0
16	12	(0.9)	10.7±3.3	(0.8)	100.0
17	5	(0.4)	8.8±3.0	(0.7)	100.0
18	5	(0.4)	7.3±2.7	(0.6)	100.0
19	6	(0.5)	6.0±2.4	(0.5)	100.0
20	10	(0.8)	5.0±2.2	(0.4)	100.0
21	3	(0.2)	4.1±2.0	(0.3)	100.0
22	5	(0.4)	3.4±1.8	(0.3)	100.0
23	7	(0.5)	2.8±1.7	(0.2)	100.0
24	4	(0.3)	2.3±1.5	(0.2)	100.0
25	0	(0.0)	1.9±1.4	(0.1)	100.0
26	5	(0.4)	1.6±1.3	(0.1)	99.9
27	1	(0.1)	1.3±1.1	(0.1)	99.8
28	1	(0.1)	1.1±1.0	(0.1)	99.3
29	0	(0.0)	0.9±0.9	(0.1)	98.4
30	1	(0.1)	0.7±0.9	(0.1)	96.7
31	1	(0.1)	0.6±0.8	(<0.1)	94.0
32	0	(0.0)	0.5±0.7	(<0.1)	90.3
33	0	(0.0)	0.4±0.6	(<0.1)	85.4
34	1	(0.1)	0.3±0.6	(<0.1)	79.6
35	1	(0.1)	0.3±0.5	(<0.1)	73.1
38	1	(0.1)	0.2±0.4	(<0.1)	52.2
40	1	(0.1)	0.1±0.3	(<0.1)	39.6
54	1	(0.1)	<0.1±0.1	(<0.1)	3.4
总计	1,289				

* ≥1个交换的区间代表连续的重组不分离标记"箱子"间的981个间隙。只有随机标记被认为可避免因已知基因的分布而造成的偏差。

† The probability of the longest run is calculated in ref. 6. Briefly, if a coin with heads probability P is tossed n times, the length R_n of the longest head run has expected value $\mu = \log_{1/p}[(n-1)(1-p)+1]$ and the distribution of R_n is given approximately by Prob $(R_n - \mu > t) = 1 - \exp(-p^t)$. In this case, $p = 0.17$.

‡ The blocks with ≥ 1 marker represent the 1,001 bins of recombinationally separable markers. Only random markers are considered to avoid biases in distribution of known genes.

§ The probability of the longest head run is calculated with $p = 0.83$.

Our mouse genetic-mapping project is now at its conclusion. Although more SSLPs remain to be found (newly isolated repeats show < 10% overlap with our current set), we have reached the point of diminishing returns. The map covers the entire mouse genome, with the markers being sufficiently abundant, polymorphic and stable to allow the mapping of monogenic or polygenic traits in virtually any mouse cross of interest[5,8]. Moreover, the markers are sufficiently dense to facilitate positional cloning of most mouse mutations. With > 90% of the mouse genome being within 750 kb of a marker, and current mouse yeast artificial chromosome (YAC) libraries[14,15] having a mean insert size > 750 kb, the map affords ready access to the vast majority of the genome with little need for chromosomal walking, and provides a preliminary scaffold for constructing a genome-wide physical map[16].

The map also provides a common framework for the mapping of mutations and cloned genes. In addition to our integration with the Frederick cross, the SSLP map is being used as a framework for other mapping crosses, including public resources at the Jackson Laboratory[17] and the European Collaborative Interspecific Backcross (EUCIB)[18]. The EUCIB project (http://www.hgmp.mrc.ac.uk/MBx/MBxHomepage.html) is rescoring our SSLP markers in a cross with 1,000 meioses, which should yield finer resolution of order and correct remaining errors.

Together with the final report on the human genetic map[13], this paper marks the close of the first phase of the Human Genome Project: the construction of dense genetic maps of mouse and man.

(**380**, 149-152; 1996)

William F. Dietrich[*], Joyce Miller[*], Robert Steen[*], Mark A. Merchant[*], Deborah Damron-Boles[*], Zeeshan Husain[*], Robert Dredge[*], Mark J. Daly[*], Kimberly A. Ingalls[*], Tara J. O'Connor[*], Cheryl A. Evans[*], Margaret M. DeAngelis[*], David M. Levinson[*], Leonid Kruglyak[*], Nathan Goodman[*], Neal G. Copeland[†], Nancy A. Jenkins[†], Trevor L. Hawkins[*], Lincoln Stein[*], David C. Page[*‡§] & Eric S. Lander[*‡∥]

[*] Whitehead/MIT Center for Genome Research, Whitehead Institute for Biomedical Research, 9 Cambridge Center, Cambridge, Massachusetts 02142, USA

[†] Mammalian Genetics Laboratory, ABL-Basic Research Program, NCI-Frederick Cancer Research and Development Center, Frederick, Maryland 21702, USA

[‡] Department of Biology, and [§] Howard Hughes Medical Institute, Massachusetts Institute of Technology, Cambridge, Massachusetts 02139, USA

[∥] To whom correspondence should be addressed.

Received 23 October 1995; accepted 19 February 1996.

† 最大游程的概率按参考文献 6 计算。简单地讲，如果硬币正面的概率 P 是扔 n 次的结果，最大正面游程 R_n 的长度预期值 $\mu = \log_{1/p}[(n-1)(1-p)+1]$，$R_n$ 的分布可近似通过 $\mathrm{Prob}(R_n - \mu > t) = 1 - \exp(-p^t)$ 得出。在本例中，$p = 0.17$。

‡ ≥1 个标记的区间代表了重组可分离标记的 1,001 个"箱子"。只有随机标记被认为可避免因已知基因的分布而造成的偏差。

§ 最大正面游程的概率以 $p = 0.83$ 计算。

  我们的小鼠遗传图谱计划现在到了结局。虽然还有更多 SSLP 需要发现（新分离出的重复与我们现在的数据集之间的重叠小于 10%），但我们已经到达收益递减点了。这张图谱覆盖了整个小鼠基因组，标记十分丰富，具有多态性和稳定性，实际可用于任何感兴趣的小鼠杂交系的单基因和多基因性状作图 [5,8]。此外，标记密度非常高，有助于大多数小鼠突变的定位克隆。在这张图谱中，超过 90% 的小鼠基因组在 750 kb 之内都有一个标记，且目前小鼠酵母人工染色体（YAC）文库 [14,15] 的平均插入片段长度大于 750 kb，这意味着我们几乎不再需要利用染色体步移就可以获得基因组的绝大部分信息，该图谱为构建全基因组物理图提供了初步的框架 [16]。

  这张图也为突变和克隆基因作图提供了一个共同框架。除了我们与弗雷德里克杂交系的整合外，SSLP 图谱也被用作其他杂交品系作图的框架，包括杰克逊实验室 [17] 和欧洲合作种间回交（EUCIB）中的公共资源 [18]。EUCIB 计划（http://www.hgmp.mrc.ac.uk/MBx/MBxHomepage.html）正在利用一个有 1,000 个减数分裂的杂交来重新评估我们的 SSLP 标记，这将产生更高精度的排序，并校正现存的错误。

  这篇文章与人类遗传图谱最终结果 [13] 的共同发表，标志着人类基因组计划第一阶段——构建人类和小鼠高密度遗传图谱的结束。

（李梅 翻译；胡松年 审稿）

References:

1. Copeland, N. G. *et al. Science* **262**, 57-66 (1993).

2. Copeland, N.G. *et al. Science* **262**, 67-82 (1993).

3. Dietrich, W. F. *et al. Genetics* **131**, 423-447 (1992).

4. Dietrich, W. F. *et al.* in *Genetic Maps 1992* (ed. O'Brien, S.) 4.110-4.142 (Cold Spring Harbor Laboratory Press, NY, 1992).

5. Miller, J. C. *et al.* in *Genetic Variants and Strains of the Laboratory Mouse* 3rd Edn. (eds Lyons, M. F. & Searle, A.) (Oxford Univ. Press, New York, 1994).

6. Dietrich, W. F. *et al. Nature Genet.* **7**, 220-245 (1994).

7. Lander, E. S. *et al. Genomics* **1**, 174-181 (1987).

8. Lincoln, S. E. & Lander, E. S. *Genomics* **14**, 604-610 (1992).

9. Copeland, N. G. & Jenkins, N. A. *Trends Genet.* **7**, 113 (1991).

10. Ceci, J. D. *et al. Genomics* **5**, 699-709 (1989).

11. Buchberg, A. M. *et al. Genetics* **122**, 153-161 (1989).

12. Jacob, H. J. *et al. Nature Genet.* **9**, 63-69 (1995).

13. Dib, C. *et al. Nature* **380**, 152-154 (1996).

14. Larin, Z., Monaco, A. P. & Lehrach, H. *Proc. Natl. Acad. Sci. U.S.A.* **88**, 4123 (1991).

15. Kusumi, K. *et al. Mamm. Genome* **4**, 391-392 (1993).

16. Hudson, T. *et al. Science* **270**, 1945-1955 (1995).

17. Rowe, L. B. *et al. Mamm. Genome* **5**, 253-274 (1994).

18. The European Backcross Collaborative Group. *Hum. Molec. Genet.* **3**, 621-627 (1994).

19. Evans, E. in *Genetic Variants and Strains of the Laboratory Mouse* 3rd Edn (eds Lyons, M. F. & Searle, A.) (Oxford Univ. Press, New York, 1994).

Acknowledgements. We thank L. Wangchuk, D. Tsering, G. Farino and K. Norbu for technical assistance; D. Gilbert and L. Maltais for help in ascertaining official nomenclature for gene loci; and Research Genetics Inc. for making SSLP primers available to the community. This work was supported in part by a grant from the National Center for Human Genome Research (to E.S. L.). L.K. was supported by a Special Emphasis Research Career Award from the National Center for Human Genome Research.

Orbital Migration of the Planetary Companion of 51 Pegasi to Its Present Location

D. N. C. Lin *et al.*

Editor's Note

The recent discovery of a planet orbiting the Sun-like star 51 Pegasi raised serious issues, not least of which was why this Jupiter-like planet was so close to its parent star—0.04 astronomical units, or less than a tenth of the distance of Mercury from the Sun. Most of Jupiter's mass is in the form of gases in the atmosphere, but here Douglas Lin and colleagues demonstrate that, for the 51 Peg planet, such gases could not condense so close to the star. They find it a more likely explanation that the planet formed farther away from the star and then migrated inwards through an interaction with material in the disk out of which the planet formed.

The recent discovery[1] and confirmation[2] of a possible planetary companion orbiting the solar-type star 51 Pegasi represent a breakthrough in the search for extrasolar planetary systems. Analysis of systematic variations in the velocity of the star indicates that the mass of the companion is approximately that of Jupiter, and that it is travelling in a nearly circular orbit at a distance from the star of 0.05 AU (about seven stellar radii). Here we show that, if the companion is indeed a gas-giant planet, it is extremely unlikely to have formed at its present location. We suggest instead that the planet probably formed by gradual accretion of solids and capture of gas at a much larger distance from the star (~5 AU), and that it subsequently migrated inwards through interactions with the remnants of the circumstellar disk. The planet's migration may have stopped in its present orbit as a result of tidal interactions with the star, or through truncation of the inner circumstellar disk by the stellar magnetosphere.

THE first argument against the *in situ* formation of a planetary companion is based on models of the nebular disks[3] that are known to exist around young stars[4]. The standard picture of the formation of a giant planet involves the coagulation and accretion of small particles of ice and rock in the disk[5] until a core of about 15 Earth masses is built up; then gas, composed mainly of H and He, is accreted from the disk[6]. Standard disk models show that at 0.05 AU the temperature is about 2,000 K, too hot for the existence of any small solid particles. An alternative formation model[7] involves a massive disk, whose self-gravity is comparable to that of the central object, in which a gaseous subcondensation could form by contraction under its own gravity. But recent detailed calculations of such massive disks[8] indicate that they tend to form spiral arms and to transfer mass into the central star instead of fragmenting into subcondensations.

飞马座 51 的行星型伴星轨道迁移到现在位置的过程

林潮等

编者按

最近发现的绕类太阳恒星飞马座 51 公转的行星引发了很深刻的问题，不仅仅是为什么这颗类木行星与它的母星距离如此之近，只有 0.04 个天文单位，还不足水星到太阳距离的十分之一。木星大部分物质是以气体的形式存在于其大气层中，但在这篇文章中，林潮以及他的合作者证明，对于飞马座 51 的行星，这种气体无法在离恒星如此之近的距离处凝结。他们认为更为可能的解释是此行星在离恒星遥远的地方形成，之后通过与行星诞生的原恒星盘上物质的相互作用向内迁移。

近年来系外行星系统搜索的一个突破是，发现 [1] 和证实 [2] 可能存在行星型伴星环绕在太阳型恒星飞马座 51 的周围。对恒星视向速度的系统性变化的分析显示此伴星的质量与木星的质量相似，在距离恒星 0.05 AU（大约 7 倍恒星半径）处的近圆轨道上运行。这里我们证明，如果伴星的确是一颗气态巨行星，那么它极不可能在目前的位置形成。我们认为该行星可能是通过逐渐吸积固体颗粒和捕获距离恒星更远处（~5 AU）的气体形成，此后通过与星周盘遗迹作用向内迁移。由于恒星的潮汐相互作用，或者在由恒星磁层引起的星周盘内断层处，该行星可能停止迁移形成目前的轨道。

第一个不支持行星型伴星在原地形成的论点建立在星云盘 [3] 模型上。我们知道，星云盘存在于年轻恒星周围 [4]。巨行星形成的标准图景涉及盘内冰和石块小颗粒 [5] 的凝结与吸积，直到形成一个大约 15 倍地球质量的核；吸积盘内的气体主要由氢和氦组成 [6]。标准盘模型表明在 0.05 AU 处温度约为 2,000 K，太热而不可能存在任何固体小颗粒。另一个巨行星形成模型 [7] 包含一个大质量盘，其自引力和中心天体的引力大小相当，在盘内可通过自身引力收缩形成气态的子凝聚物。但是最近对大质量盘的详细计算 [8] 表明它们趋向于形成旋臂并将质量转移到中心恒星上而不是碎裂成子凝聚物。

A second problem with the formation of a planet at 0.05 AU is that although the present evaporation rate of the planet is negligible, this effect would have been of major importance in the past. At 0.05 AU, the companion's effective temperature, due to stellar irradiation, is ~1,300 K. In order to determine the planetary radius R_p in the presence of such heating, we calculated the evolution of objects in the mass range $M_p = 1$–$10\ M_J$ (jovian masses) using a standard stellar structure code[9,10] with a non-ideal interior equation of state[11]. The rotation of the planet is almost certainly tidally locked[12] so that the same hemisphere always faces 51 Peg. We assume that atmospheric motions and convection in the interior redistribute the heat so that the dark side and the bright side have nearly the same temperature.

In Fig. 1 we show the evolution of R_p for various M_p. At 8 Gyr, the estimated age of 51 Peg, $R_p = 8.3 \times 10^7$ m for $1\ M_J$, not much larger than the present radius of Jupiter $(7.0 \times 10^7$ m). For these values, the escape velocity of a hydrogen atom is 12 times larger than the mean thermal speed, and a simple calculation of the Jeans escape rate[13] shows that evaporation is negligible. A further process to be considered is hydrodynamic escape[14] in which ultraviolet and X-ray radiation from the star are absorbed by hydrogen atoms in the planetary atmosphere and drive a planetary wind. A rough estimate, based on the observed X-ray flux of young stars[14], shows that the effect of this process is also negligible. Thus the planet at present is quite safe against evaporation. The evaporation of a low-mass star or brown dwarf, another proposed explanation[15] for the existence of the companion, would be even more difficult because the object would have a much higher surface gravity. But during the early history of a planet[6] its radius is a factor of ten or more larger than the present radius, so the escape speed becomes much less and both evaporation mechanisms, along with ablation by the stellar wind, will prevent formation.

We propose that the companion was formed several AU away from the star through the standard process. Recent detailed calculations[16] for the accretion of Jupiter at 5 AU have shown that it is possible for that planet to build well before the nebula dissipates. The protoplanet interacts tidally with the disk during its growth[17]. Let v be the disk viscosity, M_* the stellar mass, ω the orbital frequency, and r_n the distance from the star at which the planet formed. If $M_p \gtrsim 40 v M_* / (\omega(r_n) r_n^2)$ when its tidal radius, $(M_p / 3 M_*)^{1/3} r_n$, exceeds H (the vertical scale height of the disk), the protoplanet induces the formation of a gap[18,19] in the disk near r_n so that growth of the planet stops. Standard disk models[3] give $H(r) \approx 0.1 r$, where r is the distance from the star. The disk evolves viscously on a timescale $\tau_v \approx r_d^2 / v$ which is inferred to be $\sim 5 \times 10^6$ yr from infrared observations[20]. The effective radius r_d which contains most of the disk mass observed in the infrared is[4] ~ 100 AU. Applying these estimates to the gap formation conditions, we find $M_p \approx M_J$.

在 0.05 AU 处形成行星的第二个问题是，尽管行星目前的蒸发率可忽略，但该效应在过去是一大重要因素。在 0.05 AU 处，由于恒星辐射，伴星的有效温度约为 1,300 K。为了确定在这样加热机制下的行星半径 R_P，我们使用非理想内部状态方程 [11] 的标准恒星结构程序 [9,10] 计算了质量在 $M_P = 1\,M_J \sim 10\,M_J$（$M_J$ 为木星质量）范围内天体的演化。行星的自转几乎已经被潮汐锁定 [12]，所以同一半球总是面对着飞马座 51。我们假设其内部的大气运动和对流使得热量重新分布，所以暗面和亮面几乎具有相同温度。

图 1 中我们展示了各种 M_P 下 R_P 的演化。在飞马座 51 的估计年龄为 8 Gyr 时，质量为 $1\,M_J$ 的天体，$R_P = 8.3 \times 10^7\,\text{m}$，比木星目前的半径（$7.0 \times 10^7\,\text{m}$）大不了多少。从这些值得出，氢原子的逃逸速度是平均热运动速度的 12 倍，简单计算金斯逃逸率 [13] 结果显示蒸发是可忽略的。值得进一步考虑的机制是流体力学逃逸 [14]，恒星的紫外和 X 射线辐射被行星大气里的氢原子吸收并驱动行星风形成。根据观测的年轻恒星的 X 射线流量 [14] 的初步计算结果，这个过程的效应也可以忽略。因此，该行星目前非常安全，不会被蒸发。关于伴星存在的另一个解释——小质量恒星或褐矮星的蒸发 [15]——更难实现，因为这种天体需要具有更大的表面重力。但是在行星的早期历史中 [6]，其半径为目前半径的 10 倍甚至更多，所以逃逸速度变得很小，蒸发机制和星风的烧蚀会共同阻止行星的形成。

我们提出伴星通过标准机制在距离恒星几个天文单位处形成。最近对木星在 5 AU 处吸积的详细计算 [16] 结果表明，该行星有可能在星云消散之前就已经形成。原行星在成长过程中与盘发生潮汐作用 [17]。令 v 为盘的黏度，M_* 为恒星质量，ω 为轨道频率，r_n 为行星形成处与恒星的距离。假如 $M_P \geqslant 40 v M_* / (\omega (r_n) r_n^2)$，当潮汐半径 $(M_P / 3 M_*)^{1/3} r_n$ 大于 H（盘的垂直标高）时，原行星在盘内 r_n 附近处形成空隙 [18,19] 致使行星增长停止。标准盘模型 [3] 给出 $H(r) \approx 0.1r$，这里 r 是行星与恒星的距离。盘的黏性演化时标 $\tau_v \approx r_d^2 / v$，红外观测 [20] 得出这个值为 $\sim 5 \times 10^6$ yr。包含大部分红外观测到的盘质量 [4] 的有效半径 r_d 为 ~ 100 AU。将这些估计值应用到空隙形成条件，我们得到 $M_P \approx M_J$。

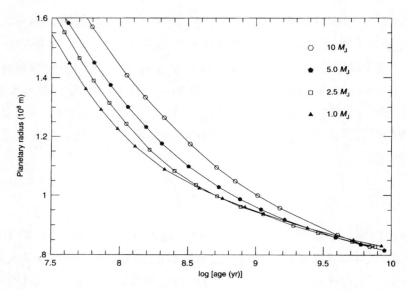

Fig. 1. Planetary radius as a function of log age for objects (bottom trace to top trace) of masses 1, 2.5, 5 and 10 M_J. The calculation assumes that the planet migrated to its present position during its first ten million years of existence. The plot shows the subsequent evolution, during which the orbit of the planet was stationary and it was heated by a central star whose luminosity was constant in time. For this evolutionary history, evaporation is not important.

After the gap formation, angular momentum transfer continues and the protoplanet undergoes orbital migration coupled to the viscous evolution of the disk[21,22]. The orbital radius of the planet (r_p) and that of the gap (both are still embedded in the disk) decrease on the timescale[22,23] of τ_v. The planet essentially follows the material of the inner disk as it evolves towards the star. We now propose two possible mechanisms which suggest that this migration can terminate at ~0.05 AU and that the planet will not plunge into 51 Peg.

Mechanism 1. As the planet approaches 51 Peg, tidal friction can induce angular momentum exchange between the planet's orbital motion and the spin of the star. If R_* is the stellar radius and P the orbital period of the planet, the timescale for tidal evolution is[12]

$$\tau_r = r_p \left(\frac{dr_p}{dt} \right)^{-1} = \frac{P}{9\pi} \left(\frac{r_p}{R_*} \right)^5 \left(\frac{M_*}{M_p} \right) Q_* \tag{1}$$

We estimate the dissipation parameter $Q_* = 1.5 \times 10^5$ for a main sequence star based on the observation[24] that the orbits of short-period pre-main-sequence binary stars and the main-sequence binary stars in the Pleiades cluster are circularized for $P \lesssim 5$ and 7 days, respectively. As young stars rotate more rapidly than their main-sequence counterparts[25], we assume that 51 Peg was rotating rapidly enough that the co-rotation point τ_{CR} (the distance from the star where an orbiting object has the same angular frequency as the stellar rotation) was inside 0.05 AU. The tidal effect then results in outward migration of the planet. Thus there may exist a radius r_c where the protoplanet's radial migration was

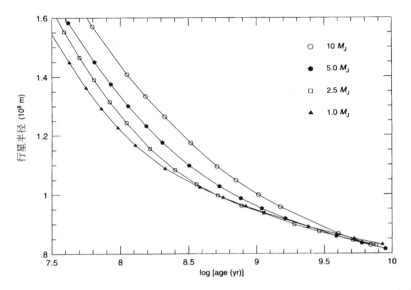

图 1. 质量分别为 $1\,M_J$、$2.5\,M_J$、$5\,M_J$ 和 $10\,M_J$ 的行星（由下到上）的半径与年龄对数的关系。该计算假设行星在形成后的一千万年内迁移到目前的位置。图中显示行星之后的演化，在此期间行星轨道稳定，且行星由亮度恒定的中心恒星加热。对这段演化历史，蒸发并不重要。

在空隙形成后，角动量继续转移，原行星开始进行轨道迁移 [21,22] 并与盘的黏性演化相耦合。行星的轨道半径 (r_p) 和空隙的半径（两者都位于盘内）随着时标 τ_v 减小 [22,23]。行星随着盘内的物质流逐渐向恒星演化。我们现在提出两个可能的机制，表明此迁移会在 ~0.05 AU 处终止，行星不会落入飞马座 51。

机制 1。当行星趋近飞马座 51 时，潮汐摩擦导致角动量在行星轨道运动和恒星自转之间交换。假设 R_* 为恒星半径，P 为行星轨道周期，潮汐演化的时标为 [12]：

$$\tau_r = r_p \left(\frac{dr_p}{dt} \right)^{-1} = \frac{P}{9\pi} \left(\frac{r_p}{R_*} \right)^5 \left(\frac{M_*}{M_p} \right) Q_* \tag{1}$$

根据观测，昴星团里短周期前主序双星和主序双星分别对于周期 $P \lesssim 5$ 天和 7 天的轨道是圆化的 [24]，我们估计主序星的耗散参数为 $Q_* = 1.5 \times 10^5$。因为年轻恒星比其对应的主序星旋转得更快 [25]，我们假设飞马座 51 旋转得足够快让共转点 τ_{CR}（天体公转角频率和恒星自转相同时与恒星的距离）位于 0.05 AU 内。潮汐效应将导致行星向外迁移。因此可能存在一个半径 r_c，在这点由盘引起的向内推力和来自飞马座 51 的向外推力达到平衡，原行星停止径向迁移。在这个半径处，整个盘内的角动量转移

halted by a balance between the inward push on it by the disk and the outward push from 51 Peg. At that point, the angular momentum transfer equilibrium throughout the disk[19] implies $\tau_v \approx \tau_r$ such that $r_c \equiv (9\pi\tau_v M_P / P_* Q_* M_*)^{2/13} R_*$, where P_* is the keplerian orbital period at R_*. Based on an estimate[26] of $R_* = 4R_\odot$ (where $R_\odot$ is the solar radius) during its early history, we find that this equilibrium can be established at 0.05 AU during the early epoch of 51 Peg.

But this equilibrium is only temporary. The disk material between the planet and the star will accrete onto the latter, leaving the planet with the remaining disk outside its orbit. The disk's surface density adjusts until a quasi-equilibrium state is attained in which the angular momentum flux is approximately constant with distance from the star. At this stage the planet's equilibrium radius is determined by the condition that the star's tidal torque on it, $M_p r_p^2 \omega_p / \tau_r$, is balanced by the angular momentum flux through the disk, $\sim M_d r_d^2 \omega_d / \tau_v$, where ω_d is a mean angular frequency of the disk and M_d is its mass. For $R_* = 4R_\odot$ we find that $r_c \approx 0.03 (M_p / M_d)^{1/6} (\tau_v / 5 \times 10^6 \text{ yr})^{1/6}$ AU. If the disk then dissipates sufficiently so that its mass $M_d \approx M_p$ and its evolution timescale lengthens so that $\tau_v \approx 10^8$ yr, then r_c could be close to the present orbital position of the planet. The dissipation must occur before the star contracts substantially ($< 10^7$ yr) or spins down ($> 10^8$ yr). In view of the rather precise timing and the relatively large R_* needed for this mechanism to work, we consider an alternative, as follows.

Mechanism 2. The spin periods of classical T Tauri stars are clustered[27] around 8 days, longer than those of the weak line T Tauri stars. One explanation for the 8-day periods is that the spin rate is controlled by coupling between the stellar magnetosphere and the disk[28]. The presence of the magnetosphere would also clear[29] the inner disk out to a point slightly less than r_{CR} (0.08 AU for an 8-day period). Once the planet has spiralled in to $r_p = 0.05$ AU, angular momentum exchange between it and the disk occurs only via the 2:1 resonance at a reduced (by $\sim M_p / M_*$) rate[17,30]. Because $r_p < r_{CR}$, the stellar tidal effect also continues to induce an inward migration. But as long as $R_* < 3R_\odot$, consistent with evolutionary tracks[26], τ_r is larger than the stellar contraction timescale, and the migration effectively stops near 0.05 AU.

After this time, in either case, τ_r and τ_v increase rapidly because the star contracts on a relatively short timescale, and the disk dissipates. During its contraction to the main sequence, 51 Peg may have spun up, if it conserved angular momentum, but once it reached the main sequence, the star would have spun down[31] because of angular momentum loss via stellar wind. Eventually in both cases r_p becomes less than r_{CR} and $R_* \approx R_\odot$, causing the companion to migrate inwards on the timescale $\tau_r \approx 14 \sin i_p$ Gyr, which is much longer than the age of the star for all reasonable values of the inclination angle i_p between the normal to the orbital plane and the line of sight. This is the configuration we observe today. The requirement that the tidal migration timescale (τ_r) be large compared with the life span of a typical solar-type star is a further piece of evidence that supports the interpretation that the companion is a planet with $M_p \approx M_J$ rather than a more massive object.

(**380**, 606-607; 1996)

平衡 [19]，意味着 $\tau_v \approx \tau_r$，因此 $r_c \equiv (9\pi\tau_v M_p/P_* Q_* M_*)^{2/13} R_*$，这里 P_* 是在 R_* 处的开普勒轨道周期。根据早期历史过程中 $R_* = 4R_\odot$ 的估计 [26]（这里 $R_\odot$ 是太阳半径），我们发现这个平衡在飞马座 51 的早期历元就能够在 0.05 AU 处建立。

但是这个平衡只是暂时的。行星和恒星之间盘内的物质将吸积到后者上，留下行星与其轨道外的剩余盘物质。盘的面密度不断调节直到实现准平衡态，该状态下距离恒星的角动量通量近似恒定。在这个阶段，行星的平衡半径由恒星对其潮汐力矩 $M_p r_p^2 \omega_p/\tau_r$ 和通过盘的角动量通量 $\sim M_d r_d^2 \omega_d/\tau_v$ 的平衡状况决定，这里 ω_d 是盘的平均角频率，M_d 是盘的质量。对于 $R_* = 4R_\odot$ 我们发现 $r_c \approx 0.03 (M_p/M_d)^{1/6} (\tau_v/5 \times 10^6 \text{ yr})^{1/6}$ AU。如果接下来盘完全消散，那么它的质量 $M_d \approx M_p$，其演化时标也增长，$\tau_v \approx 10^8$ yr，从而 r_c 接近于行星目前的轨道位置。耗散必然发生在恒星充分收缩（$< 10^7$ yr）或者自转变慢（$> 10^8$ yr）之前。这个机制需要相当精确的时间和相对较大的 R_*，因此我们考虑下面一种可能。

机制 2。 经典金牛 T 型星的自转周期一般集中在 8 天左右 [27]，比那些弱线金牛 T 型星的周期长。关于 8 天周期的一个解释是自转速度受到恒星磁层和盘耦合 [28] 的控制。磁层的存在也解释了在半径稍小于 r_{CR}（对于 8 天周期，为 0.08 AU）距离处的内盘 [29]。一旦行星旋入 $r_p = 0.05$ AU 内，行星和盘只能通过 2:1 共振以一个减少的速率（通过 $\sim M_p/M_*$）[17,30] 发生角动量的交换。因为 $r_p < r_{CR}$，恒星潮汐效应也持续引起向内的迁移。但是只要 $R_* < 3R_\odot$ 和演化轨迹一致 [26]，那么 τ_r 就会比恒星收缩时标大，且迁移在 0.05 AU 附近就会有效停止。

之后，在以上两种情形的任意一种中，由于恒星在相对较短的时标内收缩，τ_r 和 τ_v 迅速增大，并且盘开始消散。在恒星收缩到主序时，如果角动量守恒，飞马座 51 可能已经完成加速，但是一旦到达主序，恒星风带走的角动量损失将导致恒星自转变慢 [31]。最后在两个情形下，r_p 比 r_{CR} 小，并且 $R_* \approx R_\odot$，导致伴星以时标 $\tau_r \approx 14 \sin i_p$ Gyr 向内迁移。这个时标远比任何轨道面法线和视线方向倾角 i_p 值对应的恒星年龄都长。这是我们现在观测到的状况。潮汐迁移时标（τ_r）比典型太阳型恒星的寿命要长的要求进一步支持了伴星是一颗 $M_p \approx M_J$ 的行星，而不是更大质量天体的观点。

（肖莉 翻译；周济林 审稿）

D. N. C. Lin[*], **P. Bodenheimer**[*] & **D. C. Richardson**[†]

[*] UCO / Lick Observatory, Board of Studies in Astronomy and Astrophysics, University of California, Santa Cruz, California 95064, USA

[†] Canadian Institute for Theoretical Astrophysics, McLennan Laboratories, University of Toronto, 60 St George Street, Toronto, Ontario, Canada M5S 1A7

Received 24 October 1995; accepted 5 March 1996.

References:

1. Mayor, F. & Queloz, D. *Nature* **378**, 355-359 (1995).

2. Marcy, G. & Butler, R. P. *IAU Circ. No.* 6251 (1995).

3. Lin, D. N. C. & Papaloizou, J. in *Protostars and Planets II* (eds Black, D. C. & Matthews, M. S.) 981-1072 (Univ. Arizona Press, Tucson, 1985).

4. Beckwith, S. V. W., Sargent, A. I., Chini, R. & Güsten, R. *Ast. J.* **99**, 924-945 (1990).

5. Wetherill, G. W. *A. Rev. Astr. Astrophys.* **18**, 77-113 (1980).

6. Bodenheimer, P. & Pollack, J. B. *Icarus* **67**, 391-408 (1986).

7. Cameron, A. G. W. *Moon Planets* **18**, 5-40 (1978).

8. Laughlin, G. & Bodenheimer, P. *Astrophys. J.* **436**, 335-354 (1994).

9. Laughlin, G. & Bodenheimer, P. *Astrophys. J.* **403**, 303-314 (1993).

10. Stringfellow, G., Black, D. C. & Bodenheimer, P. *Astrophys. J.* **349**, L59-L62 (1990).

11. Saumon, D., Chabrier, G. & Van Horn, H. M. *Astrophys. J. Suppl. Ser.* **99**, 713-741 (1995).

12. Goldreich, P. & Soter, S. *Icarus* **5**, 375-389 (1966).

13. Shu, F. H. *The Physical Universe* 441 (University Science Books, Mill Valley, CA, 1982).

14. Zahnle, K. in *Protostars and Planets III* (eds Levy, E. & Lunine, J.) 1305-1338 (Univ. Arizona Press, Tucson, 1993).

15. Burrows, A. & Lunine, J. *Nature* **378**, 333 (1995).

16. Pollack, J. B. *et al. Icarus* (submitted).

17. Lin, D. N. C. & Papaloizou, J. C. B. *Mon. Not. R. astr. Soc.* **186**, 799-812 (1979).

18. Papaloizou, J. C. B. & Lin, D. N. C. *Astrophys. J.* **285**, 818-834 (1984).

19. Lin, D. N. C. & Papaloizou, J. C. B. in *Protostars and Planets III* (eds Levy, E. & Lunine, J.) 749-836 (Univ. Arizona Press, Tucson, 1993).

20. Strom, S. E., Edwards, S. & Skrutskie, M. F. in *Protostars and Planets III* (eds Levy, E. & Lunine, J.) 837-866 (Univ. Arizona Press, Tucson, 1993).

21. Goldreich, P. & Tremaine, S. *Astrophys. J.* **241**, 425-441 (1980).

22. Lin, D. N. C. & Papaloizou, J. C. B. *Astrophys. J.* **309**, 846-857 (1986).

23. Takeuchi, T., Miyama, S. & Lin, D. N. C. *Astrophys. J.* (in the press).

24. Mathieu, R. D. *A. Rev. Astr. Astrophys.* **32**, 465-530 (1994).

25. Skumanich, A. *Astrophys. J.* **171**, 565-567 (1972).

26. D'Antona, F. & Mazzitelli, I. *Astrophys. J. Suppl. Ser.* **90**, 467-500 (1994).

27. Bouvier, J., Cabrit, S., Fernandez, M., Martin, E. L. & Matthews, J. M. *Ast. Astrophys.* **272**, 176-206.

28. Königl, A. *Astrophys. J.* **370**, L39-L43 (1991).

29. Shu, F. H. *et al. Astrophys. J.* **429**, 781-796 (1994).

30. Goldreich, P. & Tremaine, S. *Astrophys. J.* **233**, 857-871 (1979).

31. MacGregor, K. & Bremner, M. *Astrophys. J.* **376**, 204-213 (1991).

Acknowledgements. We thank G. Marcy for providing us with his data before publication, and P. Artymowicz, G. Basri, D. O. Gough, L. Hartmann, R. D. Mathieu, F. H. Shu, S. Sigurdsson and A. Title for conversations. D.C.R. was supported by a fellowship from the Natural Sciences and Engineering Research Council (Canada). This work was supported in part by the US NSF and in part by a NASA astrophysics theory programme which supports a joint Center for Star Formation Studies at NASA-Ames Research Center, UC Berkeley and UC Santa Cruz.

840

A 3.5-Gyr-old Galaxy at Redshift 1.55

J. Dunlop *et al.*

Editor's Note

The Hubble constant (quantifying the expansion rate of the universe) was accurately measured in the 1990s, enabling a good estimate of the age of the Universe. Here James Dunlop at the University of Edinburgh and colleagues identify a problem with that figure. They report a very red galaxy (containing old stars) at a redshift of 1.55, and determine that the galaxy is at least 3.5 billion years old. Yet, at that time, the age of the Universe was considered to be just 2 billion years. The researchers point out the inconsistency, but have no explanation. It became clear two years later that the answer lies in the fact that the expansion rate of the Universe was slower in the past.

One of the most direct methods of constraining the epoch at which the first galaxies formed—and thereby to constrain the age of the Universe—is to identify and date the oldest galaxies at high redshift. But most distant galaxies have been identified on the basis of their abnormal brightness in some spectral region[1-4]; such selection criteria are biased towards objects with pronounced nuclear activity or young star-forming systems, in which the spectral signature of older stellar populations will be concealed. Here we report the discovery of a weak and extremely red radio galaxy (53W091) at $z = 1.55$, and present spectroscopic evidence that its red colour results from a population of old stars. Comparing our spectral data with models of the evolution of stellar populations, we estimate that we are observing this galaxy at least 3.5 Gyr after star-formation activity ceased. This implies an extremely high formation redshift ($z > 4$) for 53W091 and, by inference, other elliptical galaxies. Moreover, the age of 53W091 is greater than the predicted age of the Universe at $z = 1.55$, under the assumption of a standard Einstein–de Sitter cosmology (for any Hubble constant greater than $50 \, \text{km} \, \text{s}^{-1} \, \text{Mpc}^{-1}$), indicating that this cosmological model can be formally excluded.

IT is relatively easy for a short-lived burst of star-formation[5], or re-processed light from an active nucleus[6,7], to dominate the appearance of a galaxy in the rest-frame optical–ultraviolet, concealing the presence of an older underlying stellar population[8]. It is thus the reddest objects at a given redshift which are of greatest importance for constraining the first epoch of galaxy formation[9-11], and the correlation between the ultraviolet and radio properties of powerful radio galaxies[12,13] indicates that radio-based searches for passive elliptical galaxies at $z > 1$ should be confined to millijansky flux-density levels. We are therefore investigating the properties of radio galaxies with flux densities at $1.4 \, \text{GHz} \, S_{1.4\text{GHz}} > 1 \, \text{mJy}$ selected from the Leiden–Berkeley

红移 1.55 处的一个年龄为 3.5 Gyr 的星系

邓洛普等

编者按

在二十世纪九十年代，哈勃常数（用以描述宇宙膨胀率）已被准确测量，这使得我们可以很好地估计出宇宙年龄。然而在本文中，爱丁堡大学的詹姆斯·邓洛普与他的同事们却在该图像下发现了一个问题。他们发现了红移 1.55 处的一个极红星系（包含老年恒星），其年龄至少可以达到 35 亿年，而当时人们估计出的宇宙年龄大约只有 20 亿年。虽然研究人员指出了两者的不一致性，但是却并未给出相应的解释。直到大约两年后，人们才开始意识到造成两者不一致的主要原因可能是宇宙膨胀率（过去宇宙拥有更慢的膨胀率）。

发现最古老的高红移星系并确定它们的年龄，是界定第一代星系形成时间并进而界定宇宙年龄最直接的方法之一。但是大多数遥远的星系都是依据它们某些频谱区 [1-4] 中的反常亮度来进行确定的，这些选择标准倾向于识别出具有明显核活动的天体或者那些年轻星形成的系统，在这些天体系统中较年老星族的光谱特征并不明显。本文中，我们报告了一个在红移 $z = 1.55$ 处发现的极红的弱射电星系（53W091），相应光谱分析结果证实其色指数偏红是由星系中的老年恒星星族造成的。通过比较光谱数据与恒星星族演化模型，我们估计被观测的这个星系在恒星形成活动停止后至少还经历了 3.5 Gyr 的演化。这意味着该星系是在极高红移（$z > 4$）处形成的，由此推断其他的椭圆星系也是如此。另外，在标准爱因斯坦－德西特宇宙学的假设下（对于任何哈勃常数大于 50 km·s^{-1}·Mpc^{-1} 的情况），53W091 的年龄会大于理论预言的红移 $z = 1.55$ 时的宇宙年龄，这就表明我们的观测结果正式排除了这个宇宙学模型。

在静止参考系的光学－紫外波段，短时标爆发的恒星形成过程 [5] 或活动核辐射的再发射 [6,7] 容易湮没年老星族 [8] 的贡献，从而主导星系的辐射全貌。因此在一个给定的红移处，最红的天体对于限制星系形成的最初时刻 [9-11] 具有重大意义。而强射电星系在紫外和射电波段特征的相关性 [12,13] 表明用射电方法寻找 $z > 1$ 的被动演化椭圆星系时，其流量密度应该被限制在毫央（mJy）的水平上。因此我们研究了在 1.4 GHz 处 $S_{1.4GHz} > 1$ mJy 的射电星系的性质，这些射电星系选自莱顿－伯克利深度巡天（LBDS）以及该巡天的后续扩展观测 [14-17]。现在我们拥有一个包含 77 个星系完

deep survey (**LBDS**) and its extensions[14-17]. We now possess optical–infrared photometry down to $V \approx 26$ mag and $K \approx 20$ mag for a complete sample of 77 galaxies, enabling us to estimate redshifts both from spectral fitting[13] and from a modified version of the infrared Hubble diagram[18]. From this sample we have isolated a subset of 10 extremely red ($R - K > 5$) potentially high-redshift (estimated redshift $z_{est} > 1.5$) objects for intensive spectroscopic study.

The galaxy 53W091, one of the reddest in the sample ($R = 24.6 \pm 0.20$ mag and $K = 18.75 \pm 0.05$ mag within a 4-arcsec aperture) was observed for 1.5 hours on 25 July 1995 with the Low Resolution Imaging Spectrograph (LRIS) on the 10-m W. M. Keck Telescope on Mauna Kea, Hawaii. This observation yielded the detection of a faint and very red continuum, but no emission-line redshift. Therefore, in an attempt to constrain the galaxy redshift, we obtained deep J- and H-band images with IRCAM3 on the United Kingdom Infrared Telescope in August 1995. The ease with which the galaxy was detected at J and H ($J = 20.5 \pm 0.1$ mag, $H = 19.5 \pm 0.1$ mag; Fig. 1a) revealed that, if its red R–K colour was in part due to a redshifted 4,000 Å break (the most prominent spectral feature displayed by an old stellar population at optical wavelengths), this feature must lie at observed wavelength $\lambda_{obs} < 1.2$ μm, constraining the redshift to $z < 2$.

Finally, on 31 August and 1 September 1995 we re-observed 53W091 for a total of 4 hours, again with LRIS on the 10-m Keck Telescope (Fig. 1b). The spectrum produced by co-adding all 5.5 hours of integration is shown in Fig. 1c, plotted in the rest frame of the radio galaxy assuming $z = 1.552$. This unambiguous redshift was deduced from numerous absorption lines and two strong spectral breaks (at rest wavelength $\lambda_{rest} = 2,635$ and $2,897$ Å), features whose existence in the near-ultraviolet spectrum of the Sun and other low-mass dwarfs is long-established[19], and which are evident in the ultraviolet spectra of low-redshift ellipticals such as M32 (Fig. 1c). This is, to our knowledge, the first time that such a high galaxy redshift has been derived successfully from late-type absorption features; indeed, with $V \approx 26$ mag, this is probably the faintest galaxy for which an absorption-line redshift has ever been determined.

整样本的光学-红外测光数据，其 V 波段和 K 波段星等分别约为 26 mag（mag，星等）和 20 mag。通过该样本，我们可以同时利用光谱拟合[13]方法或基于修改后的红外哈勃图[18]来估计这些星系的红移。为了深入地进行光谱分光研究，我们从该样本中挑出了 10 个极红的（$R-K>5$）、可能是高红移（估计红移 $z_{est}>1.5$）的天体进行后续的分析。

星系 53W091 是该样本中最红的星系之一（在 4 arcsec 的孔径中，$R=24.6\pm0.20$ mag，$K=18.75\pm0.05$ mag）。我们于 1995 年 7 月 25 日利用夏威夷冒纳凯阿火山上的 10 m 凯克望远镜的低分辨率成像光谱仪（LRIS）对该星系进行了观测，曝光时间为 1.5 小时。虽然本次观测探测到该星系非常红的暗弱连续谱，但是我们却无法通过发射线测量出该星系的红移。为了试图限制星系的红移，我们在 1995 年 8 月利用英国红外望远镜配备的 IRCAM3 观测得到该星系在 J 波段和 H 波段上的深场图像。由于在 J 波段和 H 波段（$J=20.5\pm0.1$ mag，$H=19.5\pm0.1$ mag，图 1a）能轻易地探测到该星系，这表明如果该星系的 $R-K$ 色指数偏红是部分由红移后的 4,000 Å 不连续（年老星族在光学波段最明显的光谱特征）导致的，那么该特征一定位于观测波长 $\lambda_{obs}<1.2$ μm 处，这将意味着该星系的红移 $z<2$。

最后，在 1995 年 8 月 31 日和 9 月 1 日，我们再次利用 10 m 凯克望远镜的 LRIS 对 53W091 进行了总计 4 个小时的观测（图 1b）。对该星系总计 5.5 小时的曝光观测进行叠加并假设其红移为 $z=1.552$，我们得到该射电星系在静止参考系中的光谱，如图 1c 所示。这里，该星系的准确红移是利用大量吸收线以及两个显著的光谱不连续特征（在静止波长 $\lambda_{rest}=2,635$ Å 和 2,897 Å 处）确定下来的，很早之前我们就发现这两个近紫外波段显著的光谱不连续特征存在于太阳和其他小质量矮星中[19]，而在一些低红移的椭圆星系中，例如 M32（图 1c）的紫外光谱中也存在这一明显现象。据我们所知，利用晚型吸收特征成功确定如此高的星系红移尚属首例。事实上在 $V\approx26$ mag 时，该星系可能是迄今为止用吸收线方法确定红移的最暗的星系。

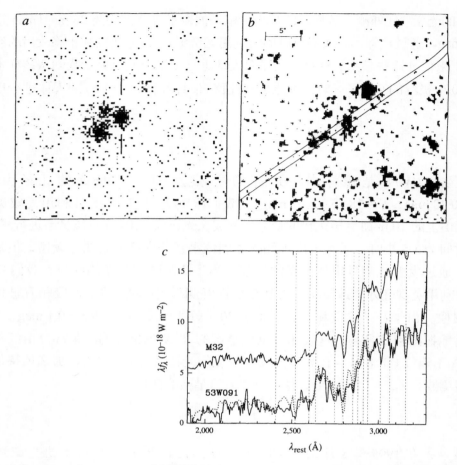

Fig. 1. Imaging and spectroscopy of 53W091. *a*, An infrared image of 53W091 produced by combining the IRCAM3 *J*- and *H*-band images. The field is 30-arcsec square and the radio galaxy identification is indicated by two bars. The position of this object is coincident with the centroid of the radio source (right ascension 17 h 21 min 17.81s, declination +50° 08′ 47.5″ (1950)) to within 0.5 arcsec. *b*, A 10-minute *R*-band image of the same field taken with the 10-m Keck Telescope, with lines superimposed to indicate the position and orientation of the LRIS slit which was used to obtain the optical spectrum. The position of the optical identification is coincident, to within the errors, with that of the near-infrared identification (in contrast to the highly wavelength-dependent morphologies often displayed by more powerful high-redshift galaxies such as 3C324[8]). In this 1-arcsec seeing optical image the radio galaxy is resolved, with a deconvolved full-width at half-maximum of 1.3 arcsec. The orientation of the LRIS slit (126°) was chosen to be close to the parallactic angle (which varied between 100° and 150° during the spectroscopic observations) and to enable a spectrum to also be obtained of a second red galaxy which lies a few arcsec southeast of 53W091. This galaxy appears to be at the same redshift as 53W091, ($z = 1.55$), and, interestingly, has an almost identical SED, providing further circumstantial evidence that the optical–infrared properties of 53W091 are essentially unaffected by its active nucleus. At radio wavelengths, 53W091 is a steep-spectrum source ($\alpha_{1.41\mathrm{GHz}}^{0.61\mathrm{GHz}} = 1.3 \pm 0.13$, where $f_v \propto v^{-\alpha}$) with $S_{1.41\mathrm{GHz}} = 22.5 \pm 1.0$ mJy (ref. 17), and is extended (by ~4 arcsec) along a position angle of 131° (ref. 16). *c*, The 5.5-h Keck spectrum of 53W091 (lower solid line) from 25 July, 31 August and 1 September, plotted in terms of rest wavelength (assuming $z = 1.552$) and compared both with the (scaled) ultraviolet spectrum of the nearby elliptical M32 (upper solid line) and with the best-fitting model spectrum (dotted line). (The model spectrum was produced by synthesizing the spectrum produced by a Scalo IMF with a main-sequence turn-off mass of $1.35 M_\odot$ (equivalent to spectral type F2), corresponding to an age of 3.5 Gyr.) The data for M32 and

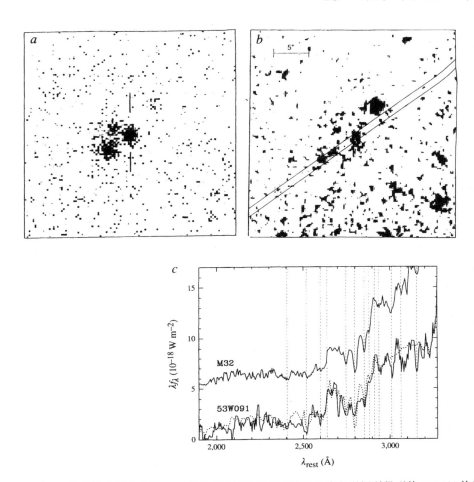

图 1. 53W091 的成像观测和光谱。a，结合 IRCAM3 的 J 波段和 H 波段观测所得到的 53W091 的红外图像。视场大小为 30 arcsec^2。两条竖线之间的天体为识别出的射电星系。该天体的位置与射电源（赤经：17 h 21 min 17.81 s，赤纬：$+50° 08' 47.5''$（1950））的中心重合，二者之间的位置偏离不超过 0.5 arcsec。b，用 10 m 凯克望远镜在 R 波段曝光 10 min，拍摄的相同视场所得到的图像。图上所画的两条直线表示的是拍摄光学光谱所用的 LRIS 狭缝的位置和方向。光学确认的位置与近红外确认的位置在误差范围内重合（与之不同的是，对于一些辐射更强的高红移星系进行观测，例如 3C324[8]，在不同波段进行观测其形态各异）。在视宁度为 1 arcsec 的观测条件下，经过半峰全宽为 1.3 arcsec 的退卷积之后，在光学图像中可以分辨出该射电星系。LRIS 狭缝（126°）方向的选取接近于星位角（在光谱分光观测期间，星位角在 100° 至 150° 之间变化），这样的选取还能同时获得位于 53W091 东南方，距离几个角秒的另一个红星系的光谱。该星系看起来与 53W091 具有相同的红移（$z = 1.55$），有趣的是它们几乎具有相同的光谱能量分布，这一点为证明 53W091 的光学 – 红外性质本质上不受活动核影响提供了进一步的旁证。在射电波段，53W091 是一个沿着 131° 的位置角延伸（~4 arcsec）[16]、$S_{1.41GHz} = 22.5 \pm 1.0$ mJy 的陡谱源（$\alpha^{0.61GHz}_{1.41GHz} = 1.3 \pm 0.13$，此处 $f_v \propto v^\alpha$）（参考文献 17）。c，用凯克望远镜在 7 月 25 日，8 月 31 日和 9 月 1 日，观测 5.5 小时所得到的 53W091 的光谱（下方的实线）。图中所示为静止参考系的光谱（假设红移 $z = 1.552$），与之相比较的是近邻椭圆星系 M32（调整后）的紫外光谱（上方的实线）和最佳拟合给出的模型光谱（虚线）。（这里，通过假设主序星拐点质量为 $1.35M_\odot$（等效于 F2 光谱型，对应于 3.5 Gyr 年龄），并基于 Scalo 初始质量函数，通过光谱合成得到模型光谱。）为使 M32 和 53W091 的数据达到相

53W091 have been rebinned to the same (5 Å) resolution, with an additional median smooth being applied to the latter. For ease of comparison, the spectrum of M32 has been scaled to the same amplitude as that of 53W091 at $\lambda_{rest} = 2{,}897$ Å and then offset vertically by 5×10^{-18} W m^{-2}. The unambiguous nature of the redshift is demonstrated by the existence of at least 11 absorption features and two strong spectral breaks in the spectrum of 53W091 (indicated by vertical dashed lines) which are all reproduced in the rest-frame spectrum of M32 (in particular the "top-hat" feature between 2,640 and 2,750 Å is a feature unique to this spectral range, and rules out the (remote) possibility that the break observed at 7,400 Å could be the 4,000 Å break at lower redshift). These features (all except the reddest three of which are also reproduced in the model spectrum) are essentially those which are seen in the near-ultraviolet spectra of F and G stars, as can be judged by comparison with the near-ultraviolet spectrum of the Sun[19], vindicating our belief that the red colours of the millijansky radio galaxies are a result of their evolved stellar populations. Such features have not been detected before in the spectrum of a high-redshift galaxy, not even in the Keck spectrum of the reddest powerful radio galaxy at $z \sim 1$, 3C65, in which they are apparently swamped by broad Mg II emission[11].

The strength of such stellar features combined with the lack of detectable emission lines (Mg II is seen in absorption, in contrast to the situation in 3C65 (ref. 9)) indicates that the ultraviolet–optical light from radio galaxies selected at milijansky flux densities is essentially free from the contaminating effects (either direct or indirect) of their active nuclei. Moreover, the similarity of this near-ultraviolet spectrum to that of low-mass main-sequence stars suggest that the red optical–infrared colour of this galaxy results from an evolved stellar population rather than, for example, a significant contribution from a dust-obscured quasar[20-22] (a viewpoint supported by the very similar appearance of 53W091 at optical and infrared wavelengths; Fig. 1).

To investigate the extent to which our data can constrain the age of 53W091, we first calculated the best-fit age produced by an updated version of the evolutionary synthesis models of Guider-doni and Rocca-Volmerange[23]. Considering a model in which 53W091 is formed in a single burst of star-formation and evolves passively thereafter, we find that the observed optical spectrum and the infrared colours ($R-K = 5.8, J-K = 1.7, H-K = 0.8$) are all perfectly reproduced by the models only at a time of 4 Gyr after cessation of star-formation activity. Next, we considered the most recent versions of the models of Bruzual and Charlot[24]. It is known that red optical–infrared colours are produced more rapidly by these models, and indeed we found that at $z = 1.55$ the observed optical–infrared colour is reproduced after only 1.5 Gyr. But the dependence of $R-K$ colour on age is controversial (see below) and so it was with interest that we found these same models could not reproduce the shape of the Keck spectrum until an age > 3 Gyr, while to produce spectral breaks at $\lambda_{rest} = 2{,}635$ and 2,897 Å of the strength observed in 53W091 requires an age > 4 Gyr. Third, we considered the models of Bressan, Chiosi and Fagotto[25], which, assuming solar metallicity, yielded a best-fit age of 3 Gyr (again in good agreement with the above results).

We derived ages using these three alternative models of galaxy evolution because it is well known that different models can produce significantly different ages from a given set of data[26]. But much of the difference between these models lies in different treatments of post-main-sequence evolution, and although this is expected to have a significant effect

同的光谱分辨率 (5 Å)，我们进行了重新分区间统计，而对于后者我们还采用了额外的中值平滑。为了便于比较，我们还将 M32 的光谱进行缩放，使其振幅与 53W091 在 λ_{rest} = 2,897 Å 处的振幅相同，并将其垂直移动了 5×10^{-18} W·m^{-2}。53W091 存在至少 11 个吸收特征和 2 个很强的光谱不连续特征 (由垂直虚线表示)，因此可以证明红移的准确性，这些光谱特征全都可以在 M32 的静止参考系光谱中找到对应 (尤其是介于 2,640 Å 和 2,750 Å 之间该谱段独一无二的 "高帽" 特征，这一特征可以排除我们在 7,400 Å 观测到的不连续特征是由低红移处的 4,000 Å 不连续所导致的 (极小的) 可能性)。本质上，这些特征 (除了可以由模型光谱重现的最红的 3 个光谱特征以外) 可以在 F 型星和 G 型星的近紫外光谱中观测到，这一点可以通过与太阳的近紫外光谱[19] 比较得到验证，以上结果表明：中央射电星系中偏红的色指数是由它们当中演化的星族所造成的。在此之前，在高红移星系的光谱中还没有探测到这些特征。即使在 z~1 处最红的强射电星系 3C65 的凯克光谱中，这些特征也明显被宽的 Mg II 发射所淹没，从而没有被探测到[11]。

考虑到该星系的这些恒星特征的强度以及在星系中没有探测到明显的发射线 (与 3C65 相反，这里 MgII 是吸收线[9])，这表明流量密度在毫央范围的射电星系的紫外–光学辐射实质上没有被活动星系核 (直接或间接地) 污染。此外，该星系的近紫外光谱与小质量主序星的光谱相似，这表明该星系的光学–红外色指数偏红是由演化的星族所导致，而并非源于尘埃遮蔽类星体[20-22] 的显著贡献 (53W091 在光学和红外波段的观测图像非常相似支持了这一观点；图 1)。

为了研究我们的数据对该星系年龄的限制能力，我们首先利用古德尔多尼和罗尔–沃尔默朗然[23] 的演化星族合成模型计算了该星系年龄的最佳拟合结果。假设 53W091 在一次单一的星暴中形成，随后被动演化，我们发现观测到的光学光谱和红外色指数 (R–K = 5.8，J–K = 1.7，H–K = 0.8) 与恒星形成活动停止后 4 Gyr 的模型预言符合得相当好。接着我们考虑最近的布鲁苏阿尔和夏洛的模型[24]。众所周知，用这些模型可以更快地得到偏红的光学–红外色指数。事实上我们发现在红移 z = 1.55 处，观测到的光学–红外色指数可以由恒星形成活动停止后 1.5 Gyr 时的模型预言得到。但是这样得到的 R–K 色指数对年龄的依赖是有争议的 (请见下文)，这是一个有趣的现象，因为我们发现只有当星系年龄大于 3 Gyr 时，这些相同的模型才能再现凯克望远镜观测到的谱形。不仅如此，为了拟合在 53W091 中观测到的在 λ_{rest} = 2,635 Å 和 2,897 Å 处的光谱不连续特征，这就要求星系年龄大于 4 Gyr。再者，我们还考虑了布雷森、基奥西和法戈托[25] 的模型，在假设太阳的金属丰度下给出的最佳拟合年龄是 3 Gyr (再次很好地符合了上面的结果)。

众所周知，对于一组给定的数据，因为不同的模型可以给出非常不同的年龄[26]，所以我们用三种不同的星系演化模型计算星系年龄。但是这些模型的主要差别在于对主序后演化采取了不同的处理方法，尽管我们预期这些不同会对理论预言的星系

on the predicted infrared–optical luminosity of the galaxy, its effect on the predicted near-ultraviolet spectral energy distribution (SED) should be minimal (an expectation apparently borne out by the fact that all three models are in good agreement over the age required to reproduce the ultraviolet SED). Indeed, because it is well documented that the near-ultraviolet spectrum ($\lambda < 3,000$ Å) of a stellar population with an age of a few Gyr should be determined simply by the turn-off point of the main sequence[27], and as the main-sequence lifetime of A $\rightarrow$ G stars is probably the best understood area of stellar evolution, it should be possible to date 53W091 in an appealingly model-independent manner by simply determining the spectral type of the main-sequence turn-off point. We have therefore used the latest stellar atmosphere models of Kurucz[28] to investigate the spectra produced by main-sequence stars at a variety of ages, and find that the single stellar spectral type which best describes the near-ultraviolet light from 53W091 between $\lambda \approx 2,000$ and 3,500 Å is F5 (with an effective temperature $T_{eff} = 6,500$ K). Furthermore, an independent comparison with the International Ultraviolet Explorer satellite spectra of stars of various spectral types produces exactly the same result. However, to set a realistic limit on the age of this galaxy, one must integrate over the initial mass function (IMF) of stars from very low masses ($\sim 0.1 M_\odot$) up to the stellar mass at which the synthesized spectrum becomes unacceptably blue. Assuming a Scalo IMF[29], we find that the best-fitting main-sequence turn-off point occurs at spectral type F2 ($T_{eff} = 6,900$ K), equivalent to a stellar mass of $1.35 M_\odot$. The main-sequence lifetime of a star of this mass is well established (to within 5%) to be 3.5 Gyr. Such an age is reassuringly consistent with the ages indicated by the different evolutionary synthesis codes considered above, and the fact that this simple model provides such an excellent description of the data confirms that we are justified in ignoring the contribution of post-main-sequence stars (Fig. 1c).

We have considered carefully the robustness of our result, paying particular attention to the ways in which we could possibly have over-estimated the age of 53W091. First, if the validity of the models at near-ultraviolet wavelengths is accepted, an age younger than 3 Gyr is strongly excluded by the overall shape of the ultra-violet SED of 53W091 (Fig. 2a). Of course, the inferred age may in principle be reduced by truncating the stellar IMF at almost exactly $1.35 M_\odot$, but this requires considerable fine tuning (any significant population of A stars will dominate the spectrum for $\sim$3 Gyr) and, if true, it would be expected that the galaxy would display other signs of youth, such as strong emission lines which are not seen.

的红外–光学光度产生显著影响，但是它们对理论预言的近紫外光谱能量分布（SED）的影响应当非常小（为重现星系紫外光谱能量分布，三个模型均得到了相一致的星系年龄限制，因此这是一个很显然的推论）。事实上，有案可稽的是年龄为几十亿年的恒星星族的近紫外光谱（$\lambda < 3{,}000$ Å）是由主序的拐点确定的，同时 A 型星至 G 型星在主序阶段的寿命可能是在恒星演化领域中研究得最好的，因此我们有可能利用不依赖于模型的方法，通过简单地确定主序[27]拐点的光谱型来判断 53W091 的年龄。所以我们利用库鲁茨[28]最新的恒星大气模型来研究不同年龄主序星的光谱。结果发现能将 53W091 从波长 2,000 Å 至 3,500 Å 之间的近紫外辐射描述得最好的是单一恒星光谱型 F5 型星（有效温度 $T_{\mathrm{eff}} = 6{,}500$ K）。此外，通过将 53W091 与国际紫外探测卫星（IUE）观测到的不同光谱型恒星光谱进行比较，我们得出了几乎完全相同的结果。然而，要对该星系的年龄给出一个真实限制，我们必须对初始质量函数（IMF）从非常小的质量（$\sim 0.1\,M_{\odot}$）开始进行积分，直至某一质量上限，使得当时的合成光谱蓝到超出了可接受的范围。采用 Scalo 的初始质量函数[29]，我们发现最佳拟合的主星序拐点与 F2 光谱型相对应（$T_{\mathrm{eff}} = 6{,}900$ K），等效恒星质量为 $1.35\,M_{\odot}$。该质量范围的恒星其公认的主序星寿命为 3.5 Gyr（在 5% 的误差范围内）。这里得到的年龄结果再次被确认与上面提到的利用不同演化合成模型得到的年龄相一致。该简单模型能够如此好地描述观测数据，证实了我们忽略后主序星（图 1c）的贡献是合理的。

我们仔细地考虑了我们结果的稳定性和可靠性，特别关注了那些有可能高估 53W091 年龄的方法。首先，如果我们认为模型在近紫外波段是可靠的，那么 53W091 星系在紫外波段的光谱能量分布的整体形状（图 2a）可以强烈地排除该星系年龄小于 3 Gyr 的可能性。当然从原理上讲，虽然可以在近似等于 $1.35\,M_{\odot}$ 处对恒星的初始质量函数进行截断来减小所推断的星系年龄，但是这就要求相当精确地调整参数（任何明显的 A 型星星族成分将会主导年龄 ~ 3 Gyr 的星系光谱特征）。而且如果以上想法确实是正确的，那么我们可以预期在该星系中探测到表征年轻的其他特征，例如强的发射线，然而我们并没有观测到。

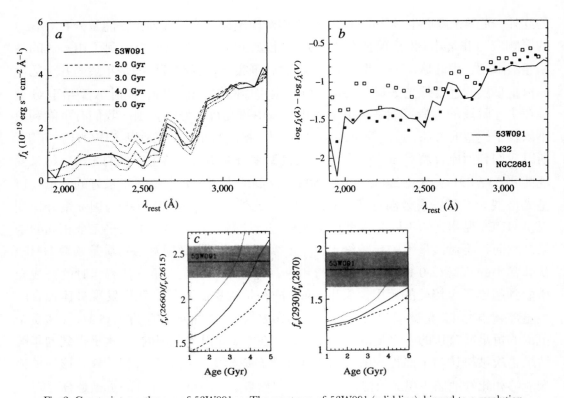

Fig. 2. Constraints on the age of 53W091. *a*, The spectrum of 53W091 (solid line), binned to a resolution of 50 Å, plotted in terms of f_λ, and compared with the SED produced by the passively evolving main-sequence model at ages of 2, 3, 4 and 5 Gyr after cessation of star-formation activity. The model spectra have been normalized to the observed flux density at 3,200 Å to illustrate why ages $\leqslant 3$ Gyr can be formally rejected at a high level of significance on the basis of the overall shape of the ultraviolet SED. Models younger than 3 Gyr overpredict the flux density at $\lambda \approx 2,100$ Å by ~100% (the relative flux-calibration of the spectrum is accurate to ~10–15% across the full wavelength range). We stress that, in the regime of interest here, the connection between the spectral type of the main-sequence turn-off point and age is well-established (to within 5%), because stellar ages for main-sequence stars in the mass range 1–1.5 $M_\odot$ are essentially unaffected by uncertainties such as assumed mass loss, choice of convection theory or equation of state, and the opacities in the corresponding temperature range are well known. *b*, The spectrum of 53W091 (solid line), binned to a resolution of 50-Å, and this time plotted in terms of $\log f_\lambda\ (\lambda) - \log f_\lambda\ (V)$ to allow direct comparison with the normalized ultraviolet SEDs of two nearby early-type galaxies, M32 (filled squares) and NGC2681 (open squares)[30]. The rest-frame *V*-band flux density, $f_\lambda(V)$, of 53W091 was determined from a weighted average of the observed *J*- and *H*-band flux densities, measured through an aperture equivalent to that used in the flux calibration of the optical spectrum. Recent studies of M32 both at optical[31] and ultraviolet[27] wavelengths are in agreement that the most recent star-formation activity in this galaxy occurred 4–5 Gyr ago, whereas in NGC2681 star formation appears to have ceased 1–2 Gyr before the epoch of observation[32]. The level and shape of the rest-frame ultraviolet SED of 53W091 is more like that of M32, consistent with an age of 3–4 Gyr for this high-redshift galaxy. *c*, The observed strength of the spectral breaks at 2,635 Å (left-hand plot) and 2,897 Å (right-hand plot) compared with the break strengths predicted by the evolving main-sequence model as a function of age for three different choices of metallicity—solar (solid line), twice solar (dotted line) and 0.2 × solar (dashed line). In each plot the horizontal line indicates the break strength as measured from the spectrum shown in Fig. 1*c*, and the shaded area indicates the uncertainty in this estimate. The strength of the breaks in both the data and the models was determined from the ratio of the average value of f_v in 30-Å bins centred on the two wavelengths indicated on the vertical axis of each plot. Based on the (reddening-independent) strength of these features the inferred

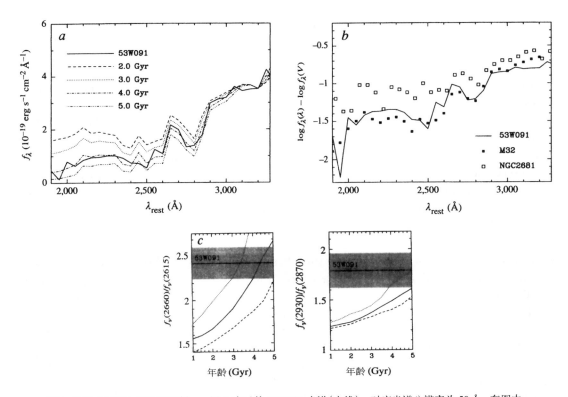

图 2. 关于 53W091 年龄的限制。a，用 f_λ 表示的 53W091 光谱（实线），对应光谱分辨率为 50 Å。在图中，我们将恒星形成活动停止后 2 Gyr、3 Gyr、4 Gyr、5 Gyr，由被动演化的主序星模型给出的光谱能量分布与 53W091 光谱进行了比较。我们对这些模型光谱进行归一化，使得 3,200 Å 处的模型光谱强度与观测流量密度一致，这样模型与观测所得的紫外光谱能量分布的整体形态的比较结果很自然地解释了可以以很高的置信度水平正式排除该星系年龄 ≤3 Gyr 的原因。年龄小于 3 Gyr 的模型所预言的流量密度在波长 $\lambda \approx 2,100$ Å 处高出观测结果将近 ~100%（在整个波长范围内，光谱相对流量定标精度约为 10% ~15%）。我们强调，在本文所感兴趣的范围内，主序星拐点对应的光谱型与年龄的联系是公认的（在 5% 内），这是因为对于质量范围在 $1\,M_\odot$ ~$1.5\,M_\odot$ 的主序星而言，恒星年龄本质上不受某些不确定因素影响，例如假设的质量损失，所选取的对流理论或物态方程；并且在对应温度范围内恒星的不透明度也是众所周知的。b，用 $\log f_\lambda(\lambda) - \log f_\lambda(V)$ 表示的 53W091 的光谱（实线），这样可以直接与两个近邻早型星系（M32，实心方块；NGC2681，空心方块）[30] 的归一化紫外光谱能量分布相比较，对应光谱分辨率为 50 Å。53W091 在静止参考系中 V 波段的流量密度 $f_\lambda(V)$ 是由观测到的 J 波段和 H 波段流量密度的加权平均确定的，测量孔径与光谱流量定标所采用的孔径一样。最近在光学 [31] 和紫光 [27] 波段对 M32 的研究结果支持该星系最近的恒星形成活动发生在 4~5 Gyr 之前，而 NGC2681 的恒星形成看起来停止于观测时期 [32] 之前的 1~2 Gyr。由于在静止参考系中，53W091 紫外光谱能量分布的强度和形状与 M32 更相像，因此这将符合该高红移星系的年龄为 3~4 Gyr 的推断。c，在 2,635 Å（左图）和 2,897 Å（右图）处观测得到的光谱不连续特征的强度。与之相比较的是演化主序星模型在三种不同金属丰度（太阳金属丰度，实线；2 倍太阳金属丰度，点线；0.2 倍太阳金属丰度，虚线）下所预言的光谱不连续的强度随年龄的变化。两幅图中的水平线表示利用图 1c 中光谱所测量出的光谱不连续特征的强度，阴影区域表示对应的误差范围。根据每幅图纵坐标，我们以两个波长为中心，在其 30 Å 范围内计算 f_ν 的平均值，再根据它们的比值分别得到了数据和模型光谱不连续的强度。根据这些特征的（与红化无关的）强度可以推断出 53W091 的年龄超过 4 Gyr，即使假设该天体拥有超太阳金属丰度，要用小于 3 Gyr 的年龄来解释我们

age of 53W091 is > 4 Gyr, and it is hard to reconcile the data with an age younger than 3 Gyr even if one assumes super-solar metallicity. The observed strengths of the corresponding breaks in the observed spectrum of M32 are 1.6 and 2.1 respectively, consistent with an age of ~4 Gyr.

Second, an independent check of our derived age is provided by comparing the ultraviolet properties of 53W091 with those of nearby early-type galaxies whose ages have been determined by other means. In Fig. 2b the normalized rest-frame ultraviolet SED of 53W091 is compared with the IUE spectra of M32 and NGC2681[30]. Recent studies of M32 both at optical[31] and ultraviolet[27] wavelengths agree that the most recent star-formation activity in this galaxy occurred 4–5 Gyr ago, whereas in NGC2681 star formation appears to have ceased 1–2 Gyr before the epoch of observation[32]. The level and shape of the rest-frame ultraviolet SED of 53W091 is undoubtedly more like that of M32, again consistent with an age of 3–4 Gyr for this high-redshift galaxy.

A third concern is that in comparing the ultraviolet SED of 53W091 both with models and with nearby ellipticals we may have over-estimated the age of 53W091 by ignoring the possible reddening effect of dust. But if this were the case, then it would be expected that reddening-independent features such as the strengths of the spectral breaks at $\lambda = 2,635$ Å, 2,897 Å would indicate a younger age. In fact these two features in the spectrum of 53W091 appear stronger than the corresponding breaks in the ultraviolet spectrum of M32, and when compared with the predictions of the main-sequence model, each break independently yields an age > 3.5 Gyr (Fig. 2c). This impressive agreement leads us to conclude that although a dusty torus may be present in the centre of this galaxy (obscuring the active nucleus) its effect on the integrated starlight of the galaxy is negligible.

The only remaining issue is the sensitivity of the derived age to the assumed value of metallicity. We have therefore investigated the effect of varying the metallicity both in our own main-sequence models, and in the full spectral synthesis code of Bressan. Both models yield very similar results; the derived age increases to 4.5 Gyr if 1/5 of solar metallicity is assumed, but is reduced by 0.5 Gyr (to 3 Gyr) if the metallicity is doubled to twice solar (Fig. 2c). Thus, although the age–metallicity degeneracy is hard to break (similar results are obtained by fitting either to the overall SED or to the strength of the two breaks), we conclude that very large values of metallicity are required to reduce the derived age of 53W091 to less than 3 Gyr.

Having considered the ways in which we might have overestimated the age of 53W091, we should stress that we regard it as more plausible that 3.5 Gyr may be a significant under-estimate of the true age of this galaxy. First, the spectral breaks indicate a larger age. Second, and more importantly, all of the model fits discussed above assume that this large elliptical galaxy was formed in an instantaneous burst after which star-formation completely ceased; if one assumes a burst of significant duration, or subsequent star-formation activity the derived age increases accordingly (for a 1-Gyr formation starburst,

的数据仍然十分困难。在 M32 的观测光谱中对应的光谱不连续的强度分别是 1.6 和 2.1，这与该星系的年龄约为 4 Gyr 是一致的。

　　其次，我们还通过将 53W091 与用其他方法确定年龄的近邻早型星系的紫外性质进行比较，来独立检验我们得到的星系年龄。图 2b 显示了 53W091 星系在静止参考系中归一化的紫外光谱能量分布与 M32 和 NGC2681[30] 的 IUE 光谱的比较结果。最近对 M32 在光学[31] 和紫外[27] 波段的研究证实在该星系中绝大多数恒星形成活动发生在 4~5 Gyr 之前。然而 NGC2681 中的恒星形成看上去停止于观测时刻前的 1~2 Gyr[32]。在静止参考系中 53W091 紫外光谱能量分布的幅度和形状无疑与 M32 更相似，这再次佐证了该高红移星系的年龄为 3~4 Gyr。

　　第三，通过比较 53W091 与模型和近邻椭圆星系的紫外光谱能量分布发现，我们也许由于忽略了可能的由尘埃引起的红化效应而高估了该星系的年龄。但如果确实如此，那么我们将期望那些不依赖红化的光谱特征，例如在 $\lambda = 2{,}635$ Å 和 2,879 Å 处光谱不连续的强度，能够表征更小的星系年龄。实际上，53W091 光谱中的这两个不连续特征看上去要强于 M32 光谱中的情况，因此当把 53W091 光谱与主序星模型预言的光谱相比较时，每一个不连续特征都能独立给出该星系年龄大于 3.5 Gyr 这一结果（图 2c）。这个令人印象深刻的一致性使得我们得出结论：尽管尘埃环可能存在于该星系的中心（遮挡住活动核），但它对该星系的整体星光分布的影响可以忽略不计。

　　最后，剩下的唯一问题是我们得到的年龄是否敏感依赖于所假设的金属丰度。为此我们在主序模型和完整的布雷森光谱合成模型中研究了金属丰度变化所带来的影响。这两个模型均给出了非常类似的结果：如果假设金属丰度为太阳金属丰度的 1/5，那么所得到的年龄将增加到 4.5 Gyr；但是如果当金属丰度为太阳金属丰度的 2 倍时，所得年龄将减小 0.5 Gyr（即等于 3 Gyr）（图 2c）。因此，尽管很难打破年龄－金属丰度简并（不管是通过拟合整个光谱能量分布，还是拟合那两个光谱不连续特征的强度时，都可以得到类似的简并结果），我们仍然可以得出结论：非常高的金属丰度才能使得计算出的 53W091 年龄小于 3 Gyr。

　　在考虑了可能导致高估 53W091 年龄的不同因素之后，我们应当强调这里更合理的情形是 3.5 Gyr 的结论可能大大低估了该星系的真实年龄。首先，以上提到的两个光谱不连续特征暗示了比 3.5 Gyr 更大的年龄。其次，更为重要的是，以上所有讨论的模型拟合都假设这个大椭圆星系是由一个瞬时星暴形成，而在此之后恒星形成完全停止。如果假设星暴具有明显的持续时间或者随后仍有恒星形成活动存在，那么推导出的星系年龄也将会相应增加（对于一个持续 1 Gyr 的星暴，即使采用太阳的

the best-fit age is 4.5 Gyr even if solar metallicity is assumed).

We now consider briefly the far-reaching implications of a 3.5-Gyr-old galaxy at $z = 1.55$. This is the first time that such an unambiguously old object has been discovered at such large look-back times, and its existence sets strong constraints both on the first epoch of galaxy formation and on cosmological models. The age of the Universe at this epoch is $1.6h^{-1}$ Gyr if $\Omega = 1$, increasing to $2.7h^{-1}$ Gyr for $\Omega = 0.2$, or at most $3.5h^{-1}$ Gyr for $\Omega = 0.2$, $\Lambda = 0.8$ ($h \equiv H_0/100$ km s^{-1} Mpc^{-1}). Obviously the Einstein–de Sitter model is in difficulty, and even in a low-density Universe an age > 3 Gyr at $z = 1.55$ requires a formation redshift $z_f > 4$ (for $h = 0.65$). It thus seems clear that at least some galaxies formed at redshifts greatly in excess of the recent formation era inferred from data on field galaxies[33], and the existence of similarly old galaxies at still higher redshifts would potentially allow one to infer a non-zero cosmological constant.

(**381**, 581-584; 1996)

James Dunlop[*], **John Peacock**[†], **Hyron Spinrad**[‡], **Arjun Dey**[§], **Raul Jimenez**[†], **Daniel Stern**[‡] & **Rogier Windhorst**[‖]

[*] Institute for Astronomy, Department of Physics and Astronomy, The University of Edinburgh, Edinburgh EH9 3HJ, UK

[†] Royal Observatory, Edinburgh EH9 3HJ, UK

[‡] Astronomy Department, University of California, Berkeley, California 94720, USA

[§] NOAO/KPNO, 950 North Cherry Avenue, Tucson, Arizona 85726, USA

[‖] Department of Physics and Astronomy, Arizona State University, Tempe, Arizona 85287-1504, USA

Received 17 January; accepted 23 April 1996.

References:

1. McCarthy, P. J. *A. Rev. Astr. Astrophys.* **31**, 639-688 (1993).

2. Steidel, C. C., Pettini, M. & Hamilton, D. *Astr. J.* **110**, 2519-2536 (1995).

3. Steidel, C. C., Giavalisco, M., Pettini, M., Dickinson, M. & Adelberger, K. L. *Astrophys. J.* **462**, L17-L20 (1996).

4. Petitjean, P., Pécontal, E., Valls-Gabaud, D. & Charlot, S. *Nature* **380**, 411-413 (1996).

5. Dunlop, J. S., Guiderdoni, B., Rocca-Volmerange, B., Peacock, J. A. & Longair, M. S. *Mon. Not. R. astr. Soc.* **240**, 257-284 (1989).

6. di Serego Alighieri, S., Fosbury, R. A. E., Quinn, P. J. & Tadhunter, C. N. *Nature* **341**, 307-309 (1989).

7. Tadhunter, C. N., Scarrott, S. M., Draper, P. & Rolph, C. *Mon. Not. R. astr. Soc.* **256**, 53P-58P (1992).

8. Rigler, M. A., Lilly, S. J., Stockton, A., Hammer, F., Le Fèvre, O. *Astrophys. J.* **385**, 61-82 (1991).

9. Hamilton, D. *Astrophys. J.* **297**, 371-389 (1985).

10. Lilly, S. J. *Astrophys. J.* **333**,161-167 (1988).

11. Stockton, A., Kellogg, M. & Ridgway, S. *Astrophys. J.* **443**, L69-L72 (1995).

12. Rawlings, S. & Saunders, R. *Nature* **349**, 138-140 (1991).

13. Dunlop, J. S. & Peacock, J. A. *Mon. Not. R. astr. Soc.* **263**, 936-966 (1993).

14. Windhorst, R. A., van Heerde, G. M. & Katgert, P. *Astr. Astrophys. Suppl. Ser.* **58**, 1-37 (1984).

15. Oort, M. J. A. & van Langevelde, H. J. *Astr. Astrophys. Suppl. Ser.* **71**, 25-38 (1987).

16. Oort, M. J. A., Katgert, P., Steeman, F. W. M. & Windhorst, R. A. *Astr. Astrophys.* **179**, 41-59 (1987).

17. Neuschaefer, L. W. & Windhorst, R. A. *Astrophys. J. Suppl. Ser.* **96**, 371-399 (1995).

18. Dunlop, J. S., Peacock, J. A. & Windhorst, R. A. in *Galaxies in the Young Universe* 84-87 (Springer, Berlin, 1995).

19. Morton, D. C., Spinrad, H., Bruzual, G. A. & Kurucz, R. L. *Astrophys. J.* **212**, 438-445 (1977).

20. McCarthy, P. J. *Publs, astr. Soc. Pacif.* **105**, 1051-1057 (1993).

21. Lacy, M., Rawlings, S., Eales, S. & Dunlop, J. S. *Mon. Not. R. astr. Soc.* **273**, 821-826 (1995).

22. Webster, R. L, Francis, P. J., Peterson, B. A., Drinkwater, M. J. & Masci, F. J. *Nature* **375**, 469- 471 (1995).

金属丰度，最佳拟合的年龄为 4.5 Gyr）。

现在我们简要地讨论在红移 $z = 1.55$ 处发现年龄为 3.5 Gyr 年老星系的深远意义。首先，这是首次在如此大的回溯时间上发现的一个确凿无疑的年老天体。该天体的存在对星系形成的初始时刻和宇宙学模型都给出了很强的限制。假设 $\Omega = 1$，那么在该时刻宇宙的年龄是 $1.6h^{-1}$ Gyr。对于 $\Omega = 0.2$，宇宙年龄增加到 $2.7h^{-1}$ Gyr，而在 $\Omega = 0.2$，$\Lambda = 0.8$（$h \equiv H_0 / 100$ km·s^{-1}·Mpc^{-1}）的情况下，宇宙年龄最多为 $3.5h^{-1}$ Gyr。很明显在爱因斯坦-德西特模型下解释 53W091 的年龄是有困难的，即使在一个低密度的宇宙中，在红移 $z = 1.55$ 处，星系年龄 > 3 Gyr 也将要求星系形成的红移 $z_f > 4$（当 $h = 0.65$ 时）。因此比较清楚的是，根据场星系的数据 [33]，我们发现在高红移处一些星系的形成时间超过了现在的形成纪元，加之在更高红移存在同样年老的星系，这可能使我们得到一个非零的宇宙学常数。

（李海宁 翻译；吴学兵 审稿）

23. Guiderdoni, B. & Rocca-Volmerange, B. *Astr. Astrophys.* **186**, 1-21 (1987).

24. Bruzual, G. B. & Charlot, S. *Astrophys. J.* **405**, 538-553 (1993).

25. Bressan, A., Chiosi, C. & Fagotto, F. *Astrophys. J. Suppl. Ser.* **94**, 63-115 (1994).

26. Charlot, S., Worthey, G. & Bressan, A. *Astrophys. J.* **457**, 626-644 (1996).

27. Magris, G. C. & Bruzual, G. A. *Astrophys. J.* **417**, 102-113 (1993).

28. Kurucz, R. *ATLAS9 Stellar Atmosphere Programs and 2km/s Grid CDROM* Vol. 13 (Smithsonian Astrophysical Observatory, Cambridge, MA, 1992).

29. Scalo, J. M. *Fund. Cosm. Phys.* **11**, 1-278 (1986).

30. Burstein, D., Bertola, F., Buson, L. M., Faber, S. M. & Lauer, T. R. *Astrophys. J.* **328**, 440-462 (1988).

31. Bressan, A., Chiosi, C. & Fagotto, F. *Astrophys. J. Suppl. Ser.* **94**, 63-115 (1994).

32. Windhorst, R. A. *et al. Astrophys. J.* **380**, 362-383 (1991).

33. Cowie, L. L., Hu, E. M. & Songaila, A. *Nature* **377**, 603-605 (1995).

Acknowledgements. We thank J. Davies for making the IRCAM3 service observations, A. Bressan for providing the age–metallicity models, and D. Burstein for supplying the IUE spectrum of M32. The United Kingdom Infrared Telescope is operated by the Royal Observatories on behalf of the UK Particle Physics and Astronomy Research Council. The W.M. Keck Observatory is a scientific partnership between the University of California and the California Institute of Technology, made possible by the generous gift of the W.M. Keck Foundation. This work was supported by the US National Science Foundation.

A Search for Human Influences on the Thermal Structure of the Atmosphere

B. D. Santer *et al.*

Editor's Note

By the mid-1990s, the likelihood that human emissions of greenhouse gases were creating significant global warming had become a major concern. Although this was widely suspected to be happening, climatologists continued to be cautious about that conclusion, for there were other ways of interpreting the apparent correlation between increasing levels of atmospheric carbon dioxide and rising temperatures. Here Ben Santer and colleagues supply one of the clinching pieces of evidence that human activities are implicated. Their detailed computer modelling shows that the observed global spatial pattern of warming closely matches that predicted on the basis of greenhouse-gas emissions. Despite its careful wording, this study identified a telltale "fingerprint" of anthropogenic global warming and made alternative explanations seem considerably less tenable.

The observed spatial patterns of temperature change in the free atmosphere from 1963 to 1987 are similar to those predicted by state-of-the-art climate models incorporating various combinations of changes in carbon dioxide, anthropogenic sulphate aerosol and stratospheric ozone concentrations. The degree of pattern similarity between models and observations increases through this period. It is likely that this trend is partially due to human activities, although many uncertainties remain, particularly relating to estimates of natural variability.

CHANGES in the vertical structure of atmospheric temperature have been proposed as a possible "fingerprint" of greenhouse-gas-induced climate change[1-4]. Until recently, most of the information about such a fingerprint resulted from experiments in which an atmospheric general circulation model (AGCM) coupled to a mixed-layer ocean was forced by a doubling of atmospheric CO_2 levels.[5,6] For annually averaged changes, these experiments show a hemispherically symmetrical pattern of stratospheric cooling and tropospheric warming, with a warming maximum in the tropical upper troposphere (Fig. 1a). One recent study[7] compared such model-predicted signals with observed radiosonde measurements[8] and concluded that this fingerprint was increasingly evident in observed data. The degree of time-increasing similarity was judged to be statistically significant—that is, unlikely to be due to natural climate variability alone.

The work reported here differs from this earlier work in four respects. First, we examine

人类对大气温度结构影响的研究

桑特等

编者按

20 世纪 90 年代中期，人类排放的温室气体可能造成全球明显变暖这个问题成为大家关注的焦点。虽然大家普遍猜测这正在发生，但由于有其他的方法能够解释大气中二氧化碳浓度的升高与温度上升之间的明显相关性，所以气候学家对这一结论仍持谨慎态度。本文中本·桑特及其同事们提供了人类活动参与其中的一个决定性证据。他们精细的计算机模拟结果显示出已观测到的全球变暖的空间分布型与基于温室气体排放所预测出的空间分布型相吻合。尽管这种措辞较为小心谨慎，但本项研究明确了一种人为引起全球变暖的证据，而且使其他的解释变得似乎非常站不住脚。

1963~1987 年间观测到的自由大气中温度变化的空间分布型，与利用目前最先进的气候模式结合不同的二氧化碳、人为硫酸盐气溶胶以及平流层臭氧浓度的组合所预测出的结果相似。在该段时期里模拟结果与实测结果的分布型相似度随时间逐渐增加。人类活动很可能是造成这种趋势的原因之一，不过仍存在许多不确定因素，特别是有关对自然变化的估计。

大气温度垂直结构的变化被认为是温室气体导致的气候变化的"指纹"[1-4]。直到最近，关于该指纹的多数信息仍主要来自实验，即，当大气 CO_2 浓度倍增时，它所驱动的大气环流模式（AGCM）与混合层海洋的耦合结果[5,6]。对于年平均变化，此类实验显示为平流层变冷和对流层变暖均呈半球对称，且增暖最高值出现在热带对流层上层(图 1a)。最近的一项研究[7]把该类模式预测信号与无线电探空仪的测定结果[8]作了比较，结果发现在实测数据中该指纹日益明显。经检验这种相似性随时间的增加程度具有统计学意义——也就是说，并非仅由自然气候变化所致。

本文介绍的研究与上述早期工作的差别在于四个方面。首先，我们对大气 CO_2

the relative detectability of vertical temperature-change signals due to individual and combined changes in atmospheric CO_2 and anthropogenic sulphate aerosols[9,10]. Previous detection work involving temperature changes in the free atmosphere has used signals due to increases in CO_2 only. We consider signals due to combined CO_2 and aerosol forcing because recent studies of near-surface temperature changes show that a combined signal may be easier to identify in the observations than a signal due to changes in CO_2 alone[10,11].

Second, we use signal data from two different models in order to explore the sensitivity of our results to model-dependent uncertainties in the definition of an anthropogenic signal. These uncertainties arise from model differences in physics, resolution, representation of aerosol effects, and modelling strategy.

Third, we consider how a combined CO_2+aerosol vertical temperature-change signal might be modified by observed changes in stratospheric ozone. The observed reduction in stratospheric ozone over the past two decades is attributable largely to the industrial production of halocarbons[12]. One recent study in which an AGCM was forced by changes in both CO_2 and stratospheric ozone showed that the inclusion of ozone effects improves model agreement with the radiosonde temperature data, particularly in the upper troposphere[13,14]. As results are not yet available from experiments with combined changes in CO_2, anthropogenic sulphate aerosols and stratospheric ozone, we perform a simple sensitivity study of possible ozone effects by linearly combining results from CO_2+aerosol[9] and ozone-only[15] model studies.

Fourth, we use information from three long control runs performed with coupled atmosphere–ocean GCMs (CGCMs) to assess the significance of trends in model-versus-observed pattern similarity. Such integrations provide estimates of internally generated natural climate variability on a range of space and timescales. Comparable information on the multi-decadal natural climate variability crucial to the detection problem is impossible to obtain from the short (< 40-year) radiosonde temperature record.

Model Signals and Observational Data

We use model data from experiments with fixed levels of anthropogenic pollutants ("equilibrium experiments") and from integrations in which the atmospheric concentrations of greenhouse gases and aerosols increase over time ("transient experiments"). The equilibrium CO_2-only and CO_2+aerosol vertical temperature-change signals were taken from experiments performed by Taylor and Penner[9] (henceforth TP) with a tropospheric chemistry model[16,17] coupled to an AGCM with a simple mixed-layer ocean[18]. The chemistry–climate model considers only the direct radiative effects of sulphate aerosols (reflection of incident solar radiation)[19]. In addition to a control run with nominal pre-industrial levels of CO_2 (270 parts per million by volume, p.p.m.v.) and no anthropogenic sulphur emissions, three perturbation experiments were performed: a sulphate-only experiment

与人为硫酸盐气溶胶[9,10]中单个作用和联合作用下垂直温度变化信号的相对可检测性作了研究。之前涉及自由大气温度变化的检测工作采用了只 CO_2 浓度升高时形成的信号。我们之所以考虑 CO_2 与气溶胶联合影响下的信号情况是因为，对近地表温度变化的新近研究表明，在实测结果中，与仅由 CO_2 变化形成的信号相比，组合信号更容易识别[10,11]。

其次，我们采用了两种不同模式的信号数据，从而能够检验在确定人为信号时我们的结果对基于模式的不确定性的敏感度。这些不确定性是由模式的物理过程差异、分辨率差异、对气溶胶效应的描述差异以及建模策略的不同所致。

第三，我们还对平流层中实际观测到的臭氧变化如何影响 CO_2 和气溶胶联合作用下的垂直温度变化信号作了研究。据观测，过去 20 年中平流层臭氧不断减少，这主要应归因于卤代烃的工业化生产[12]。一项最新研究使用了由 CO_2 和平流层臭氧浓度变化来驱动的大气环流模式进行实验，结果显示，将臭氧效应包含在内以后，提高了模式与探空仪温度数据的一致性，特别是在对流层上层[13,14]。由于目前还没有可用的 CO_2、人为气溶胶和平流层臭氧综合变化下的实验结果，所以我们将含有 CO_2 和气溶胶作用的模式结果[9]与单纯臭氧作用下的模式结果[15]作了线性叠加，进而对潜在臭氧效应作了简单的敏感性研究。

第四，我们利用海气耦合 GCMs(CGCMs) 在三个长期对照实验下得到的信息，估计了在模拟结果与实测分布之间具有相似性变化趋势的显著性。这样的模式积分有助于研究在一定时间和空间范围内内在的自然气候变化。而仅依靠短期的（不到 40 年）探空仪温度记录是不足以提供对检测问题至关重要的多年代际自然气候变化的类似信息的。

模拟信号与实测数据

我们采用的模式数据来自人为污染浓度一定时（"平衡实验"）以及大气中温室气体和气溶胶的浓度均随时间而增加时（"瞬变实验"）的模拟结果。仅含 CO_2 和 CO_2+气溶胶联合作用下的两种垂直温度变化信号均取自泰勒和彭纳[9]（后文将以 TP 表示）利用对流层化学模式[16,17]耦合 AGCM 和简单混合层海洋[18]所作的实验。该化学气候模式仅考虑了硫酸盐气溶胶的直接辐射效应（即对入射太阳辐射的反射）[19]。除了以工业化以前的 CO_2 水平(270 ppmv)且无人为硫酸盐释放条件下作的对照实验外，还进行了三项扰动实验：仅含硫酸盐 (S-TP) 的实验，其中硫酸盐含量与现今人为硫

(S-TP) with near-present-day anthropogenic sulphur emissions, a CO_2-only experiment (C-TP) with near-present-day CO_2 levels (345 p.p.m.v.), and an experiment with combined present-day CO_2 levels and anthropogenic sulphur emissions (SC-TP)[9]. The differences between the perturbation experiments and the control represent equilibrium changes from pre-industrial to present-day conditions.

We also consider vertical temperature-change signals from two recent transient experiments performed with the Hadley Centre (henceforth HC) CGCM[10,20]. The model has full ocean dynamics, and was forced over 1860 to 1990 with historical increases in greenhouse gases only (C-HC) and with increases in both greenhouse gases and anthropogenic SO_2 emissions (SC-HC). After 1990 the concentration of SO_2 evolved according to IPCC Scenario IS92a[21] while the concentration of equivalent CO_2 increased at 1% per year. Direct scattering effects of aerosols are represented by changes in the surface albedo[22].

To study how a reduction in stratospheric O_3 might modify the SC signal pattern, we use data from an experiment performed with the Geophysical Fluid Dynamics Laboratory (GFDL) "SKYHI" atmospheric GCM[15]. The model was forced with observed monthly-mean zonal average changes in stratospheric ozone over the period 1979–90, and was run with fixed cloud distributions in the troposphere and sea-surface temperature prescribed according to climatology. An idealized vertical structure of ozone losses was imposed, with constant percentage reductions in an atmospheric region extending from the tropopause to roughly 7 km above[15].

The radiosonde temperature analyses were available as anomalies for December–January–February (DJF), June–July–August (JJA) and annually averaged data relative to a reference period of 1963–73, and spanned the period 1963–87[8]. The data are in the form of zonal averages for seven atmospheric levels (850, 700, 500, 300, 200, 100 and 50 hPa). The principal data uncertainties have been described previously[7,8,23].

Comparisons between the radiosonde data and satellite-derived estimates of vertical temperature changes indicate that the two data sets are in good agreement over the period of overlap, at least in terms of the global[24] and hemispheric[8] means. For the present study we compared the radiosonde data with a reanalysis of operationally produced climate data[25]. The seasonal patterns of (zonally averaged) linear trends as a function of latitude and height were in close agreement for the period of overlap between the two data sets (1979–87), despite differences in the spatial coverage of the radiosonde data (primarily land only) and the reanalysis (land+ocean).

Note that the amplitudes of the observed changes and model signals are not directly comparable, as they represent responses to radiative forcing changes over different periods. If the radiative forcing histories and lags between forcing and response were known exactly for O_3, CO_2 and sulphate aerosols, it would be possible to make a more meaningful comparison of the amplitudes of observed and modelled vertical

化物释放量接近；仅含 CO_2 的实验（C-TP），其中 CO_2 浓度与现今接近（345 ppmv）；以及以现今 CO_2 水平与人为硫化物释放量条件下进行的实验（SC-TP）[9]。扰动实验与对照实验之间的差异表征了从工业化以前到现在的变化。

我们还利用哈德利中心（后文将以 HC 表示）新近进行的两次 CGCM 瞬变实验[10,20]对垂直温度变化信号作了研究。该模式充分考虑了海洋动力特征，在 1860 年至 1990 年期间，分别在仅有逐渐增加的温室气体（C-HC）和温室气体与人为 SO_2 排放共存（SC-HC）的条件下运行。在 1990 年后，SO_2 浓度根据 IPCC 的 IS92a 方案[21]随时间演变，相应的 CO_2 的浓度则以每年 1% 的速度递增。气溶胶的直接散射效应均以地表反射率的变化来表示[22]。

为了研究平流层 O_3 的损耗如何影响 SC 的信号分布，我们采用了由地球物理流体动力学实验室（GFDL）的"SKYHI"大气 GCM[15]实验得到的数据。该模式以 1979 年至 1990 年间平流层臭氧的纬向平均实测值的月平均值的变化来驱动，同时假定其对流层中的云量分布不变而海表温度由气候学的观测结果给定。设臭氧损耗的垂直结构为理想分布，即从对流层顶到上部约 7 km 处的大气内其递减的百分比不变[15]。

无线电探空仪测定的 1963~1987 年的温度可用来分析相对于参考时段 1963~1973 年间的 12–1–2 月份（DJF）、6–7–8 月份（JJA）温度异常以及年平均温度异常[8]。所有数据均表示为七个大气高度上（850 hPa、700 hPa、500 hPa、300 hPa、200 hPa、100 hPa 和 50 hPa）的纬向平均值。其中主要的数据不确定性之前已有论述[7,8,23]。

根据无线电探空仪数据和卫星数据得到的垂直温度变化的对比结果显示，两组数据在重叠时段内至少在全球平均值[24]和半球平均值[8]上具有很好的一致性。本次研究中，我们将无线电探空仪数据和业务产生的气候数据的再分析结果[25]进行比较。尽管无线电探空仪数据（仅陆地）和再分析数据（陆地和海洋）在空间覆盖范围有所不同，但是作为纬度和高度的函数的（纬向平均的）线性趋势的季节性分布在两组数据的重叠时段（1979~1987）非常接近。

值得注意的是，实测变化的振幅与模拟信号的振幅没有直接可比性，这是因为它们代表着不同时段辐射强迫的变化。倘若能够确切知道 O_3、CO_2 和硫酸盐气溶胶的辐射强迫的历史变化及其强迫与响应之间的滞后时间，那么将有可能根据整体响应差异，通过缩放使实测的与模拟的垂直温度变化的振幅之间的对比更具指示意义。

temperature changes by scaling according to differences in overall response. Large forcing uncertainties, particularly for sulphate aerosol effects, make such scaling exercises very difficult. We circumvent some of these difficulties by using a comparison statistic that focuses on patterns rather than amplitudes of temperature change. The issue of amplitude differences is important in the linear superposition of O_3 and SC signals, and we return to it later.

Patterns of Vertical Temperature Change

Modelled and observed patterns of annual-mean zonal-mean temperature change as a function of latitude and height are shown in Fig. 1. The pattern of stratospheric cooling and tropospheric warming in C-TP (Fig. 1a) is in accord with previous modelling work[5-7] and represents the direct radiative signature of the change in CO_2. Maximum warming occurs in the tropical upper troposphere, and temperature changes are hemispherically symmetric. In contrast, both the S-TP (Fig. 1b) and SC-TP (Fig. 1c) signals show a hemispherically asymmetric response, with (respectively) increased cooling and reduced warming in the Northern Hemisphere, where anthropogenic sulphate aerosol forcing is largest[9,22]. The SC-TP integration (like C-TP) also shows the dipole structure of stratospheric cooling/tropospheric warming characteristic of CO_2 changes, whereas there is minimal stratospheric response in S-TP.

The C-HC and SC-HC transient results (Fig. 1d, e) have features which are qualitatively similar to the equilibrium response patterns from the corresponding TP experiments (Fig. 1a, c). Both types of experiment yield stratospheric cooling and tropospheric warming (C and SC) and reduced warming in the Northern Hemisphere (SC only). We return to this point later, because it is relevant to the issue of the usefulness of equilibrium signals in climate-change detection studies.

Vertical temperature changes due to stratospheric O_3 reduction (Fig. 1f) are characterized by stratospheric cooling, with maximum cooling at high latitudes in both hemispheres. Owing to dynamical effects, cooling occurs throughout the lower stratosphere, even at low latitudes where the imposed ozone changes are negligible[15,26]. The response is not hemispherically symmetric: stratospheric cooling that is statistically significant[15] occurs over a wider latitude range in the Northern Hemisphere than in the Southern Hemisphere. This is primarily due to a hemispheric asymmetry in the observed ozone changes. Some of the model–observed temperature differences in Fig. 1f and j, such as the warming above about 70 hPa poleward of 45°S, are probably related to the idealized altitudinal profile of ozone loss[26]. Other differences are due to the different time periods considered in the model experiment and in the observations.

然而，强迫因子的不确定性，特别是硫酸盐气溶胶效应的不确定性，使得这种缩放变得非常困难。为了绕开这些困难，我们选择了对温度变化的分布型而非振幅来进行比较统计。振幅差异的问题在 O_3 和 SC 信号的线性叠加方面非常重要，关于这一点我们稍后再作讨论。

垂直温度变化的分布型

模拟和实测的年均纬向平均温度变化随纬度和高度的分布情况见图 1。C-TP（图 1a）中平流层的降温变冷和对流层的变暖与之前的模拟研究结果[5-7]一致，并且它们代表着 CO_2 变化的直接辐射特征。最高的增温出现在热带对流层上部，温度变化在南北半球对称分布。与此相反，S-TP（图 1b）和 SC-TP（图 1c）信号则显示为半球不对称响应，在人为硫酸盐气溶胶强迫最大的北半球，两者分别表现为降温的加快和变暖的减缓[9,22]。SC-TP 积分（与 C-TP 类似）也表现出像 CO_2 变化导致的平流层降温而对流层变暖的偶极子结构，而 S-TP 中的平流层响应则最小。

从性质上来说，C-HC 和 SC-HC 的瞬变结果（图 1d 和 e）的特征与相应的 TP 实验（图 1a 和 c）中的平衡响应分布相似。两类实验的结果均为平流层变冷而对流层变暖（C 和 SC），并且在北半球呈较弱的变暖（仅 SC）。关于这一点我们稍后讨论，因为它与气候变化检测研究中平衡信号的可用性问题有关。

因平流层 O_3 减少而引起的垂直温度变化（图 1f）均以平流层的变冷为特征，且最大降温均出现在南北半球的高纬度地区。由于动力学效应，整个平流层底层都存在降温现象，即使在臭氧变化可忽略不计的低纬地区亦是如此[15,26]。不过这种响应在南北半球并不对称：统计上显著的平流层降温[15]在北半球发生的纬度范围要大于南半球。这主要是因为实测臭氧变化在南北半球表现为非对称分布。图 1f 和 j 中某些模拟与实测结果的温度变化差异，例如，在 45°S 以南的 70 hPa 以上区域的变暖，很可能与臭氧损耗的理想化的垂直剖面有关[26]。其他差异则是由模式实验和实测结果中的时段不同所致。

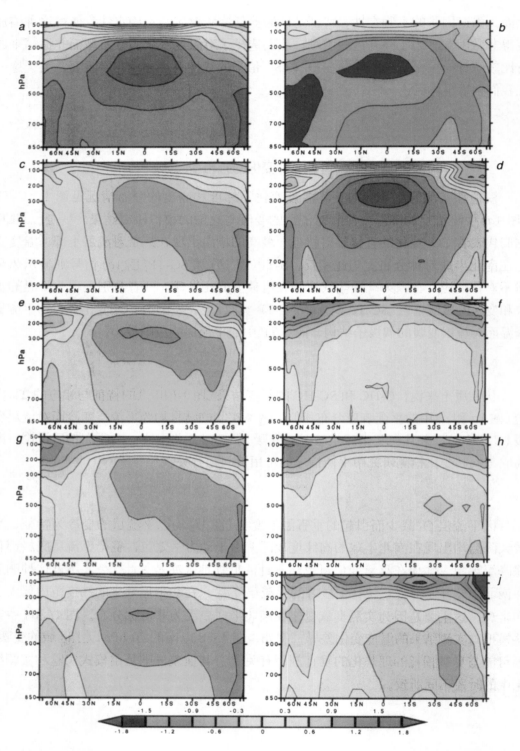

Fig. 1. Modelled and observed zonal-mean annually averaged changes (°C) in the thermal structure of the atmosphere. The equilibrium experiments by Taylor and Penner (TP)[9] simulate temperature changes for

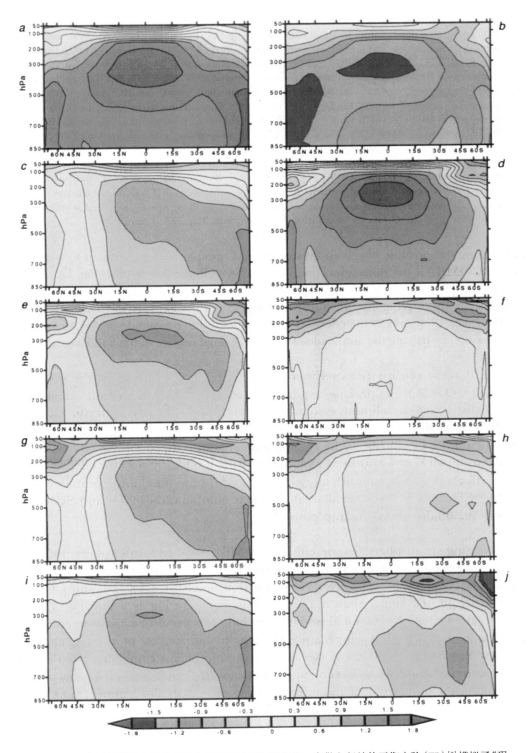

图1. 模拟和实测数据的大气热力结构的纬向平均年均变化。泰勒和彭纳的平衡实验(TP)[9]模拟了"现

nominal "present-day" levels of atmospheric CO_2 only (C-TP; *a*), anthropogenic sulphate aerosols only (S-TP; *b*), and combined forcing by CO_2+sulphate aerosols (SC-TP; *c*) relative to a control run with pre-industrial levels of CO_2 and no anthropogenic sulphur emissions. All TP integrations were at least 30 years in duration, and temperature-change signals were computed using averages over the last 20 years of the control run and each perturbation experiment. Patterns of the response to time-varying increases in greenhouse gases only (C-HC; *d*) and in greenhouse gases and aerosols (SC-HC; *e*) were taken from simulations performed with the Hadley Centre CGCM[10,20]. Temperature-change signals are the decadal averages of C-HC and SC-HC for the modelled "1990s" expressed relative to the respective C-HC and SC-HC averages over 1880-1920. The possible effects of stratospheric ozone reduction over the period 1979–90 (*f*) are from a recent equilibrium experiment by Ramaswamy *et al.*[15] The sensitivity studies COMB1 (SC-TP+O_3; *g*) and COMB2 ($\frac{1}{2}$ SC-TP+O_3; *h*) consider the possible effects of stratospheric O_3 depletion on the SC-TP signal. COMB3 ($\frac{1}{2}$ S-TP+C-TP; *i*) illustrates the sensitivity of model–observed pattern similarities to a possible overestimate of direct aerosol effects in TP. Observed changes (*j*) are radiosonde-based temperature measurements from the data set by Oort[8], and are expressed as total least-squares linear trends (°C) over the 25-year period extending from May 1963 to April 1988.

To examine the possible effects of stratospheric O_3 depletion we perform two sensitivity studies. COMB1 is the unweighted sum of the SC-TP and O_3 signals (Fig. 1*g*). COMB2 (Fig. 1*h*) explores uncertainties in the relative amplitudes of the SC-TP and O_3 signal components by halving the amplitude of the SC-TP signal. A third sensitivity study (COMB3; Fig. 1*i*), considers the effect of uncertainties in the magnitude of the aerosol forcing (and response) by halving the amplitude of the S-TP signal relative to the C-TP signal.

For any of these sensitivity experiments to be a realistic estimate of the response to combined CO_2+SO_4+O_3 forcing requires the relative weights of the individual forcings to be realistic and the climate system to respond quasi-linearly to perturbations. We have tested this linear superposition assumption and found it to be valid for combining the C-TP and S-TP signals[27]. The assumption cannot be tested for the HC experiments (owing to the lack of a transient experiment with forcing by aerosol effects alone) or for O_3 effects (because suitable model studies with individual and combined forcing by CO_2+SO_4+O_3 were not available). A linear combination of O_3 and SC effects is probably reasonable above the tropopause[28]

Incorporating stratospheric ozone effects (COMB1, COMB2) intensifies stratospheric cooling and reduces the height of the transition between stratospheric cooling and tropospheric warming[14]. However, the transition height in COMB1 and COMB2 is still roughly 50 hPa higher than in observations (compare Fig. 1*g*, *h* and Fig. 1*j*). There are several possible reasons for this. These include: uncertainties in observed O_3 losses and thus in the simulated temperature changes in the vicinity of the tropopause[15,26]; concerns regarding the validity of the linearity assumption for combining SC-TP and O_3 signals; and the (neglected) effects of upper tropospheric O_3 changes. The coarse vertical resolution of the observed data and most of the model signals also hampers more accurate determination of discrepancies in transition height.

The magnitude of direct anthropogenic sulphate aerosol forcing in TP (roughly $-0.9\,W\,m^{-2}$) is just above the upper end of the range estimated in recent reviews[29,30],

今"水平下，分别在仅含大气 CO_2（C-TP；a）、仅含人为硫酸盐气溶胶（S-TP；b）以及 CO_2 和硫酸盐气溶胶的综合强迫下（SC-TP；c）的情况下，相对于工业化以前的 CO_2 水平和无人为硫释放物为条件进行的对照模拟结果的温度变化。所有 TP 实验的积分长度都在 30 年以上，其温度变化信号是根据对照模拟结果和各个扰动实验得出的最后 20 年的平均值算出的。仅含温室气体时（C-HC；d）、温室气体和气溶胶共同作用下（SC-HC；e）两种情况随时间增加的响应分布都来自哈德利中心的 CGCM[10,20] 的模拟结果。图中所示温度变化信号为 1990 年代 C-HC 和 SC-HC 模拟结果的十年平均值，分别相对于 C-HC 和 SC-HC 实验在 1880~1920 年间的平均值的变化值。1979~1990 年间平流层臭氧减少带来的潜在效应（f）来自拉马斯瓦米等[15]新近的平衡实验。敏感性研究 COMB1（SC-TP+O_3；g）和 COMB2（$\frac{1}{2}$SC-TP+O_3；h）考虑了平流层臭氧损耗对 SC-TP 信号的可能影响。COMB3（$\frac{1}{2}$S-TP+C-TP；i）则阐明了模拟结果与实测分布之间的相似性对 TP 实验中直接气溶胶效应可能被高估的敏感度。实测变化（j）是来自奥尔特[8]的无线电探空仪温度测定结果，并以 1963 年 5 月到 1988 年 4 月这 25 年间总的最小二乘线性趋势表示（℃）。

为了检验平流层 O_3 损耗的潜在效应，我们实施了两项敏感性研究。COMB1 为 SC-TP 和 O_3 信号的非加权和（图 1g）。COMB2（图 1h）通过使 SC-TP 信号的振幅减半研究了 SC-TP 和 O_3 信号中各分量的相对振幅的不确定性。第三项敏感性研究（COMB3，图 1i）则通过令 S-TP 信号相对于 C-TP 信号的振幅减半对气溶胶强迫（和响应）的量级的不确定性作了评估。

要想使上述实验研究得到的 CO_2+SO_4+O_3 的综合强迫的响应接近真实情况，就要求各个强迫所占的比重接近实际并且气候系统对扰动的响应为准线性。我们对上述线性叠加假设作了检验，结果发现 C-TP 与 S-TP 信号的结合是有效的[27]。对于 HC 实验（因为缺少仅含气溶胶效应强迫的瞬变实验结果）和 O_3 效应（因为没有单个强迫和 CO_2+SO_4+O_3 综合强迫的合适的模式结果），无法对该假设作出检验。在对流层顶往上，O_3 与 SC 效应的线性叠加应该是合理的[28]。

纳入平流层臭氧效应后（COMB1 和 COM2），平流层的降温现象加强，而平流层降温与对流层变暖之间过渡层的高度减小[14]。不过，COMB1 和 COMB2 中过渡层的高度仍比实测值高出 50 hPa 左右（对比图 1g，h 和图 1j）。造成这种情况的可能原因有多个。其中包括：实测臭氧亏损值的不确定及其导致的模拟温度变化在对流层顶附近的不确定性[15,26]；关于 SC-TP 和 O_3 综合信号的线性假定的有效性考虑；以及（忽略掉的）对流层上层 O_3 变化的影响等。实测数据和多数模式模拟信号的垂直分辨率较低，也使得人们难以更精确地确定过渡层高度的差异。

TP 中直接人为硫酸盐气溶胶强迫的量级（约为 $-0.9\ \mathrm{W\cdot m^{-2}}$）虽然明显处于给定的硫酸盐气溶胶强迫总值（直接 + 间接）范围内，但却恰好高于最新综述中[29,30]所估

although clearly within the range given for total (direct+indirect) sulphate aerosol forcing. It is relevant in this regard that the hemispheric-scale patterns of forcing due to aerosol direct and indirect effects may be similar[31-34]. The effect in COMB3 of halving the temperature response in S-TP relative to C-TP is to reduce the interhemispheric asymmetry in the low- to mid-troposphere and enhance the temperature-change contrast between the stratosphere and troposphere (Fig. 1i).

Figure 1j shows observed temperature changes, expressed as linear trends over 1963–87. The observations show two prominent features: stratospheric cooling and tropospheric warming, and reduced warming in the Northern Hemisphere between 850 and 300 hPa. These have been documented in previous investigations[3,4,7,35]. The pattern of stratospheric cooling and tropospheric warming is common to the observations and all model signals shown in Fig. 1 (with the exception of the "ozone-only" and S-TP signals). In the lower atmosphere, it is clear that the observations are in better accord with combined greenhouse-gas and aerosol signals than with "CO_2-only" signals[10,11].

Model–Observed Pattern Similarity

To compare model and observed vertical temperature-change patterns we use a so-called "centred" correlation statistic[11], $R(t)$:

$$R(t) = \frac{\left[\sum_{x=1}^{n} (\Delta D(x,t) - \widehat{\Delta D}(t))(\Delta M(x) - \widehat{\Delta M})\right]}{[n s_D(t) s_M]} \tag{1}$$

ΔD and ΔM are temperature-change fields for observed data and model output, respectively, and x and t are discrete indices over space ($x = 1, \ldots n$, the combined latitude–height dimension of the radiosonde data) and time ($t = 1963, \ldots 1987$). Observed changes are anomalies relative to the average over 1963–73, and model changes are differences between time averages of perturbation and control experiments (see Fig. 1). The $\frown$ indicates a spatial average. The observed spatial variance $s_D^2(t)$ is

$$s_D^2(t) = \frac{\sum_{x=1}^{n} [\Delta D(x,t) - \widehat{\Delta D}(t)]^2}{n-1} \tag{2}$$

with the model spatial variance s_M^2 defined similarly.

If the observed time-varying patterns of temperature change are becoming increasingly similar to the model-predicted responses, the $R(t)$ statistic will show a sustained positive trend[36]. This trend is unlikely to be linear and monotonic, as the observations reflect a response to the real (as opposed to the modelled) anthropogenic forcing and to other

计范围的上限。与此相关的是由于直接和间接气溶胶效应引起的半球尺度上的强迫分布可能是类似[31-34]的。在 COMB3 中，将 S-TP 相对于 C-TP 的温度响应减半，目的是为了减少中低对流层中南北半球的不对称性，从而加强平流层和对流层之间温度变化的对比（图 1*i*）。

图 1*j* 所示为实测温度的变化情况，以 1963~1987 年间的线性变化趋势表示。实测结果显示出两个重要特征：平流层降温和对流层变暖；在北半球 850 hPa 到 300 hPa 之间较小的变暖趋势。这两点在之前的研究[3,4,7,35]中已经得到了证明。在实测值和所有模拟信号中平流层降温和对流层变暖的特征是共同的，如图 1 所示（"仅含臭氧效应"的信号和 S-TP 信号除外）。在低层大气中，综合了温室气体和气溶胶的模式信号要比"仅含 CO_2"的模式信号更接近于观测结果[10,11]。

模拟结果与实测分布型的相似性

为了比较模拟与实测的垂直温度变化分布特征，我们采用了一种所谓的"中心式"相关统计方法[11]，$R(t)$：

$$R(t) = \frac{\left[\sum_{x=1}^{n} \left(\Delta D(x,t) - \widehat{\Delta D}(t) \right) \left(\Delta M(x) - \widehat{\Delta M} \right) \right]}{\left[n s_{\mathrm{D}}(t) s_{\mathrm{M}} \right]} \tag{1}$$

其中 ΔD 和 ΔM 分别为实测数据和模式输出结果中的温度变化场，x 和 t 为它们在空间（$x = 1, \cdots, n$，为无线电探空仪数据的纬度和高度范围）和时间（$t = 1963, \cdots, 1987$）上的离散指数。实测变化数据是相对于 1963~1973 年间的平均值的异常值，而模拟出的变化为瞬变实验和对照实验的时间平均值的差异值（见图 1）。符号 $\frown$ 代表空间上的平均值。实测空间方差 $s_{\mathrm{D}}^2(t)$ 为

$$s_{\mathrm{D}}^2(t) = \frac{\sum_{x=1}^{n} \left[\left(\Delta D(x,t) - \widehat{\Delta D}(t) \right) \right]^2}{n-1} \tag{2}$$

模式结果中空间方差 s_{M}^2 的定义与此类似。

如果实测温度变化随时间的变化分布与模式预测出的响应越来越类似，则 $R(t)$ 统计量会表现为连续正向趋势[36]。然而，该趋势不可能是线性的，也不是单调的，因为实测值反映了对实际（与模拟结果形成对照）人为强迫以及模拟实验中未包含的

human-induced and natural forcings not included in the model experiments. Additionally, any overall $R(t)$ trend will be modulated by internally generated natural climate variability. There are two main issues of interest: whether trends in $R(t)$ could be due to natural internal variability alone, and whether they are different for different model signals.

For comparisons over 50–850 hPa (Fig. 2a), the behaviour of $R(t)$ is similar for all signals except S-TP: trends are positive over the full 25-year period, indicating an increasing expression of the model-predicted patterns in the observed annually averaged data. These similarities are due partly to the large-amplitude pattern of stratospheric cooling/ tropospheric warming common to all signals that incorporate CO_2 effects (see Fig. 1). Differences in the magnitude of this common pattern in the individual signals are reduced since they are scaled by different model spatial variances, s_M^2. Similarities in $R(t)$ are also related to the removal of different spatial mean values $(\widehat{\Delta M})$ from the model signal patterns, which has the effect of making the height of the transition from stratospheric cooling to tropospheric warming more similar in the individual signals.

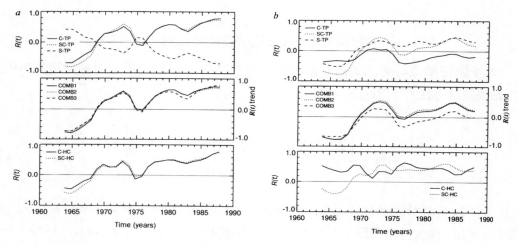

Fig. 2. Time series of centred pattern correlations, $R(t)$, between model-predicted and observed changes in zonal-mean latitude–height profiles of atmospheric temperature. For sources of model and observed data, refer to Fig. 1. Observed changes are expressed as a sequence of anomaly patterns spanning the period 1963–87, and were smoothed with a 5-term binomial filter to suppress variability on timescales shorter than a decade (for example, associated with ENSO events and the quasi-biennial oscillation)[11]. For each model experiment, one pattern characterizes the response to the imposed anthropogenic forcing (see Fig. 1). This fixed pattern is correlated with the observed time-varying spatial patterns. Results are for temperature-change patterns defined over the full vertical extent of the radiosonde data (50–850 hPa; a) and over the mid- to lower-troposphere only (500–850 hPa; b). The premise underlying the use of a centred correlation for attribution is that different "causes" (forcing mechanisms) have different response patterns. If one can demonstrate time-increasing correspondence between the observations and a model-predicted pattern of change, and show that correspondence exists at hemispheric or smaller spatial scales—not only at the surface, but also in the full three-dimensional structure of the atmosphere—then it is less likely that forcing mechanisms other than the ones being considered could match the predicted response pattern. The pattern correlations shown here were computed using annual averages and with pressure- and area-weighted data. Trends in $R(t)$ were relatively insensitive to the choice of averaging period for defining observed anomalies[11].

其他人为诱导因素和自然强迫的响应。此外，任何 $R(t)$ 的总趋势都会被内生的自然气候变化所调控。这里有两个主要的感兴趣的问题：一是 $R(t)$ 的趋势是否仅来自自然的内部变化，二是对不同的模式信号结果是否也不同。

对比了 50~850 hPa 之间的分布结果（图 2a），$R(t)$ 的变化趋势与除 S-TP 外的所有信号都很相似：此种情况在整整 25 年内表现出正的趋势，表明模式预测的分布型可以解释的实测年平均值部分逐渐增加。这种相似性的部分原因是平流层变冷或对流层变暖的大范围分布，这种分布对纳入 CO_2 影响后的所有信号都是很普遍的（见图 1）。因为结果都除以了不同模式的空间方差 s_M^2，故单个信号中的这种普遍分布型的量级差异会有所减少。$R(t)$ 的相似性也与从模式信号分布型中去除不同的空间平均值（$\widehat{\Delta M}$）有关，这会使得在单个的信号中，从平流层变冷向对流层变暖的转变高度更为相似。

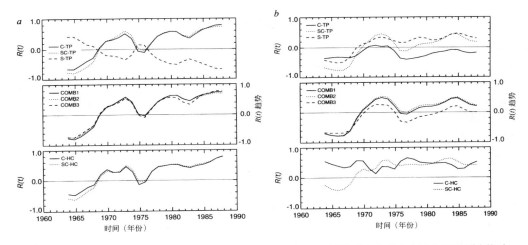

图 2. 大气温度的纬向平均纬度–高度剖面中模式预测数据和实测变化的中心式分布相关关系 $R(t)$ 的时间序列。模拟和实测数据的来源参见图 1。实测变化表示为 1963~1987 年间的一系列异常分布，这些数据经过了 5 次二项式的滤波，从而除去了时间尺度短于 10 年的那些变化（例如，与 ENSO 事件和准两年周期振荡有关的变化）[11]。对于每个模式实验，都有一种以施加其上的人为强迫响应为特征的分布（见图 1）。这种确定的分布与实测的随时间变化的空间分布有关。图中所示结果包括了无线电探空仪数据的全部垂直范围（50~850 hPa；a）和中低对流层（500~850 hPa；b）上的温度变化。采用中心式相关法找原因的前提是不同的“影响因素”（强迫机制）具有不同的响应分布。如果可以证明实测值与模式预测的变化分布之间的相关性随时间增长而增加，并且该相关性在半球尺度甚至更小空间上也存在——不仅仅是地表，而且在完整的三维大气结构中——那么，除了已经考虑到的因素以外，就不太可能有其他强迫机制与预测到的响应分布相匹配了。这里所给出的分布型相关是利用年平均值并对压力和面积作加权后计算出来的。$R(t)$ 的变化趋势对于确定实测异常值时取平均的时段的选择相对不敏感[11]。

To focus on hemispheric asymmetry differences in the various signals, we then restricted pattern comparisons to 500–850 hPa (Fig. 2b). There is now a clear distinction between CO_2-only signals and signals that additionally incorporate aerosol effects. Annual $R(t)$ time series show overall positive trends for the SC-TP, SC-HC, S-TP, COMB1 and COMB2 signals, but little or no trend for the CO_2-only signals and a smaller positive trend for COMB3. The primary reason for this discrimination is the interhemispheric asymmetry common to the observations and the signals with combined CO_2+aerosol forcing. This common asymmetry occurs also in DJF and JJA.

Although visibly apparent (Fig. 1), the benefit of incorporating stratospheric O_3 effects is not clearly shown in the $R(t)$ results. It becomes more obvious in an uncentred statistic, which retains the spatial means of the two fields being compared. This, however, has other limitations in the context of attributing observed changes to a specific causal factor[11,37].

Trend Significance

Are the positive $R(t)$ trends in Fig. 2 unusually large relative to the trends we might expect in the absence of any anthropogenic forcing—that is, due to natural variability of the climate system? To address this issue, we use (internally generated) natural variability information from multi-century CGCM control experiments performed at the Hadley Centre (HC)[10], the Max-Planck Institute for Meteorology in Hamburg (MPI)[38] and GFDL[39]. All integrations were run with no changes in natural external or anthropogenic forcings.

A number of studies have attempted to assess how reliably these three CGCMs simulate real-world natural variability[39-42]. On timescales of 10–30 years there is good agreement between the GFDL and HC spectra and the observed spectrum for global-mean annually averaged near-surface temperature[39,43]. Comparisons of model and observed patterns of surface temperature variability show that similarities exist on timescales of 5–10 years, although there are differences on shorter timescales[39,41,44].

More rigorous validation of the model-estimated internal variability of vertical temperature changes is difficult because the radiosonde record is short and represents a convolution of natural variability and anthropogenic effects. For the purposes of this investigation we must therefore assume that the CGCMs used here provide credible estimates of the spectrum and patterns of internal natural variability on timescales ranging from 10 to 25 years. Our use of noise information from multiple control runs provides an indication of the robustness of our significance estimates to uncertainties in the model-estimated noise.

In the significance-testing procedure[11], each model signal pattern (with the exception of the O_3 and S-TP signals) is correlated with the sequences of vertical temperature-change

为了集中研究各种信号中南北半球的不对称性差异，我们将分布型的比较限制在 500~850 hPa 之间的结果（图 2b）。现在仅含 CO_2 的信号与额外考虑了气溶胶效应的信号之间有明显的差别。年际 $R(t)$ 时间序列显示，SC-TP、SC-HC、S-TP、COMB1 和 COMB2 信号总体呈正趋势，而在仅含 CO_2 的信号中则趋势很小或没有趋势，以及在 COMB3 中的正趋势也小得多。出现上述差异的主要原因是，实测值以及综合考虑了 CO_2 和气溶胶强迫的信号通常具有两半球间的不对称性。这种常见的不对称性也发生于 DJF 和 JJA 期间。

虽然将平流层 O_3 效应考虑在内后看上去有明显的改善（图 1），但在 $R(t)$ 结果中并未有清楚的表现。在保留空间平均值的非中心统计检验中，加臭氧强迫与不加臭氧强迫的差异却是明显的。不过，这种方法在将实测变化与具体的因果因素进行归因时又存在其他的局限性[11,37]。

趋势的显著性

图 2 中正的 $R(t)$ 趋势相对于我们在不考虑任何人为因素时的预期值——即由气候系统的自然变化所形成的趋势——大很多吗？为了解答这一问题，我们采用了由哈德利中心（HC）[10]、德国汉堡的马克斯－普朗克气象研究所（MPI）[38] 和 GFDL[39] 实施的数百年尺度上的 CGCM 对照实验得到的（内生）自然变化信息。所有积分都是在不改变自然的外部变化或人为因素的前提下进行的。

已有大量研究尝试对上述三个 CGCM 模拟现实世界自然变化实验的可靠性作出评估[39-42]。在 10~30 年的时间尺度上 GFDL 和 HC 谱与全球平均年均近地表温度的实测曲线之间有很好的一致性[39,43]。对比近地表温度变化的模拟与实测分布显示，两者在 5~10 年的时间尺度上具有相似性，而在更短的时间尺度上则存在差异[39,41,44]。

由于无线电探空仪记录较短并且它代表了自然变化和人为影响的综合作用结果，所以很难对模式研究得到的垂直温度变化的内在变化给出更准确的估值。因此，为达到本研究的目的，我们必须假定这里所采用的 CGCM 模型提供出的 10~25 年时间尺度上的内生自然变化的范围及分布型是值得信赖的。利用多个对照实验运行得出的噪声信息显示，我们的显著性评估结果对模式评估出的噪声中的不确定性是稳健的。

在显著性检验过程[11]中，每一个模式信号分布型（O_3 和 S-TP 信号除外）都与三个 CGCM 对照实验模拟的垂直温度变化型序列作了对比。由此获得的时间序列为我

patterns simulated in each of the three CGCM control runs. The resulting time series provide information on the behaviour of the $R(t)$ statistic in the absence of external forcing. By fitting 10-, 15-, and 25-year linear trends to overlapping chunks of these "natural" $R(t)$ time series, we generate sampling distributions of unforced $R(t)$ trends. The "signal" trends in $R(t)$ over the past 10 to 25 years (Fig. 2a, b) are then compared with these sampling distributions to determine whether changes in model–observed pattern similarity with time are statistically unusual (Fig. 3).

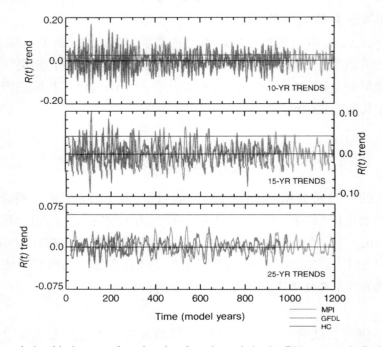

Fig. 3. The relationship between forced and unforced trends in the $R(t)$ pattern similarity statistic. "Unforced" $R(t)$ time series were computed by correlating the fixed pattern of annually-averaged vertical temperature changes in the SC-TP experiment (Fig. 1c) with the time-varying temperature-change patterns form the 310-, 1,000- and 1,260-year HC, GFDL, and MPI control integrations (respectively). Model anomaly patterns were defined relative to the overall time-mean of each control run, and were filtered in the same way as the observations (see Fig. 2). The figure shows the result of fitting overlapping linear trends to 10-, 15- and 25-year segments of the unforced $R(t)$ time series, and then plotting the magnitude (at any point in time) of the linear trend in $R(t)$. The overlap between trends is by all but one year. This yields sampling distributions of all possible unforced $R(t)$ trends for the three selected timescales. The purple horizontal lines in each panel give the magnitude of the $R(t)$ trend for the comparison of the SC-TP signal with observations over 1978–87, 1973–87 and 1963–87 (see Fig. 2a). All trends are expressed as the change in $R(t)$ per year. The level of time-increasing similarity between the observed vertical temperature-change patterns and the SC signal over the last 25 years is highly unusual relative to the unforced 25-year $R(t)$ trends estimated from all three control integrations. In contrast, recent 10-year trends in $R(t)$ are not unusual occurrences. Note that the magnitude of the unforced $R(t)$ trends decreases as the length of $R(t)$ trends increases. The results shown here are for annually averaged data and for temperature-change patterns defined over 50–850 hPa. $R(t)$ trends are plotted on the central year of the trend.

For model–observed comparisons over 50–850 hPa, the positive 25-year $R(t)$ trends for all signals considered (CO_2-only, CO_2+aerosols, and the three sensitivity studies)

们提供了没有外部强迫时 $R(t)$ 统计结果的特征信息。通过将 10 年、15 年和 25 年的线性趋势与上述"自然"$R(t)$ 时间序列的重叠部分相拟合，我们生成了非强迫 $R(t)$ 趋势的抽样分布。然后，将上述过去 $10 \sim 25$ 年间 $R(t)$ 的信号趋势（图 $2a$ 和 b）与上述抽样分布相比较，从而确定模拟与实测分布型的相似性随时间的变化是否具有统计学意义（图 3）。

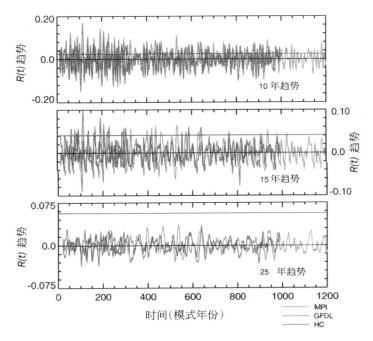

图 3. $R(t)$ 分布的相似性统计量中强迫趋势与非强迫趋势之间的关系。"非强迫"$R(t)$ 时间序列是通过将 SC-TP 实验中年均垂直温度变化的固定分布型（图 $1c$）分别与构成 310 年，1,000 年和 1,260 年的 HC、GFDL 和 MPI 对照积分相关得到。模拟结果的异常分布是相对每个对照实验的总时间平均值来定义的，并采用了与实测结果相同的滤波方法（见图 2）。图中给出了非强迫 $R(t)$ 时间序列在近 10 年、15 年和 25 年上线性趋势重叠部分的拟合结果，同时还画出了 $R(t)$ 线性趋势的量级（任意时间点）。各趋势之间的重叠部分只有一年。由此得出了所选三个时间尺度上所有可能非强迫 $R(t)$ 趋势的采样分布。各图中的紫色水平线代表 $R(t)$ 趋势的量级，用于 SC-TP 信号与实测信号在 $1978 \sim 1987$、$1973 \sim 1987$ 和 $1963 \sim 1987$ 年间的比较（见图 $2a$）。所有趋势都以每年的 $R(t)$ 变化表示。过去 25 年里，实测垂直温度变化分布型与 SC 信号的相似性随时间而递增的水平远远高于所有三个对照实验得到的这 25 年中的非强迫 $R(t)$ 结果。相反，$R(t)$ 在近 10 年中的变化趋势则未见异常。值得注意的是，非强迫 $R(t)$ 趋势的量级随 $R(t)$ 趋势长度的增加而减小。这里所给出的结果都是指年均数据，并且均为针对 $50 \sim 850$ hPa 之间的温度变化型而言。图中所示 $R(t)$ 趋势都是在趋势变化的中间年份上画出的。

对于 $50 \sim 850$ hPa 之间模拟–实测特征的对比结果，所有信号（仅 CO_2、$CO_2 +$ 气溶胶以及三项敏感性研究）在 25 年里的正 $R(t)$ 趋势都与非强迫趋势存在显著差异

differ significantly from unforced trends (Table 1a). This result shows that the observed pattern of change over 1963–87 is similar to model-predicted signals that incorporate CO_2 effects, whereas "natural" patterns of change over 25-year periods are not[45].

Table 1. Significance test results

Season	Signal	Trend lengths (years)								
		10			15			25		
		MPI	GFDL	HC	MPI	GFDL	HC	MPI	GFDL	HC
a 50–850 hPa										
DJF	C-TP	0.01	0.00	0.05	0.00	0.00	0.01	0.00	0.00	0.00
	C-HC	0.06	0.03	0.21	0.02	0.00	0.09	0.01	0.00	0.02
	SC-TP	0.02	0.02	0.12	0.00	0.00	0.02	0.00	0.00	0.00
	SC-HC	0.07	0.02	0.23	0.02	0.00	0.11	0.00	0.00	0.01
	COMB1	0.02	0.04	0.05	0.00	0.00	0.00	0.00	0.00	0.00
	COMB2	0.02	0.05	0.03	0.00	0.00	0.00	0.00	0.00	0.00
	COMB3	0.01	0.00	0.05	0.00	0.00	0.01	0.00	0.00	0.00
JJA	C-TP	0.08	0.20	0.25	0.02	0.08	0.16	0.00	0.00	0.00
	C-HC	0.23	0.35	0.39	0.07	0.17	0.22	0.00	0.00	0.00
	SC-TP	0.10	0.17	0.24	0.07	0.10	0.20	0.00	0.00	0.00
	SC-HC	0.13	0.25	0.32	0.02	0.10	0.17	0.00	0.00	0.00
	COMB1	0.10	0.18	0.20	0.06	0.10	0.14	0.00	0.00	0.00
	COMB2	0.10	0.20	0.20	0.05	0.11	0.14	0.00	0.00	0.00
	COMB3	0.10	0.19	0.24	0.05	0.09	0.15	0.00	0.00	0.00
ANN	C-TP	0.16	0.24	0.33	0.01	0.01	0.11	0.00	0.00	0.00
	C-HC	0.20	0.26	0.36	0.04	0.04	0.19	0.00	0.00	0.01
	SC-TP	0.23	0.27	0.38	0.04	0.03	0.15	0.00	0.00	0.00
	SC-HC	0.20	0.26	0.36	0.05	0.04	0.18	0.00	0.00	0.00
	COMB1	0.26	0.34	0.38	0.04	0.04	0.10	0.00	0.00	0.00
	COMB2	0.30	0.38	0.38	0.03	0.05	0.07	0.00	0.00	0.00
	COMB3	0.15	0.21	0.33	0.02	0.01	0.13	0.00	0.00	0.00
b 500–850 hPa										
DJF	C-TP	0.08	0.15	0.20	0.06	0.12	0.15	0.08	0.12	0.25
	C-HC	0.55	0.53	0.53	0.49	0.51	0.48	0.20	0.28	0.27
	SC-TP	0.29	0.37	0.40	0.30	0.38	0.36	0.01	0.04	0.02
	SC-HC	0.48	0.50	0.47	0.51	0.52	0.50	0.00	0.02	0.01
	COMB1	0.20	0.29	0.29	0.32	0.37	0.36	0.00	0.03	0.01
	COMB2	0.16	0.26	0.21	0.33	0.39	0.37	0.00	0.02	0.01
	COMB3	0.10	0.17	0.19	0.12	0.21	0.18	0.07	0.11	0.09

（表 1*a*）。该结果表明，1963~1987 年间实测变化分布型与考虑了 CO_2 效应的模式预测信号相似，而为期 25 年的"自然"变化分布型则不然[45]。

表 1. 显著性检验结果

季节	信号	趋势长度（年）								
		10			15			25		
		MPI	GFDL	HC	MPI	GFDL	HC	MPI	GFDL	HC
		a 50~850 hPa								
DJF	C-TP	0.01	0.00	0.05	0.00	0.00	0.01	0.00	0.00	0.00
	C-HC	0.06	0.03	0.21	0.02	0.00	0.09	0.01	0.00	0.02
	SC-TP	0.02	0.02	0.12	0.00	0.00	0.02	0.00	0.00	0.00
	SC-HC	0.07	0.02	0.23	0.02	0.00	0.11	0.00	0.00	0.01
	COMB1	0.02	0.04	0.05	0.00	0.00	0.00	0.00	0.00	0.00
	COMB2	0.02	0.05	0.03	0.00	0.00	0.00	0.00	0.00	0.00
	COMB3	0.01	0.00	0.05	0.00	0.00	0.01	0.00	0.00	0.00
JJA	C-TP	0.08	0.20	0.25	0.02	0.08	0.16	0.00	0.00	0.00
	C-HC	0.23	0.35	0.39	0.07	0.17	0.22	0.00	0.00	0.00
	SC-TP	0.10	0.17	0.24	0.07	0.10	0.20	0.00	0.00	0.00
	SC-HC	0.13	0.25	0.32	0.02	0.10	0.17	0.00	0.00	0.00
	COMB1	0.10	0.18	0.20	0.06	0.10	0.14	0.00	0.00	0.00
	COMB2	0.10	0.20	0.20	0.05	0.11	0.14	0.00	0.00	0.00
	COMB3	0.10	0.19	0.24	0.05	0.09	0.15	0.00	0.00	0.00
ANN	C-TP	0.16	0.24	0.33	0.01	0.01	0.11	0.00	0.00	0.00
	C-HC	0.20	0.26	0.36	0.04	0.04	0.19	0.00	0.00	0.01
	SC-TP	0.23	0.27	0.38	0.04	0.03	0.15	0.00	0.00	0.00
	SC-HC	0.20	0.26	0.36	0.05	0.04	0.18	0.00	0.00	0.00
	COMB1	0.26	0.34	0.38	0.04	0.04	0.10	0.00	0.00	0.00
	COMB2	0.30	0.38	0.38	0.03	0.05	0.07	0.00	0.00	0.00
	COMB3	0.15	0.21	0.33	0.02	0.01	0.13	0.00	0.00	0.00
		b 500~850 hPa								
DJF	C-TP	0.08	0.15	0.20	0.06	0.12	0.15	0.08	0.12	0.25
	C-HC	0.55	0.53	0.53	0.49	0.51	0.48	0.20	0.28	0.27
	SC-TP	0.29	0.37	0.40	0.30	0.38	0.36	0.01	0.04	0.02
	SC-HC	0.48	0.50	0.47	0.51	0.52	0.50	0.00	0.02	0.01
	COMB1	0.20	0.29	0.29	0.32	0.37	0.36	0.00	0.03	0.01
	COMB2	0.16	0.26	0.21	0.33	0.39	0.37	0.00	0.02	0.01
	COMB3	0.10	0.17	0.19	0.12	0.21	0.18	0.07	0.11	0.09

Continued

Season	Signal	Trend lengths (years)								
		10			15			25		
		MPI	GFDL	HC	MPI	GFDL	HC	MPI	GFDL	HC
		b 500–850 hPa								
JJA	C-TP	0.34	0.46	0.43	0.45	0.48	0.43	0.55	0.51	0.44
	C-HC	0.81	0.66	0.63	0.50	0.52	0.46	0.53	0.51	0.52
	SC-TP	0.17	0.28	0.31	0.18	0.29	0.28	0.02	0.11	0.10
	SC-HC	0.20	0.31	0.31	0.22	0.33	0.31	0.01	0.04	0.06
	COMB1	0.18	0.28	0.30	0.20	0.29	0.28	0.02	0.11	0.09
	COMB2	0.20	0.28	0.29	0.21	0.31	0.28	0.03	0.12	0.09
	COMB3	0.19	0.33	0.36	0.21	0.33	0.33	0.07	0.16	0.13
ANN	C-TP	0.24	0.37	0.36	0.32	0.43	0.41	0.27	0.40	0.37
	C-HC	0.66	0.57	0.54	0.61	0.55	0.52	0.44	0.47	0.43
	SC-TP	0.29	0.41	0.38	0.22	0.31	0.31	0.00	0.03	0.04
	SC-HC	0.54	0.49	0.48	0.47	0.50	0.49	0.00	0.02	0.02
	COMB1	0.33	0.42	0.40	0.27	0.35	0.34	0.00	0.02	0.03
	COMB2	0.37	0.44	0.41	0.32	0.38	0.37	0.00	0.02	0.00
	COMB3	0.19	0.35	0.34	0.21	0.34	0.33	0.02	0.08	0.06

Significance levels (*p*-values) for seasonal and annual vertical temperature-change signals from the TP and HC experiments with forcing by CO_2 only and CO_2+aerosols and from the three sensitivity studies (COMB1, COMB2, COMB3). The first column gives the season of interest, while the second column indicates the experiment from which the signal pattern was taken. The remaining columns give the model experiments used to obtain natural variability estimates (on three different timescales). The signals of interest are the linear trends for the most recent 10, 15 and 25 years of the $R(t)$ time series shown in Fig. 2*a* and *b*—that is, the trends over 1978–87, 1973–87, and 1963–87. These trends provide information on the degree of time-increasing pattern similarity between the observations and the model simulations. Distributions of "unforced" $R(t)$ trends on 10-, 15- and 25-year timescales were generated as described in Fig. 3. Significance levels were then computed by comparing the "signal" $R(t)$ trends with the appropriate sampling distributions for unforced trends[11]. Shaded boxes denote results that achieve significance at the 5% level or better. In these cases, the time-increasing similarity between model signal patterns and observations is unlikely to be due to (model estimated) internally-generated natural variability. Results are for model–observed comparisons over 50–850 hPa (*a*) and over 500–850 hPa (*b*).

On shorter timescales (10 and 15 years) signal-to-noise ratios decrease and significance results show a seasonal dependence, with fewer significant trends for both JJA and annually averaged data. There is also a dependence on the CGCM used to estimate noise properties, with higher noise levels (see Fig. 3) and fewer significant results for noise estimates obtained from the HC control run. The reverse applies for the MPI noise estimates. The 10- and 15-year results show why natural variability makes it difficult to evaluate the significance of short timescale trends, such as the lower tropospheric temperature changes estimated since 1979 from the satellite-based Microwave Sounding Unit[46,47].

续表

季节	信号	趋势长度（年）								
		10			15			25		
		MPI	GFDL	HC	MPI	GFDL	HC	MPI	GFDL	HC
		b 500~850 hPa								
JJA	C-TP	0.34	0.46	0.43	0.45	0.48	0.43	0.55	0.51	0.44
	C-HC	0.81	0.66	0.63	0.50	0.52	0.46	0.53	0.51	0.52
	SC-TP	0.17	0.28	0.31	0.18	0.29	0.28	0.02	0.11	0.10
	SC-HC	0.20	0.31	0.31	0.22	0.33	0.31	0.01	0.04	0.06
	COMB1	0.18	0.28	0.30	0.20	0.29	0.28	0.02	0.11	0.09
	COMB2	0.20	0.28	0.29	0.21	0.31	0.28	0.03	0.12	0.09
	COMB3	0.19	0.33	0.36	0.21	0.33	0.33	0.07	0.16	0.13
ANN	C-TP	0.24	0.37	0.36	0.32	0.43	0.41	0.27	0.40	0.37
	C-HC	0.66	0.57	0.54	0.61	0.55	0.52	0.44	0.47	0.43
	SC-TP	0.29	0.41	0.38	0.22	0.31	0.31	0.00	0.03	0.04
	SC-HC	0.54	0.49	0.48	0.47	0.50	0.49	0.00	0.02	0.03
	COMB1	0.33	0.42	0.40	0.27	0.35	0.34	0.00	0.02	0.03
	COMB2	0.37	0.44	0.41	0.32	0.38	0.37	0.00	0.02	0.00
	COMB3	0.19	0.35	0.34	0.21	0.34	0.33	0.02	0.08	0.06

在仅有 CO_2 和 CO_2＋气溶胶强迫的 TP 和 HC 实验中以及三项敏感性研究（COMB1、COMB2、COM3）中的季节和年际垂直温度变化信号的显著性水平（p 值）。第一列表示研究季节，第二列为所提取的信号分布型来源的实验。其余各列所示为用以获得自然变化估计值的模拟实验（三种不同时间尺度）。图 2a 和 b 所示的是最近的 10 年、15 年和 25 年的 $R(t)$ 时间序列的线性趋势，即 1978~1987 年、1973~1987 年和 1963~1987 年的三个时段内的趋势。这些变化趋势提供的信息从一定程度上说明，模式模拟结果与实测分布之间的相似性随时间的增长而提高。生成的 $R(t)$ 在 10、15 和 25 年的时间尺度上的"非强迫"分布趋势见图 3。随后通过对比各"信号"的 $R(t)$ 趋势和非强迫趋势的取样分布计算出显著性水平[11]。阴影框表示显著性水平达 5% 或更高。在这些例子中，模式信号分布与实测值之间的相似性随时间增长而提高应该并非由（模式预测的）内生自然变化所致。表中所列结果包含了 50~850 hPa(a) 和 500~850 hPa(b) 之间模式与实测值的对比结果。

在较短的时间尺度上（10 年和 15 年），信噪比有所降低，并且显著性结果也具有季节依赖性，同时 JJA 和年均数据中的显著性趋势较少。另外，研究噪声性质时对采用的 CGCM 也具有依赖性，HC 对照实验结果中噪音信号越强（见图 3），显著性也越低。对于 MPI 噪声估计的结果则相反。10 年和 15 年时间尺度上的结果显示了自然变化为什么使得短期趋势的显著性评估变得困难的原因，例如 1979 年以来通过星载微波探测装置数据对低对流层温度变化的估计[46,47]。

Restricting pattern comparisons to 500–850 hPa yields a clear discrimination between the CO_2-only signals and signals that incorporate aerosol effects (Table 1b). In DJF and in the annually averaged data, the 25-year $R(t)$ signal trends are highly significant for the SC-TP, SC-HC, COMB1 and COMB2 signals, but not for COMB3 (except for annually averaged data relative to the MPI noise) or the CO_2-only signals. As noted above, this result arises mainly from the relatively lower Northern Hemisphere warming that is common to the observations and the combined forcing signals. Again, none of the shorter-timescale trends in $R(t)$ achieve significance at the 5% level or better.

Equilibrium and Transient Signal Similarity

We have shown above that the TP equilibrium and HC transient signals yield very similar detection results when compared with the observed radiosonde data. This does not necessarily signify that the TP and HC signals are *themselves* correlated. Such similarity between equilibrium and transient signal patterns is implicitly assumed in any detection study that makes use of equilibrium signals[48]. To test this assumption in a rigorous way would require signal estimates from both types of experiment performed with the same model. These were not available here. We gain some indication of the similarity between equilibrium and transient results by computing pattern correlations (see equation (1)) between the TP and HC signals over the 50–850 hPa and 500–850 hPa domains. For the full vertical domain, the key correlations for annually averaged data (and for HC signals that are decadal averages for the 1990s) are $R\{C\text{-}TP\text{:}C\text{-}HC\} = 0.87$; $R\{SC\text{-}TP\text{:}SC\text{-}HC\} = 0.85$. For the low- to mid-troposphere the key result is $R\{SC\text{-}TP\text{:}SC\text{-}HC\} = 0.61$. Note, however, that the CO_2-only signals in the TP and HC experiments are uncorrelated over 500–850 hPa ($R\{C\text{-}TP\text{:}C\text{-}HC\} = -0.05$).

A further assumption underlying our detection strategy is that the transient signal is relatively stable with time over the period relevant for a comparison with observations[48]. We tested this by computing correlations between decadally averaged HC signal patterns for the modelled "1980s" and "1990s" $R\{C\text{-}HC80\text{:}C\text{-}HC90\} = 0.97$; $R\{SC\text{-}HC80\text{:}SC\text{-}HC90\} = 0.98$ (for 50–850 hPa) and $R\{SC\text{-}HC80\text{:}SC\text{-}HC90\} = 0.93$ (for 500–850 hPa).

These results illustrate that the signal components of most interest here—stratospheric cooling/tropospheric warming (in experiments that incorporate CO_2 effects) and hemispheric-scale temperature asymmetry (in experiments that include aerosol effects)—are similar in the TP and HC experiments and are relatively stable over the time period of the HC integrations relevant for comparison with the radiosonde data. We note, however, that these findings are not necessarily of general applicability to different models, climate variables and geographical domains.

将限定在 500~850 hPa 范围内的形态分布进行对比发现，在仅含 CO_2 的信号和同时考虑了气溶胶的信号之间存在明显差异（表 1b）。在 DJF 和年均数据中，SC-TP、SC-HC、COMB1 和 COMB2 信号在 25 年的 $R(t)$ 信号趋势均具有很高的显著性，而 COMB3（除年均数据相对于 MPI 噪声以外）和仅含 CO_2 的信号则不然。如前所述，该结果主要是由于在实测数据和综合强迫信号中，北半球变暖的层位相对较低所致。而且，$R(t)$ 中没有一个更短时间尺度上的趋势能达到 5% 或以上的显著性水平。

平衡信号和瞬变信号的相似性

前文我们已经证明，当与实测无线电探空仪数据相比较时，TP 平衡信号和 HC 瞬变信号产生的检测结果非常相似。这并不表示 TP 和 HC 信号**本身**具有相关性。平衡信号与瞬变信号变化分布之间的这种相似性已经暗含在采用了平衡信号的检测研究中[48]。为了能够严格检验该假设，需要有来自相同模式的两类实验得出的信号评估结果。而这一条件在这里我们无法达到。我们通过计算 50~850 hPa 和 500~850 hPa 上 TP 与 HC 信号间的分布型的相关性（见方程（1）），获得了一些平衡信号与瞬变信号结果的相似性指征。在全部垂直范围内，年均数据（以及 20 世纪 90 年代 HC 信号的 10 年平均值）的主要相关关系为 $R\{C\text{-}TP:C\text{-}HC\} = 0.87$；$R\{SC\text{-}TP:SC\text{-}HC\} = 0.85$。对于中－低层对流层，关键结果为 $R\{SC\text{-}TP:SC\text{-}HC\} = 0.61$。不过需要注意的是，在 500~850 hPa 之间，TP 和 HC 实验中仅包含 CO_2 的信号没有相关性（$R\{C\text{-}TP:C\text{-}HC\} = -0.05$）。

在我们的检验方法中暗含的另一项假设是，在与实测值进行比较的时段上，瞬变信号随时间变化相对更稳定[48]。我们通过计算 HC 信号分布型在 20 世纪 80 年代和 20 世纪 90 年代的模拟结果的 10 年平均值之间的相关性对此作了检验，其相关系分别为 $R\{C\text{-}HC80:C\text{-}HC90\} = 0.97$，$R\{SC\text{-}HC80:SC\text{-}HC90\} = 0.98$（50~850 hPa 之间）和 $R\{SC\text{-}HC80:SC\text{-}HC90\} = 0.93$（500~850 hPa 之间）。

上述结果证明，本文研究的大多数信号分量——平流层降温、对流层变暖（考虑了 CO_2 效应的实验中）以及半球尺度上的温度不对称性（包含气溶胶效应的实验中）——在 TP 和 HC 实验中都很相似，并且在 HC 积分的时间段上与无线电探空仪数据相比较相对比较稳定。不过我们需要注意，上述发现不见得通用于不同模式、不同气候变量和不同的地理区域。

Conclusions

Our results suggest that the similarities between observed and model-predicted changes in the zonal-mean vertical patterns of temperature change over 1963–87 are unlikely to have resulted from natural internally generated variability of the climate system. This conclusion holds for pattern comparisons over 50–850 hPa, which focus on the large-amplitude signal of stratospheric cooling and tropospheric warming, and for comparisons over 500–850 hPa, which emphasize hemispheric-scale temperature asymmetries in the lower atmosphere. Stratospheric cooling and tropospheric warming are common to the observations and all signals that incorporate CO_2 effects, whereas hemispheric asymmetry is an observed feature that is found only in model experiments that incorporate aerosol effects.

The main uncertainties in our work relate to:

(1) Estimates of the relative magnitudes and spatial and temporal evolution of the different forcings[29,30], including those human factors represented here (greenhouse gases, direct sulphate aerosol effects and stratospheric ozone), those not specifically represented here (such as indirect aerosol effects[31,32,49], other anthropogenic aerosols[50-52], tropospheric ozone and other non-CO_2 greenhouse gases[53]), and purely natural forcings (for example, variations in solar output and volcanic aerosol loadings).

(2) The simulated response to forcing, including model-dependent factors such as global and regional sensitivity, which in turn depend on model parametrizations (for example, for clouds, which directly affect global sensitivity[54], and for oceanic vertical mixing, which may affect interhemispheric asymmetry).

(3) The realism of CGCM-derived estimates of natural internal variability on decadal and longer timescales[55], and the neglect of the variability arising from natural external forcings.

(4) The existence of time-varying instrumental biases in the radiosonde data, and their incomplete spatial coverage[7,8,56,57].

Where possible, we have attempted to explore the sensitivity of our principal results to these uncertainties. For comparisons focusing on the pattern of stratospheric cooling and tropospheric warming, we have shown that the significant 25-year $R(t)$ trends are seasonally robust. They are insensitive to uncertainties in the signals examined here (as shown by our use of equilibrium and transient signals from models with differences in physical processes and in their treatment of direct aerosol effects), in the magnitude of the direct aerosol forcing (as shown by COMB3), and in the incorporation of stratospheric O_3 effects (as shown by COMB1 and COMB2). Finally, they are robust to uncertainties in the CGCM estimates of natural internal climate variability used here—to achieve

886

结　论

本文研究结果表明，1963~1987 年间温度变化的纬向平均垂直分布型的实测值与模式预测值之间的相似性可能并不是由气候系统内生的自然变化引起的。无论是对于强调平流层降温和对流层变暖的大振幅信号的 50~850 hPa 之间的分布型比较还是强调半球尺度上低层大气的 500~850 hPa 的温度非对称变化的比较，该结论都是成立的。对于实测结果和所有将 CO_2 效应考虑在内的模拟信号，平流层降温和对流层变暖都很常见；而观测到的半球尺度非对称特征则仅在包含气溶胶效应的模拟实验中才出现。

本研究的不确定性主要与下列几项有关：

（1）对不同强迫因子的相对量级及其时空演化的估计[29,30]。这些强迫因子包括本文已提到的各种人为因素（温室气体、硫酸盐气溶胶的直接影响以及平流层臭氧），本文并未明确指出的因素（例如气溶胶的间接效应[31,32,39]、其他人为成因的气溶胶[50-52]、对流层臭氧以及其他非 CO_2 的温室气体[53] 等）和纯自然强迫（例如，太阳辐射输出和火山气溶胶浓度的变化）。

（2）对强迫模拟的响应。这包括模式依赖的因素，如全球和区域敏感度等，而这些因素反过来又取决于模式参数（如，云层参数，它可以直接影响全球敏感度[54]；以及海洋垂直混合参数，它可能影响到半球间的非对称性）。

（3）根据 CGCM 模式得到的十年甚至更长时间尺度[55]上的内部自然变化估计值的真实性，以及对由外部自然强迫引起的变化的忽略。

（4）无线电探空仪数据中存在的随时间变化的仪器偏差，及其空间覆盖范围的不完整性[7,8,56,57]。

在条件允许的地方，我们已试着探讨了本文的主要结果对这些不确定性的敏感性。对关于平流层降温和对流层变暖分布型的对比结果，我们已经证明，显著的 25 年 $R(t)$ 趋势具有季节性的稳健性。它们对本文研究的信号（如我们所用的平衡和瞬变信号，它们是通过采用不同的物理过程及在气溶胶的直接影响的处理方面存在差异的模式得到的）、气溶胶直接影响因素的量级（如 COMB3 所示）以及结合了平流层 O_3 效应的信号（如 COMB1 和 COMB2 所示）等的不确定性并不敏感。最后，它们对本文所采用的 CGCM 模式中气候内部自然变化的估计值的不确定性是稳健的——

non-significant results on 25-year timescales would require noise levels for "unforced" $R(t)$ trends to be roughly twice as large as those estimated here.

The situation is more equivocal for model–observed comparisons focusing on hemispheric temperature-change asymmetries in the lower atmosphere. Here, too, the 25-year $R(t)$ temperature trends are generally robust to CGCM differences in natural internal variability and to signal uncertainties arising from model differences in physical processes and in the representation of direct aerosol effects. They are, however, sensitive to uncertainties in the magnitude of the aerosol forcing (as shown by COMB3). Although this points towards the need for caution in the interpretation of our results, we note that the observations are in better agreement with the larger aerosol forcing and hemispheric asymmetry in COMB1 and COMB2 than with the reduced forcing and asymmetry in COMB3. This may reflect our effective incorporation of some of the pattern characteristics of indirect aerosol forcing in the response to direct forcing[27]. For this to be the case would require a hemispherically asymmetric indirect aerosol effect, and there is evidence to support this in recent modelling studies[31,32] and satellite observations of interhemispheric differences in cloud liquid-water droplet size[33].

This investigation shows the clear need for modelling experiments with simultaneous changes in CO_2, O_3 and anthropogenic sulphate aerosols. Our use of linear superposition to assess the possible effects of ozone changes on a CO_2+aerosol signal should be regarded as a sensitivity study only. The incorporation of stratospheric O_3 effects in this way improves the fit with observations by reducing the height of the transition from stratospheric cooling to tropospheric warming. The implication of this result and other recent work[14,15] is that climate-change detection investigations that ignore possible ozone effects are likely to be searching for a sub-optimal signal (at least in terms of vertical temperature changes).

There is scope to reduce uncertainties in the observational data. We tested the robustness of our results to these uncertainties by comparing the radiosonde data with a reanalysis of operationally produced climate data. At present, this comparison is only possible after 1979. The extension of this reanalysis back to the early 1960s will allow better evaluation of the reliability of long-term trends in the radiosonde data. This will also be facilitated by other reanalysis efforts[58] and compilations of quality-controlled radiosonde data[57,59].

Although we have identified a component of the observational record that shows a statistically significant similarity with model predictions, we have not quantified the relative magnitude of natural and human-induced climate effects. This will require improved histories of radiative forcing due to natural and anthropogenic factors, and numerical experiments that better define an anthropogenic climate-change signal and the variability due to purely natural causes.

(**382**, 39-46; 1996)

为了获取 25 年时间尺度上的非显著性结果要求"非强迫性"$R(t)$趋势的噪声水平达到本文估计值的约两倍大。

低层大气中模拟值与实测值在南北半球温度变化的非对称性方面的比较结果更为模棱两可。同样，在这里，为期 25 年的 $R(t)$ 温度变化趋势对于 CGCM 在内部自然变化上的差异以及由物理过程和描述直接气溶胶效应引起的模式差异导致的信号不确定性都具有稳健性。不过，对于气溶胶强迫在量级上的不确定性它们是敏感的（如 COMB3 所示）。这提醒我们，在结果解释中需要格外谨慎，不过我们也注意到，实测值与 COMB1 和 COMB2 中较大的气溶胶强迫和半球非对称性的一致性，要好于实测值与 COMB3 中较小的强迫和非对称性的一致性。这说明在直接强迫的响应中我们对气溶胶间接影响的部分分布型特征的纳入可能是有效的[27]。为了做到这一点，需要有半球非对称的间接气溶胶效应，而这一点在新近的模拟研究结果[31,32]和南北半球云层中液态水大小不同的卫星实测值[33]中也找到了证据支持。

本研究结果显示，当前非常需要进行同时包含 CO_2、O_3 和人为硫酸盐气溶胶变化的模拟实验。我们用于获取臭氧变化对 CO_2 和气溶胶信号的潜在效应的线性叠加结果，仅能作为一项敏感度研究。引入平流层臭氧效应通过降低从平流层降温带到对流层变暖带之间的转换高度提高了它与实测值的吻合度。上述结果与近期其他研究工作[14,15]表明，忽略潜在的臭氧效应的气候变化检测研究所得到的很可能仅是一个次优信号（至少从垂直温度变化来说是如此）。

降低实测数据的不确定性是有可能的。通过对比无线电探空仪数据和业务上得到的气候数据的再分析资料，我们对本研究结果的不确定性的稳健性作了检验。目前还只能对 1979 年后的数据作上述比较。倘若将这种再分析方法延伸至 20 世纪 60 年代早期，那么将可对无线电探空仪数据中的长期趋势的可靠性作出更好的评估。其他再分析数据的建立[58]和质量控制的无线电探空资料的汇编[57,59]等也将促进该项工作的进展。

虽然我们已经确定，实测记录的某个分量与模式预测结果显示出统计上显著的相似性，但我们未能量化出自然与人为气候效应的相对量级。要达到这一点，需要有更好的由自然和人为因素导致的辐射强迫的变化数据，同时还需要大量实验来更好地界定人为气候变化信号与纯自然因素导致的变化。

（齐红艳 翻译；陈文 审稿）

B. D. Santer[*], **K. E. Taylor**[*†], **T. M. L. Wigley**[‡], **T. C. Johns**[§], **P. D. Jones**[∥], **D. J. Karoly**[¶], **J. F. B. Mitchell**[§], **A. H. Oort**[#], **J. E. Penner**[†], **V. Ramaswamy**[#], **M. D. Schwarzkopf**[#], **R. J. Stouffer**[#] & **S. Tett**[§]

[*] Program for Climate Model Diagnosis and Intercomparison, [†]Atmospheric Science Division, Lawrence Livermore National Laboratory, Livermore, California 94550, USA

[‡] National Center for Atmospheric Research, Boulder, Colorado 80307-3000, USA

[§] Hadley Centre for Climate Prediction and Research, Meteorological Office, Bracknell RG12 2SY, UK

[∥] Climatic Research Unit, University of East Anglia, Norwich NR4 7TJ, UK

[¶] Cooperative Research Centre for Southern Hemisphere Meteorology, Monash University, Clayton VIC 3168, Australia

[#] NOAA/Geophysical Fluid Dynamics Laboratory, PO Box 308, Princeton University, Princeton, New Jersey 08542, USA

Received 9 April; accepted 30 May 1996.

References:

1. Madden, R. A. & Ramanathan, V. *Science* **209**, 763-768 (1980).
2. Epstein, E. S. *J. Appl. Met.* **21**, 1172-1182 (1982).
3. Karoly, D. J. *Geophys. Res. Lett.* **14**, 1139-1141 (1987).
4. Karoly, D. J. *Geophys. Res. Lett.* **16**, 465-468 (1989).
5. Schlesinger, M. E. & Mitchell, J. F. B. *Rev. Geophys.* **25**, 760-798 (1987).
6. Mitchell, J. F. B., Manabe, S., Meleshko, V. & Tokioka, T. in *Climate Change: The IPCC Scientific Assessment* (eds Houghton, J. T., Jenkins, G. J. & Ephraums, J. J.) 131-172 (Cambridge Univ. Press, 1990).
7. Karoly, D. J. *et al. Clim. Dyn.* **10**, 97-105 (1994).
8. Oort, A. H. & Liu, H. *J. Clim.* **6**, 292-307 (1993).
9. Taylor, K. E. & Penner, J. E. *Nature* **369**, 734-737 (1994).
10. Mitchell, J. F. B., Johns, T. C., Gregory, J. M. & Tett, S. F. B. *Nature* **376**, 501-504 (1995).
11. Santer, B. D. *et al. Clim. Dyn.* **12**, 77-100 (1995).
12. Prather, M. *et al.* in *Climate Change 1994: Radiative Forcing of Climate Change and an Evaluation of the IPCC IS92 Emission Scenarios* (eds Houghton, J. T. *et al.*) 73-126 (Cambridge Univ. Press, 1994).
13. Hansen, J. E., Lacis, A., Ruedy, R., Sato, M. & Wilson, H. *Nat. Geogr. Res. Expl.* **9**, 142-158 (1993).
14. Hansen, J. E. *et al. Clim. Change* **30**, 103-117 (1995).
15. Ramaswamy, V., Schwarzkopf, M. D. & Randel, W. J. *Nature* (submitted).
16. Walton, J. J., MacCracken, M. C. & Ghan, S. J. *J. Geophys. Res.* **93**, 8339-8354 (1988).
17. Penner, J. E., Atherton, C. A. & Graedel, T. E. in *Global Atmospheric-Biospheric Chemistry* (ed. Prinn, R.) 223-248 (Plenum, New York, 1994).
18. Taylor, K. E. & Ghan, S. J. *J. Clim.* **5**, 906-919 (1992).
19. Charlson, R. J. & Wigley, T. M. L. *Scient. Am.* **270**, 48-57 (1994).
20. Johns, T. C. *et al. Clim. Dyn.* (submitted).
21. Houghton, J. T., Callander, B. A. & Varney, S. K. (eds) *Climate Change 1992: The Supplementary Report to the IPCC Scientific Assessment* (Cambridge Univ. Press, 1992).
22. Mitchell, J. F. B., Davis, R. A., Ingram, W. J. & Senior, C. A. *J. Clim.* **8**, 2364-2386 (1995).
23. Karl, T. R. *Nature* **371**, 380-381 (1994).
24. Christy, J. R. *Clim. Change* **31**, 455-474 (1995).
25. Kalnay, E. *et al. Bull. Am. Met. Soc.* **77**, 437-471 (1996).
26. Mahlman, J. D., Pinto, J. P. & Umscheid, L. J. *J. Atmos. Sci.* **51**, 489-508 (1994).
27. Penner, J. E., Wigley, T. M. L., Jaumann, P., Santer, B. D. & Taylor, K. E. in *Communicating About Climate: the Story of the Model Evaluation Consortium for Climate Assessment* (eds Howe, W. & Henderson-Sellers, A.) (Gordon & Breach, in the press).
28. Ramaswamy, V. & Bowen, M. M. *J. Geophys. Res.* **99**, 18909-18921 (1994).
29. Shine, K. P., Fouquart, Y., Ramaswamy, V., Solomon, S. & Srinivasan, J. in *Climate Change 1994: Radiative Forcing of Climate Change and an Evaluation of the IPCC IS92 Emission Scenarios* (eds Houghton, J. T. *et al.*) 163-203 (Cambridge Univ. Press, 1994).
30. Shine, K. P., Fouquart, Y., Ramaswamy, V., Solomon, S. & Srinivasan, J. in *Climate Change 1995: The Science of Climate Change* (eds Houghton, J. T. *et al.*) 108-118 (Cambridge Univ. Press, 1996).
31. Jones, A., Roberts, D. L. & Slingo, A. *Nature* **370**, 450-453 (1994).
32. Erickson, D. J., Oglesby, R. J. & Marshall, S. *Geophys. Res. Lett.* **22**, 2017-2020 (1995).
33. Boucher, O. *J. Clim.* **8**, 1403-1409 (1995).
34. Chuang, C. C., Penner, J. E., Taylor, K. E., Grossmann, A. S. & Walton, J. J. *J. Geophys. Res.* (submitted).

35. Angell, J. K. *J. Clim.* **1**, 1296-1313 (1988).

36. Barnett, T. P. & Schlesinger, M. E. *J. Geophys. Res.* **92**, 14772-14780 (1987).

37. Wigley, T. M. L. & Barnett, T. P. in *Climate Change: The IPCC Scientific Assessment* (eds Houghton, J. T., Jenkins, G. J. & Ephraums, J. J.) 239-255 (Cambridge Univ. Press, 1990).

38. Hasselmann, K. *et al. Rep. No. 168* (Max-Planck-Institut für Meteorologie, Hamburg, 1995).

39. Stouffer, R. J., Manabe, S. & Vinnikov, K. Ya. *Nature* **367**, 634-636 (1994).

40. Tett, S., Johns, T. C. & Mitchell, J. F. B. *Clim. Dyn.* (submitted).

41. Manabe, S. & Stouffer, R. J. *J. Clim.* **9**, 376-393 (1996).

42. Hegerl, G. C. *et al. J. Clim.* (in press).

43. Santer, B. D., Wigley, T. M. L., Barnett, T. P. & Anyamba, E. in *Climate Change 1995: The Science of Climate Change* (eds Houghton, J. T. *et al.*) 407-443 (Cambridge Univ. Press, 1996).

44. Gates, W. L. *et al.* in *Climate Change 1995: The Science of Climate Change* (eds Houghton, J. T. *et al.*) 229-284 (Cambridge Univ. Press, 1996).

45. Vinnikov, K. Ya., Robock, A., Stouffer, R. J. & Manabe, S. *Geophys. Res. Lett.* (in the press).

46. Christy, J. R. & McNider, R. T. *Nature* **367**, 325 (1994).

47. Jones, P. D. *Geophys. Res. Lett.* **21**, 1149-1152 (1994).

48. Barnett, T. P., Schlesinger, M. E. & Jiang, X.-J. in *Greenhouse-Gas-Induced Climatic Change: A Critical Appraisal of Simulations and Observations* (ed. Schlesinger, M. E.) 537-558 (Elsevier, Amsterdam, 1991).

49. Wigley, T. M. L. *Nature* **339**, 365-367 (1989).

50. Penner, J. E., Dickinson, R. & O'Neill, C. *Science* **256**, 1432-1434 (1992).

51. Tegen, I. & Fung, I. *J. Geophys. Res.* **100**, 18707-18726 (1995).

52. Penner, J. E. *et al. Bull. Am. Met. Soc.* **75**, 375-400 (1994).

53. Wang, W.-C., Dudek, M. P., Liang, X.-Z. & Kiehl, J. T. *Nature* **350**, 573-577 (1991).

54. Mitchell, J. F. B., Senior, C. A. & Ingram, W. J. *Nature* **341**, 132-134 (1989).

55. Barnett, T. P., Santer, B. D., Jones, P. D., Bradley, R. S. & Briffa, K. R. *Holocene* (in the press).

56. Gaffen, D. J. *J. Geophys. Res.* **99**, 3667-3676 (1994).

57. Parker, D. E. & Cox, D. I. *Int. J. Climatol.* **15**, 473-496 (1995).

58. Trenberth, K. E. *Clim. Change* **31**, 427-453 (1995).

59. Eskridge, R. E. *et al. Bull. Am. Met. Soc.* **76**, 1759-1775 (1995).

Acknowledgements. We thank J. Boyle, M. Fiorino, D. Gaffen, L. Gates, T. Karl, J. Mahlman, S. Manabe, A. Robock, H. Rodhe and four reviewers for helpful suggestions; L. Corsetti (PCMDI) for providing programming assistance; J.-S. von Storch and G. Hegerl for supplying data from the MPI control integration; and D. Williams, R. Mobley and R. Drach for developing software used to produce the colour graphics. Work at Lawrence Livermore National Laboratory was performed under the auspices of the US Department of Energy, Environmental Sciences Division. Support for T. J., J.M. and S.T. was provided by the UK Department of the Environment. T.M.L.W. and P.D.J. were supported by the US Department of Energy, Environmental Sciences Division. T.M.L.W. was also supported under the NOAA Climate Change, Data and Detection Program. The MECCA Program supplied some of the computer time required for the TP integrations.

Correspondence should be addressed to B.D.S. (e-mail: bsanter@rainbow.llnl.gov).

Seismological Evidence for Differential Rotation of the Earth's Inner Core

Xiaodong Song and Paul G. Richards

Editor's Note

The Earth's inner core is made of solid iron, crystalline despite its heat because of the high pressure. It rotates inside an outer core of molten iron, which supplies a lubricating layer separating it from the mantle. So the two solid bodies are potentially "decoupled" and can rotate independently. Here geophysicists Xiaodong Song and Paul Richards provide the first good evidence for that. Using seismic-wave data dating back to the 1960s, which reveal the inner core's orientation, they discover that it rotates faster than the mantle and crust by about one degree per year. The inner core has thus performed over a quarter of a complete revolution, relative to the rest of the solid Earth, during the past century.

The travel times of seismic waves that traverse the Earth's inner core show a small but systematic variation over the past three decades. This variation is best explained by a rotation of the inner core that moves the symmetry axis of its known seismic anisotropy. The inferred rotation rate is on the order of 1° per year faster than the daily rotation of the mantle and crust.

THE Earth's liquid iron core was formed very early in the planet's history, after which slow cooling has led to the formation and growth of the solid inner core. The inner core was discovered by seismological methods in 1936[1]. Its slow growth to a present radius of about 1,220 km has provided a source of energy as liquid iron freezes at the inner-core boundary. This energy is thought to drive convection in the outer core, which in turn maintains the dynamo action that generates the Earth's magnetic field[2].

As the inner core lies at the centre of a much larger, liquid outer core (radius 3,480 km) of very low viscosity[3,4], it is easy for the inner core to rotate[5,6]. We present observational evidence for inner-core rotation, at a rate that has taken the inner core through more than a quarter of a complete revolution this century, in an eastward direction. Around the equator of the inner core this rate corresponds to a speed of a few tens of kilometres per year, which is more than 100,000 times faster than the fastest relative motion of the tectonic plates of the lithosphere. Our estimate of the inner-core rotation rate comes from an interpretation of measurements of the difference in travel time between seismic body waves that pass through the inner core, and those that pass only through the outer core. We show that these measurements, made upon seismograms in archives going back to the mid-1960s, have systematically changed with time.

地球内核差异性旋转的地震学证据

宋晓东，理查兹

编者按

尽管地球内核温度很高，但是因为高压，其仍由固态铁结晶而成。内核在由熔融铁组成的外核内旋转，而外核作为内核和地幔之间的润滑层。所以这两个固态部分可能发生"解耦"，并且各自独立旋转。本文中地球物理学家宋晓东和保罗·理查兹首次为这种情况提供了有力的证据。他们利用可追溯至 20 世纪 60 年代的地震波数据，揭示出内核的指向，并发现内核的旋转速度每年要比地壳和地幔快 1°左右。因此，在过去的一个世纪中，相对于固体地球的其余部分，内核已经完成了超过四分之一的完整旋转周期。

在过去三十年间，穿过地球内核的地震波走时显示出一个较小但却有规律性的变化，这种变化最好解释为：已知地球内核具有各向异性，内核的旋转使各向异性对称轴发生了移动。推断的内核旋转速度比地幔和地壳的日常旋转快，在约每年 1°的量级上。

在地球演化史上，地球液态铁核形成非常早，之后缓慢的冷却导致了固态内核的形成和生长。地球内核在 1936 年由地震学方法发现[1]。随着液态铁在内外核边界冷却，内核缓慢生长到目前为止大约 1,220 km 的半径，这个过程释放了能量。外核的对流被认为由这些能量所驱动，并进而维持了产生地磁场的发电机作用[2]。

由于内核位于尺寸更大的（半径 3,480 km）低黏度液态外核的中心[3,4]，内核要旋转是很容易的[5,6]。我们这里展示内核旋转的观测证据，内核的旋转速率使得内核在本世纪向东旋转了超过四分之一圈。沿着内核的赤道，这样的速率对应每年几十千米的速度，是岩石圈构造板块间最快的相对运动速度的 100,000 倍。我们对于内核旋转速率的估计源自对穿过内核和仅穿过外核的两种地震体波之间走时差异测量值的解释。我们将展示：这些观测结果随着时间存在系统性的变化，而这些观测是基于自 20 世纪 60 年代中期以来的地震图档案得到的。

Essential to our interpretation of the travel-time data is the recent discovery that the inner core is anisotropic, with cylindrical symmetry about an axis aligned approximately with the Earth's north–south spin axis. Such anisotropy was first proposed[7,8] to explain the faster propagation of seismic waves that travel closer to the spin axis[9] and the anomalous splitting of certain normal modes of the whole Earth that have significant energy in the inner core[10], and has been recently confirmed[11-13] to have a significant amplitude of about 3%. The fact that the inner core is anisotropic is now well established, based on further studies of travel times and normal modes[14-22]. The cause of the inner-core anisotropy is believed to be preferred orientation of hexagonal close-packed iron (a high-pressure polymorph of iron[23]), but how the alignment occurs is still under debate[24-26]. Recent studies[11,15,18] also indicate that the inner core's axis of anisotropy is tilted by a few degrees from the north–south axis. A rotation about any axis different from the symmetry axis, including the north–south axis, will cause a systematic change in the times of waves transmitted through the inner core from a repeating seismic source, observed at the same fixed station. Moreover, we can use the arrival times of seismic waves transmitted through the outer core as reference points, as the outer core is thought to have negligible fluctuations in seismic velocity associated with its own convection[27].

We were led to our search for inner-core motion in part by the work of Glatzmaier and Roberts[28,29], who recently reported a three-dimensional, self-consistent numerical model of the geodynamo. Their model has an inner core with a differential rotation that is "as large as a few times 10^{-9} rad s^{-1} and changes on a timescale of about 500 years"[29] and is almost always rotating slightly faster than the mantle and crust. The rate that we report here is comparable with their value, is large enough to be important in many areas of geophysics and geochemistry, and adds a new dimension—time—to traditional seismological studies of the Earth's deep interior structure.

Differential Travel-time Observations

All of the seismic waves discussed here are simple short-period longitudinal waves (sound waves) with a wavelength of 5–20 km. Such waves that have propagated through the outer core are generically labelled PKP (Fig. 1). There are two possible paths, called PKP(AB) and PKP(BC), for waves that turn at the middle and the bottom of the outer core, respectively. The wave transmitted through both the outer and inner core is called PKP(DF). Our basic measurement is the time difference between the PKP(BC) and PKP(DF) arrivals, often abbreviated as the BC−DF time. Figure 1 shows that these two waves travel very closely together in the crust and mantle and in most of the outer core, so that the differential time (BC−DF) is relatively insensitive to uncertainty in source location and to three-dimensional heterogeneities of the crust and mantle along the ray paths. A standard Earth model (the Preliminary Earth Reference Model, or PREM[30]) is used to form the BC−DF residual (that is, the observed time difference minus the time difference predicted for PREM) for purposes of subsequent analysis. In addition, residuals of the differential times between PKP(AB) and PKP(BC), which pass through

对于我们解释走时数据至关重要的一点，是最近内核各向异性的发现，且此各向异性具有圆柱对称性，其对称轴近似与地球南北自转轴一致。该各向异性最初被提出来[7,8]是为了解释接近自转轴传播的地震波传播更快的现象[9]，以及在内核有显著能量分布的某些地球简振模式的异常分裂现象[10]，最近内核各向异性被确认[11-13]达到3%的幅度。对走时和简振模式的进一步研究[14-22]，很好地确定了内核存在各向异性这个事实。内核各向异性的成因被认为是六方紧密堆积铁晶体的有序排列（铁的一种高压晶体形态[23]），但这种排列是如何形成的仍未有定论[24-26]。最近的研究[11,15,18]还表明内核的各向异性轴偏离南北自转轴几度。围绕除了对称轴之外的任何轴的旋转，包括南北向轴，都会造成从一个重复震源发出、穿过内核、然后在同一固定台站观测到的地震波走时产生系统性的变化。另外，我们可以将穿过外核的地震波到时作为参照点。因为外核内部的对流，通常认为其地震波速度变化可以忽略不计[27]。

我们开展内核运动的搜寻在某种程度上是受格拉茨梅尔和罗伯茨[28,29]研究工作的启发，他们两人最近提出了一个三维自洽地球发电机数值模型。他们的模型有一个差异旋转的内核，即：速度最大可达几倍的$10^{-9}\,rad/s$，速度变化的时间尺度为500年[29]，并且几乎总是比地幔和地壳转得稍快一点。我们这里报道的速率和他们的值具有可比性，并且大到以至于在地球物理和地球化学的很多领域是很重要的，同时给传统地球深部结构地震学研究增加了一个新的维度——时间维度。

差异性走时观测

我们这里讨论的所有地震波都是波长为 5~20 km 的简单短周期纵波（声波）。穿过外核的这类波一般被标记为 PKP（图 1）。有两种可能的路径，它们被称为 PKP（AB）和 PKP（BC），分别对应于在外核中间和底部发生转折的 P 波。同时穿过外核和内核的波称为 PKP（DF）。我们的基本测量数据是 PKP（BC）和 PKP（DF）的到时差异，经常简称为 BC–DF 时间。图 1 表明这两种波在地壳和地幔及外核大部分传播路径都非常接近，所以时间差（BC–DF）对于震源的不确定性和沿着射线路径的地壳、地幔三维非均匀性相对而言是不敏感的。一个标准的模型（初始地球参考模型或 PREM[30]）被用来生成用于后续分析的 BC–DF 残差（即观测时间差减去通过 PREM 模型预测的时间差）。另外，仅穿过外核的 PKP（AB）和 PKP（BC）时差的残差被用来检查震源位置的系统性偏差。当 PKP（BC）不可观测时，PKP（AB）和 PKP（DF）

the outer core only, are used to examine possible systematic biases in source locations. Residuals of the differential times between PKP(AB) and PKP(DF) are also useful when PKP(BC) is not observable.

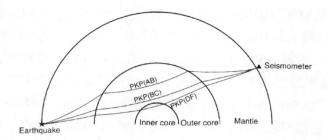

Fig. 1. Ray paths for seismic waves that pass through the Earth's cores

We began to explore time-variability in PKP(DF) times using north–south paths from nuclear explosions at Novaya Zemlya (which have well constrained locations at around 73° N, 54° E) to seismographic stations in Antarctica. Direct visual comparisons of AB–DF times in the analogue seismograms from different explosions show a decrease by about 0.2 s after about a decade—a difference not much greater than the resolution of the direct visual comparison. To improve the precision of measurement significantly will require scanning and digitization of the analogue data, ideally using the original paper records instead of microfilms (an effort that we have initiated).

We therefore turned to stations with significantly long histories of digital recordings, which permit even more precise measurement of travel times than digitized analogue data. One such station is College, Alaska (station code COL), which has 14 years of digital recordings to date (1982–96), in addition to 18 years of World Wide Standardized Seismographic Network (WWSSN) analogue recordings (1964–82). In our subsequent analysis, the data for the 1960s and 1970s are digitized from the corresponding analogue records. The north–south paths from earthquakes in the South Sandwich Islands (between South America and Antarctica) to COL had provided critical observations in previous anisotropy studies[11,12]. Figure 2 shows an overlay of PKP waveforms from such paths for two earthquakes that occurred about 15 years apart in almost exactly the same location. The time differences between BC and AB are almost exactly the same, confirming that the two event locations are indeed very close. The DF signal for the 1982 record, however, arrives earlier by about 0.4 s relative to BC than the DF signal for the 1967 record.

时差的残差也非常有用。

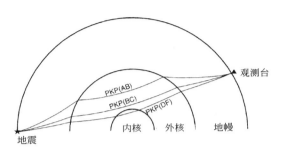

图 1. 穿过地球核部的地震波射线路径

我们开始使用从新地岛的核爆炸（位置被很好地约束在 73°N，54°E 附近）到南极洲的地震仪台站的南北路径来研究 PKP(DF)的时间差异性。直接肉眼比较记录不同爆炸的模拟地震图上的 AB－DF 时间发现，在 10 年之间有大约 0.2 s 的减小，这个差异比直接肉眼比较的精度高不了多少。为了显著地提高观测的精度，就需要对模拟数据进行扫描和数字化，同时尽可能地使用原始的纸记录而不是缩微胶片（这是我们发起的一项努力）。

所以我们转向数字记录历史明显较长的台站，使用这些数字记录可以得到比数字化后的模拟数据更精确的走时观测。其中一个这样的台站位于阿拉斯加州科利奇（台站代码 COL），它至今具有 14 年的数字化记录时间（1982~1996），另外还有全球标准化地震台网（WWSSN）18 年时间的模拟记录（1964~1982）。在我们的后续分析中，20 世纪 60 年代到 70 年代的数据都从相应的模拟数据数字化获得。在之前的各向异性研究中，由南桑威奇群岛（位于南美洲和南极洲之间）的地震到 COL 台站的南北向路径提供了关键性的观测[11,12]。图 2 给出了相隔 15 年在几乎同一位置发生的两个地震的 PKP 波形轮廓叠置图。BC 和 AB 的时间差几乎是一样的，这表明两个事件的位置确实是非常近的。但是相对于 BC，1982 年记录中的 DF 信号要比 1967 年记录中的 DF 信号早到 0.4 s。

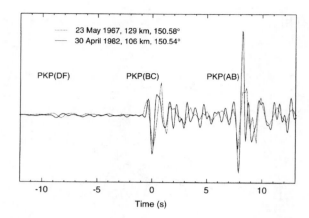

Fig. 2. An overlay of two short-period PKP seismograms from earthquakes that occurred 15 years apart at almost the same location in South Sandwich Islands, as recorded at College, Alaska (COL). Event locations in this study are taken from the Earthquake Data Reports of the US Geological Survey.

We use records such as those shown in Fig. 2 to measure BC–DF and AB–BC differential times by cross-correlation techniques. The BC–DF and AB–BC residuals obtained for the South Sandwich Islands to COL paths for a period of about 28 years (1967–95) are divided into three groups, about 12 years apart (Fig. 3). It can be seen that the BC–DF residuals increase from the 1967–75 period, to the 1980–85 period, and to the 1992–95 period (Fig. 3a), the increase amounting to about 0.3 s over the 28-year period. Possible explanations include a change in the DF (or BC) travel times, or an effect from systematic mislocation of the events. An increase in source–station distance by only 50 km would change the BC–DF time at distances near 151° by 0.3 s, so the time change could potentially be an artefact of the use of different global networks, used to locate the earthquakes in different decades. However, the distribution of the AB–BC residuals (Fig. 3b) for those records which have BC–DF measurements does not appear to have a systematic change with time, suggesting that the observed variation in AB–DF residuals is unlikely to be due to systematic event mislocations or recording instrument biases.

Figure 4 shows BC–DF residuals for three event–station pairs that are chosen to have ray directions in the inner core that make very different angles to the equatorial plane. The residuals for different distances and focal depths are corrected to a standard distance and depth by dividing the observed BC–DF residual by the time that the DF ray spends in the inner core for the distance and focal depth concerned, and multiplying by the time the DF ray spends in the inner core for a source at 151° and depth of 0 km. The residuals for South Sandwich Islands to COL paths are progressively larger from the 1960s/1970s to the 1990s, as seen before. But the paths from Kermadec to Kongsberg (KONO) and Bergen (BER), Norway, show smaller residuals for the 1990s than the 1980s. The paths from Tonga to Graefenberg, Germany (GRFO) show no such systematic differences in the data between the 1980s and 1990s. The ray directions in the inner core for the Tonga–GRFO paths are so much closer to the equatorial plane that no effect of inner core anisotropy would be expected. The deviation of the observations

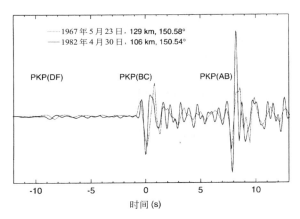

图 2. 阿拉斯加科利奇(COL)记录的、在南桑威奇群岛相隔 15 年发生的两个地震位置几乎相同的短周期 PKP 地震波形叠置图。本次研究中的地震事件位置取自美国地质调查局的地震数据报告。

我们采用互相关技术来测量如图 2 所示类似的记录中 BC－DF 和 AB－BC 时间差。沿南桑威奇群岛到 COL 台站路径得到的为期 28 年(1967~1995)的 BC－DF 和 AB－BC 残差被分成三组,相互间隔大约 12 年(图 3)。可以看到从 1967~1975 期间到 1980~1985 期间,再到 1992~1995 期间 BC－DF 时间残差在增加(图 3a),在 28 年的时间段内增加量达到约 0.3 s。可能的解释包括 DF(或 BC)走时的变化或者所有地震事件的系统性定位误差。在距离接近 151°时,震源－台站距离增加 50 km 就会使 BC－DF 时间变化 0.3 s,所以这种变化可能是在不同的年代被用于地震定位的全球台网不同而产生的人为假象。但是,对于这些具有 BC－DF 观测结果的记录,其 AB－BC 时间残差的分布(图 3b)并没有随时间表现出系统性变化,这表明观测到的 AB－DF 残差的变化不太可能是由于系统性事件定位误差或者记录设备偏差造成的。

图 4 给出了三组事件－台站对的 BC－DF 时间残差,选择这些事件－台站对是因为在内核它们的射线方向与赤道平面有差异很大的夹角。通过将观测到的不同震中距和震源深度的 BC－DF 时间残差除以对应距离和深度的 DF 射线穿过内核的时间,并乘以在 151°距离上深度为 0 km 的震源对应的 DF 射线穿过内核的时间,不同距离和震源深度的 BC－DF 时间残差被校正到一个标准的距离和深度。与之前所看到的一样,从 20 世纪 60 年代／20 世纪 70 年代到 20 世纪 90 年代,对应于南桑威奇群岛到 COL 台站路径的残差是在日益增加的。但是,自克马德克到挪威孔斯贝格(KONO)和卑尔根(BER)的路径,从 20 世纪 80 年代到 20 世纪 90 年代残差是减小的。沿汤加到德国格拉芬堡(GRFO)路径的数据则在 20 世纪 80 年代和 20 世纪 90 年代之间并未表现出系统性的差异。汤加-GRFO 路径在内核中的射线方向近乎平行于赤道平面,以至于可以预料内核各向异性不会产生影响。在 COL 台站和 KONO／BER

at COL and KONO/BER from the time-independent model (dashed curve in Fig. 4) reflects a departure of the observations from a simple constant cylindrical anisotropy of the inner core with the symmetry axis parallel to the north–south axis. We conclude from Figs 3 and 4 that there is the need to consider the effects of more complex anisotropic structure, including a time dependence.

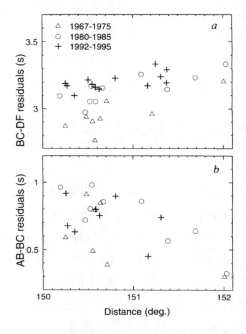

Fig. 3 Residuals for BC–DF (panel *a*) and AB–BC (panel *b*) times obtained for earthquakes grouped in three time intervals in the same region (South Sandwich Islands), observed on north–south paths at the same station (COL). Distance is measured by the angle subtended at the Earth's centre by the earthquake source and seismometer locations. The original broadband data for the 1990s are converted to the same short-period instrument response for the earlier years before the measurements. The BC–DF residuals typically increase with time. No such pattern is apparent for the AB–BC residuals, indicating that systematic event mislocations are unlikely to be the cause of time-dependent effects on BC–DF.

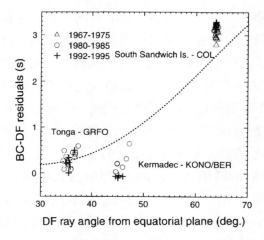

Fig. 4. Residuals for BC–DF times as a function of the angle between the inner-core part of the ray path

台站的观测值相对于不随时间变化模型的偏差（图 4 中的虚线），反映了观测值相对于一个简单不变的圆柱形各向异性内核（其对称轴平行于南北自转轴）的偏差。我们根据图 3 和图 4 得出结论，即有必要考虑更为复杂的各向异性结构的影响，包括时间依赖性。

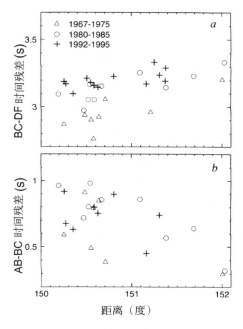

图 3. 在同一台站（COL）观测的、同一区域（南桑威奇群岛）分三个时间段获得的地震沿南北向路径的 BC-DF（图 *a*）和 AB-BC（图 *b*）时间残差。距离是由震源和观测台站分别与地球中心之间的夹角来度量的（译者注：即通常定义的震中距）。在测量之前，20 世纪 90 年代的原始宽频波段数据已被转换成了早期短周期仪器相同的响应。BC-DF 时间残差随着时间有明显的增加。但 AB-BC 残差却没有明显地表现这种模式，这表明系统性地震事件定位误差不太可能是 BC-DF 测量值随时间变化现象的原因。

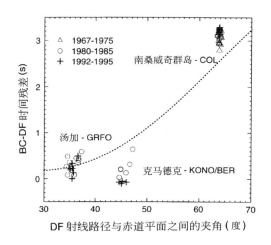

图 4. BC-DF 时间残差，显示为以内核中的射线路径与赤道平面之间夹角为变量的函数。使用了到达三

and the equatorial plane. Ray paths to three different seismographic stations are used (COL—College, Alaska; GRFO—Graefenberg, Germany; KONO/BER—Kongsberg and Bergen, Norway), each using a separate set of earthquakes in the same source region (Tonga to GRFO; Kermadec to KONO/BER; South Sandwich Islands to COL). The dashed line is the prediction for the anisotropy model of Song and Helmberger[12], which has the axis of symmetry of the inner core aligned with the north–south axis. Systematic shifts in residuals over time are absent from the near-equatorial path, and are in opposite directions for the other two paths. Such systematic shifts indicate the need to consider time-dependent effects on the fixed paths through the inner core.

Figure 5 summarizes our observations at COL as a function of the calendar time at which the South Sandwich earthquakes occurred—and also interprets them with a time-dependent model. We observe a gradual increase in the residuals from early 1967 to early 1995, suggesting that the DF ray during this period was taking a progressively faster path through the inner core. Such faster paths can be achieved by a mechanism that decreases the angle between the path within the inner core and the axis of anisotropic symmetry. As the ray path is essentially fixed, we propose that the symmetry axis is moving, owing to a rotation of the inner core. The dashed line in Fig. 5 shows our best estimate of the inner-core rotation required to explain the observed change of residuals over time, as discussed below. In this estimate, the inner core rotates about the north–south axis like the rest of the planet, but at a rate that is 1.1° per year faster. Because the symmetry axis of the anisotropy is not aligned north–south, it moves to the east as illustrated in Fig. 6.

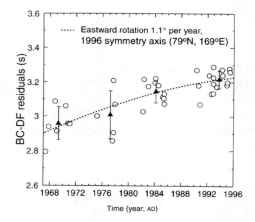

Fig. 5. Residuals for BC–DF times for South Sandwich Islands to COL paths as a function of earthquake time of occurrence. The observed residuals are indicated by open circles. The mean (filled triangles) and ± one standard deviation (error bar) are shown for the residuals over about four-year periods. The predicted times (dashed curve) are based on our best estimate of inner-core rotation about a north–south axis.

个不同地震台站的射线路径(COL：阿拉斯加科利奇；GRFO：德国格拉芬堡；KONO/BER：挪威孔斯贝格和卑尔根)，每一个台站都使用了来自某一特定区域的一组地震(汤加到 GRFO；克马德克到 KONO/BER；南桑威奇群岛到 COL)。虚线是宋晓东和黑尔姆贝格尔[12] 各向异性模型的预测值，该模型的内核对称轴和南北轴在一条线上。近赤道平面的射线路径，其残差随时间并没有系统性的变化，而另外两条路径则在两个相反的方向有系统性的变化。这种系统性的变化说明有必要考虑穿过内核固定路径的随时间变化因素的影响。

在图 5 中，我们在 COL 台站的观测被总结为一个随日历时间变化的函数，这段时间南桑威奇群岛地震持续发生，同时我们也用一个随时间变化的模型解释了这些观测值。我们观测到从 1967 年初到 1995 年初时间残差有一个逐渐的增加，这表明在这期间 DF 射线穿过内核走了一条逐渐变快的路径。通过减小穿过内核的路径和各向异性对称轴之间的夹角这种机制，可以获得这些更快的路径。由于射线路径一定是固定的，我们提出对称轴是由于内核旋转而不断移动的。正如下面所讨论的，图 5 中的虚线给出了我们对内核旋转的最佳估计，用于解释观测到的残差随时间的变化。在这个估计中，内核如地球的其他部分一样绕南北轴旋转，但是其速率每年要快 1.1°。因为各向异性对称轴和南北轴并不重合，所以各向异性对称轴是如图 6 所示向东移动的。

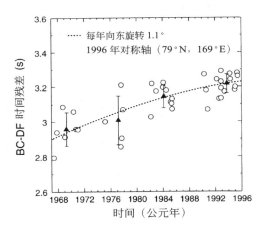

图 5. 南桑威奇群岛到 COL 路径的 BC-DF 时间残差，显示为相对于地震发生时间的函数。观测残差值由空心圆表示。平均值(实心三角形)及 ±1 个标准偏差(误差棒)表示四年时间内的偏差。预测的时间(虚线)基于我们对内核围绕南北轴旋转的最佳估计。

Fig. 6. A representation of our conclusion that the anisotropic symmetry axis of the inner core is moving owing to inner-core rotation. As the solid core and its symmetry axis rotates, there is a change in the angle between the symmetry axis and the inner-core leg of a ray for a fixed source and fixed station, resulting in the systematic shift that we see in the total time taken to travel along the ray. We show the motion of the symmetry axis since AD 1900 according to our best estimate of a 1.1° per year eastward rotation about the north–south axis.

Inferred Inner-core Motions

We have presented evidence that the inner core is moving, presumably by some type of rotation. But with the limited number of observations made so far, we can get only an approximate estimate of the rotation rate and orientation.

The inner core's moment of inertia, although only 0.07% of the Earth's total moment of inertia, is about 500 times larger than the moment of inertia of the atmosphere, whose internal motions can effect small changes in the Earth's length of day[31]. Observed changes in length of day, over a timescale of years, have been adequately explained without postulating transfer of angular momentum to or from the inner core. We therefore assume that the rotation axis and the rotation rate of the inner core do not change on the timescale of our observations.

At least eight parameters are needed to describe an appropriate model of the time variations in travel-time residuals: the latitude and longitude of the axis of symmetry at a particular time, a direction-dependent relative velocity perturbation from PREM in the form[7] $a+b\cos^2\xi+c\cos^4\xi$ (where ξ is the angle between the ray direction in the inner core and the anisotropy symmetry axis), the latitude and longitude of the fixed rotation axis, and finally the fixed rotation rate.

We carried out a grid search for the latitude and longitude of the anisotropy symmetry axis to obtain values of a, b and c and that best fitted observed travel-time residuals without rotation. Using the BC–DF measurements of Song and Helmberger[12] and the

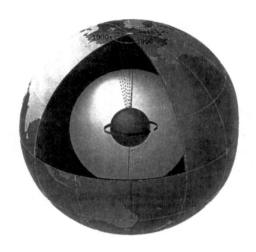

图 6. 展示我们结论的图示，即由于内核的旋转，内核的各向异性对称轴是移动的。由于固态内核及其对称轴的旋转，对一组固定的震源和台站来说，对称轴和内核中射线路径之间的夹角也是有一个变化的，这就造成我们在总射线走时中看到的系统性变化。根据我们对内核围绕南北轴每年向东旋转 1.1° 的最佳估计，给出了对称轴自公元 1900 年以来的运动。

推断内核运动

我们已经给出了内核运动的证据，据推测应该是某种类型的旋转。但是由于目前观测值数量的限制，我们只能得到旋转速率和指向的近似估计。

内核的惯性力矩，尽管只有地球总的惯性力矩的 0.07%，但却差不多是大气层的惯性力矩的 500 倍，而大气层的内部运动就能够对地球一天的长度产生小的变化[31]。不需要假设角动量转移到内核或转移自内核，已经可以解释观测到的地球日长在数年时间尺度上的变化。所以我们认为在我们观测的时间尺度内，内核旋转轴和旋转速率不发生变化。

要描述一个走时残差随时间变化的合适的模型至少需要 8 个参数：某一特定时间下对称轴的经度和纬度，相对于 PREM 模型的一个形式[7]为 $a+b\cos^2\xi+c\cos^4\xi$（这里 ξ 是内核中的射线方向和各向异性对称轴之间的夹角）的依赖于方向的相对速度扰动，固定旋转轴的经度和纬度，最后是固定的旋转速率。

我们对各向异性对称轴的经度和纬度进行网格搜索，以获得 a、b 和 c 的值和不考虑旋转情况下最佳拟合的观测走时残差。使用宋晓东和黑尔姆贝格尔[12]的

new measurements of this study with a combined time span of the past 30 years, the time-invariant best fit to the anisotropy is given by

$$\Delta\upsilon/\upsilon = 0.0042 - 0.0256\cos^2\xi + 0.0517\cos^4\xi \tag{1}$$

with symmetry axis crossing the Northern Hemisphere at 82.0° N, 175.0° E. This best fit achieves a variance reduction from the original measurement (with respect to the isotropic PREM) of 93%, not significantly better than the variance reduction of 89% achieved without allowing for a tilt of the symmetry axis. Nevertheless, our estimate of the latitude and longitude of the axis is remarkably close to previous best-fitting symmetry axes. It is only 3.5° away from 79.5° N, 160° E of Su and Dziewonski[18], estimated using PKP(DF) times of the International Seismological Centre Bulletins for years 1964–90; and 8.5° away from 80° N, 120° E of McSweeney et al.[19], estimated using differential PKP times for events in the 1980s and 1990s, as in this study. Note the range of these latitude estimates is less than 3°.

The BC–DF measurements can be used to place a minimum bound on the rotation rate, even when the orientation of the symmetry axis of anisotropy is unknown. We computed this bound by calculating the rotation rate needed to match the 0.31-s BC–DF time difference over 28 years at COL (that is, the trend of the data in Fig. 5) for every possible orientation in a grid search, and then selected the smallest. The parameters of anisotropy obtained via the time-invariant analysis were used for this calculation. When the orientation of the rotation axis is also considered unknown, the minimum bound is 0.15° per year. The minimum bound increases if we assume that the differential rotation of the inner core is around the north–south axis. With this rotation axis, the minimum rate increases as the tilt of the symmetry axis decreases, from 0.45° per year for a 15° tilt to 1.30° per year for a 5° tilt. If the BC–DF time differences at KONO are used, the minimum rates are even higher. However, the trend is less well constrained owing to fewer samples.

If we limit the tilt of the symmetry axis to between 8° and 11° away from the north–south axis, as indicated by the above time-invariant analysis, but allow the longitudinal location to vary, the least-squares solution for rotation about the north–south axis to fit the time-varying residuals at COL and KONO puts the symmetry axis at 79.2° N, 169° E at the beginning of 1996 with a rotation rate of 1.1° per year. We regard this as our best estimate, and it gives a variance reduction for COL data compared to the best-fitting time-invariant model (that is without inner-core rotation) amounting to 64%. Assuming the tilt of the symmetry axis in the best-fitting model, the allowed minimum and maximum rotation rates are estimated to be 0.4° per year and 1.8° per year, respectively, from the minimum and maximum slopes of the COL residuals (Fig. 5) constrained by the two-standard-deviation error bars. The variance reduction for the KONO data is insignificant but note that they cover only 13 years (instead of 28 years at COL), and the earlier data are quite scattered. Nevertheless, our preferred model (Fig. 6) of inner-core motion has its symmetry axis moving away from the Kermadec–Norway paths,

BC-DF 观测结果和本次研究的新测量结果，这一数据组合时间跨度达到过去 30 年，不随时间变化的各向异性最好的拟合如下：

$$\Delta v/v = 0.0042 - 0.0256\cos^2\xi + 0.0517\cos^4\xi \qquad (1)$$

且对称轴在 82.0° N，175° E 穿过北半球。这个最佳拟合获得了相对于原始测量值（以各向同性的 PREM 模型为基准）93% 的方差减小值；同不允许对称轴有所倾斜的情况下 89% 的方差减少值相比，并没有显著地改善。然而，我们对于对称轴经纬度的估计非常接近前人获得的最佳拟合对称轴。这只比苏和杰翁斯基 [18] 使用 1964~1990 年期间国际地震中心报告中的 PKP(DF) 时间得到的估计值 79.5° N，160° E 偏离了 3.5°，比麦克斯威尼等 [19] 使用 20 世纪 80 年代和 20 世纪 90 年代地震事件的 PKP 时间（与本次研究采用一样的方法）得到的估计值 80° N，120° E 偏离了 8.5°。注意这些纬度估计值的范围小于 3°。

　　BC-DF 测量值可以用来约束旋转速率的最小范围，即使各向异性对称轴的指向并不知道。通过对每一个可能满足 28 年间在 COL 台站的 0.31 秒 BC-DF 观测时间差（即图 5 中数据的趋势）的指向进行格点搜索，并选择其最小值，我们计算旋转速率，进而计算这个最小范围。在这项计算中，使用了通过时间不变性分析得到的各向异性参数。当旋转轴的指向被认为是未知的，最小范围是每年 0.15°。如果我们假设内核的差异性旋转是围绕南北轴的，则最小范围将增加。在这样的旋转轴下，最小速率随着对称轴倾斜度的减小而增加，从倾斜度 15° 对应的每年 0.45°，到倾斜度 5° 对应的每年 1.30°。如果使用 KONO 的 BC-DF 时间差，那么最小速率还会更高。但是，因为较少的采样数据，这个趋势缺少良好的约束。

　　如上面的时间不变性分析所反映的一样，如果我们限制对称轴偏离南北轴的倾斜度在 8°~11° 之间，而允许经度位置发生变化，那么，符合在 COL 和 KONO 随时间变化残差的、围绕南北轴旋转的最小二乘解，给出的对称轴位置在 1996 年初是 79.2° N，169° E，旋转速率为每年 1.1°。我们认为这是我们最好的估计，这个估计相比于最佳拟合的时间不变模型（不考虑内核旋转），可以使 COL 数据得到 64% 的方差减小量。假设在最佳拟合模型中对称轴的倾斜度，基于两个标准偏差误差棒约束的最小和最大 COL 残差斜率（图 5）可以估计：最小和最大旋转速率分别为每年 0.4° 和每年 1.8°。KONO 数据的方差减小值并不明显，但是需要注意到这些数据仅跨越了 13 年（而在 COL 则是 28 年），并且早期的数据是相当离散的。尽管如此，我们首选的内核运动模型（图 6），其对称轴远离克马德克-挪威路径，这与这些路径上观测到的 BC-DF 残差减小是一致的（图 4）。我们的首选模型对 KONO 数据的拟

consistent with the observed decrease in BC–DF residuals for these paths (Fig. 4). The fact that the preferred model does not significantly improve the fit to the KONO data suggests a need for more data samples gathered for the Kermadec–Norway paths and other paths that are sensitive to the motion of the anisotropic symmetry axis.

The main assumption underlying our best estimate of the rotation rate, namely that the rotation axis is north–south, will be examined when additional data are brought to bear. However, we can already be fairly sure from seismological observations that the rotation axis is not likely to be near the Equator, as such a rotation would cause highly nonlinear changes of travel times for north–south ray paths when the symmetry axis is rotated towards the Equator. Such changes are not seen in the shifts of travel times at COL in Fig. 5. Also in support of an axis far from the Equator is the fact that going further back, to the mid-1960s, it is still true (as today) that only paths close to the north–south spin axis show fast anomalies[12,16,18,21].

Implications of Detectable Inner-core Motions

Much tighter constraints on the rate of inner-core rotation and on the orientation of the rotation axes and symmetry axes will be possible as more recordings of north–south PKP waves are gathered and better event locations are obtained (through, for example, joint hypocentre determination[32,33], a simultaneous calculation of all hypocentres for a group of earthquakes, which gives better relative event locations). Systematic shifts in PKP(DF) times are best observed where there is the greatest change in $\Delta v/v$ with respect to ξ in equation (1), that is, $10° \leqslant \xi \leqslant 45°$. Also, the effect of inner-core rotation is likely to be amplified for waves that traverse the innermost inner core because the paths within the anisotropy are longer. Travel-time anomalies in such waves, twice as big as the anomalies for South Sandwich Islands to COL paths, have been observed[17,21]. In addition to the differential travel-time data, it is possible that the absolute travel-time data of Su and Dziewonski[18] and the normal-mode analyses of Tromp[13,22] can be reinterpreted to include possible inner-core motions. Techniques based on reflected waves may also be applicable, if lateral variability of the inner core boundary resulting in variable reflectance can be found, analogous to medical uses of ultrasound reflections to monitor organs that move inside the human body.

Numerous projects are suggested by our conclusion that inner-core motion is observable and can be quantified. New estimates of viscosity in the outer core may become available that in turn may provide information on melting conditions and temperature through the outer core, and refined estimates of the heat flux across the core–mantle boundary. New constraints may be placed on the dynamo motions underlying the geomagnetic field, leading to refinement of models that can reproduce secular variation of the field and geomagnetic reversals. New questions also arise regarding the distribution of angular momentum throughout the Earth. For example, does the inner-core rotation axis track the north–south spin axis in the precession of the equinoxes? Does the rotation of the inner core result in observable changes in the gravity field?

合并没有明显的提高，这一事实表明我们需要搜集更多的克马德克－挪威路径的数据样本，和对各向异性对称轴运动敏感的其他路径的数据样本。

构成我们关于旋转速率最佳估计基础的主要假设，即旋转轴是南北向，随着更多数据的加入，这个假设将被进一步检验。但是，从地震学的观测结果中我们已经可以相当确定地知道，旋转轴是不可能接近赤道的，因为在这样的旋转情况下，当对称轴转向赤道的时候，南北射线路径上的走时将发生高度非线性变化。这样的变化在图 5 的 COL 走时变动中并没有看到。另外一个支持旋转轴远离赤道的事实则要追溯到 20 世纪 60 年代中期，即使在今天，它仍然是正确的，即只有接近南北自转轴的路径才表现出高速异常 [12,16,18,21]。

可检测的内核运动的含义

随着更多南北路径的 PKP 地震波记录的搜集和更准确的事件位置的获取（比如，联合震源测定 [32,33]，即对一组地震所有震源的同时计算，以获得更为准确的相对事件位置），对内核旋转速率、旋转轴指向及对称轴指向更加严格的约束将会成为可能。PKP(DF) 时间的系统性变化最佳观测的位置，是在公式（1）中关于 ξ 的 $\Delta v/v$ 有最大变化的地方，即 $10° \leqslant \xi \leqslant 45°$。当然，对于穿过内核最深处的地震波来说，内核旋转的影响可能会被放大，因为其在各向异性介质中的路径更长。在这些波中，观测到的走时异常是南桑威奇群岛到 COL 台站路径异常的两倍 [17,21]。除了差异走时数据，苏和杰翁斯基 [18] 的绝对走时数据以及特龙普 [13,22] 的简振模型分析可以被重新解释以包含可能的内核运动。如果导致不同反射率的内核边界横向变化能够被找到，类似于医学上应用超声波反射来检查在人体内的器官，那么基于反射波的技术也可能是有用的。

内核运动是可观测、可定量的，我们这个结论启发了大量的研究计划。对外核黏性的新估计将成为可能，并反过来为外核的熔化条件、整个外核的温度、更准确地估计核幔边界热流提供信息。还可以为构成地磁场基础的发电机运动模型提供新的约束，并进一步优化解释磁场长期变化和极性反转的模型。地球角动量分布的新问题也被引发出来。比如，在分点岁差中内核旋转轴是跟随南北向旋转轴的吗？内核旋转会导致可以观测到的重力场变化吗？

The organization and maintenance of seismogram archives will need to be modified in order to facilitate studies of core motions. Older data should no longer be superseded by newer, but instead are vital to the accurate determination of rates of change. In this regard it is unfortunate that important sets of digital and analogue data—some of the best in the world, for our purposes—have deteriorated and/or have been destroyed. Support may be needed to recover data from certain archives that have fallen into disuse, or which were not designed for use by the research community.

Gubbins *et al.*[34] suggested that "All discussion of modes of core convection will remain speculative until some direct or indirect observational evidence is found." We believe that observational evidence is now available. The Earth's dynamo is in part composed of a rotating inner core.

(**382**, 221-224; 1996)

Xiaodong Song & Paul G. Richards
Lamont-Doherty Earth Observatory, Palisades, New York 10964, USA, and Department of Earth and Environmental Sciences, Columbia University, New York, New York 10027, USA

Received 15 March; accepted 25 June 1996.

References:

1. Lehmann, I. *Publ. Bur. Cent. Assoc. Int. Seismol.* A14, 87-115 (1936).

2. Braginsky, S. I. *Dokl. Akad. Nauk SSSR* 149, 8-10 (1963).

3. Gans, R. F. *J. Geophys. Res.* 77, 360-366 (1972).

4. Poirier, J. P. *Geophys. J.* 92, 99-105 (1988).

5. Steenbeck, M. & Helmis, G. *Geophys. J. R. astr. Soc.* 41, 237-244 (1975).

6. Gubbins, D. *J. Geophys. Res.* 86, 11695-11699 (1981).

7. Morelli, A., Dziewonski, A. M. & Woodhouse, J. H. *Geophys. Res. Lett.* 13, 1545-1548 (1986).

8. Woodhouse, J. H., Giardini, D. & Li, X.-D. *Geophys. Res. Lett.* 13, 1549-1552 (1986).

9. Poupinet, G., Pillet, R. & Souriau, A. *Nature* 305, 204-206 (1983).

10. Masters, G. & Gilbert, F. *Geophys. Res. Lett.* 8, 569-571 (1981).

11. Creager, K. C. *Nature* 356, 309-314 (1992).

12. Song, X. D. & Helmberger, D. V. *Geophys. Res. Lett.* 20, 2591-2594 (1993).

13. Tromp, J. *Nature* 366, 678-681 (1993).

14. Shearer, P. M., Toy, K. M. & Orcutt, J. A. *Nature* 333, 228-232 (1988).

15. Shearer, P. M. & Toy, K. M. *J. Geophys. Res.* 96, 2233-2247 (1991).

16. Shearer, P. M. *J. Geophys. Res.* 99, 19647-19659 (1994).

17. Vinnik, L., Romanowicz, B. & Breger, L. *Geophys. Res. Lett.* 21, 1671-1674 (1994).

18. Su, W. J. & Dziewonski, A. M. *J. Geophys. Res.* 100, 9831-9852 (1995).

19. McSweeney, T. J., Creager, K. C. & Merrill, R. T. *Phys. Earth Planet. Inter.* (submitted).

20. Song, X. D. & Helmberger, D. V. *J. Geophys. Res.* 100, 9805-9816 (1995).

21. Song, X. D. *J. Geophys. Res.* (in the press).

22. Tromp, J. *GSA Today* 5(7), 137-151 (1995).

23. Takahashi, T. & Bassett, W. A. *Science* 145, 483-486 (1964).

24. Jeanloz, R. & Wenk, H. R. *Geophys. Res. Lett.* 15, 72-75 (1988).

25. Karato, S. *Science* 262, 1708-1711 (1993).

26. Stixrude, L. & Cohen, R. E. *Science* 267, 1972-1975 (1995).

27. Stevenson, D. J. *Geophys. J. R. astr. Soc.* 88, 311-319 (1987).

28. Glatzmaier, G. A. & Roberts, P. H. *Nature* 377, 203-209 (1995).

910

地震图档案的管理和维护工作需要调整以促进对地核运动的研究。较老的数据不应该被较新的数据所取代，而应该是对变化率的准确测定起着至关重要的作用。在这方面，不幸的是一些对我们有用的、重要的数字和模拟数据集（对于我们的目标来说，其中一些是世界上最好的）已经减少并且（或者）已经被破坏了。我们需要支持以便恢复这些被废弃的或者不是被设计用于研究的档案中的数据。

格宾斯等[34]建议"我们对所有关于地核对流模型的讨论都应该保持怀疑的态度，直到一些直接或间接可观测的证据被发现"。我们相信现在已经得到了一些观测证据。地球发电机的一部分是由一个旋转的内核组成的。

（俞贵平 翻译；梁晓峰 审稿）

29. Glatzmaier, G. A. & Roberts, P. H. *Phys. Earth Planet. Inter.* **91**, 63-75 (1995).

30. Dziewonski, A. M. & Anderson, D. L. *Phys. Earth Planet. Inter.* **25**, 297-356 (1981).

31. Lambeck, K. *The Earth's Variable Rotation: Geophysical Causes and Consequences* 275-282 (Cambridge Univ. Press, London, 1980).

32. Douglas, A. *Nature* **215**, 47-48 (1967).

33. Dewey, J. W. & Algermissen, S. T. *Bull. seism. Soc. Am.* **64**, 1033-1048 (1974).

34. Gubbins, D. C., Thomson, C. J. & Whaler, K. A. *Geophys. J. R. astr. Soc.* **68**, 241-251 (1982).

Acknowledgements. We thank the IRIS DMC for easy access to data; the US NSF for long-term funding of the WWSSN archive at Lamont; J. Dewey and R. Engdahl for help with event relocations; and W. Menke, D. Kent and A. Lerner-Lam for comments on early drafts. This work was supported by the US NSF.

Correspondence should be addressed to X.S. (e-mail: xsong@LDEO.columbia.edu).

A DNA-based Method for Rationally Assembling Nanoparticles into Macroscopic Materials

C. A. Mirkin *et al.*

Editor's Note

Nanotechnology involves the arrangement of matter at the nanometre scale for a variety of technological purposes, such as information technology and chemical analysis. One of the biggest challenges is the orderly assembly of component parts at such small scales. Many researchers suspect that the answer lies in chemical self-assembly, which entails programming nanoscale structures with the information they need to assemble themselves spontaneously. Here Chad Mirkin's group at Northwestern University show that DNA provides an ideal "programmable" tag for promoting this self-assembly, thanks to the selective pairing of complementary base sequences. Mirkin later commercialized this technique in a cheap "colour-change" technology for DNA sequence recognition.

Colloidal particles of metals and semiconductors have potentially useful optical, optoelectronic and material properties[1-4] that derive from their small (nanoscopic) size. These properties might lead to applications including chemical sensors, spectroscopic enhancers, quantum dot and nanostructure fabrication, and microimaging methods[2-4]. A great deal of control can now be exercised over the chemical composition, size and polydispersity[1,2] of colloidal particles, and many methods have been developed for assembling them into useful aggregates and materials. Here we describe a method for assembling colloidal gold nanoparticles rationally and reversibly into macroscopic aggregates. The method involves attaching to the surfaces of two batches of 13-nm gold particles non-complementary DNA oligonucleotides capped with thiol groups, which bind to gold. When we add to the solution an oligonucleotide duplex with "sticky ends" that are complementary to the two grafted sequences, the nanoparticles self-assemble into aggregates. This assembly process can be reversed by thermal denaturation. This strategy should now make it possible to tailor the optical, electronic and structural properties of the colloidal aggregates by using the specificity of DNA interactions to direct the interactions between particles of different sizes and compositions.

PREVIOUS assembly methods have focused on the use of covalent "linker" molecules that possess functionalities at opposing ends with chemical affinities for the colloids of interest. One of the most successful approaches to date[5] has involved the use of gold colloids and well established thiol adsorption chemistry[6,7]. In this approach, linear alkanedithiols were used as the particle linker molecules. The thiol groups at each end

914

一种基于 DNA 将纳米颗粒合理组装成宏观材料的方法

米尔金等

编者按

纳米科技囊括了基于各种技术目的对纳米尺度的材料进行排列，比如信息技术和化学分析的需要。最大的挑战之一是对如此小尺度的组成部分进行有序组装。许多研究者猜测答案来自化学自组装，这种技术要求对纳米尺度的结构进行编码使之含有将它们进行自发组装所需之信息。这篇文章中，西北大学的查德·米尔金研究组指出 DNA 为促进这种自组装过程提供了一个理想的"可编码"标记，这得归功于互补碱基序列的选择性配对。米尔金后来基于一种用于 DNA 序列识别的廉价的"变色"技术将上述技术实现了商业化。

金属和半导体的胶体颗粒有可能具有实用的光学、光电子学和材料学的性质 [1-4]，而这些性质均来源于其小的(纳米)尺寸。这些性质可能会使之在化学传感器、光谱增强、量子点和纳米结构的制备以及显微成像方法上得到应用 [2-4]。现在对于胶体颗粒的化学组成、尺寸和多分散性 [1,2] 都可以进行控制，同时也发展出了很多方法将它们组装成为实用的聚集体和材料。这篇文章中我们介绍了一种将金胶体纳米颗粒合理并且可逆地组装成为宏观聚集体的方法。该方法涉及通过巯基与金的键合作用，将端部修饰有巯基的非互补的 DNA 寡聚片段分别附着在两批 13 nm 的金颗粒的表面。当向溶液中加入具有分别与前述嫁接的 DNA 序列互补的"黏性末端"的寡聚核苷酸双链分子时，这些纳米颗粒就自组装成为聚集体。这一组装过程可以通过热变性使之逆转。基于这种策略，利用 DNA 相互作用的特异性来控制不同尺寸和组成的颗粒之间的相互作用，将使得精确调节胶体聚集体的光学、电学和结构性质成为可能。

先前的组装方法集中于使用共价"连接"分子，这些分子两端带有对目标胶体颗粒有化学亲和力的基团。迄今为止最为成功的方法之一 [5] 涉及金胶体颗粒的使用和技术已经成熟的巯基吸附化学 [6,7]。在这种方法中，线性的双巯基烷烃作为颗粒的连接分子。连接分子每一端的巯基官能团与胶体颗粒共价相连，从而形成聚集

of the linker molecule covalently attach themselves to the colloidal particles to form aggregate structures. The drawbacks of this method are that the process is difficult to control and the assemblies are formed irreversibly. Methods for systematically controlling the assembly process are needed if the materials properties of these unusual structures are to be exploited fully.

Our oligonucleotide-based method allows the controlled and reversible assembly of gold nanoparticles into supramolecular structures. Oligonucleotides offer several advantages over nonbiological-based linker molecules. For example, discrete sequences of controlled length and with the appropriate surface binding functionality may be prepared in an automated fashion with a DNA synthesizer. In this way, the molecular recognition properties of the oligonucleotides may be used to trigger the colloidal self-assembly process. The interparticle distances and stabilities of the supramolecular structures generated by this method can be controlled through the choice of oligonucleotide sequence and length, solvent, temperature and supporting electrolyte concentration.

Others also have recognized the utility of DNA for the preparation of new biomaterials and nanofabrication methods. Previous researchers have focused on using the sequence-specific molecular-recognition properties of oligonucleotides to design impressive structures with well-defined geometric shapes and sizes[8-18]. The chemistry proposed here focuses on merging the chemistry of DNA with the chemistry of inorganic colloidal materials. In addition to generating materials with properties that are hybrids of their DNA and colloidal precursors, the union of metal-colloid and DNA chemistry offers significant opportunities relative to the construction of pure DNA materials. As noted by Seeman[19], "the theory of producing DNA [structures] is well ahead of experimental confirmation. It is much easier to design a [structure] than it is to prove its synthesis." An advantage of the DNA/colloid hybrid materials reported herein is that the assemblies can be characterized easily by transmission electron microscopy (TEM) and/or atomic force microscopy (AFM) as well as spectroscopic methods conventionally used with DNA.

Our approach to using oligonucleotides for the controlled assembly of gold nanoparticles into aggregate macroscopic structures is outlined in Fig. 1. First, 13-nm-diameter Au particles are prepared[2,20]. These particles form a dark red suspension in water, and like thin-film Au substrates[21], they are easily modified with oligonucleotides, which are functionalized with alkane thiols at their 3' termini. In a typical experiment, one solution of 17 nM (150 μl) Au colloids is treated for 24 h with 3.75 μM (46 μl) 3'-thiol-TTTGCTGA, and a second solution of colloids is treated with 3.75 μM (46 μl) 3'-thiol-TACCGTTG. Note that these oligonucleotides are non-complementary. After treatment with the thiol-capped oligonucleotides, the two colloidal Au solutions are combined, and because of the non-complementary nature of the oligonucleotides, no reaction takes place. A beneficial consequence of capping the colloids with these oligonucleotides is that they are much more stable than bare Au colloids to increased salt concentration and temperature. When heated or in a solution of high salt concentration (0.1 M NaCl), bare colloids undergo irreversible particle-growth reactions that result in their precipitation. In contrast, the

体。这种方法的弊端在于组装的过程难于控制而且这样的组装是不可逆的。如果要全面发掘这些奇异结构的材料性质，那么就需要发展出能够系统地控制组装过程的方法。

我们基于寡聚核苷酸的方法使得将金纳米颗粒可控并且可逆地组装成超分子结构成为可能。寡聚核苷酸相比非生物基的连接分子有一些优势。比如，具有可控长度及合适表面连接功能的单个序列可以通过自动运行的 DNA 合成仪来制备。这样，寡聚核苷酸的分子识别性能可以被用来引发胶体的自组装过程。这种方法制备的超分子结构的颗粒间距和稳定性可以通过对寡聚核苷酸序列及其长度、溶剂、温度和支持电解质浓度的选择来进行控制。

其他人也已经意识到了 DNA 在新型生物材料制备和纳米加工技术方面的应用。早期的研究重点是，利用寡聚核苷酸的序列特异性分子识别的性质去设计令人印象深刻的具有确定几何形状和尺寸的结构[8-18]。本文所展示的化学则着重于将 DNA 的化学与无机胶体材料的化学融合在一起。除了制备出具有所含的 DNA 和胶体前体的杂化性质的材料之外，相对于制备纯 DNA 材料而言，将金属胶体化学和 DNA 化学结合在一起提供了产生重大发现的可能性。就如西曼所指出的[19]，"制备 DNA（结构）的理论研究明显早于实验的确认。设计一个（结构）总是要比验证它的合成更为简单。"这里介绍的 DNA／胶体杂化材料的一大优点就是这种组装体可以很容易地通过透射电子显微镜（TEM）和（或）原子力显微镜（AFM）以及通常用于 DNA 研究的光谱手段来进行表征。

我们利用寡聚核苷酸将金纳米颗粒可控组装成为宏观结构聚集体的方法的简单流程如图 1 所示。首先，制备出直径为 13 nm 的金纳米颗粒[2,20]。这些颗粒在水中形成深红色的悬浮液。与薄膜金基质类似[21]，它们很容易被 3′ 端用烷基硫醇功能化的寡聚核苷酸修饰。在一个典型的实验中，17 nM（M：摩尔每升）的金胶体的溶液（150 μl）与 3.75 μM 的 3′－ 巯基 –TTTGCTGA 寡聚核苷酸片段的溶液（46 μl）反应 24 小时，同时另一份相同的金胶体溶液与 3.75 μM 的 3′－ 巯基 –TACCGTTG 溶液（46 μl）反应。需要注意的是这两种寡聚核苷酸是非互补的。经过巯基修饰的寡聚核苷酸处理之后，将这两种金胶体溶液混合起来。由于两种寡聚核苷酸的非互补性，此时没有反应发生。这种使用寡聚核苷酸修饰胶体颗粒的有利之处在于，经此处理的金胶体与裸的金胶体相比，在升高的盐浓度和温度下具有更好的稳定性。被加热时或者处于一个高盐浓度的溶液（0.1 M 的氯化钠）中时，裸的金胶体会发生不可逆的颗粒

DNA-modified Au nanoparticles reported here are stable at elevated temperatures (80 °C) and in aqueous 0.1 M NaCl solutions for days, presumably because their DNA-modified surfaces prohibit them from getting close enough to undergo particle growth. This is important because high salt concentrations are needed for the DNA hybridization events depicted in Fig. 1.

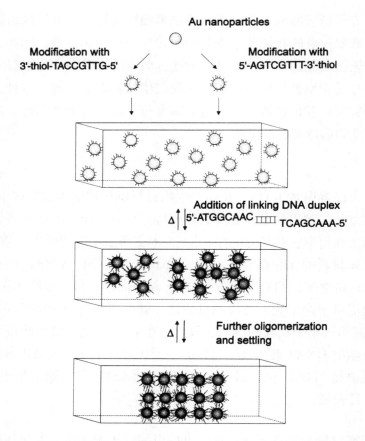

Fig. 1. Scheme showing the DNA-based colloidal nanoparticle assembly strategy (the hybridized 12-base-pair portion of the linking duplex is abbreviated as ⅢⅢ). If a duplex with a 12-base-pair overlap but with "sticky ends" with four base mismatches (5'-AAGTCAGTTATACGCGCTAG and 3'-ATATGCGCGATCAAATCACA) is used in the second step, no reversible particle aggregation is observed. The scheme is not meant to imply the formation of a crystalline lattice but rather an aggregate structure that can be reversibly annealed. Δ is the heating above the dissociation temperature of the duplex.

In the next step of the assembly scheme, a duplex consisting of 5'-ATGGCAACTATACG-CGCTAG and 3'-ATATGCGCGATCTCAGCAAA (the duplex has a 12-base-pair overlap (underlined), containing 8-base-pair sticky ends, which are complementary to the 8-base-pair oligonucleotides that are covalently attached to the Au colloids; Fig. 1) is added to the dark red solution. The solution is then diluted with aqueous NaCl (to 1 M) and buffered at pH 7 with 10 mM phosphate, conditions which are suitable for hybridization of the oligonucleotides. Significantly, an immediate colour change from red to purple is observed

918

生长反应导致沉淀产生。与之相反,本文报道的 DNA 修饰的金纳米颗粒在高温(80 ℃)和 0.1 M 的氯化钠水溶液中可以稳定数天,这大概可归因于它们经 DNA 修饰的表面阻止它们相互靠近到足以发生颗粒生长的距离。这一点非常重要,因为图 1 中描述的 DNA 杂化过程需要高的盐浓度。

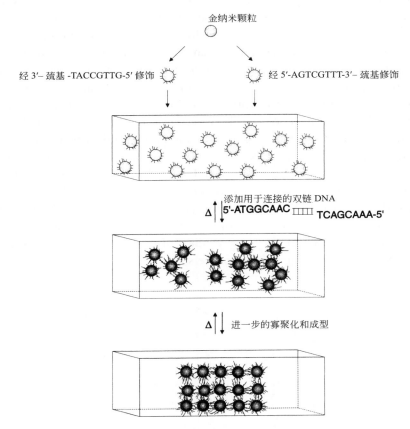

图 1. 基于 DNA 的胶体纳米颗粒的组装步骤的流程图(起连接作用的双链 DNA 的 12 对碱基杂化部分简化为 ▥)。如果在第二步使用有 12 对碱基交搭但是"黏性末端"有 4 个失配碱基的双链 DNA (5′–AAGTCAGTTATACGCGCTAG 和 3′–ATATGCGCGATCAAATCACA),那么就观察不到颗粒的可逆聚集。这个流程图并不意味着生成一晶格点阵,只是表示一个能够实现可逆退火的聚集体结构。Δ 表示加热至双链的解离温度以上。

在组装流程的下一步,一个包含链段 5′–ATGGCAAC<u>TATACGCGCTAG</u> 和链段 3′–<u>ATATGCGCGATC</u>TCAGCAAA 的双链(这个双链有 12 对碱基交搭(用下划线标出),含有 8 个配对碱基的黏性末端,这些黏性末端与共价修饰在金胶体上的带有 8 个配对碱基的寡聚核苷酸互补;图 1)被加入到深红色的溶液中。之后该溶液经氯化钠水溶液稀释(至 1 M)后加入 10 mM 的磷酸盐使之成为 pH 值为 7 的缓冲液,这样的条件适合于寡聚核苷酸的杂化。明显地,溶液颜色瞬间由红色变为紫色同时伴随

and a precipitation reaction ensues. Over the course of several hours, the solution becomes clear and a pinkish-grey precipitate settles to the bottom of the reaction vessel (Fig. 2). Presumably, the free ends of the "linking" duplex bind to the complementary oligomers anchored to the gold, thereby crosslinking the colloids, which ultimately results in the formation of the pinkish-grey polymeric DNA–colloid precipitate. To verify that this process involved both the DNA and colloids, the precipitate was collected and resuspended (by shaking) in 1 M aqueous NaCl buffered at pH 7. Then, a temperature/ time dissociation experiment was performed by monitoring both an optical absorption dependent on hybridization of DNA (260 nm) and one dependent on the degree of colloid aggregation (700 nm), Fig. 3a. As the temperature is cycled between 0 and 80 °C, which is 38 °C above the dissociation temperature (T_m) for the DNA-duplex ($T_m = 42$ °C), there is an excellent correlation between the optical signatures for both the colloids and DNA. In the absence of DNA, the ultraviolet-visible spectrum for the naked Au colloids is much less temperature-dependent (Fig. 3b). There is a substantial optical change when the polymeric DNA–colloid precipitate is heated above its melting point. The clear solution turns dark red as the polymeric biomaterial dehybridizes to generate the unlinked colloids which are soluble in the aqueous solution. This process is very reversible as evidenced by the temperature traces in Fig. 3a. In a control experiment designed to verify that this process was due to oligonucleotide hybridization, a duplex with four base-pair mismatches in each of the "sticky" ends of the linkers (step 2 in Fig. 1) did not induce the reversible particle aggregation process.

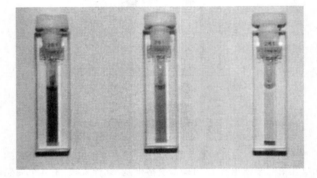

Fig. 2. Cuvettes with the Au colloids and the four DNA strands responsible for the assembly process. Left cuvette, at 80 °C with DNA-modified colloids in the unhybridized state; centre, after cooling to room temperature but before the precipitate settles; and right, after the polymeric precipitate settles to the bottom of the cuvette. Heating either of these cool solutions results in the reformation of the DNA-modified colloids in the unhybridized state (shown in the left cuvette).

有沉淀产生。数小时之后，溶液变得澄清，灰红色的沉淀沉积于反应容器的底部（图 2）。据此推测，起"连接"作用的双链的自由端连接在了与之互补的并且锚连在金上的寡聚片段上，进而使胶体颗粒发生交联，最终导致了灰红色的 DNA–胶体颗粒聚合物沉淀的形成。为了确认这一过程同时涉及 DNA 和胶体颗粒，这些沉淀被收集起来，（通过振荡的方法）重新悬浮在 pH 值为 7 的 1 M 的氯化钠缓冲液中。然后，通过同时监测与 DNA 杂化相关的光吸收（260 nm）和与胶体颗粒聚集程度有关的光吸收（700 nm）来进行一个温度 / 时间相关的解离实验，如图 3a。当温度在 0 ℃和 80 ℃之间循环时，胶体颗粒与 DNA 两者的光学信号之间有非常好的相关性，这里 80 ℃要比 DNA 双链的解离温度（$T_m = 42$ ℃）高 38 ℃。没有 DNA 的情况下，裸的金胶体颗粒的紫外–可见光谱与温度的相关性较小（图 3b）。当 DNA–胶体颗粒聚合物沉淀被加热到它的融解温度以上时，会有一个显著的光学变化。由于聚合的生物材料去杂化形成了在水溶液中可溶的非连接状态的胶体颗粒，澄清的溶液变为深红色。从图 3a 的温度响应曲线可以明显地看出这个过程是高度可逆的。在一个被设计用来确认这一过程是由寡聚核苷酸的杂化引起的对照实验中，在每个连接分子"黏性"末端都有 4 个失配碱基的双链片段（图 1 中的第二步）并不会导致颗粒的可逆聚集过程的发生。

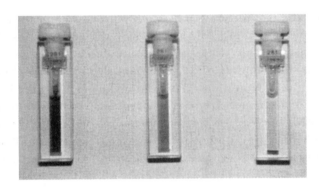

图 2. 含有金胶体颗粒和四种对组装过程有贡献的 DNA 片段的比色皿。左边的比色皿，80 ℃经过 DNA 修饰的胶体颗粒处于未杂化状态；中间，在冷却到室温之后，但在沉淀沉降之前；右边，在聚合的沉淀完全沉降于比色皿底部之后。对任何一种冷却的溶液加热都会导致处于非杂化状态的 DNA 修饰的胶体颗粒的重新生成（如左边的比色皿所示）。

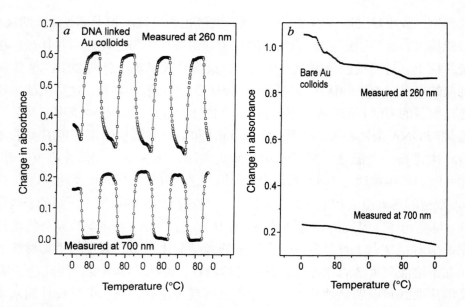

Fig. 3. *a*, Absorbance versus temperature/time profile for DNA/colloid hybridized materials. At low temperatures the Au colloids aggregate owing to the hybridization of "linking" DNA. At high temperature (80 °C), the colloids dehybridize and form a dark red solution (see Fig. 1 and Fig. 2). The temperature versus time profile shows that this is a reversible process. *b*, Results of the same procedure shown in *a*, but applied to an aqueous solution of unmodified Au colloids (5.1 nM, same concentration as in *a*).

Further evidence of the polymerization/assembly process comes from TEM studies of the polymeric precipitate (Fig. 4). TEM images of the colloids linked with hybridized DNA show large assembled networks of the Au colloids (Fig. 4*a*). Naked Au colloids do not aggregate in this manner under comparable conditions, but rather undergo particle-growth reactions[2]. Note that there is no evidence of colloid particle growth as the hybridized colloids seem to be remarkably regular in size with an average diameter of 13 nm. With TEM, because of the superposition of layers, it is difficult to assess the degree of order for three-dimensional aggregates. But smaller-scale images of single-layer, two-dimensional aggregates provide more compelling evidence of the self-assembly process (Fig. 4*b*). This figure shows close-packed assemblies of the aggregates with uniform particle separations ~60 Å. This distance is somewhat shorter than the maximum spacing (95 Å) expected for colloids connected by rigid DNA hybrids with the selected sequences. But because of the nicks in the DNA duplex, these are not rigid hybrids and are quite flexible. It should be noted that, in principle, this is a variable that can be controlled by reducing the system from four overlapping strands to three (thereby reducing the number of nicks) or by using triplexes instead of duplexes.

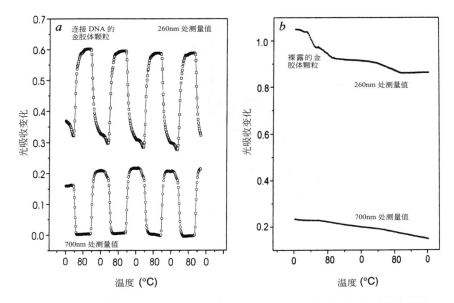

图 3. *a*，DNA/ 胶体颗粒杂化材料的光吸收随温度 / 时间的变化曲线。在低温时，起连接作用的 DNA 的杂化使得金胶体颗粒发生聚集。在高温（80℃）时，胶体颗粒去杂化形成深红色溶液（见图 1 和图 2）。温度随时间的变化反映出这是一个可逆的过程。*b*，与 *a* 中所示的相同的过程所得结果，但使用的是未经修饰的金胶体颗粒（5.1 nM，与 *a* 中同样的浓度）。

关于聚合 / 组装过程的进一步证据来自对于高聚物沉淀的透射电子显微镜研究（图 4）。由杂化 DNA 所连接的胶体颗粒的透射电子显微镜图片显示出了金胶体组装而成的大的网络结构（图 4*a*）。裸露的金胶体颗粒在相似条件下并不会以这种方式聚集，而是会发生颗粒生长反应[2]。需要指出的是，没有证据表明这里存在胶体颗粒的生长，因为杂化的胶体颗粒似乎尺寸非常均一，平均直径为 13 nm。通过透射电子显微镜观察，由于层与层之间的位置重叠，很难判断三维聚集体的有序度。但是单层、二维聚集体的小范围图像为自组装的过程提供了非常有说服力的证据（图 4*b*）。这张图片显示了聚集体的密堆积组装结构，颗粒间隙宽度均约为 60 Å。这一宽度略微短于具有选定序列的刚性 DNA 杂化连接的胶体颗粒的预期最大间隙宽度（95 Å）。但由于 DNA 双链中存在切口，因此它们并不是刚性的杂合体而是有一定的柔性。需要指出的是，原则上这一变量可以通过将体系从四段重叠链段减少为三段（同时将减少切口的数目）或者用三链 DNA 来代替双链 DNA 来控制。

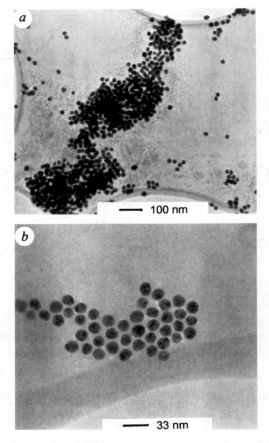

Fig. 4. TEM images of: *a*, an aggregated DNA/colloid hybrid material; *b*, a two-dimensional colloidal aggregate showing the ordering of the DNA-linked Au nanoparticles. Images were taken with a Hitachi 8100 Transmission Electron Microscope.

This work gives entry into a new class of DNA/nanoparticle hybrid materials and assemblies, which might have useful electrical, optical and structural properties that should be controllable through choice of nanoparticle size and chemical composition, and oligonucleotide sequence and length. We note that it should be possible to extend this strategy easily to other noble-metal (for example, Ag, Pt)[22] and semiconductor (for example, CdSe and CdS)[23,24] colloidal nanoparticles with well established surface coordination chemistry. Our initial results bode well for the utility of this strategy for developing new types of biosensing and sequencing schemes for DNA. The Au colloidal particles have large extinction coefficients for the bands that give rise to their colours (Fig. 2). These intense colours, which depend on particle size and concentration and interparticle distance, make these materials particularly attractive for new colorimetric sensing and sequencing strategies for DNA.

(**382**, 607-609; 1996)

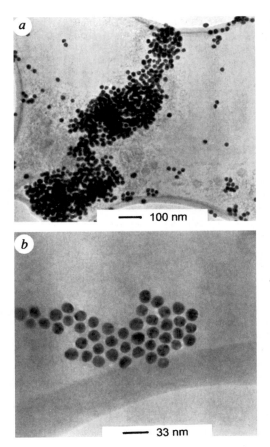

图 4. 透射电子显微镜照片：a，聚集的 DNA/ 胶体颗粒杂化材料；b，表明 DNA 连接的金纳米颗粒的排列有序性的二维胶体颗粒聚集体。照片摄自于日立 8100 型透射电子显微镜。

这一工作使得我们知道了一类新型的 DNA/ 纳米颗粒杂化材料和组装体，它们有可能具有实用的电学、光学和结构方面的性质，而通过调节纳米颗粒的尺寸和化学组成以及寡聚核苷酸序列及其长度可望实现对这些性质的控制。我们需要指出，这种策略应该可以很容易地拓展到其他的贵金属（比如，银和铂）[22] 和半导体（比如，硒化镉和硫化镉）[23,24] 等表面配位化学性质已经广为人知的胶体纳米颗粒体系。我们的初步结果预示着这一方法在发展新型的生物传感和 DNA 测序方面有着很好的应用前景。金胶体颗粒在产生其颜色的谱段有较大的消光系数（图 2）。这些强烈的颜色显著依赖于颗粒的尺寸、浓度以及颗粒间距，从而使得这种材料在新型的比色传感和 DNA 测序方面非常有吸引力。

（李琦 翻译；齐利民 审稿）

925

A DNA-based Method for Rationally Assembling Nanoparticles into Macroscopic Materials

Chad A. Mirkin, Robert L. Letsinger, Robert C. Mucic & James J. Storhoff

Department of Chemistry, Northwestern University, Evanston, Illinois 60208, USA

Received 19 April; accepted 24 June 1996.

References:

1. Schmid, G. (ed.) *Clusters and Colloids* (VCH, Weinheim, 1994).

2. Hayat, M. A. (ed.) *Colloidal Gold: Principles, Methods, and Applications* (Academic, San Diego, 1991).

3. Bassell, G. J., Powers, C. M., Taneja, K. L. & Singer, R. H. *J. Cell Biol.* **126**, 863-876 (1994).

4. Creighton, J. A., Blatchford, C. G. & Albrecht, M. G. *J. Chem. Soc., Faraday Trans. 2* **75**, 790-798 (1979).

5. Brust, M., Bethell, D., Schiffrin, D. J. & Kiely, C. J. *Adv. Mater.* **7**, 795-797 (1995).

6. Dubois, L. H. & Nuzzo, R. G. A. *Rev. Phys. Chem.* **43**, 437-463 (1992).

7. Bain, C. D. & Whitesides, G. M. *Angew. Chem. Int. Ed. Engl.* **28**, 506-512 (1989).

8. Shekhtman, E. M., Wasserman, S. A., Cozzarelli, N. R. & Solomon, M. J. *New J. Chem.* **17**, 757-763 (1993).

9. Shaw, S. Y. & Wang, J. C. *Science* **260**, 533-536 (1993).

10. Herrlein, M. K., Nelson, J. S. & Letsinger, R. L. *J. Am. Chem. Soc.* **117**, 10151-10152 (1995).

11. Chen, J. H. & Seeman, N. C. *Nature* **350**, 631-633 (1991).

12. Smith, F. W. & Feigon, J. *Nature* **356**, 164-168 (1992).

13. Wang, K. Y., McCurdy, S., Shea, R. G., Swaminathan, S. & Bolton, P. H. *Biochemistry* **32**, 1899-1904 (1993).

14. Chen, L. Q., Cai, L., Zhang, X. H. & Rich, A. *Biochemistry* **33**, 13540-13546 (1994).

15. Marsh, T. C., Vesenka, J. & Henderson, E. *Nucleic Acids Res.* **23**, 696-700 (1995).

16. Mirkin, S. M. & Frankkamenetskii, M. D. *Annu. Rev. Biophys. Biomol. Struct.* **23**, 541-576 (1994).

17. Wells, R. D. *J. Biol. Chem.* **263**, 1095-1098 (1988).

18. Wang, Y., Mueller, J. E., Kemper, B. & Seeman, N. C. *Biochemistry* **30**, 5667-5674 (1991).

19. Seeman, N. C. *et al. New J. Chem.* **17**, 739-755 (1993).

20. Grabar, K. C., Freeman, R. G., Hommer, M. B. & Natan, M. J. *Analyt. Chem.* **67**, 735-743 (1995).

21. Mucic, R. C., Herrlein, M. K., Mirkin, C. A. & Letsinger, R. L. *J. Chem. Soc., Chem. Commun.* 555-557 (1996).

22. Linnert, T., Mulvaney, P. & Henglein, A. *J. Phys. Chem.* **97**, 679-682 (1993).

23. Herron, N., Wang, Y. & Eckert, H. *J. Am. Chem. Soc.* **112**, 1322-1326 (1990).

24. Colvin, V. L., Goldstein, A. N. & Alivisatos, A. P. *J. Am. Chem. Soc.* **114**, 5221-5230 (1992).

Acknowledgements. We thank I. M. Klotz for discussions, and V. Dravid for assistance with the TEM experiments. C.A.M. was seed supported by an ONR Young Investigator award, an A. P. Sloan Foundation fellowship, a DuPont Young Professor award, an NSF Young Investigator award and a Cammille Dreyfus Teacher-Scholar Award; C.A.M. thanks the Materials Research Center of Northwestern University for the use of a TEM, which was purchased by the MRSEC Program of the National Science Foundation; R.L.L. was supported by the NIGMS.

Correspondence should be addressed to C.A.M. (e-mail: camirkin@chem.nwu.edu).

Organization of "Nanocrystal Molecules" Using DNA

A. P. Alivisatos *et al.*

Editor's Note

The use of DNA for assembling molecular-scale structures in nanotechnology was established in this paper by Paul Alivisatos and coworkers at the University of California at Berkeley, as well as in the previous paper by Mirkin *et al.* with which it was published. DNA strands carry chemical information in the form of the sequence of base pairs. A strand can thus be programmed to bind securely only to another strand with the complementary sequence, as in the double helix of chromosomes. Alivisatos and colleagues tagged gold nanoparticles with strands of DNA and let these bind to linking strands bearing complementary sequences so that the nanoparticles could be united in pairs or threes. This specific coupling of nanoparticles could be useful for making new optical and electronic devices.

Patterning matter on the nanometre scale is an important objective of current materials chemistry and physics. It is driven by both the need to further miniaturize electronic components and the fact that at the nanometre scale, materials properties are strongly size-dependent and thus can be tuned sensitively[1]. In nanoscale crystals, quantum size effects and the large number of surface atoms influence the chemical, electronic, magnetic and optical behaviour[2-4]. "Top-down" (for example, lithographic) methods for nanoscale manipulation reach only to the upper end of the nanometre regime[5]; but whereas "bottom-up" wet chemical techniques allow for the preparation of monodisperse, defect-free crystallites just 1–10 nm in size[6-10], ways to control the structure of nanocrystal assemblies are scarce. Here we describe a strategy for the synthesis of "nanocrystal molecules", in which discrete numbers of gold nanocrystals are organized into spatially defined structures based on Watson-Crick base-pairing interactions. We attach single-stranded DNA oligonucleotides of defined length and sequence to individual nanocrystals, and these assemble into dimers and trimers on addition of a complementary single-stranded DNA template. We anticipate that this approach should allow the construction of more complex two- and three-dimensional assemblies.

PREVIOUS approaches towards the preparation of coupled quantum dots include co-colloids of cadmium selenide–zinc oxide (CdSe–ZnO; ref. 11) and cadmium sulphide–silver iodide (CdS–AgI; ref. 12). In addition, small molecule crosslinking agents have been used to synthesize aggregates of Au (ref. 13) and cadmium sulphide linked to titanium oxide (CdS–TiO$_2$; ref. 14) as well as discrete dimers of cadmium selenide (CdSe;

利用 DNA 来实现"纳米晶体分子"的组装

艾利维萨托斯等

编者按

在这篇文章中加州大学伯克利分校的保罗·艾利维萨托斯及其同事们展示了在纳米科技中使用 DNA 组装分子尺度的结构的方法，这与前面发表的米尔金等人的文章类似。DNA 链以碱基对序列的方式携带化学信息。因而一条单链可以通过编码使之仅能够与另一条具有互补序列的单链牢固结合，形成与染色体中的双螺旋结构类似的结构。艾利维萨托斯及其同事们使用 DNA 链对金纳米颗粒进行标记后将之与含有互补序列起连接作用的 DNA 链相结合，这样可将纳米颗粒组装成两个或者三个一组的结构单元。这种纳米颗粒的特异性结合可用于制备新型的光学和电子学器件。

在纳米尺度上实现物质的图案化是当前材料化学和物理领域的一个重要研究目标。其推动力来自两方面：一是使电子元器件进一步微型化的需求，二是在纳米尺度下的材料性质具有强烈的尺寸依赖性并因此易于受到精细调控的事实 [1]。对于纳米尺度的晶体材料而言，它们的化学、电子学、磁学和光学性质都会受到量子尺寸效应和大量表面原子的影响 [2-4]。采用"自上而下"的方法（例如刻蚀技术）进行纳米尺度的操控仅仅只能达到纳米尺度的上限 [5]；而利用"自下而上"的湿化学法可以制备出单分散、无缺陷、仅 1~10 nm 大小的晶体材料 [6-10]，但仍缺少将纳米晶体进行可控组装得到特定结构的方法。这里我们介绍一种利用沃森－克里克的碱基配对原理制备"纳米晶体分子"的方法，该纳米晶体分子中一定数目的金纳米晶体被组装成为具有特定空间排布形式的有序结构。我们将长度和序列确定的单链 DNA 附着到单个纳米晶体上，以另外一条互补的单链 DNA 为模板组装得到纳米晶体的二聚体和三聚体。我们预期这种方法有望被应用于构造更为复杂的二维和三维组装体。

人们先前制备耦合量子点的方法涉及硒化镉－氧化锌（CdSe–ZnO，参考文献 11）和硫化镉－碘化银（CdS–AgI，参考文献 12）共胶体的制备。此外，人们利用小分子作为交联剂制备了金颗粒的聚集体（参考文献 13），硫化镉与二氧化钛的粘连体（CdS–TiO₂，参考文献 14）和分离的硒化镉二聚体（CdSe，参考文献 15）。最后，人

ref. 15). Finally, the collective properties of nanocrystals have been investigated using organic monolayers[16-22] and crystallization[23-26] to generate ordered arrays of inorganic quantum dots. It remains an open question whether self-assembly methods can be employed to generate complex sequences of nanocrystals.

Biological systems are characterized by remarkably complex structures, the assembly of which are controlled by highly selective, non-covalent interactions. For example, nucleic acids can fold into a variety of nanometre-sized structures including double helices, triplexes, knots, Holliday structures and polyhedra[27,28]. These structures are dictated by a network of specific hydrogen-bonding interactions involving the purine and pyrimidine bases. Consequently, by tagging individual nanocrystals with a DNA "codon" (a single-stranded DNA of defined length and sequences), it should be possible to self-assemble nanocrystal molecules in two and three dimensions by specific base-pairing interactions with a designed single-stranded DNA template. Furthermore, a variety of higher-order nanocrystal molecules could be accessible by attaching nanocrystals of different sizes and compositions to unique "codons" and assembling the "codons" and template strands in different geometries.

To test the feasibility of this approach, we chose as initial targets the head-to-head (antiparallel) and head-to-tail (parallel) homodimers shown in Fig. 1. Gold (Au) clusters, 1.4 nm in diameter and passivated with water-soluble phosphine ligands (Nanoprobes, Stony Brook, New York), were used for these investigations. The particles contain one N-propylmaleimide substituent per cluster which can be selectively coupled to a sulphydryl group incorporated into the single-stranded DNA "codon". Oligonucleotides, modified at either the 3' or 5' termini with a free sulphydryl group, were coupled with an excess of monomaleimido–Au particles. The oligonucleotide–Au conjugates were then combined with appropriate mounts of 37-nucleotide single-stranded templates and the resulting double-stranded complexes were purified from single-stranded precursors on a sizing column. The retention times of the DNA–Au conjugates were significantly different from the retention times of the corresponding Au–oligonucleotide duplexes. The ratio of absorbances at 280 nm to that at 420 nm (A_{280}/A_{420}), determined, indicated that the complex had spectrophotometrically the desired stoichiometries of oligonucleotide and Au cluster. The complexes were also analysed by gel electrophoresis using ethidium bromide and silver staining to visualize the oligonucleotides and oligonucleotide–Au conjugates, respectively (Fig. 2). In the case of the dimeric complexes, individual bands were observed that were assigned to double-stranded complexes containing two, one or zero Au particles. These assignments were confirmed by competing the oligonucleotide–Au conjugate with free oligomer and analysing the pattern and intensities of the resulting bands (Fig. 2).

930

们还利用有机单分子膜[16-22]和结晶化[23-26]形成无机量子点的有序阵列来研究纳米晶体的集体性质。但是，能否通过自组装的方法来得到复杂的纳米晶体序列仍是一个尚未解决的问题。

生物系统以极其复杂的结构为特点，这些结构的组装受到具有高度选择性的非共价相互作用的控制。例如，核酸可以折叠成为双螺旋、三股螺旋、扭结、霍利迪结构和多面体等一系列纳米尺度的结构[27,28]。这些结构是由嘌呤碱基和嘧啶碱基之间特定的氢键相互作用决定的。所以，通过将单个纳米晶体与 DNA"密码子"（具有特定长度和序列的单链 DNA 分子）连接，以能够与该单链 DNA 分子的碱基配对的另一单链 DNA 分子为模板，就有可能使纳米晶体自组装成为二维或者三维结构。此外，将不同大小和成分的纳米晶体与特定的"密码子"连接，以及将"密码子"与具有不同几何构型的 DNA 模板组装在一起，就有可能得到一系列具有更高级有序结构的纳米晶体分子。

为了验证这个方法的可行性，我们选择图 1 所示的头对头（反平行）和头对尾（平行）的同二聚体为初始研究对象。我们使用直径为 1.4 nm 的包覆了水溶性有机膦配体的金纳米簇（购自纽约州斯托尼布鲁克的纳米探测公司）来进行这项研究。每一个这种金颗粒上都包含有一个 $N-$ 丙基马来酰亚胺基团，这个基团可以选择性地与一个包含于单链 DNA"密码子"中的巯基基团相连接。这样，3′ 末端或 5′ 末端修饰有自由巯基基团的寡聚核苷酸就与过量的具有单一马来酰亚胺基团的金颗粒进行偶联。然后将寡聚核苷酸–金颗粒偶联体与适量的含有 37 个核苷酸的单链模板进行复合，所得到的双链复合物可以通过分子筛层析柱与单链前体分离开来。同时，DNA–金颗粒偶联体与相应的双链寡聚核苷酸–金颗粒复合物在停留时间上有明显差别。通过测量在 280 nm 和 420 nm 波长处的吸光度之比（A_{280}/A_{420}）可以确定该复合物中的寡聚核苷酸和金纳米簇是符合化学计量比的。所得到的复合物也用凝胶电泳方法进行了分析，经溴化乙锭和银染色剂着色之后可以分别显现出寡聚核苷酸和寡聚核苷酸–金颗粒偶联体（图 2）。在二聚体的电泳图中，可以分别观察到与包含了两个、一个和零个金颗粒的双链复合物相对应的染色条带。并且，我们通过寡聚核苷酸–金偶联体和自由的寡聚核苷酸的竞争，以及分析得到的这些染色条带的图案和亮度来确认这些条带的归属（图 2）。

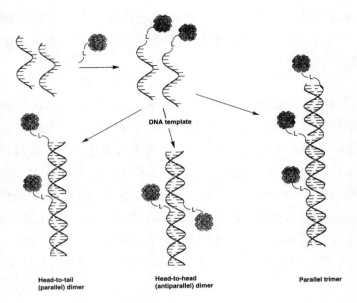

Fig. 1. Nanocrystal assembly based on Watson–Crick base-pairing interactions. Attachment of the inorganic nanocrystal (shaded) to either the 3' or 5' termini of the oligonucleotide "codon" by linker L, permits the preparation of head-to-head dimers, head-to-tail dimers, and trimers, as shown schematically here and observed in the TEM images of Fig. 3.

Methods. The "codon" and template oligonucleotides were prepared using an Applied Biosystems Model 391 DNA Synthesizer. Sulphydryl groups were introduced at the 5' or 3' termini of 18-nucleotide (nt) synthetic oligonucleotides by capping with S-trityl-6-mercaptohexylphosphoramidite or by using 1-O-dimethoxytritylpropyldisulphide-1'-succinoyl support (Glen Research, Sterling, Virginia), respectively. The 5'-thiol group was detritylated using silver nitrate and dithiothreitol following the procedure of Zuckermann *et al.*[29] Oligonucleotides thiolated at the 3'terminus were oxidized using a 0.02 M iodine solution after each coupling step and cleaved from support with 0.05 M dithiothreitol during deprotection in concentrated NH_4OH. All oligonucleotides were purified by gel electrophoresis or reverse-phase high-performance liquid chromatography (HPLC). Concentrations were determined spectrophotometrically and by titration of free thiol using 5,5'-dithiobis(2-nitrobenzoic acid). Thiolmodified oligonucleotides were stored at −20 °C in aqueous 50 mM dithiothreitol. Oligonucleotides were desalted on a Pharmacia Superdex 75 HR 10/30 column using 3 mM bis-Tris, 1 mM EDTA buffer, pH 6.5. Extinction coefficients were determined by combining standard extinction coefficients for the deoxynucleotide triphosphates (dNTPs). Sequences prepared for these experiments include: the 5'-thiol-terminated 18-nt oligomer (5'-HS-CAGTCAGGCAGTCAGTCA-3') (oligo **1**); the 37-nt template (5'-TGACTGACTGCCTGACTGTTGACTGACTGCCTGACTG-3') (template **2**); the 5'-thiol-terminated 18-nt oligomer (5'-HS-CTTGCACTAGTCCTTGAG-3') (oligo **3**); the 3'-thiol-terminated 18-nt oligomer (5'-CAGTCAGGCAGTCAGTCA-SH-3') (oligo **4**); the 37-nt template (5'-CTCAAGGACTAGTGCAAGTTGACTGACTGCCTGACTG-3') (template **5**); the 56-nt template 5'-TGACTGACTGCCTGACTGTTGACTGACTGCCTGACTGTTGACTGACTGCCTGACTG-3') (template **6**); and the unlabelled 18-nt oligomer (5'-CAGTCAGGCAGTCAGTCA-3') (oligo **7**). Oligonucleotides, modified at either the 3' or 5' termini with a free sulphydryl group (1.5 µM) were coupled with a 10-fold excess of the monomaleimido–Au particles (Nanoprobes, Stony Brook, NY) in aqueous 20 mM NaH_2PO_4, 150 mM NaCl, 1mM EDTA buffer, pH 6.5, containing 10% isopropanol at 4 °C for 24 h. The oligonucleotide–Au conjugates were then combined with the appropriate amounts of 37-nt single-stranded oligonucleotide templates and the resulting double-stranded complexes were purified from single-stranded precursors on a sizing column (Superose 12 10/30 in aqueous 5 mM NaH_2PO_4, 150 mM NaCl buffer, pH 6.5). The ratio of absorbances (A_{280}/A_{420}), determined spectrophotometrically, indicated that the complex had the desired stoichiometries of oligonucleotide and Au cluster.

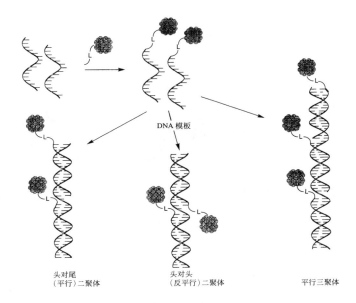

头对尾
(平行)二聚体

头对头
(反平行)二聚体

平行三聚体

图 1. 基于沃森-克里克碱基配对相互作用的纳米晶体组装。将无机纳米晶体(图中深色部分)通过连接分子 L 与 3′ 末端或者 5′ 末端的寡聚核苷酸 "密码子" 相接,就可以将之组装成为头对头二聚体、头对尾二聚体和三聚体。原理如图中所示,相应的透射电子显微镜观察结果如图 3 所示。

方法。寡聚核苷酸模板和 "密码子" 通过应用生物系统 391 型 DNA 合成仪合成。巯基基团通过硫-三苯甲基-6-巯基己基磷酰胺或者与基质相连的 1-氧-二甲氧基三苯甲基丙基二硫醚-1′-丁二酰基(购于弗吉尼亚州斯特灵的格伦研究公司)分别与 18 个核苷酸(nt)的合成寡聚核苷酸的 5′ 末端或者 3′ 末端反应引入。5′ 末端的巯基团上的三苯甲基采用楚克曼等人文献[29]中报道的方法用硝酸银和二硫苏糖醇脱除。在每一步偶联反应之后,用 0.02 M 的碘溶液来氧化 3′ 末端巯基化的寡聚核苷酸,而在浓氨水中脱保护的过程中用 0.05 M 的二硫苏糖醇溶液将其从基质上洗脱。所有的寡聚核苷酸均经过凝胶电泳或者反相高效液相色谱(HPLC)提纯。寡聚核苷酸的浓度通过分光光度法测定,也通过使用 5,5′-二硫代双(2-硝基苯甲酸)对自由的巯基进行滴定来确定。巯基化的寡聚核苷酸均在 50 mM 的二硫苏糖醇水溶液中于 −20 ℃ 保存。寡聚核苷酸经过法玛西亚公司的 Superdex 75 HR 10/30 型层析柱,用含有 3 mM bis-Tris 和 1 mM EDTA 的、pH 值为 6.5 的缓冲溶液进行脱盐处理。产物的消光系数通过与脱氧核苷酸三磷酸盐(dNTPs)的标准消光系数对照获得。在实验中用到的核苷酸序列包括:5′ 末端巯基化的 18 nt 寡聚核苷酸(5′–HS–CAGTCAGGCAGTCAGTCA–3′)(寡聚体 **1**),37 nt 模板(5′–TGACTGACTGCCTGACTGTTGACTGACTGCCTGACTG–3′)(模板 **2**),5′ 末端巯基化的 18 nt 寡聚核苷酸(5′–HS–CTTGCACTAGTCCTTGAG–3′)(寡聚体 **3**),3′ 末端巯基化的 18 nt 寡聚核苷酸(5′–CAGTCAGGCAGTCAGTCA–SH–3′)(寡聚体 **4**),37 nt 模板(5′–CTCAAGGACTAGTGCAAGTTGACTGACTGCCTGACTG–3′)(模板 **5**),56 nt 模板(5′–TGACTGACTGCCTGACTGTTGACTGACTGCCTGACTGTTGACTGACTGCCTGACTG–3′)(模板 **6**),未用巯基修饰的 18 nt 寡聚核苷酸(5′–CAGTCAGGCAGTCAGTCA–3′)(寡聚体 **7**)。3′ 末端或者 5′ 末端由一个自由巯基修饰的寡聚核苷酸(1.5 µM)与 10 倍过量的单马来酰亚胺修饰的金颗粒(购自纽约州斯托尼布鲁克的纳米探测公司)在含有 20 mM NaH_2PO_4、150 mM NaCl、1 mM EDTA 并含有 10% 异丙醇的 pH 值为 6.5 的水溶液中在 4 ℃ 下进行偶联反应 24 小时。将得到的寡聚核苷酸-金颗粒偶联体与适量的 37 nt 单链寡聚核苷酸模板混合使之结合,得到的双链复合物与单链的前体通过分子筛层析柱进行分离(Superose 12 10/30 型层析柱,含有 5 mM NaH_2PO_4、150 mM NaCl 的缓冲液,pH 值为 6.5)。分光光度法测量得到的吸光度之比(A_{280}/A_{420})表明得到的复合物中寡聚核苷酸与金纳米簇的化学计量比符合预期值。

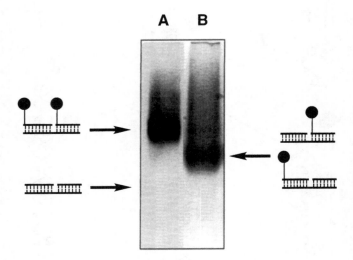

Fig. 2. Gel electrophoresis (10% acrylamide) results of DNA–Au complexes after purification by a sizing column; lane A, a 2 : 1 mixture of Au-labelled oligo **1** and the corresponding template **2**; lane B, a 1 : 1 mixture of Au-labelled oligo **1** and oligo **7** incubated with template **2**. The arrows indicate the retention times of the nucleic acid complexes containing two, one and zero Au clusters (indicated by the filled circles). Gel electrophoresis was accomplished using 10% crosslinked polyacrylamide gels[30] in 1 × TBE buffer at 80 mV. The Au-labelled oligonucleotides were visualized by development with LI Silver stain (Nanoprobes, Stony Brook, NY), and the non-Au-labelled duplexes were visualized by treatment with ethidium bromide. The band representing the template **2** annealed to two oligo **7** fragments was visualized using ethidium bromide staining but not with the LI Silver stain.

Transmission electron microscopy (TEM) was used to characterize the DNA–Au nanocrystal molecules. Dilute samples (20–30 nM) were imaged on ultra-thin carbon films coated with polylysine solution (10 mg per ml) to enhance binding of the oligonucleotides. Experiments using a double-stranded oligonucleotide–Au control showed that 90% of the Au particles are well separated, thereby excluding the possibility of aggregation due to TEM sample preparation. The TEM images (Fig. 3a, b) of the DNA–Au complexes were consistent with the expected dimeric structures. Modelling of the parallel and antiparallel dimers indicates that the centre-to-centre distances between the two Au particles can vary from 2.6 to 12.5 nm and 2.6 to 7.5 nm, respectively, due to the combined lengths of the linkers and the ligand shell. The distances observed under the TEM for the parallel and antiparallel dimers range from 2.9 ± 0.6 to 10.2 ± 0.6 nm and 2.0 ± 0.6 to 6.3 ± 0.6 nm, respectively. As additional evidence for our ability to chemically control nanocrystal molecules, we synthesized a trimeric parallel complex using a 56-nucleotide single-stranded DNA template (Fig. 3c).

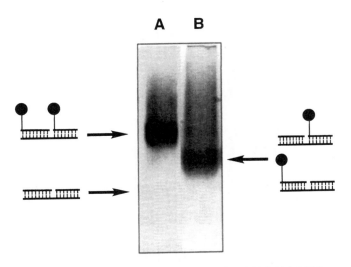

图 2. 经过分子筛层析柱提纯之后的 DNA－金颗粒复合物的凝胶电泳结果(采用含 10% 丙烯酰胺的凝胶)。A 泳道，连接有金颗粒的寡聚体 1 与相应的模板 2 以 2∶1 的比例混合后的产物；B 泳道，连接有金颗粒的寡聚体 1 与未标记金颗粒的寡聚体 7 以 1∶1 的比例混合后与模板 2 形成的复合物。图中箭头显示了包含两个、一个和零个金纳米簇的核酸复合物(示意图中的金纳米簇用实心圆表示)的停留时间。凝胶电泳实验使用浓度为 10% 的交联聚丙烯酰胺凝胶[30] 在 1×TBE 缓冲液中 80 mV 的电压下进行。连接有金颗粒的双链寡聚核苷酸用 LI 银染色剂(购自纽约州斯托布鲁克的纳米探测公司)着色，没有连接金颗粒的双链寡聚核苷酸用溴化乙锭着色。模板 2 与两个寡聚体 7 结合的双链寡聚核苷酸在使用溴化乙锭着色时可见，但使用 LI 银染色剂时不可见。

使用透射电子显微镜来表征这些 DNA－金纳米晶体分子。使用多聚赖氨酸溶液 (10 mg·ml^{-1}) 对碳膜进行了涂层以提高寡聚核苷酸与超薄碳膜之间的结合力，而后将稀释过的样品 (20~30 nM) 滴于碳膜之上用于透射电子显微镜成像。实验中观察到作为对照物的双链寡聚核苷酸－金颗粒复合物中 90% 的金颗粒是分离的，从而排除了在透射电子显微镜样品制备过程中发生金颗粒聚集的可能性。DNA－金颗粒复合物的透射电子显微镜照片(图 3a 和 b)符合预期的二聚体结构。由于连接分子的结合长度和配体外壳的存在，在平行和反平行排列的二聚体模型中两个金颗粒之间的理论中心间距应该分别在 2.6~12.5 nm 和 2.6~7.5 nm 之间。而透射电子显微镜观察到的平行排列的二聚体中金颗粒实际间距在 2.9±0.6 nm 到 10.2±0.6 nm 之间，反平行排列的二聚体中金颗粒距离在 2.0±0.6 nm 到 6.3±0.6 nm 之间。为了进一步验证这种纳米晶体分子制备方法的化学可控性，我们使用含有 56 个核苷酸的单链 DNA 为模板制备出了平行排列的三聚复合体(图 3c)。

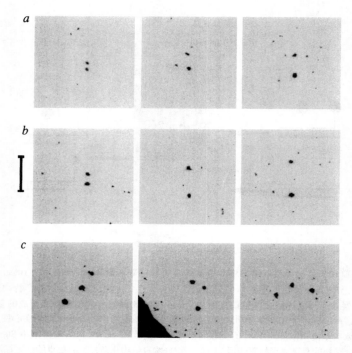

Fig. 3. Transmission electron microscopy (TEM) images of 1.4 nm Au–nucleic acid complexes. *a*, Head-to-head dimer sample in which a 2 : 1 ratio of oligo **1** was hybridized to the corresponding template **2**. From left to right are examples of the nearest, average and farthest dimers. The centre-to-centre distances range from 2.0 ± 0.6 to 6.3 ± 0.6 nm. *b*, Head-to-tail dimer sample in which a 1 : 1 ratio of oligo **3** and oligo **4** were hybridized to template **5**. From left to right are examples of the nearest, average and farthest dimmers. The centre-to-centre distances in this example ranged from 2.9 ± 0.6 to 10.2 ± 0.6 nm. *c*, Equidistant trimer sample in which oligo **1** was hybridized to the trimeric template **6**. The curvature apparent in the trimer samples may reflect the flexibility of the linkers between the Au centres and the nucleic acids or bending in the DNA. Scale bar, 10 nm. The absorbances of Au–DNA samples used for imaging was approximately 5 mAU (where AU is absorbance units). A Jeol-100CX TEM instrument, operating at 80 kV, was used to image the samples which had been deposited on 400-mesh copper grids coated with ultra-thin (2–3 nm) holey carbon films. The carbon-coated grids were subjected briefly to an air plasma (30 seconds at 50 mtorr) followed by deposition of 10–15 µl of a 10 mg per ml solution of polylysine (reactive molecular mass 10–40,000, pH 7.5; Sigma Chemical, St Louis, Missouri). The grids were dried in air, solutions of the DNA–Au complexes were deposited and the excess solution was removed by wicking. Examination of a large number of nanocrystal–DNA complexes by TEM indicated that ~70% were consistent with the expected dimeric structures.

These results demonstrate the potential of using oligonucleotides to self-assemble inorganic nanoparticles into aggregates that are discrete, well-defined, homogeneous and soluble. Further improvements in the methodology, particularly shorter and more rigid linkers and soluble, stable ligands for nanocrystals other than Au, are required before the full range of physical phenomena expected in coupled nanocrystal systems can be investigated. However, this approach should allow the chemical synthesis of complex mixtures of nanocrystals of differing sizes and compositions with the size of complete aggregate limited only by the degree of control over the nucleic acid template.

(**382**, 609-611; 1996)

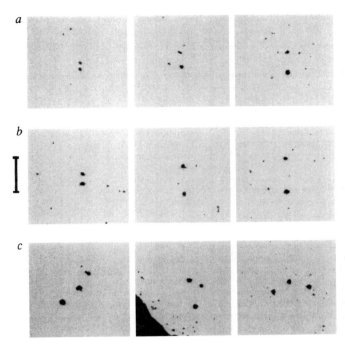

图 3. 1.4 nm 的金颗粒 – 核酸复合物的透射电子显微镜(TEM)图片。a，将连接有金颗粒的寡聚体 **1** 与相应的模板 **2** 以 2∶1 的比例复合时得到的头对头二聚体样品。从左到右的三幅图分别为金颗粒间的距离为最短、平均值和最长时的二聚体。金颗粒的中心间距在 2.0±0.6 nm 到 6.3±0.6 nm 之间。b，连接有金颗粒的寡聚体 **3** 和 **4** 的 1∶1 混合物与模板 **5** 复合形成的头对尾二聚体样品。从左到右分别对应于金颗粒之间距离为最短、平均值和最长时的二聚体。金颗粒的中心间距在 2.9±0.6 nm 到 10.2±0.6 nm 之间。c，连接有金颗粒的寡聚体 **1** 与三聚体模板 **6** 杂化形成的金颗粒之间等间距的三聚体。三聚体样品的曲率表明金颗粒与核酸之间的连接分子有一定的柔性，或者 DNA 链段发生了弯曲。图中比例尺为10 nm。用以成像的金颗粒 – DNA 复合物样品的吸光度大约为 5 mAU(其中 AU 为吸光度的单位)。将样品沉积在覆盖有超薄多孔碳膜(2~3 nm 厚)的 400 目铜网上，利用 Jeol – 100CX 型透射电子显微镜在80 kV 的加速电压下使样品成像。覆盖有碳膜的铜网经过短暂的空气等离子体轰击(轰击时间 30 秒，气压 50 毫托)之后，滴涂上 10~15 μl，10 mg·ml⁻¹ 的聚赖氨酸溶液(活性分子量在 10~40,000 之间，pH 值为 7.5；购于密苏里州圣路易斯的西格玛化学公司)。待铜网在空气中干燥后，将 DNA – 金颗粒复合物溶液滴于铜网上，再吸去多余的溶液。对大量纳米晶体 – DNA 复合物样品的透射电子显微镜观察结果表明，约 70% 的复合物具有预期的二聚体结构。

　　上述结果证实了利用寡聚核苷酸可以将无机纳米颗粒自组装成为分立的、结构规整的、均一且可溶的聚集体。在对预期存在于偶联纳米晶体系统中的物理现象进行全面的研究之前，需要对该方法进行进一步优化，尤其是选择更短、更具刚性的连接分子，以及适用于除金之外的其他纳米晶体的可溶且稳定的配体。然而，这种方法可以实现由不同尺寸和组分的纳米晶体组成的复杂混合物的化学合成，最终的聚集体的大小仅仅受限于对核酸模板的控制程度。

（李琦 翻译；齐利民 审稿）

A. Paul Alivisatos[*], **Kai P. Johnsson**[†], **Xiaogang Peng**[*], **Troy E. Wilson**[†], **Colin J. Loweth**[†], **Marcel P. Bruchez Jr**[*] & **Peter G. Schultz**[†]

[*] Department of Chemistry, University of California at Berkeley, Berkeley, California 94720, USA and Molecular Design Institute, Lawrence Berkeley National Laboratory, Berkeley, California 94701, USA

[†] Howard Hughes Medical Institute, Department of Chemistry, University of California at Berkeley, Berkeley, California 94720, USA

Received 7 June; accepted 16 July 1996.

References:

1. Alivisatos, A. P. *Science* **271**, 933-937 (1996).

2. Bawendi, M. G., Steigerwald, M. L. & Brus, L. E. *Annu. Rev. Phys. Chem* **41**, 477-496 (1990).

3. Weller, H. *Angew. Chem. Int. Ed. Engl.* **32**, 41-53 (1993).

4. Tolbert, S. H. & Alivisatos, A. P. *Annu. Rev. Phys. Chem.* **46**, 595-625 (1995).

5. Waugh, F. R. *et al. Phys. Rev. Lett.* **75**, 705-708 (1995).

6. Murray, C. B., Norris, D. J. & Bawendi, M. G. *J. Am. Chem. Soc.* **115**, 8706-8715 (1993).

7. Littau, K. A., Szajowski, P. J., Muller, A. J., Kortan, A. R. & Brus, L. E. *J. Phys. Chem.* **97**, 1224-1230 (1993).

8. Guzelian, A. A. *et al. J. Phys. Chem.* **100**, 7212-7219 (1996).

9. Schmid, G. *Chem. Rev.* **92**, 1709-1727 (1992).

10. Haneda, K. *Can. J. Phys.* **65**, 1233-1241 (1987).

11. Spanhel, L, Weller, H. & Henglein, A. *J. Am. Chem. Soc.* **109**, 6632-6635 (1987).

12. Gopidas, K. R., Bohorquez, M. & Kamat, P. V. *J. Phys. Chem.* **94**, 6435-6440 (1990).

13. Brust, M., Bethell, D., Schiffrin, D. J. & Kiely, C. J. *Adv. Mater.* **7**, 795-797 (1995).

14. Lawless, D., Kapoor, S. & Meisel, D. *J. Phys. Chem.* **99**, 10329-10335 (1995).

15. Pag, X. *et al. Angew. Chem.* (submitted).

16. Peschel, S. & Schmid, G. *Angew. Chem. Int. Ed. Engl.* **34**, 1442-1443 (1995).

17. Whetten, R. L. *et al. Adv. Mater.* **8**, 428-433 (1996).

18. Andres, R. P. *et al. Science* **272**, 1323-1325 (1996).

19. Klein, D. L., McEuen, P. L, Bowen-Katari, J. E., Roth, R., Alivisatos, A. P. *Appl. Phys. Lett.* **68**, 2574-2576 (1996).

20. Covin, V. L., Goldstein, A. N., Alivisatos, A. P. *J. Am. Chem. Soc.* **114**, 5221-5230 (1992).

21. Fendler, J. H., Meldrum, F. C. *Adv. Mater.* **7**, 607-632 (1995).

22. Peng, X. *et al. J. Phys. Chem.* **96**, 3412-3416 (1992).

23. Murray, C. B., Kagan, C. R. & Bawendi, M. G. *Science* **270**, 1335-1338 (1995).

24. Vossmeyer, T. *et al. Science* **267**, 1476-1479 (1995).

25. Herron, N., Calabrese, J. C., Farneth, W. E. & Wang, Y. *Science* **259**, 1426-1428 (1993).

26. Bentzon, M. D., van Wonterghem, J., Morup, S., Tholen, A. & Koch, C. J. W. *Phil. Mag. B* **60**, 169-178 (1989).

27. Seeman, N. C. *Mater. Res. Soc. Symp. Proc.* **292**, 123-135 (1993).

28. Niemeyer, C. M., Sano, T., Smith, C. L. & Cantor, C. R. *Nucleic Acids Res.* **22**, 5530-5539 (1994).

29. Zuckermann, R. N., Corey, D. R. & Schultz, P. G. *Nucleic Acids Res.* **15**, 5305-5321 (1987).

30. Maniatis, T., Frisch, E. F. & Sambrook, J. *Molecular Cloning: A Laboratory Manual* (Cold Spring Harbor Lab., Cold Spring Harbor, NY, 1989).

Acknowledgements. We thank S. Miller, A. Kadavanich, and the staff at the Robert Ogg Electron Microscopy Laboratory, U. C. Berkeley. This work was supported by the US Office of Naval Research, and the Director of the Office of Energy Research, US Department of Energy. P.G.S. is a Howard Hughes Medical Institute Investigator. T.E.W. was supported by fellowships from the Howard Hughes Medical Institute and the Fannie and John Hertz Foundation. K.J. was supported by the Deutsche Forschungsgemeinschaft.

Correspondence should be addressed to A.P.A. or P.G.S.

Discovery of Ganymede's Magnetic Field by the Galileo Spacecraft

M. G. Kivelson *et al.*

Editor's Note

The Earth has a fairly strong magnetic field, and Mercury a weak one. Venus and Mars do not have magnetic fields. Although Jupiter's Galilean moon Io probably has one, it is a special case because of the extreme tidal forces on the moon created by Jupiter and the fact that it is immersed in Jupiter's massive field. It was quite surprising when, in this paper, Margaret Kivelson and her colleagues reported that Ganymede, the largest of the four Galilean moons of Jupiter, generates its own internal magnetic field, probably through convection in the molten iron core—a process similar to that which generates the Earth's magnetic field. The field is strong enough to carve out a small, separate magnetosphere within Jupiter's own magnetosphere.

The Galileo spacecraft has now passed close to Jupiter's largest moon—Ganymede—on two occasions, the first at an altitude of 838 km, and the second at an altitude of just 264 km. Here we report the discovery during these encounters of an internal magnetic field associated with Ganymede (the only other solid bodies in the Solar System known to have magnetic fields are Mercury, Earth and probably Io[1]). The data are consistent with a Ganymede-centred magnetic dipole tilted by ~10° relative to the spin axis, and an equatorial surface-field strength of ~750 nT. The magnetic field is strong enough to carve out a magnetosphere with clearly defined boundaries within Jupiter's magnetosphere. Although the observations require an internal field, they do not indicate its source. But the existence of an internal magnetic field should in itself help constrain models of Ganymede's interior.

ON Galileo's first inbound pass following orbital insertion, the magnetometer[2] measurements followed reasonably closely the predictions from a recent model of the magnetic field of Jupiter's magnetosphere[3] that we refer to as the KK96 model. (This model consists of the O6 model[4] of Jupiter's internal field plus the field of a warped and hinged current sheet parametrized to fit the magnetic field measured on the Pioneer 10 outbound pass near the dawn meridian.) The field increased in magnitude with approach to Jupiter and varied in orientation at Jupiter's rotation period. Data from 00:00 UT (universal time; h:min) to 12:00 UT on 27 June 1996 are plotted in Fig. 1; the Ganymede-associated perturbation is clearly apparent at 06:29 UT. The Ganymede encounter occurred well off the jovian magnetic equator (identifiable by the reversal of sign of B_r (the coordinate system is defined in Fig. 1 legend)) and thus in a region of relatively low

伽利略木星探测器发现木卫三的磁场

基维尔森等

编者按

地球有相当强的磁场，而水星磁场较弱。金星和火星没有磁场。尽管木星的伽利略卫星木卫一(Io)可能有磁场，但这是一个特殊的例子，因为这颗卫星受到了极强的潮汐力并且处于木星的强磁场中。在本文中，玛格丽特·基维尔森和她的同事们报道了相当令人吃惊的结果，木星的四颗伽利略卫星中最大的木卫三(Ganymede)有可能通过与熔融铁核作用产生了自己的内源磁场，该过程与地球磁场的产生相似。这个磁场强到足以在木星的磁层中开拓出一个小的独立磁层。

伽利略木星探测器已经两次掠过木星最大的卫星——木卫三。第一次距木卫三表面高度 838 km，第二次高度只有 264 km。在这里，我们报道在这两次与木卫三有关的内源磁场相遇期间的发现(在太阳系其他固态天体中已知具有磁场的只有水星、地球，可能还有木卫一[1])。观测数据与以相对于木卫三自旋轴倾斜约 10°的中心磁偶极子一致，且赤道处表面场强约为 750 nT(nT，纳特)。这个磁场的强度足以在木星磁层中开拓出一个具有明确边界的磁层。虽然观测结果需要用一个内源磁场来解释，但并不确定其来源。虽然如此，内源磁场的存在本身也可以帮助我们约束木卫三内部的模型。

在伽利略号入轨后的首次降轨过程中，磁强计[2]的测量结果与近期的木星磁层的磁场模型[3]KK96 的预测结果符合得很好。(这个模型包括木星内源磁场的 O6 模型[4]加上一个翘曲铰连式的电流片，这个电流片的参数通过对先驱者 10 号在近黎明子午线附近升轨时的测量数据进行拟合得到。)在接近木星过程中场强增大，并且磁场方向变化的周期与木星自转周期相同。图 1 显示了从 1996 年 6 月 27 日 00:00 UT (世界时，小时:分钟)到 12:00 UT 的磁场数据，06:29 UT 出现了一个明显与木卫三有关的扰动。与木卫三的相遇发生在远离木星磁赤道的地方(从 B_r 的正负号反转可以看出来(坐标系的定义见图 1 注))，故在等离子体密度相对较低的区域内。最近点在木星磁层的等离子流中木卫三的下游。靠近木卫三，场强从 06:00 UT 的 107 nT

plasma density. Closest approach was downstream of Ganymede relative to the flowing plasma of Jupiter's magnetosphere. Near to Ganymede, the field increased from 107 nT at 06:00 UT to 480 nT at 06:29:07 UT (h:min:s) near closest approach, and then decreased to background, returning to 118 nT at ~07:00 UT. A considerable rotation accompanied the change in field magnitude.

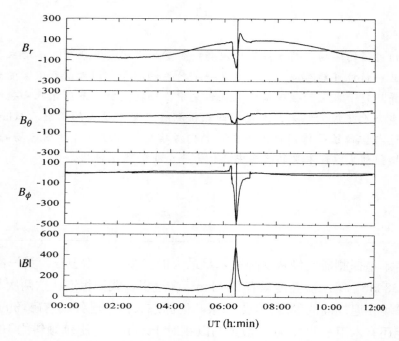

Fig. 1. Magnetometer data for the inbound pass to Jupiter on 27 June 1996 over a radial distance range from 17.44 to 13.14 jovian radii from Jupiter. The data are given in a Jupiter-centred right-handed spherical coordinate system (r, θ, ϕ) with r the radial distance, θ the angle from the spin axis, and ϕ the azimuthal angle. This is a variant of System III (1996)[14] with ϕ increasing westward. The ten-hour periodicity arises from Jupiter's rotation. Closest approach to Ganymede was at 06:29:07 UT. All times are given as spacecraft event time, which is universal time at the spacecraft. The magnetic field vector is $\mathbf{B} = (B_r, B_\theta, B_\phi)$.

The data near closest approach for this first pass are shown in Fig. 2. The field near closest approach is approximately that of a magnetic dipole centred at Ganymede with surface strength 750 nT at the equator added to the KK96 model. The dipole north pole is tilted by 10° from the spin axis towards 200° Ganymede east longitude. (Longitude of 180° is radially outward from Jupiter.) Currents flowing in the magnetospheric plasma in Ganymede's environment perturb the magnetic signature[5,6], so the actual magnetic moment of Ganymede may be slightly overestimated by the vacuum field estimate. In Fig. 3 we show projections of the trajectory and of the perturbation field vectors measured along it. (The perturbation field is the vector difference between the observed field and the KK96 model field.) The figure illustrates that the field perturbations converge towards Ganymede, as expected in the vicinity of an internal dipole.

942

增加到 06:29:07 UT(小时:分钟:秒)最近点附近的 480 nT，然后又回落到背景水平，在大约 07:00 UT 回到 118 nT。伴随磁场强度变化有可观的旋转。

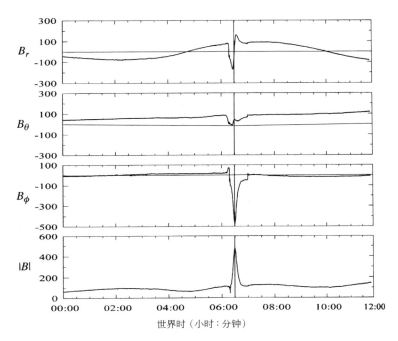

图 1. 1996 年 6 月 27 日向木星降轨过程中，径向距离从 17.44 个木星半径到 13.14 个木星半径的磁强计数据。数据基于以木星为中心的右手球坐标系 (r, θ, ϕ)，其中 r 是径向距离，θ 是相对于自转轴的角度，ϕ 是方位角。这是 System Ⅲ(1996)[14] 的一个方位角向西增大的变化形式。10 小时的周期来源于木星的自转。06:29:07 UT 到达距木卫三的最近点。所有时间都是飞船事件时间，也就是飞船上的世界时。磁场矢量 $\mathbf{B} = (B_r, B_\theta, B_\phi)$。

图 2 显示第一次经过距木卫三最近点附近的数据。最近点附近的场强大致相当于将一个以木卫三为中心且赤道表面场强为 750 nT 的磁偶极子叠加于 KK96 模型上的磁场强度。偶极子北极从自转轴向木卫三东经 200°(180° 经度是从木星径向向外)方向倾斜 10°。由于木卫三周边磁层等离子体的电流扰动了磁场形态[5,6]，所以按照真空场来估计，木卫三的实际磁矩可能被稍微高估。我们在图 3 中给出了伽利略号轨道的投影以及沿轨道测量的扰动场磁场矢量。(扰动场是指观测到的磁场与 KK96 模型场的矢量差。)此图显示扰动场汇聚于木卫三，符合内偶极子附近的预期。

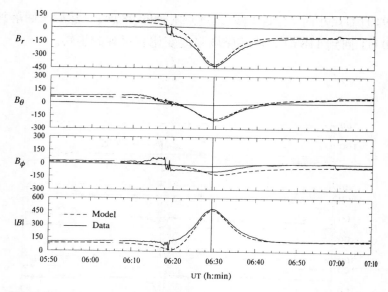

Fig. 2. Magnetic-field components and magnitude (solid lines) from 05:50 UT to 07:10 UT on 27 June 1996. The data are given in a Ganymede-centred coordinate system referenced to Ganymede's spin axis with r the radial distance, θ the angle from an axis parallel to Jupiter's spin axis and through Ganymede's centre, and ϕ the azimuthal angle, increasing eastward. Galileo's radial distance from the centre of Ganymede varied from $6.85\,R_G$ (radius of Ganymede, 2,634 km) at 05:50 UT to $1.32\,R_G$ at closest approach (marked by a vertical line) and out to $5.47\,R_G$ at 07:00 UT. Dashed lines show the superposition of a model of the jovian field[3] and the field of a Ganymede-centred magnetic moment described in the text. The data resolution is 0.333 s between 06:07 and 06:44 UT. Elsewhere the data resolution is 24 s.

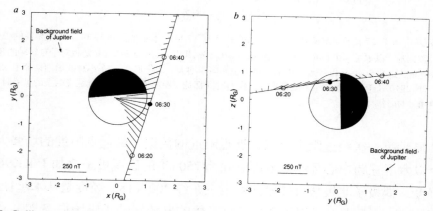

Fig. 3. Galileo's (27 June 1996) inbound towards Jupiter in the region near Ganymede (large circle, Ganymede; small circles, Galileo). The filled circle is near the closest approach to Ganymede. The plots use a coordinate system referenced to the direction of co-rotation (along $\hat{\mathbf{x}}$) and the spin axis of Jupiter, effectively the spin axis of Ganymede (along $\hat{\mathbf{z}}$). The unperturbed background field lies in the y–z plane roughly 50° outward from $-\hat{\mathbf{z}}$; $\hat{\mathbf{y}}$ is positive inward towards Jupiter. a, x–y projection, indicating the flow direction. The lines rooted along the trajectory are proportional to the projection of $\mathbf{B}-\mathbf{B}_{model}$ of Fig. 2 and the scale for the field perturbations is indicated. Key times are given. The projection direction of the background field is also shown. The night side of Ganymede is shaded. The terminator was crossed close to the centre of the wake, with the sunlit side corresponding to negative values of y. b, y–z projection of the trajectory and the perburbation field vectors. Note that the trajectory passes principally above Ganymede's equator.

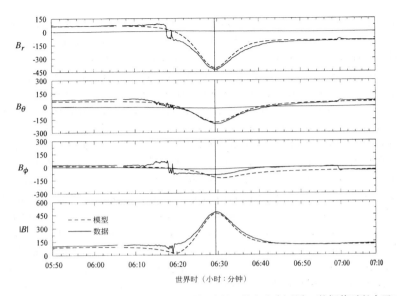

图 2. 1996 年 6 月 27 日 05:50 UT 到 07:10 UT 的磁场分量及其大小(实线)。数据基于以木卫三为中心、其自转轴为基准的坐标系。其中 r 是径向距离,θ 是相对一个平行于木星自转轴且通过木卫三中心的轴的角度,ϕ 是向东增大的方位角。伽利略号离开木卫三的径向距离从 05:50 UT 的 6.85 R_G(R_G 为木卫三半径,2,634 km)到最近点(垂直线)的 1.32 R_G,又在 07:00 UT 超过 5.47 R_G。虚线显示木星磁场模型[3]和正文中描述的木卫三为中心的磁矩的叠加。从 06:07 UT 到 06:44 UT,数据的分辨率为 0.333 s,其他地方数据的分辨率为 24 s。

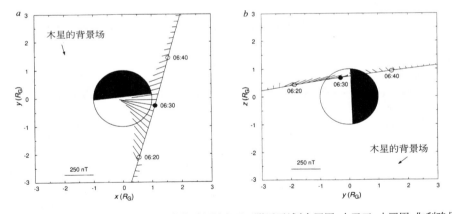

图 3. 1996 年 6 月 27 日伽利略号向木星降轨时经过木卫三附近区域(大圆圈,木卫三;小圆圈,伽利略号)。实心圆圈接近飞船距离木卫三的最近点。本图使用的坐标系是基于共转方向(沿 $\hat{x}$ 轴)以及木星自转轴,后者也基本上就是木卫三自转轴(沿 $\hat{z}$ 轴)。未受扰动的背景磁场在 y-z 平面上,从 $-\hat{z}$ 向外转大约 50°;$\hat{y}$ 轴正向向内指向木星。a,x-y 投影,显示流动方向。从轨迹发出的线段长度正比于图 2 中 $\mathbf{B}-\mathbf{B}_{\text{model}}$ 的投影,扰动场的比例尺和基本时刻点、背景场的投影方向也在图中标出。木卫三的夜半球用阴影表示。图中飞船轨迹的中点越过明暗界线,昼半球对应 y 的负值。b,轨迹的 y-z 投影以及扰动场矢量。注意轨迹主要经过木卫三赤道上方。

For the second pass, Ganymede was again located well above the jovian current sheet, probably in a region of low plasma density. The full data from the magnetometer and other particle and field instruments will be reported elsewhere, but measurements at ~1-minute resolution were acquired in advance of the full data set by operating the magnetometer[2] in a mode that averages and stores up to 200 field vectors for delayed transmission to the ground. Figure 4 presents these initial data and the vacuum field model previously described, which again provides a reasonable approximation to the data. Because of the low altitude of closest approach on this pass, the internal field dominates the signature (the field magnitude reached 1,146 nT at 18:59:45 on 6 September 1996). The small discrepancies between the data and the modelled field arise from various neglected effects. The vacuum superposition model does not allow for the fact that the external field is frozen into the flowing plasma of the jovian magnetosphere which modifies the interaction. In particular, currents that flow through the jovian plasma and close through Ganymede or a possible ionosphere[5,6] produce perturbations that tilt the field in the direction of the co-rotation flow. These neglected perturbations affect principally B_ϕ (see Fig. 2 legend) which is poorly fitted by the model. Possible contributions from higher-order multipoles of the internal field have not been considered.

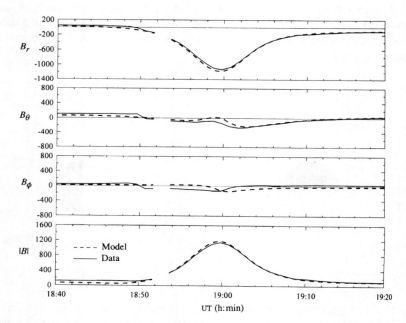

Fig. 4. Magnetic field components and magnitude (solid lines) from 18:40 to 19:20 UT on 6 September 1996 during Galileo's second fly-by of Ganymede. The coordinate system is defined in Fig. 2 legend. A short gap in the data removes artefacts associated with a programmed gain change. (The gap is covered in the recorded data.) The coordinate system is the same as in Fig. 2. Galileo's radial distance from the centre of Ganymede varied from $3.67 R_G$ at 18:40 UT to $\sim 1.10 R_G$ at closest approach and out to $3.74 R_G$ at 19:20 UT. Dashed lines show the superposition of the model fields discussed in the text. The data resolution is ~1 minute.

　　第二次经过时，木卫三同样处于木星电流片上方，可能位于低等离子体密度区域内。磁强计以及其他粒子和场测量仪器的完整数据将在另外的地方报告。但是在得到完整的数据之前，通过设定磁强计[2]模式为平均模式，并储存最多达 200 个场矢量以延迟输送到地面，先行得到了分辨率大约为 1 分钟的测量结果。图 4 展示了这些初始数据以及之前所述的真空场模型。模型与数据符合得也相当不错。由于这次经过木卫三时的高度很低，磁场特征主要由内源磁场决定（在 1996 年 9 月 6 日 18：59：45，场强达到 1,146 nT）。数据与模型的微小差别来源于各种被忽略的效应。真空叠加模型不能处理外部磁场被冻结在木星磁层的流动等离子体中的情况，这种情况对相互作用有修正。特别是穿过木星等离子体的电流和近距离流过木卫三或者可能的电离层[5,6]的电流会产生使磁场向共转流方向倾斜的扰动。这些被忽略的扰动主要影响 B_ϕ（见图 2 注），在这个分量上模型和数据符合得很差。我们没有考虑可能的内源磁场的高阶多极分量的贡献。

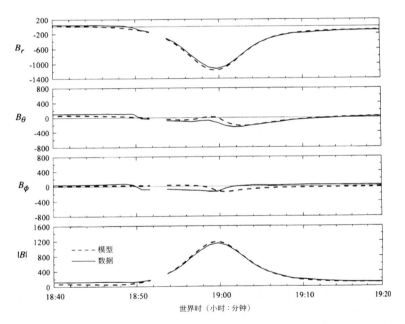

图 4. 1996 年 9 月 6 日 18：40 UT 到 19：20 UT 伽利略号第二次掠过木卫三时测得的磁场分量及其大小（实线）。坐标系定义见图 2 注。数据中间的小缺隙用来除去程序中设定的增益变化引起的假信号。（这个缺隙在记录的数据中被掩盖了。）所用坐标系与图 2 相同。伽利略号离开木卫三中心的径向距离从 18：40 UT 的 3.67 R_G 到最近点的大约 1.10 R_G，并在 19：20 UT 超过 3.74 R_G。虚线表示正文中讨论的叠加模型场。数据的分辨率为 1 分钟左右。

We have traced field lines near Ganymede in a simplified representation of the magnetic geometry (Fig. 5). The background (jovian) field is assumed uniform and tilted radially away from Jupiter. It has been added to the field of a Ganymede dipole pointing to 10° radially inward relative to the southward direction (which is the same as tilting the north pole 10° radially outward). This model neglects minor components of both the external field and the dipole moment out of the y–z plane (the coordinates are defined in Fig. 3 legend). A significant element of the schematic is the presence of field lines linked to Ganymede at both ends out to ~$2R_G$ (where R_G is the radius of Ganymede), implying that Ganymede carves out its own magnetosphere within the jovian magnetosphere. The interpretations of plasma wave emissions by Gurnett[7] are consistent with this interpretation.

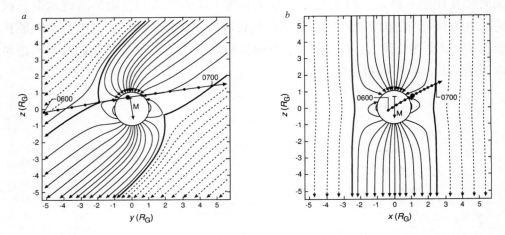

Fig. 5. Field lines in a vacuum superposition of a uniform external magnetic field of 120 nT lying in the y–z plane and tilted by 50° outward from $-z$ (a good approximation to the local value of the KK96 model field) and the field of a Ganymede-centred magnetic dipole with equatorial surface-field strength of 700 nT tilted 10° inward from $-z$. a, Field lines in the y–z plane. b, Field lines in the x–z plane. In both cases the projection of Galileo's trajectory is shown with dots every 5 minutes along the trajectory from 06:00 to 07:00 UT on 27 June 1996. Closest approach is marked with a large dot. Note that the projection in a appears to place closest approach at high latitude, but the projection in b makes clear that the actual latitude is much lower. The separatrices between field lines linked to Ganymede and field lines that do not intersect the moon, effectively the magnetopause, are shown as heavy lines. Dashed lines are jovian field lines not linked to Ganymede. Solid lines are field lines with at least one end on Ganymede. An arrow marked M is aligned with Ganymede's magnetic moment.

Figure 5 shows (heavy lines) the separatrix that encloses Ganymede's magnetosphere, identified as the region in which field lines link to Ganymede at least once. Galileo crossed into the Ganymede magnetosphere very near the boundary between field lines that intersect Ganymede's surface only once and field lines that intersect Ganymede's surface twice (see the trajectory in Fig. 5) and then passed through a region analogous to the cusp (or polar cusp) of a conventional magnetosphere[8]. The separatrix intersects the inbound trajectory at 06:20 UT, quite close to the time of the rather abrupt field rotation observed at ~06:17:45 UT, and intersects the outbound trajectory at 07:00 UT just at the time a small rotation was observed. The boundary is analogous to the magnetopause of a conventional magnetosphere, and its signature is also clear in the plasma wave data[7]. The trajectory passed

我们以简化的磁场几何表示追踪了木卫三附近的磁力线（图5）。假定背景（木星）磁场是均匀的，从木星沿径向向外倾斜。这个背景磁场被叠加到相对南方以 10° 径向向内倾斜（相当于将北极沿径向向外倾斜 10°）的木卫三磁偶极子磁场上。这个模型忽略了外部磁场的次要分量和 $y–z$ 平面之外的偶极矩次要分量（坐标系定义在图3注中）。本图的显著之处是在木卫三两边大约 $2R_G$（R_G 是木卫三的半径）范围内存在与之相连的磁力线，暗示木卫三在木星磁层中开拓出了自己的磁层。这个说法符合古奈特的等离子波发射解释[7]。

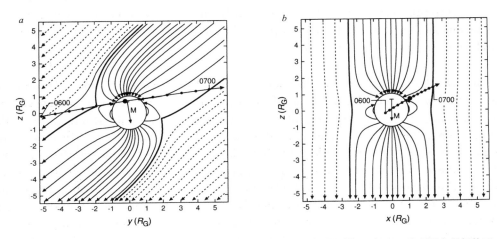

图 5. 真空叠加场的磁力线。两个叠加磁场为：$y–z$ 平面内从 $-z$ 向外倾斜 50°（KK96 模型场在局部的不错的近似值），强度为 120 nT 的均一外部磁场；木卫三为中心的赤道表面场强为 700 nT，从 $-z$ 向内倾斜 10° 的磁偶极子场。a，$y–z$ 平面内的磁力线。b，$x–z$ 平面内的磁力线。两图中伽利略号从 1996 年 6 月 27 日 06：00 UT 到 07：00 UT 的轨迹投影都以每 5 分钟一点标明。最近点用大一些尺寸的点表示。注意 a 图的投影中最近点看上去在高纬地区，但是 b 图的投影表明实际纬度要低得多。与木卫三相交的磁力线和不与这个卫星相交的磁力线的界面用粗实线表示，它实际上就相当于磁层顶。虚线是不与木卫三相交的木星磁场的磁力线。实线是与木卫三至少在一端相交的磁力线。以 M 标示的箭头显示木卫三的磁矩。

图 5 显示（粗实线）了木卫三磁层的界面，磁层定义为其磁力线至少与木卫三有一次相连的区域。伽利略号进入木卫三磁层的地点非常接近磁力线与木卫三相交一次和两次之间的边界区域（见图 5 中的轨迹），然后穿越相当于一个普通磁层[8]的尖点（极尖）的区域。界面与飞船降轨轨迹在 06：20 UT 相交，这与在大约 06：17：45 UT 观测到的磁场较突然的旋转很接近。飞船升轨轨迹与界面在 07：00 UT 相交，同时观测到小的磁场旋转。界面相当于普通磁层的磁层顶，其特征在等离子波数据[7] 中也很清楚。图中飞船轨迹穿过界面进入磁层的地点同时也恰好是它穿越磁中性线的位

through the magnetic neutral line in the schematic simultaneous with crossing of the inbound separatrix. In the data, the field magnitude dropped to 12.85 nT consistent with a near-neutral line encounter at 06:19:06 UT, more than one minute after the field rotation.

We have analysed the field rotation for the inbound magnetopause crossing. The normal to the surface lies almost in the y–z plane of Fig. 5a and is rotated radially outwards from the z-axis by 33°. This orientation suggests that in a more realistic model, the dipole centre might be shifted slightly towards positive z, the dimple in the separatrix would shift upward, and the trajectory would cross the separatrix just below the dimple. The small shift would produce a delay between the crossing of the separatrix and the encounter with the neutral line. It would account for the orientation of the magnetopause boundary during the inbound crossing, and it would hardly affect the outbound crossing. (Because the rotation at the outbound magnetopause is small, we are not able to evaluate the normal from the low-resolution data.)

It is not clear that we are justified in taking the details of a vacuum superposition model as far has been done in the above analysis, but, because the ambient jovian electron density was probably $\leq 1 \text{ cm}^{-3}$, it is likely that neither the Alfvénic Mach number (flow speed/Alfvén speed) nor the plasma β (thermal pressure/magnetic pressure) was large enough for plasma effects to displace the boundary significantly. However, the Ganymede magnetosphere must divert the jovian plasma around the $\sim 4 R_G$ (diameter) magnetic obstacle. This region of diverted flow is analogous to a traditional magnetosheath, although the diverted flow is not bounded by a shock. Just before the magnetopause crossing, low-frequency fluctuations were observed as is common in a magnetosheath. Elsewhere fluctuations are very small, although the time resolution of the data was sufficient to detect fluctuations on the scale of seconds between 06:07 UT and 06:44 UT. The absence of fluctuations suggests low plasma pressure within the magnetosphere, although a peak density of $> 45 \text{ cm}^{-3}$ has been reported[7].

The dipole moment of Ganymede ($1.4 \times 10^{13} \text{ T m}^3$ or $1.4 \times 10^{20} \text{ A m}^2$) is close to that inferred for Io[1,9]. Thus Ganymede, whose angular momentum is also close to that of Io, follows the trend of the relation between the magnetic moment and the angular momentum for magnetized planets suggested by Blackett[10]. However, the discovery of an internal field at Ganymede does not bear directly on the interpretation of the signature at Io as the properties of the two bodies differ greatly. In some ways, the conditions at Io seem more favourable for field generation than those at Ganymede. Density is higher, a large core is known to be present[11], rotation is faster, and there is a source of heat that could drive convection, even though the heat is not deposited directly in the core. However, as details of the heating and transport processes are likely to be very different at the two jovian satellites, the discovery of a Ganymede field does little to support the arguments[1,9] for an internal magnetic field of Io.

Given that the dipole moments are comparable, it may seem puzzling that the evidence for an internal field at Ganymede is unambiguous whereas the evidence for an internal field at

置。在数据中，测到磁场旋转 1 分多钟后，在接近中性线的 06：19：06 UT，场强相应地降低到 12.85 nT。

我们分析了降轨穿越磁层顶时的磁场旋转。表面的法向矢量几乎处于图 5a 的 y–z 平面中，方向从 z 轴径向向外旋转 33°。这个定向表明在更接近实际的模型中，偶极子的中心应向 z 轴正方向稍微移动一些。界面凹窝中心应该略微上移，飞船轨迹应该在紧靠凹窝下方穿越界面。这个微小偏移会使轨迹穿越界面和中性线之间产生一个延迟。这还能解释降轨穿越时磁层顶边界的定向，但是对升轨穿越不会有什么影响。（因为穿出磁层顶的旋转很小，我们无法从低分辨率数据估计其法向。）

在以上分析中使用了很多真空叠加模型的细节，也许未必完全合理。但是因为周围的木星电子密度可能不大于 1 cm⁻³，不论是阿尔文–马赫数（流体速度 / 阿尔文速度）还是等离子体 β（热压 / 磁压）都不太可能大到使等离子体效应得以显著移动边界线位置。然而，木卫三的磁层必然使得木星等离子体流改道绕过自己这个 4 R_G（直径）的磁障碍物。改道后的流体区域相当于传统的磁鞘，只是流体没有激波边界。刚好在穿越磁层顶之前观测到的低频涨落是磁鞘中的常见现象。其他地方的涨落都十分微小，不过数据的时间分辨率还是能够探测出 06：07 UT 到 06：44 UT 之间几秒范围的涨落。虽然有等离子体最大密度大于 45 cm⁻³ 的报告 [7]，但缺少涨落表明磁层中等离子体压强很低。

木卫三的偶极矩（1.4×10^{13} T·m³ 或 1.4×10^{20} A·m²）和提到的木卫一的偶极矩 [1,9] 很接近，角动量也和木卫一的差不多，符合布莱克特提出的磁化行星的磁矩和角动量关系 [10]。但是由于两个天体的性质大为不同，木卫三内源磁场的发现不能直接用来解释木卫一的特征。从某些方面看，木卫一的条件比木卫三更适于产生磁场。它密度更高、内核更大 [11]、旋转更快，并且有一个能够推动对流的热源，尽管热量并不直接加载到内核上。但是由于木星的这两个卫星加热和运输的细节可能十分不同，所以木卫三磁场的发现对木卫一具有内源磁场的论证 [1,9] 不能提供什么支持。

由于二者磁矩差不多，故木卫三内源磁场的证据十分明确，而木卫一内源磁场的证据尽管很有力却不明确，这一点可能看起来有些让人感到迷惑。造成这种不明

Io, though compelling, is not unambiguous. The ambiguity arises both because the ratio of the magnitudes of the nominal surface equatorial magnetic field to the ambient jovian magnetic field is smaller by almost an order of magnitude at Io than at Ganymede and because the signature near Io is partially obscured by strong perturbations from ion pickup and charge exchange.

The source of Ganymede's magnetic field could be dynamo action in a molten iron core (or a salty-water internal ocean) or remanent magnetization in its interior. Ganymede's internal structure and thermal state determine which of these possibilities is the most likely. Schubert et al.[12] have considered how the field might be generated by dynamo action in an iron core or a watery mantle. The magnitude of Ganymede's magnetic field, almost an order of magnitude larger at the satellite's pole than the ambient jovian magnetic field, is in accord with theoretical expectations for a dynamo-generated field as is the direction of the dipole axis approximately aligned with the rotation axis[12]. The dominantly dipolar character of the field is consistent with generation deep within the body[13]. The large ratio between the polar field and the ambient field of the jovian magnetosphere at Ganymede cannot be explained by simple reactive processes such as paramagnetism or magneto-convection.

Remanent magnetization, though unlikely, cannot be ruled out completely. Whether in a core below the Curie temperature or in a magnetized shell in the interior of the moon, iron-rich material with a magnetic moment per unit volume $\mu = 40–80$ A m^{-1} would produce the observed dipole moment. The external field required to account for such strong magnetization is in excess of the field near Ganymede in its present environment, but cannot be ruled out during its evolution. The inferred values cannot be rejected as impossibly large because the natural remanent magnetization of iron-rich meteorites can be this large in some cases.

We note that the presence of a strong internal field carries significant implications for the form of plasma flow near Ganymede. There should be no direct access of torus plasma to the surface other than in regions near the poles. Thus, deposits of sulphur-rich material from the torus should be localized near the poles. Sputtering of neutral atoms or molecules from Ganymede or its atmosphere would occur only in the polar regions, and this might inhibit significant neutral cloud formation and would certainly impose constraints on the cloud shape near the source.

(**384**, 537-541; 1996)

M. G. Kivelson[*†], K. K. Khurana[*], C. T. Russell[*†], R. J. Walker[*], J. Warnecke[*], F. V. Coroniti[‡], C. Polanskey[§], D. J. Southwood[*‖] & G. Schubert[*†]

[*] Institute of Geophysics and Planetary Physics, [†]Department of Earth and Space Sciences, [‡]Department of Physics, University of California, Los Angeles, California 90095-1567, USA

[§] Jet Propulsion Laboratory, 4800 Oak Grove Drive, Pasadena, California 91109, USA

[‖] Department of Physics, Imperial College of Science, Technology, and Medicine, London SW7 2BZ, UK

Received 30 September; accepted 5 November 1996.

确的原因既是因为就表面赤道磁场强度与周围木星磁场强度之比来看，木卫一的数值比起木卫三几乎要小一个数量级，也是因为木卫一附近的磁场特征部分地被离子俘获和电荷交换带来的强烈扰动所掩蔽。

木卫三磁场的来源可能是熔融铁核（或者内部咸水体）中的发电机作用或者内部的剩余磁化强度。木卫三的内部结构和热学状态决定哪一个机制最为可能。舒伯特等 [12] 考虑了铁核或者水体幔层中发电机作用如何产生磁场的情形。木卫三的磁场在其极区几乎比周围木星磁场大一个数量级，偶极子轴与自转轴大致平行 [12]，这些都符合发电机产生磁场的理论预期。磁场的主要偶极特性与天体内部深处产生的场的性质相符 [13]。极区场强比起周围木星磁层在木卫三处的场强大很多，不能用诸如顺磁作用或磁对流这样的简单的电抗性过程来解释。

尽管发生剩余磁化强度的概率非常小，但是也不能完全排除。不论是居里温度之下的内核还是卫星内部磁化的壳层，富铁物质单位体积内磁矩达到 $\mu = 40{\sim}80\,\text{A}\cdot\text{m}^{-1}$ 就能产生观测到的偶极矩。要达到这样的磁化强度，需要的外部磁场大于现在环境下木卫三周围的磁场。但是不能排除在其演化历史中有过这样大的场强。由于一些富铁陨石的自然剩余磁化强度就有这么大，所以不能说这是不可能的。

我们注意到存在强的内源磁场对木卫三附近的等离子体流的形式有显著影响。除了极区之外，环形等离子流不能直接到达表面。因此环形流中的富硫物质只能沉积在极区。中性原子和分子从木卫三或者其大气层向外的溅射只能发生在极区，这会抑制显著中性云的产生，而且一定会限制源附近云的形状。

（何钧 翻译；杜爱民 审稿）

References:

1. Kivelson, M. G. *et al. Science* **273**, 337-340 (1996).

2. Kivelson, M. G., Khurana, K. K., Means, J. D., Russell, C. T. & Snare, R. C. *Space Sci. Rev.* **60**, 357-383 (1992).

3. Khurana, K. K. *J. Geophys. Res.* (submitted).

4. Connerney, J. E. P. in *Planetary Radio Emissions III* (eds Rucker, H. O., Bauer, S. J. & Kaiser, M. L.) 13-33 (Osterreichischen Akademie der Wissenschaftern, Vienna, 1992).

5. Neubauer, F. M. *J. Geophys. Res.* **85**, 1171-1178 (1980).

6. Southwood, D. J., Kivelson, M. G., Walker, R. J. & Slavin, J. A . *J. Geophys. Res.* **85**, 5959-5968 (1980).

7. Gurnett, D. A., Kurth, W. S., Roux, A., Bolton, S. J. & Kennel, C. F. *Nature* **384**, 535-537 (1996).

8. Hughes, W. in *Introduction to Space Physics* (eds Kivelson, M. G. & Russell, C. T.) 227-287 (Cambridge Univ. Press, New York, 1995).

9. Kivelson, M. G., Khurana, K. K., Walker, R. J., Warnecke, J. & Russell, C. T. *Science* **274**, 396-398 (1996).

10. Blackett, P. M. S. *Nature* **159**, 658 (1947).

11. Anderson, J. D., Shogren, W. L. & Schubert, G. *Science* **272**, 709-711 (1996).

12. Schubert, G., Zhang, K., Kivelson, M. G. & Anderson, J. D. *Nature* **384**, 544-545 (1996).

13. Elphic, R. C. & Russell, C. T. *Geophys. Res. Lett.* **5**, 211-214 (1978).

14. Dressler, A. J. in *Physics of the Jovian Magnetosphere* (ed. Dressler, A. J.) 498-504 (Cambridge Univ. Press, New York, 1983).

Acknowledgements. We thank S. Joy and A. Frederick for assistance in data preparation; R. L. Snare, J. Means, R. George, T. King and R. Silva for their varied contributions to the success of this effort; Y. Mei and D. Bindschadler for their support of magnetometer planning; V. Vasyliunas for discussions; and D. Stevenson for criticism. This work was supported by the Jet Propulsion Laboratory.

Correspondence should be addressed to M.G.K. (e-mail: mkivelson@igpp.ucla.edu).

Gravitational Scattering as a Possible Origin for Giant Planets at Small Stellar Distances

S. J. Weidenschilling and F. Marzari

Editor's Note

While inward migration of Jupiter-mass planets towards the parent star can explain the presence of such planets in tight, low-eccentricity (near-circular) orbits, it cannot explain those in high-eccentricity orbits. Here Stuart Weidenschilling and Francesco Marzari show that gravitational scattering—a kind of cosmic billiards—can explain these high-eccentricity systems. They say that a second distant planet in a high-eccentricity orbit, perhaps highly inclined to the plane of rotation of the star, would offer a telltale signature of such scattering. In most cases, one might expect there to be a third planet that is ejected completely. Such free-floating planets have since been reported, although with uncertain masses.

The recent discoveries[1-4] of massive planetary companions orbiting several solar-type stars pose a conundrum. Conventional models[5,6] for the formation of giant planets (such as Jupiter and Saturn) place such objects at distances of several astronomical units from the parent star, whereas all but one of the new objects are on orbits well inside 1 AU; these planets must therefore have originated at larger distances and subsequently migrated inwards. One suggested migration mechanism invokes tidal interactions between the planet and the evolving circumstellar disk[7]. Such a mechanism results in planets with small, essentially circular orbits, which appears to be the case for many of the new planets. But two of the objects have substantial orbital eccentricities, which are difficult to reconcile with a tidal-linkage model. Here we describe an alternative model for planetary migration that can account for these large orbital eccentricities. If a system of three or more giant planets form about a star, their orbits may become unstable as they gain mass by accreting gas from the circumstellar disk; subsequent gravitational encounters among these planets can eject one from the system while placing the others into highly eccentric orbits both closer and farther from the star.

THE most generally accepted model for the origin of the giant planets, Jupiter and Saturn, in our own Solar System assumes that solid planetesimals accumulated to form cores having masses of the order of ten times Earth's mass. Each core was then able to initiate accretion of gas from the surrounding solar nebula; the mass of the accreted gas became great enough for its own gravity to continue the process until that region of the nebula was exhausted, or tidal torques formed a gap at the planet's orbit[5]. Formation of such a core is believed to have required condensation of water (and perhaps other ices)

引力散射是近邻巨行星的可能起源

魏登席林，马尔扎里

编者按

尽管木星质量的行星向母星迁移可以解释此类行星存在于近邻的低偏心率（近圆）轨道中，但是这不能解释那些高偏心率轨道上的此类行星。在此，斯图尔特·魏登席林和弗朗切斯科·马尔扎里指出，引力散射——一种宇宙台球效应——可以解释这些高偏心率系统。他们指出，远处另外一颗处于高偏心率轨道（或许相对恒星自转平面有较大倾角）中的行星可能会显示出这种散射的迹象。在大部分情形中，有可能存在被完全抛射出去的第三颗行星。这种自由漂浮的行星已有报道，尽管质量不确定。

最近发现的几颗环绕类太阳恒星的大质量行星 [1-4] 给科学界提出了一个难题。巨行星（例如木星和土星）形成的传统模型 [5,6] 认为这类天体应该在距离母星几个天文单位处形成，不过这些新发现的行星除一颗外几乎都在 1 AU 内；故这些行星一定是在较远距离处形成，然后向内迁移的。一个可能的迁移机制是行星和演化中的星周盘之间的潮汐相互作用 [7]。这样的机制导致行星具有小的圆形轨道，大部分新行星似乎是这样的情形。但是这些新行星中有两颗具有较大的轨道偏心率，这很难和潮汐相关模型一致。这里我们描述另外一个能解释这些大轨道偏心率的行星迁移模型。如果一个具有 3 个或者更多巨行星的系统在一颗恒星周围形成，由于它们通过吸积星周盘气体来获得质量，所以轨道可能变得不稳定；随后这些行星之间的引力交会可将一颗行星从系统内抛射出去，同时使其他行星进入距离恒星更近以及更远的高偏心率轨道。

关于太阳系巨行星（木星和土星）起源最为广泛接受的模型是固体星子聚集在一起形成 10 倍地球质量的核。接着每个核都能够从周围的太阳星云开始吸积气体；吸积气体的质量大到足以让自引力继续吸积气体直到那片区域的星云耗尽，或者潮汐力矩在行星轨道处形成一个空隙 [5]。我们认为这种核的形成需要水的凝结（以及其他可能的冰物质）来提供足够的质量使得核能够在气体耗散之前增长。距太阳几个天文单位之内的高温将排除这种起源。广泛认为位于 5.2 AU 处的木星是在太阳星云的

to provide enough mass to allow growth of the core before dissipation of the gas. High temperatures within a few AU of the Sun would preclude such an origin. Jupiter, at 5.2 AU, is widely believed to have formed near the boundary of ice condensation in the solar nebula[8]. In contrast, at present six planets are known with masses comparable to Jupiter and orbits well inside 1 AU; these are companions of the stars 51 Pegasi, τ Boötis, v Andromedae, 55 Cancri, HD114762 and 70 Virginis. The first three all have semimajor axes $a \approx 0.05$ AU, the next has $a \approx 0.1$ AU, and the last two are at 0.4 and 0.47 AU. In addition, a planet of 47 Ursae Majoris is at a distance of 2.1 AU.

Lin *et al.*[7] suggested that giant planets migrated inwards while tidally linked to an evolving circumstellar disk that was accreting onto the star. This mechanism implies that planets must have formed simultaneously with the star itself, but it is difficult to account for the formation of planets on such short timescales[6]. Tidal linkage to the nebula also implies that any surviving planets should have essentially circular orbits. This appears to be the case for most of the newly-discovered planets, but 70 Vir B and HD114762 B have substantial orbital eccentricities ($e \approx 0.38$ and 0.25, respectively). This circumstance has led to the suggestion[9,10] that these objects are brown dwarfs that formed during the collapse of their pre-stellar clouds, rather than planets that formed within circumstellar disks.

We suggest an alternative origin for these bodies that is compatible with the more conventional model of formation of jovian planets. The accretion of their solid cores from planetesimals is stochastic, and should produce multiple embryonic cores with the potential to accrete gas if their masses become sufficiently large. There is no *a priori* reason why these cores should form with such wide separations that the orbits of the final planets would remain stable after accretion of gas increases their mass by an order of magnitude or more. The likely outcome in many cases would be that the first core to accrete gas outstrips its neighbours, and potential rivals are either accreted or ejected from the system by its perturbations. However, stochastic growth of the cores will yield some systems with multiple cores in orbits that are stable before they accrete gas, but too close to be permanently stable after they gain additional mass from the nebula.

In the classical three-body problem, two planets initially in circular orbits cannot make close approaches if their semimajor axes, a, differ by more than $2\sqrt{3}R_H$, where R_H is the so-called Hill radius, equal to $\bar{a}[(m_1+m_2)/3M_*]^{1/3}$, where $\bar{a}=(a_1+a_2)/2$ is their mean distance from the star of mass M_*, and m_1, m_2 are the planetary masses[11]. If their orbital separation is less than this critical value, close encounters can occur. Gravitational scattering can change their orbits, but cannot produce stability; the ultimate fate of such a system is collision between the two bodies. Conservation of angular momentum decrees that the orbit of the combined body is between those of the original pair, and so does not extend the range of allowed orbits.

Very different outcomes are possible for a system of more than two planets. Chambers *et al.*[12] found that for three or more planets of comparable mass, mutual perturbations

958

冰物质凝聚边界形成的[8]。相反，目前知道的 6 颗质量和木星相当的行星轨道都在 1 AU 内；它们分别是恒星飞马座 51、牧夫座 τ、仙女座 ν、巨蟹座 55、HD114762 和室女座 70 的行星。前 3 颗行星的半长轴都为 $a \approx 0.05$ AU，随后一颗的半长轴为 $a \approx 0.1$ AU，最后两颗的半长轴分别为 0.4 AU 和 0.47 AU。此外，大熊座 47 的一颗行星位于 2.1 AU 处。

林潮等人[7]认为巨行星和正被吸积到恒星的演化中的星周盘发生潮汐相互作用时会向内迁移。这个机制表明行星一定是和恒星本身同时形成的，但是难以解释如何在这么短的时标内形成行星[6]。与星云的潮汐联系也表明任何存在的行星本来应该有圆形轨道。大部分新发现的行星似乎都是这个情况，但室女座 70 B 和 HD114762 B 具有显著的轨道偏心率（分别为 $e \approx 0.38$ 和 $e \approx 0.25$）。这个情况表明这些天体是在其星前云坍缩时形成的褐矮星，而不是在星周盘内形成的行星[9,10]。

我们提出这些天体的另外一种起源。这与更传统的类木行星形成模型一致。星子吸积形成固体核是随机的，并且应该形成多个胚胎核，当它们质量足够大时将能够吸积气体。没有先验的理由来解释为什么这些核应该在这么宽的间距内形成，以保证在吸积气体质量增加一个量级以上后，行星的轨道仍然保持稳定。很多情形中的可能结果是首个核吸积气体超过邻近核，潜在的竞争对手要么被吸积，要么因为受到这个核扰动而被抛射出系统。不过，核的随机增长将形成一些多核的系统，这些核的轨道在它们吸积气体之前稳定，但在它们从星云获得额外质量后由于距离太近而不能永久保持稳定。

在经典三体问题中，两颗开始处于圆轨道中的行星，如果它们的半长轴 a 相差大于 $2\sqrt{3}\,R_{\mathrm{H}}$ 就不能靠得太近，这里 R_{H} 是所谓的希尔半径，等于 $\bar{a}[(m_1+m_2)/3M_*]^{1/3}$，此处 $\bar{a} = (a_1+a_2)/2$ 是它们距离质量为 M_* 的恒星的平均距离，m_1、m_2 是行星质量[11]。如果它们的轨道间距比这个临界值小，则可能发生密近交会。引力散射能够改变它们的轨道，从而引起轨道不稳定；这样一个系统的最终命运是两个天体发生碰撞。角动量守恒使得合并后的天体的轨道位于它们初始轨道之间，并且不会超过允许的轨道范围。

超过两颗行星的系统的结果将非常不同。钱伯斯等人[12]发现对于三颗或者更多

could produce crossing orbits, even though each pair of bodies considered separately meets the Hill stability criterion. There appears to be no absolute stability in such systems; the timescale for orbits to become crossing merely increases with initial separation. With three (or more) planets, a greater variety of outcomes is possible as the result of close encounters. Angular momentum can be partitioned unequally among the planets, and the system need not remain completely bound to the star. The idea that systems of massive planets could be dynamically unstable was first mentioned by Farinella[13] in 1980. However, this suggestion was forgotten, as no such planets had been detected at that time, and there was no consensus as to how such systems could form.

We have carried out a series of numerical integrations of the orbits of three Jupiter-mass planets about a solar-mass star, using Everhart's[14] integrator. The initial orbits were circular, and separated by 4–5 Hill radii. Simulations were performed for coplanar orbits and for small ($1–2°$) initial inclinations, with similar outcomes. Mutual perturbations rapidly increased eccentricities until close approaches became possible. There followed a period of chaotic evolution with close encounters among the planets. The vast majority resulted in one planet being ejected on a hyperbolic trajectory. The remaining two planets usually had stable orbits. If the initial orbits were not strictly coplanar, the final orbits could also have significant mutual inclinations. There was no preference as to their fate; any of the three might be ejected, or end up in either the inner or outer orbit.

One example of such an outcome is shown in Fig. 1. Three Jupiter-mass planets had initially circular orbits at $a = 5.0$, 7.25 and 9.5 AU. After about 20,000 yr, the planet originally in the innermost orbit was ejected. The outermost original planet was left in a close orbit with $a = 2$ AU, $e = 0.78$, while the planet initially in the middle had a distant orbit with $a = 29$ AU, $e = 0.44$. These final orbits are stable against further encounters. The starting conditions were chosen to minimize computation time, and resulted in evolution on a timescale much shorter than the $\sim 10^6$ yr needed for the planets to reach their assumed masses by accretion of gas[6]. We have carried out other simulations with larger initial separations, in which orbits became crossing only after several million years.

Although ejection of one planet is by far the most common outcome, other end states are possible. A small fraction of cases end with collisions between planets, or sequential ejection of two planets, leaving a single planet orbiting the star. Impact of a planet onto the star itself cannot be ruled out, though we have no examples of such an outcome. It is beyond the scope of this Letter to explore the full range of possibilities. We note that such systems are chaotic, that is, the outcome is sensitive to small differences in initial conditions. Even for a fixed set of planetary masses and initial semimajor axes, different angular separations at the start of the simulation can lead to very different final configurations. Much additional work will be needed to map out the full range of outcomes and their statistical distributions as functions of the masses and initial orbits of the planets. The present work established that dynamical interactions can alter the cosmogonically imposed initial state of a planetary system.

颗质量相近行星，相互的扰动能够产生相交轨道，尽管分别对每对天体的考虑都符合希尔稳定性判据。在这样的系统中似乎没有绝对的稳定；轨道开始相交的时标仅随初始间距增加而增加。在三颗（或者更多颗）行星的系统中，由于密近交会而产生的结果可能会更为多种多样。角动量在这些行星间分配不均，系统不一定完全束缚于恒星。大质量行星系统可能动力学不稳定的想法首先是由法里内拉[13]于1980年提出的。不过，这个想法被人们遗忘，因为当时还没有探测到这样的行星，并且对如何能够形成这种系统没有共识。

我们使用埃弗哈特[14]的积分器对围绕太阳质量恒星的三颗具有木星质量的行星的轨道进行了一系列数值积分。初始轨道为圆形，间距4~5希尔半径。对共面轨道和初始小倾角轨道(1°~2°)的模拟结果类似。行星间的相互扰动使得偏心率迅速增大，直到行星间可能发生密近交会。接下来是行星发生密近交会的混沌演化时期。多数结果是一颗行星沿着双曲线轨道被抛射出去。剩下的两颗行星一般具有稳定的轨道。如果初始轨道不是严格共面，最终的轨道之间可能也具有明显的倾角。这对它们的命运没有太大影响；三颗行星中的任何一颗都有可能被抛射，或者最终处于靠内轨道或靠外轨道。

图1展示了这种结果的一个例子。三颗木星质量行星起初具有 $a = 5.0$ AU、7.25 AU和9.5 AU的圆轨道。大约20,000年后，最初在最内轨道的行星被抛射出去。初始在最外的行星留存在 $a = 2$ AU，$e = 0.78$ 的近轨道上，开始处于中间的行星位于 $a = 29$ AU，$e = 0.44$ 的较远轨道上。这些最终轨道很稳定，不存在进一步的交会。初始条件的选择是为了使计算时间最小化，并且在比行星通过吸积气体[6]达到其假设质量所需的一百万年短得多的时标上有演化。我们进行了更大初始间距的模拟，结果是轨道在仅仅几百万年后就开始相交。

尽管一颗行星的抛射是目前最常见的结果，但其他结局也是可能的。一小部分结果是行星之间发生碰撞或者相继抛射出两颗行星，只剩下一颗行星围绕恒星运转。一颗行星和恒星碰撞本身也不能够排除，尽管我们目前还没有这样的例子。探索所有可能性超过了本快报的范畴。我们注意到这样的系统是混沌的，即结果对初始条件的微小变化敏感。甚至对固定的行星质量和初始半长轴，模拟开始时不同的角间距也能导致非常不同的结果。想要得到全部可能的结果及其统计分布作为行星质量和初始轨道的函数，还需要很多额外的工作。目前的工作确定了动力学作用能够改变行星系统起源时的初始状态。

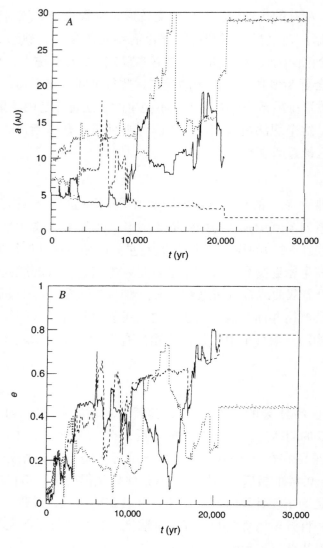

Fig. 1. Evolution of semimajor axes (panel *A*) and eccentricities (panel *B*) of a trio of Jupiter-mass planets orbiting a solar-mass star. Initial orbits are circular and coplanar, at distances of 5.0, 7.25 and 9.5 AU from the star. Their orbits become crossing, and after a series of close encounters the original inner planet is ejected hyperbolically at 21,000 yr. The planet originally in the outermost orbit is left in a close orbit ($a = 2$ AU, $e = 0.78$). The remaining planet has a distant orbit ($a = 29$ AU, $e = 0.44$).

Wetherill[15,16] has pointed out that there are problems with the timescale of formation of gas-giant planets by the core-accretion model (although these are less severe than for origin within a still-evolving disk). These considerations, and the lack of detection of such planets in earlier surveys, led him to suggest that they might be very rare[16]. If so, then it is surprising that our own system contains two such bodies, Jupiter and Saturn. It seems plausible that other planetary systems could produce three (or perhaps more) gas giants, particularly if their circumstellar nebulae were more massive than our own. If systems of multiple giant planets in unstable orbits are a common outcome of

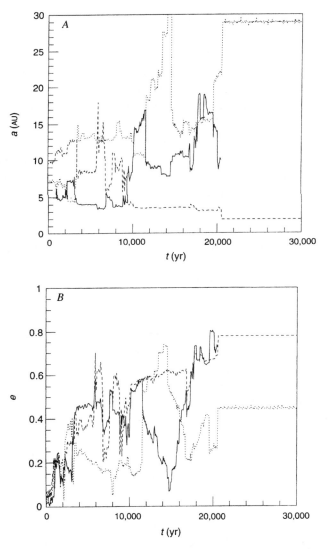

图 1. 一颗太阳质量恒星周围环绕的 3 颗木星质量行星的半长轴（A 图）和偏心率（B 图）的演化。初始轨道为圆形且共面，分别距离恒星 5.0 AU、7.25 AU 和 9.5 AU。它们的轨道开始相交，在经过一系列密近交会后，初始靠内的行星在 21,000 年通过双曲轨道被抛射。初始最靠外的行星则留在最近的轨道（$a = 2$ AU，$e = 0.78$）。另一颗行星的轨道很远（$a = 29$ AU，$e = 0.44$）。

韦瑟里尔[15,16]指出核吸积模型形成巨气体行星的时标有问题（尽管这些问题没有一个正在演化的盘的起源问题严重）。这些考虑，以及在较早的巡天中没有探测到这样的行星，导致他提出巨气体行星可能很少见[16]。如果是这样，那么我们自己的太阳系包含两个这样的天体——木星和土星——着实令人惊讶。其他行星系统能够形成三颗（或者可能更多）巨气体行星看起来是可能的，特别是如果它们的星周云比太阳系星云质量更大的话。如果不稳定轨道中的多颗巨行星系统是随机形成的核吸

stochastic core formation followed by gas accretion, then there are other implications for cosmogony. Many potential systems of terrestrial-type planets may be disrupted by a gas giant in their midst; we would owe our existence to the possibly fortuitous circumstance that only two cores in our own system, Jupiter and Saturn, grew large enough to accrete gas. It is not clear whether this fortunate outcome was purely stochastic, or influenced by the mass and density distribution of the solar nebula. There should also be a population of interstellar "Jupiters" that were ejected from forming systems.

Our model can account, at least qualitatively, for the large eccentricities observed for 70 Vir B and HD114762 B. It cannot explain the other planets unless some additional process acted to circularize their orbits after they were scattered inwards. Processes that could reduce eccentricities include tidal interactions with the circumstellar disk[17], drag of nebular gas enhanced by the planet's gravity[18], and accretion of a portion of the nebula by the planet after migration to a new orbit. Any or all of these might explain the low eccentricity observed for 47 UMa B, whereas the disks about 70 Vir and HD114762 may have had insufficient mass or lifetimes too short to accomplish such damping.

It is more difficult to account for very close orbits such as that of 51 Peg B. In principle, gravitational encounters can produce an eccentric orbit with very small periastron, which could then be circularized by the processes mentioned above, or by tidal dissipation within the star and the planet (Mayor and Queloz[1] derived a timescale of a few billion years for such tides to damp the eccentricity of 51 Peg B). The subsequent discoveries of other planets in similar orbits make this explanation unlikely, as such "star-grazing" orbits are rarely produced in our simulations. Observations suggest that a few per cent of solar-type stars may possess large planets at distances of 0.1 AU or less. Radial velocity surveys are most sensitive to close orbits, but it is unclear whether this bias can explain their apparent abundance. At present, there appear to be two classes of orbits: those that are circular and very near their stars, and more distant ones that may have significant eccentricities. If this trend is confirmed by additional discoveries, it would suggest that two mechanisms for planetary migration were effective. The close orbits may be the product of tidal locking to an evolving disk, while the eccentric ones are due to gravitational scattering.

One test of the two mechanisms is the existence of other planetary companions. Tidal locking does not require that other planets exist around a given star, but if they do, their orbits should be coplanar with the inner one. Gravitational scattering implies that a star with one close planet should have at least one other planet of comparable mass in a distant eccentric orbit; the two orbits may have high mutual inclination. Detection of such a distant companion will be difficult. Radial velocity perturbations vary in amplitude as $a^{-1/2}$, but their period increases as $a^{3/2}$. In the example of Fig. 1, the effect of the outer planet would be about 1/4 as large as that of the inner one, but its period more than 50 times longer. Detection of a planet by radial velocity variations requires a length of observation comparable to the orbital period. As high-precision radial velocity surveys have been conducted for about a decade, it is not surprising that the only planets discovered to date are close to their stars. More distant companions should be found

964

积气体的一般结果，那么这对天体演化还有其他意义。许多潜在的类地行星系统可能被巨气体行星瓦解；我们把我们的存在归功于可能的幸运环境——太阳系只有两个核（木星与土星）生长到足够大以吸积气体。目前还不清楚这样的幸运单纯是随机结果，还是受到太阳星云质量和密度分布的影响。应该存在一批从正在形成的系统抛射出去的星际"木星"。

我们的模型至少能够定性解释观测到的室女座 70 B 和 HD114762 B 的大偏心率。这不能解释其他行星，除非其他机制在它们被向内散射后发生作用以圆化其轨道。能够减小偏心率的机制包括与星周盘的潮汐相互作用[17]、被行星引力增强的星云气体的拖曳阻力[18] 和行星迁移到新轨道后对一部分星云气体的吸积。任何一个或者所有这些机制都可能解释观测到的大熊座 47 B 的低偏心率，而室女座 70 和 HD114762 的盘可能是由于没有足够的质量或是寿命太短，从而无法实现这样的偏心率减小。

对飞马座 51 B 这样非常近的轨道，解释起来更加困难。原则上，引力交会能够形成近星点非常小的偏心轨道，然后轨道可以通过上面提到的机制或者通过恒星与行星的潮汐耗散作用所圆化（梅厄和奎洛兹[1] 推导出对这种潮汐阻尼衰减飞马座 51 B 偏心率的时标为几十亿年）。随后在类似轨道发现的其他行星排除了这个解释，因为这种"掠过恒星"轨道在我们的模拟中很少出现。观测表明百分之几的类太阳恒星可能在 0.1 AU 甚至更近的距离处拥有大行星。视向速度巡天对近轨道最灵敏，但是尚不清楚这种偏向性能否解释它们的视丰度。目前，似乎有两类轨道：圆形并且非常接近恒星的轨道，以及可能具有明显偏心率的较远的轨道。如果这个趋势被其他的发现证实，这将表明行星迁移的这两个机制都是有效的。近轨道可能是潮汐锁定到正在演化的盘的结果，而偏心轨道是引力散射的结果。

对这两个机制的一个检验是其他似行星伴天体的存在与否。潮汐锁定不需要在给定恒星周围存在其他行星，但是如果存在，它们的轨道应该跟靠内的轨道共面。引力散射表明具有较近行星的恒星应该至少另外有一颗在远距离偏心轨道中、质量相当的行星；这两个轨道的相对倾角可能很大。探测这样的远距离伴天体将是很困难的。视向速度扰动在幅度上以 $a^{-1/2}$ 变化，但是它们的周期以 $a^{3/2}$ 增加。在图 1 的例子中，外行星的作用是内行星作用的 1/4，其周期是后者的 50 多倍。通过视向速度变化来探测行星需要观测时间和轨道周期相当。因为高精度视向速度巡天已经进行了约十

eventually by long-term monitoring of stellar radial velocities. They may also be revealed by their perturbations on the orbits of the inner planets, by astrometry, or by direct imaging.

Note added in proof: Cochran *et al.*[19] have discovered another extra-solar planet with an eccentric orbit. This companion to the star 16 Cygni B has $a = 1.7$ AU, $e = 0.65$, and mass at least 1.6 times that of Jupiter. Rasio and Ford[20] have independently developed a model for planetary migration similar to ours.

(**384**, 619-621; 1996)

Stuart J. Weidenschilling* & **Francesco Marzari**†

* Planetary Science Institute/SJI, 620 North Sixth Avenue, Tucson, Arizona 85705, USA

† Dipartimento di Fisica, Universita di Padova, Via Marzolo 8, I-35131 Padova, Italy

Received 8 April; accepted 30 October 1996.

References:

1. Mayor, M. & Queloz, D. *Nature* **378**, 355-359 (1995).

2. Latham, D. W., Mazeh, T., Stefanik, R. P., Mayor, M. & Burki, G. *Nature* **339**, 38-40 (1989).

3. Marcy, G. W. & Butler, R. P. *Astrophys. J.* **464**, L147-L152 (1996).

4. Butler, R. P. & Marcy, G. W. *Astrophys. J.* **464**, L153-L156 (1996).

5. Lissauer, J. *Icarus* **69**, 249-265 (1987).

6. Pollack, J. *et al. Icarus* (in the press).

7. Lin, D. N. C., Bodenheimer, P. & Richardson, D. C. *Nature* **380**, 606-607 (1996).

8. Boss, A. *Science* **267**, 360-362 (1995).

9. Boss, A. *Nature* **379**, 397-398 (1995).

10. Beckwith, S. & Sargent, A. *Nature* **383**, 139-144 (1996).

11. Gladman, B. *Icarus* **106**, 247-263 (1993).

12. Chambers, J., Wetherill, G. W. & Boss, A. *Icarus* **119**, 261-268 (1996).

13. Farinella, P. *Moon Planets* **22**, 25-29 (1980).

14. Everhart, E. in *Dynamics of Comets: Their Origin and Evolution* (eds Carusi, A. & Valsecchi, G.) 185-202 (Reidel, Dordrecht, 1985).

15. Wetherill, G. W. *Nature* **373**, 470 (1995).

16. Wetherill, G. W. *Astrophys. Space Sci.* **212**, 23-32 (1994).

17. Ward, W. R. *Icarus* **73**, 330-348 (1988).

18. Takeda, H., Matsuda, T., Sawada, K. & Hayashi, C. *Prog. Theor. Phys.* **74**, 272-287 (1985).

19. Cochran, W. D., Hatzes, A. P., Butler, R. P. & Marcy, G. W. *Bull. Am. Astron. Soc.* **28**, 1111 (1996).

20. Rasio, F. A. & Ford, E. B. *Science* (in the press).

Acknowledgements. We thank D. R. Davis and W. K. Hartmann for discussions and comments. This work was supported by NASA Planetary Geology and Geophysics Program and the Italian Space Agency.

Correspondence should be addressed to S.J.W. (e-mail: sjw@psi.edu).

年，目前仅发现距离恒星近的行星是不足为奇的。更多远距离伴天体通过长期恒星视向速度监测最终应该能被发现。它们也可能通过对内行星轨道的扰动、天体测量或者直接成像被发现。

　　附加说明：科克伦等[19]已经发现另外一颗具有偏心轨道的太阳系外行星——天鹅座 16 B，这颗行星的轨道为 $a = 1.7\,AU$，$e = 0.65$，质量至少是木星的 1.6 倍。拉西奥和福特[20]已经独立建立了一个和我们的模型类似的行星迁移模型。

（肖莉 翻译；周济林 审稿）

2.5-million-year-old Stone Tools from Gona, Ethiopia

S. Semaw *et al.*

Editor's Note

For many years, the earliest-known stone tools were from Olduvai, found alongside *Homo habilis* and *Zinjanthropus boisei*, and dated to around 1.8 million years ago. Further work in Ethiopia and Kenya pushed the earliest archaeology to around 2.3 million years. This report, from the Gona river drainage in Ethiopia, described primitive "Oldowan" (Olduvai-style) artefacts securely dated to 2.5 million years old, then the earliest known artefacts from anywhere in the world. But who made them? The world of the late Pliocene was occupied by australopithecines as well as early *Homo*. Louis Leakey's association of stone tools with *Homo*, so boldly made in 1964, had never looked so uncertain. Could the world's first tool-makers have been ape-men?

The Oldowan Stone tool industry was named for 1.8-million-year-old (Myr) artefacts found near the bottom of Olduvai Gorge, Tanzania. Subsequent archaeological research in the Omo (Ethiopia) and Turkana (Kenya) also yielded stone tools dated to 2.3 Myr. Palaeoanthropological investigations in the Hadar region of the Awash Valley of Ethiopia[1], revealed Oldowan assemblages in the adjacent Gona River drainage[2]. We conducted field work in the Gona study area of Ethiopia between 1992 and 1994 which resulted in additional archaeological discoveries as well as radioisotopic age control and a magnetic polarity stratigraphy of the Gona sequence. These occurrences are now securely dated between 2.6–2.5 Myr. The stone tools are thus the oldest known artefacts from anywhere in the world. The artefacts show surprisingly sophisticated control of stone fracture mechanics, equivalent to much younger Oldowan assemblages of Early Pleistocene age. This indicates an unexpectedly long period of technological stasis in the Oldowan.

IN 1976 the first archaeological occurrences of stone tools were identified in a fine-grained context at Gona[3], and two additional sites were reported later[4]. Fieldwork in 1992–94 increased the number of reported sites (Fig. 1a) and has provided the impetus for a reassessment of the geological context, age and character of the Gona archaeological concentrations.

埃塞俄比亚戈纳发现 250 万年前石制工具

塞马夫等

编者按

多年来，奥杜威地区与能人及鲍氏种东非人一起被发现的、距今约 180 万年前的石制品一直被学术界认为是最早的石制工具，随后在埃塞俄比亚和肯尼亚进一步的工作将这一年代向前推进到距今约 230 万年前。本文描述了在埃塞俄比亚戈纳河流域发现的、明确可以追溯到距今 250 万年前的远古"奥杜威文化"（奥杜威模式）的石制品，它们是世界上目前已知最早的人工制品。那么，这些石器的制造者究竟是何人呢？上新世晚期，南方古猿和早期人属成员同时生活在我们的星球上。路易斯·利基 1964 年提出制作石器工具是人属成员所独有的技能，这一激进观点从未面临如此严峻的挑战。难道最早的石制工具确是由猿人制造的吗？

坦桑尼亚奥杜威峡谷谷底附近发现的、距今 180 万年前的石制品被命名为奥杜威石器工业。随后奥莫（埃塞俄比亚）和图尔卡纳（肯尼亚）考古工作中所获得的石制品测年数据为距今 230 万年前。在埃塞俄比亚阿瓦什河谷哈达尔地区 [1] 进行的古人类调查显示，附近戈纳河流域 [2] 同样存在奥杜威石器工业制品。1992 年到 1994 年间，我们在埃塞俄比亚戈纳地区进行的田野工作中，发现了更为丰富的考古学遗存，并且获得了戈纳遗址地层的放射性同位素年龄和磁极性地层学信息。由于该地区石制品的年代可断定为距今 260 万年到 250 万年间，因此这些石器应是目前所知的、世界上最古老的人工制品。令人惊奇的是，这些石制品显示其生产者已经能熟练地掌握石料的断裂力学，具有与时代更晚的早更新世奥杜威石制品组合相同的加工工艺，这显示奥杜威石器技术的停滞期远比我们想象的久远。

1976 年，在戈纳的细粒地层沉积物中首次发现了石器考古遗存 [3]。随后，另外两处遗址也陆续被报道出来 [4]。1992~1994 年间的野外工作使所报道遗址的数目有所增加（图 1a），为重新认识戈纳地区考古遗址群的地质环境、年代和特征提供了契机。

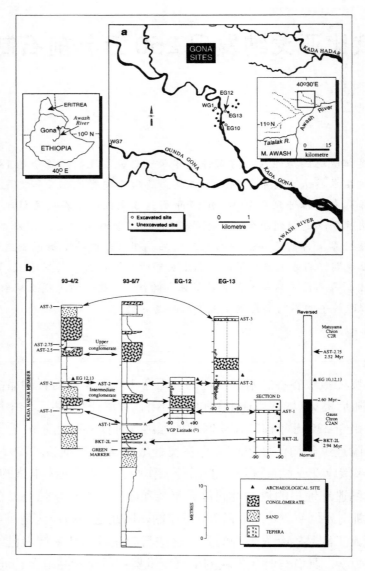

Fig. 1. **a**, Map of the Gona River drainage showing locations of the archaeological sites. **b**, Stratigraphic context of the Gona sites. Lithostratigraphy and markers from the East Gona exposures; composite sections (93-4/2 and 93-6/7) are correlated with results of magnetic polarity sampling from EG12/EG13 and section D (at 93-6/7). The profiles represent composite sections of the Gona stratigraphic sequence. Significant stratigraphic markers are listed next to the columns and correlations shown with solid lines. Filled circles indicate normal polarity, open circles reversed polarity. Chronostratigraphic context with units of the magnetic polarity timescale (MPTS) and isotopic age determinations are given on the right.

Strata associated with the Gona sites comprise three sedimentary intervals within the Kada Hadar Member of the Hadar Formation: an upward-coarsening interval of lacustrine and deltaic strata at the base of the sequence, five upward-fining fluvial cycles, and a predominantly fine-grained sequence of fluvial deposits capping the sequence. These sediments record

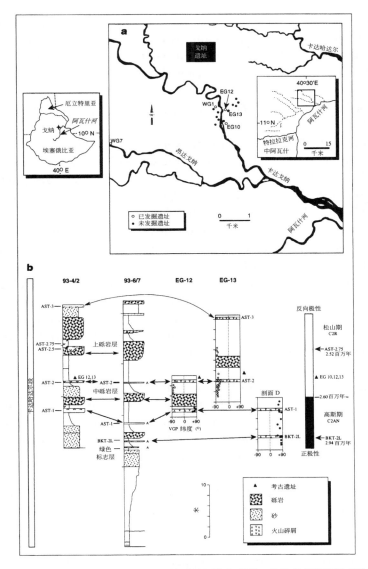

图 1. **a**，戈纳河流域考古遗址位置图。**b**，戈纳遗址地层堆积序列。戈纳东部岩相地层及标志层露头；组合剖面（93-4/2 和 93-6/7）与 EG12/EG13 以及剖面 D（93-6/7 位置）的地磁极性结果对比。该图为戈纳各地点的地层层序剖面集合。重要的地层标志在旁边纵列栏中列出，并以实线标示出它们之间的相互关系。实心代表正极性，空心代表反向极性。右侧标示的是包含地磁极性年代（MPTS）单位的年代地层环境和同位素年龄。

与戈纳旧石器时代考古遗址相关的地层包含了哈达尔组卡达哈达尔段中的三次沉积间断：地层层序底部沉积颗粒向上逐渐变粗的湖相和三角洲间隔层、五个颗粒向上逐渐变细的河流相旋回以及覆盖在此层序之上的一层主要由细微颗粒构成的河流沉积物。这些沉积物记录了整个遗址区湖盆被填充、随之而来的三角洲平原的进

the infilling of a lake basin, subsequent progradation of a delta plain, and cycling of fluvial channel and floodplain environments across the localities. The archaeological occurrences are found in floodplain environments, close to margins of channels that carried the volcanic cobbles used as raw materials for tool manufacture.

Relationships between Gona and Hadar strata are given in Fig. 1b. In the Gona, a series of marker beds consisting of vitric tephra and bentonites (altered vitric tephra) provide local correlation and tie the sequence to the Kada Hadar Member to the east. The lowest of these is a greenish bentonite in the Gona, the Green Marker. It correlates on lithologic and stratigraphic grounds with BKT-2L$_l$ in the Kada Hadar. A few metres above this is a discontinuous anorthoclase-phyric tephra, which correlates with BKT-2L. The next two markers, vitric tephra AST-1 and AST-2, have not yet been recognized outside the Gona. Between these tephra is a prominent conglomerate termed the Intermediate Conglomerate[5]. Another prominent conglomerate above AST-2 is the Upper Conglomerate, and a bentonite channelled into this conglomerate (cinerite III[5]) we refer to as AST-2.5. In outcrops immediately above this restricted exposure of AST-2.5 is plagioclase-phyric bentonite AST-2.75. This portion of the sequence is capped by a third vitric tephra, AST-3. None of the ASTs have been correlated into the Kada Hadar sequence. However, we have chronostratigraphic date on AST-2.75, and magnetic polarity stratigraphy through the sequence to provide additional control.

The age of the Gona artefact sites is constrained by a combination of radioisotopic dating and magnetic polarity stratigraphy (Fig. 1b). Magnetic stratigraphy revealed a transition from normally magnetized basal strata to reversed polarities at the level of the Intermediate Conglomerate, between tephra AST-1 and 2. Tuffs BKT-2L$_l$ and BKT-L have been identified near the bottom of the Gona sequence on the basis of lithologic similarity and outcrop tracing. In the adjacent Kada Hadar drainage, they underlie a third Bouroukie Tuff, BKT-2u. Ages of 2.95 Myr for BKT-2L and 2.92 Myr for BKT-2u have been recently cited[6], although no uncertainties were reported, nor have data been published. We report here new data documenting an age of 2.94 Myr for BKT-2L and 2.52 Myr for AST-2.75 (Fig. 2 and Table 1). This establishes the normal magnetozone at the base of the Gona sequence as the upper Gauss Chron, and the overlying reversed magnetozone as the lowermost Matuyama Chron. The Gauss–Matuyama Chron transition occurred at 2.6 Myr (ref. 7). The two excavated sites EG10 and EG12 directly overlie AST-2 and fall stratigraphically below AST-2.75. They are thus tightly bracketed between 2.6 and 2.5 Myr.

Table 1. Ar/Ar analytical data for AST-2.75 and BKT-2L

Lab no. (watts)	^{40}Ar(mol) ($\times 10^{-15}$)	^{40}Ar/^{39}Ar	^{37}Ar/^{39}Ar	^{36}Ar/^{39}Ar ($\times 10^{-3}$)	^{40}Ar*/^{39}Ar	%^{40}Ar*	Age (Myr)	±σ (Myr)
AST-2.75 (Single crystal total fusion)								
8302-01	1.165	4.856	3.084	5.101	3.604	74.0	2.557	0.311
8302-02	2.014	7.017	2.485	12.385	3.562	50.7	2.527	0.260

积作用以及河道和河漫滩环境的循环过程。发现于河漫滩上的考古学遗存临近河道边缘，河流所携带的火山岩砾石可作为加工石制工具的原料。

戈纳地区和哈达尔地区地层之间的关系见图 1b。在戈纳地区，由火山玻璃碎屑和膨润土（蚀变的火山玻璃碎屑）所构成的一系列标志层提供了当地地层堆积之间的相互关系，并且将该地区的地层与卡达哈达尔段的东部区域联系起来。在戈纳地区的这些地层中，堆积物最下部是一个绿色的膨润土层，即绿色标志层，其岩性和地层层序与卡达哈达尔 BKT-2L₁ 相关。该层之上几米处与 BKT-2L 相关的是一层不连续的歪长石斑状火山碎屑。接下来的两处标志层是在戈纳以外的地方从未发现过的火山玻璃碎屑 AST-1 和 AST-2。这些火山玻璃碎屑之间有一层明显的砾岩，称为中砾岩层[5]。在 AST-2 之上另一层明显的砾岩层是上砾岩层，还有我们称为 AST-2.5 的、一处嵌在该砾岩层中的膨润土（火山凝灰岩 III[5]）。在 AST-2.5 暴露出来的有限区域之上，刚露头的部分是斜长石膨润土层 AST-2.75，该部分层序被第三层火山玻璃碎屑，即 AST-3 所覆盖。没有一个 AST 层位与卡达哈达尔的地层相关。但我们有 AST-2.75 的地层年代，磁极性地层学数据则给出了整个地层的年代控制。

戈纳遗址石制品的年代由放射性同位素年代测定法和磁极性地层学两种方法共同确定（图 1b）。磁性地层学数据揭示了在火山碎屑 AST-1 和 AST-2 之间发生的从下部正极性到中砾岩层反向极性的倒转。根据岩性地层的相似性和追踪露头，在接近戈纳层序的底部确定了凝灰岩层 BKT-2L₁ 和 BKT-L。在相邻的卡达哈达尔流域，它们下伏在第三种伯乌罗凯凝灰岩层 BKT-2u 之下。尽管没有年代数据不确定性的报道，结果也尚未发表，但最近已经有人引用 BKT-2L 的年代为 295 万年，BKT-2u 的年代为 292 万年[6]。我们这里报道的新数据证实 BKT-2L 的年代为 294 万年，而 AST-2.75 的年代为 252 万年（图 2 和表 1）。这确立了以戈纳地层底部的正极性地层为高斯正极性时晚期，而覆盖在上面的反向极性地层为松山反向极性时的初期。高斯–松山极性倒转事件发生在距今 260 万年前（参考文献 7）。两处发掘地点 EG10 和 EG12 刚好处在 AST-2 地层之上、AST-2.75 地层之下，因此这两个遗址地层的年代恰好被严格控制在距今 260 万年到 250 万年之间。

表 1. AST-2.75 和 BKT-2L 的氩–氩法（Ar/Ar）分析数据

实验编号（watts）	$^{40}Ar(mol)$（× 10^{-15}）	$^{40}Ar/^{39}Ar$	$^{37}Ar/^{39}Ar$	$^{36}Ar/^{39}Ar$（× 10^{-3}）	$^{40}Ar*/^{39}Ar$	%$^{40}Ar*$	年代（百万年）	±σ（百万年）
AST-2.75（激光单颗粒全熔）								
8302-01	1.165	4.856	3.084	5.101	3.604	74.0	2.557	0.311
8302-02	2.014	7.017	2.485	12.385	3.562	50.7	2.527	0.260

Continued

Lab no. (watts)	^{40}Ar(mol) ($\times 10^{-15}$)	^{40}Ar/^{39}Ar	^{37}Ar/^{39}Ar	^{36}Ar/^{39}Ar ($\times 10^{-3}$)	^{40}Ar*/^{39}Ar	%^{40}Ar*	Age (Myr)	$\pm\sigma$ (Myr)
AST-2.75 (Single crystal total fusion)								
8302-03	3.106	6.054	3.030	9.675	3.445	56.8	2.444	0.163
8302-04	1.062	21.970	13.955	63.094	4.489	20.2	3.184	1.710
8302-05	0.651	5.269	2.812	8.941	2.858	54.1	2.028	0.597
8302-06	1.783	7.873	2.472	17.899	2.787	35.3	1.977	0.432
8302-07	0.533	6.698	2.934	12.699	3.187	47.5	2.261	0.857
8302-08	0.504	27.587	0.046	72.863	6.059	22.0	4.297	4.210
8302-09	0.577	4.694	3.120	7.706	2.672	56.8	1.896	0.480
8302-10	0.553	5.456	2.730	6.544	3.748	68.6	2.659	0.503
8302-11	0.341	5.942	3.197	9.146	3.503	58.8	2.485	0.926
8302-12	0.678	6.195	3.497	10.013	3.525	56.7	2.501	0.547
8302-13	2.049	5.610	0.004	6.637	3.649	65.0	2.589	0.181
8302-14	1.188	7.851	2.582	15.958	3.348	42.6	2.376	0.483
8302-15	0.754	19.284	1.172	56.896	2.567	13.3	1.821	1.971
8302-16	0.275	4.465	3.489	1.797	4.224	94.4	2.996	1.176
8302-20	82.311	33.003	0.033	70.249	12.247	37.1	*8.674*	*0.083*
8302-21	0.237	15.566	38.207	21.730	12.566	78.4	*8.899*	*1.505*
8302-22	0.282	4.903	3.050	4.711	3.763	76.6	2.670	0.474
8302-23	4.541	42.883	1.816	2.477	42.355	98.6	*29.823*	*0.296*
8302-24	6.624	35.672	0.816	8.843	33.144	92.9	*23.379*	*0.162*
8302-25	0.467	10.666	3.110	23.173	4.077	38.1	2.892	0.483
8302-26	0.704	10.816	4.077	24.397	3.945	36.4	2.799	0.318
8302-27	24.226	40.627	0.010	19.737	34.796	85.6	*24.536*	*0.087*
8302-28	0.785	6.732	4.952	12.390	3.480	51.5	2.469	0.198
8302-29	16.982	35.005	0.143	0.447	34.888	99.7	*24.601*	*0.075*
8302-30	0.454	5.000	3.201	4.392	3.967	79.2	2.814	0.303
8302-31	6.865	57.853	4.131	176.057	6.178	10.6	4.381	0.454
8302-32	0.258	5.389	3.075	6.967	3.585	66.4	2.543	0.629
Weighted mean								2.517 ± 0.075
BKT-2L (Single crystal total fusion)								
7201-01	2.099	3.495	0.633	0.344	3.438	98.5	2.936	0.070
7201-02	3.564	3.515	0.230	0.303	3.438	97.9	2.936	0.037
7201-03	2.195	3.541	0.857	0.490	3.458	97.7	2.953	0.057
7201-04	4.744	3.447	0.224	0.072	3.439	99.9	2.936	0.027
7201-05	2.825	3.507	0.231	0.163	3.472	99.1	2.965	0.054

实验编号 (watts)	$^{40}Ar(mol)$ $(\times 10^{-15})$	$^{40}Ar/^{39}Ar$	$^{37}Ar/^{39}Ar$	$^{36}Ar/^{39}Ar$ $(\times 10^{-3})$	$^{40}Ar^*/^{39}Ar$	$\%^{40}Ar^*$	年代 (百万年)	$\pm\sigma$ (百万年)
AST-2.75（激光单颗粒全熔）								
8302-03	3.106	6.054	3.030	9.675	3.445	56.8	2.444	0.163
8302-04	1.062	21.970	13.955	63.094	4.489	20.2	3.184	1.710
8302-05	0.651	5.269	2.812	8.941	2.858	54.1	2.028	0.597
8302-06	1.783	7.873	2.472	17.899	2.787	35.3	1.977	0.432
8302-07	0.533	6.698	2.934	12.699	3.187	47.5	2.261	0.857
8302-08	0.504	27.587	0.046	72.863	6.059	22.0	4.297	4.210
8302-09	0.577	4.694	3.120	7.706	2.672	56.8	1.896	0.480
8302-10	0.553	5.456	2.730	6.544	3.748	68.6	2.659	0.503
8302-11	0.341	5.942	3.197	9.146	3.503	58.8	2.485	0.926
8302-12	0.678	6.195	3.497	10.013	3.525	56.7	2.501	0.547
8302-13	2.049	5.610	0.004	6.637	3.649	65.0	2.589	0.181
8302-14	1.188	7.851	2.582	15.958	3.348	42.6	2.376	0.483
8302-15	0.754	19.284	1.172	56.896	2.567	13.3	1.821	1.971
8302-16	0.275	4.465	3.489	1.797	4.224	94.4	2.996	1.176
8302-20	82.311	33.003	0.033	70.249	12.247	37.1	*8.674*	*0.083*
8302-21	0.237	15.566	38.207	21.730	12.566	78.4	*8.899*	*1.505*
8302-22	0.282	4.903	3.050	4.711	3.763	76.6	2.670	0.474
8302-23	4.541	42.883	1.816	2.477	42.355	98.6	*29.823*	*0.296*
8302-24	6.624	35.672	0.816	8.843	33.144	92.9	*23.379*	*0.162*
8302-25	0.467	10.666	3.110	23.173	4.077	38.1	2.892	0.483
8302-26	0.704	10.816	4.077	24.397	3.945	36.4	2.799	0.318
8302-27	24.226	40.627	0.010	19.737	34.796	85.6	*24.536*	*0.087*
8302-28	0.785	6.732	4.952	12.390	3.480	51.5	2.469	0.198
8302-29	16.982	35.005	0.143	0.447	34.888	99.7	*24.601*	*0.075*
8302-30	0.454	5.000	3.201	4.392	3.967	79.2	2.814	0.303
8302-31	6.865	57.853	4.131	176.057	6.178	10.6	4.381	0.454
8302-32	0.258	5.389	3.075	6.967	3.585	66.4	2.543	0.629
加权平均值								2.517 ± 0.075
BKT-2L(激光单颗粒全熔)								
7201-01	2.099	3.495	0.633	0.344	3.438	98.5	2.936	0.070
7201-02	3.564	3.515	0.230	0.303	3.438	97.9	2.936	0.037
7201-03	2.195	3.541	0.857	0.490	3.458	97.7	2.953	0.057
7201-04	4.744	3.447	0.224	0.072	3.439	99.9	2.936	0.027
7201-05	2.825	3.507	0.231	0.163	3.472	99.1	2.965	0.054

Continued

Lab no. (watts)	$^{40}Ar(mol)$ ($\times 10^{-15}$)	$^{40}Ar/^{39}Ar$	$^{37}Ar/^{39}Ar$	$^{36}Ar/^{39}Ar$ ($\times 10^{-3}$)	$^{40}Ar*/^{39}Ar$	$\%^{40}Ar*$	Age (Myr)	$\pm\sigma$ (Myr)
BKT-2L (Single crystal total fusion)								
7201-06	4.568	3.469	0.233	0.196	3.424	98.8	2.924	0.033
7201-07	5.078	3.492	0.250	0.216	3.443	98.7	2.940	0.028
7201-08	4.639	3.462	0.228	0.017	3.470	100.4	2.963	0.025
7201-09	2.098	3.699	0.218	0.762	3.485	94.4	2.976	0.059
7201-10	3.603	3.481	0.224	0.125	3.457	99.4	2.952	0.035
7201-14	5.612	3.654	0.227	0.579	3.496	95.8	2.985	0.021
7201-15	5.201	3.552	0.233	0.385	3.451	97.3	2.947	0.020
7201-16	3.695	3.494	0.229	0.377	3.395	97.3	2.899	0.025
7201-17	2.412	3.511	0.227	0.336	3.424	97.7	2.924	0.039
7201-18	6.018	3.488	0.246	0.154	3.457	99.2	2.952	0.017
7201-19	4.206	3.472	0.230	0.106	3.453	99.6	2.949	0.024
7201-20	5.572	3.488	0.231	0.067	3.481	99.9	2.972	0.017
7201-21	2.002	3.574	0.734	0.510	3.475	97.3	2.968	0.045
7201-22	3.935	3.491	0.224	0.310	3.412	97.9	2.914	0.023
7201-24	0.513	3.800	0.205	1.104	3.484	91.8	2.976	0.175
7201-25	7.476	3.561	0.234	0.604	3.395	95.5	2.900	0.013
Weighted mean							2.940 ± 0.006	
BKT-2L (Bulk-step heating)								
(2.1)	0.306	7.275	1.158	19.628	1.559	21.4	1.332	0.619
(2.5)	0.342	4.939	0.860	11.467	1.611	32.6	1.376	0.337
(2.8)	0.700	5.477	0.617	9.346	2.758	50.4	2.356	0.213
(3.0)	0.428	3.810	0.559	0.937	3.572	93.8	3.050	0.364
(3.3)	0.432	3.563	0.526	0.516	3.446	96.8	2.943	0.315
(3.6)	0.441	3.495	0.516	0.902	3.263	93.5	2.787	0.289
(3.9)	0.606	4.047	0.527	2.159	3.445	85.2	2.942	0.173
(4.4)	1.502	3.607	0.396	0.804	3.395	94.2	2.900	0.057
(4.7)	0.361	3.509	0.488	0.485	3.399	97.0	2.902	0.374
(5.1)	0.670	3.627	0.636	1.148	3.332	92.0	2.846	0.127
(5.6)	0.648	3.865	0.597	1.668	3.413	88.4	2.915	0.136
(6.0)	0.665	3.581	0.618	1.085	3.303	92.3	2.821	0.130
(6.5)	0.608	3.432	0.603	0.142	3.432	100.1	2.931	0.219
(7.0)	0.782	3.467	0.604	0.640	3.320	95.9	2.835	0.150
(7.5)	2.301	4.457	0.866	3.643	3.443	77.3	2.941	0.053
(8.0)	3.219	3.422	0.818	0.263	3.403	99.5	2.906	0.026

实验编号 （watts）	$^{40}Ar(mol)$ （$\times 10^{-15}$）	$^{40}Ar/^{39}Ar$	$^{37}Ar/^{39}Ar$	$^{36}Ar/^{39}Ar$ （$\times 10^{-3}$）	$^{40}Ar*/^{39}Ar$	$\%^{40}Ar*$	年代 （百万年）	$\pm\sigma$ （百万年）
BKT-2L（激光单颗粒全熔）								
7201-06	4.568	3.469	0.233	0.196	3.424	98.8	2.924	0.033
7201-07	5.078	3.492	0.250	0.216	3.443	98.7	2.940	0.028
7201-08	4.639	3.462	0.228	0.017	3.470	100.4	2.963	0.025
7201-09	2.098	3.699	0.218	0.762	3.485	94.4	2.976	0.059
7201-10	3.603	3.481	0.224	0.125	3.457	99.4	2.952	0.035
7201-14	5.612	3.654	0.227	0.579	3.496	95.8	2.985	0.021
7201-15	5.201	3.552	0.233	0.385	3.451	97.3	2.947	0.020
7201-16	3.695	3.494	0.229	0.377	3.395	97.3	2.899	0.025
7201-17	2.412	3.511	0.227	0.336	3.424	97.7	2.924	0.039
7201-18	6.018	3.488	0.246	0.154	3.457	99.2	2.952	0.017
7201-19	4.206	3.472	0.230	0.106	3.453	99.6	2.949	0.024
7201-20	5.572	3.488	0.231	0.067	3.481	99.9	2.972	0.017
7201-21	2.002	3.574	0.734	0.510	3.475	97.3	2.968	0.045
7201-22	3.935	3.491	0.224	0.310	3.412	97.9	2.914	0.023
7201-24	0.513	3.800	0.205	1.104	3.484	91.8	2.976	0.175
7201-25	7.476	3.561	0.234	0.604	3.395	95.5	2.900	0.013
加权平均值								2.940±0.006
BKT-2L（块状逐步加热）								
(2.1)	0.306	7.275	1.158	19.628	1.559	21.4	1.332	0.619
(2.5)	0.342	4.939	0.860	11.467	1.611	32.6	1.376	0.337
(2.8)	0.700	5.477	0.617	9.346	2.758	50.4	2.356	0.213
(3.0)	0.428	3.810	0.559	0.937	3.572	93.8	3.050	0.364
(3.3)	0.432	3.563	0.526	0.516	3.446	96.8	2.943	0.315
(3.6)	0.441	3.495	0.516	0.902	3.263	93.5	2.787	0.289
(3.9)	0.606	4.047	0.527	2.159	3.445	85.2	2.942	0.173
(4.4)	1.502	3.607	0.396	0.804	3.395	94.2	2.900	0.057
(4.7)	0.361	3.509	0.488	0.485	3.399	97.0	2.902	0.374
(5.1)	0.670	3.627	0.636	1.148	3.332	92.0	2.846	0.127
(5.6)	0.648	3.865	0.597	1.668	3.413	88.4	2.915	0.136
(6.0)	0.665	3.581	0.618	1.085	3.303	92.3	2.821	0.130
(6.5)	0.608	3.432	0.603	0.142	3.432	100.1	2.931	0.219
(7.0)	0.782	3.467	0.604	0.640	3.320	95.9	2.835	0.150
(7.5)	2.301	4.457	0.866	3.643	3.443	77.3	2.941	0.053
(8.0)	3.219	3.422	0.818	0.263	3.403	99.5	2.906	0.026

Continued

Lab no. (watts)	$^{40}Ar(mol)$ ($\times 10^{-15}$)	$^{40}Ar/^{39}Ar$	$^{37}Ar/^{39}Ar$	$^{36}Ar/^{39}Ar$ ($\times 10^{-3}$)	$^{40}Ar*/^{39}Ar$	$\%^{40}Ar*$	Age (Myr)	$\pm\sigma$ (Myr)
BKT-2L (Bulk-step heating)								
(8.5)	0.124	2.951	0.342	−1.199	3.327	112.9	2.841	0.804
(8.5)	0.201	3.491	0.359	0.383	3.401	97.5	2.904	0.565
(8.5)	5.930	3.461	0.458	0.152	3.447	99.7	2.943	0.010
Plateau age								2.936±0.010

Methods. Palaeomagnetic sampling and analysis were done as described previously[23]. Ar/Ar dating used methods and facilities described in refs 24, 25. Samples were irradiated in the Oregon State University Triga reactor for 1.5 h using the cadmium-lined CLICKIT facility. Data for BKT-2L and AST-2.75 are presented in Table 1: isotope ratios are corrected for background, mass discrimination (1.00657 ± 0.00151 to 1.00873 ± 0.0010 per atomic mass unit, measured by routine automated analysis of air pipette samples) and radioactive decay. Sensitivities of the mass spectrometer–electron multiplier systems were $(5-10) \times 10^{13}$ nA per mol for argon isotopes. Nucleogenic interference corrections were made based on $(^{39}Ar/^{39}Ar)_{Ca} = 0.00764 \pm 0.0000557$, $(^{36}Ar/^{37}Ar)_{Ca} = 0.0002705 \pm 0.0000105$, $(^{40}Ar/^{39}Ar)_{Ca} = 0.00014 \pm 0.00060$. Calculated ages are based on J values (0.0003935 ± 0.0000003 for AST-2.75, 0.0004737 ± 0.0000003 for BKT-2L) derived from replicate analysis of the Fish Canyon sanidine standard, with an age of 27.84 Myr[24,25]. Age calculations are based on decay constants $\lambda = 5.543 \times 10^{-10}$ Y^{-1}. Uncertainties in ages reflect uncertainties in isotope abundances and all corrections, but do not reflect uncertainty in the age of the standard. The arithmetic mean and standard error of the mean are 2.58 ± 0.11 Myr, whereas the inverse variance weighted mean is 2.52 ± 0.08 Myr; we adopt the latter as more appropriate because of the heterogeneous precision of individual analyses. Samples with ages shown in italics (AST-2.75) are contaminants and were excluded from the mean age calculations.

Figure 1a maps the Gona archaeological sites. Systematic excavations at EG10 (13 m^2) and at EG12 (9 m^2) yielded the largest and most informative artefact assemblages ($n = 2,970$ stone artefacts, 1,114 of these being *in situ*). The artefacts were restricted to a 10-cm interval of a 6-m-thick, well consolidated clay-rich palaeovertisol. An additional 43 surface and excavated artefacts were recovered in 1994 from WG7, increasing the geographical distribution of the archaeological occurrences to include the Ounda Gona catchment. The fine-grained context, the limited vertical dispersion, the fresh quality of the artefacts and the lack of artefact-size sorting suggests a low-energy depositional environment.

The excavated and surface artefact assemblages at EG10 and EG12 primarily comprise simple cores, whole flakes and flaking debris. Unifacially and bifacially flaked cores comprise the "flaked pieces" category. There are numerous examples of several generations of flake scars on the cores, indicating that Late Pliocene hominids had mastered the skills of basic stone knapping (Fig. 3). Moreover, the large number of well struck flakes with conspicuous bulbs of percussion indicate a clear understanding of conchoidal fracture mechanics. "Detached pieces" are numerically dominant, with values in the range of 75–95%. There are a few "pounded pieces", namely pieces modified or shaped by pounding or battering, like hammerstones, anvils or battered cobbles.

实验编号 （watts）	$^{40}Ar(mol)$ （×10⁻¹⁵）	$^{40}Ar/^{39}Ar$	$^{37}Ar/^{39}Ar$	$^{36}Ar/^{39}Ar$ （×10⁻³）	$^{40}Ar*/^{39}Ar$	%$^{40}Ar*$	年代 （百万年）	±σ （百万年）
BKT-2L（块状逐步加热）								
(8.5)	0.124	2.951	0.342	−1.199	3.327	112.9	2.841	0.804
(8.5)	0.201	3.491	0.359	0.383	3.401	97.5	2.904	0.565
(8.5)	5.930	3.461	0.458	0.152	3.447	99.7	2.943	0.010
坪年龄								2.936±0.010

方法。古地磁采样和分析的方法参见之前的描述[23]。Ar/Ar 年代测定使用的方法和设备在参考文献 24 和 25 中有描述。使用镉谱线 CLICKIT 设施，在俄勒冈州立大学的 Triga 反应堆中照射样本 1.5 小时。BKT-2L 和 AST-2.75 的数据在表 1 中列出：同位素比值经过背景校正、质量歧视校正（通过空气移液管样本的常规自动分析测定每原子质量单位 $1.00657±0.00151$ 到 $1.00873±0.0010$）和放射性衰变校正。质谱仪电子倍增系统的敏感性对氩同位素而言是每摩尔 $(5\sim10)×10^{13}$ nA。元素的核源干扰修正是在 $(^{39}Ar/^{39}Ar)_{Ca}=0.00764±0.0000557$、$(^{36}Ar/^{37}Ar)_{Ca}=0.0002705±0.0000105$、$(^{40}Ar/^{39}Ar)_{Ca}=0.00014±0.00060$ 的基础上进行的。计算出来的年代是根据菲什峡谷透长石标准的重复分析推出的 J 值（AST-2.75 的 J 值是 $0.0003935±0.0000003$，BKT-2L 的 J 值是 $0.0004737±0.0000003$）得到的，其年代为 2,784 万年[24,25]。年代的计算依据是衰变常数 $λ=5.543×10^{-10}$ Y^{-1}。年代的不确定性反映了同位素丰度和所有校正值的不确定性，但是并不反映标准年代的不确定性。算术平均值和均值的标准误差是 $(258±11)$ 万年，而方差倒数加权均值是 $(252±8)$ 万年；因为个体分析存在异质精确性，所以我们认为后者更准确。年代用斜体表示的样本（AST-2.75）是污染物，在计算均值时将它们排除在外。

图 1a 为戈纳考古遗址图。在 EG10（13 平方米）和 EG12（9 平方米）两处进行的系统发掘工作获取了数量最多、信息最为丰富的人工制品组合（石制品 2,970 件，其中 1,114 件为原位埋藏）。这些石制品夹杂在 6 米厚的、致密的、富含黏土的古土壤层的 10 厘米厚的文化层中。另外，1994 年在 WG7 地表采集和发掘出土了 43 件人工制品，它们将考古发现的地理分布区域扩展到了整个昂达戈纳流域。细微颗粒的沉积环境、分布在有限的垂直地层、人工制品的新鲜程度以及人工制品尺寸缺乏变化暗示着一种比较稳定的沉积环境。

在 EG10 和 EG12 发掘出土和地表采集的人工制品主要包括简单的石核、完整的石片类工具和剥片废屑。单面和两面剥片的石核类工具组成"剥片类"工具。石核体上有大量不同剥片阶段的石片疤，说明上新世晚期的人科成员已经掌握了基本的剥片技术（图 3）。此外，大量带有明显打击泡的石片说明制造者清楚地了解石料贝壳状断裂力学。"剥落石片类"数量居多，比例为 75%~95%。通过击打或敲打来进行剥片或修形的石锤、石砧或砾石等"打击类"工具数量较少。

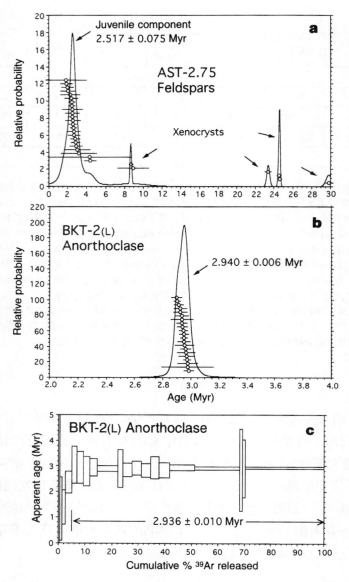

Fig. 2. Age-probability plots for **a,** AST-2.75, and **b,** BKT-2L for single-crystal laser fusion $^{40}Ar/^{39}Ar$ analyses. **c,** Apparent age spectrum for bulk argon-ion laser heating of BKT-2L.

Trachyte was the main raw material source, comprising $> 70\%$ of the artefacts. Other volcanics such as rhyolite and basalt were also used. The likely sources of raw materials were nearby stream conglomerates. Clasts from the level of the Intermediate Conglomerate show that trachyte cobbles were the most abundant, comprising about 50% of the total sample that also includes chalcedony, breccia and other lavas. The high proportion of trachyte artefacts could be taken to mean an appreciation of the flaking properties and selectivity for this particular raw material over others. There is a good correspondence between the sizes of the stone clasts and the sizes of the excavated stone artefacts. The

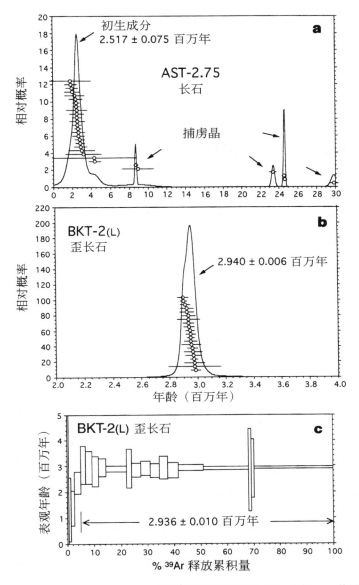

图 2. 年龄概率图：**a**，AST-2.75 和 **b**，BKT-2L 的激光单颗粒熔融 $^{40}Ar/^{39}Ar$ 分析。**c**，使用块状氩离子激光加热得到的 BKT-2L 表观年龄谱。

　　粗面岩是加工石制品的主要原料，占石制品的 70% 以上。其他的火山岩如流纹岩和玄武岩也有使用。这些原料可能出自附近溪流的砾岩层。从中砾岩层得到的岩块表明，粗面岩砾石最为丰富，约占标本总量的 50%。标本中也含玉髓、角砾岩和其他熔岩。粗面岩石制品的高比例可能意味着相较其他原料而言，古人类更倾向于选择这种熟悉的、便于剥片的原料。碎屑岩的大小和发掘出土的人工石器制品尺寸

close proximity of raw material sources may account for the less exhausted nature of the "flaked pieces" and the very low numbers of "unmodified pieces" (manuports) found at the archaeological sites.

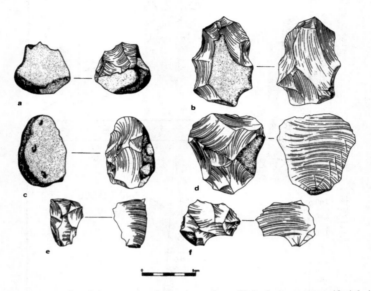

Fig. 3. Sketches of a sample of the excavated Gona artefacts. Flaked pieces: **a,** unifacial side chopper, EG12; **b,** discoid, EG10; **c,** unifacial side chopper, EG10. Detached pieces: **d–f,** whole flakes, EG10. Note that the maximum dimension of **d** is as large as some of the flaked pieces.

The artefact collections from Olduvai Gorge, Koobi Fora and the Omo[8-11] are the largest and best-studied samples of Oldowan artefacts. The oldest reliably dated among these are those from Lokalalei[12], which are constrained to be younger than the Kalochoro Tuff (= Tuff F of the Shungura Fm) at 2.36 ± 0.05 Myr. The Gona artefacts are thus at least 160 Kyr $\pm$ 90 Kyr older than these, the ages being distinguishable with greater than 92% confidence. All these stone assemblages are characterized by simple flaked cores made on cobbles and blocks, and associated flaking debris. The composition of the Gona assemblages is very similar to Plio-Pleistocene sites elsewhere, except for lower diversity of the cores from Gona and the high incidence of utilized pieces and manuports at Olduvai Gorge.

In addition to the lower diversity of the types seen in the Gona core forms, other contrasts exist between these and the Early Pleistocene assemblages. There are no retouched flakes such as light duty flake scrapers at Gona, which are present in small quantities in the Olduvai assemblages. In contrast to these minimal differences, we see strong parallels among all Plio-Pleistocene assemblages dated between 2.5–1.5 Myr. Assemblages from Olduvai and Koobi Fora show a greater degree of core reduction, but knowledge of fundamental conchoidal fracture mechanics suggests that the Gona artefacts are not significantly different. Indeed, the greater core reduction witnessed at Koobi Fora and Olduvai may be due to the considerable distances of these sites from the sources of raw materials compared to Gona.

之间有很好的一致性。原料来源近可以解释遗址中较少发现高损耗的"剥片类"制品和"未使用石料"的现象。

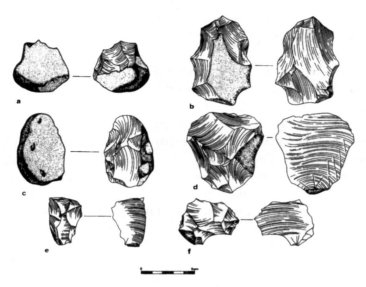

图 3. 戈纳发掘出土石制品线图。剥片类:**a**,单面砍砸器,EG12;**b**,饼状石核,EG10;**c**,单面砍砸器,EG10。剥落的石片类:**d~f**,完整石片,EG10。注意:**d** 的最大尺寸与一些剥片类的尺寸近似。

　　奥杜威工业数量最集中、研究最为充分的人工制品样本来自奥杜威峡谷、库比福勒和奥莫 [8-11],其中最早的可靠年代数据来自罗卡拉雷 [12],它们被认定比卡罗卓洛凝灰岩(= 上古拉地层的凝灰岩 F)更年轻,距今约(236±5)万年。因此戈纳人工制品至少比这些要早 16 万年 ± 9 万年,其可辨年代的置信度大于92%。所有这些石制品组合都是由毛坯为砾石或岩块的、简单剥片的石核和剥片废屑构成。戈纳遗址的石制品组合与其他地方上新世–更新世遗址的组合非常相似,只是戈纳遗址的石核变化少,而奥杜威峡谷遗址群中使用的片类工具和未使用石料比例较高。

　　除了戈纳石核形态多样性较低外,戈纳遗址的石制品与早更新世石制品组合之间还存在其他差异。戈纳无二次加工修理的工具如轻型刮削器,而这种工具在奥杜威石制品组合中少量存在。与这些细小的差异相比,我们发现所有距今 250 万年到150 万年之间的上新世–更新世石制品组合都表现出高度的一致性。奥杜威和库比福勒发现的石制品组合显示出较高程度的石核剥片率,但是人类对贝壳状断裂力学最基本的了解表明,戈纳石制品并没有显著的不同之处。事实上,在库比福勒和奥杜威出现的石核高剥片率现象可能是由于与戈纳相比,这些地点离原料产地的距离更远。

The presence of large concentrations of stone artefacts at the early Gona sites shows that by 2.5 Myr some populations of Late Pliocene hominids had already mastered the basics of stone tool manufacture. The working edges of the majority of Gona artefacts are very fresh and sharp. Many of the cores show evidence of pitting and bruising. This suggests that in addition to being sources of sharp-edged flakes[13], the cores were used as multipurpose tools, for example as hammerstones and for other pounding activities.

The Gona evidence extends the known age of the Oldowan Industrial Complex to 2.5 Myr, and obviates the need to posit a "pre-Oldowan"[14] or an early facies of the Omo industrial complex[10,12]. Clearly, all the Oldowan assemblages group together because of the simplicity of craft practices in fashioning simple cores and the resultant flakes. These contrast with Acheulean assemblages that show elements of much more specific and preconceived designs[15]. The very early age of the Gona artefacts shows a techno-logical stasis in the Oldowan industrial complex for over a period of 1 million years. The Acheulean appears abruptly at about 1.6–1.5 Myr with large bifacial tool forms such as handaxes and cleavers that were unknown in the Oldowan (*sensu stricto*)[16-18].

The hominids responsible for the manufacture of the Gona artefacts remain unidentified. There is, as yet, no evidence of stone artefacts in sediments older than 2.6 Myr within the Gona. Two contemporaneous hominid species *Homo* and *A. aethiopicus* are known elsewhere in eastern Africa from deposits that are comparable in age with the Gona[19,20]. However, no hominid specimens have yet been found associated with Late Pliocene stone tools.

The sophisticated understanding of conchoidal fracture evidence at Gona implies that the hominids that lived about 2.5 Myr ago were not novices to lithic technology. We predict that even older artefacts will be found. Future research in the Gona study area will be directed towards searching for archaeological evidence in the older deposits and towards assessing contrasting hypotheses linking global climatic changes, the origin of the genus *Homo*, and the beginning of stone-tool manufacture and use[21,22].

(**385**, 333-336; 1997)

S. Semaw[*], P. Rennet[†], J. W. K. Harris[*], C. S. Feibel[*], R. L. Bernor[‡], N. Fesseha[‡] & K. Mowbray[*]

[*] Department of Anthropology, Douglass Campus, Rutgers University, New Brunswick, New Jersey 08903, USA
[†] Berkeley Geochronology Center, 2455 Ridge Road, Berkeley, California 94709, USA
[‡] Laboratory of Paleobiology, Department of Anatomy, College of Medicine, Howard University, Washington DC 20059, USA

Received 18 June; accepted 25 November 1996.

References:

1. Johanson, D. C. *et al. Am. J. Phys. Anth.* **57**, 373-402 (1982).
2. Corvinus, G. & Roche, H. *L'Anthropologie* **80**, 315-324 (1976).
3. Harris, J. W. K. *Afr. Arch. Rev.* **1**, 3-31 (1983).
4. Harris, J. W. K. & Semaw, S. *Nyame Akuma* **31**, 19-21 (1989).
5. Roche, H. & Tiercelin, J. J. *C. r. hebd. Séanc. Acad. Sci. Paris* **284D**, 1871-1874 (1977).

在时代较早的戈纳遗址中，石制品的大量集中出现表明，在距今 250 万年前，一些上新世晚期的人科成员已经掌握了基本的石器制造技术。大部分戈纳遗址石制品的工作刃缘都非常新鲜且锐利。不少石核体上显示出挖掘和摩擦的痕迹，表明这些石核除了用于剥落刃缘锋利的石片之外[13]，还被用作多用途的工具，如作为石锤、用于其他敲砸活动。

戈纳遗址将已知的奥杜威工业范畴的年代拓展到了距今 250 万年，从而排除了有"前奥杜威"[14] 或早期奥莫工业[10,12] 存在的可能。很显然，因为石核－石片加工工艺十分简单，所以所有奥杜威工业的石制品组合都很类似，这与阿舍利石制品组合所呈现出的具有更加专业化趋向及预先设计的元素形成了鲜明的对比[15]。戈纳石制品年代之早表明奥杜威石器工业技术曾历经 100 多万年的技术停滞期。阿舍利工业在距今约 160 万年到 150 万年间突然出现了大型的两面工具，如手斧和薄刃斧，这些在狭义的奥杜威工业中都是前所未见的[16-18]。

现在尚无法确定戈纳遗址石制品的制造者究竟是哪一人科种群，也没有证据表明戈纳地区沉积物中存在早于距今 260 万年前的石制品。目前已知的、在东非与戈纳遗址时代相同的堆积物中发现的人科成员有两种——人属和南方古猿埃塞俄比亚种[19,20]，但尚未发现与上新世晚期石器相伴随的人科化石标本。

在戈纳发现的人类熟练掌握石料贝壳状断裂力学的证据表明，生活在距今约 250 万年前的原始人类并不是制作石制工具的新手，我们预测未来将有更古老的石制品被发现。戈纳地区后续的研究工作将瞄准在更古老的地层堆积物中搜寻考古学证据以及甄别莫衷一是的全球气候变化、人属起源以及石制工具的出现与使用等方面关系的假说[21,22] 上。

（刘皓芳 翻译；王社江 审稿）

6. Kimbel, W. H. *et al. Nature* **368**, 449-451 (1994).

7. McDougall, I. *et al. Geophys. Res. Lett.* **19**, 2349-2352 (1992).

8. Leakey, M. D. *Olduvai Gorge* Vol. 3 (Cambridge University Press, UK, 1971).

9. Isaac, G. L. in *Earliest Man and Environments in the Lake Rudolf Basin* (eds Coppens, Y., Howell, F. C., Isaac, G. L. & Leakey, R. E. F.) 552-564 (University of Chicago Press, Illinois, 1976).

10. Chavaillon, J. in *Earliest Man and Environments in the Lake Rudolf Basin* (eds Coppens, Y., Howell, F. C., Isaac, G. L. & Leakey, R. E. F.) 565-573 (University of Chicago Press, Illinois, 1976).

11. Merrick, H. V. & Merrick, J. P. S. in *Earliest Man and Environments in the Lake Rudolf Basin* (eds Coppens, Y., Howell, F. C., Isaac, G. L. & Leakey, R. E. F.) 574-589 (University of Chicago Press, Illinois, 1976).

12. Kibunjia, M. *J. Hum. Evol.* **27**, 159-171 (1994).

13. Toth, N. *J. Archaeol. Sci.* **12**, 101-120 (1985).

14. Piperno, M. in *Hominidae: Proc. 2nd Intern. Congr. Hum. Paleont.* 189-195 (Jaca Books, Milan, Italy, 1989).

15. Gowlett, J. A. J. in *Stone Age Prehistory* (eds Bailey, G. N. & Callow, P.) 243-260 (Cambridge University Press, UK, 1986).

16. Isaac, G. L. & Curtis, G. H. *Nature* **249**, 624-627 (1974).

17. Asfaw, B. *et al. Nature* **360**, 732-735 (1992).

18. Dominguez-Rodrigo, M. *Complutum* **7**, 7-15 (1996).

19. Walker, A. *et al. Nature* **322**, 517-522 (1986).

20. Hill, A. *et al. Nature* **355**, 719-722 (1992).

21. Vrba, E. S. in *Evolutionary History of the Robust Australopithecines* (ed. Grine, F.) 405-426 (de Gruyter, New York, 1988).

22. deMenocal, P. B. *Science* **270**, 53-59 (1995).

23. Renne, P. R. *et al. Geophys. Res. Lett.* **20**, 1067-1070 (1993).

24. Deino, A. & Potts, R. *J. Geophys. Res.* **95**, 8453-8470 (1990).

25. WoldeGabriel, G. *et al. Nature* **371**, 330-333 (1994).

Acknowledgements. Permission for this research was granted by the CRCCH and the National Museum of Ethiopia in the Ministry of Culture and Information. On behalf of members of the Gona research project, the two principal investigators (S.S. and J.W.K.H.) thank the Government of Ethiopia and the Afar People. We also thank J. D. Clark, T. White, and F. C. Howell and S. Asrat for their help; B. Asfaw, Y. Beyene and G. WoldeGabriel for encouragement, advice and laboratory assistance at the Museum in Addis; the NTO of Ethiopia and drivers; Y. Haile Selassie, A, Ademassu, J. Haile-Mariam and J. Wynn for overall support; M. Kahasai, A. Asfaw, A. Humet, A. Habib and the Afars at Eloha, Busidima and Talalak for support in the field; Y. Kanaa, M. Siegel and P. Jung for illustrations; T. Assebework and S. Eshete for fieldwork; J. Butterworth for palaeomagnetic analyses; and T. White, R. Blumenschine, D. Lieberman, M. Domínguez-Rodrigo and M. Rogers for comments on the manuscript. We thank the NSF, the L. S. B. Leakey Foundation, the Boise Fund, Ann and Gordon Getty Foundation, D. Holt, Z. Zelazo, and Rutgers University for financial support.

Correspondence and requests for materials should be addressed to S.S. (e-mail: semaw@eden.rutgers. edu).

Viable Offspring Derived from Fetal and Adult Mammalian Cells

I. Wilmut *et al.*

Editor's Note

Soon after Morag and Megan, the first mammals cloned from an established cell line, cloning pioneer Ian Wilmut and colleagues report the arrival of Dolly the sheep, the first mammal cloned from an adult cell. Dolly was proof that nuclear transfer could be used to reprogram adult DNA, raising the prospect of tailor-making patient-matched stem cells for use in regenerative medicine and of cloning other animals. Many species including dogs, horses and mice have been cloned subsequently, and nuclear transfer-derived human stem cells are being used to study development and disease. Dolly prompted researchers to devise new egg-free methods for making stem cells without destroying embryos, and it is believed these will greatly aid basic and applied biological research.

Fertilization of mammalian eggs is followed by successive cell divisions and progressive differentiation, first into the early embryo and subsequently into all of the cell types that make up the adult animal. Transfer of a single nucleus at a specific stage of development, to an enucleated unfertilized egg, provided an opportunity to investigate whether cellular differentiation to that stage involved irreversible genetic modification. The first offspring to develop from a differentiated cell were born after nuclear transfer from an embryo-derived cell line that had been induced to become quiescent[1]. Using the same procedure, we now report the birth of live lambs from three new cell populations established from adult mammary gland, fetus and embryo. The fact that a lamb was derived from an adult cell confirms that differentiation of that cell did not involve the irreversible modification of genetic material required for development to term. The birth of lambs from differentiated fetal and adult cells also reinforces previous speculation[1,2] that by inducing donor cells to become quiescent it will be possible to obtain normal development from a wide variety of differentiated cells.

IT has long been known that in amphibians, nuclei transferred from adult keratinocytes established in culture support development to the juvenile, tadpole stage[3]. Although this involves differentiation into complex tissues and organs, no development to the adult stage was reported, leaving open the question of whether a differentiated adult nucleus can be fully reprogrammed. Previously we reported the birth of live lambs after nuclear transfer from cultured embryonic cells that had been induced into quiescence. We suggested that inducing the donor cell to exit the growth phase causes changes

胎儿和成年哺乳动物的细胞可以产生存活后代

威尔穆特等

编者按

由已建立的细胞系克隆得到的首批哺乳动物莫拉格和梅甘出生后不久，克隆先驱伊恩·威尔穆特和他的同事们报道了第一只由成年体细胞克隆得到的哺乳动物——多莉羊的诞生。多莉羊表明通过核移植可实现成体 DNA 的重编程，这为定制与患者相匹配的用于再生医学的干细胞以及克隆其他动物带来了希望。随后，包括狗、马和小鼠在内的其他物种也实现了克隆，源于核移植的人类干细胞被用来研究发育和疾病问题。多莉羊促使研究者设计新的无卵方法在不破坏胚胎的情况下获得干细胞，也会为基础生物研究和应用生物研究提供巨大帮助。

哺乳动物的卵细胞受精后出现连续的细胞分裂和渐进分化，最开始出现早期的胚胎，随后分化为组成成年动物所需的各类细胞。将发育特定阶段的单个细胞核移植到摘除细胞核的未受精的卵细胞内，为研究细胞分化到这个阶段是否发生了不可逆的遗传修饰提供了契机。由分化细胞发育而来的第一批后代是在转入已诱导为静止的胚胎来源细胞系的核后产生的[1]。采用相同的方法，我们从成年母羊乳腺、胎儿和胚胎建立的三个新细胞群中获得了活羊羔。从成体细胞发育出羊羔这个事实证实了这一细胞的分化并不包括完成体内发育所需遗传物质的不可逆修饰。这些来源于分化的胎儿细胞和成体细胞的小羊的出生也加强了先前的推测[1,2]，即通过诱导供体细胞进入静止期就可能实现不同分化阶段细胞的正常发育。

很久以前人们就知道，在两栖动物中，用培养的成体角质形成细胞的细胞核进行核移植，可以支持个体发育到幼年蝌蚪阶段[3]。尽管这一过程涉及复杂的组织和器官的分化，但是尚无报道称其能发育至成年阶段。因此，分化的成体细胞核能否完全重编程是一个有待解决的问题。先前我们报道了培养的胚胎细胞经诱导为静止状态后，经过核移植能够发育成活的小羊。我们认为诱导供体细胞退出其生长周期能引起染色质结构的改变，从而促进了基因表达的重编程；而且如果以类似的方式

in chromatin structure that facilitate reprogramming of gene expression and that development would be normal if nuclei are used from a variety of differentiated donor cells in similar regimes. Here we investigate whether normal development to term is possible when donor cells derived from fetal or adult tissue are induced to exit the growth cycle and enter the G0 phase of the cell cycle before nuclear transfer.

Three new populations of cells were derived from (1) a day-9 embryo, (2) a day-26 fetus and (3) mammary gland of a 6-year-old ewe in the last trimester of pregnancy. Morphology of the embryo-derived cells (Fig. 1) is unlike both mouse embryonic stem (ES) cells and the embryo-derived cells used in our previous study. Nuclear transfer was carried out according to one of our established protocols[1] and reconstructed embryos transferred into recipient ewes. Ultrasound scanning detected 21 single fetuses on day 50–60 after oestrus (Table 1). On subsequent scanning at ~14-day intervals, fewer fetuses were observed, suggesting either mis-diagnosis or fetal loss. In total, 62% of fetuses were lost, a significantly greater proportion than the estimate of 6% after natural mating[4]. Increased prenatal loss has been reported after embryo manipulation or culture of unreconstructed embryos[5]. At about day 110 of pregnancy, four fetuses were dead, all from embryo-derived cells, and post-mortem analysis was possible after killing the ewes. Two fetuses had abnormal liver development, but no other abnormalities were detected and there was no evidence of infection.

Table 1. Development of embryos reconstructed with three different cell types

Cell type	No. of fused couplets (%)*	No. recovered from oviduct (%)	No. cultured	No. of morula/ blastocyst (%)	No. of morula or blastocysts transferred†	No. of pregnancies/ no. of recipients (%)	No. of live lambs (%)‡
Mammary epithelium	277 (63.8)[a]	247 (89.2)	–	29 (11.7)[a]	29	1/13 (7.7)	1 (3.4%)
Fetal fibroblast	172 (84.7)[b]	124 (86.7)	–	34 (27.4)[b]	34	4/10 (40.0)	2 (5.9%)
			24	13 (54.2)[b]	6	1/6 (16.6)	1 (16.6%) §
Embryo-derived	385 (82.8)[b]	231 (85.3)	–	90 (39.0)[b]	72	14/27 (51.8)	4 (5.6%)
			92	36 (39.0)[b]	15	1/5 (20.0)	0

* As assessed 1 h after fusion by examination on a dissecting microscope. Superscripts a or b within a column indicate a significant difference between donor cell types in the efficiency of fusion ($P < 0.001$) or the proportion of embryos that developed to morula or blastocyst ($P < 0.001$).

† It was not practicable to transfer all morulae/blastocysts.

‡ As a proportion of morulae or blastocysts transferred. Not all recipients were perfectly synchronized.

§ This lamb died within a few minutes of birth.

对不同分化程度的供体细胞进行处理后，其发育也会是正常的。这里我们研究了当来源于胎儿组织或者成体组织的供体细胞被诱导脱离生长周期并在核移植之前进入细胞周期的 G0 期后，是否还有可能完成正常的发育。

这三个新的细胞群分别来源于：（1）第 9 天的胚胎；（2）第 26 天的胎儿；（3）6 岁母羊孕晚期的乳腺。胚胎来源的细胞形态（图 1）不同于我们之前实验中使用过的小鼠胚胎干细胞（ES）和胚胎来源的细胞。根据我们建立的方案 [1] 进行核移植，然后将重组的胚胎移植到受体母羊中。发情期后第 50~60 天超声检测到了 21 个单独的胚胎（表 1）。随后在大约以 14 天为间隔的扫描检测中发现，看到的胚胎数越来越少，暗示出现了错误诊断或者胎儿死亡。胎儿损失率共计 62%，显著高于自然交配的估计值 6%[4]。有研究报道，胚胎处理或者非重组胚胎的培养会增加胎儿损失率 [5]。大约在孕期的第 110 天，四个胎儿死亡，它们都来源于胚胎细胞核衍生的细胞，处死母羊后即可进行验尸分析。其中两个胎儿的肝脏发育异常，但是没有发现其他异常或者感染的证据。

表 1. 三种不同类型细胞重组胚胎的发育

细胞类型	融合胚胎的数量 (%)*	输卵管中收回的胚胎数量 (%)	培养的胚胎数量	桑椹胚／胚泡数量 (%)	移植的桑椹胚或胚泡数量†	怀孕母羊数目／受体母羊数目 (%)	存活小羊数目 (%)‡
乳腺上皮细胞	277 (63.8)ᵃ	247 (89.2)	–	29 (11.7)ᵃ	29	1/13 (7.7)	1 (3.4%)
胎儿成纤维细胞	172 (84.7)ᵇ	124 (86.7)		34 (27.4)ᵇ	34	4/10 (40.0)	2 (5.9%)
			24	13 (54.2)ᵇ	6	1/6 (16.6)	1 (16.6%)§
胚胎来源细胞	385 (82.8)ᵇ	231 (85.3)	–	90 (39.0)ᵇ	72	14/27 (51.8)	4 (5.6%)
			92	36 (39.0)ᵇ	15	1/5 (20.0)	0

* 在融合 1 小时后用解剖显微镜进行检查。上标 a 或者 b 表示供体细胞融合的效率显著差异（$P < 0.001$）或者胚胎发育成桑椹胚或者胚泡的比例显著差异（$P < 0.001$）。
† 要移植所有的桑椹胚或胚泡是不可行的。
‡ 占移植的桑椹胚或胚泡的比例。并不是所有的受体都能完全同步。
§ 该小羊出生后几分钟内死亡。

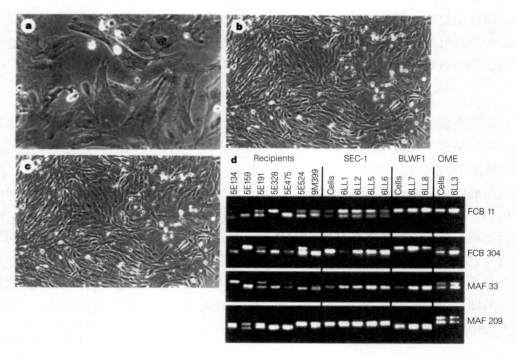

Fig. 1. Phase-contrast photomicrograph of donor-cell populations: **a**, Embryo-derived cells (SEC1); **b**, fetal fibroblasts (BLWF1); **c**, mammary-derived cells (OME). **d**, Microsatellite analysis of recipient ewes, nuclear donor cells and lambs using four polymorphic ovine markers[22]. The ewes are arranged from left to right in the same order as the lambs. Cell populations are embryo-derived (SEC1), fetal-derived (BLW1), and mammary-derived (OME), respectively. Lambs have the same genotype as the donor cells and differ from their recipient mothers.

Eight ewes gave birth to live lambs (Table 1, Fig. 2). All three cell populations were represented. One weak lamb, derived from the fetal fibroblasts, weighed 3.1 kg and died within a few minutes of birth, although post-mortem analysis failed to find any abnormality or infection. At 12.5%, perinatal loss was not dissimilar to that occurring in a large study of commercial sheep, when 8% of lambs died within 24 h of birth[6]. In all cases the lambs displayed the morphological characteristics of the breed used to derive the nucleus donors and not that of the oocyte donor (Table 2). This alone indicates that the lambs could not have been born after inadvertent mating of either the oocyte donor or recipient ewes. In addition, DNA microsatellite analysis of the cell populations and the lambs at four polymorphic loci confirmed that each lamb was derived from the cell population used as nuclear donor (Fig. 1). Duration of gestation is determined by fetal genotype[7], and in all cases gestation was longer than the breed mean (Table 2). By contrast, birth weight is influenced by both maternal and fetal genotype[8]. The birth weight of all lambs was within the range for single lambs born to Blackface ewes on our farm (up to 6.6 kg) and in most cases was within the range for the breed of the nuclear donor. There are no strict control observations for birth weight after embryo transfer between breeds, but the range in weight of lambs born to their own breed on our farm is 1.2–5.0 kg, 2–4.9 kg and 3–9 kg for the Finn Dorset, Welsh Mountain and Poll Dorset genotypes, respectively. The attainment of sexual maturity in the lambs is being monitored.

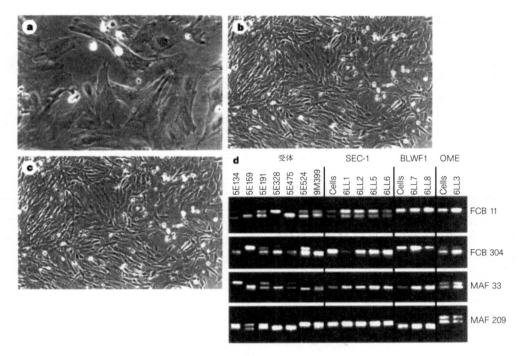

图 1. 供体细胞群的相差显微照片：**a**，胚胎来源的细胞（SEC1）；**b**，胎儿成纤维细胞（BLWF1）；**c**，乳腺来源的细胞（OME）。**d**，使用四种多态性绵羊标记物对受体母羊、细胞核供体细胞和小羊进行微卫星分析[22]。母羊从左到右排列的顺序和羊羔一致。细胞群分别是胚胎来源的细胞（SEC1）、胎儿来源的细胞（BLW1）和乳腺来源的细胞（OME）。小羊和供体细胞具有相同的基因型，而与受体母羊不同。

八只母羊生出了活的小羊（表 1，图 2），包含了所有三个细胞群来源。其中一只较弱的小羊来源于胎儿成纤维细胞，重 3.1 kg，并在出生后几分钟内死亡，然而验尸分析没有发现任何异常或者感染。12.5% 的围产期损失率与商品羊大型研究中大约 8% 的小羊在出生后 24 小时内死亡[6] 的损失率相似。所有的小羊都表现出细胞核供体的形态特征，而不是卵细胞供体的特征（表 2）。仅仅这点就表明这些小羊的出生并非是卵细胞供体或者受体母羊偶然交配的结果。此外，利用 DNA 微卫星对细胞群和小羊的四个多态性基因座进行分析也证实了每只小羊均来自核供体细胞群（图 1）。妊娠期的长短由胎儿的基因型决定[7]，而且在所有例子中妊娠期都比品种平均妊娠期长（表 2）。相比之下，出生体重则受到母体和胎儿基因型的影响[8]。所有小羊的出生体重均在我们农场的黑面母羊生出的单胎羊羔的体重范围内（最重 6.6 kg），而且在大多数情况下都在核供体品种的体重范围内。对于不同品种间胚胎移植后的出生体重没有进行严格的对照观察，但是在我们农场中出生的芬兰多塞特、威尔士山和无角多塞特三个品种小羊的体重范围分别是 1.2~5.0 kg、2~4.9 kg 和 3~9 kg。小羊的性成熟程度也在监测之中。

Table 2. Delivery of lambs developing from embryos derived by nuclear transfer from three different donor cells types, showing gestation length and birth weight

Cell type	Breed of lamb	Lamb identity	Duration of pregnancy (days)*	Birth weight (kg)
Mammary epithelium	Finn Dorset	6LL3	148	6.6
Fetal fibroblast	Black Welsh	6LL7	152	5.6
	Black Welsh	6LL8	149	2.8
	Black Welsh	6LL9†	156	3.1
Embryo- derived	Poll Dorset	6LL1	149	6.5
	Poll Dorset	6LL2‡	152	6.2
	Poll Dorset	6LL5	148	4.2
	Poll Dorset	6LL6‡	152	5.3

* Breed averages are 143, 147 and 145 days, respectively for the three genotypes Finn Dorset, Black Welsh Mountain and Poll Dorset.

† This lamb died within a few minutes of birth.

‡ These lambs were delivered by caesarian section. Overall the nature of the assistance provided by the veterinary surgeon was similar to that expected in a commercial flock.

Fig. 2. Lamb number 6LL3 derived from the mammary gland of a Finn Dorset ewe with the Scottish Blackface ewe which was the recipient.

Development of embryos produced by nuclear transfer depends upon the maintenance of normal ploidy and creating the conditions for developmental regulation of gene expression. These responses are both influenced by the cell-cycle stage of donor and recipient cells and the interaction between them (reviewed in ref. 9). A comparison of development of mouse and cattle embryos produced by nuclear transfer to oocytes[10,11] or enucleated zygotes[12,13] suggests that a greater proportion develop if the recipient is an oocyte. This may be because factors that bring about reprogramming of gene expression in a transferred nucleus are required for early development and are taken up by the pronuclei during development of the zygote.

994

表 2. 由三种不同类型供体细胞核移植后得到的胚胎发育而成的小羊的妊娠期时间和出生体重

细胞类型	小羊品种	小羊代号	妊娠期长度(天)*	出生体重(kg)
乳腺上皮细胞	芬兰多塞特	6LL3	148	6.6
胎儿成纤维细胞	黑面威尔士	6LL7	152	5.6
	黑面威尔士	6LL8	149	2.8
	黑面威尔士	6LL9†	156	3.1
胚胎来源细胞	无角多塞特	6LL1	149	6.5
	无角多塞特	6LL2‡	152	6.2
	无角多塞特	6LL5	148	4.2
	无角多塞特	6LL6‡	152	5.3

* 三种基因型的羊——芬兰多塞特羊、黑面威尔士山羊和无角多塞特羊的品种平均妊娠期分别是 143 天、147 天和 145 天。

† 该小羊出生后几分钟内死亡。

‡ 这些羊出生都采用剖腹取胎术。兽医提供的帮助与商品羊中的相似。

图 2. 6LL3 号小羊，来源于芬兰多塞特母羊的乳腺细胞，受体母羊是苏格兰黑面羊。

通过核移植产生的胚胎的发育依赖于正常染色体倍性的保持以及基因表达的发育调控环境的创造。这些反应都受到供体细胞和受体细胞的细胞周期以及它们之间相互作用的影响(参考文献 9 中的综述)。将核移植到卵母细胞[10,11] 或者无核的受精卵[12,13] 中得到的小鼠和牛胚胎的发育情况的对比结果表明，如果受体是卵母细胞，那么大部分胚胎发育。这可能是因为在早期发育时就需要那些能引起移植的细胞核中基因表达重编程的因子，但是在受精卵的发育中这些因子已经被原核消耗了。

If the recipient cytoplasm is prepared by enucleation of an oocyte at metaphase II, it is only possible to avoid chromosomal damage and maintain normal ploidy by transfer of diploid nuclei[14,15], but further experiments are required to define the optimum cell-cycle stage. Our studies with cultured cells suggest that there is an advantage if cells are quiescent (ref. 1, and this work). In earlier studies, donor cells were embryonic blastomeres that had not been induced into quiescence. Comparisons of the phases of the growth cycle showed that development was greater if donor cells were in mitosis[16] or in the G1 (ref. 10) phase of the cycle, rather than in S or G2 phases. Increased development using donor cells in G0, G1 or mitosis may reflect greater access for reprogramming factors present in the oocyte cytoplasm, but a direct comparison of these phases in the same cell population is required for a clearer understanding of the underlying mechanisms.

Together these results indicate that nuclei from a wide range of cell types should prove to be totipotent after enhancing opportunities for reprogramming by using appropriate combinations of these cell-cycle stages. In turn, the dissemination of the genetic improvement obtained within elite selection herds will be enhanced by limited replication of animals with proven performance by nuclear transfer from cells derived from adult animals. In addition, gene targeting in livestock should now be feasible by nuclear transfer from modified cell populations and will offer new opportunities in biotechnology. The techniques described also offer an opportunity to study the possible persistence and impact of epigenetic changes, such as imprinting and telomere shortening, which are known to occur in somatic cells during development and senescence, respectively.

The lamb born after nuclear transfer from a mammary gland cell is, to our knowledge, the first mammal to develop from a cell derived from an adult tissue. The phenotype of the donor cell is unknown. The primary culture contains mainly mammary epithelial (over 90%) as well as other differentiated cell types, including myoepithelial cells and fibroblasts. We cannot exclude the possibility that there is a small proportion of relatively undifferentiated stem cells able to support regeneration of the mammary gland during pregnancy. Birth of the lamb shows that during the development of that mammary cell there was no irreversible modification of genetic information required for development to term. This is consistent with the generally accepted view that mammalian differentiation is almost all achieved by systematic, sequential changes in gene expression brought about by interactions between the nucleus and the changing cytoplasmic environment[17].

Methods. Embryo-derived cells were obtained from embryonic disc of a day-9 embryo from a Poll Dorset ewe cultured as described[1], with the following modifications. Stem-cell medium was supplemented with bovine DIA/LIF. After 8 days, the explanted disc was disaggregated by enzymatic digestion and cells replated onto fresh feeders. After a further 7 days, a single colony of large flattened cells was isolated and grown further in the absence of feeder cells. At passage 8, the modal chromosome number was 54. These cells were used as nuclear donors at passages 7–9. Fetal-derived cells were obtained from an eviscerated Black Welsh Mountain fetus recovered at autopsy on day 26 of pregnancy. The head was removed before tissues were cut into small pieces and the cells dispersed by exposure to trypsin. Culture was in BHK 21 (Glasgow MEM; Gibco Life Sciences) supplemented with

996

如果受体细胞质是通过将处于减数第二次分裂中期的卵母细胞去核制备的，这只可能通过移植二倍体细胞核来避免染色体的损伤并保持正常的倍性[14,15]，但是需要进一步的研究来确定最佳细胞周期。我们用培养的细胞进行的研究表明，如果细胞是静止的会有一些优势（参考文献 1 和本工作）。在早期的研究中，供体细胞是没有被诱导静止的胚胎卵裂球。各个细胞周期细胞的对比结果表明，供体细胞处于有丝分裂期[16]或者 G1 期（参考文献 10）比处于 S 期或者 G2 期的胚胎发育更好。使用 G0、G1 或有丝分裂期的供体细胞可以促进发育，这表明在此时卵母细胞的细胞质内可能存在更易获取的重编程因子。但是我们需要在同一个细胞群中直接比较不同时期的细胞，以便更加清楚地了解潜在的机制。

这些结果表明，不同细胞类型来源的细胞核通过合适的细胞周期组合提高重编程的机会之后应该具有全能性。反过来，用成年动物的细胞核进行移植可以确定基因优良的动物，在挑选好的良种动物群中通过有限的繁殖就可以达到基因改良的目的。此外，通过修饰后细胞群体的核移植可实现家畜的基因打靶，这将为生物技术提供新的机会。本文描述的这种技术也为研究表观遗传改变的持久性和影响提供了机会，比如基因印迹和端粒缩短，这两者被认为分别在体细胞的发育和衰老中发生。

据我们所知，这只由乳腺细胞核移植培育出的小羊是从成体组织中培养出的首个哺乳动物。供体细胞的表型不清楚。原代培养物中主要含有乳腺上皮细胞（超过 90%）以及其他分化的细胞类型，包括肌上皮细胞和成纤维细胞。我们不能排除存在小比例相对未分化的干细胞的可能，它们能在妊娠期支持乳腺的再生。小羊的出生表明在乳腺细胞的发育过程中没有完成体内发育所需遗传信息的不可逆修饰。这和普遍接受的观点一致，即哺乳动物的分化主要是通过细胞核和变化的细胞质环境相互作用引起的基因表达过程中系统且有序的改变实现的[17]。

方法。胚胎来源的细胞是按参考文献所述的方法[1]，从培养的无角多塞特母羊第 9 天胚胎的胎盘中获得的，并经过了以下处理。在干细胞基质中加入小牛 DIA/LIF。8 天后，用酶消化裂解移植的胎盘组织，将细胞置于新的饲养细胞上。再过 7 天，分离出一个大的扁平的细胞集落，然后在没有饲养细胞的情况下进一步培养。第 8 代的模式染色体数目是 54。第 7 代至第 9 代的细胞用作核供体。胎儿来源的细胞取自一只去除内脏的妊娠期 26 天的黑面威尔士山羊胎儿尸体。去除该尸体的头部，然后将组织切成碎片并用胰蛋白酶消化使细胞分散。培养基是加有 L–谷氨酰胺（2 mM）、丙酮酸钠（1 mM）和 10% 胎牛血清的 BHK 21（GMEM

L-glutamine (2 mM), sodium pyruvate (1 mM) and 10% fetal calf serum. At 90% confluency, the cells were passaged with a 1:2 division. At passage 4, these fibroblast-like cells (Fig. 1) had modal chromosome number of 54. Fetal cells were used as nuclear donors at passages 4–6. Cells from mammary gland were obtained from a 6-year-old Finn Dorset ewe in the last trimester of pregnancy[18]. At passages 3 and 6, the modal chromosome number was 54 and these cells were used as nuclear donors at passage numbers 3–6.

Nuclear transfer was done according to a previous protocol[1]. Oocytes were recovered from Scottish Blackface ewes between 28 and 33 h after injection of gonadotropin-releasing hormone (GnRH), and enucleated as soon as possible. They were recovered in calcium- and magnesium-free PBS containing 1% FCS and transferred to calcium-free M2 medium[19] containing 10% FCS at 37 °C. Quiescent, diploid donor cells were produced by reducing the concentration of serum in the medium from 10 to 0.5% for 5 days, causing the cells to exit the growth cycle and arrest in G0. Confirmation that cells had left the cycle was obtained by staining with antiPCNA/cyclin antibody (Immuno Concepts), revealed by a second antibody conjugated with rhodamine (Dakopatts).

Fusion of the donor cell to the enucleated oocyte and activation of the oocyte were induced by the same electrical pulses, between 34 and 36 h after GnRH injection to donor ewes. The majority of reconstructed embryos were cultured in ligated oviducts of sheep as before, but some embryos produced by transfer from embryo-derived cells or fetal fibroblasts were cultured in a chemically defined medium[20]. Most embryos that developed to morula or blastocyst after 6 days of culture were transferred to recipients and allowed to develop to term (Table 1). One, two or three embryos were transferred to each ewe depending upon the availability of embryos. The effect of cell type upon fusion and development to morula or blastocyst was analysed using the marginal model of Breslow and Clayton[21]. No comparison was possible of development to term as it was not practicable to transfer all embryos developing to a suitable stage for transfer. When too many embryos were available, those having better morphology were selected.

Ultrasound scan was used for pregnancy diagnosis at around day 60 after oestrus and to monitor fetal development thereafter at 2-week intervals. Pregnant recipient ewes were monitored for nutritional status, body condition and signs of EAE, Q fever, border disease, louping ill and toxoplasmosis. As lambing approached, they were under constant observation and a veterinary surgeon called at the onset of parturition. Microsatellite analysis was carried out on DNA from the lambs and recipient ewes using four polymorphic ovine markers[22].

(**385**, 810-813; 1997)

I. Wilmut, A. E. Schnieke*, J. McWhir, A. J. Kind* & K. H. S. Campbell
Roslin Institute (Edinburgh), Roslin, Midlothian EH25 9PS, UK
* PPL Therapeutics, Roslin, Midlothian EH25 9PP, UK

Received 25 November 1996; accepted 10 January 1997.

References:
1. Campbell, K. H. S., McWhir, J., Ritchie, W. A. & Wilmut, I. Sheep cloned by nuclear transfer from a cultured cell line. *Nature* **380**, 64-66 (1996).

培养基，Gibco 生命科学公司）。这些细胞达到 90% 的覆盖率后，就按照 1：2 的比例进行传代培养。到第 4 代时这些成纤维细胞样细胞（图 1）就有 54 个模式染色体。选用第 4 代至第 6 代的胎儿细胞作为核供体。乳腺细胞来自一只 6 岁的妊娠晚期芬兰多塞特母羊[18]。在第 3 代和第 6 代，模式染色体达到 54 个，因此第 3 代至第 6 代的细胞都被用作核供体。

根据参考文献的方法进行核移植[1]。注射促性腺激素释放激素（GnRH）后 28 到 33 小时之间从苏格兰黑面母羊中获得卵母细胞，并尽快去核。它们在含有 1% FCS 的无钙镁 PBS 溶液中恢复，然后转移到 37℃ 下含有 10% FCS 的无钙 M2 培养基中[19]。通过减少培养基中血清的浓度（5 天内从 10% 减到 0.5%）制备静止的二倍体供体细胞，这一方法使得细胞退出细胞周期并静止在 G0 期。利用抗 PCNA／细胞周期蛋白抗体（美国 Immuno Concepts 公司）进行染色，并用结合罗丹明的二抗（丹麦 Dakopatts 公司）进行显色，最终确定这些细胞退出细胞周期。

注射 GnRH 到供体母羊中 34~36 小时后，用同样的电脉冲诱导供体细胞和去核卵母细胞的融合以及卵母细胞的激活。大部分的重组胚胎如以前一样培养在羊结扎的输卵管中，但是一些通过胚胎来源细胞或者胎儿成纤维细胞核移植产生的胚胎培养在化学成分确定的培养基中[20]。经过 6 天培养后发育成桑椹胚或者胚泡的大部分胚胎都被移植到受体中并发育直到分娩（表 1）。根据胚胎的有效性，每只母羊中移植 1 个、2 个或 3 个胚胎。使用布雷斯洛和克莱顿[21]的边缘模型来分析细胞类型对细胞融合以及发育到桑椹胚或者胚泡的影响。发育到足月进行比较不太可能，因为将所有发育到一定阶段可以移植的胚胎都进行移植并不好操作。如果有太多的胚胎可供选择，那么形态较好的就被选中。

发情期后 60 天左右用超声进行妊娠诊断，此后每两周检测一次胎儿的发育情况。怀孕的受体母羊需要监测营养状况，身体状况，实验性变态反应性脑脊髓炎、Q 热、边界病、跳跃病和弓形体病的症状。产期临近时，进行实时监护，兽医随时准备接生。使用四个多态性羊标记物对小羊和受体母羊的 DNA 进行微卫星分析[22]。

（毛晨晖 翻译；方向东 审稿）

2. Solter, D. Lambing by nuclear transfer. *Nature* **380**, 24-25 (1996).

3. Gurdon, J. B., Laskey, R. A. & Reeves, O. R. The developmental capacity of nuclei transplanted from keratinized skin cells of adult frogs. *J. Embryol. Exp. Morph.* **34**, 93-112 (1975).

4. Quinlivan, T. D., Martin, C. A., Taylor, W. B. & Cairney, I. M. Pre- and perinatal mortality in those ewes that conceived to one service. *J. Reprod. Fert.* **11**, 379-390 (1966).

5. Walker, S. K., Heard, T. M. & Seamark, R. F. *In vitro* culture of sheep embryos without co-culture: successes and perspectives. *Therio* **37**, 111-126 (1992).

6. Nash, M. L., Hungerford, L. L., Nash, T. G. & Zinn, G. M. Risk factors for perinatal and postnatal mortality in lambs. *Vet. Rec.* **139**, 64-67 (1996).

7. Bradford, G. E., Hart, R., Quirke, J. F. & Land, R. B. Genetic control of the duration of gestation in sheep. *J. Reprod. Fert.* **30**, 459-463 (1972).

8. Walton, A. & Hammond, J. The maternal effects on growth and conformation in Shire horse–Shetland pony crosses. *Proc. R. Soc.* B**125**, 311-335 (1938).

9. Campbell, K. H. S., Loi, P., Otaegui, P. J. & Wilmut, I. Cell cycle co-ordination in embryo cloning by nuclear transfer. *Rev. Reprod.* **1**, 40-46 (1996).

10. Cheong, H.-T., Takahashi, Y. & Kanagawa, H. Birth of mice after transplantation of early-cell-cycle-stage embryonic nuclei into enucleated oocytes. *Biol. Reprod.* **48**, 958-963 (1993).

11. Prather, R. S. *et al.* Nuclear transplantation in the bovine embryo. Assessment of donor nuclei and recipient oocyte. *Biol. Reprod.* **37**, 859-866 (1987).

12. McGrath, J. & Solter, D. Inability of mouse blastomere nuclei transferred to enucleated zygotes to support development *in vitro. Science* **226**, 1317-1318 (1984).

13. Robl, J. M. *et al.* Nuclear transplantation in bovine embryos. *J. Anim. Sci.* **64**, 642-647 (1987).

14. Campbell, K. H. S., Ritchie, W. A. & Wilmut, I. Nuclear-cytoplasmic interactions during the first cell cycle of nuclear transfer reconstructed bovine embryos: Implications for deoxyribonucleic acid replication and development. *Biol. Reprod.* **49**, 933-942 (1993).

15. Barnes, F. L. *et al.* Influence of recipient oocyte cell cycle stage on DNA synthesis, nuclear envelope breakdown, chromosome constitution, and development in nuclear transplant bovine embryos. *Mol. Reprod. Dev.* **36**, 33-41 (1993).

16. Kwon, O. Y. & Kono, T. Production of identical sextuplet mice by transferring metaphase nuclei from 4-cell embryos. *J. Reprod. Fert.* Abst. Ser. **17**, 30 (1996).

17. Gurdon, J. B. The control of gene expression in animal development (Oxford University Press, Oxford, 1974).

18. Finch, L. M. B. *et al.* Primary culture of ovine mammary epithelial cells. *Biochem. Soc. Trans.* **24**, 369S (1996).

19. Whitten, W. K. & Biggers, J. D. Complete development *in vitro* of the preimplantation stages of the mouse in a simple chemically defined medium. *J. Reprod. Fertil.* **17**, 399-401 (1968).

20. Gardner, D. K., Lane, M., Spitzer, A. & Batt, P. A. Enhanced rates of cleavage and development for sheep zygotes cultured to the blastocyst stage *in vitro* in the absence of serum and somatic cells. Amino acids, vitamins, and culturing embryos in groups stimulate development. *Biol. Reprod.* **50**, 390-400 (1994).

21. Breslow, N. E. & Clayton, D. G. Approximate inference in generalized linear mixed models. *J. Am. Stat. Assoc.* **88**, 9-25 (1993).

22. Buchanan, F. C., Littlejohn, R. P., Galloway, S. M. & Crawford, A. L. Microsatellites and associated repetitive elements in the sheep genome. *Mammal. Gen.* **4**, 258-264 (1993).

Acknowledgements. We thank A. Colman for his involvement throughout this experiment and for guidance during the preparation of this manuscript; C. Wilde for mammary-derived cells; M. Ritchie, J. Bracken, M. Malcolm-Smith, W. A. Ritchie, P. Ferrier and K. Mycock for technical assistance; D. Waddington for statistical analysis; and H. Bowran and his colleagues for care of the animals. This research was supported in part by the Ministry of Agriculture, Fisheries and Food. The experiments were conducted under the Animals (Scientific Procedures) Act 1986 and with the approval of the Roslin Institute Animal Welfare and Experiments Committee.

Correspondence should be addressed to I.W. (e-mail Ian.Wilmut@bbsrc.ac.uk).

Evidence for Deep Mantle Circulation from Global Tomography

R. D. van der Hilst *et al.*

Editor's Note

Convection in the Earth's mantle seems to happen largely in two layers. But how, if at all, are the flow patterns related, and what do they look like? Here Rob van der Hilst and his co-workers offer one of the first clear pictures of those issues. Using seismic waves to "image" the structure of the deep Earth, they find that some large-scale non-uniformities in the lower mantle are associated with slabs of cold material sinking into the upper mantle at subduction zones. This indicates that sinking slabs may penetrate the boundary between the upper and lower mantle and persist all the way down to the Earth's core. Thus, at least a part of the convective structure involves the entire mantle.

Seismic tomography based on P-wave travel times and improved earthquake locations provides further evidence for mantle-wide convective flow. The use of body waves makes it possible to resolve long, narrow structures in the lower mantle some of which can be followed to sites of present-day plate convergence at the Earth's surface. The transition from subduction-related linear structures in the mid-mantle to long-wavelength heterogeneity near the core–mantle boundary remains enigmatic, but at least some slab segments seem to sink to the bottom of the mantle.

GLOBAL tomography, a technique pioneered in the 1970s and early 1980s[1,2] to interpret the observed seismic wave field in terms of seismic properties at depth, is revolutionizing our knowledge of the Earth's interior. However, decades of research and spirited debate have not led to a consensus on the scale of mantle convection and the nature of coupling between motions in the deep interior and tectonic processes at the surface. Resolution of this issue is important for better understanding of the thermal and chemical evolution of our planet[3,4]. There is increasing agreement on large-scale (> 4,000 km) structural features in global images[5-7], which represent the integrated effects of mantle processes over long periods of time[8,9]. The shorter-wavelength components in the models, however, have appeared sensitive to the type of data and model parametrization used in the inversions and have so far not shown convincing correlation. This lack of agreement prevents the effective use of global models to constrain reconstructions of past plate motion and numerical flow simulations at high Rayleigh numbers, and to discriminate unambiguously between end-member circulation models known as layered-mantle and whole mantle convection. For recent reviews see refs 6, 10–13.

深部地幔流动的全球层析成像证据

地球的地幔对流似乎主要是分两层进行的，但若果真如此，不同的流动模式是如何相互关联的？它们看起来是什么样的？罗布·范德希尔斯特和他的同事们在本文中首次给出了关于这些问题的清晰图像。他们利用地震波对地球内部结构进行"成像"，发现下地幔一些大规模非均质体与俯冲带中下沉至上地幔的冷板片物质有关。这说明下沉板片可能穿透上、下地幔之间的边界，一路沉至地核附近。因此，至少一部分对流结构是涉及整个地幔的。

基于 P 波走时和修正后的地震位置的地震层析成像为地幔范围内的对流流动提供了进一步的证据。体波的使用使得解析下地幔长而窄的结构成为可能，其中一些结构可以被追踪到现今地球表面板块汇聚的位置。从地幔中部与俯冲有关的线性结构，到核幔边界附近的长波长非均匀体的过渡，仍然是个谜，但至少一些板片碎块看起来像是沉到了地幔底部。

全球层析成像是一种开创于 20 世纪 70 年代和 80 年代早期的技术 [1,2]，它根据地球深部的地震属性来解释观测到的地震波场，正在使我们对地球内部的认识产生革命性的变化。但是，对地幔对流的尺度以及地球深部运动和地表构造过程之间的耦合性这些问题，经过数十年的研究和激烈的争论后，并没有达成一个共识。这些问题的解决对于更好地理解地球的热与化学演化十分重要 [3,4]。在全球图像的大尺度（大于 4,000 km）结构特征方面现已有了越来越多的共识 [5-7]，这些结构代表着长时间内地幔过程的综合效应 [8,9]。但是这些模型中的较短波长部分，对反演中使用的数据和模型参数化类型都表现敏感，目前还没有显示出令人信服的相关性。这种一致性的缺乏，对有效使用全球模型来约束过往板块运动的重建和高瑞利数的数值流动模拟，以及明确区分端元地幔循环模型（被称为层状地幔对流）和全地幔对流模型等方面，都构成了阻碍。最近的综述请参考文献 6 和 10~13。

Several lines of geophysical evidence support flow across the boundary between the upper and lower mantle, defined here by the seismic discontinuity at approximately 660 km depth. The magnitude of lateral variations in depth to this interface[14] is consistent with an endothermic phase change in the $(Mg, Fe)_2SiO_4$ system[15] that is by itself too weak to stratify flow[16]. Global tomography models lack the increased heterogeneity near 660 km depth expected for a thermal boundary layer at that depth[17], anomalous travel times of high-frequency waves are consistent with slab penetration into the lower mantle in some subduction systems[11,18-25], and long-wavelength gravity data can be explained by dynamic models of deep circulation in a high-viscosity lower mantle[5,12,26]. On the other hand, regional seismological studies have demonstrated stagnation of some slabs in the upper-mantle transition zone[20,21]. In addition, the long-term survival of distinct chemical reservoirs of primordial mantle as deduced from isotope and trace-element data has been used as evidence for layered convection (for reviews see refs 3 and 4). However, these data are not inconsistent with mantle-wide distribution of compositional heterogeneity[12,27], for which there seems to be increasing observational seismological evidence[28,29].

Here we present results of the inversion of carefully processed travel times, mainly from first-arriving P-waves, for aspherical variations in compressional wave speed in the Earth's mantle. The uneven sampling limits the resolution of aspherical structure in the upper mantle, but the new data reveal deep structure in unprecedented detail, which helps to assess the ultimate fate of the subducted slabs and their role in lower-mantle flow. We infer long, linear structures that locally connect to seismogenic slabs in the upper mantle and that divide the mid-mantle into large domains of shorter-wavelength heterogeneity. The transition from the linear subduction–related structures in the mid-mantle to long-wavelength heterogeneity near the core–mantle boundary (CMB) remains enigmatic, but our study reveals segments of slab that connect to structural heterogeneity in the CMB region. Along with results of regional studies that reveal structural complexity in the transition zone, these findings suggest that the Earth's present-day convective regime is predominated by some form of whole mantle overturn and their intermittent mantle stratification is a local[30] and transient[31,32] phenomenon only.

Data and Tomographic Method

Shear-wave models are often based on carefully processed digital waveforms and can exploit the excellent spatial data coverage provided by a combination of direct and surface-reflected body[22] and surface waves[33-35] and by constraints of free oscillation data[7,36]. In contrast, global P-wave models are typically based on relatively noisy short-period travel-time data reported to international data centres by thousands of station operators worldwide[1,2,5,21,37,38]. An important novel aspect of our global imaging is the use of better travel-time data and earthquake locations than previously available.

In a major effort, Engdahl and co-workers[39] reprocessed the entire database published

一系列地球物理学证据支持流动穿过上下地幔边界，这里的上下地幔边界定义为在约 660 km 深处的地震不连续面。深度达到这一界面时，横向变化的幅度[14] 与 $(Mg, Fe)_2SiO_4$ 体系中的一种吸热相变[15] 是一致的，但这种相变自身太弱不足以使流动分层[16]。在全球层析成像模型中，660 km 深度附近缺少增强的非均匀性，而如果这个深度存在一个热边界层的话，应该存在增强的非均匀性[17]；同时，高频地震波的走时异常与在某些俯冲带系统中俯冲板片插入下地幔的情况是一致的[11,18-25]；并且，长波长的重力数据可以由在高黏度下地幔中的深部环流动力学模型来解释[5,12,26]。另一方面，一些区域性的地震学研究已经证明了在上地幔过渡带有一些板片滞留的现象[20,21]。另外，依据同位素和痕量元素数据可以推断出原生地幔存在化学成分截然不同的蓄积区，而这些蓄积区的长期存在，已经被作为层状对流的一种证据（综述见参考文献 3 和 4）。然而，这些数据与在地幔范围内广泛分布的成分非均匀性并非不一致[12,27]，而且似乎有越来越多的地震学观测证据支持这种成分非均匀性的广泛分布[28,29]。

这里我们给出了经过仔细处理的走时（主要是 P 波初至走时）的反演结果，目的是获得地幔中的压缩波速度（即 P 波速度，译者注）非球对称变化结果。不均匀采样限制了上地幔中非球对称结构的分辨率，但是新的数据揭示了深部结构前所未有的细节，这些细节有助于评估俯冲板片的最终命运，以及它们在下地幔流动中所扮演的角色。我们推断存在长且线性的结构，这些结构与上地幔孕震板片局部性连接，并将中地幔切分成包含较短波长非均匀体的一些大的区域。从中地幔的线性俯冲相关结构到核幔边界（CMB）长波长非均匀体的过渡仍然是未解之谜，不过我们的研究揭示了板片碎块的存在，这些板片碎块连接着核幔边界区域的结构非均匀体。与揭示地幔过渡带内部结构复杂性的区域性研究结果相结合，这些发现表明地球现在的对流体系是以某种形式的全地幔倒转为主的，而间歇性地幔分层只是一种局部[30] 而短暂[31,32] 的现象。

数据和层析成像方法

剪切波模型通常基于经过仔细处理的数字波形，并且能够利用由直达的和界面反射的体波[22]、面波[33-35] 混合的数据，以及由自由振荡数据约束[7,36] 共同提供的良好的空间数据覆盖。相比之下，全球 P 波模型通常基于有相当噪声的短周期走时数据，而这些数据由全球范围内成千上万的台站操作员报告到国际数据中心[1,2,5,21,37,38]。我们全球成像的一项重要的革新就是使用了比前人更好的走时数据和震源位置。

恩达尔和合作者[39] 的一项主要成果是重新处理了整个数据库，这个数据库是由

by the International Seismological Centre (ISC) and, for recent years, the US Geological Survey's National Earthquake Information Center. Using robust statistics, an improved global travel-time model[40], and the arrival times of direct P- and S-phases, depth phases (pP, sP and the ocean-surface-reflected pwP), and PKP core phases, they relocated in an iterative, nonlinear procedure all teleseismically well-constrained earthquakes occurring between 1 January 1964 and 31 December 1995 (Fig. 1a). Upon application of appropriate corrections and event selection criteria, this procedure minimizes focal depth errors and the mapping of source heterogeneity into mislocation, thereby creating a significantly improved database for tomographic imaging. We used an iterative, conjugate-gradient algorithm[41] to invert all available P and pP travel-time residuals for effects of source mislocation due to three-dimensional structure and for P-wave speed in about 300,000 constant velocity blocks. We did not account for effects of aspherical structure on path geometry. This may underestimate the amplitude and overestimate the width of the anomalies in the upper mantle but does not affect the conclusions based on relatively large-scale lower-mantle structures.

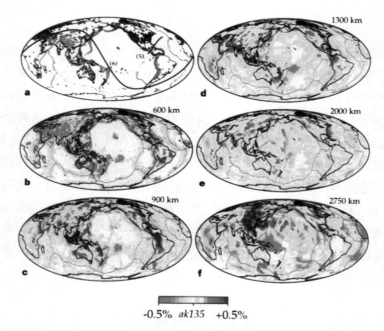

-0.5% *ak135* +0.5%

Fig. 1. **a,** Pacific-centred Mollweide projection depicting the locations of the almost 80,000 earthquakes (red dots) and 3,500 stations (triangles) that produced the 7.3 million P and 0.3 million pP phases used in the inversions resulting in the P-wave-speed anomalies as displayed at 600 km (**b**), 900 km (**c**), 1,300 km (**d**), 2,000 km (**e**) and 2,700 km (**f**) depth in the Earth's mantle. Dark blue lines in **a** depict the locations of the cross-sections of Figs 5 and 6. To suppress noise and reduce the spatial imbalance in data coverage we grouped data associated with event and station clusters into summary rays[25], which reduced the total number of data used in the inversions from 7.6 million to 500,000. Wave speed variations are relative to the radially stratified *ak135* model[40]; see colour scale. Blue (red) colours represent fast (slow) wave propagation; grey depicts mantle regions of poor sampling. In these map views, no *a posteriori* smoothing or interpolation is used other than regridding from 2° × 2° to 1° × 1° blocks. The amplitude is, however, poorly constrained and therefore not used in the discussions. The perturbations may underestimate the actual values because of (1) the effect of regularization (damping) of the inversion, (2) trade-offs with earthquake location (on

国际地震中心（ISC）及近些年美国地质调查局国家地震信息中心发布的。他们使用稳健统计学，改进的全球走时模型[40] 以及直达 P 震相、S 震相、深度震相（pP，sP 和海洋表面反射的 pwP）和 PKP 核震相的走时，并采用一种迭代的非线性方法，对所有具有良好远震约束的地震进行了重新定位，这些地震发生在 1964 年 1 月 1 日至 1995 年 12 月 31 日之间（图 1a）。在使用合适的校正和事件选择标准之后，这种处理使得震源非均匀性到定位误差的映射和震源深度误差最小化，因而为层析成像提供了一个显著改进的资料库。我们使用一种迭代共轭梯度算法[41]，反演所有可以得到的 P 和 pP 走时残差，以获得三维结构引起的震源定位误差和在 300,000 个常速度块体中的 P 波速度。我们没有考虑非球面结构对路径几何形态的影响。这可能造成对上地幔异常幅度的低估和对异常宽度的高估，但是这并不影响我们基于相对大尺度的下地幔结构的结论。

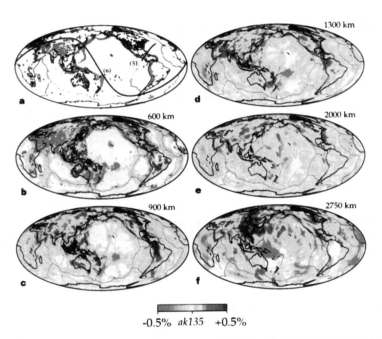

-0.5% *ak135* +0.5%

图 1. a，以太平洋为中心的莫尔韦德投影描绘了近 80,000 个地震（红点）和 3,500 个台站（三角形）的位置，其中涉及反演中使用的 7,300,000 个 P 相位和 300,000 个 pP 相位，并得出了深度在 600 km（b），900 km（c），1,300 km（d），2,000 km（e）和 2,700 km（f）处的地幔 P 波速度异常。图 a 中深蓝色的线描绘了图 5 和 6 的横截面位置。为了抑制噪声并减少数据空间覆盖的不平衡，我们将相关地震事件与台站群的数据分组成概括型射线[25]，这使得反演中使用的数据量从 7,600,000 降到了 500,000。波速变化是相对于径向分层的 ak135 模型的[40]；具体请参考色标。蓝色（红色）代表快（慢）的传播速度；灰色表示采样差的地幔区域。在这些地图视图中，没有做过后期的光滑处理或者插值，仅仅从 2°×2° 的块体到 1°×1° 的块体重新进行了网格化。但是，幅值约束得不好，所以在讨论中没有采用。速度扰动值可能被低估了，原

1007

inversion, the hypocentre relocation parameters can in principle absorb substantial signal; in practice this is limited by the effective control on focal depth by the depth phases[39]), and (3) the neglect of ray bending effects. The regularization applied is a combination of norm and gradient damping; in absence of strong data constraints the former produces a bias towards the reference values (that is, zero anomalies) and the latter minimizes the difference in amplitude between adjacent blocks, which results in a smooth model. The model shown reduces the variance of the summary ray data by almost 50%, in addition to the ~15% variance reduction pre-processing of the original ISC data[20,39]. The thin red lines depict the location of plate boundaries.

The Earth's mantle is probably heterogeneous at all scales but the choice of a particular parametrization sets a minimum resolution length and excludes smaller structure from observation. Models based on spherical harmonics[33-36] constrain long-wavelength anomalies, but do not resolve in detail trajectories of mantle flow such as descending slabs. The local basis functions used in our study (constant-velocity blocks with a dimension of $2° \times 2° \times 200$ km in the lower mantle) begin to provide the resolution required to investigate the continuity of structure between upper and lower mantle and the pattern of convective flow at larger depth. However, the uneven source/receiver distribution (Fig. 1a) and the effective restriction of inversions for P-wave speed to body waves necessarily renders large regions where the solution is not constrained, in particular in the upper mantle and transition zone (Fig. 1b). Body-wave sampling improves significantly in the mid-mantle (Fig. 1c–e) but degrades again in the lowermost mantle, especially in the Southern Hemisphere (Fig. 1f). Here we focus on the part of the solution pertinent to lower-mantle structure; detailed images of slabs in the upper mantle are better obtained by regional studies or global studies that allow for variable block size, which would ideally be based on three-dimensional ray tracing to account for effects of ray bending.

Aspherical Mantle Structure

Our results for the upper mantle (not shown) are in general agreement with surface-wave studies[6,7,33-35]; low wave speeds characterize marginal basins and tectonic continental regions, and zones of fast wave propagation outline stable continental cratons. The data reveal numerous fast anomalies in the upper-mantle transition zone beneath the circumpacific region (Fig. 1b), which agrees with inferences from Earth's free oscillations[36].

In the top half of the lower mantle, inversion of our improved data brings out prominent high-wave speed structures that continue intermittently over horizontal distances in excess of 10,000 km beneath the Americas and the southern margin of Eurasia (Fig. 1c, d). These outstanding structures correlate with anomalies in models based on spectral techniques (Fig. 2) but are narrower than inferred from these previous results, in particular at depths less than 1,500 km. With a width of 500–1,000 km in map view their shape is not controlled by the block size used. We infer that the lower-mantle structure beneath the Americas is laterally coherent for depths up to approximately 1,700 km, but the slab signature vanishes at about 1,300 km depth beneath South America[22]. The deep anomaly connects to upper-mantle structures that are more fragmented as a result of

因是：(1) 反演中正则化(阻尼)的影响，(2) 与地震位置间存在的折中关系(反演中，震源重定位参数能够吸收有效信号；在实践中，这种影响通过深震相对震源深度的有效控制可以得到限制[39])，(3) 忽略射线弯曲造成的影响。使用的正则化方法是范数和梯度阻尼的组合；在缺少强数据约束的情况下，前者产生倾向于参考值(即零异常)的偏差，后者则使相邻块体幅值差异最小，即得到一个光滑的模型。除了对 ISC 原始数据进行预处理而减少的 15% 方差之外[20,39]，给出的模型使概括型射线数据的方差减少了近 50%。细红线描绘了板块边界的位置。

地幔在任何尺度可能都是非均匀的，但是选择一种特定的参数化方式就设置了一个最小分辨长度，进而从观测中排除了更小尺度的结构。基于球谐函数的模型[33-36]约束了长波长异常，但是并没有分辨地幔流动轨迹的细节，比如说下沉中的板片。在我们的研究中使用的局部基函数(在下地幔的常速度块体尺度为 2°×2°×200 km)，开始为调查上下地幔之间结构的连续性和更大深度的对流模式提供了分辨率。但是，不均匀的震源和接收点分布(图 1a)及对 P 波速度反演的有效制约，必然使得许多区域的解没有约束，尤其是在上地幔和过渡带(图 1b)。在中地幔，体波采样得到了显著改善(图 1c~e)，但是到下地幔底部又变差了，尤其是在南半球(图 1f)。这里我们主要讨论有关下地幔结构的解；而在上地幔中板片的精细图像可以由区域性研究获得，或者由允许块体尺寸变化的全球性研究获得，在理想情况下，这些研究应当是基于考虑了射线弯曲效应的三维射线追踪进行的。

非球面地幔结构

我们结果中的上地幔部分(这里没有展示)和面波的研究结果[6,7,33-35]在整体上是一致的；边缘盆地和构造活动活跃的大陆区域以低波速为特征，而高速传播区则勾画了稳定大陆克拉通。数据揭示了在环太平洋区域下方，上地幔过渡带内部存在大量的高速异常(图 1b)，这与基于地球自由振荡得到的推论[36]是一致的。

在下地幔的上半部分，我们改进数据后的反演结果显示存在明显的高速结构，这个高速结构在南北美洲和欧亚大陆南缘下面断续延伸超过 10,000 km 的水平距离(图 1c 和 d)。这些显著的结构和基于谱技术得到的模型中的异常(图 2)相对应，但相比于先前结果推断出的结构更窄，尤其是在深度小于 1,500 km 的地方。当地图视图宽度为 500~1,000 km 时，它们的形状不受所采用的模型块体尺寸的控制。我们推断在南北美洲下方的下地幔结构是横向相关的，其最深约达 1,700 km，但是在南美洲下方，板片特征在约 1,300 km 深度消失[22]。深部异常同上地幔结构相连接，但是这些上地幔结构由于东太平洋和加勒比海区域的新生代构造运动而显得更支离破碎。

Cenozoic tectonic activity in the eastern Pacific and Caribbean region. Beneath eastern Europe and Indonesia a fast anomaly can be traced from mid- to upper-mantle depths, but it is elsewhere only inferred between about 1,000 and at least 1,700 km in depth. The vertical dimension of both lineaments exceed the depth uncertainty in the images of about 300 km as determined by resolution tests with fabricated slab models (S.W. and R.D.v.d.H., manuscript in preparation). Outside these large-scale structures there is substantial scatter of smaller-scale heterogeneity, some of which may be real on the basis of correlation with independent results[22,42].

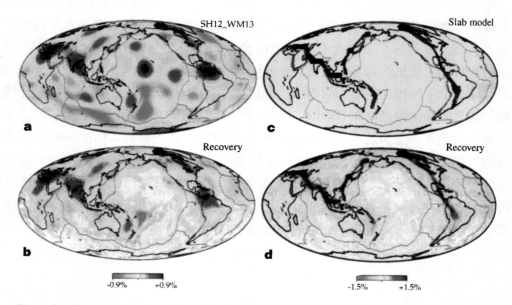

Fig. 2. Resolution of long-wavelength (**a, b**) and short-wavelength (**c, d**) structure. We investigated the potential resolution of certain structural features in aspherical Earth models by inverting synthetic data calculated from assumed input models. We added gaussian noise to the synthetic data to simulate data errors and applied the same parameters (number of iterations, amount of regularization) as in the inversion of reported phase data. **a,** Lateral variation in shear-wave speed in the mid-mantle (at 1,300 km depth) according to *SH12_WM13* by Su and co-workers[33], and **b,** structure according to this model as it would have been imaged using the body-wave paths used in our study. Comparison of the input (**a**) and the recovery after inversion (**b**) demonstrates first, that our data coverage is sufficient, in particular in the Northern Hemisphere, to resolve large-scale structural features, and second, that there is significant agreement between the models if structures in *SH12_WM13* represent long-wavelength images of narrower structures (Figs 1d and 3). **c,** Artificial slab structure at 1,300 km depth with a peak anomaly of 3% (off-scale). The result of the inversion of the (noisy) synthetic data (**d**) demonstrates that narrow structure in the lower mantle can be resolved by our data, in particular in the Northern Hemisphere, and that the width of the anomaly may not be significantly overestimated. These tests also indicate that insufficient sampling by our body waves precludes the resolution of lower-mantle structures in large parts of the Southern Hemisphere. (Note that our colour coding intentionally de-emphasizes structure of near-zero amplitude. Inversion with random noise and the assessment of effects of, for instance, source mislocation and uneven data coverage suggest that structure with near-zero amplitude is not necessarily indicative of Earth's structure).

在东欧和印尼的下方有一个高速异常可以从中地幔追踪到上地幔深度，但是在其他地方同样的异常却只能推测在 1,000 km 和至少 1,700 km 深度之间。两组特征的垂直维度都超过了图像中大约 300 km 的深度不确定性，这个深度不确定性是由假定板片模型的分辨率测试所确定的（维迪扬托罗和范德希尔斯特，稿件准备中）。在这些大尺度的结构之外，有较大量散布的小尺度非均匀体，基于相互独立结果 [22,42] 之间的相关性可知，其中一些非均匀体可能是真实存在的。

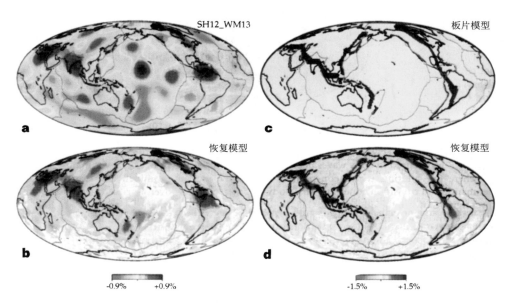

图 2. 长波长（**a**、**b**）和短波长（**c**、**d**）结构的分辨率。通过对基于假定输入模型计算得到的合成数据进行反演，我们对反演获得的非球面地球模型的某些结构性特征的潜在分辨率进行了研究。我们在合成数据中加入了高斯噪声以模拟数据误差，并在反演中使用了同反演报道的震相数据相同的参数（迭代次数，正则化的程度）。**a**，根据苏和合作者 [33] 的 SH12_WM13 模型得到的中地幔（深度在 1,300 km）剪切波速度的横向变化，**b**，根据这一模型得到的结构，使用我们研究中相同的体波路径成像得到的结果。输入模型（**a**）和经过反演恢复的模型（**b**）的比较得出：第一，我们的数据量是足够恢复大尺度的结构特征的，尤其在北半球；第二，如果 SH12_WM13 模型的结构代表的是狭窄结构的长波长图像，两组模型之间有显著一致性（图 1d 和图 3）。**c**，在 1,300 km 处具有 3%（超出正常范围）的峰值异常的人造板片结构。**d**，带噪声的合成数据反演结果表明，使用我们的数据可以解析下地幔狭窄结构（尤其在北半球），并且异常的宽度可能并没有被显著高估。这些测试也表明，我们的体波采样不足会影响相当大一部分南半球下地幔大尺度结构的分辨率。（注意：我们的色标有意不过分强调幅值接近于零的结构。带有随机噪声的反演和对例如震源定位误差、非均匀速度覆盖影响的评估表明，接近于零值振幅的结构未必是对地球结构的反映。）

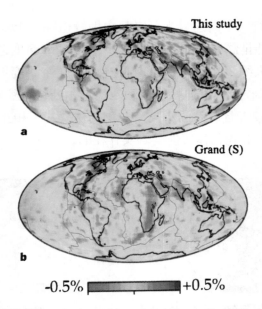

This study

a

Grand (S)

b

-0.5% ▬▬▬▬▬▬ +0.5%

Fig. 3. Africa-centred Mollweide projections of lateral variation in P- and S-wave speed at a depth of 1,350 km in different tomographic models of the Earth's mantle. The linear high-wave-speed anomalies revealed by inversion of our P-wave data (**a**) are in very good agreement with the results of S-wave inversions by Grand[22,42] (**b**). Grand's model is based on a careful analysis of direct and multiply reflected shear waves, and is continually being upgraded with more data. The wave-speed perturbations are plotted on the same scale, that is between ±0.5% relative to the reference models used. For this comparison we choose to use a different projection than in Figs 1, 2 and 4 because mantle structure beneath the western Pacific is not yet well constrained in Grand's current models.

In the mid-mantle, slow anomalies appear isolated in map view. Their shape seems more equidimensional than the fast structures, but this is not well constrained owing to poor data coverage. A slow anomaly is visible from the Earth's surface to at least 2,000 km depth beneath the southwestern Pacific Ocean (Society islands) and from about 800 km depth to the CMB beneath southern and central Africa.

At about 1,700 km depth the character of heterogeneity begins to change: the linear structures (Fig. 1c, d) gradually disintegrate into smaller-scale anomalies that show less lateral continuity (Fig. 1e). In the lowermost mantle (2,300 km depth to the CMB), mantle structure is again dominated by long-wavelength features (Fig. 1f), but the general appearance of heterogeneity in this depth range is strikingly different from the linear structures at shallower depth (compare, for instance, Fig. 1d, f). There is general agreement between our results and independent studies of the region just above the CMB (see Wysession[43] and references therein), although there seem to be some differences between P- and S-wave speed that are not yet fully understood[42]. Our data do not satisfactorily resolve Southern Hemisphere structure but the global distribution of fast and slow anomalies is consistent with the heterogeneity pattern inferred from waveform data[33-35]. The images also reveal small-scale features that we think are real. For example, the short-wavelength variations at mid-latitudes in the western Pacific are in excellent agreement with anomalous core-phase (PKP) times (K. C. Creager, personal communication).

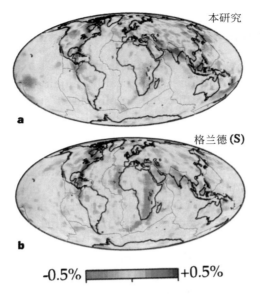

本研究

a

格兰德 (S)

b

-0.5% ▬▬▬▬▬ +0.5%

图 3. 在不同层析成像的地幔模型中 1,350 km 深处的 P 波和 S 波速度横向变化的、以非洲为中心的莫尔韦德投影图。由我们的 P 波数据反演揭示的线性高速异常（a）与格兰德 [22,42] 的 S 波速度反演结果（b）具有高度的一致性。格兰德的模型是基于对直达的和多次反射的剪切波的仔细分析得到的，并随着数据的增加在持续更新。波速扰动以同样的尺度绘制出，即相对于使用的参考模型的 ±0.5% 之间。对于本次比较，我们采用了不同于图 1、2 和 4 的投影，因为在格兰德现在的模型中西太平洋下方的地幔结构并没有得到很好地约束。

　　在中地幔，在地图视图中低速异常表现得互相孤立。它们的形状相比高速结构看起来长短轴更接近，但由于较差的数据覆盖，它们的形态并不能被很好地约束。在西南太平洋（社会群岛）下方从地表到至少 2,000 km 深度，以及非洲南部和中部下方从约 800 km 深度到核幔边界，两处分别可以观察到一个低速异常。

　　大约在 1,700 km 深度，非均匀性的特征开始变化：线性结构（图 1c 和 d）渐渐瓦解成小尺度的异常，表现出更少的横向连续性（图 1e）。在地幔的最底端（从 2,300 km 深度到核幔边界），地幔结构重新为长波长特征所主导（图 1f）；但是，在这一深度范围内非均匀性的普遍形态和深度较浅处的线性结构具有惊人的不同（例如对比图 1d 和 f）。我们的结果和针对核幔边界正上方区域开展的独立研究结果（详见维瑟逊 [43] 的文章及其后的参考文献）总的来说是一致的，尽管还有一些尚未完全理解的 P 波和 S 波速度差异 [42]。我们的数据并没有很好地解析南半球的结构，但是全球高速和低速异常的分布与波形数据推断出的非均匀性模式是一致的 [33-35]。图像同时揭示了一些我们认为是真实的小尺度特征。比如，在西太平洋中纬度地区短波长的变化与异常的核震相（PKP）时间是高度一致的（克里杰，个人交流）。

Are Narrow Structures in the Mid-mantle Real?

The inference that narrow features are prominent to at least 1,700 km depth in the Earth's mantle is perhaps surprising as spherical-harmonic representations of the Earth's interior shear structure indicate that the amplitude of structure in the mid-mantle is significantly lower than that in the upper and lowermost mantle structure, at least out to degree 16 (refs 33–35).

The length of the linear features exceeds by far the distance over which body waves propagate horizontally, indicating that a large number of data with coherent structural signal must contribute to the mapping of these structures. The narrow width of the lower-mantle lineaments is not an artefact owing to preferential sampling or the use of local basis functions for model parametrization (Fig. 2). With the body-wave paths used in the actual data inversion we computed travel times using the long-wavelength model by Su and co-workers[33]. We inverted these synthetic data and compared the output to the input model. The excellent model recovery indicates that our inversion technique does not bias towards short-wavelength anomalies in regions of dense sampling and implies that long-wavelength lower-mantle structures will be mapped accurately by our method if the data contain signal pertinent to such structures. This interpretation, if correct, suggests that spectral methods map similar structural features but may significantly overestimate their true width. Our resolution degrades in areas of poor sampling and substantial parts of the long-wavelength models cannot be tested against our results. Such tests thus help isolate structures for which a model comparison is meaningful.

Resolution tests also demonstrate that narrow structures can be resolved in most parts of the lower mantle and that their width can probably be inferred fairly accurately from Figs 1 and 3 (Fig. 2c, d). The increasing agreement between independent models further suggests that the linear anomalies are real. Once identified, the linear structures can be recognized in the long-wavelength models[33-35] (Fig. 2) and in images based on ISC data[37,38] but these models typically show high-amplitude structure in other regions as well, which complicates interpretation. Particularly exciting is the excellent correlation between the narrow structures in our P-wave maps and similar features in the S-wave model by Grand[22,42] (Fig. 3). There is good agreement also at depths other shown in Fig. 3 but differences exist in regions of poor data coverage in one or the other model, or both[42]. The spectacular correlation of structural detail in models deduced independently from different data and analysis procedures marks significant progress in global imaging.

Cold Downwellings in the Lower Mantle

Figure 4a shows the lateral distribution (planform) of downwellings in the mid-mantle according to a synthesized three-dimensional slab model[9] based on plate convergence in the past 180 Myr (ref. 44) and a simple simulation of whole-mantle flow. Our data

中部地幔的狭窄结构是真实的吗？

狭窄结构特征在地幔内至少 1,700 km 深度内都很显著，这个推断可能是令人吃惊的，因为地球内部剪切结构的球谐波模型指出，中地幔处结构的幅度要明显比上地幔和地幔最底部处的低，至少外推到 16 阶（参考文献 33~35）。

线性特征的长度超过了体波水平传播的距离，这表明包含相关结构信号的大量数据一定对探测这些结构有贡献。下地幔异常特征的狭窄宽度并不是由于优势采样或是在模型参数化时使用局部基函数而造成的人为假象（图 2）。依据在实际数据反演中使用的体波路径，我们采用苏及其同事 [33] 的长波长模型计算了走时。我们对这些合成数据进行了反演，并将输出模型和输入模型做了比较。优秀的模型恢复表明我们的反演技术在采样密集的区域并不偏向于短波长异常，还暗示了长波长的下地幔结构可以通过我们的方法被精确地绘制，如果数据中包含和这些结构相关的信号的话。这一解释，如果正确的话，表明谱方法可以对相似的结构特征成像，但可能会明显地高估它们的实际宽度。在采样较差的区域我们的分辨率降低了，同时，长波长模型大部分不能被证明与我们的结论是相矛盾的。这样的测试有助于分离一些结构，而模型之间的比较对分离这些结构是很有意义的。

分辨率测试同样证实可以分辨下地幔大部分地方的狭窄结构，从图 1 和 3（图 2c 和 d）来看他们的宽度或许也是可以被相当准确地推断的。这种独立模型之间不断增加的一致性进一步表明，线性异常是真实存在的。一旦被识别，这些在长波长模型 [33-35]（图 2）和基于 ISC 数据的图像 [37,38] 中的线性结构就可以被认可，但是这些模型通常也在其他区域显示出高幅值结构，这使得解释变得复杂。尤其令人兴奋的是在我们 P 波图中的狭窄结构和格兰德 [22,42] 的 S 波模型中的相似特征具有高度的相关性（图 3）。在图 3 中其他深度显示的图像也同样具有很好的一致性，但是在数据覆盖较差的地方差异是存在的，数据覆盖差可能出现在这个模型或者那个模型，或者同时出现在两个模型中 [42]。从不同数据和分析程序中独立推断出来的模型中结构性细节的高度相关性，标志着全球成像的显著进展。

下地幔中冷的下降流

图 4a 显示了中地幔下降流的横向分布（平面图），这是依据合成的三维板片模型 [9] 得到的，该模型是建立在过去 1.8 亿年来的板块汇聚（参考文献 44）和对全地幔

coverage is sufficient to map out the structure as predicted (Fig. 4), except for the region south of South America, which implies that many observed differences from the tomograms are meaningful.

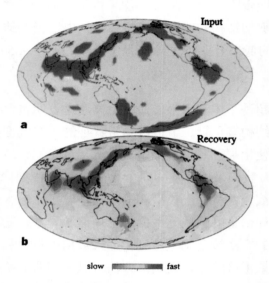

Fig. 4. Illustration of the resolution of large-scale structures at depths between 1,800 and 2,000 km using a synthesized three-dimensional slab model[9] that is based on plate convergence in the past 180 Myr (refs 8, 44). This model is produced by "simply" dropping spherical particles, called slablets, into the mantle beneath a convergence margin and does not account for ambient mantle flow or dynamical effects of the transition zone. The "slabs" sink vertically across the upper/lower mantle interface, but at a reduced rate due to an increase in viscosity. We inverted synthetic data calculated from the three-dimensional slab model, shown in **a** at a depth of 1,900 km, and compared the recovered model (**b**) to the input model. We tested the resolution of such large-scale structures at ~1,900 km because this represents the depth interval where inversion of the actual data indicates a patchwork of smaller scale structure. The comparison suggests that: (1) upon the damped inversion there is a substantial loss of amplitude; (2) our data coverage is not sufficient to resolve structure in the Southern Hemisphere and the central Pacific; and (3) the circumpacific and south Asia anomalies would be well resolved, but smearing can produce structures with amplitudes less than ~20% of the peak values. Tests such as those illustrated here and in Figs 2 and 5 have several advantages over more standard "chess-board" tests. In particular, one can investigate more directly whether the data used can resolve a hypothetical pattern of structural heterogeneity. This technique can help, for instance, to explore the class of seismic data required to verify certain aspects in numerical models.

The subduction model predicts significant slab structure in the mid-mantle beneath North America (subduction of the Farallon plate), southern Eurasia (Tethys ocean floor), the northwestern Pacific (Izanagi, Kula and Pacific plates) and Tonga (Pacific plate). The Farallon anomaly, the first lower-mantle structure associated with subduction[45] and discussed in more detail by Grand[22], is prominent in our images and appears to be continuous from the upper mantle to the CMB beneath central America (Fig. 5). In the upper 300 km, the narrow slab does not leave a signature in $2° \times 2°$ blocks but shows up clearly when a smaller block size is used (H. Bijwaard *et al.*, personal communication). The subduction of former African lithosphere beneath Europe, often referred to as the Aegean slab, forms the western boundary of the Tethys anomaly in the

流动的一个简单模拟的基础上的。除了南美洲的南部区域，我们的数据覆盖对于反演预测的结构来说是足够的（图 4），这表明在层析成像中观测到的许多差异是有意义的。

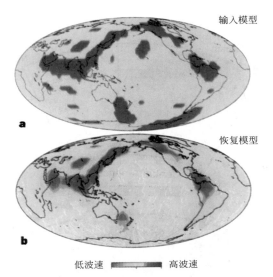

图 4. 1,800 km 到 2,000 km 深度间大尺度结构的分辨率图解，这些结构是利用基于过去 1.8 亿年的板块汇聚历史建立的合成三维板片模型 [9] 而得到的（参考文献 8 和 44）。这个模型是通过"简单地"使球形颗粒（称之为微板片）下沉到汇聚边缘下方的地幔中，并且不考虑周围地幔流和过渡带的动力学影响。"板片"垂向下沉并穿过上下地幔之间的界面，但是由于黏度的增加，速率是在下降的。我们反演了依据三维板片模型计算得到的合成数据，1,900 km 深度的三维板片模型如图 a 所示，并将恢复的模型（b）和输入模型做了比较。我们对深度大约在 1,900 km 的这种大尺度结构的分辨率进行了测试，因为这代表着实际数据反演所反映的小尺度结构群的深度区间。比较的结果表明：（1）由于阻尼反演的影响，幅值有显著的损失；（2）我们的数据覆盖对于解析南半球和太平洋中部的结构不够充分；（3）环太平洋和南亚的异常将会被很好地解析，但是拖尾效应会形成小于峰值幅度 20% 的结构。例如这里图示的以及图 2 和图 5 中这样的测试，相比于更加标准的"棋盘测试"有几个优点。尤其是人们可以更加直接地检查所使用的数据是否能够解析结构非均匀性的某种假定模式。在核实数值模型的某些因素等研究中对需要的地震数据类别的探索等方面，这个技术是很有帮助的。

俯冲模型预测在北美洲（法拉荣板块的俯冲）、欧亚大陆南部（特提斯洋底）、太平洋西北部（伊泽纳崎板块、库拉板块和太平洋板块）和汤加（太平洋板块）下方的中地幔存在显著的板片结构。法拉荣异常是第一个同俯冲关联的下地幔结构 [45]，并且由格兰德 [22] 给出了详细的讨论，在我们的图像中这个异常是非常明显的，并且在中美洲下方从上地幔连续延伸到核幔边界（图 5）。在上部 300 km，在 2°×2° 的块体中，狭窄的板片并没有留下踪迹，但是当使用更小尺寸的块体时就清晰地显示出来（拜瓦尔德等，个人交流）。在欧洲下方早期非洲岩石圈的俯冲，经常被称为爱琴板片，形成了位于欧亚大陆南部下方中地幔特提斯异常的西边界（图 6a）。爱琴板片看起来

mid-mantle beneath southern Eurasia (Fig. 6a). The Aegean slab seems to be continuous to approximately 1,500 km depth (Fig. 6b), which is in accord with a regional study[23]. The eastern edge of the Tethys structure is marked by subduction of the Indo-Australian plate beneath the Sunda arc[25].

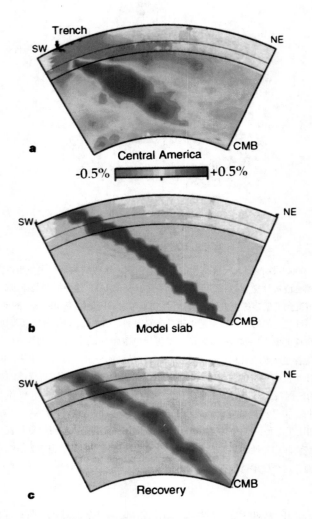

Fig. 5. **a,** Vertical mantle section through our global P-wave model from the Earth's surface to the core–mantle boundary across the convergent margin in Central America (see Fig. 1a for cross-section location). This anomaly was one of the first lower-mantle structures interpreted as lithospheric slab in the lower mantle[45]; see Lay[13] for a recent review of this and other subduction-zone structures. The fast anomaly in the lower mantle has a peak value of almost 1% of the *ak135* reference model, but this value is not well constrained. As before, the poorly sampled mantle regions are masked. CMB, core–mantle boundary; NE and SW denote geographical orientation. The word "trench" marks the location at the surface of the Middle America trench. Thin lines at constant depth depict the location of the 410 and 660 km discontinuities. The comparison of the input with a peak anomaly of 3% (**b**) and output (**c**) of test inversions with synthetic data (see Figs 2 and 4 for description) demonstrates that both the width and amplitude of the high-wave-speed anomaly beneath Central America are influenced by irregular sampling but that the slab is probably not much narrower than inferred from **a**. Results of studies at higher resolution

连续延伸到约 1,500 km 的深度（图 6b），这与一项区域性研究的结果 [23] 是相吻合的。特提斯结构的东部边界是以巽他弧下方的印度 – 澳大利亚板块的俯冲为标志的 [25]。

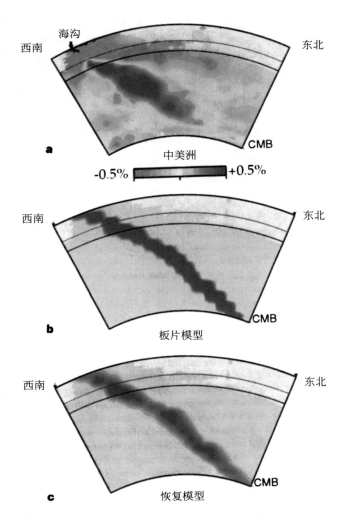

图 5. a，通过我们的全球 P 波模型得到的从地球表面到核幔边界穿过中美洲汇聚边界的地幔垂直剖面图（看图 1a 中给出的纵剖面的位置）。这个异常是在下地幔中最早被解释为岩石圈板片的几个下地幔结构之一 [45]；请参考莱 [13] 最近关于这个俯冲带结构及其他俯冲带结构的综述文章。在下地幔中的高速异常有约为 ak135 参考模型的 1% 的峰值，但是这个值没有得到较好的约束。和之前一样，采样较差的地幔区域被遮盖起来了。CMB 表示核幔边界；西南和东北表示相应的地理方位。图中"海沟"表示地表上中美洲海沟的位置。在固定深度的细线描绘了 410 km 和 660 km 不连续界面的位置。具有 3% 峰值异常的输入模型（b）和使用合成数据测试反演得到的输出模型（c）之间的比较（请看图 2 和图 4 的描述）证明了，中美洲下方的高速异常的宽度和幅值均受不规则采样的影响，但是板片可能并不比图 a 中推断出的宽度窄许多。更高分辨率的研究结果（维迪扬托罗和范德希尔斯特，稿件准备中）表明连续的法拉荣板片穿

(S.W. and R.D.v.d.H., manuscript in preparation) indicate continuity of the Farallon slab across the shallow mantle but that it is too narrow to be resolved in our current global inversion. Similar tests show that for Tonga the data cannot discriminate between penetration to ~1,800 km or to a larger depth.

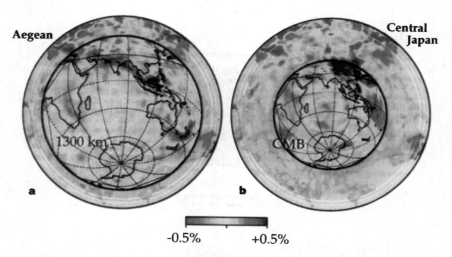

-0.5%   +0.5%

Fig. 6. Mantle cross-sections along the great circle depicted in Fig. 1a to a depth of 1,300 km (**a**) and 2,750 km (**b**). In the centre of the vertical sections we plotted in map view the anomalies at the corresponding depth (that is 1,300 and 2,750 km) in an equal-area projection. The cross-section through the upper 1,300 km of the mantle demonstrates that the deep subduction of the African plate beneath eastern Europe[23] forms the western edge of the long linear structure that continues as an intermittent high-wave-speed anomaly beneath the southern margin of Asia and connects to the deep slab beneath Indonesia[25]. Beneath eastern Europe, the Aegean slab does not seem to have sunk deeper than about 1,500 km, in accord with the narrow width of the western part of the Mesozoic Tethys ocean. The depth to the leading edge of this slab is well constrained. Beneath central Japan we infer that the slab plunges into the lower mantle with an increased dip angle, which corroborates earlier studies based on residual sphere analyses[18] and travel-time inversion[19]. Beneath central Japan the narrow structure seems to be continuous to the core–mantle boundary, where it connects to the well studied seismic anomaly beneath southeastern Asia. This vertical continuity is only observed for rather narrow segments of the Japan slab; the results of extensive resolution tests suggest, however, that such detail can be resolved by the data used (for instance Fig. 2c, d). The map view at 1,300 km reveals that this deep subduction of the Pacific plate has not resulted in a linear structure large enough to be detected by our current study. This lack of structure is representative for the depth range between 800 and 1,400 km.

The pattern of mantle flow beneath the northwestern Pacific remains enigmatic. On the basis of plate reconstructions for this region[8,9,44] one would expect a slab-related anomaly in the lower mantle that is as prominent as the Tethys and Farallon structures (Fig. 4). Even though our data coverage is sufficient to detect such a feature (Fig. 2c, d) we do not observe it in the depth range between approximately 700 and 1,400 km (Fig. 1c, d). This concurs with global models based on spherical harmonics: a circumpacific high is usually inferred, but in the top of the lower mantle beneath east Asia the fast anomaly is often either absent or significantly reduced in amplitude[33-35] (Fig. 2; H. Bolten and G. Masters, personal communication). At approximately 1,500 km depth a large-scale anomaly re-emerges that continues to the CMB (Fig. 1). Locally, narrow fast anomalies seem to pierce through the "gap" in the uppermost lower mantle and connect to (and, indeed, cause) the pronounced high-wave-speed anomaly in the CMB region beneath eastern Asia (Fig. 6b).

过浅部的地幔，但是在我们目前的全球反演中因其太窄而不能被分辨。相同的测试表明，对于汤加而言，我们的数据不能区分穿透深度达到 1,800 km 或更深的情况。

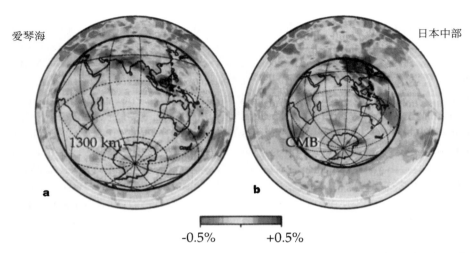

图 6. 沿着图 1a 中描绘的大圆的地幔截面图，深度达到 1,300 km（**a**）和 2,750 km（**b**）。在垂直剖面图的中心，我们也画出了在相应深度（即 1,300 km 和 2,750 km）的等面积投影的地图视图异常图。穿过地幔上部 1,300 km 的截面图证明了，位于东欧下方的非洲板块的深部俯冲[23]形成了具有绵长线性结构的西部边界，该线性结构作为一个间歇性高速异常连续出现在亚洲南部边缘的下方，并和印尼下方的深部板片相连接[25]。在东欧下的爱琴海板片看起来并没有下沉到比 1,500 km 更深的地方，这跟中生代特提斯洋西部较窄的宽度有关。这一板片的前缘深度得到了很好的约束。在日本中部下方，我们推断板片以一个不断增加的倾角插下地幔，这证实了早期基于残差球分析[18]和走时反演[19]的研究。在日本中部下方，狭窄结构似乎一直延续到核幔边界，并与研究较充分的亚洲东南部下方的地震异常相连。只在日本板片相当狭窄的部分观测到这种垂向连续性；但是大量的分辨率测试结果表明，通过所使用的数据可以分辨这些细节（比如图 2c 和 d）。在 1,300 km 深度的地图视图揭示，太平洋板块的这种深俯冲并没有形成一个大到足以被我们目前的研究能探测到的线性结构。这种结构在 800 km 到 1,400 km 的深度之间缺失是很具有代表性的。

　　在西北太平洋下方的地幔流动模式依然是未解之谜。基于针对这一区域的板块重建[8,9,44]，人们期待在下地幔出现与特提斯和法拉荣结构一样明显的俯冲板片相关的异常（图 4）。尽管我们的数据覆盖是足够探测这一特征的（图 2c 和 d），但是我们在大约 700 km 到 1,400 km 的深度范围内并没有观测到这样的异常（图 1c 和 d）。这与基于球谐函数观测的全球模型是一致的：通常推断存在一个环太平洋高速异常，但是在东亚下方的下地幔顶部，高速异常经常要么缺失，要么幅度明显减弱[33-35]（图 2；博尔腾和马斯特斯，个人交流）。在约 1,500 km 的深度，一个大尺度异常再次出现，并一直延续到核幔边界（图 1）。狭窄的高速异常似乎在局部穿透了下地幔最上部的"缺口"，并且和东亚下方核幔边界区域的明显高速异常相连接（而且，实际上导致了这个显著的高速异常）（图 6b）。

Deep Circulation in the Earth's Mantle

Figures 1, 5 and 6 suggest that fast anomalies are continuous across the "660-km" discontinuity to at least 1,700 km depth beneath many convergent margins and that the long narrow structures in the mid-mantle are related to subduction of former oceanic lithosphere, with some slab segments probably sinking all the way to the CMB. Lower-mantle flow is required to explain these observations—the distance to the upper mantle is simply too large for them to be the result of conductive cooling alone—and must be causally related to upper-mantle flow unless the inferred spatial correlation of wavespeed anomalies is just coincidental. Flow across the seismic discontinuity offers the simplest explanation of the observed continuity of amplitude and geometry (for example, dip angle) of the anomalies. In particular, our results argue against worldwide mantle stratification by a flow-impeding interface at 660 km or stagnation of slab material in the lower mantle above 1,100 km (ref. 46). Penetrative convection—a hybrid flow model in which slab material flows back to the upper mantle after initial penetration into a chemically distinct lower mantle with slightly higher intrinsic density[10]—may explain our observations, in particular if the chemical boundary occurs at such a large depth that downwarping to the CMB is plausible or if large depressions of the boundary nucleate downwellings that control the planform of convection in the layer beneath them (mechanical coupling) and show up as fast anomalies. Either alternative is not easily distinguished from simple whole mantle flow on the basis of seismic imaging alone.

Local intermittence of flow into the lower mantle. Although inconsistent with worldwide stratification at 660 km depth, the interplay of plate tectonic motions, radial increases in viscosity, and (perhaps) endothermic phase changes can locally distort mantle flow. Beneath the northwestern Pacific region, for example, some slabs deflect in the transition zone[20,21] whereas others penetrate to larger depth[18-20] (for example, Fig. 6b). Slab structure is here not well defined in the top of the lower mantle but re-emerges at larger depth (~1,500 km) and then continues to the CMB. We argue that this structural complexity is in keeping with the complex tectonic evolution of the region and that mantle stratification is a local and transient[30-32] phenomenon with a characteristic timescale that is much shorter than that of mantle-wide overturn[47].

Lithospheric plates had been subducting along the eastern margin of continental Asia since at least 140 Myr ago (ref. 8) when Eocene (~45 Myr ago) plate reorganizations in the Pacific realm caused the separation of Japan from continental Asia and initiation of subduction beneath the Philippine Sea plate along the proto Izu Bonin and Mariana trenches. Post-Eocene clockwise migration of the newly formed arc system resulted in slab deflection in the transition zone beneath the Izu Bonin arc[47], which switched off the supply to the older downwelling in the lower mantle beneath the east Asian margin. The formation of the inferred 600 km or so slab window in the uppermost lower mantle during the past 40 Myr implies a minimum sinking rate of about 1.5 cm yr^{-1} in the lower mantle, which concurs with inferences from South America[22]. Trench migration may have

地幔中的深部循环

图 1、5 和 6 表明，在许多汇聚板块边缘下方，高速异常穿过"660 km"不连续面并一直连续延伸到 1,700 km 深度，并且中地幔的狭长结构和古大洋岩石圈的俯冲相关，甚至有些板片碎块已经一直下沉到核幔边界。解释这些观测结果需要下地幔流动，因为对这些高速异常而言到上地幔的距离太远，不可能是纯粹传导冷却的结果；并且下地幔流动必须同上地幔流动成因果联系，除非推断的大片波速异常的空间相关性仅仅是个巧合。穿过地震不连续界面的流动为观测到的幅值和几何（比如倾角）连续性给出了最简单的解释。我们的结果尤其不支持全球地幔分层模型，而这些模型是依据 660 km 处阻碍流动的界面或者在下地幔 1,100 km 上方的板片物质停滞（参考文献 46）进行分层研究的。穿透对流，作为一种混合流动模型（即在刚开始穿入化学性质迥异、具有略高密度的下地幔之后，其板片物质将流回上地幔[10]），或许能够解释我们的观测结果，尤其是当化学边界出现在这样深的深度以至于向下弯曲到核幔边界是有可能的，或者是有大规模边界沉降使下降流在这些边界下方的层内成核，下降流控制着对流的平面分布（机械耦合），并且显示为高速异常。仅靠地震成像是不能轻易将这两种替代模型同简单全地幔流动区别开来的。

进入下地幔的局部流动间歇。尽管和 660 km 深度的全球性分层不一致，板块构造运动之间的相互作用、黏度径向增加和（可能的）吸热相变也能够使地幔流动发生局部性扰动。比如在西北太平洋区域的下方，一些板片在过渡带就发生偏移[20,21]，而其他的板片则穿入更深的深度[18-20]（比如，图 6b）。在这里，板片结构在下地幔顶部不能被很好地界定，但在更大的深度（~1,500 km）它再次出现并一直延续到核幔边界。我们认为这种结构复杂性是和该区域的复杂构造演化相一致的，并且地幔分层是一个具有特征时间尺度的局部暂时性[30-32]现象，该时间尺度明显比地幔范围内倒转的时间尺度[47]要短。

至少从 1.4 亿年前以来（参考文献 8），岩石圈板块就一直沿着亚洲大陆东缘俯冲，在始新世（大约 4,500 万年前）时，太平洋区域的板块重组造成了日本从亚洲大陆分离，以及在菲律宾海板块下方沿"原"伊豆－小笠原海沟和马里亚纳海沟俯冲的开始。始新世之后，新形成的弧系统顺时针迁移造成了伊豆－小笠原弧下方过渡带内板片的偏移[47]，这导致亚洲东部边缘下方下地幔较老下降流的物质供应停止。过去 4,000 万年间，在下地幔顶部大约 600 km 的板片窗口的形成，暗示了在下地幔约每年 1.5 cm 的最小下沉速率，这与来自南美洲的推断[22]是一致的。海沟迁移可能

caused local deflection of the Japan slab[47], but beneath central Japan subduction of the Pacific plate seems to have continued along a shallowly dipping conduit to a previously established downwelling anchored in the lower mantle[48] (Fig. 6b). Horizontal slabs are gravitationally unstable[49] and will eventually become entrained in lower-mantle flow through Rayleigh–Taylor instabilities; this process may produce narrow downwellings that may be hard to detect by seismic imaging.

Is there a lower-mantle transition zone? We infer from the images that flow in the shallow mantle connects, at least locally, to structural heterogeneity just above the CMB (Figs 5 and 6b), confirming previous suggestions of such a relationship[12,13,27,43,50], but the long narrow structures in the mid-mantle are strikingly different from the long-wavelength features just above the CMB (compare, for instance, Fig. 1d and f). This suggests that the downwellings that reach the CMB (Fig. 6b) lose the characteristic planar geometry across a transitional interval (approximately 1,800–2,300 km depth). A change in shape of the downwellings from sheet-like to more cylindrical is in accord with numerical flow simulations[51]. Comparison with other models also suggests that the change in character of heterogeneity is real. We remark that the inferred transition in heterogeneity coincides with a change in proportionality between P and S speed[52], indicated by the Poisson's ratio, which may indicate a compositional change[53]. There are several caveats. Although resolution tests demonstrate that the inferred breakdown of the linear structures is not a result of reduced sampling (Fig. 4) we realize that data coverage in the lowermost mantle is not satisfactory. Moreover, structural signal from heterogeneity in the deepest mantle may be lost from travel-time data owing to a mechanism known as wavefront healing[54]. At this stage we cannot exclude the possibility that the change in geometry of the anomalies is causally related to past changes in plate motion, without the need for a change in physical state. Conversely, it is exciting to realize that the detailed structures revealed by global imaging may now begin to constrain reconstructions of past plate motion.

It is obvious that several aspects of the tomographic model presented can—and will—be improved. There are important issues that require further study (uneven sampling, interpretation of deep structure, remaining differences with long-wavelength models), but there seems to be increasing consensus from seismology for deep convective circulation in the mantle. A concerted effort of seismic imaging, plate reconstruction, numerical flow modelling, and chemical mass-balancing is required to unravel reaming mysteries of the deep Earth and to explain the flow behaviour in a lower-mantle transition zone and the isotope record. The increasing similarity between flow patterns deduced from global seismic imaging and numerical flow simulation[55,56] (H.-P. Bunge and M. Richards, personal communication), and the fact that, for the first time, independent global wave-speed models begin to show excellent correlation of small-scale (< 1,000 km) structure,[42] mark important and exciting contributions towards understanding the dynamic and thermal evolution of our planet.

(**386**, 578-584; 1997)

造成了日本板片的局部偏移[47]，但是日本中部下方太平洋板块的俯冲，看起来已经沿着一个较浅角度倾斜的通道，连续延伸到一个之前形成的扎根到下地幔的下降流[48]（图6b）。水平板片在重力下是不稳定的[49]，并最终会通过瑞利–泰勒不稳定性卷入下地幔流动；这个过程可能会形成难以被地震成像所探测的狭窄下降流。

存在下地幔过渡带吗？ 我们从图像中推断，地幔浅部的流动至少在局部地区同核幔边界上方的结构非均匀体相连（图5和图6b），这证实了前人认为存在这一关系的想法[12,13,27,43,50]，但是中地幔内的狭长结构显然和核幔边界上方的长波长特征不一致（比如比较图1d和f）。这表明到达核幔边界的下降流（图6b）穿过一个过渡区后（大约1,800~2,300 km深）失去了特征的平面几何形态。下降流的形状从片状变成了更接近圆柱体，这同数值流动模拟结果是相一致的[51]。和其他模型的比较也表明非均匀性特征的变化是真实存在的。我们注意到推断的非均匀性过渡变化与通过泊松比反映的P波和S波速度比的变化一致[52]，这可能反映了一种成分变化[53]。有几点需要附加说明的情况。尽管分辨率测试显示推断的线性结构瓦解并不是采样减少造成的（图4），但是我们意识到在地幔最底部的数据覆盖是不那么令人满意的。另外，由于波前愈合效应[54]，地幔最深处的非均匀性结构信号可能会从走时数据中丢失[54]。在现在这个阶段，我们不能排除这样一种可能性，即异常的几何变化是由过去板块运动的变化引起的，而不需要物理状态的变化。反过来，意识到现在可以开始用全球成像揭示的详细结构来约束过去板块运动的重建，这是令人兴奋的一件事。

显然，这里给出的层析成像模型有很多方面都能够并将会被改进。有许多重要的问题（如不均匀采样、深部结构的解释、与长波长模型仍存在的差异）值得进一步研究，但是似乎地震学对于地幔中的深对流循环有着越来越多的共识。解开地球深部的秘密、解释下地幔转换带的流动行为和同位素记录，需要地震成像、板块重建、数值流动模拟、化学物质平衡等多学科研究方向的共同努力。从全球地震成像中推断出来的流动模式和数值流动模拟结果之间有着越来越多的相似性[55,56]（邦奇和理查兹，个人交流），而且，不同的相互独立的全球波速模型首次开始显示出很好的小尺度（小于1,000 km）相关性[42]，这些成果标志着人们在地球的动力学和热演化研究方面重要和令人兴奋的贡献。

（俞贵平 翻译；梁晓峰 审稿）

R. D. van der Hilst*, **S. Widiyantoro**[†] **& E. R. Engdahl**[‡]

* Massachusetts Institute of Technology, Department of Earth, Atmospheric, and Planetary Sciences, Rm 54-514, Cambridge Massachusetts 02139, USA

[†] Australian National University, Research School of Earth Sciences, Canberra ACT 0200, Australia

[‡] US Geological Survey, DFC, MS 967, PO Box 25046, Denver, Colorado 80225, USA

Received 2 September 1996; accepted 11 March 1997.

References:

1. Dziewonski, A. M., Hager, B. H. & O'Connell, R. J. Large-scale heterogeneities in the lower mantle. *J. Geophys. Res.* **82**, 239-255 (1977).

2. Dziewonski, A. M. Mapping the lower mantle: determination of lateral heterogeneity in P velocity up to degree and order 6. *J. Geophys. Res.* **89**, 5929-5952 (1984).

3. Carlson, R. W. Mechanisms of Earth differentiation: consequences for the chemical structure of the mantle. *Rev. Geophys.* **32**, 337-362 (1994).

4. Hofmann, A. Mantle geochemistry: the message from oceanic volcanism. *Nature* **385**, 219-229 (1997).

5. Hager, B. H., Clayton, R. W., Richards, M. A., Comer, R. P. & Dziewonski, A. M. Lower mantle heterogeneity, dynamic topography and the geoid. *Nature* **313**, 541-545 (1985).

6. Montagner, J.-P. Can seismology tell us anything about convection in the mantle? *Rev. Geophys.* **32**, 115-138 (1994).

7. Ritzwoller, M. H. & Lavely, E. M. Three-dimensional seismic model of the Earth's mantle. *Rev. Geophys.* **33**, 1-66 (1995).

8. Richards, M. A. & Engebretson, D. C. Large-scale mantle convection and the history of subduction. *Nature* **355**, 437-440 (1992).

9. Ricard, Y., Richards, M. A., Lithgow-Bertelloni, C. & Le Stunff, Y. A geodynamic model of mantle density heterogeneity. *J. Geophys. Res.* **98**, 21895-21909 (1993).

10. Silver, P. G., Carlson, R. W. & Olson, P. Deep slabs, geochemical heterogeneity, and the large-scale structure of mantle convection: investigations of an enduring paradox. *Rev. Earth Planet. Sci.* **16**, 477-541 (1988).

11. Jordan, T. H., Lerner-Lam, A. L. & Creager, K. C. in *Mantle Convection* (ed. Peltier, W. R.) 98-201 (Gordon & Breach Scientific, New York, 1989).

12. Davies, G. F. & Richards, M. A. Mantle convection. *J. Geol.* **100**, 151-206 (1992).

13. Lay, T. The fate of descending slabs. *Annu. Rev. Earth Planet. Sci.* **22**, 33-61 (1994).

14. Shearer, P. & Masters, G. Global mapping of topography on the 660-km discontinuity. *Nature* **355**, 791-796 (1992).

15. Ito. E. & Takahashi, E. Postspinel transformations in the system $Mg_2SiO_4-Fe_2SiO_4$ and some geophysical implications. *J. Geophys. Res.* **94**, 10637-10646 (1989).

16. Christensen, U. R. & Yuen, D. A. The interaction of subducting lithospheric slab with a chemical or phase boundary. *J. Geophys. Res.* **89**, 4389-4402 (1984).

17. Puster, P. & Jordan, T. H. How stratified is mantle convection? *J. Geophys. Res.* **102**, 7625-7646 (1997).

18. Creager, K. C. & Jordan, T. H. Slab penetration into the lower mantle below the Mariana and other island arcs of the northwest Pacific. *J. Geophys. Res.* **91**, 3573-3589 (1986).

19. Kamiya, S., Miyatake, T. & Hirahara, K. How deep can we see the high velocity anomalies beneath the Japan island arcs? *Geophys. Res. Lett.* **15**, 828-831 (1988).

20. Van der Hilst, R. D., Engdahl, E. R., Spakman, W. & Nolet, G. Tomographic imaging of subducted lithosphere below northwest Pacific island arcs. *Nature* **353**, 37-43 (1991).

21. Fukao, Y., Obayashi, M., Inoue, H. & Nenbai, M. Subducting slabs stagnant in the mantle transition zone. *J. Geophys. Res.* **97**, 4809-4822 (1992).

22. Grand, S. P. Mantle shear structure beneath the Americas and the surrounding oceans. *J. Geophys. Res.* **99**, 11591-11621 (1994).

23. Spakman, W., Van der Lee, S., Van der Hilst, R. D. Travel-time tomography of the European- Mediterranean mantle down to 1400 km. *Phys. Earth Planet. Inter.* **79**, 3-74 (1993).

24. Van der Hilst, R. D. Complex morphology of subducted lithosphere in the mantle beneath the Tonga trench. *Nature* **374**, 154-157 (1995).

25. Widiyantoro, S. & Van der Hilst, R. D. The slab of subducted lithosphere beneath the Sunda arc, Indonesia. *Science* **271**, 1566-1570 (1996).

26. King, S. D. The viscosity structure of the mantle. *Rev. Geophys. Suppl.* **33**, 11-17 (1995).

27. Loper, D. E. A simple model of whole mantle convection. *J. Geophys. Res.* **90**, 1809-1836 (1985).

28. Hedlin, M., Shearer, P. & Earle, P. S. Seismic evidence for small-scale heterogeneity throughout the Earth's mantle. *Nature* (in the press).

29. Krüger, F., Weber, M., Scherbaum, F. & Schlittenhardt, J. Evidence for normal and inhomogenous lowermost mantle and core–mantle boundary structure under the Arctic and northern Canada. *Geophys. J. Int.* **122**, 637-657 (1995).

30. Thoraval, C., Machetal, P. & Cazenave, A. Locally layered convection inferred from dynamic models of the Earth's mantle. *Nature* **375**, 777-780 (1995).

31. Machetel, P. & Weber, P. Intermittent layered convection in a model mantle with an endothermic phase change at 670km. *Nature* **350**, 55-57 (1991).

32. Tackley, P. Mantle dynamics: Influence of the transition zone. *Rev. Geophys. Suppl.* **33**, 275-282 (1995).

33. Su, W.-J., Woodward, R. L. & Dziewonski, A. M. Degree 12 model of shear velocity heterogeneity in the mantle. *J. Geophys. Res.* **99**, 6945-6981 (1994).

34. Li, X.-D. & Romanowicz, B. Global mantle shear-velocity model developed using nonlinear asymptotic coupling theory. *J. Geophys. Res.* **101**, 22245-22272 (1996).

35. Masters, G., Johnson, S., Laske, G. & Bolton, H. A shear-velocity model of the mantle. *Phil. Trans. R. Soc. Lond. A* **354**, 1385-1411 (1996).

36. Masters, G., Jordan, T. H., Silver, P. G. & Gilbert, F. A spherical Earth structure from fundamental spheroidal-mode data. *Nature* **298**, 609-613 (1982).

37. Inoue, H., Fukao, Y., Tanabe, K. & Ogata, Y. Whole mantle P-wave travel-time tomography. *Phys. Earth Planet. Inter.* **59**, 294-328 (1990).

38. Vasco, D. W., Johnson, L. R., Pulliam, R. J. & Earle, P. S. Robust inversion of IASP91 travel time residuals for mantle P and S velocity structure. *J. Geophys. Res.* **99**, 13727-13755 (1994).

39. Engdahl, E. R., Van der Hilst, R. D. & Buland, R. P. Global teleseismic earthquake relocation with improved travel times and procedures for depth determination. *Bull. Seismol. Soc. Am.* (submitted).

40. Kennett, B. L. N., Engdahl, E. R. & Buland, R. Constraints on seismic velocities in the Earth from traveltimes. *Geophys. J. Int.* **122**, 108-124 (1995).

41. Nolet, G. Solving or resolving inadequate and noisy tomographic systems. *J. Comput. Phys.* **61**, 463-482 (1985).

42. Grand, S. P., Van der Hilst, R. D. & Widiyantoro, S. Global seismic tomography: a snapshot of convection in the earth. *Geol. Soc. Am. Today* (in the press).

43. Wysession, M. E. Continents of the core. *Nature* **381**, 373-374 (1996).

44. Lithgow-Bertelloni, C., Richards, M. A., Ricard, Y., O'Connell, R. J. & Engebretson, D. C. Toroidal-poloidal partitioning of plate motions since 120 Ma. *Geophys. Res. Lett.* **20**, 375-378 (1993).

45. Jordan, T. H. & Lynn, W. S. A velocity anomaly in the lower mantle. *J. Geophys. Res.* **79**, 2679-2685 (1974).

46. Wen, L. & Anderson, D. L. The fate of slabs inferred from seismic tomography and 130 million years of subduction. *Earth Planet. Sci. Lett.* **133**, 185-198 (1995).

47. Van der Hilst, R. D. & Seno, T. Effects of relative plate motion on the deep structure and penetration depth of slabs below the Izu-Bonin and Mariana island arcs. *Earth Planet. Sci. Lett.* **120**, 375-407 (1993).

48. Griffiths, R. W., Hackney, R. & Van der Hilst, R. D. A laboratory investigation of trench migration and the fate of subducted slabs. *Earth Planet. Sci. Lett.* **133**, 1-17 (1995).

49. Christensen, U. R. The influence of trench migration on slab penetration into the lower mantle. *Earth Planet. Sci. Lett.* **140**, 27-39 (1996).

50. Kendall, J.-M. & Silver, P. G. Constraints from seismic anisotropy on the nature of the lowermost mantle. *Nature* **381**, 409-412 (1996).

51. Bercovici, D., Schubert, G. & Glatzmaier, G. 3-dimensional spherical-models of convection in the Earth's mantle. *Science* **244**, 950-955 (1989).

52. Bolton, H. & Masters, G. A region of anomalous d lnV$_s$/d ln V$_p$ in the deep mantle, (abstr.) *Eos* 77, F6g7 (1996).

53. Loper, D. & Lay, T. The core–mantle boundary region. *J. Geophys. Res.* **100**, 6397-6420 (1995).

54. Nolet, G. & Moser, T.-J. Teleseismic delay times in a 3-dimensional Earth and a new look at the S-discrepancy. *Geophys. J. Int.* **114**, 185-195 (1993).

55. Puster, P., Hager, B. H.& Jordan, T. H. Mantle convection experiments with evolving plates. *Geophys. Res. Lett.* **22**, 2223-2226 (1995).

56. Bunge, H.-P., Richards, M. A. & Baumgardner, J. R. The effect of viscosity stratification on mantle convection. *Nature* **379**, 436-438 (1996).

Acknowledgements. We thank B. Kennett and J. Braun for providing graphics software; S. Grand, C. Lithgow-Bertelloni and W.-J. Su for access to their models; T. Jordan, B. Hager, S. Grand and C. Froidevaux for discussions; and G. Masters for a review. This work was supported in part by the US National Science Foundation.

Correspondence and requests for materials should be addressed to R.D.v.d.H. (e-mail: hilst@mit.edu).

Transient Optical Emission from the Error Box of the γ-ray Burst of 28 February 1997

J. van Paradijs *et al.*

Editor's Note

Mysterious flashes of gamma rays in the sky have been reported since 1973, when it was thought that they originated within our solar system. Many theories were proposed to explain them, but the observation of a counterpart object at any other wavelength would constrain these considerably. Here Jan van Paradijs and colleagues describe such an object for the first time, using the Beppo-SAX satellite. They report a visible-light counterpart seen in less than 21 hours after the burst GRB 970228, which shows that the burst is associated with a faint galaxy, probably at high redshift. We know now that most "long" bursts like this are very distant, and seem to arise in peculiar types of supernovae (exploding stars).

For almost a quarter of a century[1], the origin of γ-ray bursts—brief, energetic bursts of high-energy photons—has remained unknown. The detection of a counterpart at another wavelength has long been thought to be a key to understanding the nature of these bursts (see, for example, ref. 2), but intensive searches have not revealed such a counterpart. The distribution and properties of the bursts[3] are explained naturally if they lie at cosmological distances (a few Gpc)[4], but there is a countervailing view that they are relatively local objects[5], perhaps distributed in a very large halo around our Galaxy. Here we report the detection of a transient and fading optical source in the error box associated with the burst GRB970228, less than 21 hours after the burst[6,7]. The optical transient appears to be associated with a faint galaxy[7,8], suggesting that the burst occurred in that galaxy and thus that γ-ray bursts in general lie at cosmological distance.

G RB970228 was detected[9] with the Gamma-ray Burst Monitor[10] on board the Italian–Dutch BeppoSAX satellite[11] on 1997 February 28, UT 02 h 58 min 01 s. The event lasted ~80 s and reached peak fluxes of $\sim4 \times 10^{-6}$, $\sim6 \times 10^{-6}$ and $\sim10^{-7}$ erg cm^{-2} s^{-1} in the 40–600 keV, 40–1,000 keV and 1.5–7.8 keV ranges, respectively[9,12] (note that the peak flux of 0.23 Crab quoted in ref. 9 is in error). It occurred in the field of view of one of the BeppoSAX Wide Field Cameras (WFCs)[13]. The spectrum of the event is characteristic of classical γ-ray bursts (GRBs)[12]. Its position (about halfway between α Tauri and γ Orionis) was determined with an accuracy of 3′ (radius)[7] at right ascension (RA) 05 h 01 min 57 s, declination (dec.)+11° 46.4′. Application of the long-baseline timing technique[14] to the GRB data obtained with the Ulysses spacecraft, and with the BeppoSAX and the Wind satellites, respectively, constrained this location to be within each of two parallel annuli,

1997 年 2 月 28 日伽马射线暴误差框内的暂现光学辐射

帕拉基斯等

编者按

从 1973 年开始，神秘的伽马射线在天空中的闪光就有所报道。当时认为，闪光发生在我们的太阳系里。科学家们提出了很多理论去解释它们，但是在其他波段观测到的对应体会很大程度地限制这些理论。这里帕拉基斯及他的合作者们第一次用 BeppoSAX 卫星对它们进行描述。他们报道了在伽马射线暴 GRB970228 爆发后 21 小时内观测到的一个光学对应体，并表明该暴和一个可能处于高红移处的暗星系成协。我们现在知道，大多数类似的"长"暴都发生在很远的地方，并且似乎都产生于特殊类型的超新星（爆炸的恒星）之中。

将近 25 年的时间中 [1]，伽马射线暴——短暂的、巨大能量的高能光子爆发——的起源一直不为人所知。长期以来人们认为探测到其他波段的对应体将是理解这些暴本质的关键（例如，见参考文献 2），可是密集的搜寻并没有发现这样的对应体。如果这些暴位于宇宙学距离上（几十亿个秒差距）[4]，那么它们的分布和性质 [3] 可以很自然地得到解释。但是也有相反的观点，认为它们是相对邻近的天体 [5]，可能分布在银河系周围很大尺度的晕里。这里我们报道 GRB970228 爆发后 21 小时内在其误差圈里探测到一个暂现并衰减的光学源 [6,7]。这个光学暂现源似乎和一个暗星系成协 [7,8]，这表明伽马射线暴发生在那个星系里，因此伽马射线暴大体上是处于宇宙学距离上的。

GRB970228 是于 1997 年 2 月 28 日，世界时 (UT)02 h 58 min 01 s，由安装在意大利 – 荷兰的 BeppoSAX 卫星 [11] 上的伽马射线暴监测器 [10] 探测到的 [9]。这个事件持续了 ~80 s，在 40~600 keV、40~1,000 keV 和 1.5~7.8 keV 能段的峰值流量分别为 $\sim 4 \times 10^{-6}$ erg·cm^{-2}·s^{-1}、$\sim 6 \times 10^{-6}$ erg·cm^{-2}·s^{-1} 和 $\sim 10^{-7}$ erg·cm^{-2}·s^{-1}[9,12]（注意：参考文献 9 引用的 0.23 倍蟹状星云的峰值流量是错误的）。它发生在 BeppoSAX 大视场照相机（WFCs）[13] 的一个视场里。这个事件的光谱具有典型伽马射线暴（GRBs）的特征 [12]。它的位置（大约在金牛座 α 和猎户座 γ 的中间）确定为赤经 (RA)05 h 01 min 57 s，赤纬 (dec.)+11°46.4′，精度为 3′（半径）[7]。分别对尤里西斯号太阳探测器 (Ulysses)、BeppoSAX 和 Wind 卫星观测到的伽马射线暴的数据应用长基线计时

with half-widths[15,16] of 31″ (3σ), and 30″ (3σ), respectively, which intersect the WFC error circle (Fig. 1).

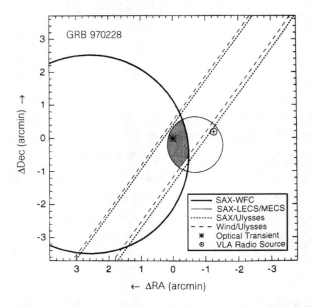

Fig. 1. The position of the optical transient, indicated with an asterisk, is shown with respect to the 3′ (radius) WFC location error circle, the 50″ (radius) error circles of the BeppoSAX X-ray transient, and the two annuli obtained from the differences between the times the GRB was detected with Ulysses, and with BeppoSAX and Wind, respectively. The area in common between these error regions in hatched. The coordinates are given in units of arcmin with respect to the position of the optical transient (RA 05 h 01 min 46.66 s, dec. +11° 46′ 53.9″, J2000). The position of an unrelated radio source[49] in the error circle of the X-ray transient is indicated with the square symbol.

Eight hours after the burst occurred, BeppoSAX was reoriented so that the GRB position could be observed with the LECS and MECS detectors[17,18]. A weak X-ray source was then found[19] at RA 05 h 01 min 44 s, dec. +11° 46.7′ (error radius 50″), near the edge of the WFC error circle[9] (Fig. 1). The 2–10 keV (MECS) flux of this source was 2.4×10^{-12} erg cm^{-2} s^{-1}. The LECS instrument measured a 0.1–10 keV source flux of $(2.6 \pm 0.6) \times 10^{-12}$ erg cm^{-2} s^{-1}. The source spectrum was consistent with a power-law model with photon index 2.7, reduced at low energy by a column density N_H of 5.6×10^{21} cm^{-2}. During an observation with the same instruments on March 3, UT 17 h 37 min this flux had decreased by a factor of 20 (ref. 19). With ASCA the X-ray source was detected[20] on 7 March at a 2–10 keV flux of $(0.8 \pm 0.2) \times 10^{-13}$ erg cm^{-2} s^{-1}.

On February 28, UT 23 h 48 min, 20.8 hours after the GRB occurred, before we had any knowledge of the X-ray transient, we obtained a V-band and an I-band image (exposure times 300 s each) of the WFC error box with the Prime Focus Camera of the 4.2-m William Herschel Telescope (WHT) on La Palma[21]. The 1,024 × 1,024 pixel CCD frames (pixel size 24 μm, corresponding to 0.421″) cover a 7.2′ × 7.2′ field, well matched to the size of the GRB error box. The limiting magnitudes of the images are $V = 23.7$, and

技术 [14]，把位置限制在两个半宽 [15,16] 分别为 31″（3σ）和 30″（3σ）的平行环内，和 WFC 误差圈相交在一起（图 1）。

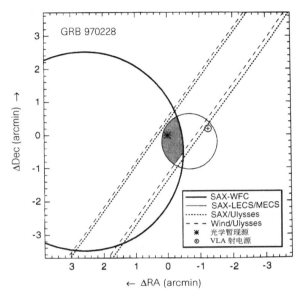

图 1. 光学暂现源的位置，用星号标示。相应的图中显示了 3′（半径）的 WFC 位置误差圈，50″（半径）的 BeppoSAX X 射线暂现源的误差圈，以及由 Ulysses 测量到的伽马射线暴时间分别与 BeppoSAX 和 Wind 测量到的伽马射线暴时间的差值得到的两个环。这些误差范围的重合区域画上了阴影。坐标表示光学暂现源的位置（RA 05 h 01 min 46.66 s，dec.+11°46′53.9″，J2000），以 arcmin 为单位。在 X 射线暂现源误差圈内一个不相干的射电源 [49] 的位置由 ⊕ 表示。

爆发 8 小时后，再次调整 BeppoSAX 的方向以使得伽马射线暴的位置能够被 LECS 和 MECS 探测器观测到 [17,18]。在 WFC 误差圈 [9] 的边缘附近 RA 05 h 01 min 44 s，dec.+11°46.7′（误差半径为 50″）处发现了一个弱的 X 射线源 [19]（图 1）。这个源在 2~10 keV（MECS）范围内的流量为 2.4×10^{-12} erg·cm^{-2}·s^{-1}。LECS 仪器测量源在 0.1~10 keV 范围内的流量为 $(2.6 \pm 0.6) \times 10^{-12}$ erg·cm^{-2}·s^{-1}。这个源的能谱和光子指数为 2.7 的幂律谱模型一致，在低能处流量由柱密度 N_H 为 5.6×10^{21} cm^{-2} 的吸收导致减少。在 3 月 3 日 UT 17 h 37 min，相同仪器观测到这个源的流量减少为原来的 1/20（参考文献 19）。3 月 7 日 ASCA 探测到的这个 X 射线源 [20]，在 2~10 keV 的流量为 $(0.8 \pm 0.2) \times 10^{-13}$ erg·cm^{-2}·s^{-1}。

在 2 月 28 日 UT 23 h 48 min，伽马射线暴爆发 20.8 小时后，在不知道 X 射线暂现源之前，我们利用拉帕尔马的 4.2 m 威廉·赫歇尔望远镜（WHT）的主焦点照相机得到 WFC 误差圈的 V 波段和 I 波段图像（每幅图曝光时间 300 s）[21]。1,024 × 1,024 像素的 CCD 图像（像素大小为 24 μm，对应于 0.421″）覆盖了 7.2′ × 7.2′ 的天区，和伽马射线暴误差圈的大小符合得很好。成像的极限星等为 $V = 23.7$ 和 $I = 21.4$。3 月

$I = 21.4$. We obtained a second I-band image on March 8, UT 21 h 12 min with the same instrument on the WHT (exposure time 900 s), and a second V-band image on March 8, UT 20 h 42 min with the Isaac Newton Telescope (INT) on La Palma (exposure 2,500 s). Photometric calibration was obtained from images of standard star number 336 and Landolt[22] field 104. The images were reduced using standard bias subtraction and flatfielding.

A comparison of the two image pairs immediately revealed one object with a large brightness variation[6]: it is clearly detected in both the V- and I-band images taken on 28 February, but not in the second pair of images taken on 8 March (Fig. 2). From a comparison with positions of nearby stars that were obtained using the Digitized Sky Survey we find for its location RA 05 h 01 min 46.66 s, dec. +11° 46′ 53.9″ (equinox J2000); this position has an estimated (internal) accuracy of 0.2″. The object is located in the error box defined by the WFC position, the Ulysses/BeppoSAX/Wind annuli, and the transient X-ray source position (Fig. 1).

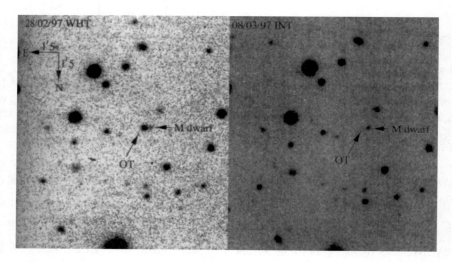

Fig. 2. V-band images of a 1.5′ × 1.5′ region of the sky containing the position of the optical transient. The left image was obtained with the WHT on 1997 28 February, UT 23 h 48 min, the right image with the INT on 8 March, UT 20 h 42 min. The optical transient is indicated by "OT". The M dwarf, separated from the optical transient by 2.9″, is also indicated.

Using aperture photometry software we determined the magnitudes of the variable as follows[6]: $V = 21.3 \pm 0.1$, $I = 20.6 \pm 0.1$ on 28 February and $V > 23.6$, $I > 22.2$ on 8 March. The shape of the source in both the 28 February V- and I-band images is consistent with that of the point-spread function, as determined for 15 stars in the same images.

Close to the optical transient is a star, located 2.85″ away at RA 05 h 01 min 46.47 s, dec. +11° 46′ 54.0″, with $V = 23.1$, $I = 20.5$. A spectrum of this star, taken on March 1, UT 0 h with the ESO 3.6-m telescope using the EFOSC1 spectrograph and the R1000 grating (resolution of 14 Å per pixel), covering the 5,600–11,000 Å region, reveals the

8 日 UT 21 h 12 min，我们使用 WHT 上相同的仪器得到第二幅 I 波段图像（曝光时间 900 s），3 月 8 日 UT 20 h 42 min 使用拉帕尔马的艾萨克·牛顿望远镜（INT）得到第二幅 V 波段图像（曝光时间 2,500 s）。测光定标通过 336 号标准恒星和朗多[22] 场星 104 的图像完成。图像通过标准偏差扣除与平场处理得到还原。

　　紧接着对两组图的比较显示出一个亮度大幅变化的源[6]：它在 2 月 28 日拍的 V 波段和 I 波段图像上都清楚地出现，但是在 3 月 8 日拍的第二对图像中（图 2）没有被探测到。通过比较数字化巡天得到的附近恒星的位置，我们得到其坐标为 RA 05 h 01 min 46.66 s，dec.+11° 46′ 53.9″（春分点 J2000）；这个位置估计（固有）精度为 0.2″。这个天体位于由 WFC 的位置、Ulysses/BeppoSAX/Wind 环和 X 射线暂现源位置决定的误差框区域内（图 1）。

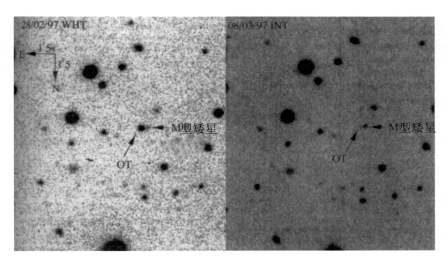

图 2. 包含光学暂现源位置 1.5′×1.5′ 天区的 V 波段图。左边图像是用 WHT 在 1997 年 2 月 28 日 UT 23 h 48 min 观测的，右边图像是用 INT 于 3 月 8 日 UT 20 h 42 min 观测的。光学暂现源用"OT"标示。距离光学暂现源 2.9″ 处的 M 型矮星也被标示出。

　　使用孔径测光软件我们得到变源的星等为[6]：2 月 28 日 $V = 21.3 \pm 0.1$，$I = 20.6 \pm 0.1$ 和 3 月 8 日 $V > 23.6$，$I > 22.2$。这个源在 2 月 28 日 V 波段和 I 波段的图像上的形状都和从相同图像上 15 颗恒星得到的点扩散函数一致。

　　靠近光学暂现源的是一颗恒星，位于 2.85″ 的距离，坐标为 RA 05 h 01 min 46.47 s，dec.+11° 46′ 54.0″，$V = 23.1$，$I = 20.5$。3 月 1 日 UT 0 h 利用 ESO（欧南台）3.6 m 望远镜获得了该恒星的一个光谱，其中利用了 EFOSC1 光谱仪和 R1000 光栅（分辨率为每像素 14 Å），覆盖了 5,600～11,000 Å 波段。光谱显示 TiO 带的存在，这表明它

presence of TiO bands, which indicate it is an M-type star. With foreground absorption $A_v = 0.4 \pm 0.3$ mag (ref. 23), (substantially smaller than the value inferred from the low-energy cut off in the LECS spectrum), its colour index, $V-I = 2.6$, corresponds to an M2 star[24]. It is most likely to be an M dwarf at a distance of ~3 kpc (an early M-type giant would be located at a distance of ~0.4 Mpc, which we consider much less likely).

Further images were obtained with the Nordic Optical Telescope (NOT, La Palma) on 4 March, with the INT on 9 March, and with the ESO New Technology Telescope (NTT) on 13 March (see Table 1 for a summary). The transient was not detected in these images, which puts a lower limit on its average decay rate (in 4 days) of 0.7 mag per day. The NTT image shows that at the location of the variable object there is an extended object, probably a galaxy[7,8] (Fig. 3); this object is also seen in the INT B- and R-band images. From differential astrometry relative to the nearby M star for both the V- and I-band images, we find that the centres of the optical transient and the galaxy have a relative distance $(0.22 \pm 0.12)''$ (1σ; quadratic addition of the errors in the two relative positions). The relative position of the optical transient did not change by more than $0.2''$ between the 28 February V- and I-band images. From the NTT image and the 9 March INT image we measured[7] the galaxy's magnitude to be $R = 23.8 \pm 0.2$ and 24.0 ± 0.2, respectively, consistent with the value $R = 24.0$ reported by Metzger et al.[8], and $B = 25.4 \pm 0.4$ (Table 1).

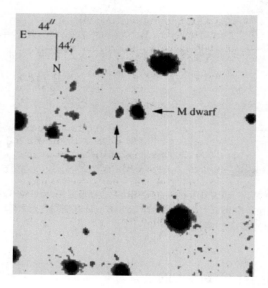

Fig. 3. R-band image of a $44'' \times 44''$ region of the sky containing the position of the optical transient, obtained with the NTT on 1997 13 March UT 0 h. The faint galaxy coincident with the optical transient (A) and the M-dwarf are indicated.

是一颗 M 型恒星。考虑前景吸收 $A_v = 0.4 \pm 0.3$ mag(参考文献 23,实质上的比 LECS 光谱低能截断得到的值小得多),它的色指数为 $V-I = 2.6$,对应于 M2 型恒星 [24]。这颗恒星很可能是颗距离为 ~3 kpc 的 M 型矮星(早期 M 型巨星位于距离 ~0.4 Mpc 处,我们认为这种可能性小很多)。

更多的图像于 3 月 4 日利用北欧光学望远镜(NOT,拉帕尔马),3 月 9 日利用 INT 以及 3 月 13 日利用 ESO 的新技术望远镜(NTT)得到(总结见表 1)。暂现源在这些图像中没有被探测到,从而得到其平均衰减率(4 天内)的下限为每天 0.7 mag。NTT 的图像显示在变源位置处存在一个延展天体,可能是一个星系 [7,8](图 3);这个天体也在 INT 的 B 波段和 R 波段图像上呈现。通过在 V 波段和 I 波段的图像上相对邻近的 M 型恒星的较差天体测量,我们发现光学暂现源的中心和星系的中心相对距离为 $(0.22 \pm 0.12)''$(1σ;两个相对位置误差的平方和)。光学暂现源在 2 月 28 日的 V 波段和 I 波段图像上的相对位置变化不超过 0.2″。从 NTT 的图像和 3 月 9 日 INT 的图像我们测量出 [7] 星系的星等分别为 $R = 23.8 \pm 0.2$ 和 24.0 ± 0.2,和梅茨格等人 [8] 报道的 $R = 24.0$ 和 $B = 25.4 \pm 0.4$ 一致(表 1)。

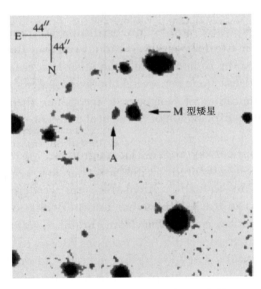

图 3. 1997 年 3 月 13 日 UT 0 h 利用 NTT 观测到的包含光学暂现源位置 44″×44″ 天区的 R 波段图。与光学暂现源重合的暗星系(A)和 M 型矮星都已被标出。

Table1. Summary of optical observations

Date (1997)	Time (UT)	Telescope	Band	Integration time (s)	Magnitude	Remarks
28 Feb.	23 h 48 min	WHT	V	300	$V = 21.3$	Transient
28 Feb.	23 h 53 min	WHT	I	300	$I = 20.6$	Transient
04 Mar.	20 h 42 min	NOT	V	900	$V > 24.2$	–
08 Mar.	20 h 42 min	INT	V	2,500	$V > 23.6$	–
08 Mar.	21 h 12 min	WHT	I	300	$V > 22.2$	–
09 Mar.	21 h 30 min	INT	R	1,200	$R = 24.0$	Extended
09 Mar.	20 h 30 min	INT	B	2,500	$B = 25.4$	Extended
13 Mar.	0 h 0 min	NTT	R	3,600	$R = 23.8$	Extended

Known types of optical transient events (novae, supernovae, dwarf novae, flare stars) are unlikely to account for the optical transient for a variety of reasons, such as the amplitude and short timescale of its variability, its colour index, or its inferred distance.

The GRB source is located relatively close to the ecliptic, at latitude −11°, and this raises the possibility that the optical transient is an asteroid. However, on 1 March asteroids in the direction of the GRB have proper motions of at least 0.1° per day (T. Gehrels, personal communication), which would have led to easily detectable motion ($> 2.5''$) during the 600-s total exposure time of our two separate images. On the basis of its proper motion during our two exposures we cannot rule out that the optical transient is a Kuiper belt object. However, its non-detection on other images taken in the week following the GRB, the low surface density (one per several hundred square degrees at 21st magnitude; T. Gehrels, personal communication) of Kuiper belt objects, and their very red colours[25], make such objects a highly unlikely explanation of the optical transient.

The variability of the optical sky above 21st magnitude, on timescales of a few days, has not yet been extensively explored[26,27], and it is therefore not possible to make a firm estimate of the probability that the optical transient we detected is a faint, strongly variable AGN unrelated to the GRB, or has another (unknown) origin unrelated to the GRB. Some information is available from the faint-galaxy monitoring program of Kochanski et al.[28] which covered 2,830 galaxies (down to $B = 24.8$, $R = 23.3$) in a $16' \times 16'$ field during 10 years. They found that near $B = 24$ only ~0.5% of these varied by more than 0.03 mag on a timescale of months to years; none varied by more than a magnitude. Variability of blazars on timescales of minutes to hours does not exceed 0.3 mag; day-to-day variations of a factor of two or more have been observed[50].

Although we cannot firmly exclude that the optical transient in the error box of GRB970228 is caused by some unknown event unrelated to the GRB, the temporal coincidence between the optical and X-ray transients, and their spatial coincidence with the GRB lead us to believe that both the optical transient and the decaying BeppoSAX X-ray source are associated with GRB970228.

表 1. 光学观测总结

日期 (1997)	时间 (UT)	望远镜	波段	积分时间 (s)	星等	标注
2 月 28 日	23 h 48 min	WHT	V	300	$V = 21.3$	暂现源
2 月 28 日	23 h 53 min	WHT	I	300	$I = 20.6$	暂现源
3 月 4 日	20 h 42 min	NOT	V	900	$V > 24.2$	–
3 月 8 日	20 h 42 min	INT	V	2,500	$V > 23.6$	–
3 月 8 日	21 h 12 min	WHT	I	300	$V > 22.2$	–
3 月 9 日	21 h 30 min	INT	R	1,200	$R = 24.0$	延展
3 月 9 日	20 h 30 min	INT	B	2,500	$B = 25.4$	延展
3 月 13 日	0 h 0 min	NTT	R	3,600	$R = 23.8$	延展

　　光学暂现源的已知类型（新星、超新星、矮新星、耀星）因为各种原因，例如光变的幅度和短时标，色指数或者推断的距离等，都解释不了这个光学暂现源。

　　伽马射线暴源所在纬度为 $-11°$，相对接近于黄道，这提出了光学暂现源是小行星的可能性。不过，3 月 1 日在该星方向的小行星的自行至少为每天 0.1°（赫雷尔斯，个人交流），在我们两幅独立的、总曝光时间为 600 s 的图像上应该很容易探测到其运动（$> 2.5''$）。根据两次曝光测到的自行，我们不能排除这个光学暂现源为柯伊伯带天体。不过，在伽马射线暴之后的一个星期内拍摄的其他图像并没有探测到这个暂现源，以及柯伊伯带天体的低面密度（21 星等的天体每几百平方度中才有 1 个；赫雷尔斯，个人交流）和它们非常红的色指数[25]，使得光学暂现源几乎不可能是柯伊伯带天体。

　　在 21 星等之上，时标为几天的光学变源目前还没有得到广泛的研究[26,27]，因此不大可能准确估计所探测到的光学暂现源是暗的、和伽马射线暴无关的、光变幅度较大的 AGN 的可能性，或者是来自其他（未知）和伽马射线暴无关的起源的可能性。我们从科汉斯基等人[28]10 年内在 $16' \times 16'$ 的天区覆盖 2,830 个星系（最暗能探测到：$B = 24.8$，$R = 23.3$）的弱星系监测项目中得到一些信息。他们发现在 $B = 24$ 附近只有 ~0.5% 的星系在几个月到几年时标上变化超过 0.03 mag；没有星系变化超过一个星等。耀变体在几分钟到几小时时标上的变化不会超过 0.3 mag；以天为时标，幅度达到 2 倍或更多的变化已经被观测到[50]。

　　尽管我们不能明确排除 GRB970228 误差圈内的光学暂现源是由一些和伽马射线暴无关的事件引起的可能性。但是光学暂现源和 X 射线暂现源在时间上的一致，以及它们和该暴在空间位置上的一致，让我们相信光学暂现源和衰减的 BeppoSAX X 射线源两者都与 GRB970228 成协。

Radio observations (at 6 cm wavelength) of the GRB error box[6] made with the Westerbork Radio Synthesis telescope on February 28, UT 23 h 17 min (for 1.2 h; 20.4 h after the GRB, simultaneous with the observations at the WHT), and on March 1, UT 18 h and March 2, UT 18 h (each lasting 12 hours) show that at the position of the optical transient there is then no radio point source with a flux exceeding 1.0, 0.33 and 0.33 mJy, respectively (2σ upper limit).

Some rough spectral information on the optical/X-ray transient can be obtained if we assume that between the two BeppoSAX X-ray observations, made 4 days apart, the X-ray flux of the transient decreased with time since the GRB as a power law. Approximating the spectrum by $F_v \propto v^\alpha$ we estimate from $F_X \simeq 0.04$ μJy (inter-polated) and $F_V \simeq 10$ μJy, that $\alpha = -0.7 \pm 0.1$. Extrapolation of this spectrum to the radio region would lead to an expected radio flux density of 10–100 mJy, far exceeding the observed upper limit. This indicates that the X-ray, optical and radio flux densities of the transient cannot be represented by a single power law.

The close positional coincidence between the optical transient and the galaxy suggests that the transient may be located in that galaxy. In an effort to quantify this we adopt a Bayesian approach. We consider three disjoint and exhaustive hypotheses for the source of the optical transient. The hypotheses are: H_c, the optical transient is in the centre of a galaxy; H_g, the optical transient is in a galaxy but not at its centre; and H_n, the optical transient is not in a galaxy.

We assume that there is a single optical transient detected in the field of view of angular area A and that n non-overlapping galaxies are detected in the field. The transient is at distance $r \pm \sigma_r$ from the nearest galaxy, where the error includes the uncertainty in the positions of the centroids of both the galaxy and the transient. The probability density at r under H_c is $P(r|H_c) = (2\pi\sigma_r^2 n)^{-1}\exp[-(r^2/2\sigma_r^2)]$. The probability density under H_g depends on the size, shape and inclination of the galaxy and the specifics of the model for the distribution of sources in the galaxy. For simplicity, we assume the probability density to be gaussian with width σ_g. Then $P(r|H_g) = (2\pi\sigma_g^2 n)^{-1}\exp[-(r^2/2\sigma_g^2)]$. The probability density under H_n is uniform over the field of view, so $P(r|H_n) = A^{-1}$. The posterior probability of each hypothesis H is $P(H|r) = kP(H)P(r|H)$, where $P(H)$ is the prior probability and the normalization constant k is obtained by the requirement that $P(H_c|r) + P(H_g|r) + P(H_n|r) = 1$.

For the NTT observation we find seven galaxies in $A = (44'')^2$ field, that is, $n = 13$ per arcmin^2, $r = 0.22''$, $\sigma_r = 0.12''$. A reasonable estimate for the galaxy width is $\sigma_g = 1''$. With these values the probability densities at r are $P(r|H_c) = 0.294$, $P(r|H_g) = 0.022$ and $P(r|H_n) = 0.0005$, all in units of arcsec^{-2}. Assuming equal priors $P(H_c) = P(H_g) = P(H_n) = 1/3$, the posterior probabilities are $P(H_c|r) = 0.928$, $P(H_g|r) = 0.070$ and $P(H_n|r) = 0.0016$. The posterior probability for H_g depends sensitively on the assumed σ_g. However, the posterior probability, $P(H_n|r)$, that the transient is not associated with a galaxy is in the range 0.09–0.18%, for any assumptions about the size of faint galaxies. Within the range of assumed values for σ_r between $0.08''$ and $0.2''$ the values of $P(H_n|r)$ increase by less than a factor of 3.

伽马射线暴误差圈的射电观测 [6]（在 6 cm 波长）于 2 月 28 日 UT 23 h 17 min（伽马射线暴爆发后 20.4 h，持续 1.2 h，和 WHT 观测同时进行），3 月 1 日 UT 18 h 和 3 月 2 日 UT 18 h（每次持续 12 h）利用韦斯特博克综合孔径射电望远镜完成，结果显示在光学暂现源的位置上流量分别没有超过 1.0 mJy、0.33 mJy 和 0.33 mJy 的射电点源（2σ 上限）。

如果假设在两次间隔 4 天的 BeppoSAX X 射线观测之间，暂现源的 X 射线流量在伽马射线暴后随着时间呈幂律变化，我们能得到光学/X 射线暂现源一些大体的光谱信息。通过 $F_\nu \propto \nu^\alpha$ 近似拟合光谱，我们从 $F_X \approx 0.04$ μJy（内插）和 $F_V \approx 10$ μJy 估计得到 $\alpha = -0.7 \pm 0.1$。将这个谱外推到射电波段将得到预期的射电流量密度 10~100 mJy，远高于观测上限。这表明暂现源的 X 射线、光学和射电流量密度不能用单个幂律谱来表示。

光学暂现源和星系在位置上的一致性表明暂现源可能位于那个星系中。我们采用贝叶斯方法来定量计算这一点。关于光学暂现源的来源，我们提出三个不相干但完备的假设，分别是：H_c，光学暂现源位于星系中心；H_g，光学暂现源位于星系内但是不在中心；H_n，光学暂现源不在星系内。

我们假设在角面积 A 的视场内探测到一个光学暂现源和 n 个不重叠的星系。暂现源离最近的星系的距离为 $r \pm \sigma_r$，其中误差包括了星系中心位置和暂现源中心位置的误差。在 H_c 条件下暂现源在 r 处的概率密度为 $P(r|H_c) = (2\pi\sigma_r^2 n)^{-1} \exp[-(r^2/2\sigma_r^2)]$。在 H_g 条件下的概率密度依赖于星系的大小、形状和倾角以及星系内源分布的模型。为了简化，我们假设概率密度是宽度为 σ_g 的高斯分布。因而 $P(r|H_g) = (2\pi\sigma_g^2 n)^{-1} \exp[-(r^2/2\sigma_g^2)]$。在 H_n 条件下的概率密度是在视场内均匀分布的，所以 $P(r|H_n) = A^{-1}$。每个假设 (H) 的后验概率为 $P(H|r) = kP(H)P(r|H)$，这里 $P(H)$ 是先验概率，而归一化常数 k 是从 $P(H_c|r) + P(H_g|r) + P(H_n|r) = 1$ 的条件中获得的。

从 NTT 的观测结果中，我们在 $A = (44'')^2$ 的视场内发现 7 个星系，即 $n = 13$ arcmin^{-2}，$r = 0.22''$，$\sigma_r = 0.12''$。对星系宽度的合理估计为 $\sigma_g = 1''$。使用以上数值，在 r 处的概率密度为 $P(r|H_c) = 0.294$，$P(r|H_g) = 0.022$ 和 $P(r|H_n) = 0.0005$，全部以 arcsec^{-2} 为单位。假设先验概率相等 $P(H_c) = P(H_g) = P(H_n) = 1/3$，后验概率为 $P(H_c|r) = 0.928$，$P(H_g|r) = 0.070$ 和 $P(H_n|r) = 0.0016$。H_g 的后验概率非常灵敏地依赖于假设的 σ_g 值。不过对于任何暗星系大小的假设，后验概率 $P(H_n|r)$，即暂现源不和星系成协，都是在 0.09%~0.18% 的范围内。假设 σ_r 的值在 0.08'' 到 0.2'' 范围内，$P(H_n|r)$ 的值将增加为不到原来的 3 倍。

The above analysis suggests that the optical transient is related to the faint galaxy, which provides support for the cosmological distance scale for GRBs.

A rough estimate of the expected redshift, z, of the galaxy may be made by assuming that its absolute magnitude is in the range −21 to −16, which covers the bulk of normal galaxies[29]. For an assumed Hubble constant of $60\,km\,s^{-1}\,Mpc^{-1}$, this corresponds to z in the range 0.2–2.

The close proximity of the optical transient to the centre of the faint galaxy, and the presence of relatively bright quasars in the 8 arcmin^2 error box of GRB781119 ($V = 20$)[30-32], and in the 3′ (radius) error box[33] of GRB960720 ($R = 18.8$)[34-36] raise the possibility that GRBs occur preferentially, or exclusively, in or near galactic nuclei.

Searches for an optical counterpart to a GRB have been continually attempted for the past 20 years. Recent reviews and descriptions of serendipitous, rapid follow-up, and delayed searches for optical counterparts of GRBs[36-44] show that these previous searches were generally made a week or longer after the GRB, or they were not as deep ($V < 20$) as the images presented here. The most sensitive rapid follow-up observations so far had delay times (δt) and limiting magnitudes (m) as follows: $\delta t = 1.85$ d, $m < 23$ (ref. 45), and $\delta t = 4.0$ d, $m_B < 22$ (ref. 38).

It was not until the launch of BeppoSAX in 1996 that accurate (several arcmin) locations for GRBs became available within hours of detection, hence facilitating rapid follow-up observations at large ground-based optical telescopes for those bursts which happened to be in the field of the WFC. The continued operation of BeppoSAX and the approval of the High Energy Transient Explorer-2 (HETE-2) mission bode well for great progress in the rapid follow-up observations of GRBs. Also, near-real-time, fully automated optical systems linked to the BATSE–BACODINE[37] system are becoming operational, and their sensitivity is continually improving[46,47].

We expect that X-ray and optical transients associated with GRBs will again be seen (though perhaps not in all cases[48]) in the near future. This could be a turning point in GRB astronomy. Detailed studies (light curves and spectra) of such transients can be expected within a year, and we are optimistic that the distance scale as well as the mechanism behind the enigmatic GRBs are now within reach.

Note added in proof: After this paper was submitted, an HST observation was made of the optical transient (K. Sahu *et al.*, *IAU Circ. No.* 6606). This observation confirms that the transient is associated with an extended emission region, but seems to exclude that the transient is located at the centre of that region.

(**386**, 686-689; 1997)

以上的分析表明光学暂现源和暗星系相关，支持了伽马射线暴是处在宇宙学距离尺度上的说法。

对该星系红移 z 的粗略估计可以通过假设星系的绝对星等位于 $-21 \sim -16$ 的范围来获得，这个范围覆盖了大部分正常星系[29]。假定哈勃常数为 $60 \text{ km} \cdot \text{s}^{-1} \cdot \text{Mpc}^{-1}$，得到 z 的范围为 $0.2 \sim 2$。

光学暂现源接近暗星系的中心，以及在 GRB781119 ($V = 20$)[30-32] 的 8 arcmin² 误差圈和 GRB960720 ($R = 18.8$)[34-36] 的 3′（半径）误差圈[33]内存在相对较亮的类星体，这些都提出了伽马射线暴倾向于，或者说仅发生在星系核或附近的可能性。

在过去的 20 年内，人们一直致力于寻找到伽马射线暴的光学对应体。最近的综述和叙述文章表明，无论是偶然的、快速跟踪的还是延后的对伽马射线暴光学对应体的搜寻[36-44]，之前的这些搜寻工作大部分都在伽马射线暴发生一周甚至更长时间之后进行，或者它们也没有像这里的图像这么深的曝光（$V < 20$）。目前最灵敏快速的跟踪观测得到的伽马射线暴的延后时间（δt）和极限星等（m）如下：$\delta t = 1.85$ 天，$m < 23$（参考文献 45），和 $\delta t = 4.0$ 天，$m_{\text{B}} < 22$（参考文献 38）。

直到 1996 年 BeppoSAX 的发射才使得在探测到伽马射线暴几个小时之后就获得到伽马射线暴的精确定位（几个角分）成为可能，进而促使大型地面光学望远镜对这些发生在 WFC 视场内的伽马射线暴能进行快速跟踪观测。BeppoSAX 的继续运行和已经获得批准的高能暂现源探测器 2 号（HETE-2）项目预示着伽马射线暴的快速跟踪观测将取得很大的进步。另外，与 BATSE-BACODINE 系统[37]连接的，近实时、全自动的光学系统也正变得可操作，而且它们的灵敏度也在不断地提高[46,47]。

我们预期和伽马射线暴成协的 X 射线和光学暂现源在不久的将来会再次被观测到（尽管可能不是所有暴的对应体都能被发现[48]）。这可能是伽马射线暴天文学的一个转折点。对这些暂现源详细的研究（光变曲线和光谱）可望在一年内开展，我们乐观地认为，谜一样的伽马射线暴的距离尺度及其背后机制正在被揭开。

附加说明： 在这篇文章投稿后，HST 对这个光学暂现源进行了观测（萨胡等，*IAU Circ. No.* 6606）。观测证实这个暂现源和一个延展的辐射区域成协，但是似乎排除了暂现源位于该区域中心的可能性。

（肖莉 翻译；黎卓 审稿）

J. van Paradijs[1,2], P. J. Groot[1], T. Galama[1], C. Kouveliotou[3,4], R. G. Strom[5,1], J. Telting[5,6], R. G. M. Rutten[5,6], G. J. Fishman[4], C. A. Meegan[4], M. Pettini[7], N. Tanvir[8], J. Bloom[8], H. Pedersen[9], H. U. Nørdgaard-Nielsen[10], M. Linden-Vørnle[10], J. Melnick[11], G. van der Steene[11], M. Bremer[12], R. Naber[13], J. Heise[14], J. in't Zand[14], E. Costa[15], M. Feroci[15], L. Piro[15], F. Frontera[16], G. Zavattini[16], L. Nicastro[17], E. Palazzi[17], K. Bennet[18], L. Hanlon[19] & A. Parmar[18]

[1] Astronomical Institute "Anton Pannekoek", University of Amsterdam, and Center for High Energy Astrophysics, Kruislaan 403, 1098 SJ Amsterdam, The Netherlands.

[2] Physics Department, University of Alabama in Huntsville, Huntsville, Alabama 35899, USA.

[3] Universities Space Research Association.

[4] NASA Marshall Space Flight Center, ES-84, Huntsville, Alabama 35812, USA.

[5] Netherlands Foundation for Research in Astronomy, Postbus 2, 7990 AA Dwingeloo, The Netherlands.

[6] Isaac Newton Group, Apartado de Correos 321, 38780 Santa Cruz de La Palma, Tenerife, Canary Islands.

[7] Royal Greenwich Observatory, Madingley Road, Cambridge CB3 0EZ, UK.

[8] Institute of Astronomy, Madingley Road, Cambridge CB3 0HA, UK.

[9] Copenhagen University Observatory, Juliane Maries Vej 30, 2100 Copenhagen, Denmark.

[10] Danish Space Research Institute, Juliane Maries Vej 30, 2100 Copenhagen, Denmark.

[11] European Southern Observatory, Casilla 19001, Santiago 19, Chile.

[12] Leiden Observatory, Postbus 9513, 2300 RA Leiden, The Netherlands.

[13] Kapteyn Astronomical Institute, Postbus 800, 9700 AV Groningen, The Netherlands.

[14] SRON Laboratory for Space Research, Sorbonnelaan 2, 3584 CA Utrecht, The Netherlands.

[15] Istituto di Astrofisica Spaziale CNR, Via Enrico Fermi 21/23, Frascati CP 67, Italy.

[16] Dipartimento di Fisica, Universita di Ferrara, Via Paradiso 12,44100 Ferrara, Italy.

[17] Istituto Tecnologie e Studio Radiazione Extraterrestrie CNR, Via Gobetti 101, 40129 Bologna, Italy.

[18] ESA/ESTEC, Space Science Department, Postbus 299, 2200 AG Noordwijk, The Netherlands.

[19] Physics Department, University College Dublin, Belfield, Stillorgan Road, Dublin, Ireland.

Received 25 March; accepted 29 March 1997.

References:

1. Klebesadel, R. W., Strong, I. B. & Olson, R. A. Observations of gamma-ray bursts of cosmic origin. *Astrophys. J.* **182**, L85-L88 (1973).

2. Fishman, G. J. & Meegan, C. A. Gamma-ray bursts. *Annu. Rev. Astron. Astrophys.* **33**,415-458 (1995).

3. Meegan, C. A. *et al.* Spatial distribution of gamma-ray bursts observed by BATSE. *Nature* **355**, 143-145 (1992).

4. Paczyński, B. Gamma-ray bursters at cosmological distances. *Astrophys. J.* **308**, L43-L46 (1986).

5. Podsiadlowski, Ph., Rees, M. J. & Ruderman, M. Gamma-ray bursts and the structure of the Galactic halo. *Mon. Not. R. Astron. Soc.* **273**, 755-771 (1995).

6. Groot, P. J. *et al. IAU Circ. No.* 6584 (1997).

7. Groot, P. J. *et al. IAU Circ. No.* 6588 (1997).

8. Metzger, M. R. *et al. IAU Circ. No.* 6588 (1997).

9. Costa, E. *et al. IAU Circ. No.* 6572 (1997).

10. Frontera, F. *et al.* The high-energy X-ray experiment PDS on board the SAX satellite. *Adv. Space Res.* **11**, 281-286 (1991).

11. Piro, L., Scarsi, L. & Butler, R. C. SAX: the wideband mission for X-ray Astronomy, *Proc. SPIE* **2517**, 169-181 (1995).

12. Palmer, D. *et al. IAU Circ. No.* 6577 (1997).

13. Jager, R., Heise, J., In't Zand, J. & Brinkman, A. C. Wide field cameras for SAX. *Adv. Space Res.* **13**, 315-318 (1995).

14. Hurley, K. *et al.* The Ulysses supplement to the BATSE 3B Catalog. *AIP Proc.* **384**, 422-426 (1996).

15. Cline, T. L. *et al. IAU Circ. No.* 6593 (1997).

16. Hurley, K. *et al. IAU Circ. No.* 6594 (1997).

17. Parmar, A. N. *et al.* The low-energy concentrator spectrometer on-board the SAX X-Ray astronomy satellite. *Astron. Astrophys.* (in the press).

18. Bonura, A. *et al.* Performance characteristics of the scientific model of the medium energy concentrator spectrometer on board the X-ray astronomy satellite SAX. *Proc. SPIE* **1743**, 510-522 (1992).

19. Costa, E. *et al. IAU Circ.No.* 6576 (1997).

20. Yoshida, A. *et al. IAU Circ.No.* 6593 (1997).

21. Groot, P. *et al. IAU Circ.No.* 6574 (1997).

22. Landolt, A.UBVRI photometric standard stars in the magnitude range 11.5-16.0 around the celestial equator. *Astron.J.* **104**, 340-376 (1992).

23. Hakkila, J., Myers, J.M., Stidham, B. J. & Hartmann, D. H. A computerized model of large-scale visual interstellar extinction. *Astron.J* (submitted).

24. Johnson, H.L. Astronomical measurements in the infrared. *Annu. Rev. Astron. Astrophys.* **4**, 191-206(1996).

25. Luu, J. & Jewitt, D. Color diversity among the Centaurs and Kuiper Belt Objects. *Astron. J.* **112**, 2310-2318 (1996).

26. Paczynski, B. *Variable Stars and the Astrophysical Returns of Microlensing Surveys* (ed. Ferlet, R. and Maillard, J.-P.)(Proc. 12th AIP Collop., in the press).

27. Trevese, D., Pittella, G., Kron, R. G., Koo, D. C. & Bershady, M. A survey for faint variable objects in SA 57. *Astron. J.* **98**, 108-116(1989).

28. Kochanski, G. P., Tyson, J. A. & Fischer, P. Flickering faint galaxies: few and far between. *Astron J.* (in the press).

29. Schechter, P. An analytic expression for the luminosity function for galaxies. *Astrophys. J.* **203**, 297- 306 (1976).

30. Pedersen, H. *et al.* Optical candidates for the 1978 November 19 gamma-ray burst source. *Astrophys. J.* **270**, L43-L47 (1983).

31. Pedersen, H. & Hansen, J. A quasar in the 1978 November 19 gamma-ray burst error box. *Astrophys. J.* (submitted).

32. Boer, M. *et al.* ROSAT detection and high precision localization of X-ray sources in the November 19, 1978 gamma-ray burst error box. *Astrophys. J.* (in the press).

33. In't Zand, J. *et al. IAU Circ. No.* 6969 (1997).

34. Greiner, J. & Heise, J. *IAU Circ. No.* 6570 (1997).

35. Piro, L. *et al. IAU Circ. No.* 6570 (1997).

36. Walsh, D. *et al.* Spectroscopy of 26 QSO candidates from the Jodrell Bank 966-MHz survey. *Mon. Not. R. Astron. Soc.* **211**, 105-109 (1984).

37. Barthelmy, S. *et al.* Progress with the real-time GRB coordinates distribution Network (BACODINE). *AIP Proc.* **384**, 580-584 (1996).

38. McNamara, B. *et al.* Ground-based gamma-ray burst follow-up efforts: results from the first two years of the BATSE/COMPTEL/NMSU Rapid Response Network. *Astrophys. J. Suppl. Ser.* **103**, 173-181 (1996).

39. Vrba, F., Hartmann, D. & Jennings, M. Deep optical counterpart searches of gamma-ray burst localizations. *Astrophys. J.* **446**, 115-149 (1995).

40. Vrba, F. Searches for gamma-ray burst counterparts: current status and future prospects. *AIP Proc.* **384**, 565-574 (1996).

41. Luginbuhl, C., Vrba, F., Hudec, R., Hartmann, D. & Hurley, K. Results from the USNO quiescent optical counterpart search of IPN[3] GRB and optical transient localizations. *AIP Proc.* **384**, 676-679 (1996).

42. McNamara, B. *et al.* Ground-based γ-ray burst follow-up efforts: the first three years of the BATSE/COMPTEL/NMSU γ-Ray Burst Rapid Response Network. *AIP Proc.* **384**, 680-684 (1996).

43. Castro-Tirado, A., Brandt, S., Lund, N. & Guziy, A. Optical follow-up of gamma-ray bursts observed by WATCH. *AIP Proc.* **307**, 404-407 (1994).

44. Klose, S. Search for an optical counterpart of the source of GRB911001. *Astrophys. J.* **446**, 357-360 (1995).

45. Schaefer, B. *et al.* Rapid searches for counterparts of GRB 930131. *Astrophys. J.* **422**, L71-L74 (1994).

46. Park, H. S. *et al.* Limits on Real-time Optical Emission from Gamma-Ray Bursts Measured by the GROCSE Experiment. *Astrophys. J.* (submitted).

47. Lee, B. *et al.* Results from GROCSE: a real-time search for gamma-ray burst optical counterparts. *Astrophys. J.* (submitted).

48. Castro-Tirado, A. *et al. IAU Circ. No.* 6598 (1997).

49. Frail, D. *et al. IAU Circ. No.* 6576 (1997).

50. Miller, H. R. & Noble, J. C. The microvariability of blazars and related AGN. *ASP Conf. Ser.* **110**, 17-29 (1996).

Acknowledgements. We thank T. Courvoisier, T. Gehrels, J. Hakkila, D. Hartmann, M. Kippen, S. Perlmutter, P. Sackett, T. Tyson and M. Urry for their helpful answers to our many questions. We also thank W. Lewin and M. van der Klis and the referee, F. Vrba, for their critical comments on this Letter.

Correspondence should be addressed to C.K. (e-mail: chryssa.kouveliotou@msfc.nasa.gov).

Spectral Constraints on the Redshift of the Optical Counterpart to the γ-ray Burst of 8 May 1997

M. R. Metzger *et al.*

Editor's Note

Although the first optical counterpart (an object seen at visible wavelengths) to a gamma-ray burst had been found a couple of months earlier than this work, there was still uncertainty about how far away the bursts are. Here Mark Metzger and colleagues report the spectrum of an optical object at the same position as the burst GRB 970508. There are numerous absorption lines in the spectrum, analogous to the ones seen in the spectra of distant quasars. The researchers interpret these lines as arising from gas inside the host galaxy of the burst, and assigned it a redshift of 0.835. This clearly demonstrated that such GRBs lie far beyond our galaxy.

Brief, intense bursts of γ-rays occur approximately daily from random directions in space, but their origin has remained unknown since their initial detection almost 25 years ago[1]. Arguments based on their observed isotropy and apparent brightness distribution[2] are not sufficient to constrain the location of the bursts to a local[3] or cosmological origin[4]. The recent detection of a counterpart to a γ-ray burst at other wavelengths[5,6] has therefore raised the hope that the sources of these energetic events might soon be revealed. Here we report spectroscopic observations of the possible optical counterpart[7,8] to the γ-ray burst GRB970508. The spectrum is mostly featureless, except for a few prominent absorption lines which we attribute to the presence of an absorption system along the line of sight at redshift $z = 0.835$. Coupled with the absence of Lyman-α forest features in the spectra, our results imply that the optical transient lies at $0.835 \leqslant z \leqslant 2.3$. If the optical transient is indeed the counterpart of GRB970508, our results provide the first direct limits on the distance to a γ-ray burst, confirming that at least some of these events lie at cosmological distances, and are thus highly energetic.

ON 8 May 1997 UT, a moderate-fluence classical γ-ray burst (GRB970508) was detected by instruments aboard the Italian–Dutch satellite BeppoSAX[9]; the burst was localized initially to an error region of 5-arcmin radius[10] and later to a region of 3-arcmin radius[11]. A potential optical counterpart was identified within two days[7,8], which we refer to as OT J065349+79163 (here OT stands for optical transient). Interest in this object was heightened when the appearance of a bright X-ray source was reported[12] that was not seen in a previous X-ray all-sky survey, and included OT J065349+79163 in the 45-arcsec-radius error circle. The presence of a new and bright X-ray source in a γ-ray burst (GRB) error circle has been seen in the recent three GRBs observed by BeppoSAX.

对 1997 年 5 月 8 日伽马射线暴光学
对应体红移的光谱限制

梅茨格等

编者按

尽管第一个伽马射线暴的光学对应体（在光学波段观测到的天体）在这篇文章发表几个月前就被发现了，但是这些暴离我们到底有多远仍然不确定。这里马克·梅茨格以及他的合作者报道了和伽马射线暴 GRB 970508 相同位置的光学天体的光谱。在光谱中存在着许多的吸收线，这和遥远的类星体光谱中的吸收线类似。研究者认为这些吸收线是由该暴寄主星系内的气体造成的，并且确定其红移为 0.835。这很明确地证明这样的伽马射线暴发生在我们的星系之外很远的地方。

短暂、强烈的伽马射线暴几乎每天都在太空的不同方向随机发生，但是自从 25 年前首次被发现以来，它们的起源就一直处于未知的状态[1]。以观测到的伽马射线暴各向同性和视亮度分布为基础的论证[2] 尚不足以限制这些暴的源头处于近邻区域[3] 还是处在宇宙距离上[4]。最近在其他波段探测到伽马射线暴的对应体[5,6] 唤起了可能很快揭示这些高能事件起源的希望。这里我们报道对伽马射线暴 GRB970508 可能的光学对应体[7,8] 的光谱观测。这个光谱大体上是无特征的，除了一些明显的吸收线（这些吸收线我们认为是由于在视线方向上红移 $z = 0.835$ 处存在一个吸收系统）。结合光谱上缺少莱曼 α 森林特征的事实，我们的结果表明这个光学暂现源位于红移 $0.835 \leqslant z \leqslant 2.3$ 之内。假如这个光学暂现源真是 GRB970508 的对应体，我们的结果首次直接限制了伽马射线暴的距离，并证实至少有一些爆发事件处在宇宙学距离，因而具有很高的能量。

世界时（UT）1997 年 5 月 8 日，安装在意大利-荷兰卫星 BeppoSAX[9] 上的仪器探测到一个中等能流的经典伽马射线暴（GRB970508）；这个暴开始定位于半径为 5 arcmin 的误差区域内[10]，随后定位于一个半径为 3 arcmin 的区域内[11]。在探测到这个伽马射线暴之后的 2 天内认证出一个可能的光学对应体[7,8]，记为 OT J065349+79163（这里 OT 代表光学暂现源）。当有报道发现了一个之前的 X 射线全天巡天中不存在的亮 X 射线源[12]，并且它的半径为 45 arcsec 的误差圆内包含了 OT J065349+79163 后，人们对这个光学暂现源的研究兴趣大为增大。在最近 BeppoSAX

In the first such case, a decaying optical source[5] was also seen and these authors suggested that such fading (X-ray and optical) sources are the afterglow of γ-ray bursts. It has been suggested[13] that because OT J065349+79163 exhibits unusual variability at optical and X-ray wavelengths, it represents a similar optical afterglow to GRB970508.

We obtained spectra of OT J065349+79163 with the Keck II 10-m telescope on 11 May 1997 UT, using the Low Resolution Imaging Spectrograph[14] (LRIS) with a 2,048 × 2,048 pixel CCD (charge-coupled device). Starting at 05:44 UTC, a sequence of three 10-minute spectra were obtained with a 1.0-arcsecond-wide slit oriented along the direction of the atmospheric dispersion. The spectrograph was configured with a 300 lines mm^{-1} grating blazed at 5,000 Å, covering the region 3,850–8,550 Å. We obtained two further spectra of 10 minutes each on 12 May 1997 UT. Calibration Hg–Kr–Ar and flat lamp spectra were taken at the end of each exposure sequence. Owing to the extremely low elevation angle of the telescope during the observations (~25°) and a problem with the Keck II lower shutter, approximately half of the telescope aperture was blocked during the exposures. Instrumental sensitivity was calibrated by an observation of the standard star[15] BD+284211, but owing to an approximate correction for the occulted aperture the absolute calibration is only rough.

The resulting combined spectra from 11 May is shown in Fig. 1a. It is customary to represent the spectral flux density (F_v) of a non-thermal source by a power law, $F_v \propto v^{\alpha}$; here v is the frequency. The optical index computed from the spectrum is $\alpha_0 = -0.9 \pm 0.3$. The large uncertainty is due to the uncertain correction for atmospheric extinction in the blue region of the spectrum at the large zenith angles of our observations.

Several absorption features are evident; the strongest, near 7,600 and 6,870 Å, are due to telluric O_2. In the region between 4,300 and 5,300 Å (Fig. 1b), there are several significant absorption features[16] that we identify. The identifications were made based on Mg II doublet (5,129 and 5,143 Å) line ratios, and assigning further rough identification of other metal lines based on wavelength ratios between these and the Mg doublet. Table 1 shows the lines identified in the spectrum; independent redshifts are computed from each line. This reveals a relatively strong[17] metal line absorption system at $z = 0.8349 \pm 0.0002$, and a weaker Mg II system at $z = 0.768$. The eight lines present in the strong absorption system make the redshift assignment unambiguous. The continuum source is either more distant and absorbed by a gas cloud at this redshift, or perhaps is located physically within the cloud, but the absorption places a firm lower limit to the redshift of the source, $z \geqslant 0.835$.

探测到的三例伽马射线暴（GRB）中，我们都发现伽马射线暴的误差圆内存在新的 X 射线亮源。在第一个这种事例中同时发现有衰减的光源[5]，研究作者们认为这些衰减的（X 射线和光学）源是伽马射线暴的余晖。这是因为 OT J065349+79163 在光学和 X 射线波段都存在不寻常的变化，它的表现类似 GRB970508 的光学余晖[13]。

我们于 1997 年 5 月 11 日 UT 利用 Keck II 10 m 望远镜通过装载着 $2,048 \times 2,048$ 像素 CCD（电荷耦合器件）的低分辨率成像摄谱仪[14]（LRIS）得到 OT J065349+79163 的光谱。05:44 UTC（协调世界时）开始，通过沿着大气色散方向放置 1.0 arcsec 宽的狭缝获得了 3 次曝光 10 分钟的光谱。摄谱仪配置有每毫米 300 条狭缝的光栅，照射中心为 5,000 Å，覆盖波长范围 3,850~8,550 Å。我们于 1997 年 5 月 12 日 UT 得到另外两次曝光 10 分钟的光谱。在曝光之后对每段光谱都进行了 Hg–Kr–Ar 和平谱校准。由于观测时望远镜仰角极低（~25°）以及 Keck II 低遮光板的问题，曝光时望远镜接近一半的孔径都被遮住。仪器灵敏度是通过对标准星[15]BD+284211 的观测来校准的，但是由于对孔径遮盖只是近似修正，这里绝对校准是较为粗糙的。

5 月 11 日得到的合并后光谱在图 1a 中展示。按惯例用幂律来描述非热源的光谱流量密度（F_ν），$F_\nu \propto \nu^\alpha$；这里 ν 是频率。从光谱得到的光学指数为 $\alpha_\circ = -0.9 \pm 0.3$。比较大的不确定度主要来自在大天顶角观测时对光谱蓝端大气消光修正的误差。

从光谱中可以明显看到一些吸收特征；在 7,600 Å 和 6,870 Å 附近的最强吸收线来自地球大气的 O_2。在 4,300~5,300 Å 区域（图 1b）我们认证出好几条吸收线[16]。这些认证是根据 Mg II 双重线（5,129 Å 和 5,143 Å）的谱线比来实现的，其他金属谱线的进一步粗略认证是根据这些金属谱线和 Mg 双重线的波长比来实现的。表 1 显示了光谱中认证出的谱线；对每条谱线都独立计算出红移。结果显示在 $z = 0.8349 \pm 0.0002$ 红移处是相对较强[17]的金属谱线吸收系统，在 $z = 0.768$ 处有相对而言较弱的 Mg II 吸收系统。强吸收系统的 8 条谱线很清楚地确定出红移。连续谱发射源可能位于更远处，谱线被处于这个红移处的一团气体云吸收，或者可能发射源本身就处于气体云里，但是吸收特征能够确定这个源红移的下限，即 $z \geqslant 0.835$。

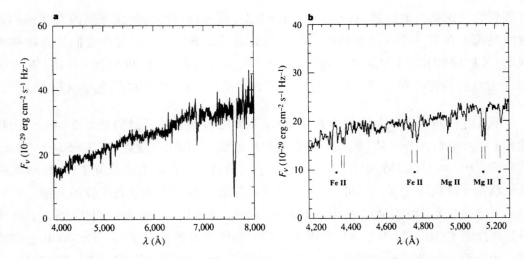

Fig. 1. The spectrum of the optical variable. **a**, Full spectrum; **b**, expansion of a limited region, with strong absorption lines and identifications indicated. The lines marked with an asterisk are identified with an absorption system at redshift $z = 0.835$, the others at $z = 0.767$. The spectrum has been smoothed with a three-pixel boxcar filter. A few additional weak features (not shown) have also been tentatively identified with the $z = 0.767$ system. F_v is the flux density, and d is the wavelength in Å.

Table 1. OT J065349+79163 absorption lines

λ_{vac} (Å)	Unc.	W_λ (Å)	Unc.	λ_{rest} (Å)	z	Assignment
4,302.5	1.8	1.3	0.3	2,344.2	0.8354 (8)	Fe II
4,359.7	1.4	1.3	0.3	2,374.5	0.8360 (6)	Fe II
4,372.2	1.5	1.4	0.3	2,382.8	0.8349 (6)	Fe II
4,746.7	1.7	1.0	0.4	2,586.7	0.8350 (7)	Fe II
4,769.7	1.3	2.3	0.2	2,600.2	0.8344 (5)	Fe II
4,941.1	1.5	1.3	0.3	2,796.4	0.7670 (5)	Mg II
4,953.9	1.5	1.0	0.4	2,803.5	0.7670 (5)	Mg II
5,130.4	1.1	2.7	0.2	2,796.4	0.8346 (4)	Mg II
5,144.0	1.1	3.0	0.2	2,803.5	0.8348 (4)	Mg II
5,232.6	1.3	1.8	0.2	2,853.0	0.8341 (5)	Mg I

Table gives measured parameters for identified absorption lines in OT J065349+79163 and the inferred redshift of each feature. λ_{vac} is the measured wavelength of each line, corrected to vacuum, and the following column is the uncertainty (in Å); W_λ is the observed (not rest frame) equivalent width of the line in Å, along with the corresponding uncertainty; the last three columns list the assigned physical absorption for each line, with rest vacuum wavelength (λ_{rest}), implied redshift, and element/ionization state.

Such absorption systems are commonly seen in the spectra of high-redshift quasi-stellar objects (QSOs)[17]. An imaging study of such systems[18] reveals that most are associated with normal galaxies close to the line of sight to the QSO. An analysis of these systems[19] at redshift similar to the system we identify in OT J065349+79163 indicates a correlation

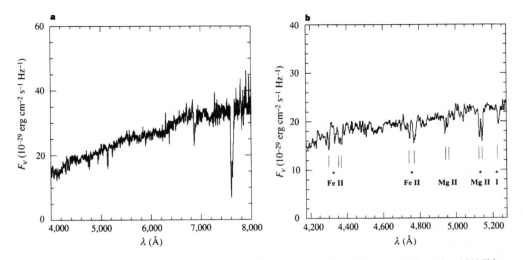

图 1. 光学变源的光谱。**a**，光谱整体；**b**，光谱一部分的放大图，强吸收线和认证被标示出。用星号标记的线被认为是红移 $z = 0.835$ 处的吸收系统，其他的则被认为是 $z = 0.767$ 处的吸收系统。光谱经过三个像素的 boxcar 滤波器的平滑处理。一些额外的弱特征（这里没有显示出）已经初步被认证为对应于 $z = 0.767$ 的系统。F_ν 是流量密度，d 是以 Å 为单位的波长。

表 1. OT J065349+79163 吸收线

λ_{vac}(Å)	误差	W_λ(Å)	误差	λ_{rest}(Å)	z	认证
4,302.5	1.8	1.3	0.3	2,344.2	0.8354 (8)	Fe II
4,359.7	1.4	1.3	0.3	2,374.5	0.8360 (6)	Fe II
4,372.2	1.5	1.4	0.3	2,382.8	0.8349 (6)	Fe II
4,746.7	1.7	1.0	0.4	2,586.7	0.8350 (7)	Fe II
4,769.7	1.3	2.3	0.2	2,600.2	0.8344 (5)	Fe II
4,941.1	1.5	1.3	0.3	2,796.4	0.7670 (5)	Mg II
4,953.9	1.5	1.0	0.4	2,803.5	0.7670 (5)	Mg II
5,130.4	1.1	2.7	0.2	2,796.4	0.8346 (4)	Mg II
5,144.0	1.1	3.0	0.2	2,803.5	0.8348 (4)	Mg II
5,232.6	1.3	1.8	0.2	2,853.0	0.8341 (5)	Mg I

表格给出 OT J065349+79163 认证出的吸收线测量参数和对每个特征推测得到的红移。λ_{vac} 是每条线在真空里的测量波长，随后一列是波长的误差，以 Å 为单位；W_λ 是谱线的等值宽度的观测值（非静止系），以 Å 为单位，而对应的误差列在后一列；最后三列列出每条线所确定的物理吸收，包括静止真空波长（λ_{rest}）、确定的红移和元素（或电离态）。

    这样的吸收系统经常出现在高红移类星体（QSOs）的光谱中[17]。对这种系统[18]的成图研究显示大部分吸收系统和 QSO 视线方向附近的正常星系成协。对类似 OT J065349+79163 红移处这些系统[19]的分析显示谱线等值宽度和碰撞参数有一定的相关性（弥散较大）。正因为看到的吸收和 QSO 系统的类似，我们预期深度曝光的

(with significant scatter) between line equivalent width and impact parameter. As the absorption we see should be similar to QSO systems, we expect that deep images (perhaps taken after the transient fades) would reveal a galaxy responsible for this absorption system, though it is difficult to predict its brightness or separation from the transient. A hint of such an object has already been suggested[20]. Note that as the OT was far brighter than any other nearby object, any contamination of the spectrum is negligible and thus the OT features were a physical absorption.

At these redshifts, the number of Mg II absorption systems with rest equivalent widths $W_\lambda > 0.3$ Å per unit redshift is of the order of unity[17]. Detection of one or two such absorption systems in our spectrum is thus not unusual. However, the ratio of line strengths (Mg I/Mg II) seems unusually high, and combined with the high strength of the Mg II absorption system provides some evidence for a dense foreground interstellar medium. This implies either a small impact parameter[19], or, more likely, that the $z = 0.835$ system is due to the GRB host galaxy itself. We can also place an approximate upper limit to the source redshift from the absence of apparent Lyman-α absorption features in our spectra. The short-wavelength limit of our data corresponds to $z_{Ly\alpha} \approx 2.3$. In addition to the lack of individual lines, the mean observed continuum decrement at this redshift is[21,22] $D_A \approx 0.1$–0.2, and it increases with redshift. If present, such a continuum drop should be detected in our data for wavelength $\lambda > 4,000$ Å. We can thus place an approximate upper limit to the source redshift of $z \lesssim 2.3$.

One might ask whether from current observations we should expect to see a host galaxy for the burst, if such a galaxy were present. If we assume a minimum redshift of $z = 0.835$ in a standard Friedmann cosmology with $H_0 = 70$ km s^{-1} Mpc^{-1} and $\Omega_0 = 0.2$, the luminosity distance is 1.49×10^{28} cm. The B band would be redshifted just slightly past the Gunn i band, and for observations[13] made on 10 May UT, the observed flux in the redshifted B band is ~39 μJy. For the assumed redshift and cosmology, this implies an absolute magnitude of $M_B \approx -22.6$ mag, or a lower limit for $L_B \approx 7 L_*$, where L_* is a characteristic galaxy luminosity[33]. Thus, OT J065349+79163 is still significantly outshining any host galaxy for the most probable host luminosity range. The properties of the Mg absorption lead us to expect that once the OT has faded, the galaxy could be identified optically.

Taken together, the source's compact optical appearance, a featureless continuum, X-ray emission and high redshift suggest a possible classification (independent of a burst event) as a BL Lac object[23]. One of the known characteristics of BL Lac objects is their variability from radio to γ-ray wavelengths. We now evaluate the a posteriori probability that we might be seeing a BL Lac object by random coincidence with the γ-ray error box. The surface density of BL Lac objects with Rosat X-ray flux $f_X \lesssim 10^{-12}$ erg cm^{-2} s^{-1} is not very well known, but there are indications that this distribution is quite flat at low flux densities. A simple extrapolation for the expected number of BL Lacs with $f_X > 6 \times 10^{-13}$ erg cm^{-2} s^{-1} is[24] 0.03 per square degree. Thus the probability of finding a BL Lac object within the 3-arcmin-radius localization region is ~2×10^{-4}. The amplitude of the variability detected in the counterpart[13] over a few days is also larger than has been observed in studies of BL

图像（可能在暂现源衰退之后）将显示产生这个吸收系统的星系，尽管很难预计星系的亮度以及离开暂现源的距离。已经有人提供了存在这样一个星系的线索[20]。注意因为这个光学暂现源比附近任何天体都亮得多，任何光谱污染都可忽略，因此这个光学暂现源的光谱特征确实来自物理吸收。

在这些红移处，每单位红移静止等值宽度 $W_\lambda > 0.3$ Å 的 Mg II 吸收系统的数目是 1 的量级[17]。因此在我们的系统中探测到一个或两个这样的吸收系统是正常的。不过，谱线强度比（Mg I/Mg II）似乎过高，结合 Mg II 吸收系统的高强度特征绘出了一些存在前景稠密星际介质的证据。这表明或者碰撞参数很小[19]，或者更可能的是这个红移 0.835 的系统是来自伽马射线暴寄主星系本身。我们也从光谱缺少明显的莱曼 $-\alpha$ 吸收特征来估计源的红移上限。我们的数据在短波端的极限对应于 $z_{Ly\alpha} \approx 2.3$。除了缺少单独的谱线，这个红移处观测到的平均连续谱减幅为 $D_A \approx 0.1 \sim 0.2$，并且随着红移增大。这样的连续谱陡降如果存在，在波长 $\lambda > 4{,}000$ Å 处应该能在我们的数据中探测到。因此，我们能大概限制源的红移上限为 $z \lesssim 2.3$。

你可能会问如果存在这个伽马射线暴的寄主星系，那么我们是否能从目前的观测中观测到它。假设最小红移为 0.835，那么在 $H_0 = 70$ km $\cdot$ s^{-1} $\cdot$ Mpc^{-1} 和 $\Omega_0 = 0.2$ 的标准弗里德曼宇宙，光度距离为 1.49×10^{28} cm。B 波段将轻微红移过冈恩 i 波段，5 月 10 日 UT 在红移后的 B 波段观测[13]的流量为 ~39 mJy。在假设的红移和宇宙学模型下，得出绝对星等 $M_B \approx -22.6$ mag，或者下限 $L_B \approx 7L_*$，这里 L_* 是星系特征光度[33]。因此，在最可能的寄主星系光度范围内 OT J065349+79163 仍然比它的寄主星系都要闪耀。Mg 吸收的性质让我们预期一旦光学暂现源光度衰弱，我们就能在光学上探测到该星系。

综合考虑该源的致密光学外观、无特征的连续谱、X 射线辐射和高红移这些因素，可将其归类（与该爆发事件无关）为 BL Lac 天体[23]。目前知道的 BL Lac 天体的一个特征是它们从射电到 γ 射线波段都存在光变。我们现在估计 BL Lac 天体随机落在 γ 射线误差圆内的后验概率。虽然伦琴 X 射线流量为 $f_X \lesssim 10^{-12}$ erg $\cdot$ cm^{-2} $\cdot$ s^{-1} 的 BL Lac 天体的面密度目前不是很清楚，但是有迹象表明在低流量密度处面密度分布比较平。简单外推得到 $f_X > 6 \times 10^{-13}$ erg $\cdot$ cm^{-2} $\cdot$ s^{-1} 的 BL Lac 天体的预计个数[24]为每平方度 0.03 个。因此在半径为 3 arcmin 的范围内发现 BL Lac 天体的概率为 ~2×10^{-4}。所探测到的对应体在几天内的光变幅度[13]也比目前 BL Lac 天体光变研究中观测到

Lac object variability[25,26]. Although we cannot completely exclude the possibility that OT J065349+79163 is a chance coincidence of a BL Lac object with the GRB error circle, the probability of finding a random BL Lac object which also exhibits variability that is temporally correlated with a γ-ray burst is quite small. Thus we conclude that the OT is probably associated with GRB970508, regardless of classification, though the strongest constraints naturally come from higher-energy emission.

The high redshift of OT J065349+79163, its featureless spectrum and slowly decaying optical flux are consistent with the so-called fireball models for cosmological bursts[27-29], which are efficient at emitting γ-rays and produce power-law spectral energy distributions. The fluence[30] of GRB970508 in the energy range 20–1,000 keV was 3×10^{-6} erg cm^{-2}, and at the minimum redshift implied for OT J065349+79163, this burst would have a total γ-ray energy of 7×10^{51} erg (assuming isotropic emission). This falls in the general range of typical γ-ray burst energies from various cosmological models[31,32].

The remarkable progress in detecting X-ray and optical counterparts to GRBs has been made possible only by rapid localization of the burst by BeppoSAX and prompt dissemination of the coordinates by the BeppoSAX team. Further progress in understanding GRBs requires many more optical counterparts to be identified. It is clear from experience of the first two optical counterparts that, in order to obtain the critical data, the counterparts must be discovered and followed up spectroscopically within a few days. It now seems that an understanding of the physical mechanisms behind γ-ray bursts is within reach.

(387, 878-880; 1997)

M. R. Metzger[*], S. G. Djorgovski[*], S. R. Kulkarni[*], C. C. Steidel[*], K. L. Adelberger[*], D. A. Frail[†], E. Costa[‡] & F. Frontera[§]

[*] Palomar Observatory, 105-24, California Institute of Technology, Pasadena, California 91125, USA
[†] National Radio Astronomy Observatory, Socorro, New Mexico 87801, USA
[‡] Istituto di Astrofisica Spaziale CNR, 00044 Frascati, Italy
[§] Dipartimento di Fisica, Universita' di Ferrara and Istituto TESRE-CNR, 40129 Bologna, Italy

Received 21 May; accepted 3 June 1997.

References:

1. Klebesadel, R. W., Strong, I. B. & Olsen, R. A. Observations of gamma-ray bursts of cosmic origin. *Astrophys. J.* **182**, L85-L88 (1973).

2. Meegan, C. A. *et al.* Spatial distribution of gamma-ray bursts observed by BATSE. *Nature* **355**, 143- 145 (1992).

3. Lamb, D. Q. The distance scale to gamma-ray bursts. *Publ. Astron. Soc. Pacif.* **107**, 1152-1166 (1995).

4. Paczyński, B. How far away are gamma-ray bursters? *Publ. Astron. Soc. Pacif.* **107**,1167-1175 (1995).

5. van Paradijs, J. *et al.* Transient optical emission from the error box of the γ-ray burst of 28 February 1997. *Nature* **386**, 686-689 (1997).

6. Costa E. *et al. IAU Circ.* No. 6576 (1997).

7. Bond, H.E. *IAU Circ.* No. 6654 (1997).

8. Djorgovski, S. *et al. IAU Circ.* No. 6655 (1997).

9. Boella, G. *et al.* BeppoSAX, the wide band mission for X-ray astronomy. *Astron. Astrophys. Suppl.* **122**, 299 (1997).

10. Costa, E. *et al. IAU Circ.* No. 6649 (1997).

11. Heise, J. *et al. IAU Circ.* No. 6654 (1997).

12. Piro, L. *et al. IAU Circ.* No. 6656 (1997).

13. Djorgovski, S. G. *et al.* The optical counterpart to the γ-ray burst GRB970508. *Nature* **387**, 876-878 (1997).

的 [25,26] 大。尽管我们不能完全排除 OT J065349+79163 是偶然落入 GRB 误差圆的 BL Lac 天体的可能性，但是发现随机的一个 BL Lac 天体显示的光变在时间上与一个伽马射线暴相关的概率非常小。因此我们得出结论，不论是什么类别，这个光源暂现源可能和 GRB970508 有关，尽管最强的限制理应来自于更高能的辐射。

OT J065349+79163 的高红移、无特征的光谱和缓慢衰减的光学流量都与宇宙学伽马射线暴的所谓火球模型 [27-29] 一致。火球模型能有效产生 γ 射线并产生幂律的能谱。GRB970508 在 20~1,000 keV 能量段的能量 [30] 为 3×10^{-6} erg·cm^{-2}，在 OT J065349+79163 可能的最小红移值处，这个暴产生的总 γ 射线能量为 7×10^{51} erg（假设各向同性辐射）。这个能量处于各种宇宙学模型下典型伽马射线暴的一般能量范围内 [31,32]。

伽马射线暴的 X 射线和光学对应体探测的显著进展是通过 BeppoSAX 快速定位伽马射线暴的位置和 BeppoSAX 团队即时发布坐标信息才变得可能。进一步理解伽马射线暴的性质需要发现更多的光学对应体。从最早的两例光学对应体的发现经验可知，为了得到关键的数据，必须在伽马射线暴发生的几天内利用光谱发现并跟踪对应体。目前看来，对伽马射线暴背后的物理机制的理解正逐步成为可能。

（肖莉 翻译；黎卓 审稿）

14. Oke, J. B. *et al.* The Keck low-resolution imaging spectrometer. *Publ. Astron. Soc. Pacif.* **107**, 375-385 (1995).

15. Massey, P., Strobel, K., Barnes, J. V. & Anderson, E. Spectrophotometric standards. *Astrophys. J.* **328**, 315-333 (1988).

16. Metzger, M. R. *et al. IAU Circ.* No. 6655 (1997).

17. Steidel, C. C. & Sargent, W. L. W. Mg II absorption in the spectra of 103 QSOs: implications for the evolution of gas in high-redshift galaxies. *Astrophys. J. Suppl. Ser.* **80**, 1-108 (1992).

18. Steidel, C. C., Dickinson, M. & Persson, S. E. Field galaxy evolution since z approximately 1 from a sample of QSO absorption-selected galaxies. *Astrophys. J.* **437**, L75-L78 (1994).

19. Steidel, C. C. in *QSO Absorption Lines* (ed. Meylan, G.) 139-152 (Springer, Berlin, 1995).

20. Djorgovski, S. *et al. IAU Circ.* No. 6660 (1997).

21. Oke, J. B. & Korycansky, D. G. Absolute spectrophotometry of very large redshift quasars. *Astrophys. J.* **255**, 11-19 (1982).

22. Zuo, L. & Lu, L. Measurements of D_A for a large QSO sample and determination of evolution of Lyman-alpha clouds. *Astrophys. J.* **418**, 601-616 (1993).

23. Stocke, J. T. *et al.* The Einstein Observatory extended medium-sensitivity survey. II – The optical identifications. *Astrophys. J. Suppl. Ser.* **76**, 813-874 (1991).

24. Nass, P. *et al.* BL Lacertae objects in the ROSAT All-Sky Survey: new objects and comparison of different search techniques. *Astron. Astrophys.* **309**, 419-430 (1996).

25. Miller, H. R. & Noble, J. C. The microvariability of blazars and related AGN. 17-29 (ASP Conf. Ser. 110, Astron. Soc. Pacif., 1996).

26. Heidt, J. & Wagner, S. J. Statistics of optical intraday variability in a complete sample of radio-selected BL Lacertae objects. *Astron. Astrophys.* **305**, 42-52 (1995).

27. Nészáros, P. & Rees, M. J. Gamma-ray bursts; multiwaveband spectral predictions for blast wave models. *Astrophys. J.* **418**, L59-L62 (1993).

28. Paczyński, B. & Rhoads, J. E. Radio transients from gamma-ray bursters. *Astrophys. J.* **418**, L5-L8 (1993).

29. Waxman, E. Gamma-ray burst after-glow: confirming the cosmological fireball model. *Astrophys. J.* (submitted).

30. Kouveliotou, C. *et al. IAU Circ.* No. 6660 (1997).

31. Fenimore, E. E. *et al.* The intrinsic luminosity of gamma-ray bursts and their host galaxies. *Nature* **366**, 40-42 (1993).

32. Fenimore, E. E. & Bloom, J. S. Determination of distance from time dilation of cosmological gamma-ray bursts. *Astrophys. J.* **453**, 25-36 (1995).

33. Schachter, P. An analytic expression for the luminosity function of galaxies. *Astrophys. J.* **203**, 297-306 (1976).

Acknowledgements. We thank the BeppoSAX team for their efforts in disseminating information to observers for rapid identification of an optical transient, making this work possible. We thank W. Sargent and M. Pahre for discussions, and the Keck Observatory staff for assistance at the telescope. This work is based on observations obtained at the W. M. Keck Observatory, which is jointly operated by the California Institute of Technology and the University of California. M.R.M. was supported by Caltech; S.R.K. was supported by NASA and NSF; S.G.D. was supported by NSF and the Bressler Foundation; C.C.S. was supported by NSF and the Sloan Foundation.

Correspondence should be addressed to M.R.M. (e-mail: mrm@astro.caltech.edu).

Size and Morphology of the Chicxulub Impact Crater

J. Morgan *et al.*

Editor's Note

It is widely believed that the end of the Cretaceous period 65 million years ago was marked by the impact on Earth of a large asteroid, perhaps triggering environmental changes that hastened the extinction of the dinosaurs. A large impact crater partly offshore the coast of Mexico at Chicxulub is of the right age and size to match this suspected impact. Here a team of geologists map out the size and shape of the Chicxulub crater, constraining its dimensions more accurately than before and thereby permitting improved estimates of the energy release in the impact.

The Chicxulub impact in Mexico has been linked to the mass extinction of species at the end of the Cretaceous period. From seismic data collected across the offshore portion of the impact crater, the diameter of the transient cavity is determined to be about 100 km. This parameter is critical for constraining impact-related effects on the Cretaceous environment, with previous estimates of the cavity diameter spanning an order of magnitude in impact energy. The offshore seismic data indicate that the Chicxulub crater has a multi-ring basin morphology, similar to large impact structures observed on other planets, such as Venus.

ON the basis of an anomalous clay layer observed at the Cretaceous/Tertiary (K/T) boundary, Alvarez *et al.*[1] proposed that there had been a large impact at the end of the Cretaceous period (65 Myr ago). The Chicxulub crater in Mexico[2-7], which is the largest known Phanerozoic impact structure, is now widely accepted as the site of this event. The crater is located partly offshore; onshore its main surface expression (Fig. 1) is a roughly 165 km diameter semicircular ring of cenotes[8] (sink-holes in the carbonate platform). The crater is covered by post-impact Tertiary sediments that thicken from a few hundred metres outside the cenote ring to more than a kilometre in the interior of the basin. The crater has a clear gravitational (Fig. 1) and magnetic signature[9-12].

The formation of simple bowl-shaped impact craters of less than a few kilometres in diameter is well understood from field observations, simulations of impacts in laboratory experiments, and theoretical calculations[13]. As craters increase in size, they undergo gravity-driven modification where the floor of the initial transient cavity rebounds upwards, and the crater margins collapse inwards, to form broad, shallow, complex craters. The smallest complex craters have central peaks. As crater size increases further, this central peak is replaced by a peak ring, typically an irregular ring of hills and massifs, that lacks

希克苏鲁伯撞击坑的大小和形态

摩根等

编者按

人们普遍认为，6,500 万年前的白垩纪晚期，一颗大的小行星撞击地球可能引起了环境的巨变，并加速恐龙的灭绝。在墨西哥近海岸希克苏鲁伯地区存在一个巨型撞击坑，表征了可能存在的撞击发生时间和规模。在这里，一支由地质学家组成的团队绘制出了希克苏鲁伯撞击坑的大小和形态，较之前对撞击坑大小的限定更为准确，从而更好地估算出这次撞击释放的能量。

人们已将墨西哥的希克苏鲁伯撞击坑与白垩纪末期的物种大规模灭绝相联系。根据撞击坑近海部分收集的地震数据，确定瞬态空腔的直径约 100 km。该参数对于限定对白垩纪环境产生的与撞击相关的影响至关重要，而以往对空腔直径的估计使撞击能量跨了一个数量级。近海地震数据表明，希克苏鲁伯撞击坑具有多环盆地形态，和其他行星如金星上观测到的大撞击坑结构类似。

基于在白垩纪／第三纪（K／T）地层边界观测到的异常黏土层，阿尔瓦雷斯等人 [1] 提出，白垩纪末期（6,500 万年前）有一次大的撞击。墨西哥希克苏鲁伯撞击坑 [2-7]——目前已知的最大显生宙撞击结构——已被广泛接受为该事件的发生地。该撞击坑部分位于海上；其岸上部分的主要地表特征（图 1）表现为由直径约 165 km 的洞状陷穴（碳酸盐岩地台上的灰岩坑）组成的半圆环 [8]。该撞击坑被其后的第三纪沉积物覆盖，沉积厚度从洞状陷穴环外的几百米增加到盆地内的一千多米。撞击坑还有明显的重力特征（图 1）和磁场特征 [9-12]。

通过野外考察、实验室模拟撞击以及理论计算 [13]，对直径小于几千米的简单碗状撞击坑的形成已有很好的理解。随着撞击坑的增大，它们会经历重力驱动下的改变，初始瞬态空腔的底部向上回弹，撞击坑边缘向内塌陷，形成宽阔且浅的复合撞击坑。最小的复合撞击坑存在中央峰。随着撞击坑规模的扩大，中央峰被峰环代替，通常表现为山脉和丘陵构成的不规则环，它们没有明显的不对称边界陡坡。

prominent asymmetric bounding scarps. The largest craters, at least on the Moon and Venus, appear as multi-ring basins. These may contain a peak ring, and, by definition, contain two or more prominent rings showing inward-facing asymmetric scarps. The mechanism of ring-formation in multi-ring basins remains obscure, not least because of the lack of clear terrestrial analogues and the difficulty of making high-resolution subsurface observations on other planets.

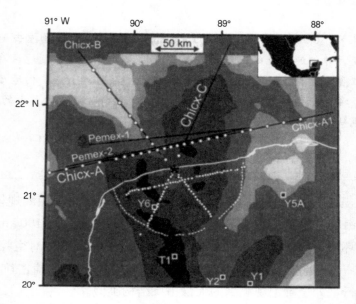

Fig. 1. The Chicxulub seismic experiment. Solid lines show offshore reflection lines, white dots show wide-angle receivers. Shading shows Bouguer gravity anomaly; the crater is marked by a ~30 mGal circular gravity low. The dashed white line marks the position of the cenote ring. Squares show well locations; Y6 is ~1.6 km deep and T1, Y1, Y2 and Y5a are 3–4 km deep. We calculated all radii using a nominal centre at 89.54° W, 21.3° N, located by an asterisk. There is ambiguity in defining an exact centre as the inner and outer gravity structures, the cenote ring and the magnetic data all have slightly different centres[8,11,12].

On Earth the transition from central-peak to peak-ring morphology occurs at a diameter of about 25 km (refs 13, 14). On Venus, which is comparable to the Earth in terms of its gravity, the transition occurs at around the same diameter, and the transition from peak-ring to multi-ring morphology occurs between about 110 and 150 km diameter[14]. We might therefore expect that craters on Earth greater than about 150 km in diameter would also have a multi-ring basin morphology[12], although it remains to be proven whether such an expectation is justified, as the transition may be rheologically rather than gravitationally controlled. There are three craters of > 150 km diameter known on Earth: Vredefort, Sudbury and Chicxulub. The morphology of the first two remains equivocal; they are both around 2 Gyr old, Vredefort is deeply eroded and Sudbury is tectonically deformed. Chicxulub therefore represents our best opportunity to understand the dynamics and structure of large terrestrial craters.

最大的撞击坑表现为多环的盆地，至少在月球和金星上是这样的。这些撞击坑可能含有一个峰环，或者根据定义，含有两个或多个突起的环，以面向内的不对称陡坡形式表现出来。多环盆地中环的形成机制仍不清楚，相当一部分原因是缺乏清晰的地内类比物以及难以在其他行星上进行高分辨率的地下观测。

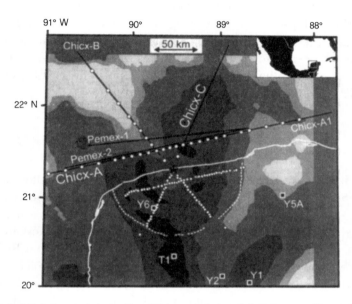

图 1. 希克苏鲁伯地震实验。实线表示近海反射测线，白点表示宽角接收器。阴影显示布格重力异常；撞击坑表现为约 30 毫伽（mGal，译者注：1 伽 =1 厘米每平方秒（cm/s²），1 伽 =1,000 毫伽）的环状重力低值。白色虚线标示了洞状陷穴环的位置。方块显示了测井的位置；Y6 深约 1.6 km，T1、Y1、Y2 和 Y5a 深约 3~4 km。我们取 89.54° W，21.3° N 位置为所谓的中心计算所有半径，该中心以星号表示。中心的精准界定有一定的不确定性，因为内外重力结构、洞状陷穴环和磁场数据都有略微不同的中心 [8,11,12]。

　　在地球上，从中央峰到峰环形态的转变发生在直径约 25 km 处（参考文献 13 和 14）。在金星上，其重力与地球相当，这一转变发生在大约相同的直径，而从峰环到多环形态的转变发生在直径约 110 km 和 150 km 之间 [14]。因此我们预期地球上直径大于 150 km 左右的撞击坑可能也有多环盆地的形态 [12]，尽管仍有待验证该预言是否合理，因为这一转变可能是受流变性影响而非受重力控制。地球上已知有三个直径大于 150 km 的撞击坑：维勒德福特、萨德伯里和希克苏鲁伯。前两个的形态仍然不清楚；它们的年龄都在 20 亿年左右，维勒德福特侵蚀严重而萨德伯里有构造变形。因此，希克苏鲁伯撞击坑提供了了解大型地球撞击坑动力学过程和结构的最好机会。

The precise size and morphology of the Chicxulub crater has been in dispute; it has been interpreted as a ~180 km peak-ring crater[2,9,11], a ~250 km peak-ring crater[5,8], and a ~300 km multi-ring basin[4,12,15]. This size difference could represent an order of magnitude difference in impact energy with quite different consequences for potential environmental perturbation. Our new seismic data image the offshore portion of the structure from the crater floor to the base of the crust. These data show why previously there has been ambiguity in determining crater dimensions. The radial extent of the inner edge of the collapsed transient cavity is confirmed to have been close to the minimum estimates previously proposed[9]. However, the outer structure seems to extend further than might be expected on the basis of this small inner cavity, because the crater, at least offshore, appears to have a multi-ring basin morphology. Elements of both end-member models[4,11] turn out to have been substantially correct.

The Seismic Reflection Data

The Chicxulub impact occurred on a carbonate platform, into shallow water, in an area otherwise tectonically and magmatically inactive. The crater floor was subsequently buried beneath about 1 km of Tertiary carbonates, and remains relatively pristine and undeformed. Its shallow burial, and location partly offshore, make Chicxulub an ideal target for seismic investigation. In October 1996 the British Institutions Reflection Profiling Syndicate (BIRPS) acquired ~650 km of marine seismic reflection profile (Fig. 1) across the crater, recorded to 18 s two-way travel-time (TWTT). The reflection data were recorded on a 6-kilometre array of towed hydrophones, and the airgun shots fired to generate these reflection data were also recorded at large offsets on land and on the sea bed, providing high-resolution velocity control throughout the crust. These seismic data, together with the existing gravity, magnetic and well data, provide the clearest image yet of the crater in three dimensions.

Here we describe the main features observed on the deep reflection profiles (Chicx-A, A1, B and C), and on two shallow industry profiles (Pemex 1 and 2) acquired by Petroleos Mexicanos in 1992 (ref. 6). Pemex 2, which is close to Chicx-A, was reprocessed as part of this project.

Target stratigraphy. The seismic reflection data image the pre-impact target stratigraphy, labelled A in Fig. 2, as a series of bright, continuous, subhorizontal layered reflectors between 0.5 and 2.5 s TWTT around the periphery of the crater. These reflectors can be traced as they deepen towards the crater centre and disappear at a diameter of about 85 km and a depth of about 3.5 s (7–9 km), B in Fig. 2. We assume that material originally inside this diameter has been excavated, and that the disappearance of this stratigraphy marks the inner edge of the collapsed transient cavity.

有关希克苏鲁伯撞击坑的准确大小和形态争论颇多；它曾被解释为一个约 180 km 的峰环撞击坑 [2,9,11]、约 250 km 的峰环撞击坑 [5,8] 或者约 300 km 的多环盆地 [4,12,15]。大小的差异可以代表撞击能量一个数量级的差别，其对环境造成的潜在影响完全不同。我们新的地震数据给出了撞击坑底到地壳底部的近海部分的成像。这些数据显示了为什么以前在确定撞击坑尺度上会含糊不清。塌陷了的瞬态空腔内边缘的径向范围被证实接近以前给出的最小估计值 [9]。然而，其外部结构似乎比基于以上较小的内腔体预测的延伸得更远，因为撞击坑，至少是近海部分，看起来有多环盆地的形态。两个端元模型 [4,11] 基本内容实质上都是正确的。

地震反射数据

希克苏鲁伯撞击发生在碳酸盐岩地台上，属于浅水，是构造和岩浆活动均不活跃的区域。撞击坑底随后被埋在 1 km 厚的第三纪碳酸盐岩之下，相对稳定、未产生变形。较浅的埋深和部分近海的位置使得希克苏鲁伯成为地震探测的理想目标。1996 年 10 月，英国反射剖面探地联盟（BIRPS）获得了约 650 km 横跨该撞击坑的海洋地震反射剖面（图 1），记录长度可达 18 s 双程走时（TWTT）。反射数据由 6 km 孔径的拖曳式检波器阵列记录，产生这些反射数据的气枪信号同时也在较远观测距离的陆地和海床上被记录下来，为整个地壳的高分辨率速度成像提供了较好的约束。这些地震数据加上已有的重力、磁场和测井数据提供了到目前为止撞击坑最清晰的三维图像。

本文将描述深反射剖面（Chicx-A、A1、B 和 C）以及墨西哥国家石油公司在 1992 年得到的两个浅层工业剖面（Pemex 1 和 2）中观测到的主要特征（文献 6）。Pemex 2 的位置接近 Chicx-A，作为这个项目的一部分，我们对 Pemex 2 进行了重新处理。

目标地层。地震反射数据反映了撞击之前的目标地层，在图 2 中标注为 A，表现为一系列明亮、连续、近水平层状反射体，它们位于撞击坑边缘，双程走时介于 0.5~2.5 s 之间。这些反射体可以被追踪，它们向撞击坑中央逐步变深，在直径约 85 km、深度约 3.5 s（7~9 km）处消失，图 2 中用 B 表示。我们假设该直径内原有物质已被清空，该地层的消失标志了塌陷的瞬态空腔的内边缘。

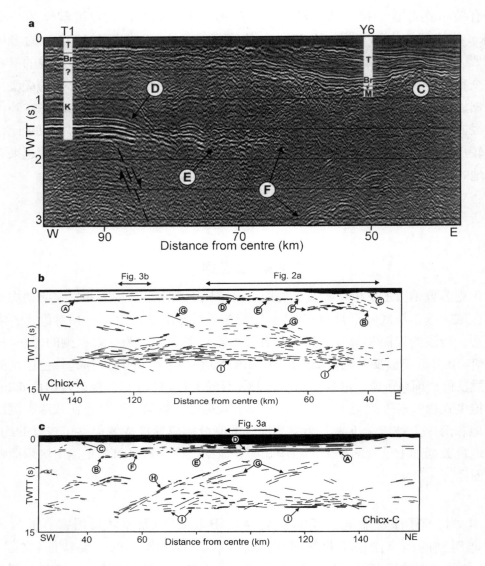

Fig. 2. Seismic reflection data along part of Chicx-A and Chicx-C; the data are unmigrated. **a**, Close-up Chicx-A. **b**, Line drawing of Chicx-A. **c**, Line drawing of Chicx-C. Highly reflective target stratigraphy, labelled (A), lies at ~1.6 s on Chicx-A, and at ~2.5 s on Chicx-C. This stratigraphy deepens by 200 ms across a monocline (D), remains subhorizontal for ~20 km (E), and then slumps (F) to between 3 and 4 s to form a series of slumped blocks before disappearing at the inner edge of the collapsed transient cavity (B). The peak ring is labelled (C), the suite of dipping reflectors (G and H), and the Moho reflector at the base of the crust (I). In **a** we have projected the stratigraphy in wells Y6 and T1 on to the seismic section at their respective radial distances; T represents Tertiary rocks, Br impact breccia, K the pre-impact Cretaceous stratigraphy, and M melt breccia[7,12].

In Fig. 2a we show the stratigraphy encountered in onshore well T1 projected onto the seismic line at its equivalent radius. No wells have yet been drilled offshore. In T1 the Tertiary sequence is ~500 m thick, and is underlain by an impact breccia interpreted as being between ~400 m (refs 7, 11) and ~1,300 m thick[12]. The range in breccia thickness

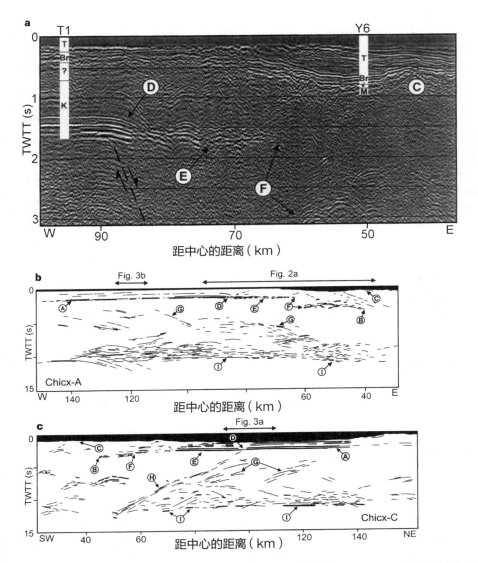

图 2. 沿 Chicx-A 和 Chicx-C 部分剖面的地震反射数据；数据未做偏移。**a**，Chicx-A 数据"特写"。**b**，Chicx-A 的"素描"图。**c**，Chicx-C"素描"图。高反射率的目标地层（标记为 A），在 Chicx-A 位于 ~1.6 s，在 Chicx-C 位于 ~2.5 s。该地层在穿过某一单斜（D）时加深了 200 ms，保持近水平状态 ~20 km（E），然后下沉（F）到 3 s 到 4 s 之间，形成一系列下陷地块后，在塌陷的瞬态空腔内边缘（B）消失。峰环标记为（C），倾斜反射体序列为（G 和 H），地壳底部的莫霍面为（I）。在 a 中我们将测井 Y6 和 T1 中的地层投影到各自径向距离的地震剖面上：T 表示第三纪岩石，Br 表示撞击角砾岩，K 表示撞击前白垩纪地层，M 表示熔融角砾岩[7,12]。

图 2a 展示了陆上测井 T1 经过的地层，我们把它投影到等半径的地震测线上。目前还没有海上的钻探测井。在 T1 中，第三纪地层大约厚 500 m，下伏一层撞击角砾岩，厚度在约 400 m（参考文献 7 和 11）到约 1,300 m 之间[12]。角砾岩厚度的范围

reflects the difficulty, when using well logs and a small number of core samples, in distinguishing between disrupted autochthonous target rock and allogenic impact breccia. On the seismic data we observe a chaotic sequence from 0.4 to 0.9 s (0.5–1.7 km). It is likely that a significant portion of this sequence is the impact breccia observed in T1. The chaotic sequence is underlain by about 0.8 s (~2 km) of weakly disturbed layered reflections originating from the Mesozoic section that is observed in nearby onshore wells T1, Y1, Y2 and Y5a (ref. 6). The bright reflective layer at ~1.6 s (~2.5 s on Chicx-C) is most probably generated by the lower Cretaceous anhydrites interbedded with carbonates that are observed in the onshore wells.

Tertiary basin and peak ring. In the central region of the crater, we observe a ~1 s deep Tertiary basin which has a radius of 68–82 km except to the northeast where the deep basin extends to radial distances of about 140 km (Fig. 2c). The region of anomalously thick Tertiary sedimentation in the northeast coincides with a region of anomalously low gravity (Fig. 1). The stratigraphy encountered in Y6 (refs 7, 12) is projected on to the seismic line in Fig. 2a. Tertiary sediments in Y6 coincide with a layered reflective sequence in the seismic data, whereas the breccias correspond to an unreflective layer. The Tertiary basin contains an outer annular trough, and a peak ring (C) with an average radius of 40 km measured to the highest peak. The peak ring is irregular, rugged, and stands a few hundred metres above the basin floor. The ring is narrow and prominent (400–600 m above crater floor) in the west and northwest (Fig. 2a and b), and broader and less prominent (200–300 m above crater floor) to the east and northeast (Fig. 2c). On several profiles, the peak ring lies directly over the inner edge of the collapsed transient cavity (Fig. 2b).

Offsets in Mesozoic strata. The pre-impact stratigraphy is most clearly imaged on lines Chicx-A and C (Fig. 2). Tracking these reflectors towards the crater centre we observe an offset (D) in the Mesozoic sequence at a radial distance of 101 km on Chicx-C and 87 km on Chicx-A. In both cases the vertical offset is 400–500 m and it is observed in the Cretaceous stratigraphy but not in the deepest Tertiary reflectors. On Chicx-A the offset occurs entirely across a monocline (Fig. 2a); on Chicx-C the offset occurs partly across a monocline and partly across a fault-bounded asymmetric graben (Fig. 3a). Inside these offsets, the stratigraphy remains subhorizontal, although internally disturbed, for at least 20 km (E). On Chicx-A the target stratigraphy is down-thrown by 4–5 km on a single fault (F) at a radial distance of 61 km to form a series of slumped blocks, whereas on Chicx-C we observe a sequence of faults with a combined throw of ~3 km. Pemex 1 shows a similar profile to Chicx-A at comparable radial distances[6], except that the inner slumping occurs over several faults as it does along Chicx-C.

反映了在使用测井曲线和少量岩芯样本来区分受到破坏的原生目标岩石和外来撞击角砾岩时遇到的困难。我们在地震数据的 0.4 s 到 0.9 s (0.5~1.7 km) 间观测到混乱层序。有可能这个层序中相当一部分就是在 T1 中观测到的撞击角砾岩。该混乱序列层下伏约 0.8 s (约 2 km) 扰动较弱的反射层，这个反射层即为附近的陆上测井 T1、Y1、Y2 和 Y5a 中观测到的中生代地层 (参考文献 6)。约 1.6 s (在 Chicx-C 大约为 2.5 s 处) 处明亮的反射层最有可能产生于陆上测井中观测到的夹杂了碳酸盐岩的下白垩统硬石膏。

第三纪盆地和峰环。在撞击坑的中心区域，我们观测到一个约 1 s 深的第三纪盆地，除了在东北方向延伸了大约 140 km 距离 (图 2c) 以外，其他方向的半径在 68~82 km 的范围内。东北部异常厚的第三纪沉积层区域和一个低重力异常区域相符 (图 1)。将 Y6 经过的地层 (参考文献 7 和 12) 投影在图 2a 中的地震测线上。Y6 中第三纪沉积层和地震数据中的层状反射序列一致，而角砾岩和无反射层一致。这个第三纪盆地有一个外围的环状槽和距最高峰平均半径 40 km 的峰环 (C)。该峰环不规则、高低不平，高于盆地底部数百米。这个环在西边和西北边 (图 2a 和 b) 窄而突出 (高出撞击坑底 400~600 m)，而在东边和东北边 (图 2c) 较宽且较不突出 (高出撞击坑底 200~300 m)。在几个剖面上，峰环都直接位于塌陷的瞬态空腔的内边缘之上 (图 2b)。

中生代地层的断错。测线 Chicx-A 和 C (图 2) 上最为清楚地显示了撞击之前的地层。向撞击坑中央追踪这些反射体，我们在 Chicx-C 剖面径向距离 101 km 和 Chicx-A 剖面径向距离 87 km 处的中生代地层中观测到一个断错 (D)。它们的垂向断错达 400~500 m，并且都在白垩纪地层而不是在最深的第三纪反射体中被观测到。Chicx-A 上的断错全部发生在一个单斜上 (图 2a)；在 Chicx-C 上，断错部分沿单斜发生，部分横跨断层界定的不对称地堑中 (图 3a)。在这些断错内部，地层尽管受到内部扰动，但仍在至少 20 km(E) 范围内保持近水平。Chicx-A 径向距离 61 km 处，目标地层受单断层错动下沉了 4~5 km(F)，形成一系列陷落地块；而在 Chicx-C 上我们观测到一组复式断错达 ~3 km 的断层。Pemex 1 在差不多的径向距离处显示了和 Chicx-A 相似的剖面[6]，除了最内的陷落位于数个断层上，就如沿着 Chicx-C 那样。

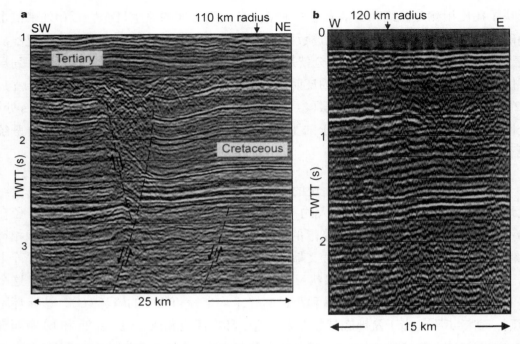

Fig. 3. Seismic sections showing deformation of the target stratigraphy. **a**, Close-up of the outer ring on Chicx-C formed by a monocline and fault-bounded graben. **b**, Close-up of the disruption in the target stratigraphy at ~120 km radius on Chicx-A.

To the northwest and east, on Chicx-B and A1, the seismic signal is strong within the region of the deep Tertiary basin, but outside this the pre-impact stratigraphy is discontinuous and not strongly reflective. We cannot use these lines to unequivocally identify offsets in the Mesozoic sequence outside the deep Tertiary basin. On Chicx-B the region of missing Cretaceous reflectivity corresponds roughly to the position and extent of the anomalous gravity high observed in the northwest sector of the crater (Fig. 1). On Chicx-A1 problems with near-surface statics appear to be responsible for the poor shallow seismic image. On this line, we do however image clearly the main normal fault (F) that bounds the slumped blocks at a radial distance of 62 km.

On Chicx-A, the shallowest pre-impact stratigraphy becomes increasingly disturbed towards the crater centre. This disturbance is a likely result of structural collapse, secondary cratering and near-surface fracturing. Such fracturing can be caused when tensile stresses produced by the rarefaction wave locally exceed overburden pressure and the tensile strength of the rocks. On Chicx-C, the uppermost Cretaceous stratigraphy seems to be absent, removed presumably during or shortly after impact by collapse into deep water to the northeast. On Chicx-A and Chicx-A1 the upper part of the Mesozoic sequence is disrupted at a radial distance of about 120 km (Fig. 3b). On both lines this disruption appears to be more easily explained by outwardly directed thrusting than by inward collapse, but its precise significance remains unclear, and it is possible that both processes were involved.

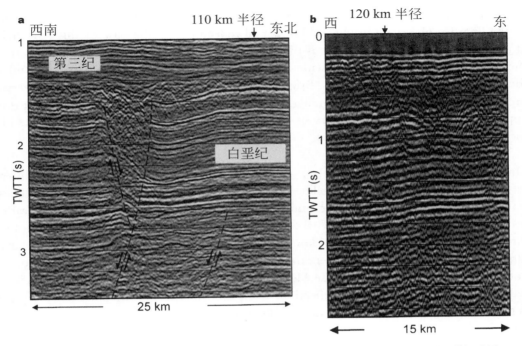

图 3. 显示出目标地层变形的地震剖面片段。**a**, 由单斜和断层界定的地堑形成的 Chicx-C 外环 "特写" 图。**b**, Chicx-A 上约 120 km 处目标地层的破坏 "特写" 图。

往西北边和东部, 在 Chicx-B 和 A1, 地震信号在深的第三纪盆地区域中较强, 但在此之外, 撞击前地层中的信号不连续且没有强反射。我们无法使用这些测线明确识别深第三纪盆地之外的中生代序列中的断错。在 Chicx-B, 缺少白垩纪反射地层的区域大致对应撞击坑西北部观测到的高重力异常值的位置和范围 (图 1)。在 Chicx-A1, 近地表静校正的问题看起来是导致浅层地震成像糟糕的原因。然而在这条测线上, 我们确实对主要正断层 (F) 进行了清晰成像, 该断层在径向距离 62 km 处界定了下陷地块。

在 Chicx-A, 越往撞击坑中央, 最浅部的撞击前地层受到的扰动越大。这个扰动可能是结构塌陷、二次成坑和近地表破裂的结果。该破裂可能是稀疏波产生的张应力超过了局部的上覆盖层压力和岩石拉伸强度造成的。在 Chicx-C, 白垩纪地层的最顶部似乎缺失, 可能是在撞击中或之后短时间塌陷到东北边的深水中去了。在 Chicx-A 和 Chicx-A1 上, 中生代序列上部在径向距离大约 120 km 处受到扰动 (图 3b)。两条测线上的扰动用朝外的逆冲比向内塌陷似乎更易解释, 但其准确含义还不清楚, 也有可能两个过程均涉及了。

Crustal reflectivity. The deep crust on all the profiles is highly reflective. Over much of the lines we observe a bright, subhorizontal reflector (I) at the base of this reflectivity at around 11 s which we interpret as the crust–mantle boundary. We see reflections from the Moho discontinuity on our wide-angle data at ~35 km depth that correspond to these normal-incidence reflections. Bright lower-crustal reflectivity is commonly observed on deep reflection lines[16], and is unlikely to be generically related to the impact. It does appear, however, that the geometry of the lower crustal reflectivity has been affected by the impact.

On all the deep reflection profiles, we observe distinctive bands of dipping, linear reflections, G and H, in the crystalline crust outside the collapsed transient cavity. These reflections dip towards the crater centre at between 30 and 40°, and extend to radial distances of 135 km. On Chicx-C the innermost reflector H in Fig. 2c, can be traced directly to the normal fault at 101 km (Fig. 3a), and, at depth, the reflections appear to offset the Moho (I) by ~1 s. Observations of linear reflectors that offset unequivocally both near-surface sediments and the Moho are extremely rare on continental deep seismic reflection profiles. The dipping reflections show no evidence that they dip less steeply at depth, nor do they intersect or detach into the collapsed transient cavity.

Transient and Excavation Cavities

The transient cavity is produced during the compressive stage of impact immediately before the gravitational collapse that leads to the formation of the final crater. The excavation cavity is formed by the boundary between material that is ejected from the crater and material that is displaced to form the transient cavity. In Fig. 4 we reconstruct the pre-impact section and the transient cavity. The asterisk marks material that lay just outside the excavated cavity, was compressed in the transient rim uplift, and, after collapse, lay on the inner edge of the collapsed transient cavity. The diameter of the transient cavity can be usefully defined in one of two ways—either by the diameter measured at the pre-impact surface, or by the rim-to-rim diameter of the transient rim uplift. The former is often referred to as the *apparent* diameter (D_{at} in Fig. 4), and the latter as the *true* diameter (D_t in Fig. 4).

On our seismic data we observe the inner edge of the collapsed transient cavity (B). To determine from this the dimensions of the uncollapsed transient cavity, we must restore this stratigraphy to its original pre-impact position and estimate the flow regime that carried this pre-impact stratigraphy outwards and upwards to form the transient rim uplift. For the purpose of estimating the dimensions of the transient and excavation cavities we have assumed a Maxwell Z-model. This is an analytical model of the excavation flow, and provides a simplified kinematic description of the cratering flow field[17]. We have used a Z value of 2.7, a value successfully applied at Ries[18] and other craters[13], and an effective depth of burst 8 km below the surface. Our calculations are not very sensitive to realistic variations in these parameters. We also assume a paraboloid

地壳反射层。所有剖面上的深地壳都表现出强烈的反射。在大部分测线上，我们在该反射层底部 11 s 附近都观测到一个近水平的反射亮层(I)，我们将其解释为壳-幔边界。在我们的宽角数据中，我们观测到来自 35 km 深的莫霍面反射，对应于正常入射的反射信号。在深反射测线上经常观测到亮的下地壳反射[16]，这一般不太可能和撞击有关。然而，看起来下地壳反射层的几何性状已经受到了撞击的影响。

在所有深反射剖面上，我们在塌陷了的瞬态空腔外的结晶地壳中都观测到了倾斜、线性反射的明显条带，G 和 H。这些反射层以 30°到 40°倾角向撞击坑中央倾斜，并且延伸到径向距离 135 km 处。在 Chicx-C，图 2c 中最内的反射体 H 可以被直接追踪到 101 km 处的正断层(图 3a)，在深部，反射层看起来将莫霍界面(I)错断了 ~1 s。在大陆深地震反射剖面中，同时将近地表沉积层和莫霍面断错的线状反射体情况极为罕见。没有证据表明倾斜的反射层在深处倾角更小，也没有证据表明它们和塌陷的瞬态空腔相交或分离。

瞬态空腔和撞蚀空腔

瞬态空腔迅速形成于撞击压缩阶段，随后重力塌陷最终导致撞击坑的形成。撞蚀空腔是在撞击坑中抛出物和发生移动形成瞬态空腔的物质之间的边界形成。在图 4 中，我们重构了撞击前的截面和瞬态空腔。星号标记了恰位于撞蚀空腔之外的物质，它们在瞬态边缘隆起部位被压缩，然后坍塌，堆积于塌陷瞬态空腔内侧边缘。瞬态空腔的直径可以由下列两种方法中的一种有效定义，撞击前地表测量的直径，或者瞬态边缘隆起的边到边直径。前者通常称为**视**直径(图 4 中的 D_{at})，而后者称为**真**直径(图 4 中的 D_t)。

在我们的地震数据中，我们观测到塌陷的瞬态空腔内边缘(B)。为了由此确定未塌陷的瞬态空腔的大小，我们必须把该地层还原到撞击之前的原初位置，并估计携带撞击前地层向外、向上形成瞬态边缘隆起的流场区域。为了估计瞬态空腔和撞蚀空腔的大小，我们假设了 Maxwell Z 模型。这是一个撞蚀流的解析模型，提供了一个简化的撞击坑流场的运动学描述[17]。我们选取 Z 值为 2.7，该 Z 值在里斯[18]和其他撞击坑[13]研究中均有成功的应用，另外还假定有效冲击深度在地下 8 km。我们的计算对这些参数实际的变化不太敏感。我们还假设了瞬态空腔具有抛物面形式。

form for the transient cavity. In Fig. 4b we show two flow lines calculated from this Z-model: the inner one defines the excavation cavity.

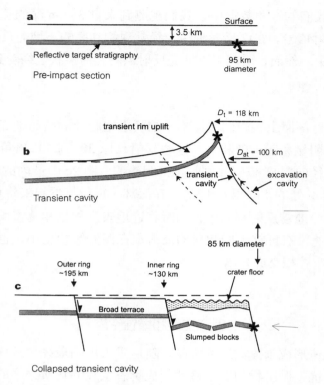

Fig. 4. Reconstruction of the rim of the transient cavity. Cartoon of **a**, the pre-impact section; **b**, the transient cavity; and **c**, the collapsed transient cavity. The pre-impact surface in **a** is shown as a horizontal dashed line in **b** and **c**. The crater floor, which is ~1 km below the pre-impact surface, is indicated by a wavy line. The short-dashed lines in **b** represent flow lines calculated using the Z-model; the inner flow line delineates the excavation cavity. The asterisk marks reflective target rock, shaded dark grey, that lay initially just outside the excavation zone, and, after the impact, lies near the inner edge of the collapsed transient cavity. The final diameters are average values obtained from Chicx-A and Chicx-C showing rings at ~130 km and ~195 km diameter at surface. Values from Chicx-B and Chicx-A1 have not been used in these averages because the outer ring is equivocal on these lines. The dashed region contains impact deposits that form the floor of the crater.

The first stage in the reconstruction is to restore the slumped blocks to their pre-impact position. We assume that the collapse of the transient cavity (from Fig. 4b to c) must occur towards and into the cavity in such a way as to reduce its volume. Restoring the slumped blocks to their original depth places the inner edge of the reflective stratigraphy at the approximate location of the excavated cavity, as measured ~3.5 km below the pre-impact surface. The second stage is to project the position of the excavated cavity to the pre-impact surface (a few hundred metres below the present-day surface), and to reconstruct the transient rim uplift using the flow model. We obtain a value for the rim-to-rim diameter of the transient rim uplift, D_t, of 118 km, and a diameter for the excavation cavity of 100 km. This diameter must be close to that of the transient cavity

在图 4b 中我们显示了用这个 Z 模型计算的两条流场线：靠内的一条是撞蚀空腔。

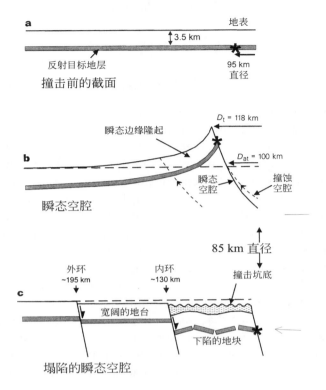

图 4. 瞬态空腔边缘的重构。a，撞击前的截面示意图；b，瞬态空腔示意图；c，塌陷的瞬态空腔示意图。a 中的撞击前地表在 b 和 c 中用水平虚线表示。撞击坑底在撞击前位于地表以下约 1 km，以波浪线表示。b 中的短虚线表示用 Z 模型计算的流线；靠内的流线描绘了撞蚀空腔。星号标记反射的目标岩层，用深灰色阴影表示，起初正好位于撞蚀区域之外，而在撞击之后位于塌陷的瞬态空腔内边缘附近。最终的直径是从 Chicx-A 和 Chicx-C 得到的值的平均，它们在地表显示为直径约 130 km 和 195 km 的环。从 Chicx-B 和 Chicx-A1 得到的值没有用于这些平均中，因为这些测线上的外环比较含糊不清。虚线区域包含了形成撞击坑底部的撞击沉积物。

　　重构的第一步是将陷落的地块恢复到撞击前的位置。我们假设瞬态空腔的塌陷（从图 4b 到 c）必须向着空腔发生，进入空腔并减小其体积。将陷落地块恢复到原初深度要把反射地层的内边缘放置在撞蚀空腔附近，正如所测量的撞击前地表下约 3.5 km 处。第二步是将撞蚀后空腔的位置投影到撞击前地表（现今地表以下几百米），并使用流体模型重构瞬态边缘隆起。我们得到瞬态边缘隆起边到边的直径 D_t 约 118 km，以及 100 km 的撞蚀空腔直径。这个直径必然接近于在地表测量的瞬态空腔直径 D_{at}。在重构过程中存在各种各样的误差来源，使得 D_{at} 的极值位于 90~105 km

measured at surface, D_{at}. There are various sources of error in this reconstruction; these allow extreme values for D_{at} to lie within the range 90–105 km, and for D_t to lie within the range 105–125 km. Note that our rim-to-rim diameter does not include any contribution from overlying ejecta.

Morphology

We recognize that any topographic highs at surface would have been subject to rapid erosion[9,12], and, because the Yucatan was immersed in a shallow sea, we would expect considerable re-distribution of the ejecta by high-energy wave action following the impact. We have therefore used major offsets in the deeper target stratigraphy to infer post-impact surface topography, accepting that this topography might have existed for only a short time. We observe a separation (E) between an inner zone of intense slumping and an outer isolated monocline (D) on Chix-A, Chicx-C and Pemex-1. This separation is much larger than the widths of individual slump terraces in central-peak and peak-ring craters[13], and is comparable to the spacing of rings in multi-ring basins. This suggests that, immediately after the impact, there were two distinct inward-facing asymmetric scarps along these profiles. We conclude therefore that Chicxulub had a multi-ring basin morphology, at least in the limited region where the seismic data and pre-existing stratigraphy are such that we would be able to identify such a structure. We have as yet no seismic reflection data around the entire southern half of the structure, and our seismic data elsewhere offshore are equivocal. It remains to be shown therefore whether these asymmetric scarps are true rings that extend around the entire crater.

Assuming that the seismic data are truly representative of the entire structure, then Chicxulub would have had at least three rings in total, a peak ring with an average diameter of 80 km, an inner ring with a diameter of about 130 km at surface, and an outer ring with a diameter of about 195 km at surface (Fig. 4c). The peak ring rose a few hundred metres above a relatively flat basin floor. Our best but poorly constrained estimates suggest that the inner ring would have had about half a kilometre of throw visible at surface above the crater floor, and the outer ring slightly less. After the impact, this structure would have appeared similar to the smaller 140-km-diameter multi-ring basin Klenova on Venus, which appears to show all the same structural elements. Klenova has a similar degree of lateral and radial variability[14] to that which we observe at Chicxulub. The apparent continuation of deep deformation to large radial distances, and disruptions in the stratigraphy at ~120 km radius on Chicx-A and Chicx-A1, hint perhaps at an additional ring outside 195 km diameter.

Implications

In principle, it is possible to calculate the energy of the impact from the size of the transient cavity. In practice, the required scaling relationships have large errors,

范围内，而 D_t 位于 105~125 km 范围内。需要注意我们的边到边直径不包括任何来自上覆抛出物的贡献。

形　态

我们意识到地表的任何隆起都已受到快速剥蚀的影响 [9,12]，并且由于尤卡坦沉入浅海，我们应该预期紧随撞击后的高能量波作用产生的抛射物分布发生了显著改变。我们因此利用了较深目标地层中的主要断错推测撞击后地表地形，并相信该地形可能只是短时间存在过。在 Chicx-A、Chicx-C 和 Pemex-1 上，我们观测到强烈陷落的内区和外部孤立的单斜（D）分隔开来（E）。该分隔比中央峰和峰环撞击坑中的单个陷落地体的宽度大很多 [13]，和多环盆地中环的间距相当。这表明紧随撞击，沿着这些剖面存在两道明显朝内的不对称陡坡。因此我们得出结论，希克苏鲁伯有一个多环盆地的形态，至少在有限区域是这样，这些区域的地震数据和之前存在的地层序列使我们可以识别出这样的结构。到目前为止在该结构的南部周围还没有地震反射数据，并且我们的其他近海地震数据不甚清楚。因此仍然需要证明这些不对称的陡坡是围绕整个撞击坑展布的真正的环。

假设地震数据对整个结构真的有代表性，那么希克苏鲁伯应该至少共有三个环，一个平均直径 80 km 的峰环，一个地表直径约 130 km 的内环和一个地表直径约 195 km 的外环（图 4c）。峰环高出相对平坦的盆地底部数百米。我们最好的但又是限定较差的估计表明，内环应该有大约半千米的落差，在撞击坑底之上的地表可见，而外环的落差稍小。撞击之后，该结构应该和金星上略小的直径为 140 km 的多环盆地克里诺娃类似，该盆地显示出完全相同的结构单元。克里诺娃有着和我们在希克苏鲁伯观测到的相似的横向和径向变化 [14]。明显的深层变形向外大范围延伸，以及在 Chicx-A 和 Chicx-A1 上约 120 km 处地层中的扰动，可能暗示在 195 km 直径外有另外一个环。

意　义

原则上有可能从瞬态空腔的尺寸计算撞击能量。而实际上，所需要的标度关系误差很大，尤其是对大的撞击更是这样。我们使用施密特–霍尔萨普尔 Pi 群标度

particularly for large impacts. We use the Schmidt–Holsapple Pi-group scaling law[19] to calculate the size of the bolide. The impact energy is about 5×10^{23} J. For an asteroid impact the required diameter is about 12 km; if the object was a comet then the required diameter lies in the range 10–14 km depending on impact velocity.

Our estimates of the size of the transient and excavated cavity place constraints on the quantities of material ejected by the impact. Using the Z-model with an effective depth of burst at 8 km, we find that the total volume of ejecta is ~80,000 km³. This is probably too high because the Z-model overestimates the depth of excavation when the depth of burst is placed below the surface[17]. The volume is likely to be closer to 50,000 km³, calculated assuming an effective depth of burst at surface. The maximum uplift of the transient crater rim was about 8 km. Scaling laws[13] place the depth of the transient cavity at between 35 and 40 km, and the maximum depth of excavation at about 12 km.

Previous calculations[20,21] of the total sulphur released into the atmosphere by the impact range from 6.5×10^{12} to 4.2×10^{15} kg. These values, which are important for modelling the environmental consequences of the impact, are poorly constrained because of uncertainties in crater size, the total volume of anhydrite in the target sequence, and the precise pressure at which sulphur is released. Using the calculations presented by Ivanov *et al.*[22] together with an apparent transient diameter of 100 km, we find that the total sulphur release was between 6×10^{13} and 1.5×10^{14} kg. These volumes are not sufficient to produce the dramatic changes in pH in surface ocean waters that were indicated by the largest previous estimates[20].

There is no general agreement on the mechanism for forming rings in multi-ring basins, and a wide variety of models have been proposed[13,23]. Prominent among these is the ring tectonic model in which material in a low-viscosity layer flows toward the crater centre as the transient cavity collapses, producing an inward drag on the base of the overlying lithosphere that creates concentric extensional faults[24]. To form a ring by this mechanism, the transient cavity must penetrate a low-viscosity channel which, on the Earth, is most likely to be formed by the lower-continental crust[25] or the asthenosphere. On our new seismic data, we observe dipping reflections on all the profiles that appear to be linear faults or shear zones in the deep crust. On Chicx-C, this dipping fault-zone is directly linked to the outer ring. We therefore have direct evidence in the subsurface for the deformation associated with the formation of a ring in a multi-ring basin. If the linear fault observed on Chicx-C continued deep into the mantle, it would reach ~70 km depth beneath the centre of the crater. If the ring tectonic model is correct, our data seem to show that the required low-viscosity zone does not correspond to either the conventionally defined asthenosphere or the lower crust.

Unlike faulting in conventional tectonics, the faults we observe at Chicxulub (G and H) would have generated their entire throw in a single period of movement lasting not more than a few minutes. Such faulting can generate large volumes of melt within the fault zone to produce extensive pseudotacholytes[26]. These are probably the reason

律[19]计算撞击体的大小。撞击能量大约是 $5×10^{23}$ 焦耳。对于小行星撞击，所需直径大约是 12 km；如果是彗星，那么所需直径界于 10~14 km 范围之间，取决于撞击速度。

我们关于瞬态空腔和撞蚀空腔大小的估计对撞击抛出物质的量给出了限定。使用有效冲击深度为 8 km 的 Z 模型，我们发现抛出物的总体积约为 80,000 km³。但考虑到冲击深度位于地表以下时，Z 模型高估了撞蚀深度[17]，因此抛出物总体积可能被高估了。若假设有效冲击深度就位于地表，则体积可能更接近 50,000 km³。瞬态撞击坑边缘的最大隆起约为 8 km。标度律[13]将瞬态空腔的深度确定为 35~40 km，将最大撞蚀深度确定在大约 12 km。

之前计算的撞击释放到大气中的总硫量值[20,21]在 $6.5×10^{12}$ kg 到 $4.2×10^{15}$ kg 之间。这些值对模拟撞击带给环境的影响至关重要，但是由于撞击坑大小、目标地层中硬石膏总体积和硫被释放的准确压力的不确定性，对这些值的限定很不好。使用伊万诺夫等人[22]的计算和 100 km 的视瞬态直径，我们发现总的硫释放量在 $6×10^{13}$ kg 到 $1.5×10^{14}$ kg 之间。这些量不足以在表层海水中产生之前最大估值[20]所暗示的剧烈的 pH 值变化。

人们对于多环盆地中成环的机制没有达成共识，并已提出过很多模型[13,23]。这些模型中较为著名的是环构造模型：随瞬态空腔的塌陷，某一低黏性层中的物质流向撞击坑中央，在上覆岩石圈底部产生一个向内的拖拽，产生同心的张性断层[24]。要以这种机制形成一个环，瞬态空腔必须穿透一个低黏度通道，在地球上该通道最可能由大陆地壳深部[25]或软流圈形成。在我们新的地震数据中，我们在所有的剖面都观测到倾斜的反射层，它们看起来是地壳深部的线状断层或剪切带。在 Chicx-C，该倾斜断层带直接和外环相连。因此我们有了近地表中的变形与多环盆地中环的形成相关的直接证据。如果在 Chicx-C 观测到的线状断层向深处延伸到地幔，它将抵达撞击坑中心以下约 70 km 的深度。如果环构造模型正确，我们的数据似乎显示，所需的低黏度带既不对应于传统意义上的软流圈也不对应于下地壳。

和传统构造学中的断层作用不同，我们在希克苏鲁伯观测到的断层(G 和 H)在持续时间不超过几分钟内就产生了整个断错。这样的断层作用可以在断层带内导致大规模熔融，产生大量假玄武玻璃[26]。这些可能是在地震数据中能看见断层的原因。

that the faults are visible on the seismic data. Rings of pseudotacholyte are observed at the Sudbury crater, where they have been interpreted as having a fault origin, and as being associated with ring formation in a multi-ring basin[27]. We suspect that the dipping reflectors that we observe in the seismic data are analogous to the rings of pseudotacholyte that exist at Sudbury.

The Chicxulub seismic survey has produced the first high-resolution whole-crustal structural image of a well-preserved large crater, together with direct evidence for a multi-ring basin on the Earth. Continued processing of the data will further refine these images, and particularly should improve the definition of shallow features at large radial distances. Analysis of the accompanying wide-angle data will provide additional lithological and structural constraints, especially in the deep crust, central uplift and peak ring.

(**390**, 472-476; 1997)

Jo Morgan[*], Mike Warner[*] and the Chicxulub Working Group, John Brittan[*], Richard Buffler[†], Antonio Camargo[‡], Gail Christeson[†], Paul Denton[§], Alan Hildebrand[‖], Richard Hobbs[¶], Hamish Macintyre[*], Graeme Mackenzie[§], Peter Maguire[§], Luis Marin[#], Yosio Nakamura[†], Mark Pilkington[‖], Virgil Sharpton[☆], Dave Snyder[¶], Gerardo Suarez[#] & Alberto Trejo[#]

[*] Department of Geology, Imperial College, London, SW7 2BP, UK
[†] University of Texas Institute for Geophysics, Austin, Texas 78759-8500, USA
[‡] Petroleos Mexicanos, Villahermosa, CP86030, Mexico
[§] University of Leicester, Leicester, LE1 7RH, UK
[‖] Geological Survey of Canada, Ottawa, K1A 0Y3, Canada
[¶] BIRPS, Bullard Laboratories, University of Cambridge, CB3 0EZ, UK
[#] Universidad Nacional Autonoma de Mexico, Mexico DF 04510, Mexico
[☆] Lunar and Planetary Institute, Houston, Texas 77058, USA

Received 18 July; accepted 14 October 1997.

References:

1. Alvarez, L. W., Alvarez, W., Azaro, F. & Michel, H. V. Extraterrestrial cause for the Cretaceous–Tertiary extinction. *Science* **208**, 1095-1108 (1980).

2. Hildebrand, A. R. *et al.* A possible Cretaceous–Tertiary boundary impact crater on the Yucatan peninsula, Mexico. *Geology* **19**, 867-871 (1991).

3. Swisher, C. C. III *et al.* Coeval ^{40}Ar/^{39}Ar ages of 65.0 million years ago from Chicxulub crater melt rock and Cretaceous–Tertiary boundary tektites. *Science* **257**, 954-958 (1992).

4. Sharpton, V. L. *et al.* Chicxulub multi-ring impact basin: Size and other characteristics derived from gravity analysis. *Science* **261**, 1564-1567 (1993).

5. Pope, K. O., Ocampo, A.C. & Duller, C. E. Surficial geology of the Chicxulub impact crater, Yucatan, Mexico. *Earth Moon Planets* **63**, 93-104 (1993).

6. Camargo-Zanoguera, A. & Suarez-Reynoso, G. Evidencia Sismica del crater impacto de Chicxulub, G. *Bol. Asoc. Mex. Geof. Expl.* **34**, 1-28 (1994).

7. Ward, W. C., Keller, G., Stinnesbeck, W. & Adatte, T. Yucatan subsurface stratigraphy: Implications and constraints for the Chicxulub impact. *Geology* **23**, 873-876 (1995).

8. Pope, K. O., Ocampo, A. C., Kinsland, G. L. & Smith, R. Surface expression of the Chicxulub crater. *Geology* **24**, 527-530 (1996).

9. Pilkington, M., Hildebrand, A. R. & Ortiz-Aleman, C. Gravity and magnetic field modelling and structure of the Chicxulub crater, Mexico. *J. Geophys. Res.* **99**, 13147-13162 (1994).

10. Espindola, J. M., Mena, M., de la Fuente, M. & Campos-Enriquez, J. O. A model of the Chicxulub impact structure (Yucatan, Mexico) based on gravity and magnetic signatures. *Phys. Earth Planet. Inter.* **92**, 271-278 (1995).

11. Hildebrand, A. R. *et al.* Size and structure of the Chicxulub crater revealed by horizontal gravity gradients. *Nature* **376**, 415-417 (1995).

12. Sharpton, V. L. *et al.* Model of the Chicxulub impact basin. *Geol. Soc. Am. Spec. Pap.* **307**, 55-74 (1996).

13. Melosh, H. J. *Impact Cratering: A Geologic Process* (Oxford Univ. Press, New York, 1989).

14. Alexopoulos, J. S. & McKinnon, W. B. Large impact craters and basins on Venus, with implications for ring mechanics on the terrestrial planets. *Geol. Soc. Am.*

萨德伯里撞击坑中观测到了假玄武玻璃环，那里被解释为断层起源，并和多环盆地中环的形成相联系[27]。我们猜测在地震数据中观测到的倾斜反射体和在萨德伯里存在的假玄武玻璃环类似。

希克苏鲁伯地震勘查获得了一个保存完好的大撞击坑的首个高分辨率地壳整体结构图像，以及地球上多环盆地的直接证据。进一步数据处理将继续精细化这些图像，特别是将会改进大径向距离浅层特征的确定。对随之而来宽角数据的分析将提供额外的对岩性和结构的限定，特别是在地壳深部、中央隆起和峰环处。

（钱磊 翻译；李娟 审稿）

Spec. Pap. **293**, 29-50 (1994).

15. Urrutia-Fucugauchi, J., Marin, L. & Trejo-Garcia, A. UNAM Scientific drilling program of the Chicxulub impact structure—Evidence for a 300-kilometre crater diameter. *Geophys. Res. Lett.* **23**, 1565-1568 (1996).

16. Warner, M. R. Basalts, water or shear zones in the lower continental crust? *Tectonophysics* **173**, 163- 174 (1990).

17. Croft, S. K. Cratering flow fields: Implications of the excavation and transient expansion stages of crater formation. *Proc. 11th Lunar Planet. Sci. Conf.* 2347-2378 (Pergamon, New York, 1980).

18. Hörz, F., Ostertag, R. & Rainey, D. A. Bunte Breccia of the Ries: Continuous deposits of large craters. *Rev. Geophys. Space Phys.* **21**, 1667-1725 (1983).

19. Holsapple, K. A. & Schmidt, R. M. On the scaling of crater dimensions 2. Impact processes. *J. Geophys. Res.* **87**, 1849-1870 (1982).

20. D'Hondt, S. *et al.* Surface-water acidification and extinction at the Cretaceous-Tertiary boundary. *Geology* **22**, 983-986 (1994).

21. Pope, K. O., Baines, K. H., Ocampo, A. C. & Ivanov, B. A. Impact winter and the Cretaceous/Tertiary extinctions: Results of a Chicxulub asteroid impact model. *Earth Planet. Sci. Lett.* **128**, 719-725 (1994).

22. Ivanov, B.A. *et al.* Degassing of sedimentary rocks due to Chicxulub impact: Hydrocode and Physical simualtions. *Geol. Soc. Am. Spec. Pap.* **307**, 125-140 (1996).

23. Schultz, P. H. & Merrill, R. B. *Multi-ring Basins* (Pergamon, New York, 1981).

24. Melosh, H. J. & McKinnon, W. B. The mechanics of ringed basin formation. *Geophys. Res. Lett.* **5**, 985-988 (1978).

25. Alexopoulos, J. S. & McKinnon, W. B. Multiringed impacts on Venus: An overview from Arecibo and Venera images, and initial Magellan data. *Icarus* **100**, 347-363 (1992).

26. Spray, J. G. Super faults. *Geology* **25**, 579-582 (1997).

27. Spray, J. G. & Thompson, L. M. Friction melt distribution in a multi-ring impact basin. *Nature* **373**, 130-132 (1996).

Acknowledgements. The reflection seismic data were acquired by BIRPS and funded by the Natural Environment Research Council and the BIRPS Industrial Associates programme. The project also received funding from the National Science Foundation, the Leverhulme Trust, the Royal Society, and the Royal Commission for the Exhibition of 1851. The data were acquired by Geco-Prakla and processed by Bedford Interactive Processing Services. We thank Petroleos Mexicanos for releasing their seismic data to us.

Correspondence should be addressed to M.W. (e-mail: m.warner@ic.ac.uk).

Experimental Quantum Teleportation

D. Bouwmeester *et al.*

Editor's Note

Exploitation of the principles of quantum physics to manipulate information in new ways is giving rise to the discipline of quantum information technology, which promises superfast quantum computers and secure quantum cryptography. One exotic possibility allowed by quantum physics is the instantaneous transfer of a quantum state over large distances: quantum teleportation. This is enabled by using the phenomenon of entanglement, in which the states of two or more quantum particles are interdependent. Here Anton Zeilinger and colleagues at the University of Innsbruck report the first experimental demonstration of quantum teleportation, in which the polarization state of one photon is transferred to another entangled photon some distance away. Realized within the laboratory here, quantum teleportation has now been achieved over more than a hundred kilometres.

Quantum teleportation—the transmission and reconstruction over arbitrary distances of the state of a quantum system—is demonstrated experimentally. During teleportation, an initial photon which carries the polarization that is to be transferred and one of a pair of entangled photons are subjected to a measurement such that the second photon of the entangled pair acquires the polarization of the initial photon. This latter photon can be arbitrarily far away from the initial one. Quantum teleportation will be a critical ingredient for quantum computation networks.

THE dream of teleportation is to be able to travel by simply reappearing at some distant location. An object to be teleported can be fully characterized by its properties, which in classical physics can be determined by measurement. To make a copy of that object at a distant location one does not need the original parts and pieces—all that is needed is to send the scanned information so that it can be used for reconstructing the object. But how precisely can this be a true copy of the original? What if these parts and pieces are electrons, atoms and molecules? What happens to their individual quantum properties, which according to the Heisenberg's uncertainty principle cannot be measured with arbitrary precision?

Bennett *et al.*[1] have suggested that it is possible to transfer the quantum state of a particle onto another particle—the process of quantum teleportation—provided one does not get any information about the state in the course of this transformation. This requirement can be fulfilled by using entanglement, the essential feature of quantum mechanics[2]. It describes correlations between quantum systems much stronger than any classical correlation could be.

量子隐形传态实验

鲍夫梅斯特等

编者按

基于量子物理的基本原理对信息以全新的方式进行操控，催生了量子信息技术，使我们有望实现超快速的量子计算和安全的量子密码。而由量子物理带来的其中一个神奇的现象是在远距离下量子态的瞬时转移：量子隐形传态。这项技术是利用纠缠态（在两个或多个粒子的纠缠态中，这些粒子的状态都是相互依赖的）的特性来实现的。在这篇文章中，来自因斯布鲁克大学的安东·蔡林格和他的同事们报道了第一个量子隐形传态的实验演示。这个实验是将一个光子的偏振态转移给远处另一个处在纠缠态的光子。自这个实验以后，如今已经可以在一百千米以上的距离实现量子隐形传态。

我们实验演示了量子隐形传态，也就是将量子系统的状态传递到任意距离之外并加以重建。本次实验过程涉及三个光子，第一个光子携带将被转移的偏振信息。第二个和第三个光子处于纠缠态，对第一个和第二个光子进行联合测量，第三个光子就可以获得第一个光子的偏振信息。第三个光子与第一个光子之间的距离可以任意远。量子隐形传态将成为量子计算网络的关键组成。

隐形传态是想通过在远处重现的方法来实现旅行的梦想。远距传送的对象可以完全由其性质来表示，在经典物理中这些性质可以由测量决定。要在一定距离之外造出对象的一个副本，我们并不需要原来的部分和零件，只要把扫描得到的信息传送过去用来重建对象就可以了。但是这样得到的原件的副本有多精确？如果那些部分和零件是电子，原子和分子呢？它们的个体量子性质会是什么情况？根据海森堡的测不准原理，这些个体量子性质是无法以任意精度测量的。

本内特等 [1] 提出，一个粒子的量子态可以被转移到另一个粒子上，前提是在转移过程中关于这个态的信息不可知，这就是量子隐形传态过程。其前提条件可以由作为量子力学本质特征的纠缠 [2] 来实现。它描述了比任何经典的相关都要强的量子系统之间的关联。

The possibility of transferring quantum information is one of the cornerstones of the emerging field of quantum communication and quantum computation[3]. Although there is fast progress in the theoretical description of quantum information processing, the difficulties in handling quantum systems have not allowed an equal advance in the experimental realization of the new proposals. Besides the promising developments of quantum cryptography[4] (the first provably secure way to send secret messages), we have only recently succeeded in demonstrating the possibility of quantum dense coding[5], a way to quantum mechanically enhance data compression. The main reason for this slow experimental progress is that, although there exist methods to produce pairs of entangled photons[6], entanglement has been demonstrated for atoms only very recently[7] and it has not been possible thus far to produce entangled states of more than two quanta.

Here we report the first experimental verification of quantum teleportation. By producing pairs of entangled photons by the process of parametric down-conversion and using two-photon interferometry for analysing entanglement, we could transfer a quantum property (in our case the polarization state) from one photon to another. The methods developed for this experiment will be of great importance both for exploring the field of quantum communication and for future experiments on the foundations of quantum mechanics.

The Problem

To make the problem of transferring quantum information clearer, suppose that Alice has some particle in a certain quantum state $|\psi\rangle$ and she wants Bob, at a distant location, to have a particle in that state. There is certainly the possibility of sending Bob the particle directly. But suppose that the communication channel between Alice and Bob is not good enough to preserve the necessary quantum coherence or suppose that this would take too much time, which could easily be the case if $|\psi\rangle$ is the state of a more complicated or massive object. Then, what strategy can Alice and Bob pursue?

As mentioned above, no measurement that Alice can perform on $|\psi\rangle$ will be sufficient for Bob to reconstruct the state because the state of a quantum system cannot be fully determined by measurements. Quantum systems are so evasive because they can be in a superposition of several states at the same time. A measurement on the quantum system will force it into only one of these states—this is often referred to as the projection postulate. We can illustrate this important quantum feature by taking a single photon, which can be horizontally or vertically polarized, indicated by the states $|\leftrightarrow\rangle$ and $|\updownarrow\rangle$. It can even be polarized in the general superposition of these two states

$$|\psi\rangle = \alpha\,|\leftrightarrow\rangle + \beta\,|\updownarrow\rangle \tag{1}$$

where α and β are two complex numbers satisfying $|\alpha|^2 + |\beta|^2 = 1$. To place this example in a more general setting we can replace the states $|\leftrightarrow\rangle$ and $|\updownarrow\rangle$ in equation (1) by $|0\rangle$ and

量子信息传送的可能性是新兴的量子通信和量子计算领域的基石之一 [3]。虽然量子信息处理的理论描述发展很快，但是由于操纵量子系统的困难性，新方案的实验演示相对滞后。除了已经演示了充满希望的量子密码 [4]（第一个被证实的保密通信方式）之外，我们还只是在前不久又成功演示了量子密集编码这种基于量子力学实现增强数据压缩的可能性 [5]。实验进展如此之慢的主要原因在于，虽然存在产生纠缠光子对的方法 [6]，但原子的纠缠到最近才被证实 [7]，并且目前为止无法产生两个量子以上的纠缠态。

本文中我们报道了量子隐形传态的首次实验证明。通过参量下转换产生纠缠光子对，并利用双光子干涉测量来分析纠缠，我们可以做到将量子特性（在我们的实验中是偏振态）从一个光子转移到另一个光子。本实验发展的方法将在量子通信领域以及未来量子力学基础检验中发挥重要作用。

问 题 阐 述

为了阐明量子信息转移的问题，我们假设艾丽斯有一个粒子处于某个量子态 $|\psi\rangle$ 并且她希望远处的鲍勃也有一个粒子处于这个态。当然，一种可能的方式是直接把自己的粒子送到鲍勃那里。但是如果艾丽斯和鲍勃之间的通信通道不够好不足以保持必要的量子相干性，或者传送过程需要的时间太长（若 $|\psi\rangle$ 是更复杂的或者更大的对象的态函数，就会很容易出现这些情况），艾丽斯和鲍勃能采取什么策略呢？

正如前面提到的一样，因为量子系统的态是不能完全由测量确定的，艾丽斯对 $|\psi\rangle$ 所能进行的测量，都不能精确到让鲍伯能够重建这个态。量子叠加性原理可以使量子系统同时处于几个态的叠加。对量子系统进行测量会迫使它处于其中的一个态，这经常被称为投影假设。我们可以通过一个光子的例子来说明这个重要的量子特征。这个光子可以处于水平偏振或者垂直偏振，分别以 $|\leftrightarrow\rangle$ 和 $|\updownarrow\rangle$ 表示。其偏振态甚至可以是这两个态的普遍叠加

$$|\psi\rangle = \alpha\,|\leftrightarrow\rangle + \beta\,|\updownarrow\rangle \tag{1}$$

其中 α 和 β 是两个复数满足 $|\alpha|^2 + |\beta|^2 = 1$。为了让这个例子更具普遍性，我们可以把

$|1\rangle$, which refer to the states of any two-state quantum system. Superpositions of $|0\rangle$ and $|1\rangle$ are called qubits to signify the new possibilities introduced by quantum physics into information science[8].

If a photon in state $|\psi\rangle$ passes through a polarizing beam splitter—a device that reflects (transmits) horizontally (vertically) polarized photons—it will be found in the reflected (transmitted) beam with probability $|\alpha|^2$ ($|\beta|^2$). Then the general state $|\psi\rangle$ has been projected either onto $|\leftrightarrow\rangle$ or onto $|\updownarrow\rangle$ by the action of the measurement. We conclude that the rules of quantum mechanics, in particular the projection postulate, make it impossible for Alice to perform a measurement on $|\psi\rangle$ by which she would obtain all the information necessary to reconstruct the state.

The Concept of Quantum Teleportation

Although the projection postulate in quantum mechanics seems to bring Alice's attempts to provide Bob with the state $|\psi\rangle$ to a halt, it was realised by Bennett *et al.*[1] that precisely this projection postulate enables teleportation of $|\psi\rangle$ from Alice to Bob. During teleportation Alice will destroy the quantum state at hand while Bob receives the quantum state, with neither Alice nor Bob obtaining information about the state $|\psi\rangle$. A key role in the teleportation scheme is played by an entangled ancillary pair of particles which will be initially shared by Alice and Bob.

Suppose particle 1 which Alice wants to teleport is in the initial state $|\psi\rangle_1 = \alpha \, |\leftrightarrow\rangle_1 + \beta \, |\updownarrow\rangle_1$ (Fig. 1a), and the entangled pair of particles 2 and 3 shared by Alice and Bob is in the state:

$$|\psi^-\rangle_{23} = \frac{1}{\sqrt{2}} \, (|\leftrightarrow\rangle_2 |\updownarrow\rangle_3 - |\updownarrow\rangle_2 |\leftrightarrow\rangle_3) \tag{2}$$

That entangled pair is a single quantum system in an equal superposition of the states $|\leftrightarrow\rangle_2 |\updownarrow\rangle_3$ and $|\updownarrow\rangle_2 |\leftrightarrow\rangle_3$. The entangled state contains no information on the individual particles; it only indicates that the two particles will be in opposite states. The important property of an entangled pair is that as soon as a measurement on one of the particles projects it, say, onto $|\leftrightarrow\rangle$ the state of the other one is determined to be $|\updownarrow\rangle$, and vice versa. How could a measurement on one of the particles instantaneously influence the state of the other particle, which can be arbitrarily far away? Einstein, among many other distinguished physicists, could simply not accept this "spooky action at a distance". But this property of entangled states has now been demonstrated by numerous experiments (for reviews, see refs 9, 10).

公式（1）中的态 $|\leftrightarrow\rangle$ 和 $|\updownarrow\rangle$ 换作 $|0\rangle$ 和 $|1\rangle$，来表示任何双态量子系统的两个态。 $|0\rangle$ 和 $|1\rangle$ 的叠加被称为量子比特，以显示量子物理为信息科学引入新的可能性[8]。

如果一个处于 $|\psi\rangle$ 态的光子通过一个偏振分束器（这种器件反射水平偏振光而透射垂直偏振光），则在反射光束中找到该光子的概率是 $|\alpha|^2$，在透射光束中找到该光子的概率是 $|\beta|^2$。测量的行为使得普通态函数 $|\psi\rangle$ 被投影到 $|\leftrightarrow\rangle$ 或者 $|\updownarrow\rangle$ 上。我们的结论是：量子力学的规则，特别是投影假设，使得艾丽斯不可能对 $|\psi\rangle$ 进行一次测量以得到所有必要的信息来重建这个态。

量子隐形传态的概念

尽管量子力学的投影假设看上去阻止了艾丽斯将 $|\psi\rangle$ 态提供给鲍勃的意图，本内特等[1] 却意识到就是这个投影假设使得 $|\psi\rangle$ 从艾丽斯到鲍勃的隐形传态成为可能。在隐形传态过程中，艾丽斯将对自己这边的量子态进行测量破坏，这时，鲍勃那边才接收到这个量子态，这个过程中，两个人都没有获知 $|\psi\rangle$ 态的信息。最初由艾丽斯和鲍勃共享的处于纠缠态的辅助粒子对在这个隐形传态方案中起到关键作用。

假定艾丽斯想要传送的粒子 1 处于初始态 $|\psi\rangle_1 = \alpha\,|\leftrightarrow\rangle_1 + \beta\,|\updownarrow\rangle_1$（图 1a），并且艾丽斯和鲍勃共享的纠缠粒子对，即粒子 2 和粒子 3 处于下列态中：

$$|\psi^-\rangle_{23} = \frac{1}{\sqrt{2}}\,(|\leftrightarrow\rangle_2|\updownarrow\rangle_3 - |\updownarrow\rangle_2|\leftrightarrow\rangle_3) \tag{2}$$

这个纠缠粒子对是 $|\leftrightarrow\rangle_2|\updownarrow\rangle_3$ 态和 $|\updownarrow\rangle_2|\leftrightarrow\rangle_3$ 态等量叠加的一个简单量子系统。纠缠态不包含任何个体粒子的信息，它仅仅表明两个粒子是处于正交的态。纠缠对的一个重要特性就是当对其中一个粒子进行测量而将其投影到比如说 $|\leftrightarrow\rangle$ 上，另一个粒子的态就确定为 $|\updownarrow\rangle$，反过来也是一样。对一个粒子的测量如何能够瞬间影响另一个可以是任意远的粒子的态？爱因斯坦还有其他很多杰出物理学家干脆不能接受这种"幽灵般的超距作用"。但是纠缠态的这个性质已经被很多实验所证实（请看参考文献 9 和 10）。

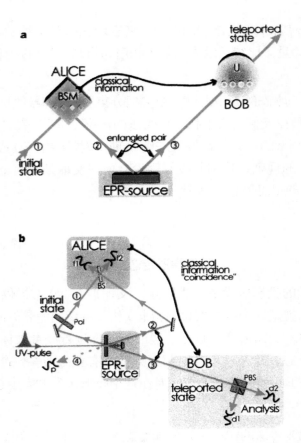

Fig. 1. Scheme showing principles involved in quantum teleportation (**a**) and the experimental set-up (**b**). **a**, Alice has a quantum system, particle 1, in an initial state which she wants to teleport to Bob. Alice and Bob also share an ancillary entangled pair of particles 2 and 3 emitted by an Einstein–Podolsky–Rosen (EPR) source. Alice then performs a joint Bell-state measurement (BSM) on the initial particle and one of the ancillaries, projecting them also onto an entangled state. After she has sent the result of her measurement as classical information to Bob, he can perform a unitary transformation (U) on the other ancillary particle resulting in it being in the state of the original particle. **b**, A pulse of ultraviolet radiation passing through a nonlinear crystal creates the ancillary pair of photons 2 and 3. After retroflection during its second passage through the crystal the ultraviolet pulse creates another pair of photons, one of which will be prepared in the initial state of photon 1 to be teleported, the other one serving as a trigger indicating that a photon to be teleported is under way. Alice then looks for coincidences after a beam splitter BS where the initial photon and one of the ancillaries are superposed. Bob, after receiving the classical information that Alice obtained a coincidence count in detectors f1 and f2 identifying the $|\psi^-\rangle_{12}$ Bell state, knows that his photon 3 is in the initial state of photon 1 which he then can check using polarization analysis with the polarizing beam splitter PBS and the detectors d1 and d2. The detector p provides the information that photon 1 is under way.

The teleportation scheme works as follows. Alice has the particle 1 in the initial state $|\psi\rangle_1$ and particle 2. Particle 2 is entangled with particle 3 in the hands of Bob. The essential point is to perform a specific measurement on particles 1 and 2 which projects them onto the entangled state:

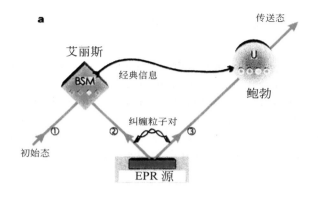

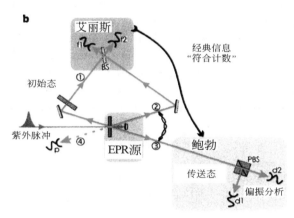

图 1. 表现量子隐形传态相关原理（a）和实验装置（b）的示意图。a，艾丽斯想把自己的量子系统也就是粒子 1 所处的初始态传送给鲍勃。艾丽斯和鲍勃共享一个从 EPR 源发出的辅助纠缠粒子对 2 和 3。艾丽斯接着对初始粒子 1 和辅助对中的一个粒子进行一个联合贝尔态测量，将其投影到一个纠缠态上。在她将测量结果以经典信息形式传送给鲍勃后，他就可以对另一个辅助粒子进行幺正变换，使之处于初始粒子 1 的状态中。b，一束紫外线脉冲通过非线性晶体时产生了辅助光子对 2 和 3。逆反射后第二次穿过晶体这个紫外脉冲又产生一对光子，其中一个将被制备到待传递的光子 1 的初始态，另一个用做触发器，表示一个待传态的光子已经上路。于是，艾丽斯查看经过分束器 BS 后初始光子和一个辅助光子叠加时的符合计数。鲍勃在收到艾丽斯已经在探测器 f1 和 f2 处获得验证贝尔态 $|\psi^-\rangle_{12}$ 的符合计数的经典信息后，就知道他的光子 3 已处于光子 1 的初始态中，并可用偏振分光器 PBS 和探测器 d1 和 d2 进行偏振分析来验证。探测器 p 提供光子正在路上的信息。

　　隐形传态方案如下面所述。艾丽斯现有粒子 2 和处于初始态 $|\psi\rangle_1$ 的粒子 1，粒子 2 与鲍勃处的粒子 3 处于纠缠态。关键之处是对粒子 1 和粒子 2 进行一个特定的测量，将它们投影到纠缠态上：

$$|\psi^-\rangle_{12} = \frac{1}{\sqrt{2}} \left(|\leftrightarrow\rangle_1 |\updownarrow\rangle_2 - |\updownarrow\rangle_1 |\leftrightarrow\rangle_2 \right) \tag{3}$$

This is only one of four possible maximally entangled states into which any state of two particles can be decomposed. The projection of an arbitrary state of two particles onto the basis of the four states is called a Bell-state measurement. The state given in equation (3) distinguishes itself from the three other maximally entangled states by the fact that it changes sign upon interchanging particle 1 and particle 2. This unique antisymmetric feature of $|\psi^-\rangle_{12}$ will play an important role in the experimental identification, that is, in measurements of this state.

Quantum physics predicts[1] that once particles 1 and 2 are projected into $|\psi^-\rangle_{12}$, particle 3 is instantaneously projected into the initial state of particle 1. The reason for this is as follows. Because we observe particles 1 and 2 in the state $|\psi^-\rangle_{12}$ we know that whatever the state of particle 1 is, particle 2 must be in the opposite state, that is, in the state orthogonal to the state of particle 1. But we had initially prepared particle 2 and 3 in the state $|\psi^-\rangle_{23}$, which means that particle 2 is also orthogonal to particle 3. This is only possible if particle 3 is in the same state as particle 1 was initially. The final state of particle 3 is therefore:

$$|\psi\rangle_3 = \alpha |\leftrightarrow\rangle_3 + \beta |\updownarrow\rangle_3 \tag{4}$$

We note that during the Bell-state measurement particle 1 loses its identity because it becomes entangled with particle 2. Therefore the state $|\psi\rangle_1$ is destroyed on Alice's side during teleportation.

This result (equation (4)) deserves some further comments. The transfer of quantum information from particle 1 to particle 3 can happen over arbitrary distances, hence the name teleportation. Experimentally, quantum entanglement has been shown[11] to survive over distances of the order of 10 km. We note that in the teleportation scheme it is not necessary for Alice to know where Bob is. Furthermore, the initial state of particle 1 can be completely unknown not only to Alice but to anyone. It could even be quantum mechanically completely undefined at the time the Bell-state measurement takes place. This is the case when, as already remarked by Bennett *et al.*[1], particle 1 itself is a member of an entangled pair and therefore has no well-defined properties on its own. This ultimately leads to entanglement swapping[12,13].

It is also important to notice that the Bell-state measurement does not reveal any information on the properties of any of the particles. This is the very reason why quantum teleportation using coherent two-particle superpositions works, while any measurement on one-particle superpositions would fail. The fact that no information whatsoever is gained on either particle is also the reason why quantum teleportation escapes the verdict of the no-cloning theorem[14]. After successful teleportation particle 1 is not available in its original state any more, and therefore particle 3 is not a clone but is really the result of teleportation.

$$|\psi^-\rangle_{12} = \frac{1}{\sqrt{2}} \ (|\leftrightarrow\rangle_1|\updownarrow\rangle_2 - |\updownarrow\rangle_1|\leftrightarrow\rangle_2) \tag{3}$$

这仅仅是任意双粒子态可以分解成的四个可能的最大纠缠态之一。双粒子任意态在四个最大纠缠态组成的一组正交完备基中任何一个态上的投影测量叫贝尔态测量。公式 3 中的态和其他三个最大纠缠态的不同之处在于交换粒子 1 和粒子 2 将导致其符号改变。$|\psi^-\rangle_{12}$ 态的这个独特的反对称特征在实验确认也就是在这个态的测量中将起到重要作用。

量子物理预言 [1] 当粒子 1 和 2 被投影到 $|\psi^-\rangle_{12}$ 态时，粒子 3 将被即时投影到粒子 1 的初始态。原因如下：因为我们测量得知粒子 1 和 2 处于 $|\psi^-\rangle_{12}$ 态中，所以我们知道无论粒子 1 处于任何态，粒子 2 一定处于正交态，也就是和粒子 1 的态正交的态中。但是我们一开始将粒子 2 和 3 置于 $|\psi^-\rangle_{23}$ 态中，也就是说粒子 2 也和粒子 3 正交。要实现这一点唯一的可能就是粒子 3 处于和粒子 1 的初始态相同的态中。由此粒子 3 的终态就是

$$|\psi\rangle_3 = \alpha|\leftrightarrow\rangle_3 + \beta|\updownarrow\rangle_3 \tag{4}$$

注意在贝尔态测量过程中粒子 1 因为与粒子 2 纠缠而失去了自身特征。因此艾丽斯这边的 $|\psi\rangle_1$ 态在隐形传态过程中被破坏。

这个结果（公式 4）值得进一步讨论。从粒子 1 到粒子 3 的量子信息的转移可以是通过任意距离，所以才有隐形传态的名字。实验证明量子纠缠能够建立在 10 千米量级的距离上 [11]。注意隐形传态方案中艾丽斯不需要知道鲍勃在哪里。另外不光是艾丽斯，其他任何人都不用知道粒子 1 的初始态。在进行贝尔态测量时，它甚至可以是在量子力学意义上完全未定义的。正像本内特等 [1] 已经指出过的，当粒子 1 自己是一个纠缠对中的一员因而没有自己的明确定义的性质时，就是这种情况。这最终导致纠缠交换 [12,13]。

另外重要的一点是贝尔态测量不揭示任何一个粒子性质的任何信息。这是为什么利用相干双粒子叠加的量子隐形传态能够成功，而任何单粒子叠加的测量都会失败的原因。未能获取任一粒子的任何信息的事实，也是量子隐形传态并不违反量子不可克隆定理 [14] 的原因。在成功的隐形传态之后，粒子 1 不再处于初始态，因而粒子 3 确实是隐形传态的结果而不是一个克隆。

A complete Bell-state measurement can not only give the result that the two particles 1 and 2 are in the antisymmetric state, but with equal probabilities of 25% we could find them in any one of the three other entangled states. When this happens, particle 3 is left in one of three different states. It can then be brought by Bob into the original state of particle 1 by an accordingly chosen transformation, independent of the state of particle 1, after receiving via a classical communication channel the information on which of the Bell-state results was obtained by Alice. Yet we note, with emphasis, that even if we chose to identify only one of the four Bell states as discussed above, teleportation is successfully achieved, albeit only in a quarter of the cases.

Experimental Realization

Teleportation necessitates both production and measurement of entangled states; these are the two most challenging tasks for any experimental realization. Thus far there are only a few experimental techniques by which one can prepare entangled states, and there exist no experimentally realized procedures to identify all four Bell states for any kind of quantum system. However, entangled pairs of photons can readily be generated and they can be projected onto at least two of the four Bell states.

We produced the entangled photons 2 and 3 by parametric down-conversion. In this technique, inside a nonlinear crystal, an incoming pump photon can decay spontaneously into two photons which, in the case of type II parametric down-conversion, are in the state given by equation (2) (Fig. 2)[6].

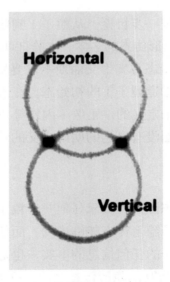

Fig. 2. Photons emerging from type II down-conversion (see text). Photograph taken perpendicular to the propagation direction. Photons are produced in pairs. A photon on the top circle is horizontally polarized while its exactly opposite partner in the bottom circle is vertically polarized. At the intersection points their polarizations are undefined; all that is known is that they have to be different, which results in entanglement.

　　一个完整的贝尔态测量不仅能给出两个粒子 1 和 2 处于反对称态的结果，我们还可能发现它们处于其他三个纠缠态中的任何一个的概率都是相等的 25%。如果发生这种情况，粒子 3 就处于三个不同的态中的一个。接着鲍勃可以在通过经典通信通道收到艾丽斯获取的是哪一个贝尔态的信息后，通过选择相应的变换，在与粒子 1 所处态无关的情况下，将粒子 3 置于粒子 1 的初始态中。我们要着重强调，即使像前面所讨论的那样我们选择只确认四个贝尔态中的一个，隐形传态仍然可以成功实现，尽管只是在四分之一的事例中。

实验的实现

　　实现隐形传态需要生成和测量纠缠态。任何实验实现都要面临这两个难题。到目前为止，能够作出纠缠态的实验技术寥寥无几，而且没有成功的实验程序来确认任何一种量子系统的所有四个贝尔态。虽然如此，纠缠光子对可以由简易方法产生并被投影到至少两个贝尔态上。

　　我们通过参量下转换产生纠缠光子对 2 和 3。在这项技术中，非线性晶体中进来一个泵浦光子可以即时衰变为两个光子。在二型参量下转换情形中，这两个光子处于公式 2 给出的态（图 2）[6]。

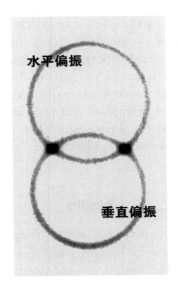

图 2. 二型参量下转换产生的光子（见正文）。相片与传播方向垂直。光子成对产生。顶圈的光子水平偏振，其严格相反的底圈同伴为垂直偏振。在相交的两点它们的偏振态是不明确的，我们只知道它们必须是不同的，这就导致纠缠。

To achieve projection of photons 1 and 2 into a Bell state we have to make them indistinguishable. To achieve this indistinguishability we superpose the two photons at a beam splitter (Fig. 1b). Then if they are incident one from each side, how can it happen that they emerge still one on each side? Clearly this can happen if they are either both reflected or both transmitted. In quantum physics we have to superimpose the amplitudes for these two possibilities. Unitarity implies that the amplitude for both photons being reflected obtains an additional minus sign. Therefore, it seems that the two processes cancel each other. This is, however, only true for a symmetric input state. For an antisymmetric state, the two possibilities obtain another relative minus sign, and therefore they constructively interfere[15,16]. It is thus sufficient for projecting photons 1 and 2 onto the antisymmetric state $|\psi^-\rangle_{12}$ to place detectors in each of the outputs of the beam splitter and to register simultaneous detections (coincidence)[17-19].

To make sure that photons 1 and 2 cannot be distinguished by their arrival times, they were generated using a pulsed pump beam and sent through narrow-bandwidth filters producing a coherence time much longer than the pump pulse length[20]. In the experiment, the pump pulses had a duration of 200 fs at a repetition rate of 76 MHz. Observing the down-converted photons at a wavelength of 788 nm and a bandwidth of 4 nm results in a coherence time of 520 fs. It should be mentioned that, because photon 1 is also produced as part of an entangled pair, its partner can serve to indicate that it was emitted.

How can one experimentally prove that an unknown quantum state can be teleported? First, one has to show that teleportation works for a (complete) basis, a set of known states into which any other state can be decomposed. A basis for polarization states has just two components, and in principle we could choose as the basis horizontal and vertical polarization as emitted by the source. Yet this would not demonstrate that teleportation works for any general superposition, because these two directions are preferred directions in our experiment. Therefore, in the first demonstration we choose as the basis for teleportation the two states linearly polarized at −45° and +45° which are already superpositions of the horizontal and vertical polarizations. Second, one has to show that teleportation works for superpositions of these base states. Therefore we also demonstrate teleportation for circular polarization.

Results

In the first experiment photon 1 is polarized at 45°. Teleportation should work as soon as photon 1 and 2 are detected in the $|\psi^-\rangle_{12}$ state, which occurs in 25% of all possible cases. The $|\psi^-\rangle_{12}$ state is identified by recording a coincidence between two detectors, f1 and f2, placed behind the beam splitter (Fig. 1b).

If we detect a f1f2 coincidence (between detectors f1 and f2), then photon 3 should also be polarized at 45°. The polarization of photon 3 is analysed by passing it through

要将光子 1 和 2 投影到一个贝尔态上我们必须让它们变得不可区分。为实现这个不可区分性我们将这两个光子在分束器处叠加（图 1b）。这样的话，如果它们从两边一边一个地入射，能不能做到出射时也是一边一个呢？显然这是可能的，只要它们都被反射或者都被透射就行。在量子物理中我们必须将这两个可能的振幅叠加。幺正性意味着两个光子都被反射的那个可能情形的振幅需要多加一个负号。这样的话这两个过程看上去互相抵消。但是只有对称入射态才是这种情况。对于反对称入射态，这两个可能情形要再加一个相对的负号，这样它们之间的干涉是相长的 [15,16]。由此，只要将探测器放在分束器的每个输出端记录同时发生的响应（符合计数），就可以将光子 1 和 2 投影到反对称态 $|\psi^-\rangle_{12}$。[17-19]

为了确保不能通过到达时间来区分光子 1 和 2，我们通过脉冲泵浦光束产生光子 1 和 2 并使其通过窄带宽滤波器来产生一个比泵浦脉冲长度长得多的相干时间 [20]。在实验中泵浦脉冲持续时间为 200 fs，重复率为 76 MHz。观测下转换产生的光子（该光子波长为 788 nm，带宽为 4 nm）得到相干时间为 520 fs。这里应当提到的是，由于光子 1 也是作为纠缠对的一部分产生的，可以用其同伴来显示它已被发出。

如何用一个实验证明未知量子态被隐形传送？首先要证明隐形传态能够在一组（完备）基矢上成功实现，任何其他态都能分解到这组已知基矢上。偏振态的基矢只有两个成分，原理上我们可以把源发射的水平和垂直偏振作为基矢。但是因为这两个方向在我们实验中是优先方向，这种演示不能证明隐形传送对任何普遍叠加态都能实现。出于这个原因，在第一个实验中我们选择 −45° 和 +45° 两个线性偏振态作为拟传送态的基矢。它们都已经是水平和垂直偏振的叠加。其次，我们必须证明对这些基矢的叠加也能实现隐形传态。为此我们还证明了圆偏振的隐形传态。

实 验 结 果

在第一个实验中光子 1 处于 45° 偏振。在所有可能情形中，光子 1 和 2 被检测到处于 $|\psi^-\rangle_{12}$ 态的概率是 25%。一旦出现这种情形，隐形传态就应当实现。$|\psi^-\rangle_{12}$ 态的确认是通过置于分束器后面两个探测器 f1 和 f2 的符合计数来实现的（图 1b）。

如果我们探测到一个 f1f2（探测器 f1 和 f2 之间的）符合事例，那么光子 3 应当也是 45° 偏振。光子 3 的偏振态的分析方法是让它通过一个选择 +45° 和 −45° 偏振

a polarizing beam splitter selecting +45° and −45° polarization. To demonstrate teleportation, only detector d2 at the +45° output of the polarizing beam splitter should click (that is, register a detection) once detectors f1 and f2 click. Detector d1 at the −45° output of the polarizing beam splitter should not detect a photon. Therefore, recording a three-fold coincidence d2f1f2 (+45° analysis) together with the absence of a three-fold coincidence d1f1f2 (−45° analysis) is a proof that the polarization of photon 1 has been teleported to photon 3.

To meet the condition of temporal overlap, we change in small steps the arrival time of photon 2 by changing the delay between the first and second down-conversion by translating the retroflection mirror (Fig. 1b). In this way we scan into the region of temporal overlap at the beam splitter so that teleportation should occur.

Outside the region of teleportation, photon 1 and 2 each will go either to f1 or to f2 independent of one another. The probability of having a coincidence between f1 and f2 is therefore 50%, which is twice as high as inside the region of teleportation. Photon 3 should not have a well-defined polarization because it is part of an entangled pair. Therefore, d1 and d2 have both a 50% chance of receiving photon 3. This simple argument yields a 25% probability both for the −45° analysis (d1f1f2 coincidences) and for the +45° analysis (d2f1f2 coincidences) outside the region of teleportation. Figure 3 summarizes the predictions as a function of the delay. Successful teleportation of the +45° polarization state is then characterized by a decrease to zero in the −45° analysis (Fig. 3a), and by a constant value for the +45° analysis (Fig. 3b).

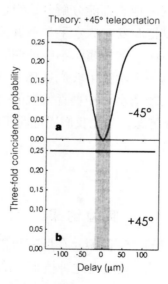

Fig. 3. Theoretical prediction for the three-fold coincidence probability between the two Bell-state detectors (f1, f2) and one of the detectors analysing the teleported state. The signature of teleportation of a photon polarization state at +45° is a dip to zero at zero delay in the three-fold coincidence rate with the detector analysing −45° (d1f1f2) (**a**) and a constant value for the detector analysis +45° (d2f1f2) (**b**). The shaded area indicates the region of teleportation.

的偏振分束器。若要证明隐形传态的实现，当探测器 f1 和 f2 响应时，必须只有偏振分束器 +45°输出端的探测器 d2 有响应，也就是记录下了一次探测，而偏振分束器 −45°输出端的探测器 d1 不应探测到光子。因此，一个三重符合计数 d2f1f2（+45° 偏振分析）的记录，加上三重符合计数 d1f1f2（−45° 偏振分析）的缺失，就成为光子 1 的偏振态已经被隐形传态到光子 3 的证据。

为满足时间重叠条件，我们通过平移逆反射镜改变第一次和第二次下转换之间的延迟来微调光子 2 的到达时间（图 1b）。用这种办法，我们逐渐进入分束器处时间重叠的区间，保证隐形传态发生。

在隐形传态区间之外，光子 1 和 2 各自可能独立奔向 f1 或者 f2。因此在 f1 和 f2 得到一个符合计数的概率是 50%。这个概率是在隐形传态区间中的两倍。光子 3 因为是纠缠对中一员，所以不应有明确定义的偏振。这样的话，d1 和 d2 都有 50% 的可能接收到光子 3。这个简单的论证得到的结果是，在隐形传态区间之外，−45° 偏振分析（d1f1f2 符合计数）和 +45° 偏振分析（d2f1f2 符合计数）都有 25% 的概率。图 3 总结了作为时间延迟函数的预测概率值。−45° 分析下降到零（图 3a）和 +45° 分析保持为一个常数（图 3b），表征 +45° 偏振态的隐形传态得到成功实现。

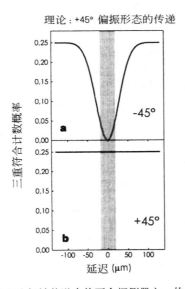

图 3. 两个贝尔态探测器（f1,f2）和分析被传递态的两个探测器之一的三重符合计数概率的理论预期。+45°光子偏振态传递的特征是：在零延迟处，−45° 偏振分析探测器三重符合计数率（d1f1f2）有一个到零概率值的下降（a），而 +45° 分析探测器三重符合计数率（d2f1f2）保持为常数（b）。阴影区为隐形传态区间。

The theoretical prediction of Fig. 3 may easily be understood by realizing that at zero delay there is a decrease to half in the coincidence rate for the two detectors of the Bell-state analyser, f1 and f2, compared with outside the region of teleportation. Therefore, if the polarization of photon 3 were completely uncorrelated to the others the three-fold coincidence should also show this dip to half. That the right state is teleported is indicated by the fact that the dip goes to zero in Fig. 3a and that it is filled to a flat curve in Fig. 3b.

We note that equally as likely as the production of photons 1, 2 and 3 is the emission of two pairs of down-converted photons by a single source. Although there is no photon coming from the first source (photon 1 is absent), there will still be a significant contribution to the three-fold coincidence rates. These coincidences have nothing to do with teleportation and can be identified by blocking the path of photon 1.

The probability for this process to yield spurious two- and three-fold coincidences can be estimated by taking into account the experimental parameters. The experimentally determined value for the percentage of spurious three-fold coincidences is $68\% \pm 1\%$. In the experimental graphs of Fig. 4 we have subtracted the experimentally determined spurious coincidences.

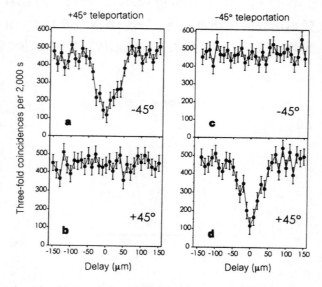

Fig. 4. Experimental results. Measured three-fold coincidence rates d1f1f2 ($-45°$) and d2f1f2 ($+45°$) in the case that the photon state to be teleported is polarized at $+45°$ (**a** and **b**) or at $-45°$ (**c** and **d**). The coincidence rates are plotted as function of the delay between the arrival of photon 1 and 2 at Alice's beam splitter (see Fig. 1b). The three-fold coincidence rates are plotted after subtracting the spurious three-fold contribution (see text). These data, compared with Fig. 3, together with similar ones for other polarizations (Table 1) confirm teleportation for an arbitrary state.

图 3 中的理论预计图可以这样来简单理解：与隐形传态区间之外相比较，在延迟为零时，两个贝尔态探测器 f1 和 f2 的符合计数率下降一半；如此一来，如果光子 3 的偏振与其他光子完全无关，三重符合计数也应该降到一半。在图 3a 中曲线下降一直到零而在图 3b 中被填平成为平坦曲线，表明设计的隐形传态得到实现。

需要指出的是，与光子 1、2 和 3 的产生同样可能发生的是单一源发出两对下转换光子。虽然这种情况中没有光子来自第一个源（光子 1 未出现），但是它对三重符合计数率仍有显著贡献。这些符合计数与隐形传态无关，可以用阻断光子 1 路径的办法确认。

这一产生乱真二重和三重符合计数的过程发生的概率可以从实验参数估计。由实验确定的乱真三重符合计数的百分比是 68%±1%。图 4 中的实验图形中我们已经扣除这个实验确定的乱真符合计数。

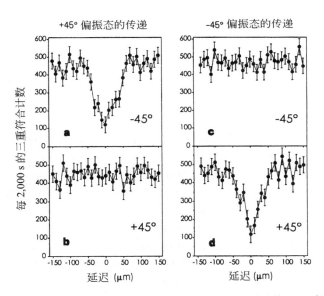

图 4. 实验结果。在待传光子为 +45° 偏振（**a** 和 **b**）或者 −45° 偏振（**c** 和 **d**）的情况下，测量 d1f1f2（−45°）和 d2f1f2（+45°）三重符合计数率。画出的符合计数率是光子 1 和 2 分别到达艾丽斯的分束器的延迟的函数（见图 1b），并扣除了乱真三重计数的贡献（见正文）。这些数据与图 3 对比，再加上其他偏振的类似结果（表 1），证实了任意一个态都可被传递。

The experimental results for teleportation of photons polarized under +45° are shown in the left-hand column of Fig. 4; Fig. 4a and b should be compared with the theoretical predictions shown in Fig. 3. The strong decrease in the −45° analysis, and the constant signal for the +45° analysis, indicate that photon 3 is polarized along the direction of photon 1, confirming teleportation.

The results for photon 1 polarized at −45° demonstrate that teleportation works for a complete basis for polarization states (right-hand column of Fig. 4). To rule out any classical explanation for the experimental results, we have produced further confirmation that our procedure works by additional experiments. In these experiments we teleported photons linearly polarized at 0° and at 90°, and also teleported circularly polarized photons. The experimental results are summarized in Table 1, where we list the visibility of the dip in three-fold coincidences, which occurs for analysis orthogonal to the input polarization.

Table 1. Visibility of teleportation in three-fold coincidences

Polarization	Visibility
+45°	0.63 ± 0.02
−45°	0.64 ± 0.02
0°	0.66 ± 0.02
90°	0.61 ± 0.02
Circular	0.57 ± 0.02

As mentioned above, the values for the visibilities are obtained after subtracting the offset caused by spurious three-fold coincidences. These can experimentally be excluded by conditioning the three-fold coincidences on the detection of photon 4, which effectively projects photon 1 into a single-particle state. We have performed this four-fold coincidence measurement for the case of teleportation of the +45° and +90° polarization states, that is, for two non-orthogonal states. The experimental results are shown in Fig. 5. Visibilities of 70% ± 3% are obtained for the dips in the orthogonal polarization states. Here, these visibilities are directly the degree of polarization of the teleported photon in the right state. This proves that we have demonstrated teleportation of the quantum state of a single photon.

图 4 左栏是 +45° 偏振光子的隐形传态的实验结果；我们应当把图 4a 和 b 与图 3 中的理论预计曲线相比较来看。−45° 分析中的猛烈下降和 +45° 分析中的稳定信号表明光子 3 与光子 1 的偏振方向相同，证实了隐形传态的实现。

−45° 偏振的光子 1 的结果证明能够对一组完备的偏振基态实现隐形传态（图 4 右栏）。为了排除对实验结果的任何经典解释，我们用另外的实验进一步证实我们的方法是成功的。在这些附加实验中我们隐形传送了 0° 和 90° 的线偏振光子以及圆偏振光子，结果总结在附表 1 中。实验中与入射偏振正交方向的三重符合计数出现下降，表中列出了这个下降的可见度。

表 1. 三重符合计数下隐形传态的可见度

偏振方向	可见度
+45°	0.63 ± 0.02
−45°	0.64 ± 0.02
0°	0.66 ± 0.02
90°	0.61 ± 0.02
圆偏振	0.57 ± 0.02

如前所述，这些可见度是扣除乱真三重符合计数引起的偏差之后得到的数值。实验上排除这些计数的办法是对三重计数再附加一个光子 4 计数的条件。这使得光子 1 实际上被投影到一个单粒子态上。我们将这个四重符合计数测量方法用到 +45° 和 +90° 偏振态这两个非正交态的隐形传态中。实验结果在图 5 中给出。得到的正交偏振态下降的可见度在 70%±3%。这些可见度直接就是被传态光子在其本态的偏振度。这表示我们已经证明了单个光子的量子态的隐形传递。

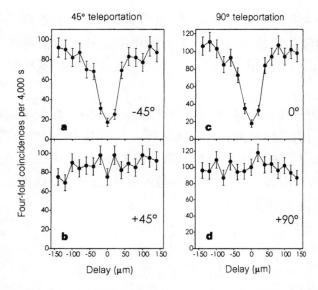

Fig. 5. Four-fold coincidence rates (without background subtraction). Conditioning the three-fold coincidences as shown in Fig. 4 on the registration of photon 4 (see Fig. 1b) eliminates the spurious three-fold background. **a** and **b** show the four-fold coincidence measurements for the case of teleportation of the +45° polarization state; **c** and **d** show the results for the +90° polarization state. The visibilities, and thus the polarizations of the teleported photons, obtained without any background subtraction are 70% ± 3%. These results for teleportation of two non-orthogonal states prove that we have demonstrated teleportation of the quantum state of a single photon.

The Next Steps

In our experiment, we used pairs of polarization entangled photons as produced by pulsed down-conversion and two-photon interferometric methods to transfer the polarization state of one photon onto another one. But teleportation is by no means restricted to this system. In addition to pairs of entangled photons or entangled atoms[7,21], one could imagine entangling photons with atoms, or phonons with ions, and so on. Then teleportation would allow us to transfer the state of, for example, fast-decohering, short-lived particles, onto some more stable systems. This opens the possibility of quantum memories, where the information of incoming photons is stored on trapped ions, carefully shielded from the environment.

Furthermore, by using entanglement purification[22]—a scheme of improving the quality of entanglement if it was degraded by decoherence during storage or transmission of the particles over noisy channels—it becomes possible to teleport the quantum state of a particle to some place, even if the available quantum channels are of very poor quality and thus sending the particle itself would very probably destroy the fragile quantum state. The feasibility of preserving quantum states in a hostile environment will have great advantages in the realm of quantum computation. The teleportation scheme could also be used to provide links between quantum computers.

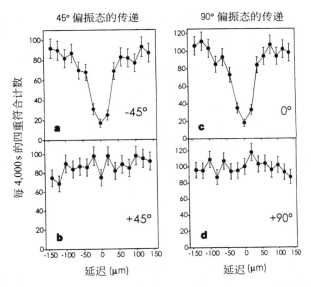

图 5. 四重符合计数率（未扣除背景）。对图 4 的三重符合计数附加一个光子 4 计数的条件（见图 1b）消除了乱真三重计数的背景。**a** 和 **b** 显示传递 +45° 偏振态的四重符合计数测量；**c** 和 **d** 是 +90° 偏振态的结果。在没有去除背景的情况下，得到的可见度，也就是被传态光子的偏振度，是 70%±3%。这两个非正交态的传递结果表明了我们已经证实单个光子的量子态的隐形传态。

展　望

我们的实验使用脉冲下转换产生的偏振纠缠光子对，并利用双光子干涉测量法来将一个光子的偏振态传递给另一个光子。但是隐形传态不只局限于这个系统。除了纠缠光子对或者纠缠原子对[7,21]，还可以设想光子和原子之间纠缠，声子和离子之间纠缠等等。隐形传态使得我们能够把比如快速退相干的短寿命粒子的态转移到其他更稳定的系统中，这使得量子存储成为可能。在量子存储中，进来的光子的信息被储存到被俘获的离子上，外界的影响被很好地屏蔽掉。

纠缠纯化[22] 是一种在存储粒子或在噪声信道传送粒子的过程中因退相干导致纠缠退化时改进纠缠质量的方案。利用纠缠纯化可以更进一步将一个粒子的量子态传至异地，哪怕当前量子通道的质量很差并且使得传递粒子本身很可能会把脆弱的量子态破坏。在不利环境中保存量子状态的可行性在量子计算领域中会带来很大优势。隐形传态的方案还可以用于两台量子计算机之间的通信。

Quantum teleportation is not only an important ingredient in quantum information tasks; it also allows new types of experiments and investigations of the foundations of quantum mechanics. As any arbitrary state can be teleported, so can the fully undetermined state of a particle which is member of an entangled pair. Doing so, one transfers the entanglement between particles. This allows us not only to chain the transmission of quantum states over distances, where decoherence would have already destroyed the state completely, but it also enables us to perform a test of Bell's theorem on particles which do not share any common past, a new step in the investigation of the features of quantum mechanics. Last but not least, the discussion about the local realistic character of nature could be settled firmly if one used features of the experiment presented here to generate entanglement between more than two spatially separated particles[23,24].

(**390**, 575-579; 1997)

Dik Bouwmeester, Jian-Wei Pan, Klaus Mattle, Manfred Eibl, Harald Weinfurter & Anton Zeilinger
Institut für Experimentalphysik, Universität Innsbruck, Technikerstr. 25, A-6020 Innsbruck, Austria

Received 16 October; accepted 18 November 1997.

References:

1. Bennett, C. H. *et al.* Teleporting an unknown quantum state via dual classic and Einstein-Podolsky-Rosen channels. *Phys. Rev. Lett.* **70**, 1895-1899 (1993).

2. Schrödinger, E. Die gegenwärtige Situation in der Quantenmechanik. *Naturwissenschaften* **23**, 807-812; 823-828; 844-849 (1935).

3. Bennett, C. H. Quantum information and computation. *Phys. Today* **48**(10), 24-30, October (1995).

4. Bennett, C. H., Brassard, G. & Ekert, A. K. Quantum Cryptography. *Sci. Am.* **267**(4), 50-57, October (1992).

5. Mattle, K., Weinfurter, H., Kwiat, P. G. & Zeilinger, A. Dense coding in experimental quantum communication. *Phys. Rev. Lett.* **76**, 4656-4659 (1996).

6. Kwiat, P. G. *et al.* New high intensity source of polarization-entangled photon pairs. *Phys. Rev. Lett.* **75**, 4337-4341 (1995).

7. Hagley, E. *et al.* Generation of Einstein-Podolsky-Rosen pairs of atoms. *Phys. Rev. Lett.* **79**, 1-5 (1997).

8. Schumacher, B. Quantum coding. *Phys. Rev. A* **51**, 2738-2747 (1995).

9. Clauser, J. F. & Shimony, A. Bell's theorem: experimental tests and implications. *Rep. Prog. Phys.* **41**, 1881-1927 (1978).

10. Greenberger, D. M., Horne, M. A. & Zeilinger, A. Multiparticle interferometry and the superposition principle. *Phys. Today* August, 22-29 (1993).

11. Tittel, W. *et al.* Experimental demonstration of quantum-correlations over more than 10 kilometers. *Phys. Rev. Lett.* (submitted).

12. Zukowski, M., Zeilinger, A., Horne, M. A. & Ekert, A. "Event-ready-detectors" Bell experiment via entanglement swapping. *Phys. Rev. Lett.* **71**, 4287-4290 (1993).

13. Bose, S., Vedral, V. & Knight, P. L. A multiparticle generalization of entanglement swapping. (preprint).

14. Wootters, W. K. & Zurek, W. H. A single quantum cannot be cloned. *Nature* **299**, 802-803 (1982).

15. Loudon, R. *Coherence and Quantum Optics VI* (eds Everly, J. H. & Mandel, L.) 703-708 (Plenum, New York, 1990).

16. Zeilinger, A., Bernstein, H. J. & Horne, M. A. Information transfer with two-state two-particle quantum systems. *J. Mod. Optics* **41**, 2375-2384 (1994).

17. Weinfurter, H. Experimental Bell-state analysis. *Europhys. Lett.* **25**, 559-564 (1994).

18. Braunstein, S. L. & Mann, A. Measurement of the Bell operator and quantum teleportation. *Phys. Rev. A* **51**, R1727-R1730 (1995).

19. Michler, M., Mattle, K., Weinfurter, H. & Zeilinger, A. Interferometric Bell-state analysis. *Phys. Rev. A* **53**, R1209-R1212 (1996).

20. Zukowski, M., Zeilinger, A. & Weinfurter, H. Entangling photons radiated by independent pulsed sources. *Ann. NY Acad. Sci.* **755**, 91-102 (1995).

21. Fry, E. S., Walther, T. & Li, S. Proposal for a loophole-free test of the Bell inequalities. *Phys. Rev. A* **52**, 4381-4395 (1995).

22. Bennett, C. H. *et al.* Purification of noisy entanglement and faithful teleportation via noisy channels. *Phys. Rev. Lett.* **76**, 722-725 (1996).

23. Greenberger, D. M., Horne, M. A., Shimony, A. & Zeilinger, A. Bell's theorem without inequalities. *Am. J. Phys.* **58**, 1131-1143 (1990).

24. Zeilinger, A., Horne, M. A., Weinfurter, H. & Zukowski, M. Three particle entanglements from two entangled pairs. *Phys. Rev. Lett.* **78**, 3031-3034 (1997).

Acknowledgements. We thank C. Bennett, I. Cirac, J. Rarity, W. Wootters and P. Zoller for discussions, and M. Zukowski for suggestions about various aspects of the experiments. This work was supported by the Austrian Science Foundation FWF, the Austrian Academy of Sciences, the TMR program of the European Union and the US NSF.

Correspondence and requests for materials should be addressed to D.B. (e-mail: Dik.Bouwmeester@uibk.ac.at).

　　量子隐形传态不仅仅是量子信息处理任务的一个重要组成，它还为量子力学基础提供新的实验和研究方法。既然任意一个态都可以被传递，作为一个纠缠对中一员的粒子的完全未确定的量子态也可以被传递。这种作法等于在粒子间传递纠缠。这样我们不但能够用长距离链式传递量子态解决退相干在途中破坏量子态的问题，而且能够对没有共同历史的粒子进行贝尔定律检测（量子力学特征研究的新步骤）。最后同样重要的一点是，如果利用本文描述的实验要素来产生两个以上的空间分离粒子的纠缠，就可能确实解决自然世界定域实在特征的争论 [23,24]。

（何钧 沈乃澂 翻译；陆朝阳 李军刚 审稿）

Localization of Light in a Disordered Medium

D. Wiersma *et al.*

Editor's Note

Quantum physics implies that particle diffusion inside disordered materials may be inhibited by destructive wave interference, if the disorder is sufficiently pronounced. This phenomenon of strong localization—or "Anderson localization", as it was originally described by physicist Philip Anderson—affects not only the behaviour of electrons in many solids, but that of photons as well. Here Diederik Wiersma and colleagues provided experimental confirmation of Anderson localization for light in semiconductor powders. They studied light transmission through gallium arsenide in a crystal and in powders with various particle sizes. They found a sharp threshold of particle size at which disorder-induced localization ultimately blocks light transmission, causing the transmission coefficient through a sample to decrease exponentially with sample thickness rather than linearly.

Among the unusual transport properties predicted for disordered materials is the Anderson localization[1] phenomenon. This is a disorder-induced phase transition in the electron-transport behaviour from the classical diffusion regime, in which the well-known Ohm's law holds, to a localized state in which the material behaves as an insulator. The effect finds its origin in the interference of electrons that have undergone multiple scattering by defects in the solid[2-10]. A similar phenomenon is anticipated for multiple scattering of electromagnetic waves, but with one important simplification: unlike electrons, photons do not interact with one another. This makes transport of photons in disordered materials an ideal model system in which to study Anderson localization[10-17]. Here we report direct experimental evidence for Anderson localization of light in optical experiments performed on very strongly scattering semiconductor powders.

MULTIPLE scattering of light is a common phenomenon in daily life, occurring for example in sugar, fog, white paint and clouds. The propagation of light in these media can in general be described by a normal diffusion process. For diffusion of light through a disordered material the same Ohm's law holds as for diffusion of electrons through any common resistor: the transmission, or conductance, decreases linearly with the system length (thickness).

Anderson localization brings classical diffusion to a complete halt. That is, on increasing the amount of scattering beyond a critical value, the material makes a transition into a localized state (see Fig. 1). This transition can best be observed in the transmission properties of the system. In the localized state, the transmission coefficient decreases exponentially instead of linearly with the thickness of a sample. At the transition, the

无序介质中光的局域化

维尔斯马等

编者按

量子物理学指出，在材料的无序程度足够显著的情况下，粒子在该材料中的扩散会被波的相消干涉所抑制。这种强烈的局域化现象，或者叫"安德森局域化"（因为该现象最早是由物理学家菲利普·安德森描述出来的），影响了电子在多种固体中的行为，而且也会影响光子的行为。在本文中，迪德里克·维尔斯马和他的同事们用实验证实了光在半导体粉末中的安德森局域化。他们研究了光在砷化镓晶体中和在具有不同粒度的几种砷化镓粉末中的透射。他们发现，光透射率在某一粒度值处出现一个显著的阈值，在该处，无序诱导的局域化完全阻挡了光的透射，导致样品的透射系数随样品厚度呈指数下降而非线性下降。

安德森局域化[1]现象是科学家预测到的无序材料不同寻常的传输性质之一。这是一种由无序环境诱导产生的电子传输行为上的相变，表现为由经典的扩散向局域态的转变，而经典扩散是众所周知的欧姆定律适用的范围，局域态则对应绝缘体材料。这个效应来源于被固体中的缺陷多次散射的电子之间的干涉[2-10]。可以预料的是，电磁波的多次散射会产生相似的现象，但是有一个重要的简化：和电子不同，光子之间不会有相互作用。这使光子在无序材料中的传输成为研究安德森局域化的理想模型[10-17]。在本文中，利用基于强散射性半导体粉末的光学实验，我们报道了光的安德森局域化的直接实验证据。

光的多次散射是生活中常见的现象，会出现在例如糖、雾、白色颜料、云中。光在这些介质中的传播通常可以用标准扩散过程来描述。对于光在无序材料中的扩散，欧姆定律依然适用，如同电子在电阻器中的扩散一样，即传导性随系统长度（厚度）线性下降。

安德森局域化使经典扩散不再适用。也就是说，一旦散射量高于某一临界值，材料就出现局域态（见图1）。观察这种变化的最佳方式是测试系统的透射。在局域态中，透射系数随样品厚度呈指数减小，而非呈线性减小。转变过程中，透射系数

transmission coefficient is expected to have a power-law dependence on the inverse thickness, which is probably quadratic[12,18].

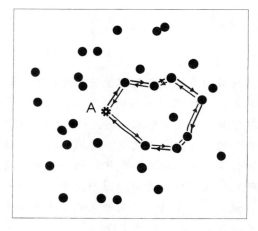

Fig. 1. Anderson localization of waves in disordered systems originates from interference in multiple elastic scattering. Here we consider a light source (like an excited atom emitting a photon) in a disordered medium at position A. The light source is denoted by a star symbol and the spheres denote the scattering elements. A random light path that returns to the light source can be followed in two opposite directions. The two waves which propagate in opposite directions along this loop will acquire the same phase and therefore interfere constructively in A. This leads to a higher probability of the wave coming back to A and consequently a lower probability of propagating away from A. On decreasing the mean free path l, the probability for such looped paths increases and at strong enough scattering the system makes a phase transition from the normal conducting state into a localized state, due to interference. In the localized regime, the system behaves as a non-absorbing insulator. Light which is incident on, for example, a slab would be almost completely reflected and the remaining transmission would decrease exponentially with the slab thickness.

The main difficulty in the search for localization of light has been the realization of strong enough scattering. The appropriate measure for the amount of scattering is the mean free path l for the light in the medium, times the magnitude of the wavevector k. Localization is expected for $kl \leqslant 1$ (ref. 19), which is known as the (modified) Ioffe–Regel criterion. This criterion can be understood intuitively if one realizes that below $kl = 1$, the electric field can not even perform one oscillation before the wave is scattered again. So far, localization effects have been reported only for microwaves in a two-dimensional system of rods[20] and for microwaves in a confined geometry (a copper tube filled with metallic and dielectric spheres)[21,22]. In the latter experiment the absorption was very large, which makes the interpretation of the data complicated. The disadvantage of experiments with microwaves compared to light waves is that it is difficult to avoid absorption.

We have been able to realize very strongly scattering samples for light waves, using semiconductor powders. Semiconductors can have a very large refractive index, while, for wavelengths in the bandgap, the absorption is extremely small. We used light at wavelength $\lambda = 1{,}064$ nm, at which the absorption coefficient κ of pure GaAs is $\kappa \ll 1$ cm^{-1} and

预计会与厚度的倒数呈幂律相关，且很有可能是二次幂律[12,18]。

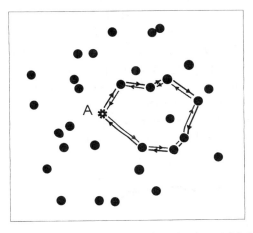

图 1. 无序系统中波的安德森局域化来源于多次弹性散射的干涉。在这里我们把无序介质中的 A 点看作是一个光源（好比一个受激原子发射出一个光子）。这个光源用星号标记，而圆点表示散射点。一条能返回到光源的不规则光路可以从相反的两个方向去实现。这两支沿着这条回路反向传播的波会具有相同的相位，从而在 A 点形成相长干涉。这种情况导致波回到 A 点的概率增加而向远离 A 点方向传播的概率减小。一旦平均自由程 l 减小，出现这种回路的概率就增加了，并且在散射足够强的情况下，干涉会导致系统发生由普通传导态到局域态的相变。在局域区，系统表现为无吸收的光绝缘体。例如，照在一块平板上的光几乎都会被反射，仅剩的一点透射光会随板的厚度呈指数衰减。

探寻光的局域化的最大难点在于实现足够强的散射。衡量散射量最恰当的方法是用光在介质中的平均自由程 l 乘以波矢量 k 的大小。局域化发生的条件为 $kl \leqslant 1$（参考文献 19），即（修正的）Ioffe–Regel 判据。如果能意识到，低于 $kl = 1$ 时，在波被再次散射前电场不能完成一次振荡，我们便能直观地理解这条判据。迄今为止，对局域化效应的报告仅限于二维棒状系统中的微波[20]和封闭空间（充满金属和电介质球的铜管）里的微波[21,22]。在后者中，微波被大量吸收，导致数据解释变得复杂。和光波实验比起来，微波实验的劣势在于吸收难以避免。

我们已利用半导体粉末实现光波的强散射。半导体可以具有很大的折射率，而对于带隙中的波长来说，吸收是极小的。我们使用波长 $\lambda = 1{,}064$ nm 的光，在这个波长下纯砷化镓的吸收系数 $\kappa \ll 1$ cm^{-1}，折射率为 3.48。我们的样品由纯的（99.999%）

the refractive index is 3.48. Our samples consist of pure (99.999%) gallium arsenide (GaAs) crystals which were ground (as a suspension in methanol) by hand in a ceramic mortar and in a planetary micromill at low speed. By varying the grinding time, we obtained samples with different average particle sizes and thereby different amounts of scattering. In grinding semiconductors one has to be careful not to introduce absorption at the wavelength at which the experiments are performed. For a powder, surface states could become more important and the grinding process (even if performed with little force) could introduce strain or lattice deformations. Surface states, strain and lattice deformations can lead to absorption tails at the edge of the bandgap. We have characterized the change of the band edge of our material by measuring the temperature dependence of the transmission (Fig. 2).

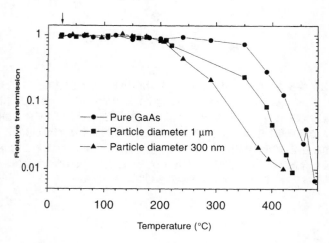

Fig. 2. Comparison of the temperature dependence of the transmission of pure GaAs crystals and powders. Data obtained using particles of size of 1 μm and 300 nm are shown. The transmission of the powder samples is measured at a thickness where the total transmission equals 1% at room temperature. All curves are scaled to have a maximum of 1. On increasing the temperature T, the bandgap shifts to lower energies $E_g(T)$ corresponding to higher wavelengths $\lambda_g = 1.24/E_g$ (in μm). The temperature dependence is given by the empirical relation: $E_g(T) = E_g(0) - \alpha T^2/(T+\beta)$, where (for GaAs) $E_g(0) = 1.522$, $\alpha = 8.871 \times 10^{-4}$ and $\beta = 572$, with T in K. This temperature-dependent shift enables the scanning of the region of the bandgap around the laser wavelength, without changing the laser wavelength itself. For example, a temperature of 200 °C corresponds to a wavelength shift of 65 nm. The arrow at top left shows the temperature where we performed all other experiments. We note that the band edge becomes less steep upon grinding the GaAs crystal; this is probably due to the increased importance of surface states and, for example, lattice deformations. But the region close to the laser wavelength remains unabsorbing.

We observe (Fig. 2) that the band edge indeed becomes less steep on grinding, and that the onset of absorption shifts into the bandgap. It is also clear, however, that the region of the absorption tails is still far enough (65 nm) below our laser wavelength as to ensure that these tails will not introduce absorption in our experiments.

To characterize the mean free path l of our samples, we used coherent backscattering. This phenomenon is a general interference effect between counter-propagating waves, which leads to a narrow cone in exact backscattering[23]. It is seen as the precursor to

砷化镓 (GaAs) 晶体构成，是在陶瓷研钵里手动碾磨 (以悬浮于甲醇的形式) 以及在微型行星式高能球磨机中低速碾磨而成的。通过改变碾磨时间，我们得到了具有不同平均粒度从而具有不同散射量的样品。碾磨半导体时，操作人员必须非常小心，以确保实验中所用波长的光不会被吸收。对于粉末来说，表面态更为重要，并且碾磨过程 (即使只用了很小的力) 会引起应变或晶格形变。表面态、应变和晶格形变都会导致带边出现吸收带尾。通过测量透射率与温度的相关性，我们描绘了材料的带边变化 (图 2)。

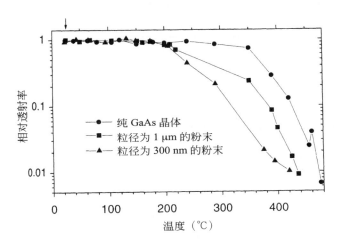

图 2. 纯 GaAs 晶体与粉末之间透射率与温度相关性的对比。图中展示了粒径为 1 μm 和 300 nm 的数据。粉末样品的透射率是在一个特定的厚度下测得的，即室温下总透射率为 1% 时的厚度。所有曲线都被按比例缩放，使得最高点是 1。一旦温度 T 升高，带隙就移向低能量 $E_g(T)$，对应于高波长 $\lambda_g = 1.24/E_g$ (单位是 μm)。和温度的相关性满足经验关系：$E_g(T) = E_g(0) - \alpha T^2/(T+\beta)$，其中 (GaAs 的) $E_g(0) = 1.522$，$\alpha = 8.871 \times 10^{-4}$，$\beta = 572$，$T$ 的单位是 K。这种依赖于温度的移动，使在不改变激光波长的情况下，遍历带隙中激光波长附近的能量成为可能。例如，200 ℃ 的温度对应于 65 nm 的波长改变量。左上角的箭头指出了我们其余全部实验的操作温度。我们注意到，在 GaAs 晶体被碾磨得更细的时候，吸收带边缘变得没那么陡直了；这很可能是因为表面态和晶格形变的影响加重了。但是激光波长附近的波长区域仍然没有吸收。

从图 2 中我们发现，在碾磨得更细的时候，吸收带边缘变得没那么陡直了，而且吸收的起始点移入带隙中了。然而另一个明确的方面是，吸收带尾所处的波长区域远比我们使用的激光的波长要小 (65 nm)，这样就保证了这种带尾不会使我们的实验里出现激光的吸收。

为确定此材料中的平均自由程 l，我们应用了相干背散射。该现象是反向传播的波之间的普通干涉效应，使背散射谱图上出现一个窄的锥形[23]。这被看作是安德森

Anderson localization and is therefore also called "weak localization of light"[24,25]. The width of the backscattering cone and the angle of its cusp are inversely proportional to l (refs 26, 27) and therefore enable the determination of the amount of scattering inside the samples. Furthermore, the cusp is due to a summation up to (in principle) infinite path length, and is therefore only present in the absence of absorption[26-28]. In Figure 3, we show backscattering cones for a coarse-grained (Fig. 3a) and a fine-grained (Fig. 3b) powder with an average particle diameter of 10 µm and 1 µm, respectively. From the angle of the cusp we find for the coarse-grained powder $l = 8.5$ µm and hence $kl = 76$. For the fine-grained powder we find $l \approx 0.17$ µm which corresponds to $kl \approx 1.5$. The observed value of $kl = 1.5$ is four times smaller than the smallest kl values that have been reported so far[30] for light waves. The shape of the coherent backscattering cone at the localization transition is interesting from both an experimental and a theoretical point of view, but will be discussed elsewhere.

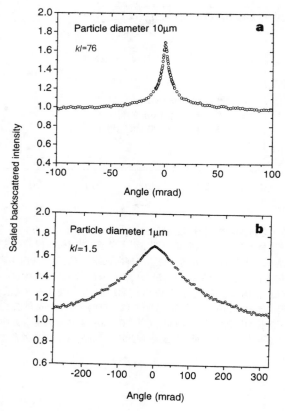

Fig. 3. Coherent backscattering cones from coarse-grained (**a**) and fine-grained (**b**) GaAs powder. The samples are strongly polydisperse with an average particle diameter of 10 µm and 1 µm, respectively. The sample is illuminated with a mode-locked Nd:YAG laser operating at 76 MHz, with a wavelength of 1,064 nm, pulse duration 100 ps, beam diameter 6 mm and incident power 100 mW. In all experiments we have checked that nonlinear absorption processes like two-photon absorption do not play a role; this was done by lowering the incident power to 20 mW, and finding that this reduction did not influence the results. Detection is performed in the polarization-conserving channel. The mean free path is calculated from the angle of the cusp[27], taking into account internal reflection[29]. This yields $l = 8.5$ µm and $kl = 76$ for the data in **a**, and $l = 0.17$ µm resulting in $kl \approx 1.5$ for the data in **b**.

局域化的前身，也因此被称为"光的弱局域化"[24,25]。背散射的锥形的宽度和尖端的角度都与 l 成反比（参考文献 26 和 27），从而使确定样品中的散射量成为可能。而且，尖端是由（理论上）无限长的光程得到的，所以只在没有吸收的情况下出现 [26-28]。图 3 中，我们展示了粗粒粉末（图 3a）和细粒粉末（图 3b）的背散射锥形，粉末的平均粒径分别为 10 μm 和 1 μm。从尖端的角度中我们发现，粗粒粉末中 $l=8.5$ μm，所以 $kl=76$，细粒粉末中 $l\approx0.17$ μm，所以 $kl\approx1.5$。观测值 $kl=1.5$ 是迄今报道过的光波的最小 kl 值的四分之一 [30]。无论从实验角度还是理论角度来看，向局域化转化的过程中，相干背散射锥的形状都很有趣，这一点会在别处讨论。

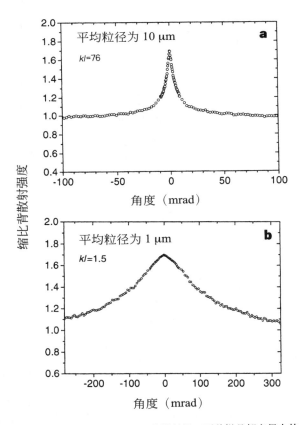

图 3. 从粗粒（a）和细粒（b）GaAs 粉末中得到的相干背散射锥。两种样品都有很大的多分散性，平均粒径分别为 10 μm 和 1 μm。用来照射样品的是锁模 Nd：YAG 激光，频率为 76 MHz，波长为 1,064 nm，脉冲宽度为 100 ps，光束直径为 6 mm，入射功率为 100 mW。在全部实验中，我们都避免了非线性吸收（如双光子吸收）。方法是把入射功率降低到 20 mW 后发现功率的降低并没有影响实验结果。检测是在保偏通道中进行的。平均自由程由锥形尖端的角度计算得出 [27]，内反射也被考虑在内 [29]。图 a 中数据得出的结果是 $l=8.5$ μm，$kl=76$，图 b 则是 $l=0.17$ μm，$kl\approx1.5$。

To observe a possible localization transition, we have measured the transmission coefficient as a function of sample thickness. In Fig. 4a, the transmission coefficient is shown for the coarse-grained powder. We see that the transmission behaves completely classically with $l = 9.8$ μm, which is consistent with the coherent backscattering data. At very large sample thicknesses ($L > 500$ μm), the transmission decreased more rapidly than linear due to the onset of absorption. This gives an upper limit for κ (defined as $\kappa = l_{in}^{-1}$) for the coarse-grained powder, of ~0.13 cm^{-1}, which shows again that the grinding process did not introduce any absorption.

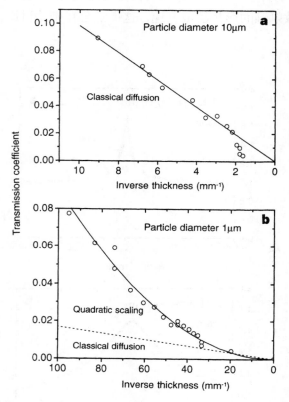

Fig. 4. Comparison of the transmission coefficients for two GaAs powders with different average particle diameters. Here the transmission coefficient is defined as the ratio between total transmitted flux and the incident flux. The total transmission is measured with an integrating sphere placed in contact with the back of the sample. The light source is as in Fig. 3, with beam diameter 0.5 mm and incident power 20 μW. The data in **a** correspond to particle a diameter of 10 μm and behave completely classically. The solid line is $T = l/L$, with $l = 9.8$ μm, which is in agreement with the backscattering data. The data in **b** correspond to a particle diameter of ~1 μm. The dashed line is the theoretical curve for classical diffusion with $l = 0.17$ μm, as obtained from the backscattering data. The solid line is a quadratic fit to the data. This quadratic dependence of the transmission coefficient on the inverse thickness is the expected behaviour at an Anderson localization transition.

In Fig. 4b, the transmission coefficient T is shown for the fine-grained powder. The dashed line is the theoretical curve for classical diffusion assuming $l = 0.17$ μm as obtained from the backscattering data. Whereas for classical diffusion T would decrease linearly with the sample

为了观测到一个可能的向局域化转化的过程，我们测量了透射系数随样品厚度的变化。图 4a 展示了粗粒粉末的透射系数。可以看出，这种透射完全表现为经典扩散，其中 $l = 9.8\ \mu m$，与相干背散射得到的数据一致。在样品厚度特别大的时候 $(L > 500\ \mu m)$，由于吸收的出现，透射率的降低速度会超线性。因此粗粒粉末的 κ 值 (定义为 $\kappa = l_{in}^{-1}$) 存在上限，约为 $0.13\ cm^{-1}$，再次说明了碾磨过程不会引入吸收。

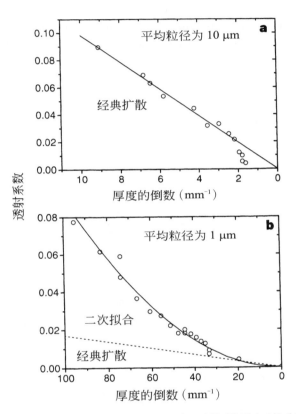

图 4. 平均粒径不同的两种 GaAs 粉末透射系数的对比。此处，透射系数被定义为总透射通量与入射通量之比。总透射量是由紧贴样品背面的积分球测出的。光源和图 3 中的一样，光束直径为 0.5 mm，发射功率为 20 μW。图 **a** 中的数据来自直径为 10 μm 的颗粒，完全表现为经典扩散。实线为 $T = l / L$，其中 $l = 9.8\ \mu m$，这和背散射数据相符。图 **b** 中的数据对应粒径约 1 μm 的情况。虚线是按经典扩散作出的理论曲线，其中 $l = 0.17\ \mu m$，由背散射数据所得。实线是实验数据的二次拟合。在转变为安德森局域化的过程中，透射系数与厚度的倒数的二次相关符合预期。

图 4b 展示了细粒粉末的透射系数 T。虚线是根据经典扩散画出的理论曲线，其中假设 $l = 0.17\ \mu m$，即由背散射数据算出的值。虽然经典扩散中的 T 值会随样品厚

thickness L, we find for these samples a quadratic dependence $(T \propto L^{-2})$. This is exactly the behaviour predicted by the scaling theory of localization at the localization transition[12,18]. We note that no classical diffusion process can show a quadratic system-size dependence.

If we decrease the particle size even further we expect (from Mie-scattering theory) to obtain even stronger scattering. In Fig. 5, the transmission coefficient is shown for a powder with an average particle diameter of 300 nm. In Fig. 5b we see that the quadratic behaviour has changed into an exponential decay in this case, as expected in the localized regime. The transport of light has come to a halt owing to interference, and the system has made a phase transition from a conducting into a localized state. The characteristic length scale for the exponential decay is called the localization length, which here is 4.3 μm.

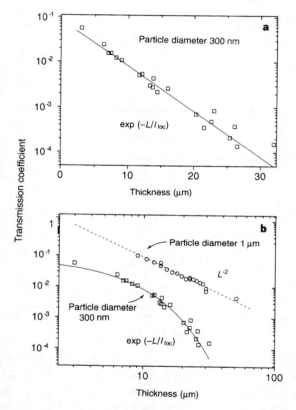

Fig. 5. The transmission coefficient of very fine GaAs powder as a function of thickness. The average particle diameter is 300 nm. In **a**, the data are plotted on a semi-logarithmic scale. The solid line is an exponential fit $\exp(-L/l_{loc})$ with a localization length of $l_{loc} = 4.3$ μm. In **b**, the same data are plotted on a double-logarithmic scale and the data of Fig. 4b are imported for comparison. We see that for the very fine powder, the quadratic behaviour changes to an exponential decay. The system goes into a localized state where it behaves as a (non-absorbing) insulator.

Different techniques could be used to map out the complete localization transition. The amount of scattering could be varied by changing the average particle diameter, the refractive index contrast, the particle density and the wavelength of the light. An

度 L 的增大呈线性下降，但我们发现这些样品中出现了二次相关（$T \propto L^{-2}$）。这和以局域化标度理论预测出的向局域化转化的表现完全一致[12,18]。我们在此特别指出，任何经典扩散过程都不会呈现与系统尺度的二次相关。

如果我们继续降低粒度，我们会（根据米氏散射理论）得到更强的散射。图 5 给出了一种平均粒径为 300 nm 的粉末的透射系数。从图 5b 中我们可以看出，在这种情况下二次相关已经变为指数衰减，符合局域区的预期。由于干涉，光不再透射，系统实现了由传导态到局域态的相变。指数衰减的特征长度尺度被称为局域化长度，此处为 4.3 μm。

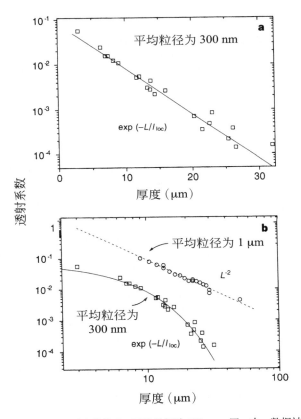

图 5. 极细 GaAs 粉末的透射系数与厚度的关系。平均粒径为 300 nm。图 **a** 中，数据被标在半对数坐标中。实线是指数化拟合曲线 $\exp(-L/l_{loc})$，其中局域化长度 $l_{loc} = 4.3$ μm。图 **b** 中，同样的数据被标在双对数坐标中，与图 4b 中的数作比较。我们可以看出，在极细的粉末中，二次相关变成了指数衰减。系统变为局域态，即表现为（无吸收的）光绝缘体。

多种方法可以用来描绘完整的向局域化转化的过程。通过改变平均粒径、折射率对比度、颗粒密度以及光的波长，可以改变散射量。时间分辨透射实验是一种重

important experiment would be a time-resolved transmission experiment in which the reduction of the diffusion constant at the Anderson localization transition is observed. Localization of classical waves is, in many ways, similar to Anderson localization of electrons. There are, however, also interesting differences between light and electrons. For experiments with light waves, coherent (laser) sources are available; the wavelength of such sources may be easily adjusted. Furthermore, for electromagnetic waves photon–photon interactions can be neglected, whereas in the case of electrons, electron–electron interactions always play a role. This latter property in particular makes light in strongly disordered media an interesting system in which to study the Anderson localization transition.

(**390**, 671-673; 1997)

Diederik S. Wiersma*, Paolo Bartolini*, Ad Lagendijk† & Roberto Righini*

* European Laboratory for Non-Linear Spectroscopy, Largo E. Fermi 2, 50125 Florence, Italy
† Van der Waals-Zeeman Laboratory, Valckenierstraat 65-67, 1018 XE Amsterdam, The Netherlands

Received 16 June; accepted 15 October 1997.

References:

1. Anderson, P. W. Absence of diffusion in certain random lattices. *Phys. Rev.* **109**, 1492-1505 (1958).

2. Bergmann, G. Quantitative analysis of weak localization in thin Mg films by electroresistance measurements. *Phys. Rev. B* **25**, 2937-2939 (1982).

3. Altshuler, B. L., Aronov, A. G., Khmel'nitskii, D. E. & Larkin, A. I. in *Quantum Theory of Solids* (ed. Lifshits, I. M.) 130-237 (MIR, Moskow, 1983).

4. Khmel'nitskii, D. E. Localization and coherent scattering of electrons. *Physica B* **126**, 235-241 (1984).

5. Lee, P. A. & Ramakrishnan, T. V. Disordered electronic systems. *Rev. Mod. Phys.* **57**, 287-337 (1985).

6. Condat, C. A., Kirkpatrick, T. R. & Cohen, S. M. Acoustic localization in one dimension in the presence of a flow field. *Phys. Rev. B* **35**, 4653-4661 (1987).

7. Souillard, B. in *Chance and Matter* (eds Souletie, J., Vannimenus, J. & Stora, R.) Ch. 5 (North-Holland, Amsterdam, 1987).

8. Ando, T. & Fukuyama, H. (eds) *Anderson Localization, Springer Proceedings in Physics* Vol. 28 (Springer, Berlin, 1988).

9. Vollhardt, D. & Wölfle, P. in *Electronic Phase Transitions* (eds Hanke, W. & Kopaev, Yu. V.) 1-78 (Elsevier, Amsterdam, 1992).

10. Sheng, P. *Introduction to Wave Scattering, Localization, and Mesoscopic Phenomena* (Academic, San Diego, 1995).

11. John, S. Electromagnetic absorption in a disordered medium near a photon mobility edge. *Phys. Rev. Lett.* **53**, 2169-2172 (1984).

12. Anderson, P. W. The question of classical localization: a theory of white paint? *Phil. Mag. B* **52**, 505-509 (1985).

13. Sheng, P. & Zhang, Z.-Q. Scalar-wave localization in a two-component composite. *Phys. Rev. Lett.* **57**, 1879-1882 (1986).

14. Arya, K., Su, Z. B. & Birman, J. L. Anderson localization of electromagnetic waves in a dielectric medium of randomly distributed metal particles. *Phys. Rev. Lett.* **57**, 2725-2728 (1986).

15. Lagendijk, A., van Albada, M. P. & van der Mark, M. B. Localization of light: the quest for the white hole. *Physica A* **140**, 183-190 (1986).

16. Kaveh, M. Localization of photons indisordered systems. *Phil. Mag. B* **56**, 693-703 (1987).

17. Soukoulis, C. M., Economou, E. N., Grest, G. S. & Cohen, M. H. Existence of Anderson localization of classical waves in a random two-component medium. *Phys. Rev. Lett.* **62**, 575-578 (1989).

18. Abrahams, E., Anderson, P. W., Licciardello, D. C. & Ramakrishnan, T. V. Scaling theory of localization: absence of quantum diffusion in two dimensions. *Phys. Rev. Lett.* **42**, 673-676 (1979).

19. Mott, N. F. *Metal-Insulator Transitions* (Taylor & Francis, London, 1974).

20. Dalichaouch, R., Armstrong, J. P., Schultz, S., Platzman, P. M. & McCall, S. L. Microwave localization by two-dimensional random scattering. *Nature* **354**, 53-55 (1991).

21. Garcia, N. & Genack, A. Z. Anomalous photon diffusion at the threshold of the Anderson localization transition. *Phys. Rev. Lett.* **66**, 1850-1853 (1991).

22. Genack, A. Z. & Garcia, N. Observation of photon localization in a three-dimensional disordered system. *Phys. Rev. Lett.* **66**, 2064-2067 (1991).

23. Kuga, Y. & Ishimaru, J. Retroflection of a dense distribution of spherical particles. *J. Opt. Soc. Am. A* **1**, 831-835 (1984).

24. Albada, M. P. & Lagendijk, A. Observation of weak localization of light in a random medium. *Phys. Rev. Lett.* **55**, 2692-2695 (1985).

25. Wolf, P. E. & Maret, G. Weak localization and coherent backscattering of photons in disordered media. *Phys. Rev. Lett.* **55**, 2696-2699 (1985).

26. Mark, M. B., Albada, M. P. & Lagendijk, A. Light scattering in strongly scattering media: multiple scattering and weak localization. *Phys. Rev. B* **37**, 3575-3592 (1988).

要的实验，在该种实验中，向安德森局域化转化的过程中，扩散常数的减小是可观测到的。经典波的局域化在很多方面都类似于电子的安德森局域化。然而，光和电子有一些有趣的不同点。在光波实验中，相干（激光）光源是可实现的；这种光源的波长是很容易调节的。而且，电磁波中的光子－光子相互作用可以忽略不计，但是电子体系中的电子－电子相互作用总是对实验有影响。后者这种特性使在强无序介质中的光成为一个研究安德森局域化转变的有趣系统。

（葛聆沨 翻译；翟天瑞 审稿）

27. Akkermans, E., Wolf, P. E., Maynard, R. & Maret, G. Theoretical study of the coherent backscattering of light by disordered media. *J. Phys.* (*Paris*) **49**, 77-98 (1988).

28. Edrei, I. & Stephen, M. J. Optical coherent backscattering and transmission in a disordered media near the mobility edge. *Phys. Rev. B* **42**, 110-117 (1990).

29. Zhu, J. X., Pine, D. J. & Weitz, D. A. Internal reflection of diffusive light in random media. *Phys. Rev. A* **44**, 3948-3957 (1991).

30. Wiersma, D. S., Albada, M. P., van Tiggelen, B. A. & Lagendijk, A. Experimental evidence for recurrent multiple scattering events of light in disordered media. *Phys. Rev. Lett.* **74**, 4193-4196 (1995).

Acknowledgements. We thank F. Bogani, M. Colocci, R. Torre and M. Gurioli for discussions, and M. Colocci also for supplying GaAs crystals. D.S.W. thanks M. van Albada for advice and continuous support during the experiments, and M. Brugmans for reading of the manuscript. A.L. was supported by the "Stichting voor Fundamenteel Onderzoek der Materie" (FOM). This work was supported by the Commission of the European Community.

Correspondence and requests for materials should be addressed to D.S.W. (e-mail: wiersma@lens.unifi.it).

Appendix: Index by Subject
附录：学科分类目录

Physics
物理学

Chemistry
化学

Biology
生物学

Astronomy
天文学

Geoscience
地球科学